1:1:86

Richard M. Sillitto

POCKETBOOK OF MATHEMATICAL FUNCTIONS

Abridged edition of

Handbook of Mathematical Functions

Milton Abramowitz and Irene A. Stegun (eds.)

Material selected by

Michael Danos and Johann Rafelski

1984

Verlag Harri Deutsch - Thun - Frankfurt/Main

CIP-Kurztitelaufnahme der Deutschen Bibliothek

Pocketbook of mathematical functions / Milton Abramowitz and Irene A. Stegun (eds.).
Material selected by Michael Danos and Johann Rafelski. — Abridged ed. of Handbook of mathematical functions. — Thun; Frankfurt/Main: Deutsch, 1984.
ISBN 3-87144-818-4
NE: Abramowitz, Milton [Hrsg.]

ISBN 3 87144 818 4

Abridged edition of „Handbook of Mathematical Functions" (edited by M. Abramowitz and I. A. Stegun) which was originally published by the National Bureau of Standards in 1964.

Printed in Germany

Foreword to the Original NBS Handbook

This volume is the result of the cooperative effort of many persons and a number of organizations. The National Bureau of Standards has long been turning out mathematical tables and has had under consideration, for at least 10 years, the production of a compendium like the present one. During a Conference on Tables, called by the NBS Applied Mathematics Division on May 15, 1952, Dr. Abramowitz of that Division mentioned preliminary plans for such an undertaking, but indicated the need for technical advice and financial support.

The Mathematics Division of the National Research Council has also had an active interest in tables; since 1943 it has published the quarterly journal, "Mathematical Tables and Aids to Computation" (MTAC), editorial supervision being exercised by a Committee of the Division.

Subsequent to the NBS Conference on Tables in 1952 the attention of the National Science Foundation was drawn to the desirability of financing activity in table production. With its support a 2-day Conference on Tables was called at the Massachusetts Institute of Technology on September 15–16, 1954, to discuss the needs for tables of various kinds. Twenty-eight persons attended, representing scientists and engineers using tables as well as table producers. This conference reached consensus on several conclusions and recommendations, which were set forth in tbe published Report of the Conference. There was general agreement, for example, "that the advent of high-speed computing equipment changed the task of table making but definitely did not remove the need for tables". It was also agreed that "an outstanding need is for a Handbook of Tables for the Occasional Computer, with tables of usually encountered functions and a set of formulas and tables for interpolation and other techniques useful to the occasional computer". The Report suggested that the NBS undertake the production of such a Handbook and that the NSF contribute financial assistance. The Conference elected, from its participants, the following Committee: P. M. Morse (Chairman), M. Abramowitz, J. H. Curtiss, R. W. Hamming, D. H. Lehmer, C. B. Tompkins, J. W. Tukey, to help implement these and other recommendations.

The Bureau of Standards undertook to produce the recommended tables and the National Science Foundation made funds available. To provide technical guidance to the Mathematics Division of the Bureau, which carried out the work, and to provide the NSF with independent judgments on grants for the work, the Conference Committee was reconstituted as the Committee on Revision of Mathematical Tables of the Mathematics Division of the National Research Council. This, after some changes of membership, became the Committee which is signing this Foreword. The present volume is evidence that Conferences can sometimes reach conclusions and that their recommendations sometimes get acted on.

Active work was started at the Bureau in 1956. The overall plan, the selection of authors for the various chapters, and the enthusiasm required to begin the task were contributions of Dr. Abramowitz. Since his untimely death, the effort has continued under the general direction of Irene A. Stegun. The workers at the Bureau and the members of the Committee have had many discussions about content, style and layout. Though many details have had to be argued out as they came up, the basic specifications of the volume have remained the same as were outlined by the Massachusetts Institute of Technology Conference of 1954.

The Committee wishes here to register its commendation of the magnitude and quality of the task carried out by the staff of the NBS Computing Section and their expert collaborators in planning, collecting and editing these Tables, and its appreciation of the willingness with which its various suggestions were incorporated into the plans. We hope this resulting volume will be judged by its users to be a worthy memorial to the vision and industry of its chief architect, Milton Abramowitz. We regret he did not live to see its publication.

P. M. Morse, *Chairman.*
A. Erdélyi
M. C. Gray
N. C. Metropolis
J. B. Rosser
H. C. Thacher, Jr.
John Todd
C. B. Tompkins
J. W. Tukey.

PREFACE

Since the publication in June, 1964 of the well known NBS Handbook, the advent of microelectronics has completely changed the needs of working scientists and engineers. Specifically, the need for numerical tables essentially has vanished while the need of a portable handbook of the analytic properties of mathematical functions has increased. Though the NBS handbook fulfills the needs admirably it is burdened by the sheer bulk of the volume resulting from, by now, superfluous material. The present volume has been designed to accommodate this changed working environment. The personal practical needs of the editors provided the impetus and the guiding light in the selection of the necessary material. The numbering of formulae and chapters of the original NBS Handbook has been retained, allowing for cross reference with the original NBS Handbook. Chapter 2 has been slightly extended and small errors have been corrected as noted in the remainder of the text.

We thank the staff of National Bureau of Standards and in particular Dr. Burton H. Colvin for their cooperation.

M. Danos
J. Rafelski

March, 1984

CONTENTS

Chapter 1 of the Original NBS Handbook has been eliminated. The numbering of formulae and chapters has been retained, allowing for cross reference.

2. Physical Constants and Conversion Factors

A.G. McNish, revised by the editors

The tables in this chapter supply some of the more commonly needed physical constants and conversion factors.

The International System of Units (SI) established in 1960 by the General Conference of Weights and Measures under the Treaty of the Meter is based upon: the meter (m) for length, defined as 1 650 763.73 wave-lengths in vacuum corresponding to the transition $2p_{10}-5d_5$ of krypton 86; the kilogram (kg) for mass, defined as the mass of the prototype kilogram at Sevres, France; the second (s) for time, defined as the duration of 9 192 631 770 periods of the radiation corresponding to the transition between the two hyperfine levels of cesium 133; the kelvin (K) for temperature, defined as 1/273.16 of the thermodynamic temperature of the triple point of water; the ampere (A) for electric current, defined as the current which, if flowing in two infinitely long parallel wires *in vacuo* separated by one meter, would produce a force of 2×10^{-7} newtons per meter of length between the wires; and the candela (cd) for luminous intensity, defined as the luminous intensity of 1/600 000 square meter of a perfect radiator at the temperature of freezing platinum.

All other units of SI are derived from these base units by assigning the value unity to the proportionality constants in the defining equations (official symbols for other SI units appear in Tables 2.1 and 2.2). Taking 1/100 of the meter as the unit for length and 1/1000 of the kilogram as the unit for mass gives rise similarly to the cgs system, often used in physics and chemistry.

SI, as it is ordinarily used in electromagnetism, is a rationalized system, i.e., the electromagnetic units of SI relate to the quantities appearing in the so-called rationalized electromagnetic equations. Thus, the force per unit length between two current-carrying parallel wires of infinite length separated by unit distance *in vacuo* is $2f = \mu_0 i_1 i_2/4\pi$, where μ_0 has the value $4\pi \times 10^{-7}$H/m. The force between two electric charges *in vacuo* is correspondingly given by $f = q_1 q_2/4\pi\epsilon_0 r^2$, ϵ_0 having the value $1/\mu_0 c^2$, where c is the speed of light in meters per second. ($\epsilon_0 \sim 8.854 \times 10^{-12}$F/m)

Setting μ_0 equal to unity and deleting 4π from the denominator in the first equation above defines the cgs-emu system. Setting ϵ_0 equal to unity and deleting 4π from the denominator in the second equation correspondingly defines the cgs-esu system. The cgs-emu and the cgs-esu systems are most frequently used in the unrationalized forms.

Table 2.1. Common Units and Conversion Factors, CGS System and SI

Quantity	SI Name	CGS Name	Factor
Force	newton (N)	dyne	10^5
Energy	joule (J)	erg	10^7
Power	watt (W)	....	10^7

Table 2.2. Names and Conversion Factors for Electric and Magnetic Units

Quantity	SI name	emu name	esu name	emu-SI factors	esu-SI factors
Current	ampere (A)	abampere	statampere	10^{-1}	$\sim 3 \times 10^9$
Charge	coulomb (C)	abcoulomb	statcoulomb	10^{-1}	$\sim 3 \times 10^9$
Potential	volt (V)	abvolt	statvolt	10^8	$\sim (1/3) \times 10^{-2}$
Resistance	ohm (Ω)	abohm	statohm	10^9	$\sim (1/9) \times 10^{-11}$
Inductance	henry (H)	centimeter	....	10^9	$\sim (1/9) \times 10^{-11}$
Capacitance	farad (F)	....	centimeter	10^{-9}	$\sim 9 \times 10^{11}$
Magnetizing force	$A \cdot m^{-1}$	oersted	....	$4\pi \times 10^{-3}$	$\sim 3 \times 10^9$
Magnetomotive force	A	gilbert	....	$4\pi \times 10^{-1}$	$\sim 3/10^6$
Magnetic flux	weber (Wb)	maxwell	....	10^8	$\sim (1/3) \times 10^{-2}$
Magnetic flux density	tesla (T)	gauss (G)	....	10^4	$\sim (1/3) \times 10^{-6}$
Electric displacement	....	....	....	10^{-5}	$\sim 3 \times 10^5$

Example: If the value assigned to a current is 100 amperes its value in abamperes is $100 \times 10^{-1} = 10$.

The values of constants given in Table 2.3 are based on an adjustment by Taylor, Parker, and Langenberg, Rev. Mod. Phys. 41, p.375 (1969). They are being considered for adoption by the Task Group on Fundamental Constants of the Committee on Data for Science and Technology, International Council of Scientific Unions. The uncertainties given are standard errors estimated from the experimental data included in the adjustment. Where applicable, values are based on the unified scale of atomic masses in which the atomic mass unit (u) is defined as 1/12 of the mass of the atom of the ^{12}C nuclide.

Table 2.3. Adjusted Values of Constants

Constant	Symbol	Value	Uncertainty ‡	Unit: Systeme International (SI)		Unit: Centimeter-gram-second (CGS)	
Speed of light in vacuum	c	2.997 925 0	±10	$\times10^{8}$	m/s	$\times10^{10}$	cm/s
Elementary charge	e	1.602 191 7	70	10^{-19}	C	10^{-20}	$cm^{1/2}g^{1/2}$ *
		4.803 250	21	....	....	10^{-10}	$cm^{3/2}g^{1/2}s^{-1}$ †
Avogadro constant	N_A	6.022 169	40	10^{23}	mol^{-1}	10^{23}	mol^{-1}
Atomic mass unit	u	1.660 531	11	10^{-27}	kg	10^{-24}	g
Electron rest mass	m_e	9.109 558	54	10^{-31}	kg	10^{-28}	g
		5.485 930	34	10^{-4}	u	10^{-4}	u
Proton rest mass	m_p	1.672 614	11	10^{-27}	kg	10^{-24}	g
		1.007 276 61	8	10^{0}	u	10^{0}	u
Neutron rest mass	m_n	1.674 920	11	10^{-27}	kg	10^{-24}	g
		1.008 665 20	10	10^{0}	u	10^{0}	u
Faraday constant	F	9.648 670	54	10^{4}	C/mol	10^{3}	$cm^{1/2}g^{1/2}mol^{-1}$*
		2.892 599	16	....	....	10^{14}	$cm^{3/2}g^{1/2}s^{-1}mol^{-1}$ †
Planck constant	h	6.626 196	50	10^{-34}	J · s	10^{-27}	erg · s
	$\hbar$	1.054 591 9	80	10^{-34}	J · s	10^{-27}	erg · s
Fine structure constant	α	7.297 351	11	10^{-3}	....	10^{-3}	....
	$1/\alpha$	1.370 360 2	21	10^{2}	....	10^{2}	....
Charge to mass ratio for electron	e/m_e	1.758 802 8	54	10^{11}	C/kg	10^{7}	$cm^{1/2}/g^{1/2}$ *
		5.272 759	16	....	....	10^{17}	$cm^{3/2}g^{-1/2}s^{-1}$ †
Quantum-charge ratio	h/e	4.135 708	14	10^{-15}	J · s/C	10^{-7}	$cm^{3/2}g^{1/2}s^{-1}$ *
		1.379 523 4	46	....	....	10^{-17}	$cm^{1/2}g^{1/2}$ †
Compton wavelength of electron	λ_C	2.426 309 6	74	10^{-12}	m	10^{-10}	cm
	$\lambda_C/2\pi$	3.861 592	12	10^{-13}	m	10^{-11}	cm
Compton wavelength of proton	$\lambda_{C,p}$	1.321 440 9	90	10^{-15}	m	10^{-13}	cm
	$\lambda_{C,p}/2\pi$	2.103 139	14	10^{-16}	m	10^{-14}	cm
Rydberg constant	R_∞	1.097 373 12	11	10^{7}	m^{-1}	10^{5}	cm^{-1}
Bohr radius	a_0	5.291 771 5	81	10^{-11}	m	10^{-9}	cm
Electron radius	r_e	2.817 939	13	10^{-15}	m	10^{-13}	cm
Gyromagnetic ratio of proton	γ	2.675 196 5	82	10^{8}	$rad \cdot s^{-1}T^{-1}$	10^{4}	$rad \cdot s^{-1}G^{-1}$ *
	$\gamma/2\pi$	4.257 707	13	10^{7}	Hz/T	10^{3}	$s^{-1}G^{-1}$ *
(uncorrected for diamagnetism,	γ'	2.675 127 0	82	10^{8}	$rad \cdot s^{-1}T^{-1}$	10^{4}	$rad \cdot s^{-1}G^{-1}$ *
H_2O)	$\gamma'/2\pi$	4.257 597	13	10^{7}	Hz/T	10^{3}	$s^{-1}G^{-1}$ *
Bohr magneton	μ_B	9.274 096	65	10^{-24}	J/T	10^{-21}	erg/G *
Nuclear magneton	μ_N	5.050 951	50	10^{-27}	J/T	10^{-24}	erg/G *
Proton moment	μ_p	1.410 620 3	99	10^{-26}	J/T	10^{-23}	erg/G *
	μ_p/μ_N	2.792 782	17	10^{0}	....	10^{0}	....
(uncorrected for diamagnetism, H_2O)	μ'_p/μ_N	2.792 709	17	10^{0}	....	10^{0}	....
Gas constant	R	8.314 34	35	10^{0}	$J \cdot K^{-1}\ mol^{-1}$	10^{7}	$erg \cdot K^{-1}\ mol^{-1}$
Normal volume perfect gas	V_0	2.241 36	39	10^{-2}	m^3/mol	10^{4}	cm^3/mol
Boltzmann constant	k	1.380 622	59	10^{-23}	J/K	10^{-16}	erg/K
First radiation constant ($8\pi hc$)	c_1	4.992 579	38	10^{-24}	J · m	10^{-15}	erg · cm
Second radiation constant	c_2	1.438 833	61	10^{-2}	m · K	10^{0}	cm · K
Stefan-Boltzmann constant	σ	5.669 61	96	10^{-8}	$W \cdot m^{-2}K^{-4}$	10^{-5}	$erg \cdot cm^{-2}s^{-1}K^{-4}$
Gravitational constant	G	6.673 2	31	10^{-11}	$N \cdot m^2/kg^2$	10^{-8}	$dyn \cdot cm^2/g^2$

‡Based on 1 std. dev; applies to last digits in preceding column. *Electromagnetic system. †Electrostatic system.

Table 2.4. Miscellaneous Conversion Factors

Standard gravity, g_0	= 9.806 65 meters per second per second*
Standard atmospheric pressure, P_0	= 1.013 25 × 10^5 newtons per square meter*
	= 1.013 25 × 10^6 dynes per square centimeter*
1 thermodynamic calorie,[1] cal_c	= 4.1840 joules*
1 IT calorie[2], cal_s	= 4.1868 joules*
1 liter, l	= 10^{-3} cubic meter*
1 angstrom unit, Å	= 10^{-10} meter*
1 bar	= 10^5 newtons per square meter*
	= 10^6 dynes per square centimeter*
1 gal	= 10^{-2} meter per second per second*
	= 1 centimeter per second per second*
1 astronomical unit, AU	= 1.496 × 10^{11} meters
1 light year	= 9.46 × 10^{15} meters
1 parsec	= 3.08 × 10^{16} meters
	= 3.26 light years

1 curie, the quantity of radioactive material undergoing 3.7 × 10^{10} disintegrations per second*.

1 roentgen, the exposure of x- or gamma radiation which produces together with its secondaries 2.082 × 10^9 electron-ion pairs in 0.001 293 gram of air.

The index of refraction of the atmosphere for radio waves of frequency less than 3 × 10^{10} Hz is given by $(n - 1)10^6 = (77.6/t)\ (p + 4810e/t)$, where n is the refractive index; t, temperature in kelvins; p, total pressure in millibars; e, water vapor partial pressure in millibars.

Factors for converting the customary United States units to units of the metric system are given in Table 2.5.

Table 2.5. Factors for Converting Customary U.S. Units to SI Units

1 yard	0.914 4 meter*
1 foot	0.304 8 meter*
1 inch	0.025 4 meter*
1 statute mile	1 609.344 meters*
1 nautical mile (international)	1 852 meters*
1 pound (avdp.)	0.453 592 37 kilogram*
1 oz. (avdp.)	0.028 349 52 kilogram
1 pound force	4.448 22 newtons
1 slug	14.593 9 kilograms
1 poundal	0.138 255 newtons
1 foot pound	1.355 82 joules
Temperature (Fahrenheit)	32 + (9/5) Celsius temperature*
1 British thermal unit[3]	1055 joules

Geodetic constants for the international (Hayford) spheroid are given in Table 2.6. The gravity values are on the basis of the revised Potsdam value. They are about 14 parts per million smaller than previous values. They are calculated for the surface of the geoid by the international formula.

Table 2.6. Geodetic Constants

a = 6 378 388 m; f = 1/297; b = 6 356 912 m

Latitude	Length of 1′ of longitude	Length of 1′ of latitude	g
	Meters	*Meters*	*m/s²*
0°	1 855.398	1 842.925	9.780 350
15	1 792.580	1 844.170	9.783 800
30	1 608.174	1 847.580	9.793 238
45	1 314.175	1 852.256	9.806 154
60	930.047	1 856.951	9.819 099
75	481.725	1 860.401	9.828 593
90	0	1 861.666	9.832 072

[1] Used principally by chemists.

[2] Used principally by engineers.

[3] Various definitions are given for the British thermal unit. This represents a rounded mean value differing from none of the more important definitions by more than 3 in 10^4.

* Exact value.

TABLE 2.7.

PHYSICAL AND NUMERICAL CONSTANTS*

PHYSICAL CONSTANTS

Quantity	Value	Uncert. (ppm)
N_A	$= 6.022\ 045(31)\times10^{23}$ mole^{-1}	5.1
V_m	$= 22413.83(70)$ cm^3 mole^{-1} = molar volume of ideal gas at STP	31
c	$= 2.997\ 924\ 58(1.2)\times10^{10}$ cm sec^{-1}	0.004
e	$= 4.803\ 242(14)\times10^{-10}$ esu $= 1.602\ 189\ 2(46)\times10^{-19}$ coulomb	2.9; 2.9
1 MeV	$= 1.602\ 189\ 2(46)\times10^{-6}$ erg	2.9
$\hbar = h/2\pi$	$= 6.582\ 173(17)\times10^{-22}$ MeV sec $= 1.054\ 588\ 7(57)\times10^{-27}$ erg sec	2.6; 5.4
$\hbar c$	$= 1.973\ 285\ 8(51)\times10^{-11}$ MeV cm = 197.32858(51) MeV fermi	2.6; 2.6
$(\hbar c)^2$	$= 0.389\ 385\ 7(20)$ GeV^2 mb	5.2
α	$= e^2/\hbar c = 1/137.03604(11)$	0.82
$k_{Boltzmann}$	$= 1.380\ 662(44)\times10^{-16}$ erg °K^{-1}	32
	$= 8.61735(28)\times10^{-11}$ MeV °K^{-1} = 1 eV/11604.50(36) °K	32; 31
$\sigma_{Stef.\ Boltz.}$	$= 5.67032(71)\times10^{-5}$ erg sec^{-1} cm^{-2} °K^{-4}	125
	$= 3.53911(44)\times10^{7}$ eV sec^{-1} cm^{-2} °K^{-4}	125
m_e	$= 0.511\ 003\ 4(14)$ MeV $= 9.109\ 534(47)\times10^{-28}$ g	2.8; 5.1
m_p	$= 938.2796(27)$ MeV $= 1836.15152(70)\ m_e = 6.722\ 775(39)\ m_{\pi^\pm}$	2.8; 0.38; 5.8
	$= 1.007\ 276\ 470(11)$ amu	0.011
1 amu	$= 1/12\ m_{C^{12}} = 931.5016(26)$ MeV	2.8
m_d	$= 1875.6280(53)$ MeV	2.8
r_e	$= e^2/m_ec^2 = 2.817\ 938\ 0(70)$ fermi (1 fermi = 10^{-13} cm)	2.5
$\lambda\!\!\!^{-}_e$	$= \hbar/m_ec = r_e\alpha^{-1} = 3.861\ 590\ 5(64)\times10^{-11}$ cm	1.6
$a_{\infty Bohr}$	$= \hbar^2/m_ee^2 = r_e\alpha^{-2} = 0.529\ 177\ 06(44)$ Å (1 Å = 10^{-8} cm)	0.82
$\sigma_{Thomson}$	$= (8/3)\pi r_e^{\ 2} = 0.665\ 244\ 8(33)$ barn (1 barn = 10^{-24} cm^2)	4.9
μ_{Bohr}	$= e\hbar/2m_ec = 0.578\ 837\ 85(95)\times10^{-14}$ MeV gauss^{-1}	1.6
μ_N	$= e\hbar/2m_pc = 3.152\ 451\ 5(53)\times10^{-18}$ MeV gauss^{-1}	1.7
μ_p/μ_{Bohr}	$= 0.001\ 521\ 032\ 209(16)$	0.011
$1/2\omega^e_{cyclotron}$	$= e/2m_ec = 8.794\ 024(25)\times10^{6}$ rad sec^{-1} gauss^{-1}	2.8
$1/2\omega^p_{cyclotron}$	$= e/2m_pc = 4.789\ 378(14)\times10^{3}$ rad sec^{-1} gauss^{-1}	2.8

Hydrogen-like atom (nonrelativistic, μ = reduced mass):

$$\frac{v}{c)_{rms}} = \frac{z\alpha}{n};\quad E_n = \frac{\mu}{2}\ v^2 = \frac{\mu}{2}\left(\frac{cz\alpha}{n}\right)^2;\ a_n = \frac{n\ \hbar}{\mu zc\alpha}$$

Quantity	Value	Uncert. (ppm)
$R_\infty = m_ee^4/2\hbar^2 = m_ec^2\alpha^2/2$	$= 13.605\ 804(36)$ eV (Rydberg)	2.6
	$= m_ec\alpha^2/2h = 109\ 737.3177(83)$ cm^{-1}	0.075
pc = 0.3 Hρ (MeV, kilogauss, cm)		
1 year (sidereal)	= 365.256 days $= 3.1558\times10^7$ sec ($\approx\pi\times10^7$ sec)	
density of dry air	= 1.204 mg cm^{-3} (at 20°C, 760 mm)	
acceleration by gravity	= 980.62 cm sec^{-2} (sea level, 45°)	
gravitational constant	$= 6.6720(41)\times10^{-8}$ cm^3 g^{-1} sec^{-2}	615
1 calorie (thermochemical)	= 4.184 joules	
1 atmosphere	= 1.01325 bar (1 bar = 10^6 dynes cm^{-2})	
1 eV per particle	= 11604.50(36) °K (from E = kT)	31

NUMERICAL CONSTANTS

π	= 3.141 592 7	1 rad	= 57.295 779 5 deg	$\sqrt{\pi}$	= 1.772 453 85
e	= 2.718 281 8	1/e	= 0.367 879 4	$\sqrt{2}$	= 1.414 213 6
ln2	= 0.693 147 2	ln10	= 2.302 585 1	$\sqrt{3}$	= 1.732 050 8
$\log_{10}2$	= 0.301 030 0	$\log_{10}e$	= 0.434 294 5	$\sqrt{10}$	= 3.162 277 7

---

* Revised 1982 by Barry N. Taylor. Originally prepared by Stanley J. Brodsky, based mainly on the "1973 Least-Squares Adjustment of the Fundamental Constants," by E. R. Cohen and B. N. Taylor, J. Phys. Chem. Ref. Data **2**, 663 (1973). The figures in parentheses correspond to the one-standard-deviation uncertainty in the last digits of the main number. The equivalent uncertainty in parts per million (ppm) is given in the last column. Note that the uncertainties of the output values of a least-squares adjustment are in general correlated, and the general law of error propagation must be used in calculating additional quantities.

The set of constants resulting from the 1973 adjustment of Cohen and Taylor has been recommended for international use by CODATA (Committee on Data for Science and Technology), and is the most up-to-date, generally accepted set currently available. However, since the publication of the 1973 adjustment, a number of new experiments have been completed, yielding improved values for some of the constants: N_A = 6.022 097 8(63)$\times10^{23}$ mole^{-1} (1.04 ppm); α^{-1} = 137.035 963(15) (0.11 ppm); m_p/m_e=1863.15300(25) (0.14 ppm); and R_∞ = 109 737.31521(11) cm^{-1} (0.001 ppm). But it must be realized that, since the output values of a least-squares adjustment are related in a complex way and a change in the measured value of one constant usually leads to corresponding changes in the adjusted values of others, one must be cautious in carrying out calculations using both the output values from the 1973 adjustment and the results of more recent experiments. A new adjustment is planned for completion by mid 1982.

TABLE 2.8.

PERIODIC TABLE OF THE ELEMENTS

IA	IIA	IIIB	IVB	VB	VIB	VIIB	VIII	VIII	VIII	IB	IIB	IIIA	IVA	VA	VIA	VIIA	
								1 H 1.0079									2 He 4.00260
3 Li 6.94	4 Be 9.01218											5 B 10.81	6 C 12.011	7 N 14.0067	8 O 15.9994	9 F 18.998403	10 Ne 20.17
11 Na 22.98977	12 Mg 24.305											13 Al 26.98154	14 Si 28.0855	15 P 30.97376	16 S 32.06	17 Cl 35.453	18 Ar 39.948
19 K 39.0983	20 Ca 40.08	21 Sc 44.9559	22 Ti 47.90	23 V 50.9415	24 Cr 51.996	25 Mn 54.9380	26 Fe 55.847	27 Co 58.9332	28 Ni 58.71	29 Cu 63.546	30 Zn 65.38	31 Ga 69.735	32 Ge 72.59	33 As 74.9216	34 Se 78.96	35 Br 79.904	36 Kr 83.80
37 Rb 85.467	38 Sr 87.62	39 Y 88.9059	40 Zr 91.22	41 Nb 92.9064	42 Mo 95.94	43 Tc 98.9062	44 Ru 101.07	45 Rh 102.9055	46 Pd 106.4	47 Ag 107.868	48 Cd 112.41	49 In 114.82	50 Sn 118.69	51 Sb 121.75	52 Te 127.60	53 I 126.9045	54 Xe 131.30
55 Cs 132.9054	56 Ba 137.33	57–71 Rare Earths	72 Hf 178.49	73 Ta 180.947	74 W 183.85	75 Re 186.207	76 Os 190.2	77 Ir 192.22	78 Pt 195.09	79 Au 196.9665	80 Hg 200.59	81 Tl 204.37	82 Pb 207.2	83 Bi 208.9804	84 Po (209)	85 At (210)	86 Rn (222)
87 Fr (223)	88 Ra 226.0254	89– Acti- nides	104 (260)	105 (260)	106 (263)												

57 La 138.9055	58 Ce 140.12	59 Pr 140.9077	60 Nd 144.24	61 Pm (145)	62 Sm 150.4	63 Eu 151.96	64 Gd 157.25	65 Tb 158.9254	66 Dy 162.50	67 Ho 164.9304	68 Er 167.26	69 Tm 168.9342	70 Yb 173.04	71 Lu 174.967	Rare earths (Lanthanide series)
89 Ac (227)	90 Th 232.0381	91 Pa 231.0359	92 U 238.029	93 Np 237.0482	94 Pu (244)	95 Am (243)	96 Cm (247)	97 Bk (247)	98 Cf (251)	99 Es (254)	100 Fm (257)	101 Md (258)	102 No (259)	103 Lr (260)	Actinide series

Upper number is atomic number, expressing the positive charge of the nucleus in multiples of the electronic charge e. Lower number is atomic mass weighted by isotopic abundance in earth's surface, relative to the mass of the carbon 12 isotope, which has been arbitrarily assigned a mass of 12.00000 atomic mass units (amu). Numbers in parentheses are mass numbers (the whole number nearest the value of the atomic mass, in amu) of most stable isotope of that element. Adapted from the Handbook of Chemistry and Physics, 62nd Ed., 1981-1982.

TABLE 2.9.

ELECTROMAGNETIC RELATIONS

Maxwell's Equations

Quantity	CGS (statcoul., statamp., sec cm^{-1})	MKSA (coul., amp., ohm)
Potentials:	$V = \sum_{\text{charges}} \frac{q}{r}$	$V = \frac{1}{4\pi\varepsilon_0} \sum_{\text{charges}} \frac{q}{r}$
	$\vec{A} = \frac{1}{c} \sum_{\text{currents}} \frac{\vec{I}}{r}$	$\vec{A} = \frac{\mu_0}{4\pi} \sum_{\text{currents}} \frac{\vec{I}}{r}$
	c = speed of light in vacuum	$\varepsilon_0 = \frac{1}{36\pi} 10^{-9}$ MKSA
		$\mu_0 = 4\pi\ 10^{-7}$ MKSA
Fields:	$\vec{E} = -\vec{\nabla}V - \frac{1}{c}\frac{\partial \vec{A}}{\partial t}$	$\vec{E} = -\vec{\nabla}V - \frac{\partial \vec{A}}{\partial t}$
	$\vec{B} = \vec{\nabla} \times \vec{A}$	$\vec{B} = \vec{\nabla} \times \vec{A}$
Materials:	$\vec{D} = \varepsilon\vec{E}, \quad \vec{B} = \mu\vec{H}$	$\vec{D} = \varepsilon\vec{E}, \quad \vec{B} = \mu\vec{H}$
Force:	$\vec{F} = q\left(\vec{E} + \frac{\vec{v}}{c} \times \vec{B}\right)$	$\vec{F} = q(\vec{E} + \vec{v} \times \vec{B})$
Maxwell:	$\vec{\nabla} \cdot \vec{D} = 4\pi\rho$	$\vec{\nabla} \cdot \vec{D} = \rho$
	$\vec{\nabla} \times \vec{E} = -\frac{1}{c}\frac{\partial \vec{B}}{\partial t}$	$\vec{\nabla} \times \vec{E} = -\frac{\partial \vec{B}}{\partial t}$
	$\vec{\nabla} \cdot \vec{B} = 0$	$\vec{\nabla} \cdot \vec{B} = 0$
	$\vec{\nabla} \times \vec{H} = \frac{4\pi\vec{j}}{c} + \frac{1}{c}\frac{\partial \vec{D}}{\partial t}$	$\vec{\nabla} \times \vec{H} = \vec{j} + \frac{\partial \vec{D}}{\partial t}$
Relativistic transformations:	$\vec{E}'_{\parallel} = \vec{E}_{\parallel}$	$\vec{E}'_{\parallel} = \vec{E}_{\parallel}$
	$\vec{E}'_{\perp} = \gamma\left(\vec{E}_{\perp} + \frac{1}{c}\vec{v} \times \vec{B}\right)$	$\vec{E}'_{\perp} = \gamma(\vec{E}_{\perp} + \vec{v} \times \vec{B})$
	$\vec{B}'_{\parallel} = \vec{B}_{\parallel}$	$\vec{B}'_{\parallel} = \vec{B}_{\parallel}$
	$\vec{B}'_{\perp} = \gamma\left(\vec{B}_{\perp} - \frac{1}{c}\vec{v} \times \vec{E}\right)$	$\vec{B}'_{\perp} = \gamma\left(\vec{B}_{\perp} - \frac{1}{c^2}\vec{v} \times \vec{E}\right)$

Impedances: Alternating Currents (MKSA)

Ohm's law: $V = ZI, \quad V = V_0 e^{i\omega t}$.

1. Impedance of self-inductance L: $Z = i\omega L$.
2. Impedance of a capacitor of capacitance C: $Z = \frac{1}{i\omega C}$.
3. Impedance of a flat conductor of width w at high frequency:

$$Z = \frac{(1+i)\rho}{w\delta} ;$$

ρ = resistivity in $10^{-8}\ \Omega m$:

~1.7 for Cu	~5.5 for W
~2.4 for Au	~73 for SS 304
~2.8 for Al	~100 for Nichrome

(Al alloys may have up to double this value.)

δ = effective skin depth

$$= \sqrt{\frac{\rho}{\pi\nu\mu}} \approx \frac{6.6 \text{ cm}}{\sqrt{\nu(\text{sec}^{-1})}} \quad \text{for Cu} .$$

4. Impedance of free space: $Z = \sqrt{\mu_0/\varepsilon_0} = 376.7\Omega$.

Capacitance C and Inductance L per Unit Length (MKSA)

1. For flat plates of width w, separated by $d \ll w$:

$$C = \frac{\varepsilon w}{d} \quad ; \qquad L = \mu\frac{d}{w} .$$

2. For coax cable of interior and exterior radii r_1 and r_2:

$$C = \frac{2\pi\,\varepsilon}{\ln(r_2/r_1)} \quad ; \qquad L = \frac{\mu}{2\pi}\ln(r_2/r_1) ;$$

ε = dielectric constant $\begin{cases} 2 \text{ to } 6 \text{ for plastics;} \\ 4 \text{ to } 8 \text{ for porcelain, glasses;} \end{cases}$

μ = magnetic susceptibility.

Transmission Lines (No Loss) (MKSA)

Velocity $= 1/\sqrt{LC} = 1/\sqrt{\mu\varepsilon}$.

Impedance $= \sqrt{L/C}$.

L and C are inductance and capacitance per unit length.

Synchrotron Radiation (CGS)

Energy loss/revolution $= \frac{4\pi}{3}\frac{e^2}{\rho}\beta^3\gamma^4$, ρ = orbit radius .

For electrons ($\beta \approx 1$), $\frac{\Delta E(\text{MeV})}{\text{rev.}} = 0.0885\,[E(\text{GeV})]^4/\rho(\text{meter})$.

Critical frequency: $\omega_c = 3\gamma^3\frac{c}{\rho}$.

Frequency spectrum (for $\gamma \gg 1$):

$$I(\omega) \cong 3.3\frac{e^2}{c}\left(\frac{\omega\rho}{c}\right)^{1/3} , \quad \omega \ll \omega_c ;$$

$$I(\omega) \cong (1.0,\ 1.6,\ 1.6,\ 0.5,\ 0.08)\frac{e^2\gamma}{c}$$

at $\frac{\omega}{\omega_c}$ = 0.01, 0.1, 0.2, 1.0, 2.0, respectively;

$$I(\omega) \cong \sqrt{3\pi}\,\frac{e^2\gamma}{c}\left(\frac{\omega}{\omega_c}\right)^{1/2} e^{-2\omega/\omega_c} , \quad \omega \gtrsim 2\omega_c .$$

The radiation is confined to angles $\lesssim 1/\gamma$ relative to the instantaneous direction of motion.

TABLE 2.10.

RADIOACTIVITY AND RADIATION PROTECTION

Unit of activity = Curie:
  1 Ci = 3.7×10^{10} disintegrations/sec
Unit of exposure dose for x and γ radiation = Roentgen:
  1 R = 1 esu/cm^3 = 87.8 erg/g (5.49×10^7 MeV/g) of air
Unit of absorbed dose = rad:
  1 rad = 100 erg/g (6.25×10^7 MeV/g) in any material
Unit of dose equivalent (for protection) = rem:
  rems (Roentgen equivalents for man) = rads × QF,
where QF (quality factor) depends upon the type of radiation and other factors. For γ rays and HE protons, QF ≈ 1; for thermal neutrons, QF ≈ 3; for fast neutrons, QF ranges up to 10; and for α particles and heavy ions, QF ranges up to 20.

Maximum permissible occupational dose for the whole body:
  5 rem/year (maximum 3 rem/calendar quarter)
Fluxes (per cm^2) to liberate 1 rad in carbon:
  3.5×10^7 minimum ionizing singly charged particles
  1.0×10^9 photons of 1 MeV energy
(These fluxes are correct to within a factor of 2 for all materials.)
Natural background: 120 to 130 millirem/year
  cosmic radiation (charged particles + neutrons) ~25 mrem/yr
  cosmic radiation (γ rays) ~25 mrem/yr
  radiation from rocks and air (γ rays) ~73 mrem/yr
Cosmic ray background in counters: ~ 1/min/cm^2/ster

3. Elementary Analytical Methods

3.1. Binomial Theorem and Binomial Coefficients; Arithmetic and Geometric Progressions; Arithmetic, Geometric, Harmonic and Generalized Means

Binomial Theorem

3.1.1

$$(a+b)^n=a^n+\binom{n}{1}a^{n-1}b+\binom{n}{2}a^{n-2}b^2+\binom{n}{3}a^{n-3}b^3+\ldots+b^n$$

(n a positive integer)

Binomial Coefficients (see chapter **24**)

3.1.2

$$\binom{n}{k}={}_nC_k=\frac{n(n-1)\ldots(n-k+1)}{k!}=\frac{n!}{(n-k)!k!}$$

3.1.3 $$\binom{n}{k}=\binom{n}{n-k}=(-1)^k\binom{k-n-1}{k}$$

3.1.4 $$\binom{n+1}{k}=\binom{n}{k}+\binom{n}{k-1}$$

3.1.5 $$\binom{n}{0}=\binom{n}{n}=1$$

3.1.6 $$1+\binom{n}{1}+\binom{n}{2}+\ldots+\binom{n}{n}=2^n$$

3.1.7 $$1-\binom{n}{1}+\binom{n}{2}-\ldots+(-1)^n\binom{n}{n}=0$$

Table of Binomial Coefficients $\binom{n}{k}$

3.1.8

n \ k	0	1	2	3	4	5	6	7	8	9	10	11	12
1	1	1											
2	1	2	1										
3	1	3	3	1									
4	1	4	6	4	1								
5	1	5	10	10	5	1							
6	1	6	15	20	15	6	1						
7	1	7	21	35	35	21	7	1					
8	1	8	28	56	70	56	28	8	1				
9	1	9	36	84	126	126	84	36	9	1			
10	1	10	45	120	210	252	210	120	45	10	1		
11	1	11	55	165	330	462	462	330	165	55	11	1	
12	1	12	66	220	495	792	924	792	495	220	66	12	1

For a more extensive table see chapter **24**.

3.1.9

Sum of Arithmetic Progression to n Terms

$$a+(a+d)+(a+2d)+\ldots+(a+(n-1)d)=na+\frac{1}{2}n(n-1)d=\frac{n}{2}(a+l),$$

last term in series $=l=a+(n-1)d$

Sum of Geometric Progression to n Terms

3.1.10

$$s_n=a+ar+ar^2+\ldots+ar^{n-1}=\frac{a(1-r^n)}{1-r}$$

$$\lim_{n\to\infty}s_n=a/(1-r)\qquad(-1<r<1)$$

Arithmetic Mean of n Quantities A

3.1.11 $$A=\frac{a_1+a_2+\ldots+a_n}{n}$$

Geometric Mean of n Quantities G

3.1.12 $$G=(a_1a_2\ldots a_n)^{1/n}\qquad(a_k>0,k=1,2,\ldots,n)$$

Harmonic Mean of n Quantities H

3.1.13

$$\frac{1}{H}=\frac{1}{n}\left(\frac{1}{a_1}+\frac{1}{a_2}+\ldots+\frac{1}{a_n}\right)\qquad(a_k>0,k=1,2,\ldots,n)$$

Generalized Mean

3.1.14 $$M(t)=\left(\frac{1}{n}\sum_{k=1}^{n}a_k^t\right)^{1/t}$$

3.1.15 $$M(t)=0\;(t<0,\text{ some }a_k\text{ zero})$$

3.1.16 $$\lim_{t\to\infty}M(t)=\max.\;(a_1,a_2,\ldots,a_n)=\max.\;a$$

3.1.17 $$\lim_{t\to-\infty}M(t)=\min.\;(a_1,a_2,\ldots,a_n)=\min.\;a$$

3.1.18 $$\lim_{t\to0}M(t)=G$$

3.1.19 $$M(1)=A$$

3.1.20 $$M(-1)=H$$

3.2. Inequalities

Relation Between Arithmetic, Geometric, Harmonic and Generalized Means

3.2.1

$A\geq G\geq H$, equality if and only if $a_1=a_2=\ldots=a_n$

3.2.2 $$\min.\;a<M(t)<\max.\;a$$

3.2.3 $\min. a < G < \max. a$

equality holds if all a_k are equal, or $t<0$ and an a_k is zero

3.2.4 $M(t)<M(s)$ if $t<s$ unless all a_k are equal, or $s<0$ and an a_k is zero.

Triangle Inequalities

3.2.5 $|a_1|-|a_2|\leq|a_1+a_2|\leq|a_1|+|a_2|$

3.2.6 $\left|\sum_{k=1}^{n} a_k\right| \leq \sum_{k=1}^{n} |a_k|$

Chebyshev's Inequality

If $a_1\geq a_2\geq a_3\geq \ldots \geq a_n$

$b_1\geq b_2\geq b_3\geq \ldots \geq b_n$

3.2.7 $n\sum_{k=1}^{n} a_kb_k\geq\left(\sum_{k=1}^{n} a_k\right)\left(\sum_{k=1}^{n} b_k\right)$

Hölder's Inequality for Sums

If $\frac{1}{p}+\frac{1}{q}=1$, $p>1$, $q>1$

3.2.8 $\sum_{k=1}^{n} |a_kb_k|\leq\left(\sum_{k=1}^{n} |a_k|^p\right)^{1/p}\left(\sum_{k=1}^{n} |b_k|^q\right)^{1/q}$;

equality holds if and only if $|b_k|=c|a_k|^{p-1}$ (c=constant>0). If $p=q=2$ we get

Cauchy's Inequality

3.2.9

$\left[\sum_{k=1}^{n} a_kb_k\right]^2\leq\sum_{k=1}^{n} a_k^2 \sum_{k=1}^{n} b_k^2$ (equality for $a_k=cb_k$, c constant).

Hölder's Inequality for Integrals

If $\frac{1}{p}+\frac{1}{q}=1$, $p>1$, $q>1$

3.2.10

$$\int_a^b |f(x)g(x)|dx\leq\left[\int_a^b |f(x)|^p dx\right]^{1/p}\left[\int_a^b |g(x)|^q dx\right]^{1/q}$$

equality holds if and only if $|g(x)|=c|f(x)|^{p-1}$ (c=constant>0).

If $p=q=2$ we get

Schwarz's Inequality

3.2.11

$$\left[\int_a^b f(x)g(x)dx\right]^2\leq\int_a^b [f(x)]^2dx\int_a^b [g(x)]^2dx$$

Minkowski's Inequality for Sums

If $p>1$ and a_k, $b_k>0$ for all k,

3.2.12

$$\left(\sum_{k=1}^{n} (a_k+b_k)^p\right)^{1/p}\leq\left(\sum_{k=1}^{n} a_k^p\right)^{1/p}+\left(\sum_{k=1}^{n} b_k^p\right)^{1/p},$$

equality holds if and only if $b_k=ca_k$ (c=constant>0).

Minkowski's Inequality for Integrals

If $p>1$,

3.2.13

$$\left(\int_a^b |f(x)+g(x)|^p dx\right)^{1/p}\leq\left(\int_a^b |f(x)|^p dx\right)^{1/p}+\left(\int_a^b |g(x)|^p dx\right)^{1/p}$$

equality holds if and only if $g(x)=cf(x)$ (c=constant>0).

3.3. Rules for Differentiation and Integration

Derivatives

3.3.1 $\frac{d}{dx}(cu)=c\frac{du}{dx}$, c constant

3.3.2 $\frac{d}{dx}(u+v)=\frac{du}{dx}+\frac{dv}{dx}$

3.3.3 $\frac{d}{dx}(uv)=u\frac{dv}{dx}+v\frac{du}{dx}$

3.3.4 $\frac{d}{dx}(u/v)=\frac{vdu/dx-udv/dx}{v^2}$

3.3.5 $\frac{d}{dx}u(v)=\frac{du}{dv}\frac{dv}{dx}$

3.3.6 $\frac{d}{dx}(u^v)=u^v\left(\frac{v}{u}\frac{du}{dx}+\ln u\frac{dv}{dx}\right)$

Leibniz's Theorem for Differentiation of an Integral

3.3.7

$$\frac{d}{dc}\int_{a(c)}^{b(c)} f(x,c)dx=\int_{a(c)}^{b(c)}\frac{\partial}{\partial c}f(x,c)dx+f(b,c)\frac{db}{dc}-f(a,c)\frac{da}{dc}$$

Leibniz's Theorem for Differentiation of a Product

3.3.8

$$\frac{d^n}{dx^n}(uv)=\frac{d^nu}{dx^n}v+\binom{n}{1}\frac{d^{n-1}u}{dx^{n-1}}\frac{dv}{dx}+\binom{n}{2}\frac{d^{n-2}u}{dx^{n-2}}\frac{d^2v}{dx^2}$$
$$+\ldots+\binom{n}{r}\frac{d^{n-r}u}{dx^{n-r}}\frac{d^rv}{dx^r}+\ldots+u\frac{d^nv}{dx^n}$$

3.3.9 $$\frac{dx}{dy}=1\Big/\frac{dy}{dx}$$

3.3.10 $$\frac{d^2x}{dy^2}=\frac{-d^2y}{dx^2}\left(\frac{dy}{dx}\right)^{-3}$$

3.3.11 $$\frac{d^3x}{dy^3}=-\left[\frac{d^3y}{dx^3}\frac{dy}{dx}-3\left(\frac{d^2y}{dx^2}\right)^2\right]\left(\frac{dy}{dx}\right)^{-5}$$

Integration by Parts

3.3.12 $$\int udv=uv-\int vdu$$

3.3.13 $$\int uvdx=\left(\int udx\right)v-\int\left(\int udx\right)\frac{dv}{dx}dx$$

Integrals of Rational Algebraic Functions

(Integration constants are omitted)

3.3.14 $$\int(ax+b)^ndx=\frac{(ax+b)^{n+1}}{a(n+1)}\qquad(n\neq-1)$$

3.3.15 $$\int\frac{dx}{ax+b}=\frac{1}{a}\ln|ax+b|$$

The following formulas are useful for evaluating $\int\frac{P(x)dx}{(ax^2+bx+c)^n}$ where $P(x)$ is a polynomial and $n>1$ is an integer.

3.3.16

$$\int\frac{dx}{(ax^2+bx+c)}=\frac{2}{(4ac-b^2)^{\frac{1}{2}}}\arctan\frac{2ax+b}{(4ac-b^2)^{\frac{1}{2}}}\qquad(b^2-4ac<0)$$

3.3.17 $$=\frac{1}{(b^2-4ac)^{\frac{1}{2}}}\ln\left|\frac{2ax+b-(b^2-4ac)^{\frac{1}{2}}}{2ax+b+(b^2-4ac)^{\frac{1}{2}}}\right|\qquad(b^2-4ac>0)$$

3.3.18 $$=\frac{-2}{2ax+b}\qquad(b^2-4ac=0)$$

3.3.19

$$\int\frac{xdx}{ax^2+bx+c}=\frac{1}{2a}\ln|ax^2+bx+c|-\frac{b}{2a}\int\frac{dx}{ax^2+bx+c}$$

3.3.20

$$\int\frac{dx}{(a+bx)(c+dx)}=\frac{1}{ad-bc}\ln\left|\frac{c+dx}{a+bx}\right|\qquad(ad\neq bc)$$

3.3.21 $$\int\frac{dx}{a^2+b^2x^2}=\frac{1}{ab}\arctan\frac{bx}{a}$$

3.3.22 $$\int\frac{xdx}{a^2+b^2x^2}=\frac{1}{2b^2}\ln|a^2+b^2x^2|$$

3.3.23 $$\int\frac{dx}{a^2-b^2x^2}=\frac{1}{2ab}\ln\left|\frac{a+bx}{a-bx}\right|$$

3.3.24 $$\int\frac{dx}{(x^2+a^2)^2}=\frac{1}{2a^3}\arctan\frac{x}{a}+\frac{x}{2a^2(x^2+a^2)}$$

3.3.25 $$\int\frac{dx}{(x^2-a^2)^2}=\frac{-x}{2a^2(x^2-a^2)}+\frac{1}{4a^3}\ln\left|\frac{a+x}{a-x}\right|$$

Integrals of Irrational Algebraic Functions

3.3.26 $$\int\frac{dx}{[(a+bx)(c+dx)]^{1/2}}=\frac{2}{(-bd)^{1/2}}\arctan\left[\frac{-d(a+bx)}{b(c+dx)}\right]^{1/2}\qquad(bd<0)$$

3.3.27 $$=\frac{-1}{(-bd)^{1/2}}\arcsin\left(\frac{2bdx+ad+bc}{bc-ad}\right)\qquad(b>0,\ d<0)$$

3.3.28 $$=\frac{2}{(bd)^{1/2}}\ln|[bd(a+bx)]^{1/2}+b(c+dx)^{1/2}|\qquad(bd>0)$$

3.3.29 $$\int\frac{dx}{(a+bx)^{1/2}(c+dx)}=\frac{2}{[d(bc-ad)]^{1/2}}\arctan\left[\frac{d(a+bx)}{(bc-ad)}\right]^{1/2}\qquad(d(ad-bc)<0)$$

3.3.30 $$=\frac{1}{[d(ad-bc)]^{1/2}}\ln\left|\frac{d(a+bx)^{1/2}-[d(ad-bc)]^{1/2}}{d(a+bx)^{1/2}+[d(ad-bc)]^{1/2}}\right|\qquad(d(ad-bc)>0)$$

3.3.31

$$\int [(a+bx)(c+dx)]^{1/2}dx$$
$$=\frac{(ad-bc)+2b(c+dx)}{4bd}[(a+bx)(c+dx)]^{1/2}$$
$$-\frac{(ad-bc)^2}{8bd}\int\frac{dx}{[(a+bx)(c+dx)]^{1/2}}$$

3.3.32

$$\int\left[\frac{c+dx}{a+bx}\right]^{1/2}dx=\frac{1}{b}[(a+bx)(c+dx)]^{1/2}$$
$$-\frac{(ad-bc)}{2b}\int\frac{dx}{[(a+bx)(c+dx)]^{1/2}}$$

3.3.33

$$\int\frac{dx}{(ax^2+bx+c)^{1/2}}$$
$$=a^{-1/2}\ln|2a^{1/2}(ax^2+bx+c)^{1/2}+2ax+b|\quad(a>0)$$

3.3.34 $$=a^{-1/2}\operatorname{arcsinh}\frac{(2ax+b)}{(4ac-b^2)^{1/2}}\quad(a>0,\ 4ac>b^2)$$

3.3.35 $$=a^{-1/2}\ln|2ax+b|\quad(a>0,\ b^2=4ac)$$

3.3.36 $$=-(-a)^{-1/2}\arcsin\frac{(2ax+b)}{(b^2-4ac)^{1/2}}$$
$$(a<0,\ b^2>4ac,\ |2ax+b|<(b^2-4ac)^{1/2})$$

3.3.37

$$\int(ax^2+bx+c)^{1/2}dx=\frac{2ax+b}{4a}(ax^2+bx+c)^{1/2}$$
$$+\frac{4ac-b^2}{8a}\int\frac{dx}{(ax^2+bx+c)^{1/2}}$$

3.3.38

$$\int\frac{dx}{x(ax^2+bx+c)^{1/2}}=-\int\frac{dt}{(a+bt+ct^2)^{1/2}}\text{ where }t=1/x$$

3.3.39

$$\int\frac{xdx}{(ax^2+bx+c)^{1/2}}$$
$$=\frac{1}{a}(ax^2+bx+c)^{1/2}-\frac{b}{2a}\int\frac{dx}{(ax^2+bx+c)^{1/2}}$$

3.3.40 $$\int\frac{dx}{(x^2\pm a^2)^{\frac{1}{2}}}=\ln|x+(x^2\pm a^2)^{\frac{1}{2}}|$$

3.3.41

$$\int(x^2\pm a^2)^{\frac{1}{2}}dx=\frac{x}{2}(x^2\pm a^2)^{\frac{1}{2}}\pm\frac{a^2}{2}\ln|x+(x^2\pm a^2)^{\frac{1}{2}}|$$

3.3.42 $$\int\frac{dx}{x(x^2+a^2)^{\frac{1}{2}}}=-\frac{1}{a}\ln\left|\frac{a+(x^2+a^2)^{\frac{1}{2}}}{x}\right|$$

3.3.43 $$\int\frac{dx}{x(x^2-a^2)^{\frac{1}{2}}}=\frac{1}{a}\arccos\frac{a}{x}$$

3.3.44 $$\int\frac{dx}{(a^2-x^2)^{\frac{1}{2}}}=\arcsin\frac{x}{a}$$

3.3.45 $$\int(a^2-x^2)^{\frac{1}{2}}dx=\frac{x}{2}(a^2-x^2)^{\frac{1}{2}}+\frac{a^2}{2}\arcsin\frac{x}{a}$$

3.3.46 $$\int\frac{dx}{x(a^2-x^2)^{\frac{1}{2}}}=-\frac{1}{a}\ln\left|\frac{a+(a^2-x^2)^{\frac{1}{2}}}{x}\right|$$

3.3.47 $$\int\frac{dx}{(2ax-x^2)^{\frac{1}{2}}}=\arcsin\frac{x-a}{a}$$

3.3.48

$$\int(2ax-x^2)^{\frac{1}{2}}dx=\frac{(x-a)}{2}(2ax-x^2)^{\frac{1}{2}}+\frac{a^2}{2}\arcsin\frac{x-a}{a}$$

3.3.49

$$\int\frac{dx}{(ax^2+b)(cx^2+d)^{\frac{1}{2}}}$$
$$=\frac{1}{[b(ad-bc)]^{\frac{1}{2}}}\arctan\frac{x(ad-bc)^{\frac{1}{2}}}{[b(cx^2+d)]^{\frac{1}{2}}}\quad(ad>bc)$$

3.3.50

$$=\frac{1}{2[b(bc-ad)]^{\frac{1}{2}}}\ln\left|\frac{[b(cx^2+d)]^{\frac{1}{2}}+x(bc-ad)^{\frac{1}{2}}}{[b(cx^2+d)]^{\frac{1}{2}}-x(bc-ad)^{\frac{1}{2}}}\right|$$
$$(bc>ad)$$

3.4. Limits, Maxima and Minima

Indeterminate Forms (L'Hospital's Rule)

3.4.1 Let $f(x)$ and $g(x)$ be differentiable on an interval $a\leq x<b$ for which $g'(x)\neq 0$.

If

$$\lim_{x\to b-}f(x)=0\text{ and }\lim_{x\to b-}g(x)=0$$

or if

$$\lim_{x\to b-}f(x)=\infty\text{ and }\lim_{x\to b-}g(x)=\infty$$

and if

$$\lim_{x\to b-}\frac{f'(x)}{g'(x)}=l\text{ then }\lim_{x\to b-}\frac{f(x)}{g(x)}=l.$$

Both b and l may be finite or infinite.

Maxima and Minima

3.4.2 (1) *Functions of One Variable*

The function $y=f(x)$ has a maximum at $x=x_0$ if $f'(x_0)=0$ and $f''(x_0)<0$, and a minimum at $x=x_0$ if $f'(x_0)=0$ and $f''(x_0)>0$. Points x_0 for which $f'(x_0)=0$ are called stationary points.

3.4.3 (2) *Functions of Two Variables*

The function $f(x, y)$ has a maximum or minimum for those values of (x_0, y_0) for which

$$\frac{\partial f}{\partial x}=0,\ \frac{\partial f}{\partial y}=0,$$

and for which $\begin{vmatrix} \partial^2 f/\partial x\partial y & \partial^2 f/\partial x^2 \\ \partial^2 f/\partial y^2 & \partial^2 f/\partial x\partial y \end{vmatrix}<0;$

(a) $f(x,y)$ has a maximum

$$\text{if } \frac{\partial^2 f}{\partial x^2}<0 \text{ and } \frac{\partial^2 f}{\partial y^2}<0 \text{ at } (x_0, y_0),$$

(b) $f(x,y)$ has a minimum

$$\text{if } \frac{\partial^2 f}{\partial x^2}>0 \text{ and } \frac{\partial^2 f}{\partial y^2}>0 \text{ at } (x_0, y_0).$$

3.5. Absolute and Relative Errors

(1) If x_0 is an approximation to the true value of x, then

3.5.1 (a) the *absolute error* of x_0 is $\Delta x=x_0-x$, $x-x_0$ is the correction to x.

3.5.2 (b) the *relative error* of x_0 is $\delta x=\frac{\Delta x}{x}\approx\frac{\Delta x}{x_0}$

3.5.3 (c) the *percentage error* is 100 times the relative error.

3.5.4 (2) The absolute error of the sum or difference of several numbers is at most equal to the sum of the absolute errors of the individual numbers.

3.5.5 (3) If $f(x_1, x_2, \ldots, x_n)$ is a function of $x_1, x_2, \ldots, x_n$ and the absolute error in x_i $(i=1, 2, \ldots n)$ is Δx_i, then the absolute error in f is

$$\Delta f\approx\frac{\partial f}{\partial x_1}\Delta x_1+\frac{\partial f}{\partial x_2}\Delta x_2+\ldots+\frac{\partial f}{\partial x_n}\Delta x_n$$

3.5.6 (4) The relative error of the product or quotient of several factors is at most equal to the sum of the relative errors of the individual factors.

3.5.7

(5) If $y=f(x)$, the relative error $\delta y=\frac{\Delta y}{y}\approx\frac{f'(x)}{f(x)}\Delta x$

Approximate Values

If $|\epsilon|<<1$, $|\eta|<<1$, $b<<a$,

3.5.8 $$(a+b)^k\approx a^k+ka^{k-1}b$$

3.5.9 $$(1+\epsilon)(1+\eta)\approx 1+\epsilon+\eta$$

3.5.10 $$\frac{1+\epsilon}{1+\eta}\approx 1+\epsilon-\eta$$

3.6. Infinite Series

Taylor's Formula for a Single Variable

3.6.1

$$f(x+h)=f(x)+hf'(x)+\frac{h^2}{2!}f''(x)+\ldots+\frac{h^{n-1}}{(n-1)!}f^{(n-1)}(x)+R_n$$

3.6.2

$$R_n=\frac{h^n}{n!}f^{(n)}(x+\theta_1 h)=\frac{h^n}{(n-1)!}(1-\theta_2)^{n-1}f^{(n)}(x+\theta_2 h)\qquad(0<\theta_{1,2}(x)<1)$$

3.6.3

$$=\frac{h^n}{(n-1)!}\int_0^1(1-t)^{n-1}f^{(n)}(x+th)dt$$

3.6.4

$$f(x)=f(a)+\frac{(x-a)}{1!}f'(a)+\frac{(x-a)^2}{2!}f''(a)+\ldots+\frac{(x-a)^{n-1}}{(n-1)!}f^{(n-1)}(a)+R_n$$

3.6.5 $$R_n=\frac{(x-a)^n}{n!}f^{(n)}(\xi)\qquad(a<\xi<x)$$

Lagrange's Expansion

If $y=f(x)$, $y_0=f(x_0)$, $f'(x_0)\neq 0$, then

3.6.6

$$x=x_0+\sum_{k=1}^{\infty}\frac{(y-y_0)^k}{k!}\left[\frac{d^{k-1}}{dx^{k-1}}\left\{\frac{x-x_0}{f(x)-y_0}\right\}^k\right]_{x=x_0}$$

3.6.7

$$g(x)=g(x_0)+\sum_{k=1}^{\infty}\frac{(y-y_0)^k}{k!}\left[\frac{d^{k-1}}{dx^{k-1}}\left(g'(x)\left\{\frac{x-x_0}{f(x)-y_0}\right\}^k\right)\right]_{x=x_0}$$

where $g(x)$ is any function indefinitely differentiable.

Binomial Series

3.6.8

$$(1+x)^\alpha=\sum_{k=0}^{\infty}\binom{\alpha}{k}x^k\qquad(-1<x<1)$$

3.6.9

$$(1+x)^{\alpha}=1+\alpha x+\frac{\alpha(\alpha-1)}{2!}x^2+\frac{\alpha(\alpha-1)(\alpha-2)}{3!}x^3+\ldots,$$

3.6.10

$$(1+x)^{-1}=1-x+x^2-x^3+x^4-\ldots \qquad (-1<x<1)$$

3.6.11

$$(1+x)^{\frac{1}{2}}=1+\frac{x}{2}-\frac{x^2}{8}+\frac{x^3}{16}-\frac{5x^4}{128}+\frac{7x^5}{256}-\frac{21x^6}{1024}+\ldots \qquad (-1<x<1)$$

3.6.12

$$(1+x)^{-\frac{1}{2}}=1-\frac{x}{2}+\frac{3x^2}{8}-\frac{5x^3}{16}+\frac{35x^4}{128}-\frac{63x^5}{256}+\frac{231x^6}{1024}-\ldots \qquad (-1<x<1)$$

3.6.13

$$(1+x)^{\frac{1}{3}}=1+\frac{1}{3}x-\frac{1}{9}x^2+\frac{5}{81}x^3-\frac{10}{243}x^4+\frac{22}{729}x^5-\frac{154}{6561}x^6+\ldots \qquad (-1<x<1)$$

3.6.14

$$(1+x)^{-\frac{1}{3}}=1-\frac{1}{3}x+\frac{2}{9}x^2-\frac{14}{81}x^3+\frac{35}{243}x^4-\frac{91}{729}x^5+\frac{728}{6561}x^6-\ldots \qquad (-1<x<1)$$

Asymptotic Expansions

3.6.15 A series $\sum_{k=0}^{\infty} a_k x^{-k}$ is said to be an asymptotic expansion of a function $f(x)$ if

$$f(x)-\sum_{k=0}^{n-1} a_k x^{-k}=O(x^{-n}) \text{ as } x\to\infty$$

for every $n=1, 2, \ldots$. We write

$$f(x)\sim\sum_{k=0}^{\infty} a_k x^{-k}.$$

The series itself may be either convergent or divergent.

Operations With Series

Let $s_1=1+a_1x+a_2x^2+a_3x^3+a_4x^4+\ldots$

$s_2=1+b_1x+b_2x^2+b_3x^3+b_4x^4+\ldots$

$s_3=1+c_1x+c_2x^2+c_3x^3+c_4x^4+\ldots$

	Operation	c_1	c_2	c_3	c_4
3.6.16	$s_3=s_1^{-1}$	$-a_1$	$a_1^2-a_2$	$2a_1a_2-a_3-a_1^3$	$2a_1a_3-3a_1^2a_2-a_4+a_2^2+a_1^4$
3.6.17	$s_3=s_1^{-2}$	$-2a_1$	$3a_1^2-2a_2$	$6a_1a_2-2a_3-4a_1^3$	$6a_1a_3+3a_2^2-2a_4-12a_1^2a_2+5a_1^4$
3.6.18	$s_3=s_1^{1/2}$	$\frac{1}{2}a_1$	$\frac{1}{2}a_2-\frac{1}{8}a_1^2$	$\frac{1}{2}a_3-\frac{1}{4}a_1a_2+\frac{1}{16}a_1^3$	$\frac{1}{2}a_4-\frac{1}{4}a_1a_3-\frac{1}{8}a_2^2+\frac{3}{16}a_1^2a_2-\frac{5}{128}a_1^4$
3.6.19	$s_3=s_1^{-1/2}$	$-\frac{1}{2}a_1$	$\frac{3}{8}a_1^2-\frac{1}{2}a_2$	$\frac{3}{4}a_1a_2-\frac{1}{2}a_3-\frac{5}{16}a_1^3$	$\frac{3}{4}a_1a_3+\frac{3}{8}a_2^2-\frac{1}{2}a_4-\frac{15}{16}a_1^2a_2+\frac{35}{128}a_1^4$
3.6.20	$s_3=s_1^n$	na_1	$\frac{1}{2}(n-1)c_1a_1+na_2$	$c_1a_2(n-1)+\frac{1}{6}c_1a_1^2(n-1)(n-2)+na_3$	$na_4+c_1a_3(n-1)+\frac{1}{2}n(n-1)a_2^2+\frac{1}{2}(n-1)(n-2)c_1a_1a_2+\frac{1}{24}(n-1)(n-2)(n-3)c_1a_1^3$
3.6.21	$s_3=s_1s_2$	a_1+b_1	$b_2+a_1b_1+a_2$	$b_3+a_1b_2+a_2b_1+a_3$	$b_4+a_1b_3+a_2b_2+a_3b_1+a_4$
3.6.22	$s_3=s_1/s_2$	a_1-b_1	$a_2-(b_1c_1+b_2)$	$a_3-(b_1c_2+b_2c_1+b_3)$	$a_4-(b_1c_3+b_2c_2+b_3c_1+b_4)$
3.6.23	$s_3=\exp(s_1-1)$	a_1	$a_2+\frac{1}{2}a_1^2$	$a_3+a_1a_2+\frac{1}{6}a_1^3$	$a_4+a_1a_3+\frac{1}{2}a_2^2+\frac{1}{2}a_2a_1^2+\frac{1}{24}a_1^4$
3.6.24	$s_3=1+\ln s_1$	a_1	$a_2-\frac{1}{2}a_1c_1$	$a_3-\frac{1}{3}(a_2c_1+2a_1c_2)$	$a_4-\frac{1}{4}(a_3c_1+2a_2c_2+3a_1c_3)$

Reversion of Series

3.6.25 Given

$$y=ax+bx^2+cx^3+dx^4+ex^5+fx^6+gx^7+\ldots$$

then

$$x=Ay+By^2+Cy^3+Dy^4+Ey^5+Fy^6+Gy^7+\ldots$$

where

$$aA=1$$

$$a^3B=-b$$

$$a^5C=2b^2-ac$$

$$a^7D=5abc-a^2d-5b^3$$

$$a^9E=6a^2bd+3a^2c^2+14b^4-a^3e-21ab^2c$$

$$a^{11}F=7a^3be+7a^3cd+84ab^3c-a^4f-28a^2bc^2-42b^5-28a^2b^2d$$

$$a^{13}G=8a^4bf+8a^4ce+4a^4d^2+120a^2b^3d+180a^2b^2c^2+132b^6-a^5g-36a^3b^2e-72a^3bcd-12a^3c^3-330ab^4c$$

Kummer's Transformation of Series

3.6.26 Let $\sum_{k=0}^{\infty} a_k=s$ be a given convergent series and $\sum_{k=0}^{\infty} c_k=c$ be a given convergent series with known sum c such that $\lim_{k\to\infty} \frac{a_k}{c_k}=\lambda\neq 0$.

Then

$$s=\lambda c+\sum_{k=0}^{\infty}\left(1-\lambda\frac{c_k}{a_k}\right)a_k.$$

Euler's Transformation of Series

3.6.27 If $\sum_{k=0}^{\infty}(-1)^k a_k=a_0-a_1+a_2-\ldots$ is a convergent series with sum s then

$$s=\sum_{k=0}^{\infty}\frac{(-1)^k\Delta^k a_0}{2^{k+1}},\ \Delta^k a_0=\sum_{m=0}^{k}(-1)^m\binom{k}{m}a_{k-m}$$

Euler-Maclaurin Summation Formula

3.6.28

$$\sum_{k=1}^{n-1} f_k=\int_0^n f(k)dk-\frac{1}{2}[f(0)+f(n)]+\frac{1}{12}[f'(n)-f'(0)]-\frac{1}{720}[f'''(n)-f'''(0)]+\frac{1}{30240}[f^{(V)}(n)-f^{(V)}(0)]-\frac{1}{1209600}[f^{(VII)}(n)-f^{(VII)}(0)]+\ldots$$

3.7. Complex Numbers and Functions

Cartesian Form

3.7.1 $$z=x+iy$$

Polar Form

3.7.2 $$z=re^{i\theta}=r(\cos\theta+i\sin\theta)$$

3.7.3 *Modulus:* $|z|=(x^2+y^2)^{\frac{1}{2}}=r$

3.7.4 *Argument:* $\arg z=\arctan(y/x)=\theta$ (other notations for arg z are am z and ph z).

3.7.5 Real Part: $x=\mathscr{R}z=r\cos\theta$

3.7.6 Imaginary Part: $y=\mathscr{I}z=r\sin\theta$

Complex Conjugate of z

3.7.7 $$\bar{z}=x-iy$$

3.7.8 $$|\bar{z}|=|z|$$

3.7.9 $$\arg\bar{z}=-\arg z$$

Multiplication and Division

If $z_1=x_1+iy_1$, $z_2=x_2+iy_2$, then

3.7.10 $$z_1z_2=x_1x_2-y_1y_2+i(x_1y_2+x_2y_1)$$

3.7.11 $$|z_1z_2|=|z_1||z_2|$$

3.7.12 $$\arg(z_1z_2)=\arg z_1+\arg z_2$$

3.7.13 $$\frac{z_1}{z_2}=\frac{z_1\bar{z}_2}{|z_2|^2}=\frac{x_1x_2+y_1y_2+i(x_2y_1-x_1y_2)}{x_2^2+y_2^2}$$

3.7.14 $$\left|\frac{z_1}{z_2}\right|=\frac{|z_1|}{|z_2|}$$

3.7.15 $$\arg\left(\frac{z_1}{z_2}\right)=\arg z_1-\arg z_2$$

Powers

3.7.16 $$z^n=r^ne^{in\theta}$$

3.7.17 $$=r^n\cos n\theta+ir^n\sin n\theta \qquad (n=0,\pm1,\pm2,\ldots)$$

3.7.18 $$z^2=x^2-y^2+i(2xy)$$

3.7.19 $$z^3=x^3-3xy^2+i(3x^2y-y^3)$$

3.7.20 $$z^4=x^4-6x^2y^2+y^4+i(4x^3y-4xy^3)$$

3.7.21 $$z^5=x^5-10x^3y^2+5xy^4+i(5x^4y-10x^2y^3+y^5)$$

3.7.22

$$z^n=\left[x^n-\binom{n}{2}x^{n-2}y^2+\binom{n}{4}x^{n-4}y^4-\ldots\right]+i\left[\binom{n}{1}x^{n-1}y-\binom{n}{3}x^{n-3}y^3+\ldots\right],$$

$$(n=1,2,\ldots)$$

If $z^n=u_n+iv_n$, then $z^{n+1}=u_{n+1}+iv_{n+1}$ where

3.7.23 $u_{n+1}=xu_n-yv_n;\ v_{n+1}=xv_n+yu_n$

$\mathscr{R} z^n$ and $\mathscr{I} z^n$ are called harmonic polynomials.

3.7.24 $$\frac{1}{z}=\frac{\bar{z}}{|z|^2}=\frac{x-iy}{x^2+y^2}$$

3.7.25 $$\frac{1}{z^n}=\frac{\bar{z}^n}{|z|^{2n}}=(z^{-1})^n$$

Roots

3.7.26 $z^{\frac{1}{2}}=\sqrt{z}=r^{\frac{1}{2}}e^{\frac{1}{2}i\theta}=r^{\frac{1}{2}}\cos\frac{1}{2}\theta+ir^{\frac{1}{2}}\sin\frac{1}{2}\theta$

If $-\pi<\theta\leq\pi$ this is the principal root. The other root has the opposite sign. The principal root is given by

3.7.27 $z^{\frac{1}{2}}=[\frac{1}{2}(r+x)]^{\frac{1}{2}}\pm i[\frac{1}{2}(r-x)]^{\frac{1}{2}}=u\pm iv$ where $2uv=y$ and where the ambiguous sign is taken to be the same as the sign of y.

3.7.28 $z^{1/n}=r^{1/n}e^{i\theta/n}$, (principal root if $-\pi<\theta\leq\pi$). Other roots are $r^{1/n}e^{i(\theta+2\pi k)/n}$ $(k=1, 2, 3, \ldots, n-1)$.

Inequalities

3.7.29 $$\big||z_1|-|z_2|\big|\leq|z_1\pm z_2|\leq|z_1|+|z_2|$$

Complex Functions, Cauchy-Riemann Equations

$f(z)=f(x+iy)=u(x,y)+iv(x,y)$ where $u(x,y)$, $v(x,y)$ are real, is *analytic* at those points $z=x+iy$ at which

3.7.30 $$\frac{\partial u}{\partial x}=\frac{\partial v}{\partial y},\ \frac{\partial u}{\partial y}=-\frac{\partial v}{\partial x}$$

If $z=re^{i\theta}$,

3.7.31 $$\frac{\partial u}{\partial r}=\frac{1}{r}\frac{\partial v}{\partial \theta},\ \frac{1}{r}\frac{\partial u}{\partial \theta}=-\frac{\partial v}{\partial r}$$

Laplace's Equation

The functions $u(x, y)$ and $v(x, y)$ are called harmonic functions and satisfy Laplace's equation:

Cartesian Coordinates

3.7.32 $$\frac{\partial^2 u}{\partial x^2}+\frac{\partial^2 u}{\partial y^2}=\frac{\partial^2 v}{\partial x^2}+\frac{\partial^2 v}{\partial y^2}=0$$

Polar Coordinates

3.7.33 $$r\frac{\partial}{\partial r}\left(r\frac{\partial u}{\partial r}\right)+\frac{\partial^2 u}{\partial\theta^2}=r\frac{\partial}{\partial r}\left(r\frac{\partial v}{\partial r}\right)+\frac{\partial^2 v}{\partial\theta^2}=0$$

3.8. Algebraic Equations

Solution of Quadratic Equations

3.8.1 Given $az^2+bz+c=0$,

$$z_{1,2}=-\left(\frac{b}{2a}\right)\pm\frac{1}{2a}q^{\frac{1}{2}},\ q=b^2-4ac,$$

$$z_1+z_2=-b/a,\ z_1z_2=c/a$$

If $q>0$, two real roots,
$q=0$, two equal roots,
$q<0$, pair of complex conjugate roots.

Solution of Cubic Equations

3.8.2 Given $z^3+a_2z^2+a_1z+a_0=0$, let

$$q=\frac{1}{3}a_1-\frac{1}{9}a_2^2;\ r=\frac{1}{6}(a_1a_2-3a_0)-\frac{1}{27}a_2^3.$$

If $q^3+r^2>0$, one real root and a pair of complex conjugate roots,
$q^3+r^2=0$, all roots real and at least two are equal,
$q^3+r^2<0$, all roots real (irreducible case).

Let

$$s_1=[r+(q^3+r^2)^{\frac{1}{2}}]^{\frac{1}{3}},\ s_2=[r-(q^3+r^2)^{\frac{1}{2}}]^{\frac{1}{3}}$$

then

$$z_1=(s_1+s_2)-\frac{a_2}{3}$$

$$z_2=-\frac{1}{2}(s_1+s_2)-\frac{a_2}{3}+\frac{i\sqrt{3}}{2}(s_1-s_2)$$

$$z_3=-\frac{1}{2}(s_1+s_2)-\frac{a_2}{3}-\frac{i\sqrt{3}}{2}(s_1-s_2).$$

If z_1, z_2, z_3 are the roots of the cubic equation

$$z_1+z_2+z_3=-a_2$$

$$z_1z_2+z_1z_3+z_2z_3=a_1$$

$$z_1z_2z_3=-a_0$$

Solution of Quartic Equations

3.8.3 Given $z^4+a_3z^3+a_2z^2+a_1z+a_0=0$, find the real root u_1 of the cubic equation

$$u^3-a_2u^2+(a_1a_3-4a_0)u-(a_1^2+a_0a_3^2-4a_0a_2)=0$$

and determine the four roots of the quartic as solutions of the two quadratic equations

$$v^2+\left[\frac{a_3}{2}\mp\left(\frac{a_3^2}{4}+u_1-a_2\right)^{\frac{1}{2}}\right]v+\frac{u_1}{2}\mp\left[\left(\frac{u_1}{2}\right)^2-a_0\right]^{\frac{1}{2}}=0$$

If all roots of the cubic equation are real, use the value of u_1 which gives real coefficients in the quadratic equation and select signs so that if

$$z^4+a_3z^3+a_2z^2+a_1z+a_0=(z^2+p_1z+q_1)(z^2+p_2z+q_2),$$

then

$$p_1+p_2=a_3, p_1p_2+q_1+q_2=a_2, p_1q_2+p_2q_1=a_1, q_1q_2=a_0.$$

If z_1, z_2, z_3, z_4 are the roots,

$$\Sigma z_i=-a_3, \Sigma z_iz_jz_k=-a_1,$$

$$\Sigma z_iz_j=a_2, z_1z_2z_3z_4=a_0.$$

3.9. Successive Approximation Methods

General Comments

3.9.1 Let $x=x_1$ be an approximation to $x=\xi$ where $f(\xi)=0$ and both x_1 and ξ are in the interval $a\leq x\leq b$. We define

$$x_{n+1}=x_n+c_nf(x_n) \qquad (n=1, 2, \ldots).$$

Then, if $f'(x)\geq 0$ and the constants c_n are negative and bounded, the sequence x_n converges monotonically to the root ξ.

If $c_n=c=\text{constant}<0$ and $f'(x)>0$, then the process converges but not necessarily monotonically.

Degree of Convergence of an Approximation Process

3.9.2 Let $x_1, x_2, x_3, \ldots$ be an infinite sequence of approximations to a number ξ. Then, if

$$|x_{n+1}-\xi|<A|x_n-\xi|^k, \qquad (n=1, 2, \ldots)$$

where A and k are independent of n, the sequence is said to have convergence of at most the kth degree (or order or index) to ξ. If $k=1$ and $A<1$ the convergence is linear; if $k=2$ the convergence is quadratic.

Regula Falsi (False Position)

3.9.3 Given $y=f(x)$ to find ξ such that $f(\xi)=0$, choose x_0 and x_1 such that $f(x_0)$ and $f(x_1)$ have opposite signs and compute

$$x_2=x_1-\frac{(x_1-x_0)}{(f_1-f_0)}f_1=\frac{f_1x_0-f_0x_1}{f_1-f_0}.$$

Then continue with x_2 and either of x_0 or x_1 for which $f(x_0)$ or $f(x_1)$ is of opposite sign to $f(x_2)$.

Regula falsi is equivalent to inverse linear interpolation.

Method of Iteration (Successive Substitution)

3.9.4 The iteration scheme $x_{k+1}=F(x_k)$ will converge to a zero of $x=F(x)$ if

(1) $|F'(x)|\leq q<1$ for $a\leq x\leq b$,

(2) $a\leq x_0\pm\frac{|F(x_0)-x_0|}{1-q}\leq b.$

Newton's Method of Successive Approximations

3.9.5

Newton's Rule

If $x=x_k$ is an approximation to the solution $x=\xi$ of $f(x)=0$ then the sequence

$$x_{k+1}=x_k-\frac{f(x_k)}{f'(x_k)}$$

will converge quadratically to $x=\xi$: (if instead of the condition (2) above),

(1) *Monotonic convergence*, $f(x_0)f''(x_0)>0$ and $f'(x)$, $f''(x)$ do not change sign in the interval (x_0, ξ), or

(2) *Oscillatory convergence*, $f(x_0)f''(x_0)<0$ and $f'(x)$, $f''(x)$ do not change sign in the interval (x_0, x_1), $x_0\leq\xi\leq x_1$.

Newton's Method Applied to Real nth Roots

3.9.6 Given $x^n=N$, if x_k is an approximation $x=N^{1/n}$ then the sequence

$$x_{k+1}=\frac{1}{n}\left[\frac{N}{x_k^{n-1}}+(n-1)x_k\right]$$

will converge quadratically to x.

If $n=2$, $x_{k+1}=\frac{1}{2}\left(\frac{N}{x_k}+x_k\right)$,

If $n=3$, $x_{k+1}=\frac{1}{3}\left(\frac{N}{x_k^2}+2x_k\right)$.

Aitken's δ^2-Process for Acceleration of Sequences

3.9.7 If x_k, x_{k+1}, x_{k+2} are three successive iterates in a sequence converging with an error which is approximately in geometric progression, then

$$\bar{x}_k=x_k-\frac{(x_k-x_{k+1})^2}{\Delta^2x_k}=\frac{x_kx_{k+2}-x_{k+1}^2}{\Delta^2x_k};$$

$$\Delta^2x_k=x_k-2x_{k+1}+x_{k+2}$$

is an improved estimate of x. In fact, if $x_k=x+O(\lambda^k)$ then $\bar{x}=x+O(\lambda^k)$, $|\lambda|<1$.

3.10. Theorems on Continued Fractions

Definitions

3.10.1

(1) Let
$$f=b_0+\cfrac{a_1}{b_1+\cfrac{a_2}{b_2+\cfrac{a_3}{b_3+\dots}}}$$
$$=b_0+\frac{a_1}{b_1+}\,\frac{a_2}{b_2+}\,\frac{a_3}{b_3+}\cdots$$

If the number of terms is finite, f is called a terminating continued fraction. If the number of terms is infinite, f is called an infinite continued fraction and the terminating fraction
$$f_n=\frac{A_n}{B_n}=b_0+\frac{a_1}{b_1+}\,\frac{a_2}{b_2+}\cdots\frac{a_n}{b_n}$$
is called the nth convergent of f.

(2) If $\lim\limits_{n\to\infty}\frac{A_n}{B_n}$ exists, the infinite continued fraction f is said to be convergent. If $a_i=1$ and the b_i are integers there is always convergence.

Theorems

(1) If a_i and b_i are positive then $f_{2n}<f_{2n+2}$, $f_{2n-1}>f_{2n+1}$.

(2) If $f_n=\frac{A_n}{B_n}$,
$$A_n=b_nA_{n-1}+a_nA_{n-2}$$
$$B_n=b_nB_{n-1}+a_nB_{n-2}$$
where $A_{-1}=1$, $A_0=b_0$, $B_{-1}=0$, $B_0=1$.

(3)
$$\begin{bmatrix}A_n\\B_n\end{bmatrix}=\begin{bmatrix}A_{n-1}&A_{n-2}\\B_{n-1}&B_{n-2}\end{bmatrix}\begin{bmatrix}b_n\\a_n\end{bmatrix}$$

(4)
$$A_nB_{n-1}-A_{n-1}B_n=(-1)^{n-1}\prod_{k=1}^{n}a_k$$

(5) For every $n\geq 0$,
$$f_n=b_0+\frac{c_1a_1}{c_1b_1+}\,\frac{c_1c_2a_2}{c_2b_2+}\,\frac{c_2c_3a_3}{c_3b_3+}\cdots\frac{c_{n-1}c_na_n}{c_nb_n}.$$

(6) $1+b_2+b_2b_3+\dots+b_2b_3\dots b_n$
$$=\frac{1}{1-}\,\frac{b_2}{b_2+1-}\,\frac{b_3}{b_3+1-}\cdots\frac{b_n}{-b_n+1}$$
$$\frac{1}{u_1}+\frac{1}{u_2}+\dots+\frac{1}{u_n}=\frac{1}{u_1-}\,\frac{u_1^2}{u_1+u_2-}\cdots\frac{u_{n-1}^2}{-u_{n-1}+u_n}$$
$$\frac{1}{a_0}-\frac{x}{a_0a_1}+\frac{x^2}{a_0a_1a_2}\dots+(-1)^n\frac{x^n}{a_0a_1a_2\dots a_n}$$
$$=\frac{1}{a_0+}\,\frac{a_0x}{a_1-x+}\,\frac{a_1x}{a_2-x+}\cdots\frac{a_{n-1}x}{+a_n-x}$$

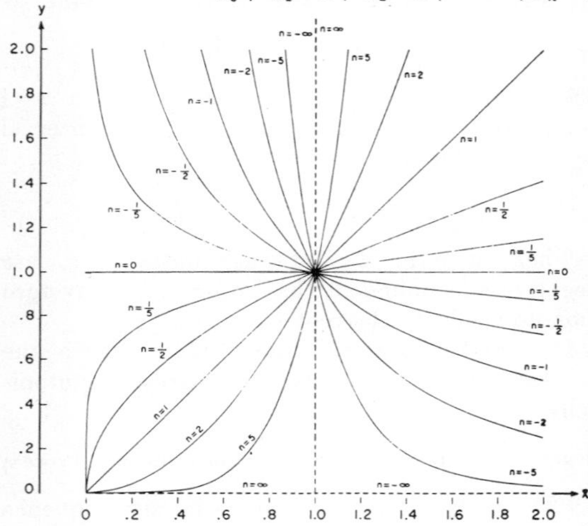

FIGURE 3.1. $y=x^n$.
$\pm n=0, \frac{1}{5}, \frac{1}{2}, 1, 2, 5.$

Logarithmic, Exponential, Circular and Hyperbolic Functions

4.1. Logarithmic Function

Integral Representation

4.1.1 $$\ln z=\int_1^z \frac{dt}{t}$$

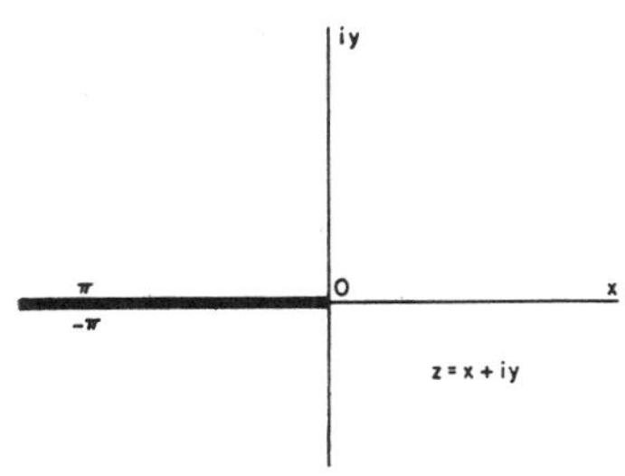

FIGURE 4.1. *Branch cut for* ln z *and* z^a.
(a not an integer or zero.)

where the path of integration does not pass through the origin or cross the negative real axis. $\ln z$ is a single-valued function, regular in the z-plane cut along the negative real axis, real when z is positive.

$$z=x+iy=re^{i\theta}.$$

4.1.2 $$\ln z=\ln r+i\theta \quad (-\pi<\theta\leq\pi).$$

4.1.3 $$r=(x^2+y^2)^{\frac{1}{2}}, \quad x=r\cos\theta, \quad y=r\sin\theta,$$
$$\theta=\arctan\frac{y}{x}.$$

The general logarithmic function is the many-valued function Ln z defined by

4.1.4 $$\text{Ln } z=\int_1^z \frac{dt}{t}$$

where the path does not pass through the origin.

4.1.5
$$\text{Ln }(re^{i\theta})=\ln(re^{i\theta})+2k\pi i=\ln r+i(\theta+2k\pi),$$

k being an arbitrary integer. $\ln z$ is said to be the *principal branch* of Ln z.

Logarithmic Identities

4.1.6 $$\text{Ln }(z_1z_2)=\text{Ln } z_1+\text{Ln } z_2.$$

(i.e., every value of Ln (z_1z_2) is one of the values of Ln z_1+Ln z_2.)

4.1.7 $$\ln(z_1z_2)=\ln z_1+\ln z_2 \quad (-\pi<\arg z_1+\arg z_2\leq\pi)$$

4.1.8 $$\text{Ln }\frac{z_1}{z_2}=\text{Ln } z_1-\text{Ln } z_2$$

4.1.9 $$\ln\frac{z_1}{z_2}=\ln z_1-\ln z_2 \quad (-\pi<\arg z_1-\arg z_2\leq\pi)$$

4.1.10 $$\text{Ln } z^n=n \text{ Ln } z \quad (n \text{ integer})$$

4.1.11 $$\ln z^n=n\ln z \quad (n \text{ integer}, \quad -\pi<n\arg z\leq\pi)$$

Special Values (see chapter 1)

4.1.12 $$\ln 1=0$$

4.1.13 $$\ln 0=-\infty$$

4.1.14 $$\ln(-1)=\pi i$$

4.1.15 $$\ln(\pm i)=\pm\tfrac{1}{2}\pi i$$

4.1.16 $\ln e=1$, e is the real number such that
$$\int_1^e \frac{dt}{t}=1$$

4.1.17 $$e=\lim_{n\to\infty}\left(1+\frac{1}{n}\right)^n=2.71828\ 18284\ldots$$
(see **4.2.21**)

Logarithms to General Base

4.1.18 $$\log_a z=\ln z/\ln a$$

4.1.19 $$\log_a z=\frac{\log_b z}{\log_b a}$$

4.1.20 $$\log_a b=\frac{1}{\log_b a}$$

4.1.21 $$\log_e z=\ln z$$

4.1.22 $$\log_{10} z=\ln z/\ln 10=\log_{10} e\ \ln z =(.43429\ \ 44819\ldots)\ln z$$

4.1.23 $\ln z = \ln 10 \log_{10} z = (2.30258\ 50929\ldots)\log_{10} z$

($\log_e x = \ln x$, called natural, Napierian, or hyperbolic logarithms; $\log_{10} x$, called common or Briggs logarithms.)

Series Expansions

4.1.24 $$\ln(1+z) = z - \tfrac{1}{2}z^2 + \tfrac{1}{3}z^3 - \ldots \qquad (|z|\le 1 \text{ and } z\ne -1)$$

4.1.25
$$\ln z = \left(\frac{z-1}{z}\right) + \frac{1}{2}\left(\frac{z-1}{z}\right)^2 + \frac{1}{3}\left(\frac{z-1}{z}\right)^3 + \ldots \qquad (\mathscr{R}z \ge \tfrac{1}{2})$$

4.1.26
$$\ln z = (z-1) - \tfrac{1}{2}(z-1)^2 + \tfrac{1}{3}(z-1)^3 - \ldots \qquad (|z-1|\le 1,\quad z\ne 0)$$

4.1.27
$$\ln z = 2\left[\left(\frac{z-1}{z+1}\right) + \frac{1}{3}\left(\frac{z-1}{z+1}\right)^3 + \frac{1}{5}\left(\frac{z-1}{z+1}\right)^5 + \ldots\right] \qquad (\mathscr{R}z \ge 0,\quad z\ne 0)$$

4.1.28 $$\ln\left(\frac{z+1}{z-1}\right) = 2\left(\frac{1}{z} + \frac{1}{3z^3} + \frac{1}{5z^5} + \ldots\right) \qquad (|z|\ge 1,\quad z\ne \pm 1)$$

4.1.29
$$\ln(z+a) = \ln a + 2\left[\left(\frac{z}{2a+z}\right) + \frac{1}{3}\left(\frac{z}{2a+z}\right)^3 + \frac{1}{5}\left(\frac{z}{2a+z}\right)^5 + \ldots\right] \qquad (a>0,\quad \mathscr{R}z \ge -a \ne z)$$

Limiting Values

4.1.30 $$\lim_{x\to\infty} x^{-\alpha}\ln x = 0 \qquad (\alpha \text{ constant},\quad \mathscr{R}\alpha > 0)$$

4.1.31 $$\lim_{x\to 0} x^{\alpha}\ln x = 0 \qquad (\alpha \text{ constant},\quad \mathscr{R}\alpha > 0)$$

4.1.32
$$\lim_{m\to\infty}\left(\sum_{k=1}^{m}\frac{1}{k} - \ln m\right) = \gamma \text{ (Euler's constant)} = .57721\ 56649\ldots$$
(see chapters **1**, **6** and **23**)

Inequalities

4.1.33 $$\frac{x}{1+x} < \ln(1+x) < x \qquad (x>-1,\quad x\ne 0)$$

4.1.34 $$x < -\ln(1-x) < \frac{x}{1-x} \qquad (x<1,\quad x\ne 0)$$

4.1.35 $$|\ln(1-x)| < \frac{3x}{2} \qquad (0<x\le .5828)$$

4.1.36 $$\ln x \le x-1 \qquad (x>0)$$

4.1.37 $\ln x \le n(x^{1/n}-1)$ for any positive n $\qquad (x>0)$

4.1.38 $$|\ln(1+z)| \le -\ln(1-|z|) \qquad (|z|<1)$$

Continued Fractions

4.1.39
$$\ln(1+z) = \frac{z}{1+}\,\frac{z}{2+}\,\frac{z}{3+}\,\frac{4z}{4+}\,\frac{4z}{5+}\,\frac{9z}{6+}\cdots$$
(z in the plane cut from -1 to $-\infty$)

4.1.40
$$\ln\left(\frac{1+z}{1-z}\right) = \frac{2z}{1-}\,\frac{z^2}{3-}\,\frac{4z^2}{5-}\,\frac{9z^2}{7-}\cdots$$
(z in the cut plane of Figure 4.7.)

Polynomial Approximations [2]

4.1.41 $$\frac{1}{\sqrt{10}} \le x \le \sqrt{10}$$

$$\log_{10} x = a_1 t + a_3 t^3 + \epsilon(x), \qquad t = (x-1)/(x+1)$$
$$|\epsilon(x)| \le 6\times 10^{-4}$$
$$a_1 = .86304 \qquad a_3 = .36415$$

4.1.42 $$\frac{1}{\sqrt{10}} \le x \le \sqrt{10}$$

$$\log_{10} x = a_1 t + a_3 t^3 + a_5 t^5 + a_7 t^7 + a_9 t^9 + \epsilon(x)$$
$$t = (x-1)/(x+1)$$
$$|\epsilon(x)| \le 10^{-7}$$

$a_1 = .86859\ 1718 \qquad a_7 = .09437\ 6476$

$a_3 = .28933\ 5524 \qquad a_9 = .19133\ 7714$

$a_5 = .17752\ 2071$

4.1.43 $$0 \le x \le 1$$

$$\ln(1+x) = a_1 x + a_2 x^2 + a_3 x^3 + a_4 x^4 + a_5 x^5 + \epsilon(x)$$
$$|\epsilon(x)| \le 1\times 10^{-5}$$

$a_1 = .99949\ 556 \qquad a_4 = -.13606\ 275$

$a_2 = -.49190\ 896 \qquad a_5 = .03215\ 845$

$a_3 = .28947\ 478$

[2] The approximations **4.1.41** to **4.1.44** are from C. Hastings, Jr., Approximations for digital computers. Princeton Univ. Press, Princeton, N.J., 1955 (with permission).

4.1.44 $0 \le x \le 1$

$$\ln(1+x)=a_1x+a_2x^2+a_3x^3+a_4x^4+a_5x^5+a_6x^6+a_7x^7+a_8x^8+\epsilon(x)$$

$$|\epsilon(x)|\le 3\times 10^{-8}$$

$a_1=$	.99999 64239	$a_5=$	.16765 40711
$a_2=$	−.49987 41238	$a_6=$	−.09532 93897
$a_3=$	.33179 90258	$a_7=$	.03608 84937
$a_4=$	−.24073 38084	$a_8=$	−.00645 35442

Approximation in Terms of Chebyshev Polynomials [3]

4.1.45 $0 \le x \le 1$

$T_n^*(x)=\cos n\theta$, $\cos\theta=2x-1$ (see chapter **22**)

$$\ln(1+x)=\sum_{n=0}^{\infty} A_n T_n^*(x)$$

n	A_n	n	A_n
0	.37645 2813	6	−.00000 8503
1	.34314 5750	7	.00000 1250
2	−.02943 7252	8	−.00000 0188
3	.00336 7089	9	.00000 0029
4	−.00043 3276	10	−.00000 0004
5	.00005 9471	11	.00000 0001

Differentiation Formulas

4.1.46 $$\frac{d}{dz}\ln z=\frac{1}{z}$$

4.1.47 $$\frac{d^n}{dz^n}\ln z=(-1)^{n-1}(n-1)!z^{-n}$$

Integration Formulas

4.1.48 $$\int\frac{dz}{z}=\ln z$$

4.1.49 $$\int \ln z\,dz=z\ln z-z$$

4.1.50

$$\int z^n\ln z\,dz=\frac{z^{n+1}}{n+1}\ln z-\frac{z^{n+1}}{(n+1)^2}\qquad (n\ne -1,\quad n \text{ integer})$$

4.1.51

$$\int z^n(\ln z)^m\,dz=\frac{z^{n+1}(\ln z)^m}{n+1}-\frac{m}{n+1}\int z^n(\ln z)^{m-1}dz\qquad (n\ne -1)$$

[3] The approximation **4.1.45** is from C. W. Clenshaw, Polynomial approximations to elementary functions, Math. Tables Aids Comp. **8**, 143–147 (1954)

4.1.52 $$\int\frac{dz}{z\ln z}=\ln\ln z$$

4.1.53

$$\int \ln[z+(z^2\pm1)^{\frac{1}{2}}]dz=z\ln[z+(z^2\pm1)^{\frac{1}{2}}]-(z^2\pm1)^{\frac{1}{2}}$$

4.1.54

$$\int z^n\ln[z+(z^2\pm1)^{\frac{1}{2}}]dz=\frac{z^{n+1}}{n+1}\ln[z+(z^2\pm1)^{\frac{1}{2}}]-\frac{1}{n+1}\int\frac{z^{n+1}}{(z^2\pm1)^{\frac{1}{2}}}dz\qquad (n\ne -1)$$

Definite Integrals

4.1.55 $$\int_0^1\frac{\ln t}{1-t}dt=-\pi^2/6$$

4.1.56 $$\int_0^1\frac{\ln t}{1+t}dt=-\pi^2/12$$

4.1.57 $$\int_0^x\frac{dt}{\ln t}=li(x)$$ (see **5.1.3**)

4.2. Exponential Function

Series Expansion

4.2.1

$$e^z=\exp z=1+\frac{z}{1!}+\frac{z^2}{2!}+\frac{z^3}{3!}+\cdots\qquad (z=x+iy)$$

where e is the real number defined in **4.1.16**

Fundamental Properties

4.2.2 $\mathrm{Ln}(\exp z)=z+2k\pi i$ (k any integer)

4.2.3 $\ln(\exp z)=z\quad(-\pi<\mathscr{I}z\le\pi)$

4.2.4 $\exp(\ln z)=\exp(\mathrm{Ln}\,z)=z$

4.2.5 $$\frac{d}{dz}\exp z=\exp z$$

Definition of General Powers

4.2.6 If $N=a^z$, then $z=\mathrm{Log}_a N$

4.2.7 $a^z=\exp(z\ln a)$

4.2.8 If $a=|a|\exp(i\arg a)\quad(-\pi<\arg a\le\pi)$

4.2.9 $|a^z|=|a|^x e^{-y\arg a}$

4.2.10 $\arg(a^z)=y\ln|a|+x\arg a$

4.2.11

$\mathrm{Ln}\,a^z=z\ln a$ for one of the values of $\mathrm{Ln}\,a^z$

4.2.12 $\ln a^x=x\ln a$ (a real and positive)

4.2.13 $|e^z|=e^x$

4.2.14 $\arg(e^z)=y$

4.2.15 $a^{z_1}a^{z_2}=a^{z_1+z_2}$

4.2.16 $a^zb^z=(ab)^z \qquad (-\pi<\arg a+\arg b\leq\pi)$

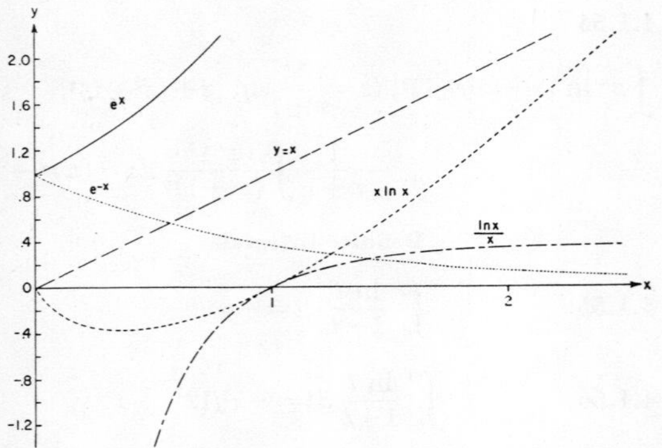

FIGURE 4.2. *Logarithmic and exponential functions.*

Periodic Property

4.2.17 $e^{z+2\pi ki}=e^z \qquad (k \text{ any integer})$

Exponential Identities

4.2.18 $e^{z_1}e^{z_2}=e^{z_1+z_2}$

4.2.19 $(e^{z_1})^{z_2}=e^{z_1z_2} \qquad (-\pi<\mathscr{I}z_1\leq\pi)$

The restriction $(-\pi<\mathscr{I}z_1\leq\pi)$ can be removed if z_2 is an integer.

Limiting Values

4.2.20

$$\lim_{|z|\to\infty} z^\alpha e^{-z}=0 \qquad (|\arg z|\leq\tfrac{1}{2}\pi-\epsilon<\tfrac{1}{2}\pi, \quad \alpha \text{ constant})$$

4.2.21 $$\lim_{m\to\infty}\left(1+\frac{z}{m}\right)^m=e^z$$

Special Values (see chapter 1)

4.2.22 $e=2.71828\ 18284\ldots$

4.2.23 $e^0=1$

4.2.24 $e^\infty=\infty$

4.2.25 $e^{-\infty}=0$

4.2.26 $e^{\pm\pi i}=-1$

4.2.27 $e^{\pm\frac{\pi i}{2}}=\pm i$

4.2.28 $e^{2\pi ki}=1 \quad (k \text{ any integer})$

Exponential Inequalities

If x is real and different from zero

4.2.29 $e^{-\frac{x}{1-x}}<1-x<e^{-x} \quad (x<1)$

4.2.30 $e^x>1+x$

4.2.31 $e^x<\frac{1}{1-x} \quad (x<1)$

4.2.32 $\frac{x}{1+x}<(1-e^{-x})<x \quad (x>-1)$

4.2.33 $x<(e^x-1)<\frac{x}{1-x} \quad (x<1)$

4.2.34 $1+x>e^{\frac{x}{1+x}} \quad (x>-1)$

4.2.35 $e^x>1+\frac{x^n}{n!} \quad (n>0, \quad x>0)$

4.2.36 $e^x>\left(1+\frac{x}{y}\right)^y>e^{\frac{xy}{x+y}} \quad (x>0, \quad y>0)$

4.2.37 $e^{-x}<1-\frac{x}{2} \quad (0<x\leq1.5936)$

4.2.38 $\frac{1}{4}|z|<|e^z-1|<\frac{7}{4}|z| \quad (0<|z|<1)$

4.2.39 $|e^z-1|\leq e^{|z|}-1\leq|z|e^{|z|} \quad (\text{all } z)$

Continued Fractions

4.2.40

$$e^z=\frac{1}{1-}\,\frac{z}{1+}\,\frac{z}{2-}\,\frac{z}{3+}\,\frac{z}{2-}\,\frac{z}{5+}\,\frac{z}{2-}\cdots \qquad (|z|<\infty)$$

$$=1+\frac{z}{1-}\,\frac{z}{2+}\,\frac{z}{3-}\,\frac{z}{2+}\,\frac{z}{5-}\,\frac{z}{2+}\,\frac{z}{7-}\cdots \qquad (|z|<\infty)$$

$$=1+\frac{z}{(1-z/2)+}\,\frac{z^2/4\cdot3}{1+}\,\frac{z^2/4\cdot15}{1+}\,\frac{z^2/4\cdot35}{1+}\cdots\frac{z^2/4(4n^2-1)}{1+}\cdots \quad (|z|<\infty)$$

4.2.41

$$e^z-e_{n-1}(z)=\frac{z^n}{n!-}\,\frac{n!z}{(n+1)+}\,\frac{z}{(n+2)-}\,\frac{(n+1)z}{(n+3)+}\,\frac{2z}{(n+4)-}\,\frac{(n+2)z}{(n+5)+}\,\frac{3z}{(n+6)-}\cdots \quad (|z|<\infty)$$

(For $e_n(z)$ see **6.5.11**)

4.2.42

$$e^{2a \arctan \frac{1}{z}}=1+\frac{2a}{z-a+}\frac{a^2+1}{3z+}\frac{a^2+4}{5z+}\frac{a^2+9}{7z+}\cdots$$

(z in the cut plane of Figure 4.4.)

Polynomial Approximations [4]

4.2.43 $0\leq x\leq \ln 2=.693\ldots$

$$e^{-x}=1+a_1x+a_2x^2+\epsilon(x)$$

$$|\epsilon(x)|\leq 3\times 10^{-3}$$

$a_1=-.9664 \qquad a_2=.3536$

4.2.44 $0\leq x\leq \ln 2$

$$e^{-x}=1+a_1x+a_2x^2+a_3x^3+a_4x^4+\epsilon(x)$$

$$|\epsilon(x)|\leq 3\times 10^{-5}$$

$a_1=-.99986\,84 \qquad a_3=-.15953\,32$
$a_2=\;\;.49829\,26 \qquad a_4=\;\;.02936\,41$

4.2.45 $0\leq x\leq \ln 2$

$$e^{-x}=1+a_1x+a_2x^2+a_3x^3+a_4x^4+a_5x^5+a_6x^6+a_7x^7+\epsilon(x)$$

$$|\epsilon(x)|\leq 2\times 10^{-10}$$

$a_1=-.99999\,99995 \qquad a_5=-.00830\,13598$
$a_2=\;\;.49999\,99206 \qquad a_6=\;\;.00132\,98820$
$a_3=-.16666\,53019 \qquad a_7=-.00014\,13161$
$a_4=\;\;.04165\,73475$

4.2.46 [5] $0\leq x\leq 1$

$$10^x=(1+a_1x+a_2x^2+a_3x^3+a_4x^4)^2+\epsilon(x)$$

$$|\epsilon(x)|\leq 7\times 10^{-4}$$

$a_1=1.14991\,96 \qquad a_3=.20800\,30$
$a_2=\;.67743\,23 \qquad a_4=.12680\,89$

4.2.47 $0\leq x\leq 1$

$$10^x=(1+a_1x+a_2x^2+a_3x^3+a_4x^4+a_5x^5+a_6x^6+a_7x^7)^2+\epsilon(x)$$

$$|\epsilon(x)|<5\times 10^{-8}$$

$a_1=1.15129\,277603 \qquad a_5=.01742\,111988$
$a_2=\;.66273\,088429 \qquad a_6=.00255\,491796$
$a_3=\;.25439\,357484 \qquad a_7=.00093\,264267$
$a_4=\;.07295\,173666$

[4] The approximations **4.2.43** to **4.2.45** are from B. Carlson, M. Goldstein, Rational approximation of functions, Los Alamos Scientific Laboratory LA-1943, Los Alamos, N. Mex., 1955

[5] The approximations **4.2.46** to **4.2.47** are from C. Hastings, Jr., Approximations for digital computers. Princeton Univ. Press, Princeton, N.J., 1955

Approximations in Terms of Chebyshev Polynomials [6]

4.2.48 $0\leq x\leq 1$

$T_n^*(x)=\cos n\theta, \quad \cos\theta=2x-1$ (see chapter **22**)

$$e^x=\sum_{n=0}^{\infty} A_nT_n^*(x) \qquad e^{-x}=\sum_{n=0}^{\infty} A_nT_n^*(x)$$

n	A_n	n	A_n
0	1.75338 7654	0	.64503 5270
1	.85039 1654	1	−.31284 1606
2	.10520 8694	2	.03870 4116
3	.00872 2105	3	−.00320 8683
4	.00054 3437	4	.00019 9919
5	.00002 7115	5	−.00000 9975
6	.00000 1128	6	.00000 0415
7	.00000 0040	7	−.00000 0015
8	.00000 0001		

Differentiation Formulas

4.2.49 $$\frac{d}{dz}e^z=e^z$$

4.2.50 $$\frac{d^n}{dz^n}e^{az}=a^ne^{az}$$

4.2.51 $$\frac{d}{dz}a^z=a^z\ln a$$

4.2.52 $$\frac{d}{dz}z^a=az^{a-1}$$

4.2.53 $$\frac{d}{dz}z^z=(1+\ln z)z^z$$

Integration Formulas

4.2.54 $$\int e^{az}dz=e^{az}/a$$

4.2.55

$$\int z^ne^{az}dz=\frac{e^{az}}{a^{n+1}}[(az)^n-n(az)^{n-1}+n(n-1)(az)^{n-2}+\ldots+(-1)^{n-1}n!(az)+(-1)^nn!] \quad (n\geq 0)$$

4.2.56

$$\int\frac{e^{az}}{z^n}dz=-\frac{e^{az}}{(n-1)z^{n-1}}+\frac{a}{n-1}\int\frac{e^{az}}{z^{n-1}}dz \quad (n>1)$$

(See chapters **5**, **7** and **29** for other integrals involving exponential functions.)

4.3. Circular Functions

Definitions

4.3.1 $$\sin z=\frac{e^{iz}-e^{-iz}}{2i} \qquad (z=x+iy)$$

4.3.2 $$\cos z=\frac{e^{iz}+e^{-iz}}{2}$$

[6] The approximations **4.2.48** are from C. W. Clenshaw, Polynomial approximations to elementary functions, Math. Tables Aids Comp. **8**, 143–147 (1954)

4.3.3 $\tan z=\frac{\sin z}{\cos z}$

4.3.4 $\csc z=\frac{1}{\sin z}$

4.3.5 $\sec z=\frac{1}{\cos z}$

4.3.6 $\cot z=\frac{1}{\tan z}$

Periodic Properties

4.3.7 $\sin (z+2k\pi)=\sin z$ (k any integer)

4.3.8 $\cos (z+2k\pi)=\cos z$

4.3.9 $\tan (z+k\pi)=\tan z$

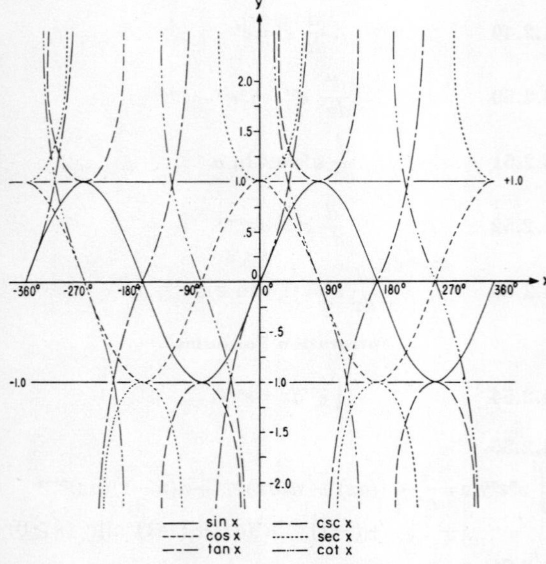

FIGURE 4.3. *Circular functions.*

Relations Between Circular Functions

4.3.10 $\sin^2 z+\cos^2 z=1$

4.3.11 $\sec^2 z-\tan^2 z=1$

4.3.12 $\csc^2 z-\cot^2 z=1$

Negative Angle Formulas

4.3.13 $\sin (-z)=-\sin z$

4.3.14 $\cos (-z)=\cos z$

4.3.15 $\tan (-z)=-\tan z$

Addition Formulas

4.3.16 $\sin (z_1+z_2)=\sin z_1 \cos z_2+\cos z_1 \sin z_2$

4.3.17 $\cos (z_1+z_2)=\cos z_1 \cos z_2-\sin z_1 \sin z_2$

4.3.18 $\tan (z_1+z_2)=\frac{\tan z_1+\tan z_2}{1-\tan z_1 \tan z_2}$

4.3.19 $\cot (z_1+z_2)=\frac{\cot z_1 \cot z_2-1}{\cot z_2+\cot z_1}$

Half-Angle Formulas

4.3.20 $\sin \frac{z}{2}=\pm\left(\frac{1-\cos z}{2}\right)^{\frac{1}{2}}$

4.3.21 $\cos \frac{z}{2}=\pm\left(\frac{1+\cos z}{2}\right)^{\frac{1}{2}}$

4.3.22 $\tan \frac{z}{2}=\pm\left(\frac{1-\cos z}{1+\cos z}\right)^{\frac{1}{2}}=\frac{1-\cos z}{\sin z}=\frac{\sin z}{1+\cos z}$

The ambiguity in sign may be resolved with the aid of a diagram.

Transformation of Trigonometric Integrals

If $\tan \frac{u}{2}=z$ then

4.3.23 $\sin u=\frac{2z}{1+z^2}, \quad \cos u=\frac{1-z^2}{1+z^2}, \quad du=\frac{2}{1+z^2}\, dz$

Multiple-Angle Formulas

4.3.24 $\sin 2z=2 \sin z \cos z=\frac{2 \tan z}{1+\tan^2 z}$

4.3.25 $\cos 2z=2 \cos^2 z-1=1-2 \sin^2 z$

$$=\cos^2 z-\sin^2 z=\frac{1-\tan^2 z}{1+\tan^2 z}$$

4.3.26 $\tan 2z=\frac{2 \tan z}{1-\tan^2 z}=\frac{2 \cot z}{\cot^2 z-1}=\frac{2}{\cot z-\tan z}$

4.3.27 $\sin 3z=3 \sin z-4 \sin^3 z$

4.3.28 $\cos 3z=-3 \cos z+4 \cos^3 z$

4.3.29 $\sin 4z=8 \cos^3 z \sin z-4 \cos z \sin z$

4.3.30 $\cos 4z=8 \cos^4 z-8 \cos^2 z+1$

Products of Sines and Cosines

4.3.31 $2 \sin z_1 \sin z_2=\cos (z_1-z_2)-\cos (z_1+z_2)$

4.3.32 $2 \cos z_1 \cos z_2=\cos (z_1-z_2)+\cos (z_1+z_2)$

4.3.33 $2 \sin z_1 \cos z_2=\sin (z_1-z_2)+\sin (z_1+z_2)$

Addition and Subtraction of Two Circular Functions

4.3.34

$$\sin z_1+\sin z_2=2 \sin\left(\frac{z_1+z_2}{2}\right) \cos\left(\frac{z_1-z_2}{2}\right)$$

4.3.35

$$\sin z_1 - \sin z_2 = 2\cos\left(\frac{z_1+z_2}{2}\right)\sin\left(\frac{z_1-z_2}{2}\right)$$

4.3.36

$$\cos z_1 + \cos z_2 = 2\cos\left(\frac{z_1+z_2}{2}\right)\cos\left(\frac{z_1-z_2}{2}\right)$$

4.3.37

$$\cos z_1 - \cos z_2 = -2\sin\left(\frac{z_1+z_2}{2}\right)\sin\left(\frac{z_1-z_2}{2}\right)$$

4.3.38

$$\tan z_1 \pm \tan z_2 = \frac{\sin(z_1 \pm z_2)}{\cos z_1 \cos z_2}$$

4.3.39

$$\cot z_1 \pm \cot z_2 = \frac{\sin(z_2 \pm z_1)}{\sin z_1 \sin z_2}$$

Relations Between Squares of Sines and Cosines

4.3.40

$$\sin^2 z_1 - \sin^2 z_2 = \sin(z_1+z_2)\sin(z_1-z_2)$$

4.3.41

$$\cos^2 z_1 - \cos^2 z_2 = -\sin(z_1+z_2)\sin(z_1-z_2)$$

4.3.42

$$\cos^2 z_1 - \sin^2 z_2 = \cos(z_1+z_2)\cos(z_1-z_2)$$

4.3.43

Signs of the Circular Functions in the Four Quadrants

Quadrant	sin csc	cos sec	tan cot
I	+	+	+
II	+	−	−
III	−	−	+
IV	−	+	−

4.3.44

Functions of Angles in Any Quadrant in Terms of Angles in the First Quadrant. ($0 \leq \theta \leq \frac{\pi}{2}$, k any integer)

	$-\theta$	$\frac{\pi}{2}\pm\theta$	$\pi\pm\theta$	$\frac{3\pi}{2}\pm\theta$	$2k\pi\pm\theta$
sin	$-\sin\theta$	$\cos\theta$	$\mp\sin\theta$	$-\cos\theta$	$\pm\sin\theta$
cos	$\cos\theta$	$\mp\sin\theta$	$-\cos\theta$	$\pm\sin\theta$	$+\cos\theta$
tan	$-\tan\theta$	$\mp\cot\theta$	$\pm\tan\theta$	$\mp\cot\theta$	$\pm\tan\theta$
csc	$-\csc\theta$	$+\sec\theta$	$\mp\csc\theta$	$-\sec\theta$	$\pm\csc\theta$
sec	$\sec\theta$	$\mp\csc\theta$	$-\sec\theta$	$\pm\csc\theta$	$+\sec\theta$
cot	$-\cot\theta$	$\mp\tan\theta$	$\pm\cot\theta$	$\mp\tan\theta$	$\pm\cot\theta$

4.3.45 Relations Between Circular (or Inverse Circular) Functions

	$\sin x=a$	$\cos x=a$	$\tan x=a$	$\csc x=a$	$\sec x=a$	$\cot x=a$
$\sin x$	a	$(1-a^2)^{\frac{1}{2}}$	$a(1+a^2)^{-\frac{1}{2}}$	a^{-1}	$a^{-1}(a^2-1)^{\frac{1}{2}}$	$(1+a^2)^{-\frac{1}{2}}$
$\cos x$	$(1-a^2)^{\frac{1}{2}}$	a	$(1+a^2)^{-\frac{1}{2}}$	$a^{-1}(a^2-1)^{\frac{1}{2}}$	a^{-1}	$a(1+a^2)^{-\frac{1}{2}}$
$\tan x$	$a(1-a^2)^{-\frac{1}{2}}$	$a^{-1}(1-a^2)^{\frac{1}{2}}$	a	$(a^2-1)^{-\frac{1}{2}}$	$(a^2-1)^{\frac{1}{2}}$	a^{-1}
$\csc x$	a^{-1}	$(1-a^2)^{-\frac{1}{2}}$	$a^{-1}(1+a^2)^{\frac{1}{2}}$	a	$a(a^2-1)^{-\frac{1}{2}}$	$(1+a^2)^{\frac{1}{2}}$
$\sec x$	$(1-a^2)^{-\frac{1}{2}}$	a^{-1}	$(1+a^2)^{\frac{1}{2}}$	$a(a^2-1)^{-\frac{1}{2}}$	a	$a^{-1}(1+a^2)^{\frac{1}{2}}$
$\cot x$	$a^{-1}(1-a^2)^{\frac{1}{2}}$	$a(1-a^2)^{-\frac{1}{2}}$	a^{-1}	$(a^2-1)^{\frac{1}{2}}$	$(a^2-1)^{-\frac{1}{2}}$	a

$\left(0\leq x\leq\frac{\pi}{2}\right)$ Illustration: If $\sin x=a$, $\cot x=a^{-1}(1-a^2)^{\frac{1}{2}}$

$\operatorname{arcsec} a = \operatorname{arccot} (a^2-1)^{-\frac{1}{2}}$

4.3.46 Circular Functions for Certain Angles

	0 0°	$\pi/12$ 15°	$\pi/6$ 30°	$\pi/4$ 45°	$\pi/3$ 60°
sin	0	$\frac{\sqrt{2}}{4}(\sqrt{3}-1)$	1/2	$\sqrt{2}/2$	$\sqrt{3}/2$
cos	1	$\frac{\sqrt{2}}{4}(\sqrt{3}+1)$	$\sqrt{3}/2$	$\sqrt{2}/2$	1/2
tan	0	$2-\sqrt{3}$	$\sqrt{3}/3$	1	$\sqrt{3}$
csc	∞	$\sqrt{2}(\sqrt{3}+1)$	2	$\sqrt{2}$	$2\sqrt{3}/3$
sec	1	$\sqrt{2}(\sqrt{3}-1)$	$2\sqrt{3}/3$	$\sqrt{2}$	2
cot	∞	$2+\sqrt{3}$	$\sqrt{3}$	1	$\sqrt{3}/3$

	$5\pi/12$ 75°	$\pi/2$ 90°	$7\pi/12$ 105°	$2\pi/3$ 120°
sin	$\frac{\sqrt{2}}{4}(\sqrt{3}+1)$	1	$\frac{\sqrt{2}}{4}(\sqrt{3}+1)$	$\sqrt{3}/2$
cos	$\frac{\sqrt{2}}{4}(\sqrt{3}-1)$	0	$\frac{-\sqrt{2}}{4}(\sqrt{3}-1)$	$-1/2$
tan	$2+\sqrt{3}$	∞	$-(2+\sqrt{3})$	$-\sqrt{3}$
csc	$\sqrt{2}(\sqrt{3}-1)$	1	$\sqrt{2}(\sqrt{3}-1)$	$2\sqrt{3}/3$
sec	$\sqrt{2}(\sqrt{3}+1)$	∞	$-\sqrt{2}(\sqrt{3}+1)$	-2
cot	$2-\sqrt{3}$	0	$-(2-\sqrt{3})$	$-\sqrt{3}/3$

	$3\pi/4$ 135°	$5\pi/6$ 150°	$11\pi/12$ 165°	π 180°
sin	$\sqrt{2}/2$	1/2	$\frac{\sqrt{2}}{4}(\sqrt{3}-1)$	0
cos	$-\sqrt{2}/2$	$-\sqrt{3}/2$	$\frac{-\sqrt{2}}{4}(\sqrt{3}+1)$	-1
tan	-1	$-\sqrt{3}/3$	$-(2-\sqrt{3})$	0
csc	$\sqrt{2}$	2	$\sqrt{2}(\sqrt{3}+1)$	∞
sec	$-\sqrt{2}$	$-2\sqrt{3}/3$	$-\sqrt{2}(\sqrt{3}-1)$	-1
cot	-1	$-\sqrt{3}$	$-(2+\sqrt{3})$	∞

Euler's Formula

4.3.47 $e^z=e^{x+iy}=e^x(\cos y+i\sin y)$

De Moivre's Theorem

4.3.48 $(\cos z+i\sin z)^\nu=\cos \nu z+i\sin \nu z$

$(-\pi<\mathscr{R}z\leq\pi$ unless ν is an integer)

Relation to Hyperbolic Functions (see 4.5.7 to 4.5.12)

4.3.49 $\sin z=-i\sinh iz$

4.3.50 $\cos z=\cosh iz$

4.3.51 $\tan z=-i\tanh iz$

4.3.52 $\csc z=i\,\mathrm{csch}\, iz$

4.3.53 $\sec z=\mathrm{sech}\, iz$

4.3.54 $\cot z=i\coth iz$

Circular Functions in Terms of Real and Imaginary Parts

4.3.55 $\sin z=\sin x\cosh y+i\cos x\sinh y$

4.3.56 $\cos z=\cos x\cosh y-i\sin x\sinh y$

4.3.57 $\tan z=\frac{\sin 2x+i\sinh 2y}{\cos 2x+\cosh 2y}$

4.3.58 $\cot z=\frac{\sin 2x-i\sinh 2y}{\cosh 2y-\cos 2x}$

Modulus and Phase (Argument) of Circular Functions

4.3.59 $|\sin z|=(\sin^2 x+\sinh^2 y)^{\frac{1}{2}}$

$=[\tfrac{1}{2}(\cosh 2y-\cos 2x)]^{\frac{1}{2}}$

4.3.60 $\arg\sin z=\arctan(\cot x\tanh y)$

4.3.61 $|\cos z|=(\cos^2 x+\sinh^2 y)^{\frac{1}{2}}$

$=[\tfrac{1}{2}(\cosh 2y+\cos 2x)]^{\frac{1}{2}}$

4.3.62 $\arg\cos z=-\arctan(\tan x\tanh y)$

4.3.63 $|\tan z|=\left(\frac{\cosh 2y-\cos 2x}{\cosh 2y+\cos 2x}\right)^{\frac{1}{2}}$

4.3.64 $\arg\tan z=\arctan\left(\frac{\sinh 2y}{\sin 2x}\right)$

Series Expansions

4.3.65

$$\sin z=z-\frac{z^3}{3!}+\frac{z^5}{5!}-\frac{z^7}{7!}+\dots \qquad (|z|<\infty)$$

4.3.66

$$\cos z=1-\frac{z^2}{2!}+\frac{z^4}{4!}-\frac{z^6}{6!}+\dots \qquad (|z|<\infty)$$

4.3.67

$$\tan z=z+\frac{z^3}{3}+\frac{2z^5}{15}+\frac{17z^7}{315}+\ldots+\frac{(-1)^{n-1}2^{2n}(2^{2n}-1)B_{2n}}{(2n)!}z^{2n-1}+\ldots\qquad\left(|z|<\frac{\pi}{2}\right)$$

4.3.68

$$\csc z=\frac{1}{z}+\frac{z}{6}+\frac{7}{360}z^3+\frac{31}{15120}z^5+\ldots+\frac{(-1)^{n-1}2(2^{2n-1}-1)B_{2n}}{(2n)!}z^{2n-1}+\ldots\qquad(|z|<\pi)$$

4.3.69

$$\sec z=1+\frac{z^2}{2}+\frac{5z^4}{24}+\frac{61z^6}{720}+\ldots+\frac{(-1)^nE_{2n}}{(2n)!}z^{2n}+\ldots\qquad\left(|z|<\frac{\pi}{2}\right)$$

4.3.70

$$\cot z=\frac{1}{z}-\frac{z}{3}-\frac{z^3}{45}-\frac{2z^5}{945}-\ldots-\frac{(-1)^{n-1}2^{2n}B_{2n}}{(2n)!}z^{2n-1}-\ldots\qquad(|z|<\pi)$$

4.3.71

$$\ln\frac{\sin z}{z}=\sum_{n=1}^{\infty}\frac{(-1)^n2^{2n-1}B_{2n}}{n(2n)!}z^{2n}\qquad(|z|<\pi)$$

4.3.72

$$\ln\cos z=\sum_{n=1}^{\infty}\frac{(-1)^n2^{2n-1}(2^{2n}-1)B_{2n}}{n(2n)!}z^{2n}\qquad(|z|<\tfrac{1}{2}\pi)$$

4.3.73

$$\ln\frac{\tan z}{z}=\sum_{n=1}^{\infty}\frac{(-1)^{n-1}2^{2n}(2^{2n-1}-1)B_{2n}}{n(2n)!}z^{2n}\qquad(|z|<\tfrac{1}{2}\pi)$$

where B_n and E_n are the Bernoulli and Euler numbers (see chapter **23**).

Limiting Values

4.3.74 $$\lim_{x\to0}\frac{\sin x}{x}=1$$

4.3.75 $$\lim_{x\to0}\frac{\tan x}{x}=1$$

4.3.76 $$\lim_{n\to\infty}n\sin\frac{x}{n}=x$$

4.3.77 $$\lim_{n\to\infty}n\tan\frac{x}{n}=x$$

4.3.78 $$\lim_{n\to\infty}\cos\frac{x}{n}=1$$

Inequalities

4.3.79 $$\frac{\sin x}{x}>\frac{2}{\pi}\qquad\left(-\frac{\pi}{2}<x<\frac{\pi}{2}\right)$$

4.3.80 $$\sin x\le x\le\tan x\qquad\left(0\le x\le\frac{\pi}{2}\right)$$

4.3.81 $$\cos x\le\frac{\sin x}{x}\le1\qquad(0\le x\le\pi)$$

4.3.82 $$\pi<\frac{\sin\pi x}{x(1-x)}\le4\qquad(0<x<1)$$

4.3.83 $$|\sinh y|\le|\sin z|\le\cosh y$$

4.3.84 $$|\sinh y|\le|\cos z|\le\cosh y$$

4.3.85 $$|\csc z|\le\operatorname{csch}|y|$$

4.3.86 $$|\cos z|\le\cosh|z|$$

4.3.87 $$|\sin z|\le\sinh|z|$$

4.3.88 $$|\cos z|<2,\quad|\sin z|\le\frac{6}{5}|z|\qquad(|z|<1)$$

Infinite Products

4.3.89 $$\sin z=z\prod_{k=1}^{\infty}\left(1-\frac{z^2}{k^2\pi^2}\right)$$

4.3.90 $$\cos z=\prod_{k=1}^{\infty}\left(1-\frac{4z^2}{(2k-1)^2\pi^2}\right)$$

Expansion in Partial Fractions

4.3.91 $$\cot z=\frac{1}{z}+2z\sum_{k=1}^{\infty}\frac{1}{z^2-k^2\pi^2}\qquad(z\ne0,\pm\pi,\pm2\pi,\ldots)$$

4.3.92 $$\csc^2 z=\sum_{k=-\infty}^{\infty}\frac{1}{(z-k\pi)^2}\qquad(z\ne0,\pm\pi,\pm2\pi,\ldots)$$

4.3.93 $$\csc z=\frac{1}{z}+2z\sum_{k=1}^{\infty}\frac{(-1)^k}{z^2-k^2\pi^2}\qquad(z\ne0,\pm\pi,\pm2\pi,\ldots)$$

Continued Fractions

4.3.94 $$\tan z=\frac{z}{1-}\,\frac{z^2}{3-}\,\frac{z^2}{5-}\,\frac{z^2}{7-}\cdots\qquad\left(z\ne\frac{\pi}{2}\pm n\pi\right)$$

4.3.95

$$\tan az=\frac{a\tan z}{1+}\,\frac{(1-a^2)\tan^2 z}{3+}\,\frac{(4-a^2)\tan^2 z}{5+}\,\frac{(9-a^2)\tan^2 z}{7+}\cdots\qquad\left(-\frac{\pi}{2}<\mathscr{R}z<\frac{\pi}{2},\quad az\ne\frac{\pi}{2}\pm n\pi\right)$$

Polynomial Approximations [7]

4.3.96 $0\leq x\leq\frac{\pi}{2}$

$$\frac{\sin x}{x}=1+a_2x^2+a_4x^4+\epsilon(x)$$

$$|\epsilon(x)|\leq 2\times 10^{-4}$$

$a_2=-.16605$ $a_4=.00761$

4.3.97 $0\leq x\leq\frac{\pi}{2}$

$$\frac{\sin x}{x}=1+a_2x^2+a_4x^4+a_6x^6+a_8x^8+a_{10}x^{10}+\epsilon(x)$$

$$|\epsilon(x)|\leq 2\times 10^{-9}$$

$a_2=-.16666\ 66664$ $a_8=\ .00000\ 27526$

$a_4=\ .00833\ 33315$ $a_{10}=-.00000\ 00239$

$a_6=-.00019\ 84090$

4.3.98 $0\leq x\leq\frac{\pi}{2}$

$$\cos x=1+a_2x^2+a_4x^4+\epsilon(x)$$

$$|\epsilon(x)|\leq 9\times 10^{-4}$$

$a_2=-.49670$ $a_4=.03705$

4.3.99 $0\leq x\leq\frac{\pi}{2}$

$$\cos x=1+a_2x^2+a_4x^4+a_6x^6+a_8x^8+a_{10}x^{10}+\epsilon(x)$$

$$|\epsilon(x)|\leq 2\times 10^{-9}$$

$a_2=-.49999\ 99963$ $a_8=\ .00002\ 47609$

$a_4=\ .04166\ 66418$ $a_{10}=-.00000\ 02605$

$a_6=-.00138\ 88397$

4.3.100 $0\leq x\leq\frac{\pi}{4}$

$$\frac{\tan x}{x}=1+a_2x^2+a_4x^4+\epsilon(x)$$

$$|\epsilon(x)|\leq 1\times 10^{-3}$$

$a_2=.31755$ $a_4=.20330$

4.3.101 $0\leq x\leq\frac{\pi}{4}$

$$\frac{\tan x}{x}=1+a_2x^2+a_4x^4+a_6x^6+a_8x^8+a_{10}x^{10}+a_{12}x^{12}+\epsilon(x)$$

$$|\epsilon(x)|\leq 2\times 10^{-8}$$

$a_2=.33333\ 14036$ $a_8=.02456\ 50893$

$a_4=.13339\ 23995$ $a_{10}=.00290\ 05250$

$a_6=.05337\ 40603$ $a_{12}=.00951\ 68091$

4.3.102 $0\leq x\leq\frac{\pi}{4}$

$$x\cot x=1+a_2x^2+a_4x^4+\epsilon(x)$$

$$|\epsilon(x)|\leq 3\times 10^{-5}$$

$a_2=-.332867$ $a_4=-.024369$

4.3.103 $0\leq x\leq\frac{\pi}{4}$

$$x\cot x=1+a_2x^2+a_4x^4+a_6x^6+a_8x^8+a_{10}x^{10}+\epsilon(x)$$

$$|\epsilon(x)|\leq 4\times 10^{-10}$$

$a_2=-.33333\ 33410$ $a_8=-.00020\ 78504$

$a_4=-.02222\ 20287$ $a_{10}=-.00002\ 62619$

$a_6=-.00211\ 77168$

Approximations in Terms of Chebyshev Polynomials [8]

4.3.104 $-1\leq x\leq 1$

$T_n^*(x)=\cos n\theta,\ \cos\theta=2x-1$ (see chapter **22**)

$$\sin\tfrac{1}{2}\pi x=x\sum_{n=0}^{\infty}A_nT_n^*(x^2)\qquad \cos\tfrac{1}{2}\pi x=\sum_{n=0}^{\infty}A_nT_n^*(x^2)$$

n	A_n	n	A_n
0	1.27627 8962	0	.47200 1216
1	−.28526 1569	1	−.49940 3258
2	.00911 8016	2	.02799 2080
3	−.00013 6587	3	−.00059 6695
4	.00000 1185	4	.00000 6704
5	−.00000 0007	5	−.00000 0047

[7] The approximations **4.3.96** to **4.3.103** are from B. Carlson, M. Goldstein, Rational approximation of functions, Los Alamos Scientific Laboratory LA-1943, Los Alamos, N. Mex., 1955

[8] The approximations **4.3.104** are from C. W. Clenshaw, Polynomial approximations to elementary functions, Math. Tables Aids Comp. **8**, 143–147 (1954)

Differentiation Formulas

4.3.105 $$\frac{d}{dz}\sin z=\cos z$$

4.3.106 $$\frac{d}{dz}\cos z=-\sin z$$

4.3.107 $$\frac{d}{dz}\tan z=\sec^2 z$$

4.3.108 $$\frac{d}{dz}\csc z=-\csc z\cot z$$

4.3.109 $$\frac{d}{dz}\sec z=\sec z\tan z$$

4.3.110 $$\frac{d}{dz}\cot z=-\csc^2 z$$

4.3.111 $$\frac{d^n}{dz^n}\sin z=\sin\left(z+\frac{1}{2}n\pi\right)$$

4.3.112 $$\frac{d^n}{dz^n}\cos z=\cos\left(z+\frac{1}{2}n\pi\right)$$

Integration Formulas

4.3.113 $$\int\sin z\,dz=-\cos z$$

4.3.114 $$\int\cos z\,dz=\sin z$$

4.3.115 $$\int\tan z\,dz=-\ln\cos z=\ln\sec z$$

4.3.116
$$\int\csc z\,dz=\ln\tan\frac{z}{2}=\ln(\csc z-\cot z)=\frac{1}{2}\ln\frac{1-\cos z}{1+\cos z}$$

4.3.117
$$\int\sec z\,dz=\ln(\sec z+\tan z)=\ln\tan\left(\frac{\pi}{4}+\frac{z}{2}\right)=\mathrm{gd}^{-1}(z)$$

=Inverse Gudermannian Function

$$\mathrm{gd}\,z=2\arctan e^z-\frac{\pi}{2}$$

4.3.118 $$\int\cot z\,dz=\ln\sin z=-\ln\csc z$$

4.3.119
$$\int z^n\sin z\,dz=-z^n\cos z+n\int z^{n-1}\cos z\,dz$$

4.3.120
$$\int\frac{\sin z}{z^n}dz=\frac{-\sin z}{(n-1)z^{n-1}}+\frac{1}{n-1}\int\frac{\cos z}{z^{n-1}}dz\qquad(n>1)$$

4.3.121 $$\int\frac{z}{\sin^2 z}dz=-z\cot z+\ln\sin z$$

4.3.122
$$\int\frac{z\,dz}{\sin^n z}=\frac{-z\cos z}{(n-1)\sin^{n-1} z}-\frac{1}{(n-1)(n-2)\sin^{n-2} z}+\frac{(n-2)}{(n-1)}\int\frac{z\,dz}{\sin^{n-2} z}\quad(n>2)$$

4.3.123
$$\int z^n\cos z\,dz=z^n\sin z-n\int z^{n-1}\sin z\,dz$$

4.3.124
$$\int\frac{\cos z}{z^n}dz=-\frac{\cos z}{(n-1)z^{n-1}}-\frac{1}{n-1}\int\frac{\sin z}{z^{n-1}}dz\quad(n>1)$$

4.3.125 $$\int\frac{z}{\cos^2 z}dz=z\tan z+\ln\cos z$$

4.3.126
$$\int\frac{z\,dz}{\cos^n z}=\frac{z\sin z}{(n-1)\cos^{n-1} z}-\frac{1}{(n-1)(n-2)\cos^{n-2} z}+\frac{(n-2)}{(n-1)}\int\frac{z\,dz}{\cos^{n-2} z}\quad(n>2)$$

4.3.127
$$\int\sin^m z\cos^n z\,dz=\frac{\sin^{m+1} z\cos^{n-1} z}{m+n}+\frac{(n-1)}{(m+n)}\int\sin^m z\cos^{n-2} z\,dz$$
$$=-\frac{\sin^{m-1} z\cos^{n+1} z}{m+n}+\frac{(m-1)}{(m+n)}\int\sin^{m-2} z\cos^n z\,dz$$
$$(m\neq-n)$$

4.3.128
$$\int\frac{dz}{\sin^m z\cos^n z}=\frac{1}{(n-1)\sin^{m-1} z\cos^{n-1} z}+\frac{m+n-2}{n-1}\int\frac{dz}{\sin^m z\cos^{n-2} z}$$
$$(n>1)$$
$$=\frac{-1}{(m-1)\sin^{m-1} z\cos^{n-1} z}+\frac{m+n-2}{m-1}\int\frac{dz}{\sin^{m-2} z\cos^n z}$$
$$(m>1)$$

4.3.129 $$\int\tan^n z\,dz=\frac{\tan^{n-1} z}{n-1}-\int\tan^{n-2} z\,dz\quad(n\neq1)$$

4.3.130 $$\int\cot^n z\,dz=-\frac{\cot^{n-1} z}{n-1}-\int\cot^{n-2} z\,dz\quad(n\neq1)$$

4.3.131

$$\int\frac{dz}{a+b\sin z}=\frac{2}{(a^2-b^2)^{\frac{1}{2}}}\arctan\frac{a\tan\left(\frac{z}{2}\right)+b}{(a^2-b^2)^{\frac{1}{2}}}\qquad(a^2>b^2)$$

$$=\frac{1}{(b^2-a^2)^{\frac{1}{2}}}\ln\left[\frac{a\tan\left(\frac{z}{2}\right)+b-(b^2-a^2)^{\frac{1}{2}}}{a\tan\left(\frac{z}{2}\right)+b+(b^2-a^2)^{\frac{1}{2}}}\right]$$

$(b^2>a^2)$

4.3.132 $$\int\frac{dz}{1\pm\sin z}=\mp\tan\left(\frac{\pi}{4}\mp\frac{z}{2}\right)$$

4.3.133

$$\int\frac{dz}{a+b\cos z}=\frac{2}{(a^2-b^2)^{\frac{1}{2}}}\arctan\frac{(a-b)\tan\frac{z}{2}}{(a^2-b^2)^{\frac{1}{2}}}\qquad(a^2>b^2)$$

$$=\frac{1}{(b^2-a^2)^{\frac{1}{2}}}\ln\left[\frac{(b-a)\tan\frac{z}{2}+(b^2-a^2)^{\frac{1}{2}}}{(b-a)\tan\frac{z}{2}-(b^2-a^2)^{\frac{1}{2}}}\right]$$

$(b^2>a^2)$

4.3.134 $$\int\frac{dz}{1+\cos z}=\tan\frac{z}{2}$$

4.3.135 $$\int\frac{dz}{1-\cos z}=-\cot\frac{z}{2}$$

4.3.136

$$\int e^{az}\sin bz\,dz=\frac{e^{az}}{a^2+b^2}(a\sin bz-b\cos bz)$$

4.3.137

$$\int e^{az}\cos bz\,dz=\frac{e^{az}}{a^2+b^2}(a\cos bz+b\sin bz)$$

4.3.138

$$\int e^{az}\sin^n bz\,dz=\frac{e^{az}\sin^{n-1}bz}{a^2+n^2b^2}(a\sin bz-nb\cos bz)+\frac{n(n-1)b^2}{a^2+n^2b^2}\int e^{az}\sin^{n-2}bz\,dz$$

4.3.139

$$\int e^{az}\cos^n bz\,dz=\frac{e^{az}\cos^{n-1}bz}{a^2+n^2b^2}(a\cos bz+nb\sin bz)+\frac{n(n-1)b^2}{a^2+n^2b^2}\int e^{az}\cos^{n-2}bz\,dz$$

Definite Integrals

4.3.140 $$\int_0^{\pi}\sin mt\sin nt\,dt=0$$

$(m\neq n,\quad m$ and n integers)

$$\int_0^{\pi}\cos mt\cos nt\,dt=0$$

4.3.141 $$\int_0^{\pi}\sin^2 nt\,dt=\int_0^{\pi}\cos^2 nt\,dt=\frac{\pi}{2}$$

(n an integer, $n\neq0$)

4.3.142 $$\int_0^{\infty}\frac{\sin mt}{t}\,dt=\frac{\pi}{2}\qquad(m>0)$$

$$=0\qquad(m=0)$$

$$=-\frac{\pi}{2}\qquad(m<0)$$

4.3.143 $$\int_0^{\infty}\frac{\cos at-\cos bt}{t}\,dt=\ln(b/a)$$

4.3.144 $$\int_0^{\infty}\sin t^2\,dt=\int_0^{\infty}\cos t^2\,dt=\frac{1}{2}\sqrt{\frac{\pi}{2}}$$

4.3.145

$$\int_0^{\pi/2}\ln\sin t\,dt=\int_0^{\pi/2}\ln\cos t\,dt=-\frac{\pi}{2}\ln 2$$

4.3.146 $$\int_0^{\infty}\frac{\cos mt}{1+t^2}\,dt=\frac{\pi}{2}e^{-m}$$

(See chapters **5** and **7** for other integrals involving circular functions.)
(See [5.3] for Fourier transforms.)

4.3.147

Formulas for Solution of Plane Right Triangles

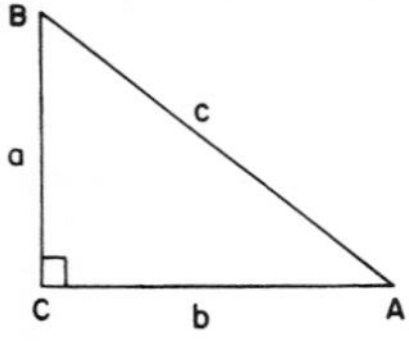

If A, B and C are the vertices (C the right angle), and a, b and c the sides opposite respectively,

$$\sin A=\frac{a}{c}=\frac{1}{\csc A}$$

$$\cos A=\frac{b}{c}=\frac{1}{\sec A}$$

$$\tan A=\frac{a}{b}=\frac{1}{\cot A}$$

versine A=vers $A=1-\cos A$

coversine A=covers $A=1-\sin A$

haversine A=hav $A=\frac{1}{2}$ vers A

exsecant A=exsec $A=\sec A-1$

4.3.148

Formulas for Solution of Plane Triangles

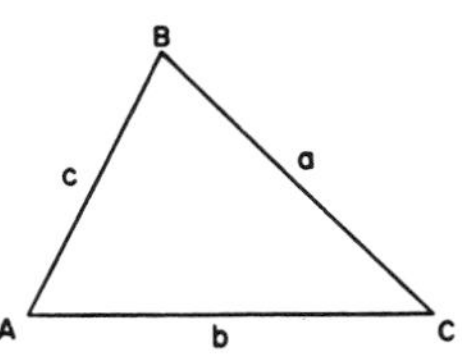

In a triangle with angles A, B and C and sides opposite a, b and c respectively,

$$\frac{a}{\sin A}=\frac{b}{\sin B}=\frac{c}{\sin C}$$

$$\cos A=\frac{c^2+b^2-a^2}{2bc}$$

$$a=b\cos C+c\cos B$$

$$\frac{a+b}{a-b}=\frac{\tan \frac{1}{2}(A+B)}{\tan \frac{1}{2}(A-B)}$$

$$\text{area}=\frac{bc\sin A}{2}=[s(s-a)(s-b)(s-c)]^{\frac{1}{2}}$$

$$s=\tfrac{1}{2}(a+b+c)$$

4.3.149

Formulas for Solution of Spherical Triangles

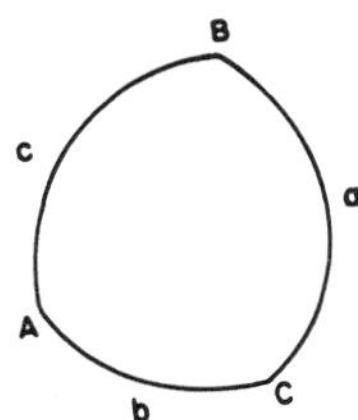

If A, B and C are the three angles and a, b and c the opposite sides,

$$\frac{\sin A}{\sin a}=\frac{\sin B}{\sin b}=\frac{\sin C}{\sin c}$$

$$\cos a=\cos b\cos c+\sin b\sin c\cos A$$

$$=\frac{\cos b\cos(c\pm\theta)}{\cos\theta}$$

where $\tan\theta=\tan b\cos A$

$$\cos A=-\cos B\cos C+\sin B\sin C\cos a$$

4.4. Inverse Circular Functions

Definitions

4.4.1

$$\arcsin z=\int_0^z \frac{dt}{(1-t^2)^{\frac{1}{2}}} \qquad (z=x+iy)$$

4.4.2

$$\arccos z=\int_z^1 \frac{dt}{(1-t^2)^{\frac{1}{2}}}=\frac{\pi}{2}-\arcsin z$$

4.4.3

$$\arctan z=\int_0^z \frac{dt}{1+t^2}$$

The path of integration must not cross the real axis in the case of **4.4.1** and **4.4.2** and the imaginary axis in the case of **4.4.3** except possibly inside the unit circle. Each function is single-valued and regular in the z-plane cut along the real axis from $-\infty$ to -1 and $+1$ to $+\infty$ in the case of **4.4.1** and **4.4.2** and along the imaginary axis from i to $i\infty$ and $-i$ to $-i\infty$ in the case of **4.4.3.**

Inverse circular functions are also written $\arcsin z=\sin^{-1} z$, $\arccos z=\cos^{-1} z$, $\arctan z=\tan^{-1} z$, ...

When $-1\leq x\leq 1$, $\arcsin x$ and $\arccos x$ are real and

4.4.4 $\quad -\frac{1}{2}\pi\leq\arcsin x\leq\frac{1}{2}\pi, \qquad 0\leq\arccos x\leq\pi$

4.4.5 $\quad \arctan z+\operatorname{arccot} z=\pm\frac{\pi}{2} \quad \begin{matrix}\mathscr{R}z\geq 0\\ \mathscr{R}z<0\end{matrix}$

4.4.6 $\quad \operatorname{arccsc} z=\arcsin 1/z$

4.4.7 $\quad \operatorname{arcsec} z=\arccos 1/z$

4.4.8 $\quad \operatorname{arccot} z=\arctan 1/z$

4.4.9 $\quad \operatorname{arcsec} z+\operatorname{arccsc} z=\frac{1}{2}\pi$

(see **4.3.45**)

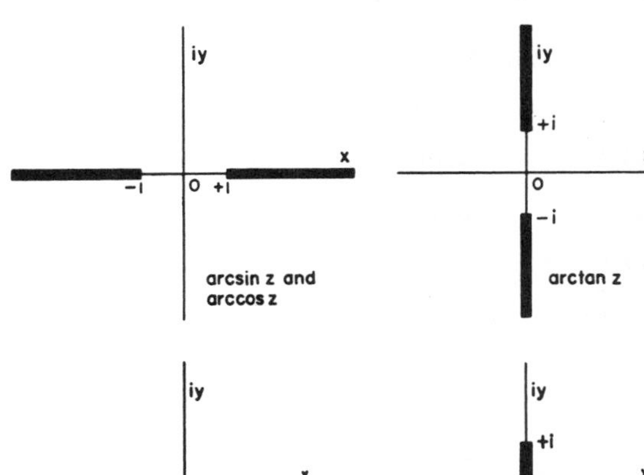

FIGURE 4.4. *Branch cuts for inverse circular functions.*

Fundamental Property

The general solutions of the equations

$$\sin t=z$$

$$\cos t=z$$

$$\tan t=z$$

are respectively

4.4.10 $t=\text{Arcsin } z=(-1)^k \arcsin z+k\pi$

4.4.11 $t=\text{Arccos } z=\pm\arccos z+2k\pi$

4.4.12
$t=\text{Arctan } z=\arctan z+k\pi \qquad (z^2\neq-1)$

where k is an arbitrary integer.

4.4.13 Interval containing principal value

	y x positive or zero	x negative
$\arcsin x$ and $\arctan x$	$0\leq y\leq\pi/2$	$-\pi/2\leq y<0$
$\arccos x$ and $\text{arcsec}\, x$	$0\leq y\leq\pi/2$	$\pi/2<y\leq\pi$
$\text{arccot}\, x$ and $\text{arccsc}\, x$	$0\leq y\leq\pi/2$	$-\pi/2\leq y<0$

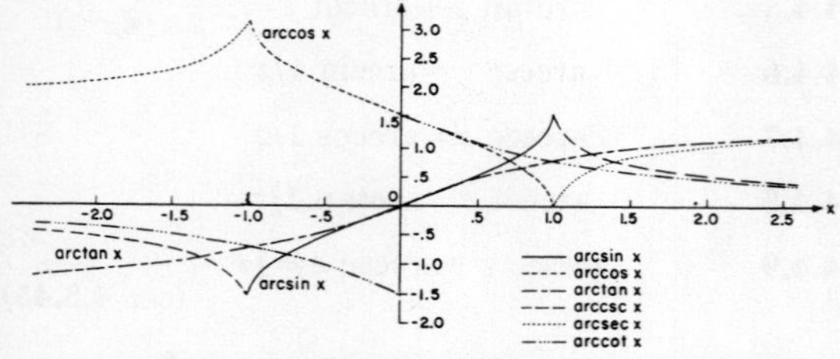

FIGURE 4.5. *Inverse circular functions.*

Functions of Negative Arguments

4.4.14 $\arcsin(-z)=-\arcsin z$

4.4.15 $\arccos(-z)=\pi-\arccos z$

4.4.16 $\arctan(-z)=-\arctan z$

4.4.17 $\text{arccsc}(-z)=-\text{arccsc}\, z$

4.4.18 $\text{arcsec}(-z)=\pi-\text{arcsec}\, z$

4.4.19 $\text{arccot}(-z)=-\text{arccot}\, z$

Relation to Inverse Hyperbolic Functions (see 4.6.14 to 4.6.19)

4.4.20 $\text{Arcsin } z=-i \text{ Arcsinh } iz$

4.4.21 $\text{Arccos } z=\pm i \text{ Arccosh } z$

4.4.22 $\text{Arctan } z=-i \text{ Arctanh } iz \qquad (z^2\neq-1)$

4.4.23 $\text{Arccsc } z=i \text{ Arccsch } iz$

4.4.24 $\text{Arcsec } z=\pm i \text{ Arcsech } z$

4.4.25 $\text{Arccot } z=i \text{ Arccoth } iz$

Logarithmic Representations

4.4.26 $\text{Arcsin } x=-i \text{ Ln}[(1-x^2)^{\frac{1}{2}}+ix] \qquad (x^2\leq1)$

4.4.27 $\text{Arccos } x=-i \text{ Ln}[x+i(1-x^2)^{\frac{1}{2}}] \qquad (x^2\leq1)$

4.4.28 $\text{Arctan } x=\frac{i}{2}\text{ Ln }\frac{1-i x}{1+i x}=\frac{i}{2}\text{ Ln }\frac{i+x}{i-x}$

$(x \text{ real})$

4.4.29 $\text{Arccsc } x=-i \text{ Ln}\left[\frac{(x^2-1)^{\frac{1}{2}}+i}{x}\right] \qquad (x^2\geq1)$

4.4.30 $\text{Arcsec } x=-i \text{ Ln}\left[\frac{1+i(x^2-1)^{\frac{1}{2}}}{x}\right] \qquad (x^2\geq1)$

4.4.31 $\text{Arccot } x=\frac{i}{2}\text{ Ln}\left(\frac{ix+1}{ix-1}\right)=\frac{i}{2}\text{ Ln}\left(\frac{x-i}{x+i}\right)$

$(x \text{ real})$

Addition and Subtraction of Two Inverse Circular Functions

4.4.32

$$\text{Arcsin } z_1\pm\text{Arcsin } z_2 =\text{Arcsin}[z_1(1-z_2^2)^{\frac{1}{2}}\pm z_2(1-z_1^2)^{\frac{1}{2}}]$$

4.4.33

$$\text{Arccos } z_1\pm\text{Arccos } z_2 =\text{Arccos}\{z_1z_2\mp[(1-z_1^2)(1-z_2^2)]^{\frac{1}{2}}\}$$

4.4.34

$$\text{Arctan } z_1\pm\text{Arctan } z_2=\text{Arctan}\left(\frac{z_1\pm z_2}{1\mp z_1z_2}\right)$$

4.4.35

$$\text{Arcsin } z_1\pm\text{Arccos } z_2 =\text{Arcsin}\{z_1z_2\pm[(1-z_1^2)(1-z_2^2)]^{\frac{1}{2}}\} =\text{Arccos}[z_2(1-z_1^2)^{\frac{1}{2}}\mp z_1(1-z_2^2)^{\frac{1}{2}}]$$

4.4.36

$$\text{Arctan } z_1\pm\text{Arccot } z_2 =\text{Arctan}\left(\frac{z_1z_2\pm1}{z_2\mp z_1}\right)=\text{Arccot}\left(\frac{z_2\mp z_1}{z_1z_2\pm1}\right)$$

Inverse Circular Functions in Terms of Real and Imaginary Parts

4.4.37

$$\text{Arcsin } z=k\pi+(-1)^k\arcsin\beta +(-1)^k i\ln[\alpha+(\alpha^2-1)^{\frac{1}{2}}]$$

4.4.38

$$\text{Arccos } z=2k\pi\pm\{\arccos\beta-i\ln[\alpha+(\alpha^2-1)^{\frac{1}{2}}]\}$$

4.4.39

$$\text{Arctan } z=k\pi+\tfrac{1}{2}\arctan\left(\frac{2x}{1-x^2-y^2}\right)+\frac{i}{4}\ln\left[\frac{x^2+(y+1)^2}{x^2+(y-1)^2}\right]\quad(z^2\neq-1)$$

where k is an integer or zero and

$$\alpha=\tfrac{1}{2}[(x+1)^2+y^2]^{\frac{1}{2}}+\tfrac{1}{2}[(x-1)^2+y^2]^{\frac{1}{2}}$$
$$\beta=\tfrac{1}{2}[(x+1)^2+y^2]^{\frac{1}{2}}-\tfrac{1}{2}[(x-1)^2+y^2]^{\frac{1}{2}}$$

Series Expansions

4.4.40

$$\arcsin z=z+\frac{z^3}{2\cdot 3}+\frac{1\cdot 3z^5}{2\cdot 4\cdot 5}+\frac{1\cdot 3\cdot 5z^7}{2\cdot 4\cdot 6\cdot 7}+\ldots\quad(|z|<1)$$

4.4.41

$$\arcsin(1-z)=\frac{\pi}{2}-(2z)^{\frac{1}{2}}\left[1+\sum_{k=1}^{\infty}\frac{1\cdot 3\cdot 5\ldots(2k-1)}{2^{2k}(2k+1)k!}z^k\right]\quad(|z|<2)$$

4.4.42

$$\arctan z=z-\frac{z^3}{3}+\frac{z^5}{5}-\frac{z^7}{7}+\ldots\quad(|z|\leq 1\text{ and }z^2\neq-1)$$

$$=\frac{\pi}{2}-\frac{1}{z}+\frac{1}{3z^3}-\frac{1}{5z^5}+\ldots(|z|>1\text{ and }z^2\neq-1)$$

$$=\frac{z}{1+z^2}\left[1+\frac{2}{3}\frac{z^2}{1+z^2}+\frac{2\cdot 4}{3\cdot 5}\left(\frac{z^2}{1+z^2}\right)^2+\ldots\right]\quad(z^2\neq-1)$$

Continued Fractions

4.4.43 $$\arctan z=\frac{z}{1+}\,\frac{z^2}{3+}\,\frac{4z^2}{5+}\,\frac{9z^2}{7+}\,\frac{16z^2}{9+}\cdots$$

(z in the cut plane of Figure 4.4.)

4.4.44 $$\frac{\arcsin z}{\sqrt{1-z^2}}=\frac{z}{1-}\,\frac{1\cdot 2z^2}{3-}\,\frac{1\cdot 2z^2}{5-}\,\frac{3\cdot 4z^2}{7-}\,\frac{3\cdot 4z^2}{9-}\cdots$$

(z in the cut plane of Figure 4.4.)

Polynomial Approximations [9]

4.4.45 $0\leq x\leq 1$

$$\arcsin x=\frac{\pi}{2}-(1-x)^{\frac{1}{2}}(a_0+a_1x+a_2x^2+a_3x^3)+\epsilon(x)$$

$$|\epsilon(x)|\leq 5\times 10^{-5}$$

$a_0=$	1.57072 88	$a_2=$	.07426 10
$a_1=$	−.21211 44	$a_3=$	−.01872 93

4.4.46 $0\leq x\leq 1$

$$\arcsin x=\frac{\pi}{2}-(1-x)^{\frac{1}{2}}(a_0+a_1x+a_2x^2+a_3x^3+a_4x^4+a_5x^5+a_6x^6+a_7x^7)+\epsilon(x)$$

$$|\epsilon(x)|\leq 2\times 10^{-8}$$

$a_0=$	1.57079 63050	$a_4=$	.03089 18810
$a_1=$	−.21459 88016	$a_5=$	−.01708 81256
$a_2=$	.08897 89874	$a_6=$	.00667 00901
$a_3=$	−.05017 43046	$a_7=$	−.00126 24911

4.4.47 $-1\leq x\leq 1$

$$\arctan x=a_1x+a_3x^3+a_5x^5+a_7x^7+a_9x^9+\epsilon(x)$$

$$|\epsilon(x)|\leq 10^{-5}$$

$a_1=$	.99986 60	$a_7=$	−.08513 30
$a_3=$	−.33029 95	$a_9=$	.02083 51
$a_5=$	.18014 10		

4.4.48 [10] $-1\leq x\leq 1$

$$\arctan x=\frac{x}{1+.28x^2}+\epsilon(x)$$

$$|\epsilon(x)|\leq 5\times 10^{-3}$$

4.4.49 [11] $0\leq x\leq 1$

$$\frac{\arctan x}{x}=1+\sum_{k=1}^{8}a_{2k}x^{2k}+\epsilon(x)$$

$$|\epsilon(x)|\leq 2\times 10^{-8}$$

$a_2=$	−.33333 14528	$a_{10}=$	−.07528 96400
$a_4=$	.19993 55085	$a_{12}=$	.04290 96138
$a_6=$	−.14208 89944	$a_{14}=$	−.01616 57367
$a_8=$	.10656 26393	$a_{16}=$	.00286 62257

[9] The approximations **4.4.45** to **4.4.47** are from C. Hastings, Jr., Approximations for digital computers. Princeton Univ. Press, Princeton, N.J., 1955

[10] The approximation **4.4.48** is from C. Hastings, Jr., Note 143, Math. Tables Aids Comp. **6**, 68 (1953)

[11] The approximation **4.4.49** is from B. Carlson, M. Goldstein, Rational approximation of functions, Los Alamos Scientific Laboratory LA–1943, Los Alamos, N. Mex., 1955

Approximations in Terms of Chebyshev Polynomials [12]

4.4.50 $$-1\leq x\leq 1$$

$T_n^*(x)=\cos n\theta, \quad \cos\theta=2x-1$ (see chapter **22**)

$$\arctan x=x\sum_{n=0}^{\infty} A_n T_n^*(x^2)$$

n	A_n	n	A_n
0	.88137 3587	6	.00000 3821
1	−.10589 2925	7	−.00000 0570
2	.01113 5843	8	.00000 0086
3	−.00138 1195	9	−.00000 0013
4	.00018 5743	10	.00000 0002
5	−.00002 6215		

For $x>1$, use $\arctan x=\frac{1}{2}\pi-\arctan(1/x)$

4.4.51 $$-\tfrac{1}{2}\sqrt{2}\leq x\leq\tfrac{1}{2}\sqrt{2}$$

$$\arcsin x=x\sum_{n=0}^{\infty} A_n T_n^*(2x^2)$$

$$0\leq x\leq\tfrac{1}{2}\sqrt{2}$$

$$\arccos x=\tfrac{1}{2}\pi-x\sum_{n=0}^{\infty} A_n T_n^*(2x^2)$$

n	A_n	n	A_n
0	1.05123 1959	5	.00000 5881
1	.05494 6487	6	.00000 0777
2	.00408 0631	7	.00000 0107
3	.00040 7890	8	.00000 0015
4	.00004 6985	9	.00000 0002

For $\frac{1}{2}\sqrt{2}\leq x\leq 1$, use $\arcsin x=\arccos(1-x^2)^{\frac{1}{2}}$, $\arccos x=\arcsin(1-x^2)^{\frac{1}{2}}$.

Differentiation Formulas

4.4.52 $$\frac{d}{dz}\arcsin z=(1-z^2)^{-\frac{1}{2}}$$

4.4.53 $$\frac{d}{dz}\arccos z=-(1-z^2)^{-\frac{1}{2}}$$

4.4.54 $$\frac{d}{dz}\arctan z=\frac{1}{1+z^2}$$

4.4.55 $$\frac{d}{dz}\operatorname{arccot} z=\frac{-1}{1+z^2}$$

4.4.56 $$\frac{d}{dz}\operatorname{arcsec} z=\frac{1}{z(z^2-1)^{\frac{1}{2}}}$$

4.4.57 $$\frac{d}{dz}\operatorname{arccsc} z=-\frac{1}{z(z^2-1)^{\frac{1}{2}}}$$

Integration Formulas

4.4.58 $$\int\arcsin z\,dz=z\arcsin z+(1-z^2)^{\frac{1}{2}}$$

4.4.59 $$\int\arccos z\,dz=z\arccos z-(1-z^2)^{\frac{1}{2}}$$

4.4.60 $$\int\arctan z\,dz=z\arctan z-\tfrac{1}{2}\ln(1+z^2)$$

4.4.61
$$\int\operatorname{arccsc} z\,dz=z\operatorname{arccsc} z\pm\ln[z+(z^2-1)^{\frac{1}{2}}]$$
$$\begin{bmatrix} 0<\operatorname{arccsc} z<\frac{\pi}{2} \\ -\frac{\pi}{2}<\operatorname{arccsc} z<0\end{bmatrix}$$

4.4.62
$$\int\operatorname{arcsec} z\,dz=z\operatorname{arcsec} z\mp\ln[z+(z^2-1)^{\frac{1}{2}}]$$
$$\begin{bmatrix} 0<\operatorname{arcsec} z<\frac{\pi}{2} \\ \frac{\pi}{2}<\operatorname{arcsec} z<\pi\end{bmatrix}$$

4.4.63
$$\int\operatorname{arccot} z\,dz=z\operatorname{arccot} z+\tfrac{1}{2}\ln(1+z^2)$$

4.4.64
$$\int z\arcsin z\,dz=\left(\frac{z^2}{2}-\frac{1}{4}\right)\arcsin z+\frac{z}{4}(1-z^2)^{\frac{1}{2}}$$

4.4.65
$$\int z^n\arcsin z\,dz=\frac{z^{n+1}}{n+1}\arcsin z-\frac{1}{n+1}\int\frac{z^{n+1}}{(1-z^2)^{\frac{1}{2}}}dz \qquad (n\neq -1)$$

4.4.66
$$\int z\arccos z\,dz=\left(\frac{z^2}{2}-\frac{1}{4}\right)\arccos z-\frac{z}{4}(1-z^2)^{\frac{1}{2}}$$

4.4.67
$$\int z^n\arccos z\,dz=\frac{z^{n+1}}{n+1}\arccos z+\frac{1}{n+1}\int\frac{z^{n+1}}{(1-z^2)^{\frac{1}{2}}}dz \qquad (n\neq -1)$$

4.4.68
$$\int z\arctan z\,dz=\frac{1}{2}(1+z^2)\arctan z-\frac{z}{2}$$

[12] The approximations **4.4.50** to **4.4.51** are from C. W. Clenshaw, Polynomial approximations to elementary functions, Math. Tables Aids Comp. **8**, 143–147 (1954)

4.4.69

$$\int z^n \arctan z\, dz = \frac{z^{n+1}}{n+1} \arctan z - \frac{1}{n+1} \int \frac{z^{n+1}}{1+z^2} dz \qquad (n \neq -1)$$

4.4.70

$$\int z \operatorname{arccot} z\, dz = \frac{1}{2} (1+z^2) \operatorname{arccot} z + \frac{z}{2}$$

4.4.71

$$\int z^n \operatorname{arccot} z\, dz = \frac{z^{n+1}}{n+1} \operatorname{arccot} z + \frac{1}{n+1} \int \frac{z^{n+1}}{1+z^2} dz \qquad (n \neq -1)$$

4.5. Hyperbolic Functions

Definitions

4.5.1 $\sinh z = \dfrac{e^z - e^{-z}}{2} \qquad (z = x+iy)$

4.5.2 $\cosh z = \dfrac{e^z + e^{-z}}{2}$

4.5.3 $\tanh z = \sinh z / \cosh z$

4.5.4 $\operatorname{csch} z = 1/\sinh z$

4.5.5 $\operatorname{sech} z = 1/\cosh z$

4.5.6 $\coth z = 1/\tanh z$

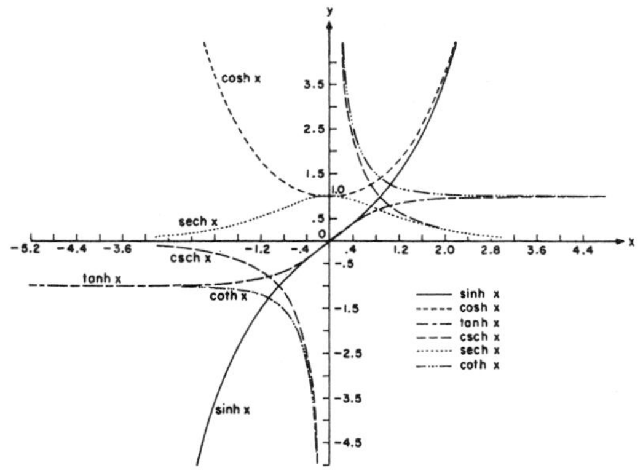

FIGURE 4.6. *Hyperbolic functions.*

Relation to Circular Functions (see 4.3.49 to 4.3.54)

Hyperbolic formulas can be derived from trigonometric identities by replacing z by iz

4.5.7 $\sinh z = -i \sin iz$

4.5.8 $\cosh z = \cos iz$

4.5.9 $\tanh z = -i \tan iz$

4.5.10 $\operatorname{csch} z = i \csc iz$

4.5.11 $\operatorname{sech} z = \sec iz$

4.5.12 $\coth z = i \cot iz$

Periodic Properties

4.5.13 $\sinh (z+2k\pi i) = \sinh z \qquad (k \text{ any integer})$

4.5.14 $\cosh (z+2k\pi i) = \cosh z$

4.5.15 $\tanh (z+k\pi i) = \tanh z$

Relations Between Hyperbolic Functions

4.5.16 $\cosh^2 z - \sinh^2 z = 1$

4.5.17 $\tanh^2 z + \operatorname{sech}^2 z = 1$

4.5.18 $\coth^2 z - \operatorname{csch}^2 z = 1$

4.5.19 $\cosh z + \sinh z = e^z$

4.5.20 $\cosh z - \sinh z = e^{-z}$

Negative Angle Formulas

4.5.21 $\sinh (-z) = -\sinh z$

4.5.22 $\cosh (-z) = \cosh z$

4.5.23 $\tanh (-z) = -\tanh z$

Addition Formulas

4.5.24 $\sinh (z_1+z_2) = \sinh z_1 \cosh z_2 + \cosh z_1 \sinh z_2$

4.5.25 $\cosh (z_1+z_2) = \cosh z_1 \cosh z_2 + \sinh z_1 \sinh z_2$

4.5.26 $\tanh (z_1+z_2) = (\tanh z_1 + \tanh z_2)/(1+\tanh z_1 \tanh z_2)$

4.5.27 $\coth (z_1+z_2) = (\coth z_1 \coth z_2 + 1)/(\coth z_2 + \coth z_1)$

Half-Angle Formulas

4.5.28

$$\sinh \frac{z}{2} = \left(\frac{\cosh z - 1}{2} \right)^{\frac{1}{2}}$$

4.5.29

$$\cosh\frac{z}{2}=\left(\frac{\cosh z+1}{2}\right)^{\frac{1}{2}}$$

4.5.30

$$\tanh\frac{z}{2}=\left(\frac{\cosh z-1}{\cosh z+1}\right)^{\frac{1}{2}}=\frac{\cosh z-1}{\sinh z}=\frac{\sinh z}{\cosh z+1}$$

Multiple-Angle Formulas

4.5.31 $\sinh 2z=2\sinh z\cosh z=\dfrac{2\tanh z}{1-\tanh^2 z}$

4.5.32 $\cosh 2z=2\cosh^2 z-1=2\sinh^2 z+1$

$=\cosh^2 z+\sinh^2 z$

4.5.33 $\tanh 2z=\dfrac{2\tanh z}{1+\tanh^2 z}$

4.5.34 $\sinh 3z=3\sinh z+4\sinh^3 z$

4.5.35 $\cosh 3z=-3\cosh z+4\cosh^3 z$

4.5.36 $\sinh 4z=4\sinh^3 z\cosh z+4\cosh^3 z\sinh z$

4.5.37 $\cosh 4z=\cosh^4 z+6\sinh^2 z\cosh^2 z+\sinh^4 z$

Products of Hyperbolic Sines and Cosines

4.5.38 $2\sinh z_1\sinh z_2=\cosh(z_1+z_2)$

$-\cosh(z_1-z_2)$

4.5.39 $2\cosh z_1\cosh z_2=\cosh(z_1+z_2)$

$+\cosh(z_1-z_2)$

4.5.40 $2\sinh z_1\cosh z_2=\sinh(z_1+z_2)$

$+\sinh(z_1-z_2)$

Addition and Subtraction of Two Hyperbolic Functions

4.5.41

$$\sinh z_1+\sinh z_2=2\sinh\left(\frac{z_1+z_2}{2}\right)\cosh\left(\frac{z_1-z_2}{2}\right)$$

4.5.42

$$\sinh z_1-\sinh z_2=2\cosh\left(\frac{z_1+z_2}{2}\right)\sinh\left(\frac{z_1-z_2}{2}\right)$$

4.5.43

$$\cosh z_1+\cosh z_2=2\cosh\left(\frac{z_1+z_2}{2}\right)\cosh\left(\frac{z_1-z_2}{2}\right)$$

4.5.44

$$\cosh z_1-\cosh z_2=2\sinh\left(\frac{z_1+z_2}{2}\right)\sinh\left(\frac{z_1-z_2}{2}\right)$$

4.5.45

$$\tanh z_1+\tanh z_2=\frac{\sinh(z_1+z_2)}{\cosh z_1\cosh z_2}$$

4.5.46

$$\coth z_1+\coth z_2=\frac{\sinh(z_1+z_2)}{\sinh z_1\sinh z_2}$$

Relations Between Squares of Hyperbolic Sines and Cosines

4.5.47

$$\sinh^2 z_1-\sinh^2 z_2=\sinh(z_1+z_2)\sinh(z_1-z_2)$$
$$=\cosh^2 z_1-\cosh^2 z_2$$

4.5.48

$$\sinh^2 z_1+\cosh^2 z_2=\cosh(z_1+z_2)\cosh(z_1-z_2)$$
$$=\cosh^2 z_1+\sinh^2 z_2$$

Hyperbolic Functions in Terms of Real and Imaginary Parts

$(z=x+iy)$

4.5.49 $\sinh z=\sinh x\cos y+i\cosh x\sin y$

4.5.50 $\cosh z=\cosh x\cos y+i\sinh x\sin y$

4.5.51 $\tanh z=\dfrac{\sinh 2x+i\sin 2y}{\cosh 2x+\cos 2y}$

4.5.52 $\coth z=\dfrac{\sinh 2x-i\sin 2y}{\cosh 2x-\cos 2y}$

De Moivre's Theorem

4.5.53 $(\cosh z+\sinh z)^n=\cosh nz+\sinh nz$

Modulus and Phase (Argument) of Hyperbolic Functions

4.5.54 $|\sinh z|=(\sinh^2 x+\sin^2 y)^{\frac{1}{2}}$

$=[\tfrac{1}{2}(\cosh 2x-\cos 2y)]^{\frac{1}{2}}$

4.5.55 $\arg\sinh z=\arctan(\coth x\tan y)$

4.5.56 $|\cosh z|=(\sinh^2 x+\cos^2 y)^{\frac{1}{2}}$

$=[\tfrac{1}{2}(\cosh 2x+\cos 2y)]^{\frac{1}{2}}$

4.5.57 $\arg\cosh z=\arctan(\tanh x\tan y)$

4.5.58 $|\tanh z|=\left(\dfrac{\cosh 2x-\cos 2y}{\cosh 2x+\cos 2y}\right)^{\frac{1}{2}}$

4.5.59 $\arg\tanh z=\arctan\left(\dfrac{\sin 2y}{\sinh 2x}\right)$

4.5.60 Relations Between Hyperbolic (or Inverse Hyperbolic) Functions

	$\sinh x=a$	$\cosh x=a$	$\tanh x=a$	$\operatorname{csch} x=a$	$\operatorname{sech} x=a$	$\coth x=a$
$\sinh x$	a	$(a^2-1)^{\frac{1}{2}}$	$a(1-a^2)^{-\frac{1}{2}}$	a^{-1}	$a^{-1}(1-a^2)^{\frac{1}{2}}$	$(a^2-1)^{-\frac{1}{2}}$
$\cosh x$	$(1+a^2)^{\frac{1}{2}}$	a	$(1-a^2)^{-\frac{1}{2}}$	$a^{-1}(1+a^2)^{\frac{1}{2}}$	a^{-1}	$a(a^2-1)^{-\frac{1}{2}}$
$\tanh x$	$a(1+a^2)^{-\frac{1}{2}}$	$a^{-1}(a^2-1)^{\frac{1}{2}}$	a	$(1+a^2)^{-\frac{1}{2}}$	$(1-a^2)^{\frac{1}{2}}$	a^{-1}
$\operatorname{csch} x$	a^{-1}	$(a^2-1)^{-\frac{1}{2}}$	$a^{-1}(1-a^2)^{\frac{1}{2}}$	a	$a(1-a^2)^{-\frac{1}{2}}$	$(a^2-1)^{\frac{1}{2}}$
$\operatorname{sech} x$	$(1+a^2)^{-\frac{1}{2}}$	a^{-1}	$(1-a^2)^{\frac{1}{2}}$	$a(1+a^2)^{-\frac{1}{2}}$	a	$a^{-1}(a^2-1)^{\frac{1}{2}}$
$\coth x$	$a^{-1}(a^2+1)^{\frac{1}{2}}$	$a(a^2-1)^{-\frac{1}{2}}$	a^{-1}	$(1+a^2)^{\frac{1}{2}}$	$(1-a^2)^{-\frac{1}{2}}$	a

Illustration: If $\sinh x=a$, $\coth x=a^{-1}(a^2+1)^{\frac{1}{2}}$

$\operatorname{arcsech} a=\operatorname{arccoth}(1-a^2)^{-\frac{1}{2}}$

4.5.61 Special Values of the Hyperbolic Functions

z	0	$\frac{\pi}{2}i$	πi	$\frac{3\pi}{2}i$	∞
$\sinh z$	0	i	0	$-i$	∞
$\cosh z$	1	0	-1	0	∞
$\tanh z$	0	∞i	0	$-\infty i$	1
$\operatorname{csch} z$	∞	$-i$	∞	i	0
$\operatorname{sech} z$	1	∞	-1	∞	0
$\coth z$	∞	0	∞	0	1

Series Expansions

4.5.62 $$\sinh z=z+\frac{z^3}{3!}+\frac{z^5}{5!}+\frac{z^7}{7!}+\ldots \qquad (|z|<\infty)$$

4.5.63 $$\cosh z=1+\frac{z^2}{2!}+\frac{z^4}{4!}+\frac{z^6}{6!}+\ldots \qquad (|z|<\infty)$$

4.5.64 $$\tanh z=z-\frac{z^3}{3}+\frac{2}{15}z^5-\frac{17}{315}z^7+\ldots+\frac{2^{2n}(2^{2n}-1)B_{2n}}{(2n)!}z^{2n-1}+\ldots \qquad \left(|z|<\frac{\pi}{2}\right)$$

4.5.65 $$\operatorname{csch} z=\frac{1}{z}-\frac{z}{6}+\frac{7}{360}z^3-\frac{31}{15120}z^5+\ldots-\frac{2(2^{2n-1}-1)B_{2n}}{(2n)!}z^{2n-1}+\ldots \qquad (|z|<\pi)$$

4.5.66 $$\operatorname{sech} z=1-\frac{z^2}{2}+\frac{5}{24}z^4-\frac{61}{720}z^6+\ldots+\frac{E_{2n}}{(2n)!}z^{2n}+\ldots \qquad \left(|z|<\frac{\pi}{2}\right)$$

4.5.67 $$\coth z=\frac{1}{z}+\frac{z}{3}-\frac{z^3}{45}+\frac{2}{945}z^5-\ldots+\frac{2^{2n}B_{2n}}{(2n)!}z^{2n-1}+\ldots \qquad (|z|<\pi)$$

where B_n and E_n are the nth Bernoulli and Euler numbers, see chapter **23.**

Infinite Products

4.5.68 $$\sinh z=z\prod_{k=1}^{\infty}\left(1+\frac{z^2}{k^2\pi^2}\right)$$

4.5.69 $$\cosh z=\prod_{k=1}^{\infty}\left[1+\frac{4z^2}{(2k-1)^2\pi^2}\right]$$

Continued Fraction

4.5.70 $$\tanh z=\frac{z}{1+}\,\frac{z^2}{3+}\,\frac{z^2}{5+}\,\frac{z^2}{7+}\cdots \qquad \left(z\neq\frac{\pi}{2}i\pm n\pi i\right)$$

Differentiation Formulas

4.5.71 $$\frac{d}{dz}\sinh z=\cosh z$$

4.5.72 $$\frac{d}{dz}\cosh z=\sinh z$$

4.5.73 $$\frac{d}{dz}\tanh z=\operatorname{sech}^2 z$$

4.5.74 $$\frac{d}{dz}\operatorname{csch} z=-\operatorname{csch} z\coth z$$

4.5.75 $$\frac{d}{dz}\operatorname{sech} z=-\operatorname{sech} z \tanh z$$

4.5.76 $$\frac{d}{dz}\coth z=-\operatorname{csch}^2 z$$

Integration Formulas

4.5.77 $$\int \sinh z\,dz=\cosh z$$

4.5.78 $$\int \cosh z\,dz=\sinh z$$

4.5.79 $$\int \tanh z\,dz=\ln \cosh z$$

4.5.80 $$\int \operatorname{csch} z\,dz=\ln \tanh \frac{z}{2}$$

4.5.81 $$\int \operatorname{sech} z\,dz=\arctan (\sinh z)$$

4.5.82 $$\int \coth z\,dz=\ln \sinh z$$

4.5.83
$$\int z^n \sinh z\,dz=z^n \cosh z-n\int z^{n-1}\cosh z\,dz$$

4.5.84
$$\int z^n \cosh z\,dz=z^n \sinh z-n\int z^{n-1}\sinh z\,dz$$

4.5.85
$$\int \sinh^m z \cosh^n z\,dz=\frac{1}{m+n}\sinh^{m+1} z\cosh^{n-1} z+\frac{n-1}{m+n}\int \sinh^m z\cosh^{n-2} z\,dz$$
$$=\frac{1}{m+n}\sinh^{m-1} z\cosh^{n+1} z-\frac{m-1}{m+n}\int \sinh^{m-2} z\cosh^n z\,dz$$
$$(m+n\neq 0)$$

4.5.86 $$\int \frac{dz}{\sinh^m z\cosh^n z}=\frac{-1}{m-1}\frac{1}{\sinh^{m-1} z\cosh^{n-1} z}-\frac{m+n-2}{m-1}\int \frac{dz}{\sinh^{m-2} z\cosh^n z}\qquad (m\neq 1)$$
$$=\frac{1}{n-1}\frac{1}{\sinh^{m-1} z\cosh^{n-1} z}+\frac{m+n-2}{n-1}\int \frac{dz}{\sinh^m z\cosh^{n-2} z}\qquad (n\neq 1)$$

4.5.87
$$\int \tanh^n z\,dz=-\frac{\tanh^{n-1} z}{n-1}+\int \tanh^{n-2} z\,dz\qquad (n\neq 1)$$

4.5.88
$$\int \coth^n z\,dz=-\frac{\coth^{n-1} z}{n-1}+\int \coth^{n-2} z\,dz\qquad (n\neq 1)$$

(See chapters **5** and **7** for other integrals involving hyperbolic functions.)

4.6. Inverse Hyperbolic Functions

Definitions

4.6.1 $$\operatorname{arcsinh} z=\int_0^z \frac{dt}{(1+t^2)^{\frac{1}{2}}}\qquad (z=x+iy)$$

4.6.2 $$\operatorname{arccosh} z=\int_1^z \frac{dt}{(t^2-1)^{\frac{1}{2}}}$$

4.6.3 $$\operatorname{arctanh} z=\int_0^z \frac{dt}{1-t^2}$$

The paths of integration must not cross the following cuts.

4.6.1 imaginary axis from $-i\infty$ to $-i$ and i to $i\infty$

4.6.2 real axis from $-\infty$ to $+1$

4.6.3 real axis from $-\infty$ to -1 and $+1$ to $+\infty$

Inverse hyperbolic functions are also written $\sinh^{-1} z$, arsinh z, $\mathscr{A}r$ sinh z, etc.

4.6.4 $\operatorname{arccsch} z=\operatorname{arcsinh} 1/z$

4.6.5 $\operatorname{arcsech} z=\operatorname{arccosh} 1/z$

4.6.6 $\operatorname{arccoth} z=\operatorname{arctanh} 1/z$

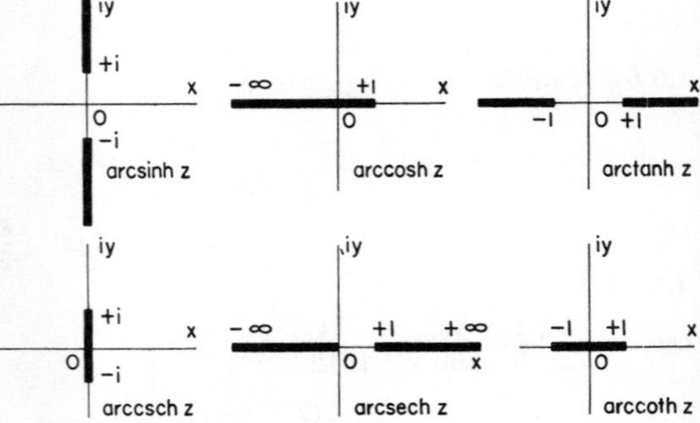

FIGURE 4.7. *Branch cuts for inverse hyperbolic functions.*

4.6.7 $\operatorname{arctanh} z = \operatorname{arccoth} z \pm \tfrac{1}{2}\pi i$

(see **4.5.60**) (according as $\mathscr{I}z \gtrless 0$)

Fundamental Property

The general solutions of the equations

$$z = \sinh t$$
$$z = \cosh t$$
$$z = \tanh t$$

are respectively

4.6.8 $t = \operatorname{Arcsinh} z = (-1)^k \operatorname{arcsinh} z + k\pi i$

4.6.9 $t = \operatorname{Arccosh} z = \pm \operatorname{arccosh} z + 2k\pi i$

4.6.10 $t = \operatorname{Arctanh} z = \operatorname{arctanh} z + k\pi i$

(k, integer)

Functions of Negative Arguments

4.6.11 $\operatorname{arcsinh}(-z) = -\operatorname{arcsinh} z$

4.6.12 $\operatorname{arccosh}(-z) = \pi i - \operatorname{arccosh} z$

4.6.13 $\operatorname{arctanh}(-z) = -\operatorname{arctanh} z$

Relation to Inverse Circular Functions (see 4.4.20 to 4.4.25)

Hyperbolic identities can be derived from trigonometric identities by replacing z by iz.

4.6.14 $\operatorname{Arcsinh} z = -i \operatorname{Arcsin} iz$

4.6.15 $\operatorname{Arccosh} z = \pm i \operatorname{Arccos} z$

4.6.16 $\operatorname{Arctanh} z = -i \operatorname{Arctan} iz$

4.6.17 $\operatorname{Arccsch} z = i \operatorname{Arccsc} iz$

4.6.18 $\operatorname{Arcsech} z = \pm i \operatorname{Arcsec} z$

4.6.19 $\operatorname{Arccoth} z = i \operatorname{Arccot} iz$

Logarithmic Representations

4.6.20 $\operatorname{arcsinh} x = \ln [x + (x^2+1)^{\frac{1}{2}}]$

4.6.21 $\operatorname{arccosh} x = \ln [x + (x^2-1)^{\frac{1}{2}}]$ $(x \geq 1)$

4.6.22 $\operatorname{arctanh} x = \tfrac{1}{2} \ln \dfrac{1+x}{1-x}$ $(0 \leq x^2 < 1)$

4.6.23 $\operatorname{arccsch} x = \ln \left[\dfrac{1}{x} + \left(\dfrac{1}{x^2}+1\right)^{\frac{1}{2}}\right]$ $(x \neq 0)$

4.6.24 $\operatorname{arcsech} x = \ln \left[\dfrac{1}{x} + \left(\dfrac{1}{x^2}-1\right)^{\frac{1}{2}}\right]$ $(0 < x \leq 1)$

4.6.25 $\operatorname{arccoth} x = \dfrac{1}{2} \ln \dfrac{x+1}{x-1}$ $(x^2 > 1)$

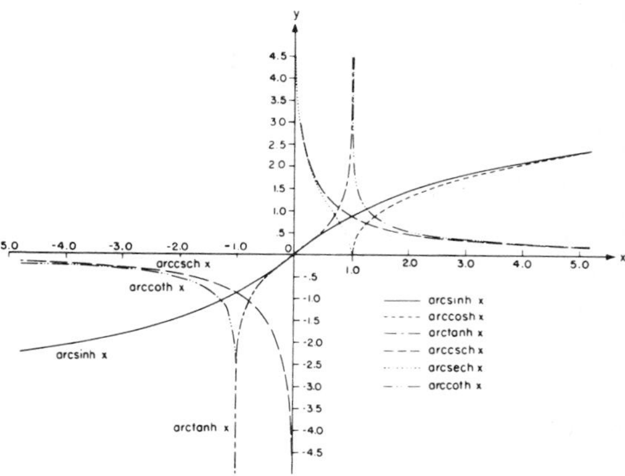

FIGURE 4.8. *Inverse hyperbolic functions.*

Addition and Subtraction of Two Inverse Hyperbolic Functions

4.6.26

$$\operatorname{Arcsinh} z_1 \pm \operatorname{Arcsinh} z_2 = \operatorname{Arcsinh} [z_1(1+z_2^2)^{\frac{1}{2}} \pm z_2(1+z_1^2)^{\frac{1}{2}}]$$

4.6.27

$$\operatorname{Arccosh} z_1 \pm \operatorname{Arccosh} z_2 = \operatorname{Arccosh} \{z_1 z_2 \pm [(z_1^2-1)(z_2^2-1)]^{\frac{1}{2}}\}$$

4.6.28

$$\operatorname{Arctanh} z_1 \pm \operatorname{Arctanh} z_2 = \operatorname{Arctanh} \left(\frac{z_1 \pm z_2}{1 \pm z_1 z_2}\right)$$

4.6.29

$$\operatorname{Arcsinh} z_1 \pm \operatorname{Arccosh} z_2 = \operatorname{Arcsinh} \{z_1 z_2 \pm [(1+z_1^2)(z_2^2-1)]^{\frac{1}{2}}\}$$
$$= \operatorname{Arccosh} [z_2(1+z_1^2)^{\frac{1}{2}} \pm z_1(z_2^2-1)^{\frac{1}{2}}]$$

4.6.30

$$\operatorname{Arctanh} z_1 \pm \operatorname{Arccoth} z_2 = \operatorname{Arctanh} \left(\frac{z_1 z_2 \pm 1}{z_2 \pm z_1}\right)$$
$$= \operatorname{Arccoth} \left(\frac{z_2 \pm z_1}{z_1 z_2 \pm 1}\right)$$

Series Expansions

4.6.31

$$\operatorname{arcsinh} z = z - \frac{1}{2\cdot 3} z^3 + \frac{1\cdot 3}{2\cdot 4\cdot 5} z^5 - \frac{1\cdot 3\cdot 5}{2\cdot 4\cdot 6\cdot 7} z^7 + \dots \qquad (|z|<1)$$

$$= \ln 2z + \frac{1}{2\cdot 2z^2} - \frac{1\cdot 3}{2\cdot 4\cdot 4z^4} + \frac{1\cdot 3\cdot 5}{2\cdot 4\cdot 6\cdot 6z^6} - \dots \qquad (|z|>1)$$

4.6.32

$$\operatorname{arccosh} z = \ln 2z - \frac{1}{2\cdot 2z^2} - \frac{1\cdot 3}{2\cdot 4\cdot 4z^4} - \frac{1\cdot 3\cdot 5}{2\cdot 4\cdot 6\cdot 6z^6} - \dots \qquad (|z|>1)$$

4.6.33 $\operatorname{arctanh} z = z + \frac{z^3}{3} + \frac{z^5}{5} + \frac{z^7}{7} + \dots \qquad (|z|<1)$

4.6.34 $\operatorname{arccoth} z = \frac{1}{z} + \frac{1}{3z^3} + \frac{1}{5z^5} + \frac{1}{7z^7} + \dots \qquad (|z|>1)$

Continued Fractions

4.6.35 $\operatorname{arctanh} z = \frac{z}{1-}\,\frac{z^2}{3-}\,\frac{4z^2}{5-}\,\frac{9z^2}{7-}\dots$

(z in the cut plane of Figure 4.7.)

4.6.36

$$\frac{\operatorname{arcsinh} z}{\sqrt{1+z^2}} = \frac{z}{1+}\,\frac{1\cdot 2z^2}{3+}\,\frac{1\cdot 2z^2}{5+}\,\frac{3\cdot 4z^2}{7+}\,\frac{3\cdot 4z^2}{9+}\dots$$

Differentiation Formulas

4.6.37 $\frac{d}{dz}\operatorname{arcsinh} z = (1+z^2)^{-\frac{1}{2}}$

4.6.38 $\frac{d}{dz}\operatorname{arccosh} z = (z^2-1)^{-\frac{1}{2}}$

4.6.39 $\frac{d}{dz}\operatorname{arctanh} z = (1-z^2)^{-1}$

4.6.40 $\frac{d}{dz}\operatorname{arccsch} z = \mp\frac{1}{z(1+z^2)^{\frac{1}{2}}}$

(according as $\mathscr{R}z \gtrless 0$)

4.6.41 $\frac{d}{dz}\operatorname{arcsech} z = \mp\frac{1}{z(1-z^2)^{\frac{1}{2}}}$

4.6.42 $\frac{d}{dz}\operatorname{arccoth} z = (1-z^2)^{-1}$

Integration Formulas

4.6.43 $\int \operatorname{arcsinh} z\,dz = z\operatorname{arcsinh} z - (1+z^2)^{\frac{1}{2}}$

4.6.44 $\int \operatorname{arccosh} z\,dz = z\operatorname{arccosh} z - (z^2-1)^{\frac{1}{2}}$

4.6.45 $\int \operatorname{arctanh} z\,dz = z\operatorname{arctanh} z + \frac{1}{2}\ln(1-z^2)$

4.6.46 $\int \operatorname{arccsch} z\,dz = z\operatorname{arccsch} z \pm \operatorname{arcsinh} z$

(according as $\mathscr{R}z \gtrless 0$)

4.6.47 $\int \operatorname{arcsech} z\,dz = z\operatorname{arcsech} z \pm \arcsin z$

4.6.48 $\int \operatorname{arccoth} z\,dz = z\operatorname{arccoth} z + \frac{1}{2}\ln(z^2-1)$

4.6.49

$$\int z\operatorname{arcsinh} z\,dz = \frac{2z^2+1}{4}\operatorname{arcsinh} z - \frac{z}{4}(z^2+1)^{\frac{1}{2}}$$

4.6.50

$$\int z^n\operatorname{arcsinh} z\,dz = \frac{z^{n+1}}{n+1}\operatorname{arcsinh} z - \frac{1}{n+1}\int\frac{z^{n+1}}{(1+z^2)^{\frac{1}{2}}}dz \qquad (n\neq -1)$$

4.6.51

$$\int z\operatorname{arccosh} z\,dz = \frac{2z^2-1}{4}\operatorname{arccosh} z - \frac{z}{4}(z^2-1)^{\frac{1}{2}}$$

4.6.52

$$\int z^n\operatorname{arccosh} z\,dz = \frac{z^{n+1}}{n+1}\operatorname{arccosh} z - \frac{1}{n+1}\int\frac{z^{n+1}}{(z^2-1)^{\frac{1}{2}}}dz \qquad (n\neq -1)$$

4.6.53

$$\int z\operatorname{arctanh} z\,dz = \frac{z^2-1}{2}\operatorname{arctanh} z + \frac{z}{2}$$

4.6.54

$$\int z^n\operatorname{arctanh} z\,dz = \frac{z^{n+1}}{n+1}\operatorname{arctanh} z - \frac{1}{n+1}\int\frac{z^{n+1}}{1-z^2}dz \qquad (n\neq -1)$$

4.6.55

$$\int z\operatorname{arccsch} z\,dz = \frac{z^2}{2}\operatorname{arccsh} z \pm \frac{1}{2}(1+z^2)^{\frac{1}{2}}$$

(according as $\mathscr{R}z \gtrless 0$)

4.6.56

$$\int z^n\operatorname{arccsch} z\,dz = \frac{z^{n+1}}{n+1}\operatorname{arccsch} z \pm \frac{1}{n+1}\int\frac{z^n}{(z^2+1)^{\frac{1}{2}}}dz \qquad (n\neq -1)$$

4.6.57
$$\int z \operatorname{arcsech} z\,dz = \frac{z^2}{2}\operatorname{arcsech} z \mp \frac{1}{2}(1-z^2)^{\frac{1}{2}}$$
(according as $\mathscr{R}z \gtreqless 0$)

4.6.58
$$\int z^n \operatorname{arcsech} z\,dz = \frac{z^{n+1}}{n+1}\operatorname{arcsech} z \pm \frac{1}{n+1}\int \frac{z^n}{(1-z^2)^{\frac{1}{2}}}\,dz$$
$(n \neq -1)$

4.6.59
$$\int z \operatorname{arccoth} z\,dz = \frac{z^2-1}{2}\operatorname{arccoth} z + \frac{z}{2}$$

4.6.60
$$\int z^n \operatorname{arccoth} z\,dz = \frac{z^{n+1}}{n+1}\operatorname{arccoth} z + \frac{1}{n+1}\int \frac{z^{n+1}}{z^2-1}\,dz$$
$(n \neq -1)$

5.1. Exponential Integral

Definitions

5.1.1 $$E_1(z)=\int_z^\infty \frac{e^{-t}}{t}\,dt \qquad (|\arg z|<\pi)$$

5.1.2 $$\mathrm{Ei}(x)=-⨍_{-x}^\infty \frac{e^{-t}}{t}\,dt=⨍_{-\infty}^{x} \frac{e^{t}}{t}\,dt \qquad (x>0)$$

5.1.3 $$\mathrm{li}(x)=⨍_0^x \frac{dt}{\ln t}=\mathrm{Ei}(\ln x) \qquad (x>1)$$

5.1.4

$$E_n(z)=\int_1^\infty \frac{e^{-zt}}{t^n}\,dt \qquad (n=0, 1, 2, \ldots; \mathscr{R}z>0)$$

5.1.5

$$\alpha_n(z)=\int_1^\infty t^n e^{-zt}dt \qquad (n=0, 1, 2, \ldots; \mathscr{R}z>0)$$

5.1.6 $$\beta_n(z)=\int_{-1}^1 t^n e^{-zt}dt \qquad (n=0, 1, 2, \ldots)$$

In **5.1.1** it is assumed that the path of integration excludes the origin and does not cross the negative real axis.

Analytic continuation of the functions in **5.1.1**, **5.1.2**, and **5.1.4** for $n>0$ yields multi-valued functions with branch points at $z=0$ and $z=\infty$.[3] They are single-valued functions in the z-plane cut along the negative real axis.[4] The function li(z), the logarithmic integral, has an additional branch point at $z=1$.

Interrelations

5.1.7

$$E_1(-x\pm i0)=-\mathrm{Ei}(x)\mp i\pi,$$
$$-\mathrm{Ei}(x)=\tfrac{1}{2}[E_1(-x+i0)+E_1(-x-i0)] \qquad (x>0)$$

[3] Some authors [5.14], [5.16] use the entire function $\int_0^z (1-e^{-t})dt/t$ as the basic function and denote it by Ein(z). We have $\mathrm{Ein}(z)=E_1(z)+\ln z+\gamma$.

[4] Various authors define the integral $\int_{-\infty}^z (e^t/t)dt$ in the z-plane cut along the positive real axis and denote it also by Ei(z). For $z=x>0$ additional notations such as $\overline{\mathrm{Ei}}(x)$ (e.g., in [5.10], [5.25]), $E^*(x)$ (in [5.2]), $\mathrm{Ei}^*(x)$ (in [5.6]) are then used to designate the principal value of the integral. Correspondingly, $E_1(x)$ is often denoted by $-\mathrm{Ei}(-x)$.

Explicit Expressions for $\alpha_n(z)$ and $\beta_n(z)$

5.1.8 $$\alpha_n(z)=n!z^{-n-1}e^{-z}\left(1+z+\frac{z^2}{2!}+\ldots+\frac{z^n}{n!}\right)$$

5.1.9

$$\beta_n(z)=n!z^{-n-1}\left\{e^z\left[1-z+\frac{z^2}{2!}-\ldots+(-1)^n\frac{z^n}{n!}\right]-e^{-z}\left(1+z+\frac{z^2}{2!}+\ldots+\frac{z^n}{n!}\right)\right\}$$

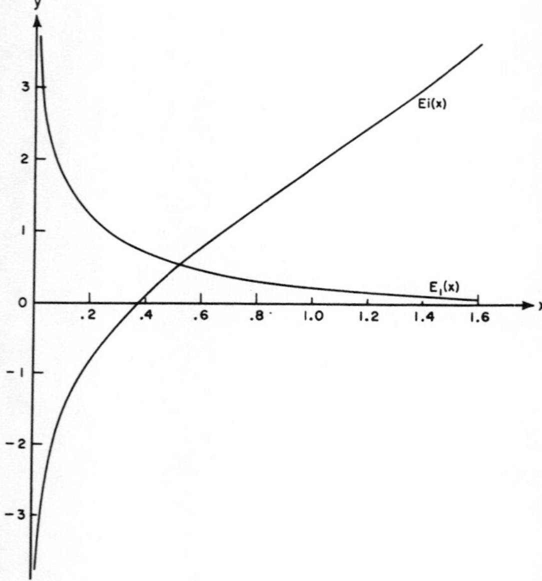

FIGURE 5.1. $y=\mathrm{Ei}(x)$ and $y=E_1(x)$.

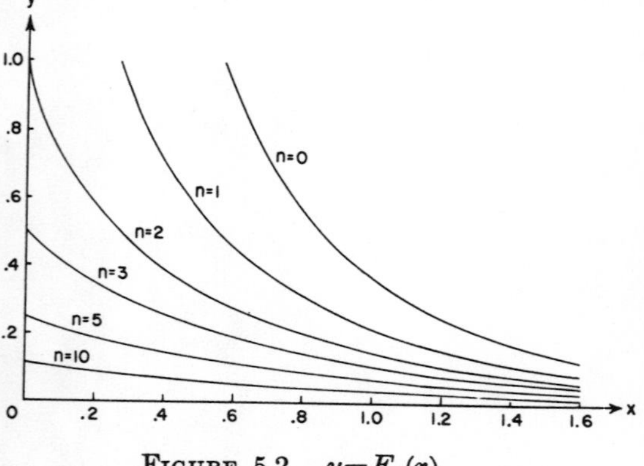

FIGURE 5.2. $y=E_n(x)$
$n=0, 1, 2, 3, 5, 10$

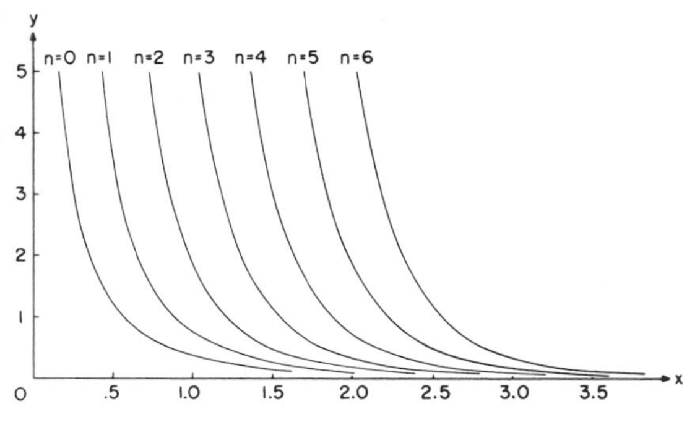

FIGURE 5.3. $y=\alpha_n(x)$
$n=0(1)6$

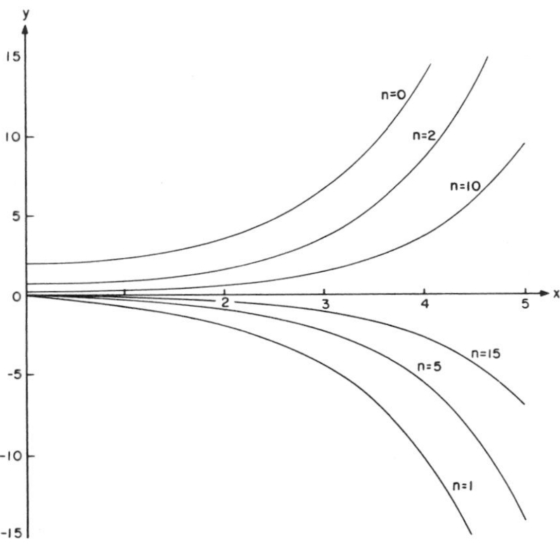

FIGURE 5.4. $y=\beta_n(x)$
$n=0, 1, 2, 5, 10, 15$

Series Expansions

5.1.10 $$\mathrm{Ei}(x)=\gamma+\ln x+\sum_{n=1}^{\infty}\frac{x^n}{n n!} \qquad (x>0)$$

5.1.11
$$E_1(z)=-\gamma-\ln z-\sum_{n=1}^{\infty}\frac{(-1)^n z^n}{n n!} \qquad (|\arg z|<\pi)$$

5.1.12
$$E_n(z)=\frac{(-z)^{n-1}}{(n-1)!}[-\ln z+\psi(n)]-\sum_{\substack{m=0\\m\neq n-1}}^{\infty}{}' \frac{(-z)^m}{(m-n+1)m!} \qquad (|\arg z|<\pi)$$

$$\psi(1)=-\gamma,\ \psi(n)=-\gamma+\sum_{m=1}^{n-1}\frac{1}{m} \qquad (n>1)$$

$\gamma=.57721\ 56649\ldots$ is Euler's constant.

Symmetry Relation

5.1.13 $$E_n(\bar{z})=\overline{E_n(z)}$$

Recurrence Relations

5.1.14
$$E_{n+1}(z)=\frac{1}{n}[e^{-z}-zE_n(z)] \quad (n=1,2,3,\ldots)$$

5.1.15 $$z\alpha_n(z)=e^{-z}+n\alpha_{n-1}(z) \qquad (n=1,2,3,\ldots)$$

5.1.16
$$z\beta_n(z)=(-1)^n e^z-e^{-z}+n\beta_{n-1}(z) \qquad (n=1,2,3,\ldots)$$

Inequalities [5.8], [5.4]

5.1.17
$$\frac{n-1}{n}E_n(x)<E_{n+1}(x)<E_n(x) \quad (x>0; n=1,2,3,\ldots)$$

5.1.18
$$E_n^2(x)<E_{n-1}(x)E_{n+1}(x) \qquad (x>0; n=1,2,3,\ldots)$$

5.1.19
$$\frac{1}{x+n}<e^x E_n(x)\leq\frac{1}{x+n-1} \qquad (x>0; n=1,2,3,\ldots)$$

5.1.20
$$\tfrac{1}{2}\ln\left(1+\frac{2}{x}\right)<e^x E_1(x)<\ln\left(1+\frac{1}{x}\right) \qquad (x>0)$$

5.1.21
$$\frac{d}{dx}\left[\frac{E_n(x)}{E_{n-1}(x)}\right]>0 \qquad (x>0; n=1,2,3,\ldots)$$

Continued Fraction

5.1.22
$$E_n(z)=e^{-z}\left(\frac{1}{z+}\,\frac{n}{1+}\,\frac{1}{z+}\,\frac{n+1}{1+}\,\frac{2}{z+}\cdots\right) \quad (|\arg z|<\pi)$$

Special Values

5.1.23 $$E_n(0)=\frac{1}{n-1} \qquad (n>1)$$

5.1.24 $$E_0(z)=\frac{e^{-z}}{z}$$

5.1.25 $$\alpha_0(z)=\frac{e^{-z}}{z},\ \beta_0(z)=\frac{2}{z}\sinh z$$

Derivatives

5.1.26 $$\frac{dE_n(z)}{dz}=-E_{n-1}(z) \qquad (n=1,2,3,\ldots)$$

5.1.27
$$\frac{d^n}{dz^n}[e^zE_1(z)]=\frac{d^{n-1}}{dz^{n-1}}[e^zE_1(z)]+\frac{(-1)^n(n-1)!}{z^n} \quad (n=1,2,3,\ldots)$$

Definite and Indefinite Integrals

(For more extensive tables of integrals see [5.3], [5.6], [5.11], [5.12], [5.13]. For integrals involving $E_n(x)$ see [5.9].)

5.1.28 $$\int_0^\infty \frac{e^{-at}}{b+t}\,dt=e^{ab}E_1(ab)$$

5.1.29
$$\int_0^\infty \frac{e^{iat}}{b+t}\,dt=e^{-iab}E_1(-iab) \qquad (a>0,\, b>0)$$

5.1.30
$$\int_0^\infty \frac{t-ib}{t^2+b^2}\,e^{iat}dt=e^{ab}E_1(ab) \qquad (a>0,\, b>0)$$

5.1.31
$$\int_0^\infty \frac{t+ib}{t^2+b^2}\,e^{iat}dt=e^{-ab}(-\mathrm{Ei}(ab)+i\pi) \qquad (a>0,\, b>0)$$

5.1.32 $$\int_0^\infty \frac{e^{-at}-e^{-bt}}{t}\,dt=\ln\frac{b}{a}$$

5.1.33 $$\int_0^\infty E_1^2(t)dt=2\ln 2$$

5.1.34
$$\int_0^\infty e^{-at}E_n(t)dt=\frac{(-1)^{n-1}}{a^n}\left[\ln(1+a)+\sum_{k=1}^{n-1}\frac{(-1)^ka^k}{k}\right] \qquad (a>-1)$$

5.1.35
$$\int_0^1 \frac{e^{at}\sin bt}{t}\,dt=\pi-\arctan\frac{b}{a}+\mathscr{I}E_1(-a+ib) \qquad (a>0,b>0)$$

5.1.36
$$\int_0^1 \frac{e^{-at}\sin bt}{t}\,dt=\arctan\frac{b}{a}+\mathscr{I}E_1(a+ib) \qquad (a>0,b \text{ real})$$

5.1.37
$$\int_0^1 \frac{e^{at}(1-\cos bt)}{t}\,dt=\frac{1}{2}\ln\left(1+\frac{b^2}{a^2}\right)+\mathrm{Ei}(a)+\mathscr{R}E_1(-a+ib) \quad (a>0,b \text{ real})$$

5.1.38
$$\int_0^1 \frac{e^{-at}(1-\cos bt)}{t}\,dt=\frac{1}{2}\ln\left(1+\frac{b^2}{a^2}\right)-E_1(a)+\mathscr{R}E_1(a+ib) \qquad (a>0,b \text{ real})$$

5.1.39 $$\int_0^z \frac{1-e^{-t}}{t}\,dt=E_1(z)+\ln z+\gamma$$

5.1.40 $$\int_0^x \frac{e^t-1}{t}\,dt=\mathrm{Ei}(x)-\ln x-\gamma \qquad (x>0)$$

5.1.41
$$\int \frac{e^{ix}}{a^2+x^2}\,dx=\frac{i}{2a}[e^{-a}E_1(-a-ix)-e^aE_1(a-ix)]+\text{const.}$$

5.1.42
$$\int \frac{xe^{ix}}{a^2+x^2}\,dx=-\frac{1}{2}[e^{-a}E_1(-a-ix)+e^aE_1(a-ix)]+\text{const.}$$

5.1.43
$$\int \frac{e^x}{a^2+x^2}\,dx=-\frac{1}{a}\mathscr{I}(e^{ia}E_1(-x+ia))+\text{const.} \quad (a>0)$$

5.1.44
$$\int \frac{xe^x}{a^2+x^2}\,dx=-\mathscr{R}(e^{ia}E_1(-x+ia))+\text{const.} \quad (a>0)$$

Relation to Incomplete Gamma Function (see 6.5)

5.1.45 $$E_n(z)=z^{n-1}\Gamma(1-n,\, z)$$

5.1.46 $$\alpha_n(z)=z^{-n-1}\Gamma(n+1,\, z)$$

5.1.47 $$\beta_n(z)=z^{-n-1}[\Gamma(n+1,\, -z)-\Gamma(n+1,\, z)]$$

Relation to Spherical Bessel Functions (see 10.2)

5.1.48 $$\alpha_0(z)=\sqrt{\frac{2}{\pi z}}\,K_{\frac{1}{2}}(z),\quad \beta_0(z)=\sqrt{\frac{2\pi}{z}}\,I_{\frac{1}{2}}(z)$$

5.1.49 $$\alpha_1(z)=\sqrt{\frac{2}{\pi z}}\,K_{3/2}(z),\quad \beta_1(z)=-\sqrt{\frac{2\pi}{z}}\,I_{3/2}(z)$$

Number-Theoretic Significance of li (x)

(Assuming Riemann's hypothesis that all non-real zeros of $\zeta(z)$ have a real part of $\frac{1}{2}$)

5.1.50 $$\text{li}(x)-\pi(x)=O(\sqrt{x}\ln x) \qquad (x\to\infty)$$

$\pi(x)$ is the number of primes less than or equal to x.

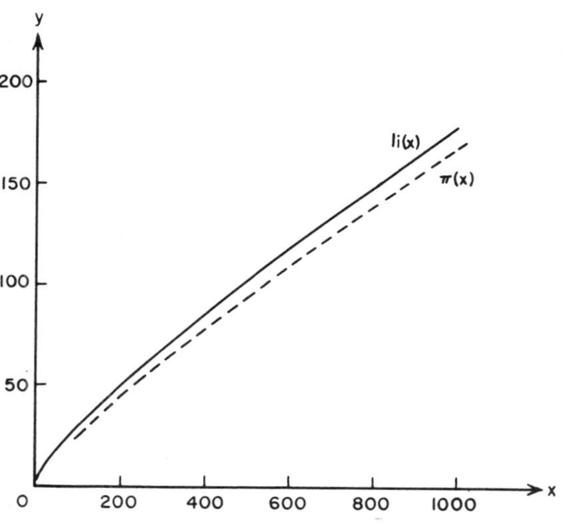

FIGURE 5.5. $y=\text{li}(x)$ and $y=\pi(x)$

Asymptotic Expansion

5.1.51

$$E_n(z)\sim\frac{e^{-z}}{z}\left\{1-\frac{n}{z}+\frac{n(n+1)}{z^2}-\frac{n(n+1)(n+2)}{z^3}+\ldots\right\} \qquad (|\arg z|<\tfrac{3}{2}\pi)$$

Representation of $E_n(x)$ for Large n

5.1.52

$$E_n(x)=\frac{e^{-x}}{x+n}\left\{1+\frac{n}{(x+n)^2}+\frac{n(n-2x)}{(x+n)^4}+\frac{n(6x^2-8nx+n^2)}{(x+n)^6}+R(n,x)\right\}$$

$$-.36n^{-4}\leq R(n,x)\leq\left(1+\frac{1}{x+n-1}\right)n^{-4} \qquad (x>0)$$

Polynomial and Rational Approximations [5]

5.1.53 $\qquad 0\leq x\leq 1$

$$E_1(x)+\ln x=a_0+a_1x+a_2x^2+a_3x^3+a_4x^4+a_5x^5+\epsilon(x)$$

$$|\epsilon(x)|<2\times10^{-7}$$

$a_0=-.57721\ 566$		$a_3=\ \ .05519\ 968$	
$a_1=\ \ .99999\ 193$		$a_4=-.00976\ 004$	
$a_2=-.24991\ 055$		$a_5=\ \ .00107\ 857$	

5.1.54 $\qquad 1\leq x<\infty$

$$xe^xE_1(x)=\frac{x^2+a_1x+a_2}{x^2+b_1x+b_2}+\epsilon(x)$$

$$|\epsilon(x)|<5\times10^{-5}$$

$a_1=2.334733 \qquad b_1=3.330657$

$a_2=\ .250621 \qquad b_2=1.681534$

5.1.55 $\qquad 10\leq x<\infty$

$$xe^xE_1(x)=\frac{x^2+a_1x+a_2}{x^2+b_1x+b_2}+\epsilon(x)$$

$$|\epsilon(x)|<10^{-7}$$

$a_1=4.03640 \qquad b_1=5.03637$

$a_2=1.15198 \qquad b_2=4.19160$

5.1.56 $\qquad 1\leq x<\infty$

$$xe^xE_1(x)=\frac{x^4+a_1x^3+a_2x^2+a_3x+a_4}{x^4+b_1x^3+b_2x^2+b_3x+b_4}+\epsilon(x)$$

$$|\epsilon(x)|<2\times10^{-8}$$

$a_1=\ 8.57332\ 87401 \qquad b_1=\ 9.57332\ 23454$

$a_2=18.05901\ 69730 \qquad b_2=25.63295\ 61486$

$a_3=\ 8.63476\ 08925 \qquad b_3=21.09965\ 30827$

$a_4=\ \ .26777\ 37343 \qquad b_4=\ 3.95849\ 69228$

5.2. Sine and Cosine Integrals

Definitions

5.2.1 $$\text{Si}(z)=\int_0^z\frac{\sin t}{t}\,dt$$

5.2.2 [6] $$\text{Ci}(z)=\gamma+\ln z+\int_0^z\frac{\cos t-1}{t}\,dt \qquad (|\arg z|<\pi)$$

5.2.3 [7] $$\text{Shi}(z)=\int_0^z\frac{\sinh t}{t}\,dt$$

5.2.4 [7] $$\text{Chi}(z)=\gamma+\ln z+\int_0^z\frac{\cosh t-1}{t}\,dt \qquad (|\arg z|<\pi)$$

[5] The approximation **5.1.53** is from E. E. Allen, Note 169, MTAC **8**, 240 (1954); approximations **5.1.54** and **5.1.56** are from C. Hastings, Jr., Approximations for digital computers, Princeton Univ. Press, Princeton, N.J., 1955; approximation **5.1.55** is from C. Hastings, Jr., Note 143, MTAC **7**, 68 (1953)

[6] Some authors [5.14], [5.16] use the entire function $\int_0^z(1-\cos t)dt/t$ as the basic function and denote it by Cin(z). We have

$$\text{Cin}(z)=-\text{Ci}(z)+\ln z+\gamma.$$

[7] The notations $\text{Sih}(z)=\int_0^z\sinh t\,dt/t$, $\text{Cinh}(z)=\int_0^z(\cosh t-1)dt/t$ have also been proposed [5.14.]

5.2.5 $$\mathrm{si}(z)=\mathrm{Si}(z)-\frac{\pi}{2}$$

Auxiliary Functions

5.2.6 $$f(z)=\mathrm{Ci}(z)\sin z-\mathrm{si}(z)\cos z$$

5.2.7 $$g(z)=-\mathrm{Ci}(z)\cos z-\mathrm{si}(z)\sin z$$

Sine and Cosine Integrals in Terms of Auxiliary Functions

5.2.8 $$\mathrm{Si}(z)=\frac{\pi}{2}-f(z)\cos z-g(z)\sin z$$

5.2.9 $$\mathrm{Ci}(z)=f(z)\sin z-g(z)\cos z$$

Integral Representations

5.2.10 $$\mathrm{si}(z)=-\int_0^{\frac{\pi}{2}} e^{-z\cos t}\cos(z\sin t)dt$$

5.2.11 $$\mathrm{Ci}(z)+E_1(z)=\int_0^{\frac{\pi}{2}} e^{-z\cos t}\sin(z\sin t)dt$$

5.2.12 $$f(z)=\int_0^\infty \frac{\sin t}{t+z}\,dt=\int_0^\infty \frac{e^{-zt}}{t^2+1}\,dt \qquad (\mathscr{R}z>0)$$

5.2.13 $$g(z)=\int_0^\infty \frac{\cos t}{t+z}\,dt=\int_0^\infty \frac{te^{-zt}}{t^2+1}\,dt \qquad (\mathscr{R}z>0)$$

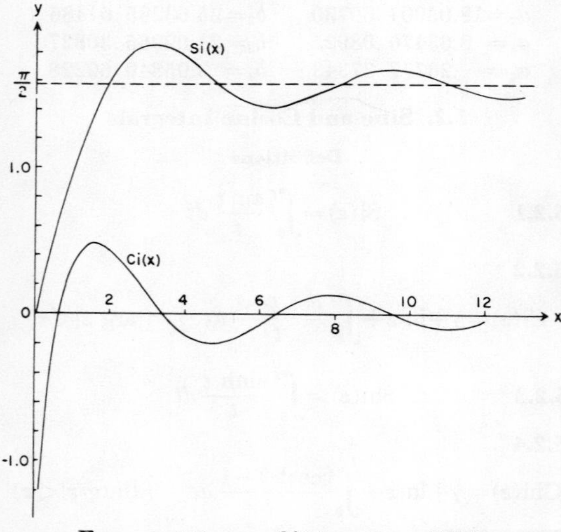

FIGURE 5.6. $y=\mathrm{Si}(x)$ *and* $y=\mathrm{Ci}(x)$

Series Expansions

5.2.14 $$\mathrm{Si}(z)=\sum_{n=0}^{\infty}\frac{(-1)^n z^{2n+1}}{(2n+1)(2n+1)!}$$

5.2.15 $$\mathrm{Si}(z)=\pi\sum_{n=0}^{\infty} J^2_{n+\frac{1}{2}}\left(\frac{z}{2}\right)$$

5.2.16 $$\mathrm{Ci}(z)=\gamma+\ln z+\sum_{n=1}^{\infty}\frac{(-1)^n z^{2n}}{2n(2n)!}$$

5.2.17 $$\mathrm{Shi}(z)=\sum_{n=0}^{\infty}\frac{z^{2n+1}}{(2n+1)(2n+1)!}$$

5.2.18 $$\mathrm{Chi}(z)=\gamma+\ln z+\sum_{n=1}^{\infty}\frac{z^{2n}}{2n(2n)!}$$

Symmetry Relations

5.2.19 $$\mathrm{Si}(-z)=-\mathrm{Si}(z),\ \mathrm{Si}(\bar{z})=\overline{\mathrm{Si}(z)}$$

5.2.20

$$\mathrm{Ci}(-z)=\mathrm{Ci}(z)-i\pi \qquad (0<\arg z<\pi)$$
$$\mathrm{Ci}(\bar{z})=\overline{\mathrm{Ci}(z)}$$

Relation to Exponential Integral

5.2.21

$$\mathrm{Si}(z)=\frac{1}{2i}[E_1(iz)-E_1(-iz)]+\frac{\pi}{2} \qquad (|\arg z|<\frac{\pi}{2})$$

5.2.22 $$\mathrm{Si}(ix)=\frac{i}{2}[\mathrm{Ei}(x)+E_1(x)] \qquad (x>0)$$

5.2.23

$$\mathrm{Ci}(z)=-\frac{1}{2}[E_1(iz)+E_1(-iz)] \qquad (|\arg z|<\frac{\pi}{2})$$

5.2.24 $$\mathrm{Ci}(ix)=\frac{1}{2}[\mathrm{Ei}(x)-E_1(x)]+i\frac{\pi}{2} \qquad (x>0)$$

Value at Infinity

5.2.25 $$\lim_{x\to\infty}\mathrm{Si}(x)=\frac{\pi}{2}$$

Integrals

(For more extensive tables of integrals see [5.3], [5.6], [5.11], [5.12], [5.13].)

5.2.26 $$\int_z^\infty \frac{\sin t}{t}\,dt=-\mathrm{si}(z) \qquad (|\arg z|<\pi)$$

5.2.27 $$\int_z^\infty \frac{\cos t}{t}\,dt=-\mathrm{Ci}(z) \qquad (|\arg z|<\pi)$$

5.2.28 $$\int_0^\infty e^{-at}\mathrm{Ci}(t)dt=-\frac{1}{2a}\ln(1+a^2) \qquad (\mathscr{R}a>0)$$

5.2.29 $$\int_0^\infty e^{-at}\,\mathrm{si}(t)dt=-\frac{1}{a}\arctan a \qquad (\mathscr{R}a>0)$$

5.2.30 $$\int_0^\infty \cos t\,\mathrm{Ci}(t)dt=\int_0^\infty \sin t\,\mathrm{si}(t)dt=-\frac{\pi}{4}$$

5.2.31 $$\int_0^\infty \mathrm{Ci}^2(t)\,dt=\int_0^\infty \mathrm{si}^2(t)\,dt=\frac{\pi}{2}$$

5.2.32 $$\int_0^\infty \mathrm{Ci}(t)\,\mathrm{si}(t)\,dt=\ln 2$$

5.2.33

$$\int_0^1 \frac{(1-e^{-at})\cos bt}{t}\,dt=\frac{1}{2}\ln\left(1+\frac{a^2}{b^2}\right)+\mathrm{Ci}(b)$$
$$+\mathscr{R}E_1(a+ib)\quad (a \text{ real},\ b>0)$$

Asymptotic Expansions

5.2.34

$$f(z)\sim\frac{1}{z}\left(1-\frac{2!}{z^2}+\frac{4!}{z^4}-\frac{6!}{z^6}+\ldots\right)\qquad (|\arg z|<\pi)$$

5.2.35

$$g(z)\sim\frac{1}{z^2}\left(1-\frac{3!}{z^2}+\frac{5!}{z^4}-\frac{7!}{z^6}+\ldots\right)\qquad (|\arg z|<\pi)$$

Rational Approximations [8]

5.2.36 $1\leq x<\infty$

$$f(x)=\frac{1}{x}\left(\frac{x^4+a_1x^2+a_2}{x^4+b_1x^2+b_2}\right)+\epsilon(x)$$

$$|\epsilon(x)|<2\times10^{-4}$$

$a_1=7.241163$ $\quad b_1=9.068580$

$a_2=2.463936$ $\quad b_2=7.157433$

5.2.37 $1\leq x<\infty$

$$g(x)=\frac{1}{x^2}\left(\frac{x^4+a_1x^2+a_2}{x^4+b_1x^2+b_2}\right)+\epsilon(x)$$

$$|\epsilon(x)|<10^{-4}$$

$a_1=7.547478$ $\quad b_1=12.723684$

$a_2=1.564072$ $\quad b_2=15.723606$

5.2.38 $1\leq x<\infty$

$$f(x)=\frac{1}{x}\left(\frac{x^8+a_1x^6+a_2x^4+a_3x^2+a_4}{x^8+b_1x^6+b_2x^4+b_3x^2+b_4}\right)+\epsilon(x)$$

$$|\epsilon(x)|<5\times10^{-7}$$

$a_1=\ 38.027264$ $\quad b_1=\ 40.021433$

$a_2=265.187033$ $\quad b_2=322.624911$

$a_3=335.677320$ $\quad b_3=570.236280$

$a_4=\ 38.102495$ $\quad b_4=157.105423$

5.2.39 $1\leq x<\infty$

$$g(x)=\frac{1}{x^2}\left(\frac{x^8+a_1x^6+a_2x^4+a_3x^2+a_4}{x^8+b_1x^6+b_2x^4+b_3x^2+b_4}\right)+\epsilon(x)$$

$$|\epsilon(x)|<3\times10^{-7}$$

$a_1=\ 42.242855$ $\quad b_1=\ 48.196927$

$a_2=302.757865$ $\quad b_2=\ 482.485984$

$a_3=352.018498$ $\quad b_3=1114.978885$

$a_4=\ 21.821899$ $\quad b_4=\ 449.690326$

[8] From C. Hastings, Jr., Approximations for digital computers, Princeton Univ. Press, Princeton, N.J., 1955

Table 5.1 SINE, COSINE AND EXPONENTIAL INTEGRALS

x	$x^{-1}\mathrm{Si}(x)$	$x^{-2}[\mathrm{Ci}(x)-\ln x-\gamma]$	$x^{-1}[\mathrm{Ei}(x)-\ln x-\gamma]$	$x^{-1}[E_1(x)+\ln x+\gamma]$
0.00	1.00000 00000	-0.25000 00000	1.00000 0000	1.00000 00000
0.01	0.99999 44444	-0.24999 89583	1.00250 5566	0.99750 55452
0.02	0.99997 77781	-0.24999 58333	1.00502 2306	0.99502 21392
0.03	0.99995 00014	-0.24999 06250	1.00755 0283	0.99254 97201
0.04	0.99991 11154	-0.24998 33339	1.01008 9560	0.99008 82265
0.05	0.99986 11215	-0.24997 39598	1.01264 0202	0.98763 75971
0.06	0.99980 00216	-0.24996 25030	1.01520 2272	0.98519 77714
0.07	0.99972 78178	-0.24994 89639	1.01777 5836	0.98276 86889
0.08	0.99964 45127	-0.24993 33429	1.02036 0958	0.98035 02898
0.09	0.99955 01094	-0.24991 56402	1.02295 7705	0.97794 25142
0.10	0.99944 46111	-0.24989 58564	1.02556 6141	0.97554 53033
0.11	0.99932 80218	-0.24987 39923	1.02818 6335	0.97315 85980
0.12	0.99920 03455	-0.24985 00480	1.03081 8352	0.97078 23399
0.13	0.99906 15870	-0.24982 40244	1.03346 2259	0.96841 64710
0.14	0.99891 17512	-0.24979 59223	1.03611 8125	0.96606 09336
0.15	0.99875 08435	-0.24976 57422	1.03878 6018	0.96371 56702
0.16	0.99857 88696	-0.24973 34850	1.04146 6006	0.96138 06240
0.17	0.99839 58357	-0.24969 91516	1.04415 8158	0.95905 57383
0.18	0.99820 17486	-0.24966 27429	1.04686 2544	0.95674 09569
0.19	0.99799 66151	-0.24962 42598	1.04957 9234	0.95443 62237
0.20	0.99778 04427	-0.24958 37035	1.05230 8298	0.95214 14833
0.21	0.99755 32390	-0.24954 10749	1.05504 9807	0.94985 66804
0.22	0.99731 50122	-0.24949 63752	1.05780 3833	0.94758 17603
0.23	0.99706 57709	-0.24944 96056	1.06057 0446	0.94531 66684
0.24	0.99680 55242	-0.24940 07674	1.06334 9719	0.94306 13506
0.25	0.99653 42813	-0.24934 98618	1.06614 1726	0.94081 57528
0.26	0.99625 20519	-0.24929 68902	1.06894 6539	0.93857 98221
0.27	0.99595 88464	-0.24924 18540	1.07176 4232	0.93635 35046
0.28	0.99565 46750	-0.24918 47546	1.07459 4879	0.93413 67481
0.29	0.99533 95489	-0.24912 55938	1.07743 8555	0.93192 94997
0.30	0.99501 34793	-0.24906 43727	1.08029 5334	0.92973 17075
0.31	0.99467 64779	-0.24900 10933	1.08316 5293	0.92754 33196
0.32	0.99432 85570	-0.24893 57573	1.08604 8507	0.92536 42845
0.33	0.99396 97288	-0.24886 83662	1.08894 5053	0.92319 45510
0.34	0.99360 00064	-0.24879 89219	1.09185 5008	0.92103 40684
0.35	0.99321 94028	-0.24872 74263	1.09477 8451	0.91888 27858
0.36	0.99282 79320	-0.24865 38813	1.09771 5458	0.91674 06533
0.37	0.99242 56078	-0.24857 82887	1.10066 6108	0.91460 76209
0.38	0.99201 24449	-0.24850 06507	1.10363 0481	0.91248 36388
0.39	0.99158 84579	-0.24842 09693	1.10660 8656	0.91036 86582
0.40	0.99115 36619	-0.24833 92466	1.10960 0714	0.90826 26297
0.41	0.99070 80728	-0.24825 54849	1.11260 6735	0.90616 55048
0.42	0.99025 17063	-0.24816 96860	1.11562 6800	0.90407 72350
0.43	0.98978 45790	-0.24808 18528	1.11866 0991	0.90199 77725
0.44	0.98930 67074	-0.24799 19870	1.12170 9391	0.89992 70693
0.45	0.98881 81089	-0.24790 00913	1.12477 2082	0.89786 50778
0.46	0.98831 88008	-0.24780 61685	1.12784 9147	0.89581 17511
0.47	0.98780 88010	-0.24771 02206	1.13094 0671	0.89376 70423
0.48	0.98728 81278	-0.24761 22500	1.13404 6738	0.89173 09048
0.49	0.98675 67998	-0.24751 22600	1.13716 7432	0.88970 32920
0.50	0.98621 48361	-0.24741 02526	1.14030 2841	0.88768 41584

$\gamma=0.57721\ 56649$

SINE, COSINE AND EXPONENTIAL INTEGRALS Table 5.1

x	Si(x)	Ci(x)	Ei(x)	$E_1(x)$
0.50	0.49310 74180	−0.17778 40788	0.45421 9905	0.55977 3595
0.51	0.50268 77506	−0.16045 32390	0.48703 2167	0.54782 2352
0.52	0.51225 15212	−0.14355 37358	0.51953 0633	0.53621 9798
0.53	0.52179 84228	−0.12707 07938	0.55173 0445	0.52495 1510
0.54	0.53132 81492	−0.11099 04567	0.58364 5931	0.51400 3886
0.55	0.54084 03951	−0.09529 95274	0.61529 0657	0.50336 4081
0.56	0.55033 48563	−0.07998 55129	0.64667 7490	0.49301 9959
0.57	0.55981 12298	−0.06503 65744	0.67781 8642	0.48296 0034
0.58	0.56926 92137	−0.05044 14815	0.70872 5720	0.47317 3433
0.59	0.57870 85069	−0.03618 95707	0.73940 9764	0.46364 9849
0.60	0.58812 88096	−0.02227 07070	0.76988 1290	0.45437 9503
0.61	0.59752 98233	−0.00867 52486	0.80015 0320	0.44535 3112
0.62	0.60691 12503	+0.00460 59849	0.83022 6417	0.43656 1854
0.63	0.61627 27944	0.01758 17424	0.86011 8716	0.42799 7338
0.64	0.62561 41603	0.03026 03686	0.88983 5949	0.41965 1581
0.65	0.63493 50541	0.04264 98293	0.91938 6468	0.41151 6976
0.66	0.64423 51831	0.05475 77343	0.94877 8277	0.40358 6275
0.67	0.65351 42557	0.06659 13594	0.97801 9042	0.39585 2563
0.68	0.66277 19817	0.07815 76659	1.00711 6121	0.38830 9243
0.69	0.67200 80721	0.08946 33195	1.03607 6576	0.38095 0010
0.70	0.68122 22391	0.10051 47070	1.06490 7195	0.37376 8843
0.71	0.69041 41965	0.11131 79525	1.09361 4501	0.36675 9981
0.72	0.69958 36590	0.12187 89322	1.12220 4777	0.35991 7914
0.73	0.70873 03430	0.13220 32879	1.15068 4069	0.35323 7364
0.74	0.71785 39660	0.14229 64404	1.17905 8208	0.34671 3279
0.75	0.72695 42472	0.15216 36010	1.20733 2816	0.34034 0813
0.76	0.73603 09067	0.16180 97827	1.23551 3319	0.33411 5321
0.77	0.74508 36664	0.17123 98110	1.26360 4960	0.32803 2346
0.78	0.75411 22494	0.18045 83335	1.29161 2805	0.32208 7610
0.79	0.76311 63804	0.18946 98290	1.31954 1753	0.31627 7004
0.80	0.77209 57855	0.19827 86160	1.34739 6548	0.31059 6579
0.81	0.78105 01921	0.20688 88610	1.37518 1783	0.30504 2539
0.82	0.78997 93293	0.21530 45859	1.40290 1910	0.29961 1236
0.83	0.79888 29277	0.22352 96752	1.43056 1245	0.29429 9155
0.84	0.80776 07191	0.23156 78824	1.45816 3978	0.28910 2918
0.85	0.81661 24372	0.23942 28368	1.48571 4176	0.28401 9269
0.86	0.82543 78170	0.24709 80486	1.51321 5791	0.27904 5070
0.87	0.83423 65953	0.25459 69153	1.54067 2664	0.27417 7301
0.88	0.84300 85102	0.26192 27264	1.56808 8534	0.26941 3046
0.89	0.85175 33016	0.26907 86687	1.59546 7036	0.26474 9496
0.90	0.86047 07107	0.27606 78305	1.62281 1714	0.26018 3939
0.91	0.86916 04808	0.28289 32065	1.65012 6019	0.25571 3758
0.92	0.87782 23564	0.28955 77018	1.67741 3317	0.25133 6425
0.93	0.88645 60839	0.29606 41358	1.70467 6891	0.24704 9501
0.94	0.89506 14112	0.30241 52458	1.73191 9946	0.24285 0627
0.95	0.90363 80880	0.30861 36908	1.75914 5612	0.23873 7524
0.96	0.91218 58656	0.31466 20547	1.78635 6947	0.23470 7988
0.97	0.92070 44970	0.32056 28495	1.81355 6941	0.23075 9890
0.98	0.92919 37370	0.32631 85183	1.84074 8519	0.22689 1167
0.99	0.93765 33420	0.33193 14382	1.86793 4543	0.22309 9826
1.00	0.94608 30704	0.33740 39229	1.89511 7816	0.21938 3934

Table 5.1 SINE, COSINE AND EXPONENTIAL INTEGRALS

x	$\mathrm{Si}(x)$	$\mathrm{Ci}(x)$	$\mathrm{Ei}(x)$	$E_1(x)$
1.00	0.94608 30704	0.33740 39229	1.89511 7816	0.21938 3934
1.01	0.95448 26820	0.34273 82254	1.92230 1085	0.21574 1624
1.02	0.96285 19387	0.34793 65405	1.94948 7042	0.21217 1083
1.03	0.97119 06039	0.35300 10067	1.97667 8325	0.20867 0559
1.04	0.97949 84431	0.35793 37091	2.00387 7525	0.20523 8352
1.05	0.98777 52233	0.36273 66810	2.03108 7184	0.20187 2813
1.06	0.99602 07135	0.36741 19060	2.05830 9800	0.19857 2347
1.07	1.00423 46846	0.37196 13201	2.08554 7825	0.19533 5403
1.08	1.01241 69091	0.37638 68132	2.11280 3672	0.19216 0479
1.09	1.02056 71617	0.38069 02312	2.14007 9712	0.18904 6118
1.10	1.02868 52187	0.38487 33774	2.16737 8280	0.18599 0905
1.11	1.03677 08583	0.38893 80142	2.19470 1672	0.18299 3465
1.12	1.04482 38608	0.39288 58645	2.22205 2152	0.18005 2467
1.13	1.05284 40082	0.39671 86134	2.24943 1949	0.17716 6615
1.14	1.06083 10845	0.40043 79090	2.27684 3260	0.17433 4651
1.15	1.06878 48757	0.40404 53647	2.30428 8252	0.17155 5354
1.16	1.07670 51696	0.40754 25593	2.33176 9062	0.16882 7535
1.17	1.08459 17561	0.41093 10390	2.35928 7800	0.16615 0040
1.18	1.09244 44270	0.41421 23185	2.38684 6549	0.16352 1748
1.19	1.10026 29760	0.41738 78816	2.41444 7367	0.16094 1567
1.20	1.10804 71990	0.42045 91829	2.44209 2285	0.15840 8437
1.21	1.11579 68937	0.42342 76482	2.46978 3315	0.15592 1324
1.22	1.12351 18599	0.42629 46760	2.49752 2442	0.15347 9226
1.23	1.13119 18994	0.42906 16379	2.52531 1634	0.15108 1164
1.24	1.13883 68160	0.43172 98802	2.55315 2836	0.14872 6188
1.25	1.14644 64157	0.43430 07240	2.58104 7974	0.14641 3373
1.26	1.15402 05063	0.43677 54665	2.60899 8956	0.14414 1815
1.27	1.16155 88978	0.43915 53815	2.63700 7673	0.14191 0639
1.28	1.16906 14023	0.44144 17205	2.66507 5997	0.13971 8989
1.29	1.17652 78340	0.44363 57130	2.69320 5785	0.13756 6032
1.30	1.18395 80091	0.44573 85675	2.72139 8880	0.13545 0958
1.31	1.19135 17459	0.44775 14723	2.74965 7110	0.13337 2975
1.32	1.19870 88649	0.44967 55955	2.77798 2287	0.13133 1314
1.33	1.20602 91886	0.45151 20863	2.80637 6214	0.12932 5224
1.34	1.21331 25418	0.45326 20753	2.83484 0677	0.12735 3972
1.35	1.22055 87513	0.45492 66752	2.86337 7453	0.12541 6844
1.36	1.22776 76460	0.45650 69811	2.89198 8308	0.12351 3146
1.37	1.23493 90571	0.45800 40711	2.92067 4997	0.12164 2198
1.38	1.24207 28180	0.45941 90071	2.94943 9263	0.11980 3337
1.39	1.24916 87640	0.46075 28349	2.97828 2844	0.11799 5919
1.40	1.25622 67328	0.46200 65851	3.00720 7464	0.11621 9313
1.41	1.26324 65642	0.46318 12730	3.03621 4843	0.11447 2903
1.42	1.27022 81004	0.46427 78995	3.06530 6691	0.11275 6090
1.43	1.27717 11854	0.46529 74513	3.09448 4712	0.11106 8287
1.44	1.28407 56658	0.46624 09014	3.12375 0601	0.10940 8923
1.45	1.29094 13902	0.46710 92094	3.15310 6049	0.10777 7440
1.46	1.29776 82094	0.46790 33219	3.18255 2741	0.10617 3291
1.47	1.30455 59767	0.46862 41732	3.21209 2355	0.10459 5946
1.48	1.31130 45473	0.46927 26848	3.24172 6566	0.10304 4882
1.49	1.31801 37788	0.46984 97667	3.27145 7042	0.10151 9593
1.50	1.32468 35312	0.47035 63172	3.30128 5449	0.10001 9582

SINE, COSINE AND EXPONENTIAL INTEGRALS Table 5.1

x	Si(x)	Ci(x)	Ei(x)	$E_1(x)$
1.50	1.32468 35312	0.47035 63172	3.30128 5449	0.10001 9582
1.51	1.33131 36664	0.47079 32232	3.33121 3449	0.09854 4365
1.52	1.33790 40489	0.47116 13608	3.36124 2701	0.09709 3466
1.53	1.34445 45453	0.47146 15952	3.39137 4858	0.09566 6424
1.54	1.35096 50245	0.47169 47815	3.42161 1576	0.09426 2786
1.55	1.35743 53577	0.47186 17642	3.45195 4503	0.09288 2108
1.56	1.36386 54183	0.47196 33785	3.48240 5289	0.09152 3960
1.57	1.37025 50823	0.47200 04495	3.51296 5580	0.09018 7917
1.58	1.37660 42275	0.47197 37932	3.54363 7024	0.08887 3566
1.59	1.38291 27345	0.47188 42164	3.57442 1266	0.08758 0504
1.60	1.38918 04859	0.47173 25169	3.60531 9949	0.08630 8334
1.61	1.39540 73666	0.47151 94840	3.63633 4719	0.08505 6670
1.62	1.40159 32640	0.47124 58984	3.66746 7221	0.08382 5133
1.63	1.40773 80678	0.47091 25325	3.69871 9099	0.08261 3354
1.64	1.41384 16698	0.47052 01507	3.73009 1999	0.08142 0970
1.65	1.41990 39644	0.47006 95096	3.76158 7569	0.08024 7627
1.66	1.42592 48482	0.46956 13580	3.79320 7456	0.07909 2978
1.67	1.43190 42202	0.46899 64372	3.82495 3310	0.07795 6684
1.68	1.43784 19816	0.46837 54812	3.85682 6783	0.07683 8412
1.69	1.44373 80361	0.46769 92169	3.88882 9528	0.07573 7839
1.70	1.44959 22897	0.46696 83642	3.92096 3201	0.07465 4644
1.71	1.45540 46507	0.46618 36359	3.95322 9462	0.07358 8518
1.72	1.46117 50299	0.46534 57385	3.98562 9972	0.07253 9154
1.73	1.46690 33404	0.46445 53716	4.01816 6395	0.07150 6255
1.74	1.47258 94974	0.46351 32286	4.05084 0400	0.07048 9527
1.75	1.47823 34189	0.46251 99967	4.08365 3659	0.06948 8685
1.76	1.48383 50249	0.46147 63568	4.11660 7847	0.06850 3447
1.77	1.48939 42379	0.46038 29839	4.14970 4645	0.06753 3539
1.78	1.49491 09830	0.45924 05471	4.18294 5736	0.06657 8691
1.79	1.50038 51872	0.45804 97097	4.21633 2809	0.06563 8641
1.80	1.50581 67803	0.45681 11294	4.24986 7557	0.06471 3129
1.81	1.51120 56942	0.45552 54585	4.28355 1681	0.06380 1903
1.82	1.51655 18633	0.45419 33436	4.31738 6883	0.06290 4715
1.83	1.52185 52243	0.45281 54262	4.35137 4872	0.06202 1320
1.84	1.52711 57165	0.45139 23427	4.38551 7364	0.06115 1482
1.85	1.53233 32813	0.44992 47241	4.41981 6080	0.06029 4967
1.86	1.53750 78626	0.44841 31966	4.45427 2746	0.05945 1545
1.87	1.54263 94066	0.44685 83813	4.48888 9097	0.05862 0994
1.88	1.54772 78621	0.44526 08948	4.52366 6872	0.05780 3091
1.89	1.55277 31800	0.44362 13486	4.55860 7817	0.05699 7623
1.90	1.55777 53137	0.44194 03497	4.59371 3687	0.05620 4378
1.91	1.56273 42192	0.44021 85005	4.62898 6242	0.05542 3149
1.92	1.56764 98545	0.43845 63991	4.66442 7249	0.05465 3731
1.93	1.57252 21801	0.43665 46388	4.70003 8485	0.05389 5927
1.94	1.57735 11591	0.43481 38088	4.73582 1734	0.05314 9540
1.95	1.58213 67567	0.43293 44941	4.77177 8785	0.05241 4380
1.96	1.58687 89407	0.43101 72752	4.80791 1438	0.05169 0257
1.97	1.59157 76810	0.42906 27288	4.84422 1501	0.05097 6988
1.98	1.59623 29502	0.42707 14273	4.88071 0791	0.05027 4392
1.99	1.60084 47231	0.42504 39391	4.91738 1131	0.04958 2291
2.00	1.60541 29768	0.42298 08288	4.95423 4356	0.04890 0511

Table 5.1 **SINE, COSINE AND EXPONENTIAL INTEGRALS**

x	$\mathrm{Si}(x)$	$\mathrm{Ci}(x)$	$xe^{-x}\mathrm{Ei}(x)$	$xe^{x}E_1(x)$
2.0	1.60541 29768	0.42298 08288	1.34096 5420	0.72265 7234
2.1	1.64869 86362	0.40051 19878	1.37148 6802	0.73079 1502
2.2	1.68762 48272	0.37507 45990	1.39742 1992	0.73843 1132
2.3	1.72220 74818	0.34717 56175	1.41917 1534	0.74562 2149
2.4	1.75248 55008	0.31729 16174	1.43711 8315	0.75240 4829
2.5	1.77852 01734	0.28587 11964	1.45162 5159	0.75881 4592
2.6	1.80039 44505	0.25333 66161	1.46303 3397	0.76488 2722
2.7	1.81821 20765	0.22008 48786	1.47166 2153	0.77063 6987
2.8	1.83209 65891	0.18648 83896	1.47780 8187	0.77610 2123
2.9	1.84219 01946	0.15289 53242	1.48174 6162	0.78130 0252
3.0	1.84865 25280	0.11962 97860	1.48372 9204	0.78625 1221
3.1	1.85165 93077	0.08699 18312	1.48398 9691	0.79097 2900
3.2	1.85140 08970	0.05525 74117	1.48274 0191	0.79548 1422
3.3	1.84808 07828	+0.02467 82846	1.48017 4491	0.79979 1408
3.4	1.84191 39833	−0.00451 80779	1.47646 8706	0.80391 6127
3.5	1.83312 53987	−0.03212 85485	1.47178 2389	0.80786 7661
3.6	1.82194 81156	−0.05797 43519	1.46625 9659	0.81165 7037
3.7	1.80862 16809	−0.08190 10013	1.46003 0313	0.81529 4342
3.8	1.79339 03548	−0.10377 81504	1.45321 0902	0.81878 8821
3.9	1.77650 13604	−0.12349 93492	1.44590 5765	0.82214 8967
4.0	1.75820 31389	−0.14098 16979	1.43820 8032	0.82538 2600
4.1	1.73874 36265	−0.15616 53918	1.43020 0557	0.82849 6926
4.2	1.71836 85637	−0.16901 31568	1.42195 6813	0.83149 8602
4.3	1.69731 98507	−0.17950 95725	1.41354 1719	0.83439 3794
4.4	1.67583 39594	−0.18766 02868	1.40501 2424	0.83718 8207
4.5	1.65414 04144	−0.19349 11221	1.39641 9030	0.83988 7144
4.6	1.63246 03525	−0.19704 70797	1.38780 5263	0.84249 5539
4.7	1.61100 51718	−0.19839 12468	1.37920 9093	0.84501 7971
4.8	1.58997 52782	−0.19760 36133	1.37066 3313	0.84745 8721
4.9	1.56955 89381	−0.19477 98060	1.36219 6054	0.84982 1778
5.0	1.54993 12449	−0.19002 97497	1.35383 1278	0.85211 0880
5.1	1.53125 32047	−0.18347 62632	1.34558 9212	0.85432 9519
5.2	1.51367 09468	−0.17525 36023	1.33748 6755	0.85648 0958
5.3	1.49731 50636	−0.16550 59586	1.32953 7845	0.85856 8275
5.4	1.48230 00826	−0.15438 59262	1.32175 3788	0.86059 4348
5.5	1.46872 40727	−0.14205 29476	1.31414 3566	0.86256 1885
5.6	1.45666 83847	−0.12867 17494	1.30671 4107	0.86447 3436
5.7	1.44619 75285	−0.11441 07808	1.29947 0536	0.86633 1399
5.8	1.43735 91823	−0.09944 06647	1.29241 6395	0.86813 8040
5.9	1.43018 43341	−0.08393 26741	1.28555 3849	0.86989 5494
6.0	1.42468 75513	−0.06805 72439	1.27888 3860	0.87160 5775
6.1	1.42086 73734	−0.05198 25290	1.27240 6357	0.87327 0793
6.2	1.41870 68241	−0.03587 30193	1.26612 0373	0.87489 2347
6.3	1.41817 40348	−0.01988 82206	1.26002 4184	0.87647 2150
6.4	1.41922 29740	−0.00418 14110	1.25411 5417	0.87801 1816
6.5	1.42179 42744	+0.01110 15195	1.24839 1155	0.87951 2881
6.6	1.42581 61486	0.02582 31381	1.24284 8032	0.88097 6797
6.7	1.43120 53853	0.03985 54400	1.23748 2309	0.88240 4955
6.8	1.43786 84161	0.05308 07167	1.23228 9952	0.88379 8662
6.9	1.44570 24427	0.06539 23140	1.22726 6684	0.88515 9176
7.0	1.45459 66142	0.07669 52785	1.22240 8053	0.88648 7675

SINE, COSINE AND EXPONENTIAL INTEGRALS **Table 5.1**

x	$\mathrm{Si}(x)$	$\mathrm{Ci}(x)$	$xe^{-x}\mathrm{Ei}(x)$	$xe^{x}E_1(x)$
7.0	1.45459 66142	0.07669 52785	1.22240 8053	0.88648 7675
7.1	1.46443 32441	0.08690 68881	1.21770 9472	0.88778 5294
7.2	1.47508 90554	0.09595 70643	1.21316 6264	0.88905 3119
7.3	1.48643 64451	0.10378 86664	1.20877 3699	0.89029 2173
7.4	1.49834 47533	0.11035 76658	1.20452 7026	0.89150 3440
7.5	1.51068 15309	0.11563 32032	1.20042 1500	0.89268 7854
7.6	1.52331 37914	0.11959 75293	1.19645 2401	0.89384 6312
7.7	1.53610 92381	0.12224 58319	1.19261 5063	0.89497 9666
7.8	1.54893 74581	0.12358 59542	1.18890 4881	0.89608 8737
7.9	1.56167 10702	0.12363 80071	1.18531 7334	0.89717 4302
8.0	1.57418 68217	0.12243 38825	1.18184 7987	0.89823 7113
8.1	1.58636 66225	0.12001 66733	1.17849 2509	0.89927 7888
8.2	1.59809 85106	0.11644 00055	1.17524 6676	0.90029 7306
8.3	1.60927 75419	0.11176 72931	1.17210 6376	0.90129 6033
8.4	1.61980 65968	0.10607 09196	1.16906 7617	0.90227 4695
8.5	1.62959 70996	0.09943 13586	1.16612 6526	0.90323 3900
8.6	1.63856 96454	0.09193 62396	1.16327 9354	0.90417 4228
8.7	1.64665 45309	0.08367 93696	1.16052 2476	0.90509 6235
8.8	1.65379 21861	0.07475 97196	1.15785 2390	0.90600 0459
8.9	1.65993 35052	0.06528 03850	1.15526 5719	0.90688 7415
9.0	1.66504 00758	0.05534 75313	1.15275 9209	0.90775 7602
9.1	1.66908 43056	0.04506 93325	1.15032 9724	0.90861 1483
9.2	1.67204 94480	0.03455 49134	1.14797 4251	0.90944 9530
9.3	1.67392 95283	0.02391 33045	1.14568 9889	0.91027 2177
9.4	1.67472 91725	0.01325 24187	1.14347 3855	0.91107 9850
9.5	1.67446 33423	+0.00267 80588	1.14132 3476	0.91187 2958
9.6	1.67315 69801	-0.00770 70361	1.13923 6185	0.91265 1897
9.7	1.67084 45697	-0.01780 40977	1.13720 9523	0.91341 7043
9.8	1.66756 96169	-0.02751 91811	1.13524 1130	0.91416 8766
9.9	1.66338 40566	-0.03676 39563	1.13332 8746	0.91490 7418
10.0	1.65834 75942	-0.04545 64330	1.13147 0205	0.91563 3339

Table 5.2

SINE, COSINE AND EXPONENTIAL INTEGRALS FOR LARGE ARGUMENTS

x^{-1}	$xf(x)$	$x^2g(x)$	$xe^{-x}\mathrm{Ei}(x)$	$xe^{x}E_1(x)$	$\langle x\rangle$
0.100	0.98191 0351	0.94885 39	1.13147 021	0.91563 33394	10
0.095	0.98353 4427	0.95323 18	1.12249 671	0.91925 68286	11
0.090	0.98509 9171	0.95748 44	1.11389 377	0.92293 15844	11
0.085	0.98660 1776	0.96160 17	1.10564 739	0.92665 90998	12
0.080	0.98803 9405	0.96557 23	1.09773 775	0.93044 09399	13
0.075	0.98940 9188	0.96938 56	1.09014 087	0.93427 87466	13
0.070	0.99070 8244	0.97302 98	1.08283 054	0.93817 42450	14
0.065	0.99193 3695	0.97649 35	1.07578 038	0.94212 92486	15
0.060	0.99308 2682	0.97976 47	1.06896 548	0.94614 56670	17
0.055	0.99415 2385	0.98283 17	1.06236 365	0.95022 55126	18
0.050	0.99514 0052	0.98568 24	1.05595 591	0.95437 09099	20
0.045	0.99604 3013	0.98830 52	1.04972 640	0.95858 41038	22
0.040	0.99685 8722	0.99068 81	1.04366 194	0.96286 74711	25
0.035	0.99758 4771	0.99282 12	1.03775 135	0.96722 35311	29
0.030	0.99821 8937	0.99469 37	1.03198 503	0.97165 49596	33
0.025	0.99875 9204	0.99629 57	1.02635 451	0.97616 46031	40
0.020	0.99920 3795	0.99761 89	1.02085 228	0.98075 54965	50
0.015	0.99955 1207	0.99865 60	1.01547 157	0.98543 08813	67
0.010	0.99980 0239	0.99940 12	1.01020 625	0.99019 42287	100
0.005	0.99995 0015	0.99985 01	1.00505 077	0.99504 92646	200
0.000	1.00000 0000	1.00000 00	1.00000 000	1.00000 00000	∞

$\mathrm{Si}(x)=\frac{\pi}{2}-f(x)\cos x-g(x)\sin x$ $\quad\mathrm{Ci}(x)=f(x)\sin x-g(x)\cos x$

$\frac{\pi}{2}=1.57079\ 63268$ $\quad\langle x\rangle=$nearest integer to x.

Table 5.3 SINE AND COSINE INTEGRALS FOR ARGUMENTS πx

x	$\mathrm{Si}(\pi x)$	$\mathrm{Cin}(\pi x)$	x	$\mathrm{Si}(\pi x)$	$\mathrm{Cin}(\pi x)$
0.0	0.00000 00	0.00000 00	5.0	1.63396 48	3.32742 23
0.1	0.31244 18	0.02457 28	5.1	1.63088 98	3.36670 50
0.2	0.61470 01	0.09708 67	5.2	1.62211 92	3.40335 81
0.3	0.89718 92	0.21400 75	5.3	1.60871 21	3.43582 68
0.4	1.15147 74	0.36970 10	5.4	1.59212 99	3.46297 82
0.5	1.37076 22	0.55679 77	5.5	1.57408 24	3.48419 47
0.6	1.55023 35	0.76666 63	5.6	1.55635 75	3.49941 45
0.7	1.68729 94	0.98995 93	5.7	1.54064 82	3.50911 89
0.8	1.78166 12	1.21719 42	5.8	1.52839 53	3.51426 89
0.9	1.83523 65	1.43932 68	5.9	1.52065 96	3.51619 81
1.0	1.85193 70	1.64827 75	6.0	1.51803 39	3.51647 44
1.1	1.83732 28	1.83737 48	6.1	1.52060 20	3.51674 38
1.2	1.79815 90	2.00168 51	6.2	1.52794 77	3.51857 25
1.3	1.74191 10	2.13821 22	6.3	1.53921 04	3.52330 06
1.4	1.67621 68	2.24595 41	6.4	1.55318 17	3.53192 30
1.5	1.60837 27	2.32581 82	6.5	1.56843 12	3.54500 55
1.6	1.54487 36	2.38040 96	6.6	1.58344 97	3.56264 55
1.7	1.49103 51	2.41370 98	6.7	1.59679 62	3.58447 72
1.8	1.45072 37	2.43067 75	6.8	1.60723 30	3.60972 10
1.9	1.42621 05	2.43680 30	6.9	1.61383 85	3.63727 15
2.0	1.41815 16	2.43765 34	7.0	1.61608 55	3.66581 26
2.1	1.42569 13	2.43844 23	7.1	1.61388 08	3.69395 05
2.2	1.44667 38	2.44365 73	7.2	1.60756 18	3.72034 97
2.3	1.47794 03	2.45676 95	7.3	1.59785 21	3.74385 98
2.4	1.51568 40	2.48004 47	7.4	1.58578 13	3.76362 13
2.5	1.55583 10	2.51446 40	7.5	1.57257 88	3.77914 01
2.6	1.59441 60	2.55975 53	7.6	1.55954 96	3.79032 64
2.7	1.62792 16	2.61452 59	7.7	1.54794 81	3.79749 22
2.8	1.65355 62	2.67647 93	7.8	1.53885 84	3.80131 21
2.9	1.66945 05	2.74269 41	7.9	1.53309 50	3.80274 91
3.0	1.67476 18	2.80993 76	8.0	1.53113 13	3.80295 56
3.1	1.66968 11	2.87498 49	8.1	1.53306 26	3.80315 83
3.2	1.65535 02	2.93491 77	8.2	1.53860 67	3.80453 88
3.3	1.63369 82	2.98737 63	8.3	1.54713 99	3.80812 16
3.4	1.60721 88	3.03074 73	8.4	1.55776 52	3.81467 97
3.5	1.57870 92	3.06427 25	8.5	1.56940 54	3.82466 68
3.6	1.55099 62	3.08807 51	8.6	1.58091 06	3.83818 15
3.7	1.52667 49	3.10310 38	8.7	1.59117 06	3.85496 61
3.8	1.50788 19	3.11100 53	8.8	1.59922 11	3.87444 05
3.9	1.49612 20	3.11393 95	8.9	1.60433 29	3.89576 52
4.0	1.49216 12	3.11435 65	9.0	1.60607 69	3.91792 84
4.1	1.49599 24	3.11475 82	9.1	1.60435 85	3.93984 77
4.2	1.50687 40	3.11746 60	9.2	1.59942 00	3.96047 61
4.3	1.52343 40	3.12441 61	9.3	1.59180 91	3.97890 22
4.4	1.54382 74	3.13699 91	9.4	1.58232 00	3.99443 58
4.5	1.56593 04	3.15595 79	9.5	1.57191 16	4.00666 94
4.6	1.58755 15	3.18134 84	9.6	1.56161 12	4.01551 22
4.7	1.60664 04	3.21256 74	9.7	1.55241 46	4.02119 22
4.8	1.62147 45	3.24843 85	9.8	1.54519 00	4.02422 80
4.9	1.63080 69	3.28734 92	9.9	1.54059 74	4.02537 29
5.0	1.63396 48	3.32742 23	10.0	1.53902 91	4.02553 78

$\mathrm{Ci}(\pi x)=\gamma+\ln\pi+\ln x-\mathrm{Cin}(\pi x)$ $\qquad\qquad$ $\gamma+\ln\pi=1.72194\ 55508$

$\mathrm{Si}(n\pi)$ are maximum values of $\mathrm{Si}(x)$ if $n>0$ is odd, and minimum values if $n>0$ is even. $\mathrm{Ci}\left[\left(n+\frac{1}{2}\right)\pi\right]$ are maximum values of $\mathrm{Ci}(x)$ if $n>0$ is even, and minimum values if $n>0$ is odd. We have

$$\mathrm{Si}(n\pi)\sim\frac{\pi}{2}-\frac{(-1)^n}{n\pi}\left[1-\frac{2!}{n^2\pi^2}+\frac{4!}{n^4\pi^4}-\cdots\right]\quad(n\to\infty)$$

$$\mathrm{Ci}\left[\left(n+\frac{1}{2}\right)\pi\right]\sim\frac{(-1)^n}{\left(n+\frac{1}{2}\right)\pi}\left[1-\frac{2!}{\left(n+\frac{1}{2}\right)^2\pi^2}+\frac{4!}{\left(n+\frac{1}{2}\right)^4\pi^4}-\cdots\right]\quad(n\to\infty)$$

EXPONENTIAL INTEGRALS $E_n(x)$ — Table 5.4

x	$E_2(x)-x\ln x$	$E_3(x)$	$E_4(x)$	$E_{10}(x)$	$E_{20}(x)$
0.00	1.00000 00	0.50000 00	0.33333 33	0.11111 11	0.05263 16
0.01	0.99572 22	0.49027 66	0.32838 24	0.10986 82	0.05207 90
0.02	0.99134 50	0.48096 83	0.32352 64	0.10863 95	0.05153 21
0.03	0.98686 87	0.47199 77	0.31876 19	0.10742 46	0.05099 11
0.04	0.98229 39	0.46332 39	0.31408 55	0.10622 36	0.05045 58
0.05	0.97762 11	0.45491 88	0.30949 45	0.10503 63	0.04992 60
0.06	0.97285 08	0.44676 09	0.30498 63	0.10386 24	0.04940 19
0.07	0.96798 34	0.43883 27	0.30055 85	0.10270 18	0.04888 33
0.08	0.96301 94	0.43111 97	0.29620 89	0.10155 44	0.04837 02
0.09	0.95795 93	0.42360 96	0.29193 54	0.10042 00	0.04786 24
0.10	0.95280 35	0.41629 15	0.28773 61	0.09929 84	0.04736 00
0.11	0.94755 26	0.40915 57	0.28360 90	0.09818 96	0.04686 29
0.12	0.94220 71	0.40219 37	0.27955 24	0.09709 34	0.04637 10
0.13	0.93676 72	0.39539 77	0.27556 46	0.09600 95	0.04588 43
0.14	0.93123 36	0.38876 07	0.27164 39	0.09493 80	0.04540 27
0.15	0.92560 67	0.38227 61	0.26778 89	0.09387 86	0.04492 62
0.16	0.91988 70	0.37593 80	0.26399 79	0.09283 12	0.04445 47
0.17	0.91407 48	0.36974 08	0.26026 96	0.09179 56	0.04398 82
0.18	0.90817 06	0.36367 95	0.25660 26	0.09077 18	0.04352 66
0.19	0.90217 50	0.35774 91	0.25299 56	0.08975 95	0.04306 98
0.20	0.89608 82	0.35194 53	0.24944 72	0.08875 87	0.04261 79
0.21	0.88991 09	0.34626 38	0.24595 63	0.08776 93	0.04217 07
0.22	0.88364 33	0.34070 05	0.24252 16	0.08679 10	0.04172 82
0.23	0.87728 60	0.33525 18	0.23914 19	0.08582 38	0.04129 03
0.24	0.87083 93	0.32991 42	0.23581 62	0.08486 75	0.04085 71
0.25	0.86430 37	0.32468 41	0.23254 32	0.08392 20	0.04042 85
0.26	0.85767 97	0.31955 85	0.22932 21	0.08298 72	0.04000 43
0.27	0.85096 76	0.31453 43	0.22615 17	0.08206 30	0.03958 46
0.28	0.84416 78	0.30960 86	0.22303 11	0.08114 92	0.03916 93
0.29	0.83728 08	0.30477 87	0.21995 93	0.08024 57	0.03875 84
0.30	0.83030 71	0.30004 18	0.21693 52	0.07935 24	0.03835 18
0.31	0.82324 69	0.29539 56	0.21395 81	0.07846 93	0.03794 95
0.32	0.81610 07	0.29083 74	0.21102 70	0.07759 60	0.03755 15
0.33	0.80886 90	0.28636 52	0.20814 11	0.07673 27	0.03715 76
0.34	0.80155 21	0.28197 65	0.20529 94	0.07587 90	0.03676 78
0.35	0.79415 04	0.27766 93	0.20250 13	0.07503 50	0.03638 22
0.36	0.78666 44	0.27344 16	0.19974 58	0.07420 06	0.03600 06
0.37	0.77909 43	0.26929 13	0.19703 22	0.07337 55	0.03562 31
0.38	0.77144 07	0.26521 65	0.19435 97	0.07255 97	0.03524 95
0.39	0.76370 39	0.26121 55	0.19172 76	0.07175 31	0.03487 98
0.40	0.75588 43	0.25728 64	0.18913 52	0.07095 57	0.03451 40
0.41	0.74798 23	0.25342 76	0.18658 16	0.07016 71	0.03415 21
0.42	0.73999 82	0.24963 73	0.18406 64	0.06938 75	0.03379 39
0.43	0.73193 24	0.24591 41	0.18158 87	0.06861 67	0.03343 96
0.44	0.72378 54	0.24225 63	0.17914 79	0.06785 45	0.03308 89
0.45	0.71555 75	0.23866 25	0.17674 33	0.06710 09	0.03274 20
0.46	0.70724 91	0.23513 13	0.17437 44	0.06635 58	0.03239 87
0.47	0.69886 05	0.23166 12	0.17204 05	0.06561 91	0.03205 90
0.48	0.69039 21	0.22825 08	0.16974 10	0.06489 07	0.03172 29
0.49	0.68184 43	0.22489 90	0.16747 53	0.06417 04	0.03139 03
0.50	0.67321 75	0.22160 44	0.16524 28	0.06345 83	0.03106 12

Table 5.4 **EXPONENTIAL INTEGRALS $E_n(x)$**

x	$E_2(x)$	$E_3(x)$	$E_4(x)$	$E_{10}(x)$	$E_{20}(x)$
0.50	0.32664 39	0.22160 44	0.16524 28	0.06345 83	0.03106 12
0.51	0.32110 62	0.21836 57	0.16304 30	0.06275 42	0.03073 56
0.52	0.31568 63	0.21518 18	0.16087 53	0.06205 80	0.03041 34
0.53	0.31038 07	0.21205 16	0.15873 92	0.06136 96	0.03009 46
0.54	0.30518 62	0.20897 39	0.15663 41	0.06068 89	0.02977 91
0.55	0.30009 96	0.20594 75	0.15455 96	0.06001 59	0.02946 70
0.56	0.29511 79	0.20297 15	0.15251 50	0.05935 05	0.02915 81
0.57	0.29023 82	0.20004 48	0.15050 00	0.05869 25	0.02885 25
0.58	0.28545 78	0.19716 64	0.14851 39	0.05804 19	0.02855 01
0.59	0.28077 39	0.19433 53	0.14655 65	0.05739 86	0.02825 08
0.60	0.27618 39	0.19155 06	0.14462 71	0.05676 26	0.02795 48
0.61	0.27168 55	0.18881 14	0.14272 53	0.05613 36	0.02766 18
0.62	0.26727 61	0.18611 66	0.14085 07	0.05551 18	0.02737 19
0.63	0.26295 35	0.18346 56	0.13900 28	0.05489 69	0.02708 50
0.64	0.25871 54	0.18085 73	0.13718 13	0.05428 89	0.02680 12
0.65	0.25455 97	0.17829 10	0.13538 55	0.05368 77	0.02652 04
0.66	0.25048 44	0.17576 58	0.13361 53	0.05309 33	0.02624 25
0.67	0.24648 74	0.17328 10	0.13187 01	0.05250 55	0.02596 75
0.68	0.24256 67	0.17083 58	0.13014 95	0.05192 43	0.02569 54
0.69	0.23872 06	0.16842 94	0.12845 33	0.05134 97	0.02542 62
0.70	0.23494 71	0.16606 12	0.12678 08	0.05078 15	0.02515 98
0.71	0.23124 46	0.16373 03	0.12513 19	0.05021 96	0.02489 62
0.72	0.22761 14	0.16143 60	0.12350 61	0.04966 40	0.02463 53
0.73	0.22404 57	0.15917 78	0.12190 31	0.04911 47	0.02437 72
0.74	0.22054 61	0.15695 49	0.12032 24	0.04857 15	0.02412 19
0.75	0.21711 09	0.15476 67	0.11876 38	0.04803 44	0.02386 92
0.76	0.21373 88	0.15261 25	0.11722 70	0.04750 33	0.02361 91
0.77	0.21042 82	0.15049 17	0.11571 15	0.04697 81	0.02337 17
0.78	0.20717 77	0.14840 37	0.11421 70	0.04645 88	0.02312 69
0.79	0.20398 60	0.14634 79	0.11274 33	0.04594 53	0.02288 46
0.80	0.20085 17	0.14432 38	0.11129 00	0.04543 76	0.02264 49
0.81	0.19777 36	0.14233 07	0.10985 67	0.04493 56	0.02240 78
0.82	0.19475 04	0.14036 81	0.10844 33	0.04443 91	0.02217 31
0.83	0.19178 10	0.13843 55	0.10704 93	0.04394 82	0.02194 08
0.84	0.18886 41	0.13653 24	0.10567 44	0.04346 28	0.02171 11
0.85	0.18599 86	0.13465 81	0.10431 85	0.04298 29	0.02148 37
0.86	0.18318 33	0.13281 22	0.10298 12	0.04250 82	0.02125 87
0.87	0.18041 73	0.13099 43	0.10166 22	0.04203 89	0.02103 61
0.88	0.17769 94	0.12920 37	0.10036 12	0.04157 49	0.02081 58
0.89	0.17502 87	0.12744 01	0.09907 80	0.04111 60	0.02059 78
0.90	0.17240 41	0.12570 30	0.09781 23	0.04066 22	0.02038 21
0.91	0.16982 47	0.12399 19	0.09656 39	0.04021 35	0.02016 87
0.92	0.16728 95	0.12230 63	0.09533 24	0.03976 98	0.01995 75
0.93	0.16479 77	0.12064 59	0.09411 77	0.03933 11	0.01974 86
0.94	0.16234 82	0.11901 02	0.09291 94	0.03889 73	0.01954 18
0.95	0.15994 04	0.11739 88	0.09173 74	0.03846 83	0.01933 72
0.96	0.15757 32	0.11581 13	0.09057 13	0.03804 41	0.01913 47
0.97	0.15524 59	0.11424 72	0.08942 11	0.03762 46	0.01893 44
0.98	0.15295 78	0.11270 63	0.08828 63	0.03720 98	0.01873 62
0.99	0.15070 79	0.11118 80	0.08716 69	0.03679 96	0.01854 01
1.00	0.14849 55	0.10969 20	0.08606 25	0.03639 40	0.01834 60

EXPONENTIAL INTEGRALS $E_n(x)$ Table 5.4

x	$E_2(x)$	$E_3(x)$	$E_4(x)$	$E_{10}(x)$	$E_{20}(x)$
1.00	0.14849 55	0.10969 20	0.08606 25	0.03639 40	0.01834 60
1.01	0.14631 99	0.10821 79	0.08497 30	0.03599 29	0.01815 39
1.02	0.14418 04	0.10676 54	0.08389 81	0.03559 63	0.01796 39
1.03	0.14207 63	0.10533 42	0.08283 76	0.03520 41	0.01777 59
1.04	0.14000 68	0.10392 38	0.08179 13	0.03481 63	0.01758 98
1.05	0.13797 13	0.10253 39	0.08075 90	0.03443 28	0.01740 57
1.06	0.13596 91	0.10116 43	0.07974 06	0.03405 35	0.01722 35
1.07	0.13399 96	0.09981 45	0.07873 57	0.03367 85	0.01704 33
1.08	0.13206 22	0.09848 42	0.07774 42	0.03330 77	0.01686 49
1.09	0.13015 62	0.09717 31	0.07676 59	0.03294 10	0.01668 84
1.10	0.12828 11	0.09588 09	0.07580 07	0.03257 84	0.01651 37
1.11	0.12643 62	0.09460 74	0.07484 83	0.03221 98	0.01634 09
1.12	0.12462 10	0.09335 21	0.07390 85	0.03186 52	0.01616 99
1.13	0.12283 50	0.09211 49	0.07298 12	0.03151 45	0.01600 07
1.14	0.12107 75	0.09089 53	0.07206 61	0.03116 78	0.01583 33
1.15	0.11934 81	0.08969 32	0.07116 32	0.03082 49	0.01566 76
1.16	0.11764 62	0.08850 83	0.07027 22	0.03048 58	0.01550 37
1.17	0.11597 14	0.08734 02	0.06939 30	0.03015 05	0.01534 14
1.18	0.11432 31	0.08618 88	0.06852 53	0.02981 89	0.01518 09
1.19	0.11270 08	0.08505 37	0.06766 91	0.02949 10	0.01502 21
1.20	0.11110 41	0.08393 47	0.06682 42	0.02916 68	0.01486 49
1.21	0.10953 25	0.08283 15	0.06599 04	0.02884 61	0.01470 94
1.22	0.10798 55	0.08174 39	0.06516 75	0.02852 90	0.01455 55
1.23	0.10646 27	0.08067 17	0.06435 55	0.02821 55	0.01440 32
1.24	0.10496 37	0.07961 46	0.06355 40	0.02790 54	0.01425 26
1.25	0.10348 81	0.07857 23	0.06276 31	0.02759 88	0.01410 35
1.26	0.10203 53	0.07754 47	0.06198 25	0.02729 55	0.01395 59
1.27	0.10060 51	0.07653 16	0.06121 22	0.02699 57	0.01381 00
1.28	0.09919 70	0.07553 26	0.06045 19	0.02669 91	0.01366 55
1.29	0.09781 06	0.07454 76	0.05970 15	0.02640 59	0.01352 26
1.30	0.09644 55	0.07357 63	0.05896 09	0.02611 59	0.01338 11
1.31	0.09510 15	0.07261 86	0.05822 99	0.02582 91	0.01324 12
1.32	0.09377 80	0.07167 42	0.05750 85	0.02554 55	0.01310 27
1.33	0.09247 47	0.07074 29	0.05679 64	0.02526 51	0.01296 57
1.34	0.09119 13	0.06982 46	0.05609 36	0.02498 78	0.01283 01
1.35	0.08992 75	0.06891 91	0.05539 98	0.02471 35	0.01269 59
1.36	0.08868 29	0.06802 60	0.05471 51	0.02444 23	0.01256 31
1.37	0.08745 71	0.06714 53	0.05403 93	0.02417 41	0.01243 17
1.38	0.08624 99	0.06627 68	0.05337 22	0.02390 88	0.01230 17
1.39	0.08506 10	0.06542 03	0.05271 37	0.02364 65	0.01217 31
1.40	0.08388 99	0.06457 55	0.05206 37	0.02338 72	0.01204 58
1.41	0.08273 65	0.06374 24	0.05142 22	0.02313 06	0.01191 98
1.42	0.08160 04	0.06292 07	0.05078 89	0.02287 70	0.01179 52
1.43	0.08048 13	0.06211 04	0.05016 37	0.02262 61	0.01167 19
1.44	0.07937 89	0.06131 11	0.04954 66	0.02237 80	0.01154 99
1.45	0.07829 30	0.06052 27	0.04893 74	0.02213 27	0.01142 91
1.46	0.07722 33	0.05974 52	0.04833 61	0.02189 01	0.01130 96
1.47	0.07616 94	0.05897 82	0.04774 25	0.02165 01	0.01119 14
1.48	0.07513 13	0.05822 17	0.04715 65	0.02141 28	0.01107 44
1.49	0.07410 85	0.05747 55	0.04657 80	0.02117 82	0.01095 86
1.50	0.07310 08	0.05673 95	0.04600 70	0.02094 61	0.01084 40
1.51	0.07210 80	0.05601 35	0.04544 32	0.02071 67	0.01073 07
1.52	0.07112 98	0.05529 73	0.04488 67	0.02048 97	0.01061 85
1.53	0.07016 60	0.05459 08	0.04433 72	0.02026 53	0.01050 75
1.54	0.06921 64	0.05389 39	0.04379 48	0.02004 33	0.01039 77
1.55	0.06828 07	0.05320 64	0.04325 93	0.01982 38	0.01028 90
1.56	0.06735 87	0.05252 83	0.04273 07	0.01960 67	0.01018 15
1.57	0.06645 02	0.05185 92	0.04220 87	0.01939 21	0.01007 50
1.58	0.06555 49	0.05119 92	0.04169 35	0.01917 98	0.00996 97
1.59	0.06467 26	0.05054 81	0.04118 47	0.01896 98	0.00986 56
1.60	0.06380 32	0.04990 57	0.04068 25	0.01876 22	0.00976 24

Table 5.4 EXPONENTIAL INTEGRALS $E_n(x)$

x	$E_2(x)$	$E_3(x)$	$E_4(x)$	$E_{10}(x)$	$E_{20}(x)$
1.60	0.06380 32	0.04990 57	0.04068 25	0.01876 22	0.00976 24
1.61	0.06294 64	0.04927 20	0.04018 66	0.01855 68	0.00966 04
1.62	0.06210 20	0.04864 67	0.03969 70	0.01835 38	0.00955 95
1.63	0.06126 98	0.04802 99	0.03921 36	0.01815 30	0.00945 96
1.64	0.06044 97	0.04742 13	0.03873 64	0.01795 43	0.00936 07
1.65	0.05964 13	0.04682 09	0.03826 52	0.01775 79	0.00926 29
1.66	0.05884 46	0.04622 84	0.03779 99	0.01756 37	0.00916 61
1.67	0.05805 94	0.04564 39	0.03734 06	0.01737 16	0.00907 03
1.68	0.05728 54	0.04506 72	0.03688 70	0.01718 16	0.00897 56
1.69	0.05652 26	0.04449 82	0.03643 92	0.01699 37	0.00888 18
1.70	0.05577 06	0.04393 67	0.03599 70	0.01680 79	0.00878 90
1.71	0.05502 94	0.04338 27	0.03556 04	0.01662 42	0.00869 72
1.72	0.05429 88	0.04283 61	0.03512 93	0.01644 24	0.00860 63
1.73	0.05357 86	0.04229 67	0.03470 37	0.01626 27	0.00851 64
1.74	0.05286 86	0.04176 45	0.03428 34	0.01608 50	0.00842 74
1.75	0.05216 87	0.04123 93	0.03386 84	0.01590 92	0.00833 94
1.76	0.05147 88	0.04072 11	0.03345 86	0.01573 54	0.00825 22
1.77	0.05079 86	0.04020 97	0.03305 39	0.01556 34	0.00816 60
1.78	0.05012 81	0.03970 51	0.03265 44	0.01539 34	0.00808 07
1.79	0.04946 70	0.03920 71	0.03225 98	0.01522 53	0.00799 63
1.80	0.04881 53	0.03871 57	0.03187 02	0.01505 90	0.00791 28
1.81	0.04817 27	0.03823 08	0.03148 55	0.01489 45	0.00783 02
1.82	0.04753 92	0.03775 22	0.03110 56	0.01473 18	0.00774 84
1.83	0.04691 46	0.03728 00	0.03073 04	0.01457 10	0.00766 74
1.84	0.04629 87	0.03681 39	0.03035 99	0.01441 19	0.00758 74
1.85	0.04569 15	0.03635 40	0.02999 41	0.01425 46	0.00750 81
1.86	0.04509 28	0.03590 01	0.02963 28	0.01409 90	0.00742 97
1.87	0.04450 24	0.03545 21	0.02927 61	0.01394 51	0.00735 21
1.88	0.04392 03	0.03501 00	0.02892 38	0.01379 29	0.00727 53
1.89	0.04334 63	0.03457 37	0.02857 59	0.01364 24	0.00719 93
1.90	0.04278 03	0.03414 30	0.02823 23	0.01349 35	0.00712 42
1.91	0.04222 22	0.03371 80	0.02789 30	0.01334 63	0.00704 98
1.92	0.04167 18	0.03329 86	0.02755 79	0.01320 07	0.00697 62
1.93	0.04112 91	0.03288 46	0.02722 70	0.01305 67	0.00690 33
1.94	0.04059 38	0.03247 59	0.02690 02	0.01291 43	0.00683 12
1.95	0.04006 60	0.03207 27	0.02657 75	0.01277 34	0.00675 99
1.96	0.03954 55	0.03167 46	0.02625 87	0.01263 41	0.00668 93
1.97	0.03903 22	0.03128 17	0.02594 40	0.01249 64	0.00661 95
1.98	0.03852 59	0.03089 39	0.02563 31	0.01236 01	0.00655 04
1.99	0.03802 67	0.03051 12	0.02532 61	0.01222 54	0.00648 20
2.00	0.03753 43	0.03013 34	0.02502 28	0.01209 21	0.00641 43

Table 5.5 EXPONENTIAL INTEGRALS $E_n(x)$ FOR LARGE ARGUMENTS

x^{-1}	$(x+2)e^xE_2(x)$	$(x+3)e^xE_3(x)$	$(x+4)e^xE_4(x)$	$(x+10)e^xE_{10}(x)$	$(x+20)e^xE_{20}(x)$	$<x>$
0.50	1.10937	1.11329	1.10937	1.07219	1.04270	2
0.45	1.09750	1.10285	1.10071	1.06926	1.04179	2
0.40	1.08533	1.09185	1.09136	1.06586	1.04067	3
0.35	1.07292	1.08026	1.08125	1.06187	1.03932	3
0.30	1.06034	1.06808	1.07031	1.05712	1.03762	3
0.25	1.04770	1.05536	1.05850	1.05138	1.03543	4
0.20	1.03522	1.04222	1.04584	1.04432	1.03249	5
0.15	1.02325	1.02895	1.03247	1.03550	1.02837	7
0.10	1.01240	1.01617	1.01889	1.02436	1.02222	10
0.09	1.01045	1.01377	1.01624	1.02182	1.02060	11
0.08	1.00861	1.01147	1.01366	1.01917	1.01883	13
0.07	1.00688	1.00927	1.01116	1.01642	1.01688	14
0.06	1.00528	1.00721	1.00878	1.01360	1.01472	17
0.05	1.00384	1.00531	1.00654	1.01074	1.01234	20
0.04	1.00258	1.00361	1.00451	1.00790	1.00973	25
0.03	1.00152	1.00217	1.00275	1.00516	1.00692	33
0.02	1.00071	1.00103	1.00133	1.00271	1.00401	50
0.01	1.00019	1.00027	1.00036	1.00081	1.00137	100
0.00	1.00000	1.00000	1.00000	1.00000	1.00000	∞

$<x>$=nearest integer to x.

EXPONENTIAL INTEGRAL FOR COMPLEX ARGUMENTS Table 5.6

$ze^zE_1(z)$

$y\backslash x$	−19 $\mathscr{R}$	−19 $\mathscr{I}$	−18 $\mathscr{R}$	−18 $\mathscr{I}$	−17 $\mathscr{R}$	−17 $\mathscr{I}$	−16 $\mathscr{R}$	−16 $\mathscr{I}$	−15 $\mathscr{R}$	−15 $\mathscr{I}$
0	1.059305	0.000000	1.063087	0.000001	1.067394	0.000002	1.072345	0.000006	1.078103	0.000014
1	1.059090	0.003539	1.062827	0.004010	1.067073	0.004584	1.071942	0.005296	1.077584	0.006195
2	1.058456	0.007000	1.062061	0.007918	1.066135	0.009032	1.070774	0.010403	1.076102	0.012118
3	1.057431	0.010310	1.060829	0.011633	1.064636	0.013226	1.068925	0.015172	1.073783	0.017579
4	1.056058	0.013410	1.059190	0.015079	1.062657	0.017075	1.066508	0.019486	1.070793	0.022432
5	1.054391	0.016252	1.057215	0.018202	1.060297	0.020512	1.063659	0.023272	1.067318	0.026598
6	1.052490	0.018806	1.054981	0.020969	1.057655	0.023505	1.060510	0.026499	1.063538	0.030055
7	1.050413	0.021055	1.052565	0.023364	1.054829	0.026044	1.057187	0.029167	1.059610	0.032823
8	1.048217	0.022996	1.050037	0.025391	1.051905	0.028141	1.053795	0.031306	1.055664	0.034957
9	1.045956	0.024637	1.047458	0.027066	1.048958	0.029824	1.050421	0.032960	1.051797	0.036527
10	1.043672	0.025993	1.044880	0.028412	1.046045	0.031130	1.047129	0.034183	1.048081	0.037609
11	1.041402	0.027086	1.042345	0.029461	1.043212	0.032102	1.043967	0.035034	1.044559	0.038282
12	1.039177	0.027940	1.039882	0.030245	1.040490	0.032781	1.040965	0.035567	1.041259	0.038616
13	1.037018	0.028581	1.037515	0.030796	1.037901	0.033211	1.038140	0.035836	1.038192	0.038677
14	1.034942	0.029034	1.035259	0.031148	1.035456	0.033431	1.035501	0.035888	1.035359	0.038520
15	1.032959	0.029326	1.033123	0.031330	1.033162	0.033476	1.033049	0.035765	1.032754	0.038193
16	1.031076	0.029477	1.031110	0.031368	1.031019	0.033377	1.030780	0.035502	1.030365	0.037735
17	1.029296	0.029511	1.029222	0.031288	1.029025	0.033162	1.028685	0.035129	1.028180	0.037179
18	1.027620	0.029445	1.027456	0.031110	1.027174	0.032855	1.026756	0.034672	1.026183	0.036552
19	1.026046	0.029296	1.025809	0.030854	1.025459	0.032474	1.024981	0.034150	1.024360	0.035873
20	1.024570	0.029080	1.024275	0.030534	1.023872	0.032037	1.023349	0.033582	1.022695	0.035160

$y\backslash x$	−14 $\mathscr{R}$	−14 $\mathscr{I}$	−13 $\mathscr{R}$	−13 $\mathscr{I}$	−12 $\mathscr{R}$	−12 $\mathscr{I}$	−11 $\mathscr{R}$	−11 $\mathscr{I}$	−10 $\mathscr{R}$	−10 $\mathscr{I}$
0	1.084892	0.000037	1.093027	0.000092	1.102975	0.000232	1.115431	0.000577	1.131470	0.001426
1	1.084200	0.007359	1.092067	0.008913	1.101566	0.011063	1.113230	0.014169	1.127796	0.018879
2	1.082276	0.014306	1.089498	0.017161	1.098025	0.020981	1.108170	0.026241	1.120286	0.033700
3	1.079313	0.020604	1.085635	0.024471	1.092873	0.029507	1.101137	0.036189	1.110462	0.045218
4	1.075560	0.026075	1.080853	0.030637	1.086686	0.036422	1.093013	0.043843	1.099666	0.053451
5	1.071279	0.030642	1.075522	0.035599	1.079985	0.041724	1.084526	0.049336	1.088877	0.058817
6	1.066708	0.034303	1.069960	0.039405	1.073185	0.045552	1.076197	0.052967	1.078701	0.061886
7	1.062046	0.037117	1.064412	0.042169	1.066578	0.048115	1.068350	0.055093	1.069450	0.063225
8	1.057448	0.039174	1.059054	0.044041	1.060352	0.049644	1.061159	0.056057	1.061235	0.063322
9	1.053021	0.040580	1.053997	0.045176	1.054606	0.050359	1.054687	0.056158	1.054046	0.062566
10	1.048834	0.041444	1.049303	0.045719	1.049380	0.050452	1.048933	0.055640	1.047807	0.061249
11	1.044928	0.041867	1.044997	0.045801	1.044674	0.050084	1.043853	0.054695	1.042417	0.059584
12	1.041320	0.041938	1.041080	0.045531	1.040464	0.049384	1.039389	0.053465	1.037766	0.057719
13	1.038010	0.041734	1.037537	0.044999	1.036713	0.048452	1.035473	0.052056	1.033752	0.055758
14	1.034989	0.041321	1.034344	0.044277	1.033378	0.047365	1.032040	0.050547	1.030282	0.053773
15	1.032241	0.040751	1.031474	0.043422	1.030414	0.046180	1.029026	0.048991	1.027274	0.051808
16	1.029747	0.040066	1.028895	0.042477	1.027781	0.044941	1.026377	0.047428	1.024658	0.049894
17	1.027486	0.039301	1.026579	0.041475	1.025438	0.043679	1.024043	0.045883	1.022375	0.048049
18	1.025437	0.038481	1.024499	0.040444	1.023352	0.042417	1.021981	0.044374	1.020375	0.046282
19	1.023580	0.037629	1.022628	0.039401	1.021489	0.041170	1.020155	0.042912	1.018617	0.044599
20	1.021896	0.036759	1.020942	0.038361	1.019824	0.039950	1.018533	0.041505	1.017066	0.043001

$y\backslash x$	−9 $\mathscr{R}$	−9 $\mathscr{I}$	−8 $\mathscr{R}$	−8 $\mathscr{I}$	−7 $\mathscr{R}$	−7 $\mathscr{I}$	−6 $\mathscr{R}$	−6 $\mathscr{I}$	−5 $\mathscr{R}$	−5 $\mathscr{I}$
0	1.152759	0.003489	1.181848	0.008431	1.222408	0.020053	1.278884	0.046723	1.353831	0.105839
1	1.146232	0.026376	1.169677	0.038841	1.199049	0.060219	1.233798	0.097331	1.268723	0.160826
2	1.134679	0.044579	1.151385	0.060814	1.169639	0.085335	1.186778	0.122162	1.196351	0.175646
3	1.120694	0.057595	1.131255	0.074701	1.140733	0.098259	1.146266	0.130005	1.142853	0.170672
4	1.106249	0.065948	1.111968	0.082156	1.115404	0.102861	1.114273	0.128440	1.105376	0.158134
5	1.092564	0.070592	1.094818	0.085055	1.094475	0.102411	1.089952	0.122397	1.079407	0.143879
6	1.080246	0.072520	1.080188	0.084987	1.077672	0.099188	1.071684	0.114638	1.061236	0.130280
7	1.069494	0.072580	1.067987	0.083120	1.064339	0.094618	1.057935	0.106568	1.048279	0.118116
8	1.060276	0.071425	1.057920	0.080250	1.053778	0.089537	1.047493	0.098840	1.038838	0.107508
9	1.052450	0.069523	1.049645	0.076885	1.045382	0.084405	1.039464	0.091717	1.031806	0.098337
10	1.045832	0.067197	1.042834	0.073340	1.038659	0.079462	1.033205	0.085271	1.026459	0.090413
11	1.040241	0.064664	1.037210	0.069803	1.033231	0.074821	1.028260	0.079488	1.022317	0.083544
12	1.035508	0.062063	1.032539	0.066381	1.028808	0.070524	1.024300	0.074315	1.019052	0.077561
13	1.031490	0.059482	1.028638	0.063128	1.025171	0.066576	1.021090	0.069688	1.016439	0.072320
14	1.028065	0.056975	1.025359	0.060070	1.022152	0.062962	1.018458	0.065542	1.014319	0.067702
15	1.025132	0.054573	1.022583	0.057215	1.019626	0.059658	1.016277	0.061817	1.012577	0.063610
16	1.022608	0.052291	1.020219	0.054559	1.017494	0.056638	1.014452	0.058460	1.011130	0.059962
17	1.020426	0.050135	1.018192	0.052094	1.015681	0.053874	1.012912	0.055424	1.009915	0.056694
18	1.018530	0.048106	1.016444	0.049806	1.014129	0.051341	1.011600	0.052670	1.008887	0.053752
19	1.016874	0.046201	1.014929	0.047684	1.012790	0.049015	1.010476	0.050161	1.008009	0.051092
20	1.015422	0.044413	1.013607	0.045714	1.011629	0.046875	1.009505	0.047870	1.007254	0.048675

For $|z|>4$, linear interpolation will yield about four decimals, eight-point interpolation will yield about six decimals.

Table 5.6 EXPONENTIAL INTEGRAL FOR COMPLEX ARGUMENTS

$ze^zE_1(z)$

$y\backslash x$	−4 $\mathcal{R}$	−4 $\mathcal{I}$	−3 $\mathcal{R}$	−3 $\mathcal{I}$	−2 $\mathcal{R}$	−2 $\mathcal{I}$	−1 $\mathcal{R}$	−1 $\mathcal{I}$	0 $\mathcal{R}$	0 $\mathcal{I}$
0	1.438208	0.230161	1.483729	0.469232	1.340965	0.850337	0.697175	1.155727	0.577216	0.000000
1	1.287244	0.263705	1.251069	0.410413	1.098808	0.561916	0.813486	0.578697	0.621450	0.343378
2	1.185758	0.247356	1.136171	0.328439	1.032990	0.388428	0.896419	0.378838	0.798042	0.289091
3	1.123282	0.217835	1.080316	0.262814	1.013205	0.289366	0.936283	0.280906	0.875873	0.237665
4	1.085153	0.189003	1.051401	0.215118	1.006122	0.228399	0.957446	0.222612	0.916770	0.198713
5	1.061263	0.164466	1.035185	0.180487	1.003172	0.187857	0.969809	0.183963	0.940714	0.169481
6	1.045719	0.144391	1.025396	0.154746	1.001788	0.159189	0.977582	0.156511	0.955833	0.147129
7	1.035205	0.128073	1.019109	0.135079	1.001077	0.137939	0.982756	0.136042	0.965937	0.129646
8	1.027834	0.114732	1.014861	0.119660	1.000684	0.121599	0.986356	0.120218	0.972994	0.115678
9	1.022501	0.103711	1.011869	0.107294	1.000454	0.108665	0.988955	0.107634	0.978103	0.104303
10	1.018534	0.094502	1.009688	0.097181	1.000312	0.098184	0.990887	0.097396	0.981910	0.094885
11	1.015513	0.086718	1.008052	0.088770	1.000221	0.089525	0.992361	0.088911	0.984819	0.086975
12	1.013163	0.080069	1.006795	0.081673	1.000161	0.082255	0.993508	0.081769	0.987088	0.080245
13	1.011303	0.074333	1.005809	0.075609	1.000119	0.076067	0.994418	0.075676	0.988891	0.074457
14	1.009806	0.069340	1.005022	0.070371	1.000090	0.070738	0.995151	0.070419	0.990345	0.069429
15	1.008585	0.064959	1.004384	0.065803	1.000070	0.066102	0.995751	0.065838	0.991534	0.065024
16	1.007577	0.061086	1.003859	0.061786	1.000055	0.062032	0.996246	0.061812	0.992518	0.061135
17	1.006735	0.057640	1.003423	0.058227	1.000043	0.058432	0.996661	0.058246	0.993342	0.057677
18	1.006025	0.054555	1.003057	0.055052	1.000035	0.055224	0.997011	0.055066	0.994038	0.054583
19	1.005420	0.051779	1.002747	0.052202	1.000028	0.052349	0.997309	0.052214	0.994631	0.051801
20	1.004902	0.049267	1.002481	0.049631	1.000023	0.049757	0.997565	0.049640	0.995140	0.049284

$y\backslash x$	1 $\mathcal{R}$	1 $\mathcal{I}$	2 $\mathcal{R}$	2 $\mathcal{I}$	3 $\mathcal{R}$	3 $\mathcal{I}$	4 $\mathcal{R}$	4 $\mathcal{I}$	5 $\mathcal{R}$	5 $\mathcal{I}$
0	0.596347	0.000000	0.722657	0.000000	0.786251	0.000000	0.825383	0.000000	0.852111	0.000000
1	0.673321	0.147864	0.747012	0.075661	0.797036	0.045686	0.831126	0.030619	0.855544	0.021985
2	0.777514	0.186570	0.796965	0.118228	0.823055	0.078753	0.846097	0.055494	0.864880	0.040999
3	0.847468	0.181226	0.844361	0.132252	0.853176	0.096659	0.865521	0.072180	0.877860	0.055341
4	0.891460	0.165207	0.881036	0.131686	0.880584	0.103403	0.885308	0.081408	0.892143	0.064825
5	0.919826	0.148271	0.907873	0.125136	0.903152	0.103577	0.903231	0.085187	0.906058	0.070209
6	0.938827	0.132986	0.927384	0.116656	0.921006	0.100357	0.918527	0.085460	0.918708	0.072544
7	0.952032	0.119807	0.941722	0.107990	0.934958	0.095598	0.931209	0.083666	0.929765	0.072792
8	0.961512	0.108589	0.952435	0.099830	0.945868	0.090303	0.941594	0.080755	0.939221	0.071700
9	0.968512	0.099045	0.960582	0.092408	0.954457	0.084986	0.950072	0.077313	0.947219	0.069799
10	0.973810	0.090888	0.966885	0.085758	0.961283	0.079898	0.957007	0.073688	0.953955	0.067447
11	0.977904	0.083871	0.971842	0.079836	0.966766	0.075147	0.962708	0.070080	0.959626	0.064878
12	0.981127	0.077790	0.975799	0.074567	0.971216	0.070769	0.967423	0.066599	0.964412	0.062242
13	0.983706	0.072484	0.979000	0.069873	0.974865	0.066762	0.971351	0.063300	0.968464	0.059630
14	0.985799	0.067822	0.981621	0.065679	0.977888	0.063104	0.974646	0.060206	0.971911	0.057096
15	0.987519	0.063698	0.983791	0.061921	0.980414	0.059767	0.977430	0.057322	0.974858	0.054671
16	0.988949	0.060029	0.985606	0.058539	0.982544	0.056723	0.979799	0.054644	0.977391	0.052371
17	0.990149	0.056745	0.987138	0.055485	0.984353	0.053941	0.981827	0.052162	0.979579	0.050200
18	0.991167	0.053792	0.988442	0.052717	0.985902	0.051394	0.983574	0.049861	0.981478	0.048160
19	0.992036	0.051122	0.989561	0.050199	0.987237	0.049057	0.985089	0.047728	0.983135	0.046245
20	0.992784	0.048699	0.990527	0.047900	0.988395	0.046909	0.986410	0.045749	0.984587	0.044449

$y\backslash x$	6 $\mathcal{R}$	6 $\mathcal{I}$	7 $\mathcal{R}$	7 $\mathcal{I}$	8 $\mathcal{R}$	8 $\mathcal{I}$	9 $\mathcal{R}$	9 $\mathcal{I}$	10 $\mathcal{R}$	10 $\mathcal{I}$
0	0.871606	0.000000	0.886488	0.000000	0.898237	0.000000	0.907758	0.000000	0.915633	0.000000
1	0.873827	0.016570	0.888009	0.012947	0.899327	0.010401	0.908565	0.008543	0.916249	0.007143
2	0.880023	0.031454	0.892327	0.024866	0.902453	0.020140	0.910901	0.016639	0.918040	0.013975
3	0.889029	0.043517	0.898793	0.034995	0.907236	0.028693	0.914531	0.023921	0.920856	0.020230
4	0.899484	0.052380	0.906591	0.042967	0.913167	0.035755	0.919127	0.030145	0.924479	0.025717
5	0.910242	0.058259	0.914952	0.048780	0.919729	0.041242	0.924336	0.035208	0.928664	0.030334
6	0.920534	0.061676	0.923283	0.052667	0.926481	0.045242	0.929836	0.039123	0.933175	0.034063
7	0.929945	0.063220	0.931193	0.054971	0.933096	0.047942	0.935365	0.041986	0.937807	0.036944
8	0.938313	0.063425	0.938469	0.056047	0.939359	0.049570	0.940731	0.043936	0.942398	0.039060
9	0.945629	0.062714	0.945023	0.056211	0.945154	0.050349	0.945812	0.045128	0.946833	0.040514
10	0.951965	0.061408	0.950850	0.055725	0.950427	0.050481	0.950535	0.045711	0.951035	0.041413
11	0.957427	0.059735	0.955987	0.054790	0.955176	0.050135	0.954870	0.045818	0.954959	0.041861
12	0.962128	0.057855	0.960495	0.053560	0.959421	0.049444	0.958814	0.045563	0.958586	0.041948
13	0.966178	0.055877	0.964444	0.052146	0.963201	0.048514	0.962379	0.045038	0.961913	0.041755
14	0.969673	0.053874	0.967903	0.050627	0.966559	0.047425	0.965591	0.044319	0.964949	0.041347
15	0.972699	0.051894	0.970935	0.049062	0.969539	0.046236	0.968477	0.043463	0.967710	0.040780
16	0.975326	0.049966	0.973557	0.047489	0.972185	0.044992	0.971067	0.042516	0.970214	0.040095
17	0.977617	0.048109	0.975940	0.045935	0.974538	0.043724	0.973393	0.041512	0.972484	0.039329
18	0.979622	0.046332	0.978009	0.044419	0.976632	0.042456	0.975481	0.040477	0.974540	0.038508
19	0.981384	0.044641	0.979839	0.042951	0.978500	0.041205	0.977357	0.039431	0.976402	0.037653
20	0.982938	0.043036	0.981465	0.041538	0.980169	0.039980	0.979047	0.038388	0.978090	0.036781

If $x>10$ or $y>10$ then (see [5.15])

$$e^zE_1(z)=\frac{0.711093}{z+0.415775}+\frac{0.278518}{z+2.29428}+\frac{0.010389}{z+6.2900}+\epsilon,\ |\epsilon|<3\times10^{-6}.$$

$$E_1(iy)=-\mathrm{Ci}(y)+i\ \mathrm{si}(y)\quad (y \text{ real})$$

EXPONENTIAL INTEGRAL FOR COMPLEX ARGUMENTS Table 5.6

$ze^zE_1(z)$

$y \backslash x$	11 ℜ	11 ℑ	12 ℜ	12 ℑ	13 ℜ	13 ℑ	14 ℜ	14 ℑ	15 ℜ	15 ℑ
0	0.922260	0.000000	0.927914	0.000000	0.932796	0.000000	0.937055	0.000000	0.940804	0.000000
1	0.922740	0.006063	0.928295	0.005212	0.933105	0.004528	0.937308	0.003972	0.941014	0.003512
2	0.924143	0.011902	0.929416	0.010258	0.934013	0.008932	0.938055	0.007847	0.941636	0.006949
3	0.926370	0.017321	0.931205	0.014991	0.935473	0.013098	0.939261	0.011540	0.942643	0.010242
4	0.929270	0.022171	0.933560	0.019295	0.937408	0.016934	0.940870	0.014974	0.943994	0.013331
5	0.932672	0.026361	0.936356	0.023091	0.939729	0.020373	0.942816	0.018095	0.945640	0.016169
6	0.936400	0.029857	0.939462	0.026339	0.942338	0.023378	0.945024	0.020867	0.947522	0.018725
7	0.940297	0.032670	0.942757	0.029036	0.945140	0.025934	0.947419	0.023273	0.949582	0.020980
8	0.944229	0.034847	0.946132	0.031205	0.948047	0.028052	0.949933	0.025315	0.951765	0.022931
9	0.948093	0.036453	0.949500	0.032887	0.950985	0.029756	0.952502	0.027004	0.954018	0.024582
10	0.951816	0.037566	0.952792	0.034134	0.953895	0.031081	0.955075	0.028365	0.956296	0.025949
11	0.955347	0.038261	0.955958	0.035004	0.956729	0.032068	0.957610	0.029426	0.958563	0.027052
12	0.958659	0.038612	0.958968	0.035552	0.959454	0.032761	0.960073	0.030221	0.960787	0.027915
13	0.961739	0.038684	0.961800	0.035833	0.962049	0.033201	0.962443	0.030781	0.962947	0.028564
14	0.964583	0.038534	0.964447	0.035893	0.964499	0.033428	0.964702	0.031140	0.965026	0.029024
15	0.967199	0.038211	0.966907	0.035775	0.966799	0.033479	0.966843	0.031327	0.967011	0.029320
16	0.969597	0.037756	0.969184	0.035515	0.968947	0.033384	0.968860	0.031370	0.968897	0.029476
17	0.971789	0.037200	0.971285	0.035144	0.970946	0.033172	0.970752	0.031293	0.970680	0.029512
18	0.973792	0.036572	0.973220	0.034687	0.972802	0.032865	0.972521	0.031117	0.972359	0.029448
19	0.975621	0.035893	0.974999	0.034166	0.974521	0.032485	0.974172	0.030862	0.973936	0.029301
20	0.977290	0.035179	0.976634	0.033597	0.976112	0.032049	0.975709	0.030542	0.975414	0.029086

$y \backslash x$	16 ℜ	16 ℑ	17 ℜ	17 ℑ	18 ℜ	18 ℑ	19 ℜ	19 ℑ	20 ℜ	20 ℑ
0	0.944130	0.000000	0.947100	0.000000	0.949769	0.000000	0.952181	0.000000	0.954371	0.000000
1	0.944306	0.003128	0.947250	0.002804	0.949897	0.002527	0.952291	0.002290	0.954467	0.002085
2	0.944829	0.006196	0.947693	0.005560	0.950277	0.005016	0.952619	0.004549	0.954752	0.004144
3	0.945678	0.009150	0.948416	0.008223	0.950898	0.007430	0.953156	0.006745	0.955219	0.006151
4	0.946824	0.011940	0.949395	0.010754	0.951741	0.009735	0.953887	0.008853	0.955856	0.008084
5	0.948226	0.014529	0.950600	0.013121	0.952782	0.011904	0.954793	0.010847	0.956650	0.009922
6	0.949842	0.016886	0.951995	0.015296	0.953995	0.013916	0.955853	0.012709	0.957581	0.011649
7	0.951624	0.018994	0.953545	0.017265	0.955349	0.015753	0.957043	0.014425	0.958631	0.013253
8	0.953527	0.020847	0.955212	0.019019	0.956815	0.017409	0.958337	0.015986	0.959779	0.014723
9	0.955509	0.022445	0.956960	0.020555	0.958363	0.018878	0.959712	0.017387	0.961004	0.016056
10	0.957530	0.023797	0.958758	0.021878	0.959966	0.020163	0.961144	0.018628	0.962288	0.017250
11	0.959559	0.024917	0.960576	0.022998	0.961598	0.021270	0.962612	0.019712	0.963611	0.018305
12	0.961568	0.025823	0.962391	0.023927	0.963238	0.022207	0.964097	0.020645	0.964956	0.019227
13	0.963534	0.026534	0.964181	0.024679	0.964868	0.022984	0.965582	0.021436	0.966310	0.020021
14	0.965443	0.027070	0.965931	0.025271	0.966472	0.023616	0.967052	0.022094	0.967658	0.020694
15	0.967280	0.027453	0.967628	0.025720	0.968039	0.024114	0.968496	0.022629	0.968990	0.021255
16	0.969038	0.027700	0.969264	0.026041	0.969558	0.024493	0.969906	0.023052	0.970297	0.021712
17	0.970712	0.027831	0.970832	0.026249	0.971023	0.024765	0.971273	0.023375	0.971571	0.022075
18	0.972300	0.027862	0.972328	0.026361	0.972430	0.024943	0.972594	0.023607	0.972808	0.022352
19	0.973800	0.027809	0.973751	0.026388	0.973775	0.025038	0.973863	0.023760	0.974004	0.022552
20	0.975215	0.027685	0.975099	0.026343	0.975057	0.025062	0.975079	0.023842	0.975155	0.022684

EXPONENTIAL INTEGRAL FOR SMALL COMPLEX ARGUMENTS Table 5.7

$e^zE_1(z)$

$y \backslash x$	−4.0 ℜ	−4.0 ℑ	−3.5 ℜ	−3.5 ℑ	−3.0 ℜ	−3.0 ℑ	−2.5 ℜ	−2.5 ℑ	−2.0 ℜ	−2.0 ℑ
0.0	-0.359552	-0.057540	-0.420509	-0.094868	-0.494576	-0.156411	-0.580650	-0.257878	-0.670483	-0.425168
0.2	-0.347179	-0.078283	-0.400596	-0.119927	-0.462493	-0.185573	-0.528987	-0.289009	-0.587558	-0.451225
0.4	-0.333373	-0.096648	-0.379278	-0.141221	-0.429554	-0.208800	-0.478303	-0.310884	-0.510543	-0.463193
0.6	-0.318556	-0.112633	-0.357202	-0.158890	-0.396730	-0.226575	-0.429978	-0.324774	-0.441128	-0.464163
0.8	-0.303109	-0.126301	-0.334923	-0.173169	-0.364785	-0.239500	-0.384941	-0.332047	-0.380013	-0.457088
1.0	-0.287369	-0.137768	-0.312894	-0.184355	-0.334280	-0.248231	-0.343719	-0.334043	-0.327140	-0.444528

$E_1(z)+\ln z$

$y \backslash x$	−2.0 ℜ	−2.0 ℑ	−1.5 ℜ	−1.5 ℑ	−1.0 ℜ	−1.0 ℑ	−0.5 ℜ	−0.5 ℑ	0 ℜ	0 ℑ
0.0	-4.261087	0.000000	-2.895820	0.000000	-1.895118	0.000000	-1.147367	0.000000	-0.577216	0.000000
0.2	-4.219228	0.636779	-2.867070	0.462804	-1.875155	0.342700	-1.133341	0.258840	-0.567232	0.199556
0.4	-4.094686	1.260867	-2.781497	0.917127	-1.815717	0.679691	-1.091560	0.513806	-0.537482	0.396461
0.6	-3.890531	1.859922	-2.641121	1.354712	-1.718135	1.005410	-1.022911	0.761122	-0.488555	0.588128
0.8	-3.611783	2.422284	-2.449241	1.767748	-1.584591	1.314586	-0.928842	0.997200	-0.421423	0.772095
1.0	-3.265262	2.937296	-2.210344	2.149077	-1.418052	1.602372	-0.811327	1.218731	-0.337404	0.946083

$y \backslash x$	0.5 ℜ	0.5 ℑ	1.0 ℜ	1.0 ℑ	1.5 ℜ	1.5 ℑ	2.0 ℜ	2.0 ℑ	2.5 ℜ	2.5 ℑ
0.0	-0.133374	0.000000	0.219384	0.000000	0.505485	0.000000	0.742048	0.000000	0.941206	0.000000
0.2	-0.126168	0.157081	0.224661	0.126210	0.509410	0.103432	0.745014	0.086359	0.943484	0.073355
0.4	-0.104687	0.312331	0.240402	0.251143	0.521123	0.205962	0.753871	0.172075	0.950289	0.146246
0.6	-0.069328	0.463961	0.266336	0.373547	0.540441	0.306707	0.768490	0.256515	0.961532	0.218215
0.8	-0.020743	0.610264	0.302022	0.492229	0.567061	0.404823	0.788664	0.339075	0.977068	0.288822
1.0	+0.040177	0.749655	0.346856	0.606074	0.600568	0.499516	0.814107	0.419185	0.996699	0.357653

6.1. Gamma (Factorial) Function

Euler's Integral

6.1.1 $$\Gamma(z)=\int_0^\infty t^{z-1}e^{-t}\,dt \qquad (\mathscr{R}z>0)$$

$$=k^z\int_0^\infty t^{z-1}e^{-kt}\,dt \qquad (\mathscr{R}z>0,\ \mathscr{R}k>0)$$

Euler's Formula

6.1.2
$$\Gamma(z)=\lim_{n\to\infty}\frac{n!\,n^z}{z(z+1)\ldots(z+n)} \qquad (z\neq 0,-1,-2,\ldots)$$

Euler's Infinite Product

6.1.3 $$\frac{1}{\Gamma(z)}=ze^{\gamma z}\prod_{n=1}^{\infty}\left[\left(1+\frac{z}{n}\right)e^{-z/n}\right] \qquad (|z|<\infty)$$

$$\gamma=\lim_{m\to\infty}\left[1+\frac{1}{2}+\frac{1}{3}+\frac{1}{4}+\ldots+\frac{1}{m}-\ln m\right]$$
$$=.57721\ 56649\ 01532\ 86061\ \ldots$$

γ is known as Euler's constant and is given to 25 decimal places in chapter 1. $\Gamma(z)$ is single valued and analytic over the entire complex plane, save for the points $z=-n\,(n=0,1,2,\ldots)$ where it possesses simple poles with residue $(-1)^n/n!$. Its reciprocal $1/\Gamma(z)$ is an entire function possessing simple zeros at the points $z=-n\,(n=0,1,2,\ldots)$.

Hankel's Contour Integral

6.1.4 $$\frac{1}{\Gamma(z)}=\frac{i}{2\pi}\int_C(-t)^{-z}e^{-t}\,dt \qquad (|z|<\infty)$$

The path of integration C starts at $+\infty$ on the real axis, circles the origin in the counterclockwise direction and returns to the starting point.

Factorial and Π Notations

6.1.5 $$\Pi(z)=z!=\Gamma(z+1)$$

Integer Values

6.1.6 $$\Gamma(n+1)=1\cdot2\cdot3\ldots(n-1)n=n!$$

6.1.7
$$\lim_{z\to n}\frac{1}{\Gamma(-z)}=0=\frac{1}{(-n-1)!} \qquad (n=0,1,2,\ldots)$$

Fractional Values

6.1.8
$$\Gamma(\tfrac{1}{2})=2\int_0^\infty e^{-t^2}\,dt=\pi^{\frac{1}{2}}=1.77245\ 38509\ldots=(-\tfrac{1}{2})!$$

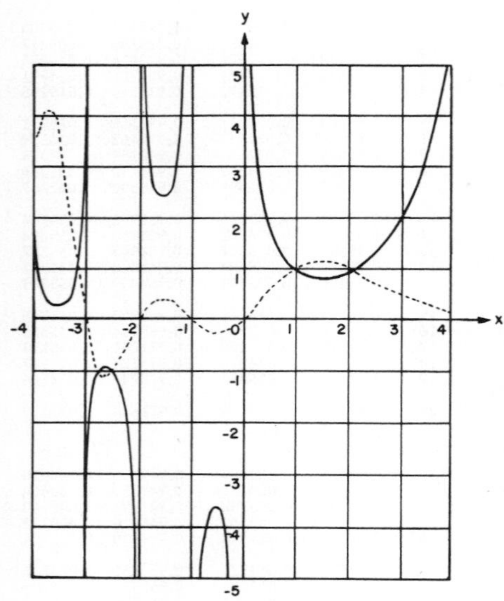

FIGURE 6.1. *Gamma function.*

———, $y=\Gamma(x)$, – – – –, $y=1/\Gamma(x)$

6.1.9 $$\Gamma(3/2)=\tfrac{1}{2}\pi^{\frac{1}{2}}=.88622\ 69254\ldots=(\tfrac{1}{2})!$$

6.1.10 $$\Gamma(n+\tfrac{1}{4})=\frac{1\cdot5\cdot9\cdot13\ldots(4n-3)}{4^n}\Gamma(\tfrac{1}{4})$$

$$\Gamma(\tfrac{1}{4})=3.62560\ 99082\ldots$$

6.1.11 $$\Gamma(n+\tfrac{1}{3})=\frac{1\cdot4\cdot7\cdot10\ldots(3n-2)}{3^n}\Gamma(\tfrac{1}{3})$$

$$\Gamma(\tfrac{1}{3})=2.67893\ 85347\ldots$$

6.1.12 $$\Gamma(n+\tfrac{1}{2})=\frac{1\cdot3\cdot5\cdot7\ldots(2n-1)}{2^n}\Gamma(\tfrac{1}{2})$$

6.1.13 $$\Gamma(n+\tfrac{2}{3})=\frac{2\cdot5\cdot8\cdot11\ldots(3n-1)}{3^n}\Gamma(\tfrac{2}{3})$$

$$\Gamma(\tfrac{2}{3})=1.35411\ 79394\ldots$$

6.1.14 $$\Gamma(n+\tfrac{3}{4})=\frac{3\cdot7\cdot11\cdot15\ldots(4n-1)}{4^n}\Gamma(\tfrac{3}{4})$$

$$\Gamma(\tfrac{3}{4})=1.22541\ 67024\ \ldots$$

Recurrence Formulas

6.1.15 $\Gamma(z+1)=z\Gamma(z)=z!=z(z-1)!$

6.1.16

$$\begin{aligned}\Gamma(n+z)&=(n-1+z)(n-2+z)\ldots(1+z)\Gamma(1+z)\\&=(n-1+z)!\\&=(n-1+z)(n-2+z)\ldots(1+z)z!\end{aligned}$$

Reflection Formula

6.1.17 $$\Gamma(z)\Gamma(1-z)=-z\Gamma(-z)\Gamma(z)=\pi\csc\pi z$$
$$=\int_0^\infty \frac{t^{z-1}}{1+t}dt \qquad (0<\mathscr{R}z<1)$$

Duplication Formula

6.1.18 $\Gamma(2z)=(2\pi)^{-\frac{1}{2}}2^{2z-\frac{1}{2}}\Gamma(z)\Gamma(z+\frac{1}{2})$

Triplication Formula

6.1.19 $\Gamma(3z)=(2\pi)^{-1}3^{3z-\frac{1}{2}}\Gamma(z)\Gamma(z+\frac{1}{3})\Gamma(z+\frac{2}{3})$

Gauss' Multiplication Formula

6.1.20 $\Gamma(nz)=(2\pi)^{\frac{1}{2}(1-n)}n^{nz-\frac{1}{2}}\prod_{k=0}^{n-1}\Gamma\left(z+\frac{k}{n}\right)$

Binomial Coefficient

6.1.21 $\binom{z}{w}=\frac{z!}{w!(z-w)!}=\frac{\Gamma(z+1)}{\Gamma(w+1)\Gamma(z-w+1)}$

Pochhammer's Symbol

6.1.22

$(z)_0=1,$

$(z)_n=z(z+1)(z+2)\ldots(z+n-1)=\frac{\Gamma(z+n)}{\Gamma(z)}$

Gamma Function in the Complex Plane

6.1.23 $\Gamma(\bar{z})=\overline{\Gamma(z)};\ \ln\Gamma(\bar{z})=\overline{\ln\Gamma(z)}$

6.1.24 $\arg\Gamma(z+1)=\arg\Gamma(z)+\arctan\frac{y}{x}$

6.1.25 $\left|\frac{\Gamma(x+iy)}{\Gamma(x)}\right|^2=\prod_{n=0}^{\infty}\left[1+\frac{y^2}{(x+n)^2}\right]^{-1}$

6.1.26 $|\Gamma(x+iy)|\leq|\Gamma(x)|$

6.1.27

$$\arg\Gamma(x+iy)=y\psi(x)+\sum_{n=0}^{\infty}\left(\frac{y}{x+n}-\arctan\frac{y}{x+n}\right)$$
$$(x+iy\neq 0,-1,-2,\ldots)$$

where $\psi(z)=\Gamma'(z)/\Gamma(z)$

6.1.28 $\Gamma(1+iy)=iy\,\Gamma(iy)$

6.1.29 $\Gamma(iy)\Gamma(-iy)=|\Gamma(iy)|^2=\frac{\pi}{y\sinh\pi y}$

6.1.30 $\Gamma(\frac{1}{2}+iy)\Gamma(\frac{1}{2}-iy)=|\Gamma(\frac{1}{2}+iy)|^2=\frac{\pi}{\cosh\pi y}$

6.1.31 $\Gamma(1+iy)\Gamma(1-iy)=|\Gamma(1+iy)|^2=\frac{\pi y}{\sinh\pi y}$

6.1.32 $\Gamma(\frac{1}{4}+iy)\Gamma(\frac{3}{4}-iy)=\frac{\pi\sqrt{2}}{\cosh\pi y+i\sinh\pi y}$

Power Series

6.1.33

$$\ln\Gamma(1+z)=-\ln(1+z)+z(1-\gamma)$$
$$+\sum_{n=2}^{\infty}(-1)^n[\zeta(n)-1]z^n/n \qquad (|z|<2)$$

$\zeta(n)$ is the Riemann Zeta Function (see chapter 23).

Series Expansion for $1/\Gamma(z)$

6.1.34 $$\frac{1}{\Gamma(z)}=\sum_{k=1}^{\infty}c_kz^k \qquad (|z|<\infty)$$

k	c_k
1	1.00000 00000 000000
2	0.57721 56649 015329
3	−0.65587 80715 202538
4	−0.04200 26350 340952
5	0.16653 86113 822915
6	−0.04219 77345 555443
7	−0.00962 19715 278770
8	0.00721 89432 466630
9	−0.00116 51675 918591
10	−0.00021 52416 741149
11	0.00012 80502 823882
12	−0.00002 01348 547807
13	−0.00000 12504 934821
14	0.00000 11330 272320
15	−0.00000 02056 338417
16	0.00000 00061 160950
17	0.00000 00050 020075
18	−0.00000 00011 812746
19	0.00000 00001 043427
20	0.00000 00000 077823
21	−0.00000 00000 036968
22	0.00000 00000 005100
23	−0.00000 00000 000206
24	−0.00000 00000 000054
25	0.00000 00000 000014
26	0.00000 00000 000001

Polynomial Approximations

6.1.35 $0 \leq x \leq 1$

$$\Gamma(x+1)=x!=1+a_1x+a_2x^2+a_3x^3+a_4x^4+a_5x^5+\epsilon(x)$$

$$|\epsilon(x)| \leq 5\times 10^{-5}$$

$a_1=-.57486\ 46$	$a_4=\ \ .42455\ 49$
$a_2=\ \ .95123\ 63$	$a_5=-.10106\ 78$
$a_3=-.69985\ 88$	

6.1.36 $0 \leq x \leq 1$

$$\Gamma(x+1)=x!=1+b_1x+b_2x^2+\ .\ .\ .\ +b_8x^8+\epsilon(x)$$

$$|\epsilon(x)| \leq 3\times 10^{-7}$$

$b_1=-.57719\ 1652$	$b_5=-.75670\ 4078$
$b_2=\ \ .98820\ 5891$	$b_6=\ \ .48219\ 9394$
$b_3=-.89705\ 6937$	$b_7=-.19352\ 7818$
$b_4=\ \ .91820\ 6857$	$b_8=\ \ .03586\ 8343$

Stirling's Formula

6.1.37

$$\Gamma(z) \sim e^{-z}z^{z-\frac{1}{2}}(2\pi)^{\frac{1}{2}}\left[1+\frac{1}{12z}+\frac{1}{288z^2}-\frac{139}{51840z^3}-\frac{571}{2488320z^4}+\cdots\right] \qquad (z\rightarrow\infty \text{ in } |\arg z|<\pi)$$

6.1.38

$$x!=\sqrt{2\pi}\, x^{x+\frac{1}{2}}\exp\left(-x+\frac{\theta}{12x}\right) \qquad (x>0,\ 0<\theta<1)$$

Asymptotic Formulas

6.1.39

$$\Gamma(az+b) \sim \sqrt{2\pi}\, e^{-az}(az)^{az+b-\frac{1}{2}} \qquad (|\arg z|<\pi,\ a>0)$$

6.1.40

$$\ln \Gamma(z) \sim (z-\tfrac{1}{2}) \ln z-z+\tfrac{1}{2} \ln (2\pi)+\sum_{m=1}^{\infty} \frac{B_{2m}}{2m(2m-1)z^{2m-1}} \qquad (z\rightarrow\infty \text{ in } |\arg z|<\pi)$$

For B_n see chapter 23

6.1.41

$$\ln \Gamma(z) \sim (z-\tfrac{1}{2}) \ln z-z+\tfrac{1}{2} \ln (2\pi)+\frac{1}{12z}-\frac{1}{360z^3}+\frac{1}{1260z^5}-\frac{1}{1680z^7}+\cdots \qquad (z\rightarrow\infty \text{ in } |\arg z|<\pi)$$

Error Term for Asymptotic Expansion

6.1.42

If

$$R_n(z)= \ln \Gamma (z)-(z-\tfrac{1}{2}) \ln z+z-\tfrac{1}{2} \ln (2\pi)-\sum_{m=1}^{n} \frac{B_{2m}}{2m(2m-1)z^{2m-1}}$$

then

$$|R_n(z)| \leq \frac{|B_{2n+2}|K(z)}{(2n+1)(2n+2)|z|^{2n+1}}$$

where

$$K(z)=\underset{u\geq 0}{\text{upper bound}}|z^2/(u^2+z^2)|$$

For z real and positive, R_n is less in absolute value than the first term neglected and has the same sign.

6.1.43

$$\mathscr{R}\ln \Gamma(iy)=\mathscr{R}\ln \Gamma(-iy)$$

$$=\tfrac{1}{2} \ln\left(\frac{\pi}{y \sinh \pi y}\right)$$

$$\sim\tfrac{1}{2} \ln (2\pi)-\tfrac{1}{2}\pi y-\tfrac{1}{2}\ln y, \qquad (y\rightarrow+\infty)$$

6.1.44

$$\mathscr{I}\ln \Gamma(iy)=\arg \Gamma(iy)=-\arg \Gamma(-iy)$$

$$=-\mathscr{I}\ln \Gamma(-iy)$$

$$\sim y \ln y-y-\tfrac{1}{4}\pi-\sum_{n=1}^{\infty} \frac{(-1)^{n-1} B_{2n}}{(2n-1)(2n)y^{2n-1}} \qquad (y\rightarrow+\infty)$$

6.1.45 $\displaystyle\lim_{|y|\rightarrow\infty}(2\pi)^{-\frac{1}{2}}|\Gamma(x+iy)|e^{\frac{1}{2}\pi|y|}|y|^{\frac{1}{2}-x}=1$

6.1.46 $\displaystyle\lim_{n\rightarrow\infty} n^{b-a}\frac{\Gamma(n+a)}{\Gamma(n+b)}=1$

6.1.47

$$z^{b-a}\frac{\Gamma(z+a)}{\Gamma(z+b)}\sim 1+\frac{(a-b)(a+b-1)}{2z}+\frac{1}{12}\binom{a-b}{2}\left(3(a+b-1)^2-a+b-1\right)\frac{1}{z^2}+\ .\ .\ .$$

as $z\rightarrow\infty$ along any curve joining $z=0$ and $z=\infty$, providing $z\neq -a,\ -a-1,\ .\ .\ .\ ;\ z\neq -b,\ -b-1,\ .\ .\ .\ .$

Continued Fraction

6.1.48

$$\ln \Gamma(z)+z-(z-\tfrac{1}{2}) \ln z-\tfrac{1}{2} \ln (2\pi) = \frac{a_0}{z+}\,\frac{a_1}{z+}\,\frac{a_2}{z+}\,\frac{a_3}{z+}\,\frac{a_4}{z+}\,\frac{a_5}{z+}\,\cdots \qquad (\mathscr{R} z > 0)$$

$$a_0=\frac{1}{12},\ a_1=\frac{1}{30},\ a_2=\frac{53}{210},\ a_3=\frac{195}{371},$$

$$a_4=\frac{22999}{22737},\ a_5=\frac{29944523}{19733142},\ a_6=\frac{109535241009}{48264275462}$$

Wallis' Formula [4]

6.1.49

$$\frac{2}{\pi}\int_0^{\pi/2}\binom{\sin}{\cos}^{2n} x\,dx=\frac{1\cdot 3\cdot 5\ldots(2n-1)}{2\cdot 4\cdot 6\ldots(2n)} =\frac{(2n)!}{2^{2n}(n!)^2}=\frac{1}{2^{2n}}\binom{2n}{n}=\frac{\Gamma(n+\frac{1}{2})}{\pi^{\frac{1}{2}}\Gamma(n+1)}$$

$$\sim\frac{1}{\pi^{\frac{1}{2}}n^{\frac{1}{2}}}\left[1-\frac{1}{8n}+\frac{1}{128n^2}-\cdots\right] \qquad (n\rightarrow\infty)$$

Some Definite Integrals

6.1.50

$$\ln \Gamma(z)=\int_0^\infty\left[(z-1)\,e^{-t}-\frac{e^{-t}-e^{-zt}}{1-e^{-t}}\right]\frac{dt}{t} \qquad (\mathscr{R} z>0)$$

$$=(z-\tfrac{1}{2})\ln z-z+\tfrac{1}{2}\ln 2\pi +2\int_0^\infty \frac{\arctan (t/z)}{e^{2\pi t}-1}\,dt \qquad (\mathscr{R} z>0)$$

6.2. Beta Function

6.2.1

$$B(z,w)=\int_0^1 t^{z-1}\,(1-t)^{w-1}\,dt=\int_0^\infty\frac{t^{z-1}}{(1+t)^{z+w}}\,dt =2\int_0^{\pi/2}(\sin t)^{2z-1}\,(\cos t)^{2w-1}\,dt \qquad (\mathscr{R} z>0,\ \mathscr{R} w>0)$$

6.2.2 $$B(z,w)=\frac{\Gamma(z)\Gamma(w)}{\Gamma(z+w)}=B(w,z)$$

6.3. Psi (Digamma) Function [5]

6.3.1 $\psi(z)=d[\ln \Gamma(z)]/dz=\Gamma'(z)/\Gamma(z)$

[4] Some authors employ the special double factorial notation as follows:

$(2n)!!=2\cdot 4\cdot 6\ldots(2n)=2^n n!$

$(2n-1)!!=1\cdot 3\cdot 5\ldots(2n-1)=\pi^{-\frac{1}{2}}\,2^n\,\Gamma(n+\frac{1}{2})$

[5] Some authors write $\psi(z)=\frac{d}{dz}\ln\Gamma(z+1)$ and similarly for the polygamma functions.

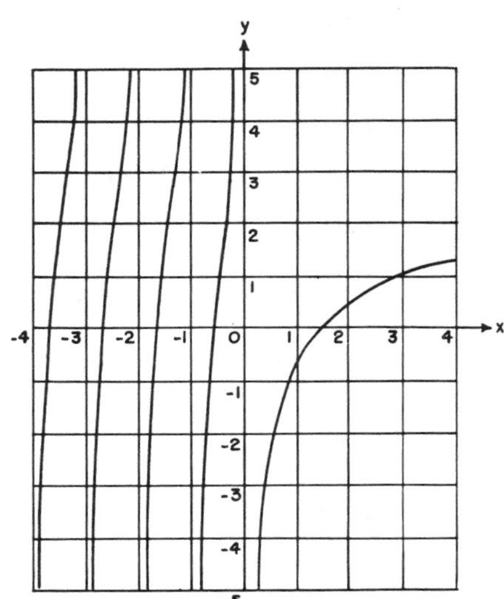

FIGURE 6.2. *Psi function.*

$y=\psi(x)=d\ln\Gamma(x)/dx$

Integer Values

6.3.2 $$\psi(1)=-\gamma,\ \psi(n)=-\gamma+\sum_{k=1}^{n-1}k^{-1} \qquad (n\geq 2)$$

Fractional Values

6.3.3

$$\psi(\tfrac{1}{2})=-\gamma-2\ln 2=-1.96351\ 00260\ 21423\ldots$$

6.3.4

$$\psi(n+\tfrac{1}{2})=-\gamma-2\ln 2+2\left(1+\frac{1}{3}+\cdots+\frac{1}{2n-1}\right) \qquad (n\geq 1)$$

Recurrence Formulas

6.3.5 $$\psi(z+1)=\psi(z)+\frac{1}{z}$$

6.3.6

$$\psi(n+z)=\frac{1}{(n-1)+z}+\frac{1}{(n-2)+z}+\cdots+\frac{1}{2+z}+\frac{1}{1+z}+\psi(1+z)$$

Reflection Formula

6.3.7 $\psi(1-z)=\psi(z)+\pi\cot\pi z$

Duplication Formula

6.3.8 $\psi(2z)=\frac{1}{2}\psi(z)+\frac{1}{2}\psi(z+\frac{1}{2})+\ln 2$

Psi Function in the Complex Plane

6.3.9 $\psi(\bar{z})=\overline{\psi(z)}$

6.3.10

$$\mathscr{R}\psi(iy)=\mathscr{R}\psi(-iy)=\mathscr{R}\psi(1+iy)=\mathscr{R}\psi(1-iy)$$

6.3.11 $\mathscr{I}\psi(iy)=\frac{1}{2}y^{-1}+\frac{1}{2}\pi\coth\pi y$

6.3.12 $\mathscr{I}\psi(\frac{1}{2}+iy)=\frac{1}{2}\pi\tanh\pi y$

6.3.13 $\mathscr{I}\psi(1+iy)=-\frac{1}{2y}+\frac{1}{2}\pi\coth\pi y$

$$=y\sum_{n=1}^{\infty}(n^2+y^2)^{-1}$$

Series Expansions

6.3.14 $\psi(1+z)=-\gamma+\sum_{n=2}^{\infty}(-1)^n\zeta(n)z^{n-1}\qquad(|z|<1)$

6.3.15

$$\psi(1+z)=\frac{1}{2}z^{-1}-\frac{1}{2}\pi\cot\pi z-(1-z^2)^{-1}+1-\gamma$$
$$-\sum_{n=1}^{\infty}[\zeta(2n+1)-1]z^{2n}\qquad(|z|<2)$$

6.3.16

$$\psi(1+z)=-\gamma+\sum_{n=1}^{\infty}\frac{z}{n(n+z)}\qquad(z\neq-1,-2,-3,\ldots)$$

6.3.17

$$\mathscr{R}\psi(1+iy)=1-\gamma-\frac{1}{1+y^2}$$
$$+\sum_{n=1}^{\infty}(-1)^{n+1}[\zeta(2n+1)-1]y^{2n}\qquad(|y|<2)$$
$$=-\gamma+y^2\sum_{n=1}^{\infty}n^{-1}(n^2+y^2)^{-1}\qquad(-\infty<y<\infty)$$

Asymptotic Formulas

6.3.18

$$\psi(z)\sim\ln z-\frac{1}{2z}-\sum_{n=1}^{\infty}\frac{B_{2n}}{2nz^{2n}}$$
$$=\ln z-\frac{1}{2z}-\frac{1}{12z^2}+\frac{1}{120z^4}-\frac{1}{252z^6}+\ldots$$
$$(z\to\infty\text{ in }|\arg z|<\pi)$$

6.3.19

$$\mathscr{R}\psi(1+iy)\sim\ln y+\sum_{n=1}^{\infty}\frac{(-1)^{n-1}B_{2n}}{2ny^{2n}}$$
$$=\ln y+\frac{1}{12y^2}+\frac{1}{120y^4}+\frac{1}{252y^6}+\ldots\qquad(y\to\infty)$$

Extrema of $\Gamma(x)$ — Zeros of $\psi(x)$

$$\Gamma'(x_n)=\psi(x_n)=0$$

n	x_n	$\Gamma(x_n)$
0	+1. 462	+0. 886
1	−0. 504	−3. 545
2	−1. 573	+2. 302
3	−2. 611	−0. 888
4	−3. 635	+0. 245
5	−4. 653	−0. 053
6	−5. 667	+0. 009
7	−6. 678	−0. 001

$x_0=1.46163\ 21449\ 68362$

$\Gamma(x_0)=\ .88560\ 31944\ 10889$

6.3.20 $x_n=-n+(\ln n)^{-1}+o[(\ln n)^{-2}]$

Definite Integrals

6.3.21

$$\psi(z)=\int_0^{\infty}\left[\frac{e^{-t}}{t}-\frac{e^{-zt}}{1-e^{-t}}\right]dt\qquad(\mathscr{R}z>0)$$
$$=\int_0^{\infty}\left[e^{-t}-\frac{1}{(1+t)^z}\right]\frac{dt}{t}$$
$$=\ln z-\frac{1}{2z}-2\int_0^{\infty}\frac{tdt}{(t^2+z^2)(e^{2\pi t}-1)}\qquad\left(|\arg z|<\frac{\pi}{2}\right)$$

6.3.22

$$\psi(z)+\gamma=\int_0^{\infty}\frac{e^{-t}-e^{-zt}}{1-e^{-t}}dt=\int_0^1\frac{1-t^{z-1}}{1-t}dt$$
$$\gamma=\int_0^{\infty}\left(\frac{1}{e^t-1}-\frac{1}{te^t}\right)dt$$
$$=\int_0^{\infty}\left(\frac{1}{1+t}-e^{-t}\right)\frac{dt}{t}$$

6.4. Polygamma Functions[7]

6.4.1

$$\psi^{(n)}(z)=\frac{d^n}{dz^n}\psi(z)=\frac{d^{n+1}}{dz^{n+1}}\ln\Gamma(z) \qquad (n=1,2,3,\ldots)$$

$$=(-1)^{n+1}\int_0^\infty \frac{t^n e^{-zt}}{1-e^{-t}}dt \qquad (\mathcal{R}z>0)$$

$\psi^{(n)}(z),(n=0,1,\ldots)$, is a single valued analytic function over the entire complex plane save at the points $z=-m(m=0,1,2,\ldots)$ where it possesses poles of order $(n+1)$.

Integer Values

6.4.2

$$\psi^{(n)}(1)=(-1)^{n+1}n!\zeta(n+1) \qquad (n=1,2,3,\ldots)$$

6.4.3

$$\psi^{(m)}(n+1)=(-1)^m m!\left[-\zeta(m+1)+1+\frac{1}{2^{m+1}}+\ldots+\frac{1}{n^{m+1}}\right]$$

Fractional Values

6.4.4

$$\psi^{(n)}(\tfrac{1}{2})=(-1)^{n+1}n!(2^{n+1}-1)\zeta(n+1) \qquad (n=1,2,\ldots)$$

6.4.5 $$\psi'(n+\tfrac{1}{2})=\tfrac{1}{2}\pi^2-4\sum_{k=1}^{n}(2k-1)^{-2}$$

Recurrence Formula

6.4.6 $$\psi^{(n)}(z+1)=\psi^{(n)}(z)+(-1)^n n! z^{-n-1}$$

Reflection Formula

6.4.7

$$\psi^{(n)}(1-z)+(-1)^{n+1}\psi^{(n)}(z)=(-1)^n\pi\frac{d^n}{dz^n}\cot\pi z$$

Multiplication Formula

6.4.8

$$\psi^{(n)}(mz)=\delta\ln m+\frac{1}{m^{n+1}}\sum_{k=0}^{m-1}\psi^{(n)}\left(z+\frac{k}{m}\right)$$

$$\delta=1,\quad n=0$$

$$\delta=0,\quad n>0$$

[7] ψ' is known as the trigamma function. ψ'', $\psi^{(3)}$, $\psi^{(4)}$ are the tetra-, penta-, and hexagamma functions respectively. Some authors write $\psi(z)=d[\ln\Gamma(z+1)]/dz$, and similarly for the polygamma functions.

Series Expansions

6.4.9

$$\psi^{(n)}(1+z)=(-1)^{n+1}\left[n!\zeta(n+1)-\frac{(n+1)!}{1!}\zeta(n+2)z+\frac{(n+2)!}{2!}\zeta(n+3)z^2-\ldots\right] \qquad (|z|<1)$$

6.4.10

$$\psi^{(n)}(z)=(-1)^{n+1}n!\sum_{k=0}^{\infty}(z+k)^{-n-1} \qquad (z\neq 0,-1,-2,\ldots)$$

Asymptotic Formulas

6.4.11

$$\psi^{(n)}(z)\sim(-1)^{n-1}\left[\frac{(n-1)!}{z^n}+\frac{n!}{2z^{n+1}}+\sum_{k=1}^{\infty}B_{2k}\frac{(2k+n-1)!}{(2k)!z^{2k+n}}\right] \qquad (z\to\infty \text{ in } |\arg z|<\pi)$$

6.4.12

$$\psi'(z)\sim\frac{1}{z}+\frac{1}{2z^2}+\frac{1}{6z^3}-\frac{1}{30z^5}+\frac{1}{42z^7}-\frac{1}{30z^9}+\ldots \qquad (z\to\infty \text{ in } |\arg z|<\pi)$$

6.4.13

$$\psi''(z)\sim-\frac{1}{z^2}-\frac{1}{z^3}-\frac{1}{2z^4}+\frac{1}{6z^6}-\frac{1}{6z^8}+\frac{3}{10z^{10}}-\frac{5}{6z^{12}}+\ldots \qquad (z\to\infty \text{ in } |\arg z|<\pi)$$

6.4.14

$$\psi^{(3)}(z)\sim\frac{2}{z^3}+\frac{3}{z^4}+\frac{2}{z^5}-\frac{1}{z^7}+\frac{4}{3z^9}-\frac{3}{z^{11}}+\frac{10}{z^{13}}-\ldots \qquad (z\to\infty \text{ in } |\arg z|<\pi)$$

6.5. Incomplete Gamma Function
(see also **26.4**)

6.5.1

$$P(a,x)=\frac{1}{\Gamma(a)}\int_0^x e^{-t}t^{a-1}dt \qquad (\mathcal{R}a>0)$$

6.5.2

$$\gamma(a,x)=P(a,x)\Gamma(a)=\int_0^x e^{-t}t^{a-1}dt \qquad (\mathcal{R}a>0)$$

6.5.3

$$\Gamma(a,x)=\Gamma(a)-\gamma(a,x)=\int_x^\infty e^{-t}t^{a-1}dt$$

6.5.4

$$\gamma^*(a,x)=x^{-a}P(a,x)=\frac{x^{-a}}{\Gamma(a)}\gamma(a,x)$$

γ^* is a single valued analytic function of a and x possessing no finite singularities.

6.5.5

Probability Integral of the χ^2-Distribution

$$P(\chi^2|\nu)=\frac{1}{2^{\frac{1}{2}\nu}\Gamma\left(\frac{\nu}{2}\right)}\int_0^{\chi^2} t^{\frac{1}{2}\nu-1}e^{-\frac{t}{2}}\,dt$$

6.5.6

(Pearson's Form of the Incomplete Gamma Function)

$$I(u,p)=\frac{1}{\Gamma(p+1)}\int_0^{u\sqrt{p+1}} e^{-t}t^p\,dt$$
$$=P(p+1,\,u\sqrt{p+1})$$

6.5.7 $$C(x,a)=\int_x^\infty t^{a-1}\cos t\,dt \qquad (\mathscr{R}a<1)$$

6.5.8 $$S(x,a)=\int_x^\infty t^{a-1}\sin t\,dt \qquad (\mathscr{R}a<1)$$

6.5.9

$$E_n(x)=\int_1^\infty e^{-xt}t^{-n}\,dt=x^{n-1}\Gamma(1-n,x)$$

6.5.10

$$\alpha_n(x)=\int_1^\infty e^{-xt}t^n\,dt=x^{-n-1}\Gamma(1+n,x)$$

6.5.11 $$e_n(x)=\sum_{j=0}^n \frac{x^j}{j!}$$

Incomplete Gamma Function as a Confluent Hypergeometric Function (see chapter 13)

6.5.12 $$\gamma(a,x)=a^{-1}x^ae^{-x}M(1,\,1+a,x)$$
$$=a^{-1}x^a\,M(a,\,1+a,-x)$$

Special Values

6.5.13

$$P(n,x)=1-\left(1+x+\frac{x^2}{2!}+\ldots+\frac{x^{n-1}}{(n-1)!}\right)e^{-x}$$
$$=1-e_{n-1}(x)e^{-x}$$

For relation to the Poisson distribution, see 26.4.

6.5.14 $$\gamma^*(-n,\,x)=x^n$$

6.5.15 $$\Gamma(0,\,x)=\int_x^\infty e^{-t}t^{-1}\,dt=E_1(x)$$

6.5.16 $$\gamma(\tfrac{1}{2},\,x^2)=2\int_0^x e^{-t^2}\,dt=\sqrt{\pi}\,\mathrm{erf}\,x$$

6.5.17 $$\Gamma(\tfrac{1}{2},x^2)=2\int_x^\infty e^{-t^2}dt=\sqrt{\pi}\,\mathrm{erfc}\,x$$

6.5.18 $$\tfrac{1}{2}\sqrt{\pi}\,x\,\gamma^*(\tfrac{1}{2},-x^2)=\int_0^x e^{t^2}dt$$

6.5.19 $$\Gamma(-n,x)=\frac{(-1)^n}{n!}\left[E_1(x)-e^{-x}\sum_{j=0}^{n-1}\frac{(-1)^jj!}{x^{j+1}}\right]$$

6.5.20 $$\Gamma(a,ix)=e^{\frac{1}{2}\pi ia}\,[C(x,a)-iS(x,a)]$$

Recurrence Formulas

6.5.21 $$P(a+1,\,x)=P(a,\,x)-\frac{x^ae^{-x}}{\Gamma(a+1)}$$

6.5.22 $$\gamma(a+1,x)=a\gamma(a,x)-x^ae^{-x}$$

6.5.23 $$\gamma^*(a-1,x)=x\gamma^*(a,x)+\frac{e^{-x}}{\Gamma(a)}$$

Derivatives and Differential Equations

6.5.24

$$\left(\frac{\partial\gamma^*}{\partial a}\right)_{a=0}=-\int_x^\infty\frac{e^{-t}dt}{t}-\ln x=-E_1(x)-\ln x$$

6.5.25 $$\frac{\partial\gamma(a,x)}{\partial x}=-\frac{\partial\Gamma(a,x)}{\partial x}=x^{a-1}e^{-x}$$

6.5.26

$$\frac{\partial^n}{\partial x^n}\,[x^{-a}\Gamma(a,x)]=(-1)^nx^{-a-n}\Gamma(a+n,x) \qquad (n=0,1,2,\ldots)$$

6.5.27

$$\frac{\partial^n}{\partial x^n}\,[e^xx^a\gamma^*(a,x)]=e^xx^{a-n}\gamma^*(a-n,\,x) \qquad (n=0,1,2,\ldots)$$

6.5.28 $$x\frac{\partial^2\gamma^*}{\partial x^2}+(a+1+x)\frac{\partial\gamma^*}{\partial x}+a\gamma^*=0$$

Series Developments

6.5.29

$$\gamma^*(a,z)=e^{-z}\sum_{n=0}^\infty\frac{z^n}{\Gamma(a+n+1)}=\frac{1}{\Gamma(a)}\sum_{n=0}^\infty\frac{(-z)^n}{(a+n)n!} \qquad (|z|<\infty)$$

6.5.30

$$\gamma(a, x+y)-\gamma(a, x) = e^{-x}x^{a-1}\sum_{n=0}^{\infty}\frac{(a-1)(a-2)\ldots(a-n)}{x^n}[1-e^{-y}e_n(y)]$$

$(|y|<|x|)$

Continued Fraction

6.5.31

$$\Gamma(a,x)=e^{-x}x^a\left(\frac{1}{x+}\,\frac{1-a}{1+}\,\frac{1}{x+}\,\frac{2-a}{1+}\,\frac{2}{x+}\cdots\right)$$

$(x>0, |a|<\infty)$

Asymptotic Expansions

6.5.32

$$\Gamma(a, z)\sim z^{a-1}e^{-z}\left[1+\frac{a-1}{z}+\frac{(a-1)(a-2)}{z^2}+\cdots\right]$$

$\left(z\to\infty \text{ in } |\arg z|<\frac{3\pi}{2}\right)$

Suppose $R_n(a,z)=u_{n+1}(a,z)+\ldots$ is the remainder after n terms in this series. Then if a,z are real, we have for $n>a-2$

$$|R_n(a,z)|\leq|u_{n+1}(a,z)|$$

and sign $R_n(a,z)=$ sign $u_{n+1}(a,z)$.

6.5.33 $\qquad \gamma(a,z)\sim\sum_{n=0}^{\infty}\frac{(-1)^n z^{a+n}}{(a+n)n!} \qquad (a\to+\infty)$

6.5.34 $\qquad \lim_{n\to\infty}\frac{e_n(\alpha n)}{e^{\alpha n}}=\begin{cases}0 \text{ for } \alpha>1\\ \frac{1}{2} \text{ for } \alpha=1\\ 1 \text{ for } 0\leq\alpha<1\end{cases}$

6.5.35

$$\Gamma(z+1,z)\sim e^{-z}z^z\left(\sqrt{\frac{\pi}{2}}z^{\frac{1}{2}}+\frac{2}{3}+\frac{\sqrt{2\pi}}{24}\frac{1}{z^{\frac{1}{2}}}+\cdots\right)$$

$(z\to\infty \text{ in } |\arg z|<\frac{1}{2}\pi)$

Definite Integrals

6.5.36

$$\int_0^{\infty}e^{-at}\Gamma(b,ct)\,dt=\frac{\Gamma(b)}{a}\left[1-\frac{c^b}{(a+c)^b}\right]$$

$(\mathscr{R}(a+c)>0, \mathscr{R}b>-1)$

6.5.37

$$\int_0^{\infty}t^{a-1}\Gamma(b,t)\,dt=\frac{\Gamma(a+b)}{a}$$

$(\mathscr{R}(a+b)>0, \quad \mathscr{R}a>0)$

6.6. Incomplete Beta Function

6.6.1 $\qquad B_x(a,b)=\int_0^x t^{a-1}(1-t)^{b-1}dt$

6.6.2 $\qquad I_x(a,b)=B_x(a,b)/B(a,b)$

For statistical applications, see **26.5**.

Symmetry

6.6.3 $\qquad I_x(a,b)=1-I_{1-x}(b,a)$

Relation to Binomial Expansion

6.6.4 $\qquad I_p(a,n-a+1)=\sum_{j=a}^{n}\binom{n}{j}p^j(1-p)^{n-j}$

For binomial distribution, see **26.1**.

Recurrence Formulas

6.6.5 $\qquad I_x(a,b)=xI_x(a-1,b)+(1-x)I_x(a,b-1)$

6.6.6 $\qquad (a+b-ax)I_x(a,b) = a(1-x)I_x(a+1,b-1)+bI_x(a,b+1)$

6.6.7 $\qquad (a+b)I_x(a,b)=aI_x(a+1,b)+bI_x(a,b+1)$

Relation to Hypergeometric Function

6.6.8 $\qquad B_x(a,b)=a^{-1}x^aF(a,1-b;\,a+1;\,x)$

7.1. Error Function

Definitions

7.1.1 $$\operatorname{erf} z=\frac{2}{\sqrt{\pi}}\int_0^z e^{-t^2}dt$$

7.1.2 $$\operatorname{erfc} z=\frac{2}{\sqrt{\pi}}\int_z^\infty e^{-t^2}dt=1-\operatorname{erf} z$$

7.1.3 $$w(z)=e^{-z^2}\left(1+\frac{2i}{\sqrt{\pi}}\int_0^z e^{t^2}dt\right)=e^{-z^2}\operatorname{erfc}(-iz)$$

In **7.1.2** the path of integration is subject to the restriction $\arg t\to\alpha$ with $|\alpha|<\frac{\pi}{4}$ as $t\to\infty$ along the path. ($\alpha=\frac{\pi}{4}$ is permissible if $\mathscr{R}t^2$ remains bounded to the left.)

Integral Representation

7.1.4

$$w(z)=\frac{i}{\pi}\int_{-\infty}^\infty \frac{e^{-t^2}dt}{z-t}=\frac{2iz}{\pi}\int_0^\infty \frac{e^{-t^2}dt}{z^2-t^2}\qquad (\mathscr{I}z>0)$$

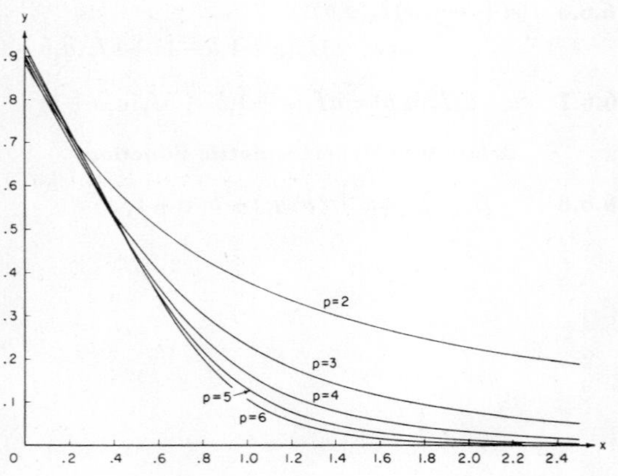

FIGURE 7.1. $y=e^{x^p}\int_x^\infty e^{-t^p}dt.$

$p=2(1)6$

Series Expansions

7.1.5 $$\operatorname{erf} z=\frac{2}{\sqrt{\pi}}\sum_{n=0}^\infty \frac{(-1)^n z^{2n+1}}{n!(2n+1)}$$

7.1.6 $$=\frac{2}{\sqrt{\pi}}e^{-z^2}\sum_{n=0}^\infty \frac{2^n}{1\cdot 3\ldots(2n+1)}z^{2n+1}$$

7.1.7 $$=\sqrt{2}\sum_{n=0}^\infty (-1)^n[I_{2n+1/2}(z^2)-I_{2n+3/2}(z^2)]$$

7.1.8 $$w(z)=\sum_{n=0}^\infty \frac{(iz)^n}{\Gamma\left(\frac{n}{2}+1\right)}$$

For $I_{n-\frac{1}{2}}(x)$, see chapter **10.**

Symmetry Relations

7.1.9 $$\operatorname{erf}(-z)=-\operatorname{erf} z$$

7.1.10 $$\operatorname{erf}\bar{z}=\overline{\operatorname{erf} z}$$

7.1.11 $$w(-z)=2e^{-z^2}-w(z)$$

7.1.12 $$w(\bar{z})=\overline{w(-z)}$$

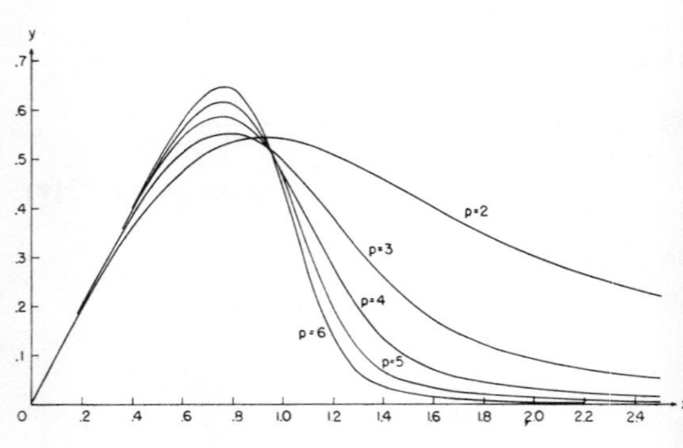

FIGURE 7.2. $y=e^{-x^p}\int_0^x e^{t^p}dt.$

$p=2(1)6$

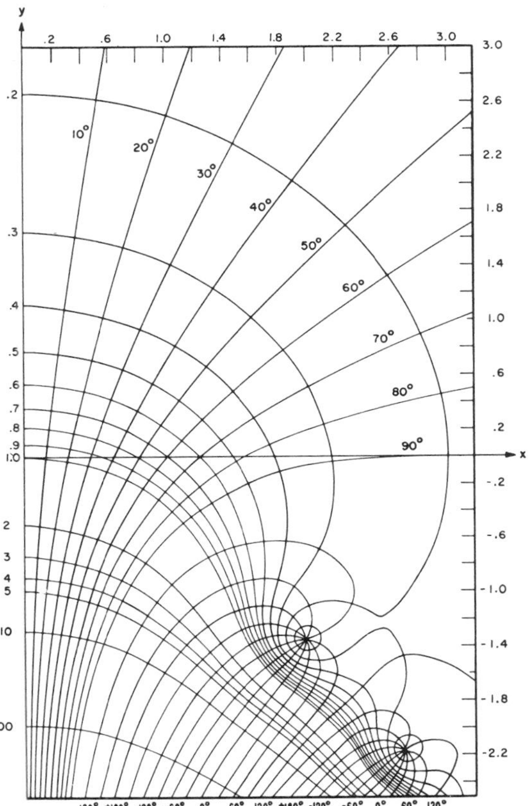

FIGURE 7.3. *Altitude Chart of $w(z)$.*

Inequalities [7.11], [7.17]

7.1.13

$$\frac{1}{x+\sqrt{x^2+2}}<e^{x^2}\int_x^\infty e^{-t^2}dt\leq \frac{1}{x+\sqrt{x^2+\frac{4}{\pi}}}\qquad (x\geq 0)$$

(For other inequalities see [7.2].)

Continued Fractions

7.1.14

$$2e^{z^2}\int_z^\infty e^{-t^2}dt=\frac{1}{z+}\,\frac{1/2}{z+}\,\frac{1}{z+}\,\frac{3/2}{z+}\,\frac{2}{z+}\cdots\quad (\mathscr{R}z>0)$$

7.1.15

$$\frac{1}{\sqrt{\pi}}\int_{-\infty}^\infty \frac{e^{-t^2}dt}{z-t}=\frac{1}{z-}\,\frac{1/2}{z-}\,\frac{1}{z-}\,\frac{3/2}{z-}\,\frac{2}{z-}\cdots$$

$$=\frac{1}{\sqrt{\pi}}\lim_{n\to\infty}\sum_{k=1}^{n}\frac{H_k^{(n)}}{z-x_k^{(n)}}\qquad (\mathscr{I}z\neq 0)$$

$x_k^{(n)}$ and $H_k^{(n)}$ are the zeros and weight factors of the Hermite polynomials. For numerical values see chapter **25**.

Value at Infinity

7.1.16 $\operatorname{erf} z\to 1\left(z\to\infty \text{ in } |\arg z|<\frac{\pi}{4}\right)$

Maximum and Inflection Points for Dawson's Integral [7.31]

$$F(x)=e^{-x^2}\int_0^x e^{t^2}dt$$

7.1.17 $F(.92413\ 88730\ldots)=.54104\ 42246\ldots$

7.1.18 $F(1.50197\ 52682\ldots)=.42768\ 66160\ldots$

Derivatives

7.1.19

$$\frac{d^{n+1}}{dz^{n+1}}\operatorname{erf} z=(-1)^n\frac{2}{\sqrt{\pi}}H_n(z)e^{-z^2}\qquad (n=0,1,2,\ldots)$$

7.1.20

$$w^{(n+2)}(z)+2zw^{(n+1)}(z)+2(n+1)w^{(n)}(z)=0\qquad (n=0,1,2,\ldots)$$

$$w^{(0)}(z)=w(z),\qquad w'(z)=-2zw(z)+\frac{2i}{\sqrt{\pi}}$$

(For the Hermite polynomials $H_n(z)$ see chapter **22**.)

Relation to Confluent Hypergeometric Function (see chapter **13**)

7.1.21

$$\operatorname{erf} z=\frac{2z}{\sqrt{\pi}}M\left(\frac{1}{2},\frac{3}{2},-z^2\right)=\frac{2z}{\sqrt{\pi}}e^{-z^2}M\left(1,\frac{3}{2},z^2\right)$$

The Normal Distribution Function With Mean m and Standard Deviation σ (see chapter **26**)

7.1.22 $$\frac{1}{\sigma\sqrt{2\pi}}\int_{-\infty}^x e^{-\frac{(t-m)^2}{2\sigma^2}}dt=\frac{1}{2}\left(1+\operatorname{erf}\left(\frac{x-m}{\sigma\sqrt{2}}\right)\right)$$

Asymptotic Expansion

7.1.23

$$\sqrt{\pi}ze^{z^2}\operatorname{erfc} z\sim 1+\sum_{m=1}^{\infty}(-1)^m\frac{1\cdot 3\ldots(2m-1)}{(2z^2)^m}$$

$$\left(z\to\infty,\ |\arg z|<\frac{3\pi}{4}\right)$$

If $R_n(z)$ is the remainder after n terms then

7.1.24

$$R_n(z)=(-1)^n \frac{1\cdot 3 \ldots (2n-1)}{(2z^2)^n}\theta,$$

$$\theta=\int_0^\infty e^{-t}\left(1+\frac{t}{z^2}\right)^{-n-\frac{1}{2}} dt \qquad \left(|\arg z|<\frac{\pi}{2}\right)$$

$$|\theta|<1 \qquad \left(|\arg z|<\frac{\pi}{4}\right)$$

For x real, $R_n(x)$ is less in absolute value than the first neglected term and of the same sign.

Rational Approximations [2] $(0\leq x<\infty)$

7.1.25

$$\text{erf } x=1-(a_1t+a_2t^2+a_3t^3)\,e^{-x^2}+\epsilon(x), \qquad t=\frac{1}{1+px}$$

$$|\epsilon(x)|\leq 2.5\times 10^{-5}$$

$p=.47047 \quad a_1=.34802\ 42 \quad a_2=-.09587\ 98 \quad a_3=.74785\ 56$

7.1.26

$$\text{erf } x=1-(a_1t+a_2t^2+a_3t^3+a_4t^4+a_5t^5)e^{-x^2}+\epsilon(x),$$

$$t=\frac{1}{1+px}$$

$$|\epsilon(x)|\leq 1.5\times 10^{-7}$$

$p=.32759\ 11 \quad a_1=.25482\ 9592 \quad a_2=-.28449\ 6736 \quad a_3=1.42141\ 3741 \quad a_4=-1.45315\ 2027 \quad a_5=1.06140\ 5429$

7.1.27

$$\text{erf } x=1-\frac{1}{[1+a_1x+a_2x^2+a_3x^3+a_4x^4]^4}+\epsilon(x)$$

$$|\epsilon(x)|\leq 5\times 10^{-4}$$

$a_1=.278393 \quad a_2=.230389$

$a_3=.000972 \quad a_4=.078108$

7.1.28

$$\text{erf } x=1-\frac{1}{[1+a_1x+a_2x^2+\cdots+a_6x^6]^{16}}+\epsilon(x)$$

$$|\epsilon(x)|\leq 3\times 10^{-7}$$

$a_1=.07052\ 30784 \quad a_2=.04228\ 20123$

$a_3=.00927\ 05272 \quad a_4=.00015\ 20143$

$a_5=.00027\ 65672 \quad a_6=.00004\ 30638$

[2] Approximations **7.1.25–7.1.28** are from C. Hastings, Jr., Approximations for digital computers. Princeton Univ. Press, Princeton, N. J., 1955

Infinite Series Approximation for Complex Error Function [7.19]

7.1.29

$$\text{erf }(x+iy)=\text{erf } x+\frac{e^{-x^2}}{2\pi x}[(1-\cos 2xy)+i\sin 2xy]$$

$$+\frac{2}{\pi}e^{-x^2}\sum_{n=1}^{\infty}\frac{e^{-\frac{1}{4}n^2}}{n^2+4x^2}[f_n(x,y)+ig_n(x,y)]+\epsilon(x,y)$$

where

$$f_n(x,y)=2x-2x\cosh ny\cos 2xy+n\sinh ny\sin 2xy$$

$$g_n(x,y)=2x\cosh ny\sin 2xy+n\sinh ny\cos 2xy$$

$$|\epsilon(x,y)|\approx 10^{-16}|\text{erf }(x+iy)|$$

7.2. Repeated Integrals of the Error Function

Definition

7.2.1

$$\text{i}^n\text{ erfc } z=\int_z^\infty \text{i}^{n-1}\text{ erfc } t\,dt \qquad (n=0,1,2,\ldots)$$

$$\text{i}^{-1}\text{ erfc } z=\frac{2}{\sqrt{\pi}}e^{-z^2},\quad \text{i}^0\text{ erfc } z=\text{erfc } z$$

Differential Equation

7.2.2 $$\frac{d^2y}{dz^2}+2z\frac{dy}{dz}-2ny=0$$

$$y=A\text{i}^n\text{ erfc } z+B\text{i}^n\text{ erfc }(-z)$$

(A and B are constants.)

Expression as a Single Integral

7.2.3 $$\text{i}^n\text{ erfc } z=\frac{2}{\sqrt{\pi}}\int_z^\infty\frac{(t-z)^n}{n!}e^{-t^2}dt$$

Power Series [3]

7.2.4 $$\text{i}^n\text{ erfc } z=\sum_{k=0}^{\infty}\frac{(-1)^kz^k}{2^{n-k}k!\,\Gamma\left(1+\frac{n-k}{2}\right)}$$

Recurrence Relations

7.2.5

$$\text{i}^n\text{ erfc } z=-\frac{z}{n}\text{i}^{n-1}\text{ erfc } z+\frac{1}{2n}\text{i}^{n-2}\text{ erfc } z \qquad (n=1,2,3,\ldots)$$

7.2.6

$$2(n+1)(n+2)\text{i}^{n+2}\text{ erfc } z=(2n+1+2z^2)\text{i}^n\text{ erfc } z-\frac{1}{2}\text{i}^{n-2}\text{ erfc } z \qquad (n=1,2,3,\ldots)$$

[3] The terms in this series corresponding to $k=n+2, n+4, n+6, \ldots$ are understood to be zero.

Value at Zero

7.2.7

$$i^n \operatorname{erfc} 0=\frac{1}{2^n\Gamma\left(\frac{n}{2}+1\right)} \qquad (n=-1,0,1,2,\ldots)$$

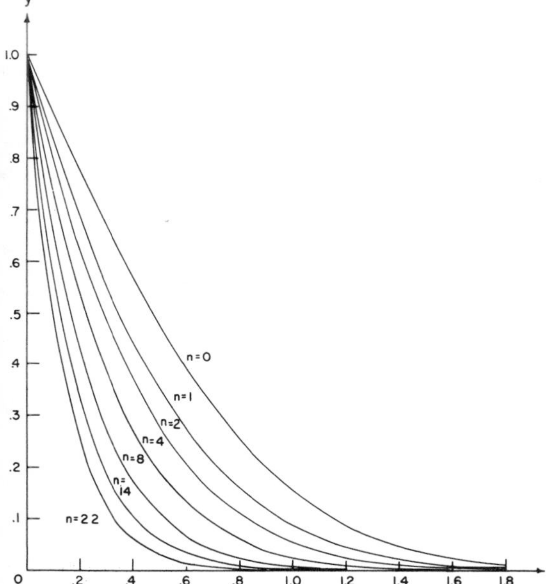

FIGURE 7.4. *Repeated Integrals of the Error Function.*

$y=2^n\Gamma\left(\frac{n}{2}+1\right) \; i^n \operatorname{erfc} x$

$n=0, 1, 2, 4, 8, 14, 22$

Derivatives

7.2.8 $$\frac{d}{dz} i^n \operatorname{erfc} z=-i^{n-1} \operatorname{erfc} z \qquad (n=0,1,2,\ldots)$$

7.2.9

$$\frac{d^n}{dz^n}(e^{z^2} \operatorname{erfc} z)=(-1)^n 2^n n!\, e^{z^2} i^n \operatorname{erfc} z \qquad (n=0,1,2,\ldots)$$

Relation to $Hh_n(z)$ (see 19.14)

7.2.10 $$i^n \operatorname{erfc} z=\frac{1}{(2^{n-1}\pi)^{\frac{1}{2}}} Hh_n(\sqrt{2}z)$$

Relation to Hermite Polynomials (see chapter 22)

7.2.11 $$(-1)^n i^n \operatorname{erfc} z+i^n \operatorname{erfc}(-z)=\frac{i^{-n}}{2^{n-1}n!} H_n(iz)$$

Relation to the Confluent Hypergeometric Function (see chapter 13)

7.2.12

$$i^n \operatorname{erfc} z=e^{-z^2}\left[\frac{1}{2^n\Gamma\left(\frac{n}{2}+1\right)} M\left(\frac{n+1}{2},\frac{1}{2},z^2\right) - \frac{z}{2^{n-1}\Gamma\left(\frac{n+1}{2}\right)} M\left(\frac{n}{2}+1,\frac{3}{2},z^2\right)\right]$$

Relation to Parabolic Cylinder Functions (see chapter 19)

7.2.13 $$i^n \operatorname{erfc} z=\frac{e^{-\frac{1}{2}z^2}}{(2^{n-1}\pi)^{\frac{1}{2}}} D_{-n-1}(z\sqrt{2})$$

Asymptotic Expansion

7.2.14

$$i^n \operatorname{erfc} z\sim\frac{2}{\sqrt{\pi}} \frac{e^{-z^2}}{(2z)^{n+1}} \sum_{m=0}^{\infty} \frac{(-1)^m(2m+n)!}{n!m!(2z)^{2m}} \qquad \left(z\to\infty,\ |\arg z|<\frac{3\pi}{4}\right)$$

7.3. Fresnel Integrals

Definition

7.3.1 $$C(z)=\int_0^z \cos\left(\frac{\pi}{2}t^2\right)dt$$

7.3.2 $$S(z)=\int_0^z \sin\left(\frac{\pi}{2}t^2\right)dt$$

The following functions are also in use:

7.3.3

$$C_1(x)=\sqrt{\frac{2}{\pi}}\int_0^x \cos t^2 dt,\ C_2(x)=\frac{1}{\sqrt{2\pi}}\int_0^x \frac{\cos t}{\sqrt{t}}\,dt$$

7.3.4

$$S_1(x)=\sqrt{\frac{2}{\pi}}\int_0^x \sin t^2 dt,\ S_2(x)=\frac{1}{\sqrt{2\pi}}\int_0^x \frac{\sin t}{\sqrt{t}}\,dt$$

Auxiliary Functions

7.3.5

$$f(z)=\left[\frac{1}{2}-S(z)\right]\cos\left(\frac{\pi}{2}z^2\right)-\left[\frac{1}{2}-C(z)\right]\sin\left(\frac{\pi}{2}z^2\right)$$

7.3.6

$$g(z)=\left[\frac{1}{2}-C(z)\right]\cos\left(\frac{\pi}{2}z^2\right)+\left[\frac{1}{2}-S(z)\right]\sin\left(\frac{\pi}{2}z^2\right)$$

Interrelations

7.3.7 $$C(x)=C_1\left(x\sqrt{\frac{\pi}{2}}\right)=C_2\left(\frac{\pi}{2}x^2\right)$$

7.3.8 $$S(x)=S_1\left(x\sqrt{\frac{\pi}{2}}\right)=S_2\left(\frac{\pi}{2}x^2\right)$$

7.3.9 $$C(z)=\frac{1}{2}+f(z)\sin\left(\frac{\pi}{2}z^2\right)-g(z)\cos\left(\frac{\pi}{2}z^2\right)$$

7.3.10 $$S(z)=\frac{1}{2}-f(z)\cos\left(\frac{\pi}{2}z^2\right)-g(z)\sin\left(\frac{\pi}{2}z^2\right)$$

Series Expansions

7.3.11 $$C(z)=\sum_{n=0}^{\infty}\frac{(-1)^n(\pi/2)^{2n}}{(2n)!(4n+1)}z^{4n+1}$$

7.3.12

$$C(z)=\cos\left(\frac{\pi}{2}z^2\right)\sum_{n=0}^{\infty}\frac{(-1)^n\pi^{2n}}{1\cdot 3\ldots(4n+1)}z^{4n+1}$$
$$+\sin\left(\frac{\pi}{2}z^2\right)\sum_{n=0}^{\infty}\frac{(-1)^n\pi^{2n+1}}{1\cdot 3\ldots(4n+3)}z^{4n+3}$$

7.3.13 $$S(z)=\sum_{n=0}^{\infty}\frac{(-1)^n(\pi/2)^{2n+1}}{(2n+1)!(4n+3)}z^{4n+3}$$

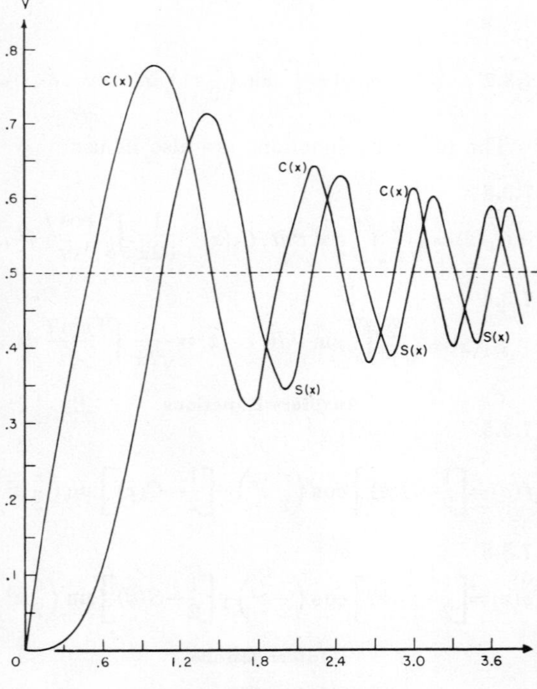

FIGURE 7.5. *Fresnel Integrals.*
$y=C(x)$, $y=S(x)$

7.3.14

$$S(z)=-\cos\left(\frac{\pi}{2}z^2\right)\sum_{n=0}^{\infty}\frac{(-1)^n\pi^{2n+1}}{1\cdot 3\ldots(4n+3)}z^{4n+3}$$
$$+\sin\left(\frac{\pi}{2}z^2\right)\sum_{n=0}^{\infty}\frac{(-1)^n\pi^{2n}}{1\cdot 3\ldots(4n+1)}z^{4n+1}$$

7.3.15 $$C_2(z)=J_{1/2}(z)+J_{5/2}(z)+J_{9/2}(z)+\ldots$$

7.3.16 $$S_2(z)=J_{3/2}(z)+J_{7/2}(z)+J_{11/2}(z)+\ldots$$

For Bessel functions $J_{n+1/2}(z)$ see chapter **10.**

Symmetry Relations

7.3.17 $$C(-z)=-C(z),\quad S(-z)=-S(z)$$

7.3.18 $$C(iz)=iC(z),\quad S(iz)=-iS(z)$$

7.3.19 $$C(\bar{z})=\overline{C(z)},\quad S(\bar{z})=\overline{S(z)}$$

Value at Infinity

7.3.20 $$C(x)\rightarrow\frac{1}{2},\qquad S(x)\rightarrow\frac{1}{2}\qquad (x\rightarrow\infty)$$

Derivatives

7.3.21 $$\frac{df(x)}{dx}=-\pi x g(x),\qquad \frac{dg(x)}{dx}=\pi x f(x)-1$$

Relation to Error Function (see 7.1.1, 7.1.3)

7.3.22

$$C(z)+iS(z)=\frac{1+i}{2}\operatorname{erf}\left[\frac{\sqrt{\pi}}{2}(1-i)z\right]$$
$$=\frac{1+i}{2}\left\{1-e^{i\frac{\pi}{2}z^2}w\left[\frac{\sqrt{\pi}}{2}(1+i)z\right]\right\}$$

7.3.23 $$g(x)=\mathscr{R}\left\{\frac{1+i}{2}w\left[\frac{\sqrt{\pi}}{2}(1+i)x\right]\right\}$$

7.3.24 $$f(x)=\mathscr{I}\left\{\frac{1+i}{2}w\left[\frac{\sqrt{\pi}}{2}(1+i)x\right]\right\}$$

Relation to Confluent Hypergeometric Function (see chapter 13)

7.3.25

$$C(z)+iS(z)=zM\left(\frac{1}{2},\frac{3}{2},i\frac{\pi}{2}z^2\right)$$
$$=ze^{i\frac{\pi}{2}z^2}M\left(1,\frac{3}{2},-i\frac{\pi}{2}z^2\right)$$

Relation to Spherical Bessel Functions (see chapter 10)

7.3.26 $$C_2(z)=\frac{1}{2}\int_0^z J_{-\frac{1}{2}}(t)dt,\quad S_2(z)=\frac{1}{2}\int_0^z J_{\frac{1}{2}}(t)dt$$

Asymptotic Expansions

7.3.27

$$\pi z f(z)\sim 1+\sum_{m=1}^{\infty}(-1)^m\frac{1\cdot 3\ldots(4m-1)}{(\pi z^2)^{2m}}\qquad \left(z\to\infty,\ |\arg z|<\frac{\pi}{2}\right)$$

7.3.28

$$\pi z g(z)\sim \sum_{m=0}^{\infty}(-1)^m\frac{1\cdot 3\ldots(4m+1)}{(\pi z^2)^{2m+1}}\qquad \left(z\to\infty,\ |\arg z|<\frac{\pi}{2}\right)$$

If $R_n^{(f)}(z)$, $R_n^{(g)}(z)$ are the remainders after n terms in **7.3.27, 7.3.28,** respectively, then

7.3.29

$$R_n^{(f)}(z)=(-1)^n\frac{1\cdot 3\ldots(4n-1)}{(\pi z^2)^{2n}}\theta^{(f)},$$

$$\theta^{(f)}=\frac{1}{\Gamma(2n+\frac{1}{2})}\int_0^{\infty}\frac{e^{-t}t^{2n-\frac{1}{2}}}{1+\left(\frac{2t}{\pi z^2}\right)^2}dt\left(|\arg z|<\frac{\pi}{4}\right)$$

7.3.30

$$R_n^{(g)}(z)=(-1)^n\frac{1\cdot 3\ldots(4n+1)}{(\pi z^2)^{2n}}\theta^{(g)},$$

$$\theta^{(g)}=\frac{1}{\Gamma(2n+\frac{3}{2})}\int_0^{\infty}\frac{e^{-t}t^{2n+\frac{1}{2}}}{1+\left(\frac{2t}{\pi z^2}\right)^2}dt\left(|\arg z|<\frac{\pi}{4}\right)$$

7.3.31 $|\theta^{(f)}|<1,\ |\theta^{(g)}|<1 \qquad \left(|\arg z|\leq\frac{\pi}{8}\right)$

For x real, $R_n^{(f)}(x)$ and $R_n^{(g)}(x)$ are less in absolute value than the first neglected term and of the same sign.

Rational Approximations[4] $(0\leq x\leq\infty)$

7.3.32

$$f(x)=\frac{1+.926x}{2+1.792x+3.104x^2}+\epsilon(x)\qquad |\epsilon(x)|\leq 2\times 10^{-3}$$

7.3.33

$$g(x)=\frac{1}{2+4.142x+3.492x^2+6.670x^3}+\epsilon(x)\qquad |\epsilon(x)|\leq 2\times 10^{-3}$$

(For more accurate approximations see [7.1].)

7.4. Definite and Indefinite Integrals

For a more extensive list of integrals see [7.5], [7 8], [7.15].

7.4.1 $$\int_0^{\infty}e^{-t^2}dt=\frac{\sqrt{\pi}}{2}$$

[4] Approximations **7.3.32, 7.3.33** are based on those given in C. Hastings, Jr., Approximations for calculating Fresnel integrals, Approximation Newsletter, April 1956, Note 10. [See also MTAC **10,** 173, 1956.]

7.4.2

$$\int_0^{\infty}e^{-(at^2+2bt+c)}dt=\frac{1}{2}\sqrt{\frac{\pi}{a}}\,e^{\frac{b^2-ac}{a}}\operatorname{erfc}\frac{b}{\sqrt{a}}\qquad (\mathscr{R}a>0)$$

7.4.3

$$\int_0^{\infty}e^{-at^2-\frac{b}{t^2}}dt=\frac{1}{2}\sqrt{\frac{\pi}{a}}\,e^{-2\sqrt{ab}}\qquad (\mathscr{R}a>0,\ \mathscr{R}b>0)$$

7.4.4

$$\int_0^{\infty}t^{2n}e^{-at^2}dt=\frac{1\cdot 3\ldots(2n-1)}{2^{n+1}a^n}\sqrt{\frac{\pi}{a}}=\frac{\Gamma(n+\frac{1}{2})}{2a^{n+\frac{1}{2}}}\qquad (\mathscr{R}a>0;n=0,1,2,\ldots)$$

7.4.5

$$\int_0^{\infty}t^{2n+1}e^{-at^2}dt=\frac{n!}{2a^{n+1}}\qquad (\mathscr{R}a>0;n=0,1,2,\ldots)$$

7.4.6

$$\int_0^{\infty}e^{-at^2}\cos(2xt)dt=\frac{1}{2}\sqrt{\frac{\pi}{a}}\,e^{-\frac{x^2}{a}}\qquad (\mathscr{R}a>0)$$

7.4.7

$$\int_0^{\infty}e^{-at^2}\sin(2xt)dt=\frac{1}{\sqrt{a}}\,e^{-x^2/a}\int_0^{x/\sqrt{a}}e^{t^2}dt\qquad (\mathscr{R}a>0)$$

7.4.8

$$\int_0^{\infty}\frac{e^{-at}dt}{\sqrt{t+z^2}}=\sqrt{\frac{\pi}{a}}\,e^{az^2}\operatorname{erfc}\sqrt{a}z\qquad (\mathscr{R}a>0,\ \mathscr{R}z>0)$$

7.4.9

$$\int_0^{\infty}\frac{e^{-at}dt}{\sqrt{t}(t+z)}=\frac{\pi}{\sqrt{z}}\,e^{az}\operatorname{erfc}\sqrt{az}\qquad (\mathscr{R}a>0,\ z\neq 0, |\arg z|<\pi)$$

7.4.10

$$\int_0^{\infty}\frac{e^{-at^2}dt}{t+x}=e^{-ax^2}\left[\sqrt{\pi}\int_0^{\sqrt{a}x}e^{t^2}dt-\frac{1}{2}\operatorname{Ei}(ax^2)\right]\qquad (a>0,\ x>0)$$

7.4.11

$$\int_0^{\infty}\frac{e^{-at^2}dt}{t^2+x^2}=\frac{\pi}{2x}\,e^{ax^2}\operatorname{erfc}\sqrt{a}x\qquad (a>0,\ x>0)$$

7.4.12 $$\int_0^1\frac{e^{-at^2}dt}{t^2+1}=\frac{\pi}{4}\,e^a[1-(\operatorname{erf}\sqrt{a})^2]\qquad (a>0)$$

7.4.13

$$\int_{-\infty}^{\infty}\frac{ye^{-t^2}dt}{(x-t)^2+y^2}=\pi\,\mathscr{R}w(x+iy)\qquad (x\text{ real},\ y>0)$$

7.4.14

$$\int_{-\infty}^{\infty}\frac{(x-t)e^{-t^2}dt}{(x-t)^2+y^2}=\pi\mathscr{I}w(x+iy)\qquad(x\text{ real},y>0)$$

7.4.15

$$\int_0^{\infty}\frac{[t^2-(x^2-y^2)]e^{-t^2}dt}{t^4-2(x^2-y^2)t^2+(x^2+y^2)^2}=\frac{\pi}{2}\mathscr{R}\frac{w(x+iy)}{y-ix}$$

$$(x\text{ real},y>0)$$

7.4.16

$$\int_0^{\infty}\frac{2xye^{-t^2}dt}{t^4-2(x^2-y^2)t^2+(x^2+y^2)^2}=\frac{\pi}{2}\mathscr{I}\frac{w(x+iy)}{y-ix}$$

$$(x\text{ real},y>0)$$

7.4.17

$$\int_0^{\infty}e^{-at}\operatorname{erf}bt\,dt=\frac{1}{a}e^{\frac{a^2}{4b^2}}\operatorname{erfc}\frac{a}{2b}$$

$$\left(\mathscr{R}a>0,|\arg b|<\frac{\pi}{4}\right)$$

7.4.18

$$\int_0^{\infty}\sin(2at)\operatorname{erfc}bt\,dt=\frac{1}{2a}[1-e^{-(a/b)^2}]\quad(a>0,\mathscr{R}b>0)$$

7.4.19

$$\int_0^{\infty}e^{-at}\operatorname{erf}\sqrt{bt}\,dt=\frac{1}{a}\sqrt{\frac{b}{a+b}}\qquad(\mathscr{R}(a+b)>0)$$

7.4.20

$$\int_0^{\infty}e^{-at}\operatorname{erfc}\sqrt{\frac{b}{t}}\,dt=\frac{1}{a}e^{-2\sqrt{ab}}\qquad(\mathscr{R}a>0,\mathscr{R}b>0)$$

7.4.21

$$\int_0^{\infty}e^{(a-b)t}\operatorname{erfc}\left(\sqrt{at}+\sqrt{\frac{c}{t}}\right)dt=\frac{e^{-2(\sqrt{ac}+\sqrt{bc})}}{\sqrt{b}(\sqrt{a}+\sqrt{b})}$$

$$(\mathscr{R}b>0,\mathscr{R}c>0)$$

7.4.22

$$\int_0^{\infty}e^{-at}\cos(t^2)dt=\sqrt{\frac{\pi}{2}}\left\{\left[\frac{1}{2}-S\left(\frac{a}{2}\sqrt{\frac{2}{\pi}}\right)\right]\cos\left(\frac{a^2}{4}\right)\right.$$

$$\left.-\left[\frac{1}{2}-C\left(\frac{a}{2}\sqrt{\frac{2}{\pi}}\right)\right]\sin\left(\frac{a^2}{4}\right)\right\}\qquad(\mathscr{R}a>0)$$

7.4.23

$$\int_0^{\infty}e^{-at}\sin(t^2)dt=\sqrt{\frac{\pi}{2}}\left\{\left[\frac{1}{2}-C\left(\frac{a}{2}\sqrt{\frac{2}{\pi}}\right)\right]\cos\left(\frac{a^2}{4}\right)\right.$$

$$\left.+\left[\frac{1}{2}-S\left(\frac{a}{2}\sqrt{\frac{2}{\pi}}\right)\right]\sin\left(\frac{a^2}{4}\right)\right\}\qquad(\mathscr{R}a>0)$$

7.4.24

$$\int_0^{\infty}e^{-at}\frac{\sin(t^2)}{t}dt=\frac{\pi}{2}\left[\frac{1}{2}-C\left(\frac{a}{2}\sqrt{\frac{2}{\pi}}\right)\right]^2$$

$$+\frac{\pi}{2}\left[\frac{1}{2}-S\left(\frac{a}{2}\sqrt{\frac{2}{\pi}}\right)\right]^2\qquad(\mathscr{R}a>0)$$

7.4.25

$$\int_0^{\infty}\frac{e^{-at}\sqrt{t}}{t^2+b^2}dt=\pi\sqrt{\frac{2}{b}}\left\{\left[\frac{1}{2}-C\left(\sqrt{\frac{2ab}{\pi}}\right)\right]\cos(ab)\right.$$

$$\left.+\left[\frac{1}{2}-S\left(\sqrt{\frac{2ab}{\pi}}\right)\right]\sin(ab)\right\}\qquad(\mathscr{R}a>0,\mathscr{R}b>0)$$

7.4.26

$$\int_0^{\infty}\frac{e^{-at}dt}{\sqrt{t}(t^2+b^2)}=\frac{\pi}{b}\sqrt{\frac{2}{b}}\left\{\left[\frac{1}{2}-S\left(\sqrt{\frac{2ab}{\pi}}\right)\right]\cos(ab)\right.$$

$$\left.-\left[\frac{1}{2}-C\left(\sqrt{\frac{2ab}{\pi}}\right)\right]\sin(ab)\right\}\qquad(\mathscr{R}a>0,\mathscr{R}b>0)$$

7.4.27

$$\int_0^{\infty}e^{-at}C(t)dt=\frac{1}{a}\left\{\left[\frac{1}{2}-S\left(\frac{a}{\pi}\right)\right]\cos\left(\frac{a^2}{2\pi}\right)\right.$$

$$\left.-\left[\frac{1}{2}-C\left(\frac{a}{\pi}\right)\right]\sin\left(\frac{a^2}{2\pi}\right)\right\}\qquad(\mathscr{R}a>0)$$

7.4.28

$$\int_0^{\infty}e^{-at}S(t)dt=\frac{1}{a}\left\{\left[\frac{1}{2}-C\left(\frac{a}{\pi}\right)\right]\cos\left(\frac{a^2}{2\pi}\right)\right.$$

$$\left.+\left[\frac{1}{2}-S\left(\frac{a}{\pi}\right)\right]\sin\left(\frac{a^2}{2\pi}\right)\right\}\qquad(\mathscr{R}a>0)$$

7.4.29

$$\int_0^{\infty}e^{-at}C\left(\sqrt{\frac{2t}{\pi}}\right)dt=\frac{1}{2a(\sqrt{a^2+1}-a)^{\frac{1}{2}}\sqrt{a^2+1}}$$

$$(\mathscr{R}a>0)$$

7.4.30

$$\int_0^{\infty}e^{-at}S\left(\sqrt{\frac{2t}{\pi}}\right)dt=\frac{1}{2a(\sqrt{a^2+1}+a)^{\frac{1}{2}}\sqrt{a^2+1}}$$

$$(\mathscr{R}a>0)$$

7.4.31 $$\int_0^{\infty}\left\{\left[\frac{1}{2}-C(t)\right]^2+\left[\frac{1}{2}-S(t)\right]^2\right\}dt=\frac{1}{\pi}$$

7.4.32

$$\int e^{-(ax^2+2bx+c)}dx=\frac{1}{2}\sqrt{\frac{\pi}{a}}e^{\frac{b^2-ac}{a}}\operatorname{erf}\left(\sqrt{a}x+\frac{b}{\sqrt{a}}\right)+\text{const.}$$

$$(a\neq 0)$$

7.4.33

$$\int e^{-a^2x^2-\frac{b^2}{x^2}}dx=\frac{\sqrt{\pi}}{4a}\left[e^{2ab}\operatorname{erf}\left(ax+\frac{b}{x}\right)+e^{-2ab}\operatorname{erf}\left(ax-\frac{b}{x}\right)\right]+\text{const.}\qquad (a\neq 0)$$

7.4.34

$$\int e^{-a^2x^2+\frac{b^2}{x^2}}dx=-\frac{\sqrt{\pi}}{4a}\,e^{-a^2x^2+\frac{b^2}{x^2}}\left[w\left(\frac{b}{x}+iax\right)+w\left(-\frac{b}{x}+iax\right)\right]+\text{const.}\qquad (a\neq 0)$$

7.4.35 $\int \operatorname{erf} x\,dx=x\operatorname{erf} x+\frac{1}{\sqrt{\pi}}\,e^{-x^2}+\text{const.}$

7.4.36

$$\int e^{ax}\operatorname{erf} bx\,dx=\frac{1}{a}\left[e^{ax}\operatorname{erf} bx-e^{\frac{a^2}{4b^2}}\operatorname{erf}\left(bx-\frac{a}{2b}\right)\right]+\text{const.}\qquad (a\neq 0)$$

7.4.37

$$\int e^{ax}\operatorname{erf}\sqrt{\frac{b}{x}}\,dx=\frac{1}{a}\left\{e^{ax}\operatorname{erf}\sqrt{\frac{b}{x}}+\frac{1}{2}\,e^{ax-\frac{b}{x}}\left[w\left(\sqrt{ax}+i\sqrt{\frac{b}{x}}\right)+w\left(-\sqrt{ax}+i\sqrt{\frac{b}{x}}\right)\right]\right\}+\text{const.}\qquad (a\neq 0)$$

7.4.38

$$\int \cos\,(ax^2+2bx+c)dx=\sqrt{\frac{\pi}{2a}}\left\{\cos\left(\frac{b^2-ac}{a}\right)C\left[\sqrt{\frac{2}{a\pi}}\,(ax+b)\right]+\sin\left(\frac{b^2-ac}{a}\right)S\left[\sqrt{\frac{2}{a\pi}}\,(ax+b)\right]\right\}+\text{const.}$$

7.4.39

$$\int \sin\,(ax^2+2bx+c)dx=\sqrt{\frac{\pi}{2a}}\left\{\cos\left(\frac{b^2-ac}{a}\right)S\left[\sqrt{\frac{2}{a\pi}}\,(ax+b)\right]-\sin\left(\frac{b^2-ac}{a}\right)C\left[\sqrt{\frac{2}{a\pi}}\,(ax+b)\right]\right\}+\text{const.}$$

7.4.40 $\int C(x)dx=xC(x)-\frac{1}{\pi}\sin\left(\frac{\pi}{2}\,x^2\right)+\text{const.}$

7.4.41 $\int S(x)dx=xS(x)+\frac{1}{\pi}\cos\left(\frac{\pi}{2}\,x^2\right)+\text{const.}$

FRESNEL INTEGRALS

Table 7.7

$$C(x)=\int_0^x \cos\left(\frac{\pi}{2}t^2\right)dt \qquad C_2(u)=\frac{1}{\sqrt{2\pi}}\int_0^u \frac{\cos t}{\sqrt{t}}dt=C\left(\sqrt{\frac{2u}{\pi}}\right)$$

$$S(x)=\int_0^x \sin\left(\frac{\pi}{2}t^2\right)dt \qquad S_2(u)=\frac{1}{\sqrt{2\pi}}\int_0^u \frac{\sin t}{\sqrt{t}}dt=S\left(\sqrt{\frac{2u}{\pi}}\right)$$

x	$u=\frac{\pi}{2}x^2$	$C(x)=C_2(u)$	$S(x)=S_2(u)$	x	$u=\frac{\pi}{2}x^2$	$C(x)=C_2(u)$	$S(x)=S_2(u)$
0.00	0.00000 00	0.00000 00	0.00000 00	1.00	1.57079 63	0.77989 34	0.43825 91
0.02	0.00062 83	0.02000 00	0.00000 42	1.02	1.63425 65	0.77926 11	0.45824 58
0.04	0.00251 33	0.04000 00	0.00003 35	1.04	1.69897 33	0.77735 01	0.47815 08
0.06	0.00565 49	0.05999 98	0.00011 31	1.06	1.76494 68	0.77414 34	0.49788 84
0.08	0.01005 31	0.07999 92	0.00026 81	1.08	1.83217 68	0.76963 03	0.51736 86
0.10	0.01570 80	0.09999 75	0.00052 36	1.10	1.90066 36	0.76380 67	0.53649 79
0.12	0.02261 95	0.11999 39	0.00090 47	1.12	1.97040 69	0.75667 60	0.55517 92
0.14	0.03078 76	0.13998 67	0.00143 67	1.14	2.04140 69	0.74824 94	0.57331 28
0.16	0.04021 24	0.15997 41	0.00214 44	1.16	2.11366 35	0.73854 68	0.59079 66
0.18	0.05089 38	0.17995 34	0.00305 31	1.18	2.18717 68	0.72759 68	0.60752 74
0.20	0.06283 19	0.19992 11	0.00418 76	1.20	2.26194 67	0.71543 77	0.62340 09
0.22	0.07602 65	0.21987 29	0.00557 30	1.22	2.33797 33	0.70211 76	0.63831 34
0.24	0.09047 79	0.23980 36	0.00723 40	1.24	2.41525 64	0.68769 47	0.65216 19
0.26	0.10618 58	0.25970 70	0.00919 54	1.26	2.49379 62	0.67223 78	0.66484 56
0.28	0.12315 04	0.27957 56	0.01148 16	1.28	2.57359 27	0.65582 63	0.67626 72
0.30	0.14137 17	0.29940 10	0.01411 70	1.30	2.65464 58	0.63855 05	0.68633 33
0.32	0.16084 95	0.31917 31	0.01712 56	1.32	2.73695 55	0.62051 11	0.69495 62
0.34	0.18158 41	0.33888 06	0.02053 11	1.34	2.82052 19	0.60181 95	0.70205 50
0.36	0.20357 52	0.35851 09	0.02435 68	1.36	2.90534 49	0.58259 73	0.70755 67
0.38	0.22682 30	0.37804 96	0.02862 55	1.38	2.99142 45	0.56297 59	0.71139 77
0.40	0.25132 74	0.39748 08	0.03335 94	1.40	3.07876 08	0.54309 58	0.71352 51
0.42	0.27708 85	0.41678 68	0.03858 02	1.42	3.16735 37	0.52310 58	0.71389 77
0.44	0.30410 62	0.43594 82	0.04430 85	1.44	3.25720 33	0.50316 23	0.71248 78
0.46	0.33238 05	0.45494 40	0.05056 42	1.46	3.34830 95	0.48342 80	0.70928 16
0.48	0.36191 15	0.47375 10	0.05736 63	1.48	3.44067 23	0.46407 05	0.70428 12
0.50	0.39269 91	0.49234 42	0.06473 24	1.50	3.53429 17	0.44526 12	0.69750 50
0.52	0.42474 33	0.51069 69	0.07267 89	1.52	3.62916 78	0.42717 32	0.68898 88
0.54	0.45804 42	0.52878 01	0.08122 06	1.54	3.72530 06	0.40997 99	0.67878 67
0.56	0.49260 17	0.54656 30	0.09037 08	1.56	3.82268 99	0.39385 29	0.66697 13
0.58	0.52841 59	0.56401 31	0.10014 09	1.58	3.92133 60	0.37895 96	0.65363 46
0.60	0.56548 67	0.58109 54	0.11054 02	1.60	4.02123 86	0.36546 17	0.63888 77
0.62	0.60381 41	0.59777 37	0.12157 59	1.62	4.12239 79	0.35351 20	0.62286 07
0.64	0.64339 82	0.61400 94	0.13325 28	1.64	4.22481 38	0.34325 29	0.60570 26
0.66	0.68423 89	0.62976 25	0.14557 29	1.66	4.32848 64	0.33481 32	0.58758 04
0.68	0.72633 62	0.64499 12	0.15853 54	1.68	4.43341 56	0.32830 61	0.56867 83
0.70	0.76969 02	0.65965 24	0.17213 65	1.70	4.53960 14	0.32382 69	0.54919 60
0.72	0.81430 08	0.67370 12	0.18636 89	1.72	4.64704 39	0.32145 02	0.52934 73
0.74	0.86016 81	0.68709 20	0.20122 21	1.74	4.75574 30	0.32122 83	0.50935 84
0.76	0.90729 20	0.69977 79	0.21668 16	1.76	4.86569 87	0.32318 87	0.48946 49
0.78	0.95567 25	0.71171 13	0.23272 88	1.78	4.97691 11	0.32733 25	0.46990 94
0.80	1.00530 96	0.72284 42	0.24934 14	1.80	5.08938 01	0.33363 29	0.45093 88
0.82	1.05620 35	0.73312 83	0.26649 22	1.82	5.20310 58	0.34203 39	0.43280 06
0.84	1.10835 39	0.74251 54	0.28414 98	1.84	5.31808 80	0.35244 96	0.41573 97
0.86	1.16176 10	0.75095 79	0.30227 80	1.86	5.43432 70	0.36476 35	0.39999 44
0.88	1.21642 47	0.75840 90	0.32083 55	1.88	5.55182 25	0.37882 93	0.38579 25
0.90	1.27234 50	0.76482 30	0.33977 63	1.90	5.67057 47	0.39447 05	0.37334 73
0.92	1.32952 20	0.77015 63	0.35904 93	1.92	5.79058 36	0.41148 24	0.36285 37
0.94	1.38795 56	0.77436 72	0.37859 81	1.94	5.91184 91	0.42963 33	0.35448 37
0.96	1.44764 59	0.77741 68	0.39836 12	1.96	6.03437 12	0.44866 69	0.34838 30
0.98	1.50859 28	0.77926 95	0.41827 21	1.98	6.15814 99	0.46830 56	0.34466 65
1.00	1.57079 63	0.77989 34	0.43825 91	2.00	6.28318 53	0.48825 34	0.34341 57

For $x\to 0: C(x)\approx x-\frac{\pi^2}{40}x^5 \qquad S(x)\approx\frac{\pi}{6}x^3-\frac{\pi^3}{336}x^7$

Table 7.7

FRESNEL INTEGRALS

$$C(x)=\int_0^x \cos\left(\frac{\pi}{2}t^2\right)dt \qquad S(x)=\int_0^x \sin\left(\frac{\pi}{2}t^2\right)dt$$

x	$C(x)$	$S(x)$	x	$C(x)$	$S(x)$	x	$C(x)$	$S(x)$
2.00	0.48825 34	0.34341 57	3.00	0.60572 08	0.49631 30	4.00	0.49842 60	0.42051 58
2.02	0.50820 04	0.34467 48	3.02	0.60383 73	0.51619 42	4.02	0.51821 54	0.42301 99
2.04	0.52782 73	0.34844 87	3.04	0.59823 78	0.53536 29	4.04	0.53675 05	0.43039 00
2.06	0.54681 06	0.35470 04	3.06	0.58910 11	0.55311 95	4.06	0.55284 04	0.44217 81
2.08	0.56482 79	0.36334 98	3.08	0.57674 01	0.56880 28	4.08	0.56543 47	0.45764 45
2.10	0.58156 41	0.37427 34	3.10	0.56159 39	0.58181 59	4.10	0.57369 56	0.47579 83
2.12	0.59671 75	0.38730 37	3.12	0.54421 58	0.59165 11	4.12	0.57705 88	0.49545 71
2.14	0.61000 60	0.40223 09	3.14	0.52525 53	0.59791 29	4.14	0.57527 76	0.51532 14
2.16	0.62117 32	0.41880 45	3.16	0.50543 56	0.60033 66	4.16	0.56844 74	0.53405 87
2.18	0.62999 53	0.43673 63	3.18	0.48552 76	0.59880 34	4.18	0.55700 75	0.55039 41
2.20	0.63628 60	0.45570 46	3.20	0.46632 03	0.59334 95	4.20	0.54171 92	0.56319 89
2.22	0.63990 31	0.47535 85	3.22	0.44858 96	0.58416 97	4.22	0.52362 06	0.57157 23
2.24	0.64075 25	0.49532 41	3.24	0.43306 55	0.57161 47	4.24	0.50396 08	0.57491 03
2.26	0.63879 28	0.51521 11	3.26	0.42040 05	0.55618 06	4.26	0.48411 63	0.57295 47
2.28	0.63403 83	0.53462 03	3.28	0.41113 97	0.53849 35	4.28	0.46549 61	0.56582 05
2.30	0.62656 17	0.55315 16	3.30	0.40569 44	0.51928 61	4.30	0.44944 12	0.55399 59
2.32	0.61649 45	0.57041 28	3.32	0.40431 99	0.49936 95	4.32	0.43712 50	0.53831 55
2.34	0.60402 69	0.58602 84	3.34	0.40709 96	0.47960 04	4.34	0.42946 40	0.51990 77
2.36	0.58940 65	0.59964 89	3.36	0.41393 66	0.46084 46	4.36	0.42704 39	0.50011 73
2.38	0.57293 44	0.61095 96	3.38	0.42455 18	0.44393 82	4.38	0.43006 79	0.48041 08
2.40	0.55496 14	0.61969 00	3.40	0.43849 17	0.42964 95	4.40	0.43833 29	0.46226 80
2.42	0.53588 11	0.62562 11	3.42	0.45514 37	0.41864 11	4.42	0.45123 59	0.44707 06
2.44	0.51612 29	0.62859 38	3.44	0.47375 96	0.41143 69	4.44	0.46781 05	0.43599 33
2.46	0.49614 28	0.62851 43	3.46	0.49348 70	0.40839 28	4.46	0.48679 41	0.42990 86
2.48	0.47641 35	0.62535 98	3.48	0.51340 62	0.40967 54	4.48	0.50671 95	0.42931 16
2.50	0.45741 30	0.61918 18	3.50	0.53257 24	0.41524 80	4.50	0.52602 59	0.43427 30
2.52	0.43961 32	0.61010 76	3.52	0.55006 11	0.42486 72	4.52	0.54318 11	0.44442 34
2.54	0.42346 72	0.59834 06	3.54	0.56501 32	0.43808 83	4.54	0.55680 46	0.45897 36
2.56	0.40939 65	0.58415 75	3.56	0.57668 02	0.45428 17	4.56	0.56578 27	0.47676 89
2.58	0.39777 91	0.56790 42	3.58	0.58446 43	0.47265 92	4.58	0.56936 57	0.49637 56
2.60	0.38893 75	0.54998 93	3.60	0.58795 33	0.49230 95	4.60	0.56723 67	0.51619 23
2.62	0.38312 73	0.53087 53	3.62	0.58694 64	0.51224 12	4.62	0.55954 81	0.53457 97
2.64	0.38052 80	0.51106 79	3.64	0.58147 10	0.53143 21	4.64	0.54691 86	0.54999 67
2.66	0.38123 50	0.49110 35	3.66	0.57178 75	0.54888 15	4.66	0.53039 13	0.56113 28
2.68	0.38525 32	0.47153 52	3.68	0.55838 18	0.56366 38	4.68	0.51135 38	0.56702 44
2.70	0.39249 40	0.45291 75	3.70	0.54194 57	0.57498 04	4.70	0.49142 65	0.56714 55
2.72	0.40277 39	0.43578 98	3.72	0.52334 49	0.58220 56	4.72	0.47232 71	0.56146 19
2.74	0.41581 68	0.42066 03	3.74	0.50357 70	0.58492 61	4.74	0.45572 30	0.55044 52
2.76	0.43125 85	0.40798 90	3.76	0.48371 94	0.58296 92	4.76	0.44308 30	0.53504 16
2.78	0.44865 46	0.39817 24	3.78	0.46487 19	0.57641 91	4.78	0.43554 28	0.51659 82
2.80	0.46749 17	0.39152 84	3.80	0.44809 49	0.56561 87	4.80	0.43379 66	0.49675 02
2.82	0.48720 04	0.38828 41	3.82	0.43434 86	0.55115 74	4.82	0.43802 47	0.47728 00
2.84	0.50717 21	0.38856 43	3.84	0.42443 43	0.53384 32	4.84	0.44786 69	0.45995 75
2.86	0.52677 66	0.39238 50	3.86	0.41894 43	0.51466 22	4.86	0.46244 40	0.44637 74
2.88	0.54538 21	0.39964 80	3.88	0.41822 16	0.49472 45	4.88	0.48042 90	0.43780 82
2.90	0.56237 64	0.41014 06	3.90	0.42233 27	0.47520 24	4.90	0.50016 10	0.43506 74
2.92	0.57718 78	0.42353 87	3.92	0.43105 68	0.45726 13	4.92	0.51979 51	0.43843 48
2.94	0.58930 60	0.43941 39	3.94	0.44389 17	0.44198 92	4.94	0.53747 34	0.44761 56
2.96	0.59830 19	0.45724 45	3.96	0.46007 70	0.43032 79	4.96	0.55150 25	0.46175 67
2.98	0.60384 56	0.47643 06	3.98	0.47863 51	0.42301 17	4.98	0.56051 94	0.47951 78
3.00	0.60572 08	0.49631 30	4.00	0.49842 60	0.42051 58	5.00	0.56363 12	0.49919 14

For $x>5$ $$\frac{C(x)}{S(x)}=0.5\pm\left(0.3183099-\frac{0.0968}{x^4}\right)\frac{\substack{\sin\\ \cos}\left(\frac{\pi}{2}x^2\right)}{x}-\left(0.10132-\frac{0.154}{x^4}\right)\frac{\substack{\cos\\ \sin}\left(\frac{\pi}{2}x^2\right)}{x^3}+\epsilon(x) \qquad |\epsilon(x)|<3\times10^{-7}$$

For $u>39$ $$\frac{C_2(u)}{S_2(u)}=0.5\pm\left(0.3989423-\frac{0.3}{u^2}\right)\frac{\substack{\sin\\ \cos}(u)}{\sqrt{u}}-\left(0.19947-\frac{0.748}{u^2}\right)\frac{\substack{\cos\\ \sin}(u)}{u\sqrt{u}}+\epsilon(u) \qquad |\epsilon(u)|<3\times10^{-7}$$

8. Legendre Functions

Notation

The conventions used are $z=x+iy$, x, y real, and in particular, x always means a real number in the interval $-1\leq x\leq +1$ with $\cos\theta=x$ where θ is likewise a real number; n and m are positive integers or zero; ν and μ are unrestricted except where otherwise indicated.

Other notations are:

$$P^n(x) \text{ for } \frac{n!P_n(x)}{(2n-1)!!}$$

$$P_{nm}(x) \text{ for } (-1)^m P_n^m(x)$$

$$T_n^m(x) \text{ for } (-1)^m P_n^m(x)$$

$$\overline{P_n^m}(x) \text{ for } (-1)^m\sqrt{\frac{(2n+1)(n-m)!}{2(n+m)!}}\,P_n^m(x)$$

$$\mathfrak{P}_\nu^\mu(z) \text{ for } P_\nu^\mu(z),\ \mathfrak{Q}_\nu^\mu(z) \text{ for } Q_\nu^\mu(z) \qquad (\mathscr{R}z>1)$$

$$\mathfrak{Q}_\nu^\mu(z) \text{ for } e^{\mu\pi i}Q_\nu^\mu(z)$$

$$Q_\nu^\mu(z) \text{ for } \frac{\sin(\nu+u)\pi}{\sin\nu\pi}\,Q_\nu^\mu(z)$$

Various other definitions of the functions occur as well as mixing of definitions.

8.1. Differential Equation

8.1.1

$$(1-z^2)\frac{d^2w}{dz^2}-2z\frac{dw}{dz}+\left[\nu(\nu+1)-\frac{\mu^2}{1-z^2}\right]w=0$$

Solutions

(Degree ν and order μ with singularities at $z=\pm 1$, ∞ as ordinary branch points—μ, ν arbitrary complex constants.)

$P_\nu^\mu(z)$, $Q_\nu^\mu(z)$—Associated Legendre Functions (Spherical Harmonics) of the First and Second Kinds [2]

$$|\arg(z\pm 1)|<\pi, \qquad |\arg z|<\pi$$

$$(z^2-1)^{\frac{1}{2}\mu}=(z-1)^{\frac{1}{2}\mu}(z+1)^{\frac{1}{2}\mu}$$

(For $P_\nu^\mu(z)$, $\mu=0$, Legendre polynomials, see chapter **22**.)

8.1.2

$$P_\nu^\mu(z)=\frac{1}{\Gamma(1-\mu)}\left[\frac{z+1}{z-1}\right]^{\frac{1}{2}\mu}F\left(-\nu,\nu+1;1-\mu;\frac{1-z}{2}\right) \qquad (|1-z|<2)$$

(For $F(a, b; c; z)$ see chapter **15.**)

8.1.3

$$Q_\nu^\mu(z)=e^{i\mu\pi}2^{-\nu-1}\pi^{\frac{1}{2}}\frac{\Gamma(\nu+\mu+1)}{\Gamma(\nu+\frac{3}{2})}z^{-\nu-\mu-1}(z^2-1)^{\frac{1}{2}\mu}F\left(1+\frac{\nu}{2}+\frac{\mu}{2},\frac{1}{2}+\frac{\nu}{2}+\frac{\mu}{2};\nu+\frac{3}{2};\frac{1}{z^2}\right) \qquad (|z|>1)$$

Alternate Forms

(Additional forms may be obtained by means of the transformation formulas of the hypergeometric function, see [8.1].)

8.1.4

$$P_\nu^\mu(z)=2^\mu\pi^{\frac{1}{2}}(z^2-1)^{-\frac{1}{2}\mu}\left\{\frac{F\left(-\frac{\nu}{2}-\frac{\mu}{2},\frac{1}{2}+\frac{\nu}{2}-\frac{\mu}{2};\frac{1}{2};z^2\right)}{\Gamma\left(\frac{1}{2}-\frac{\nu}{2}-\frac{\mu}{2}\right)\Gamma\left(1+\frac{\nu}{2}-\frac{\mu}{2}\right)}-2z\frac{F\left(\frac{1}{2}-\frac{\nu}{2}-\frac{\mu}{2},1+\frac{\nu}{2}-\frac{\mu}{2};\frac{3}{2};z^2\right)}{\Gamma\left(\frac{1}{2}+\frac{\nu}{2}-\frac{\mu}{2}\right)\Gamma\left(-\frac{\nu}{2}-\frac{\mu}{2}\right)}\right\} \qquad (|z^2|<1)$$

8.1.5

$$P_\nu^\mu(z)=\frac{2^{-\nu-1}\pi^{-\frac{1}{2}}\Gamma(-\frac{1}{2}-\nu)z^{-\nu+\mu-1}}{(z^2-1)^{\mu/2}\Gamma(-\nu-\mu)}F\left(\frac{1}{2}+\frac{\nu}{2}-\frac{\mu}{2},1+\frac{\nu}{2}-\frac{\mu}{2};\nu+\frac{3}{2};z^{-2}\right)$$
$$+\frac{2^\nu\Gamma(\frac{1}{2}+\nu)z^{\nu+\mu}}{(z^2-1)^{\mu/2}\Gamma(1+\nu-\mu)}F\left(-\frac{\nu}{2}-\frac{\mu}{2},\frac{1}{2}-\frac{\nu}{2}-\frac{\mu}{2};\frac{1}{2}-\nu;z^{-2}\right) \qquad (|z^{-2}|<1)$$

8.1.6

$$e^{-i\mu\pi}Q_\nu^\mu(z)=\frac{\Gamma(1+\nu+\mu)\Gamma(-\mu)(z-1)^{\frac{1}{2}\mu}(z+1)^{-\frac{1}{2}\mu}}{2\Gamma(1+\nu-\mu)}F\left(-\nu,1+\nu;1+\mu;\frac{1-z}{2}\right)$$
$$+\frac{1}{2}\Gamma(\mu)(z+1)^{\frac{1}{2}\mu}(z-1)^{-\frac{1}{2}\mu}F\left(-\nu,1+\nu;1-\mu;\frac{1-z}{2}\right) \qquad (|1-z|<2)$$

---

[2] The functions $Y_n^m(\theta,\varphi)=\begin{Bmatrix}\cos m\varphi\\ \sin m\varphi\end{Bmatrix}P_n^m(\cos\theta)$ called surface harmonics of the first kind, tesseral for $m<n$ and sectoral for $m=n$. With $0\leq\theta\leq\pi$, $0\leq\varphi\leq 2\pi$, they are everywhere one valued and continuous functions on the surface of the unit sphere $x^2+y^2+z^2=1$ where $x=\sin\theta\cos\varphi$, $y=\sin\theta\sin\varphi$ and $z=\cos\theta$.

8.1.7 $$e^{-i\mu\pi}Q_\nu^\mu(z)=\pi^{\frac{1}{2}}2^\mu(z^2-1)^{-\frac{1}{2}\mu}\left\{\frac{\Gamma\left(\frac{1}{2}+\frac{\nu}{2}+\frac{\mu}{2}\right)}{2\Gamma\left(1+\frac{\nu}{2}-\frac{\mu}{2}\right)}\,e^{\pm i\frac{1}{2}\pi(\mu-\nu-1)}F\left(-\frac{\nu}{2}-\frac{\mu}{2},\frac{1}{2}+\frac{\nu}{2}-\frac{\mu}{2};\frac{1}{2};z^2\right)\right.$$
$$\left.+\frac{z\Gamma\left(1+\frac{\nu}{2}+\frac{\mu}{2}\right)e^{\pm i\frac{1}{2}\pi(\mu-\nu)}}{\Gamma\left(\frac{1}{2}+\frac{\nu}{2}-\frac{\mu}{2}\right)}\,F\left(\frac{1}{2}-\frac{\nu}{2}-\frac{\mu}{2},1+\frac{\nu}{2}-\frac{\mu}{2};\frac{3}{2};z^2\right)\right\}\qquad(|z^2|<1)$$

(Upper and lower signs according as $\mathscr{I}z\gtrless0$.)

Wronskian

8.1.8
$$W\{P_\nu^\mu(z),Q_\nu^\mu(z)\}=\frac{e^{i\mu\pi}2^{2\mu}\Gamma\left(\frac{\nu+\mu+2}{2}\right)\Gamma\left(\frac{\nu+\mu+1}{2}\right)}{(1-z^2)\Gamma\left(\frac{\nu-\mu+2}{2}\right)\Gamma\left(\frac{\nu-\mu+1}{2}\right)}$$

8.1.9 $$W\{P_n(z),Q_n(z)\}=-(z^2-1)^{-1}$$

8.2. Relations Between Legendre Functions

Negative Degree

8.2.1 $$P^\mu_{-\nu-1}(z)=P^\mu_\nu(z)$$

8.2.2
$$Q^\mu_{-\nu-1}(z)=\{-\pi e^{i\mu\pi}\cos\nu\pi P_\nu^\mu(z)+Q_\nu^\mu(z)\sin[\pi(\nu+\mu)]\}/\sin[\pi(\nu-\mu)]$$

Negative Argument ($\mathscr{I}z\gtrless0$)

8.2.3
$$P_\nu^\mu(-z)=e^{\mp i\nu\pi}P_\nu^\mu(z)-\frac{2}{\pi}e^{-i\mu\pi}\sin[\pi(\nu+\mu)]Q_\nu^\mu(z)$$

8.2.4 $$Q_\nu^\mu(-z)=-e^{\pm i\nu\pi}Q_\nu^\mu(z)$$

Negative Order

8.2.5
$$P_\nu^{-\mu}(z)=\frac{\Gamma(\nu-\mu+1)}{\Gamma(\nu+\mu+1)}\left[P_\nu^\mu(z)-\frac{2}{\pi}e^{-i\mu\pi}\sin(\mu\pi)Q_\nu^\mu(z)\right]$$

8.2.6 $$Q_\nu^{-\mu}(z)=e^{-2i\mu\pi}\frac{\Gamma(\nu-\mu+1)}{\Gamma(\nu+\mu+1)}Q_\nu^\mu(z)$$

Degree $\mu+\frac{1}{2}$ and Order $\nu+\frac{1}{2}$

$\mathscr{R}z>0$

8.2.7 $$P^{-\nu-\frac{1}{2}}_{-\mu-\frac{1}{2}}\left(\frac{z}{(z^2-1)^{1/2}}\right)=\frac{(z^2-1)^{1/4}e^{-i\mu\pi}Q_\nu^\mu(z)}{(\frac{1}{2}\pi)^{1/2}\Gamma(\nu+\mu+1)}$$

8.2.8
$$Q^{-\nu-\frac{1}{2}}_{-\mu-\frac{1}{2}}\left(\frac{z}{(z^2-1)^{1/2}}\right)=-i(\tfrac{1}{2}\pi)^{1/2}\Gamma(-\nu-\mu)(z^2-1)^{1/4}e^{-i\nu\pi}P_\nu^\mu(z)$$

8.3. Values on the Cut

$(-1<x<1)$

8.3.1
$$P_\nu^\mu(x)=\tfrac{1}{2}[e^{\frac{1}{2}i\mu\pi}P_\nu^\mu(x+i0)+e^{-\frac{1}{2}i\mu\pi}P_\nu^\mu(x-i0)]$$

8.3.2
$$P_\nu^\mu(x)=e^{\pm\frac{1}{2}i\mu\pi}P_\nu^\mu(x\pm i0)$$

8.3.3
$$=i\pi^{-1}e^{-i\mu\pi}[e^{-\frac{1}{2}i\mu\pi}Q_\nu^\mu(x+i0)-e^{\frac{1}{2}i\mu\pi}Q_\nu^\mu(x-i0)]$$

8.3.4
$$Q_\nu^\mu(x)=\tfrac{1}{2}e^{-i\mu\pi}[e^{-\frac{1}{2}i\mu\pi}Q_\nu^\mu(x+i0)+e^{\frac{1}{2}i\mu\pi}Q_\nu^\mu(x-i0)]$$

(Formulas for $P_\nu^\mu(x)$ and $Q_\nu^\mu(x)$ are obtained with the replacement of $z-1$ by $(1-x)e^{\pm i\pi}$, (z^2-1) by $(1-x^2)e^{\pm i\pi}$, $z+1$ by $x+1$ for $z=x\pm i0$.)

8.4. Explicit Expressions

$(x=\cos\theta)$

8.4.1 $$P_0(z)=1\qquad P_0(x)=1$$

8.4.2
$$Q_0(z)=\frac{1}{2}\ln\left(\frac{z+1}{z-1}\right)\qquad Q_0(x)=\frac{1}{2}\ln\left(\frac{1+x}{1-x}\right)=xF(\tfrac{1}{2},1;\tfrac{3}{2};x^2)$$

8.4.3 $$P_1(z)=z\qquad P_1(x)=x=\cos\theta$$

8.4.4
$$Q_1(z)=\frac{z}{2}\ln\left(\frac{z+1}{z-1}\right)-1\qquad Q_1(x)=\frac{x}{2}\ln\left(\frac{1+x}{1-x}\right)-1$$

8.4.5
$$P_2(z)=\tfrac{1}{2}(3z^2-1)\qquad P_2(x)=\tfrac{1}{2}(3x^2-1)=\tfrac{1}{4}(3\cos2\theta+1)$$

8.4.6
$$Q_2(z)=\frac{1}{2}P_2(z)\ln\left(\frac{z+1}{z-1}\right)-\frac{3z}{2}\qquad Q_2(x)=\left(\frac{3x^2-1}{4}\right)\ln\left(\frac{1+x}{1-x}\right)-\frac{3x}{2}$$

8.5. Recurrence Relations

(Both P_ν^μ and Q_ν^μ satisfy the same recurrence relations.)

Varying Order

8.5.1
$$P_\nu^{\mu+1}(z)=(z^2-1)^{-\frac{1}{2}}\{(\nu-\mu)zP_\nu^\mu(z)-(\nu+\mu)P_{\nu-1}^\mu(z)\}$$

8.5.2

$$(z^2-1)\frac{dP_\nu^\mu(z)}{dz}=(\nu+\mu)(\nu-\mu+1)(z^2-1)^{\frac{1}{2}}P_\nu^{\mu-1}(z)-\mu zP_\nu^\mu(z)$$

Varying Degree

8.5.3

$$(\nu-\mu+1)P_{\nu+1}^\mu(z)=(2\nu+1)zP_\nu^\mu(z)-(\nu+\mu)P_{\nu-1}^\mu(z)$$

8.5.4 $$(z^2-1)\frac{dP_\nu^\mu(z)}{dz}=\nu zP_\nu^\mu(z)-(\nu+\mu)P_{\nu-1}^\mu(z)$$

Varying Order and Degree

8.5.5 $$P_{\nu+1}^\mu(z)=P_{\nu-1}^\mu(z)+(2\nu+1)(z^2-1)^{\frac{1}{2}}P_\nu^{\mu-1}(z)$$

8.6. Special Values

$x=0$

8.6.1

$$P_\nu^\mu(0)=2^\mu\pi^{-\frac{1}{2}}\cos[\tfrac{1}{2}\pi(\nu+\mu)]\Gamma(\tfrac{1}{2}\nu+\tfrac{1}{2}\mu+\tfrac{1}{2})/\Gamma(\tfrac{1}{2}\nu-\tfrac{1}{2}\mu+1)$$

8.6.2

$$Q_\nu^\mu(0)=-2^{\mu-1}\pi^{\frac{1}{2}}\sin[\tfrac{1}{2}\pi(\nu+\mu)]\Gamma(\tfrac{1}{2}\nu+\tfrac{1}{2}\mu+\tfrac{1}{2})/\Gamma(\tfrac{1}{2}\nu-\tfrac{1}{2}\mu+1)$$

8.6.3

$$\left[\frac{dP_\nu^\mu(x)}{dx}\right]_{x=0}=2^{\mu+1}\pi^{-\frac{1}{2}}\sin[\tfrac{1}{2}\pi(\nu+\mu)]\,\Gamma(\tfrac{1}{2}\nu+\tfrac{1}{2}\mu+1)/\Gamma(\tfrac{1}{2}\nu-\tfrac{1}{2}\mu+\tfrac{1}{2})$$

8.6.4

$$\left[\frac{dQ_\nu^\mu(x)}{dx}\right]_{x=0}=2^\mu\pi^{\frac{1}{2}}\cos[\tfrac{1}{2}\pi(\nu+\mu)]\,\Gamma(\tfrac{1}{2}\nu+\tfrac{1}{2}\mu+1)/\Gamma(\tfrac{1}{2}\nu-\tfrac{1}{2}\mu+\tfrac{1}{2})$$

8.6.5

$$W\{P_\nu^\mu(x),Q_\nu^\mu(x)\}_{x=0}=\frac{2^{2\mu}\Gamma(\tfrac{1}{2}\nu+\tfrac{1}{2}\mu+1)\Gamma(\tfrac{1}{2}\nu+\tfrac{1}{2}\mu+\tfrac{1}{2})}{\Gamma(\tfrac{1}{2}\nu-\tfrac{1}{2}\mu+1)\Gamma(\tfrac{1}{2}\nu-\tfrac{1}{2}\mu+\tfrac{1}{2})}$$

$\mu=m=1, 2, 3, \ldots$

8.6.6

$$P_\nu^m(z)=(z^2-1)^{\frac{1}{2}m}\frac{d^mP_\nu(z)}{dz^m},$$

$$P_\nu^m(x)=(-1)^m(1-x^2)^{\frac{1}{2}m}\frac{d^mP_\nu(x)}{dx^m}$$

8.6.7

$$Q_\nu^m(z)=(z^2-1)^{\frac{1}{2}m}\frac{d^mQ_\nu(z)}{dz^m},$$

$$Q_\nu^m(x)=(-1)^m(1-x^2)^{\frac{1}{2}m}\frac{d^mQ_\nu(x)}{dx^m}$$

$\mu=\pm\frac{1}{2}$

8.6.8

$$P_\nu^{\frac{1}{2}}(z)=(z^2-1)^{-1/4}(2\pi)^{-1/2}\{[z+(z^2-1)^{1/2}]^{\nu+\frac{1}{2}}+[z+(z^2-1)^{1/2}]^{-\nu-\frac{1}{2}}\}$$

8.6.9

$$P_\nu^{-\frac{1}{2}}(z)=\left(\frac{2}{\pi}\right)^{1/2}\frac{(z^2-1)^{-1/4}}{2\nu+1}\{[z+(z^2-1)^{1/2}]^{\nu+\frac{1}{2}}-[z+(z^2-1)^{1/2}]^{-\nu-\frac{1}{2}}\}$$

8.6.10

$$Q_\nu^{\frac{1}{2}}(z)=i(\tfrac{1}{2}\pi)^{1/2}(z^2-1)^{-1/4}[z+(z^2-1)^{1/2}]^{-\nu-\frac{1}{2}}$$

8.6.11

$$Q_\nu^{-\frac{1}{2}}(z)=-i(2\pi)^{1/2}\frac{(z^2-1)^{-1/4}}{2\nu+1}[z+(z^2-1)^{1/2}]^{-\nu-\frac{1}{2}}$$

8.6.12

$$P_\nu^{\frac{1}{2}}(\cos\theta)=(\tfrac{1}{2}\pi)^{-\frac{1}{2}}(\sin\theta)^{-\frac{1}{2}}\cos[(\nu+\tfrac{1}{2})\theta]$$

8.6.13

$$Q_\nu^{\frac{1}{2}}(\cos\theta)=-(\tfrac{1}{2}\pi)^{\frac{1}{2}}(\sin\theta)^{-\frac{1}{2}}\sin[(\nu+\tfrac{1}{2})\theta]$$

8.6.14

$$P_\nu^{-\frac{1}{2}}(\cos\theta)=(\tfrac{1}{2}\pi)^{-\frac{1}{2}}(\nu+\tfrac{1}{2})^{-1}(\sin\theta)^{-\frac{1}{2}}\sin[(\nu+\tfrac{1}{2})\theta]$$

8.6.15

$$Q_\nu^{-\frac{1}{2}}(\cos\theta)=(2\pi)^{\frac{1}{2}}(2\nu+1)^{-1}(\sin\theta)^{-\frac{1}{2}}\cos[(\nu+\tfrac{1}{2})\theta]$$

$\mu=-\nu$

8.6.16 $$P_\nu^{-\nu}(z)=\frac{2^{-\nu}(z^2-1)^{\frac{1}{2}\nu}}{\Gamma(\nu+1)}$$

8.6.17 $$P_\nu^{-\nu}(\cos\theta)=\frac{2^{-\nu}(\sin\theta)^\nu}{\Gamma(\nu+1)}$$

$\mu=0,\ \nu=n$

(Rodrigues' Formula)

8.6.18 $$P_n(z)=\frac{1}{2^nn!}\frac{d^n(z^2-1)^n}{dz^n}$$

8.6.19 $$Q_n(x)=\frac{1}{2}P_n(x)\ln\frac{1+x}{1-x}-W_{n-1}(x)$$

where

$$W_{n-1}(x)=\frac{2n-1}{1\cdot n}P_{n-1}(x)+\frac{2n-5}{3(n-1)}P_{n-3}(x)+\frac{2n-9}{5(n-2)}P_{n-5}(x)+\ldots$$

$$=\sum_{m=1}^n\frac{1}{m}P_{m-1}(x)P_{n-m}(x)$$

$W_{-1}(x)=0$

$$\nu=0,1$$

8.6.20 $\left[\frac{\partial P_\nu(\cos\theta)}{\partial\nu}\right]_{\nu=0}=2\ln(\cos\tfrac{1}{2}\theta)$

8.6.21 $\left[\frac{\partial P_\nu^{-1}(\cos\theta)}{\partial\nu}\right]_{\nu=0}=-\tan\tfrac{1}{2}\theta-2\cot\tfrac{1}{2}\theta\ln(\cos\tfrac{1}{2}\theta)$

8.6.22 $\left[\frac{\partial P_\nu^{-1}(\cos\theta)}{\partial\nu}\right]_{\nu=1}=-\tfrac{1}{2}\tan\tfrac{1}{2}\theta\sin^2\tfrac{1}{2}\theta+\sin\theta\ln(\cos\tfrac{1}{2}\theta)$

8.7. Trigonometric Expansions $(0<\theta<\pi)$

8.7.1 $P_\nu^\mu(\cos\theta)=\pi^{-1/2}2^{\mu+1}(\sin\theta)^\mu\frac{\Gamma(\nu+\mu+1)}{\Gamma(\nu+\frac{3}{2})}\sum_{k=0}^\infty\frac{(\mu+\frac{1}{2})_k(\nu+\mu+1)_k}{k!\,(\nu+\frac{3}{2})_k}\sin[(\nu+\mu+2k+1)\theta]$

8.7.2 $Q_\nu^\mu(\cos\theta)=\pi^{1/2}2^\mu(\sin\theta)^\mu\frac{\Gamma(\nu+\mu+1)}{\Gamma(\nu+\frac{3}{2})}\sum_{k=0}^\infty\frac{(\mu+\frac{1}{2})_k(\nu+\mu+1)_k}{k!(\nu+\frac{3}{2})_k}\cos[(\nu+\mu+2k+1)\theta]$

8.7.3 $P_n(\cos\theta)=\frac{2^{2n+2}(n!)^2}{\pi(2n+1)!}\left[\sin(n+1)\theta+\frac{n+1}{2n+3}\sin(n+3)\theta+\frac{1\cdot3}{2!}\frac{(n+1)(n+2)}{(2n+3)(2n+5)}\sin(n+5)\theta+\ldots\right]$

8.7.4 $Q_n(\cos\theta)=\frac{2^{2n+1}(n!)^2}{(2n+1)!}\left[\cos(n+1)\theta+\frac{n+1}{2n+3}\cos(n+3)\theta+\frac{1\cdot3}{2!}\frac{(n+1)(n+2)}{(2n+3)(2n+5)}\cos(n+5)\theta+\ldots\right]$

8.8. Integral Representations

(z not on the real axis between -1 and $-\infty$)

8.8.1 $P_\nu^\mu(z)=\frac{2^{-\nu}(z^2-1)^{-\frac{1}{2}\mu}}{\Gamma(-\nu-\mu)\Gamma(\nu+1)}\int_0^\infty(z+\cosh t)^{\mu-\nu-1}(\sinh t)^{2\nu+1}dt$ $\qquad(\mathscr{R}(-\mu)>\mathscr{R}\nu>-1)$

8.8.2 $Q_\nu^\mu(z)=\frac{e^{i\mu\pi}\sqrt{\pi}2^{-\mu}}{\Gamma(\mu+\frac{1}{2})}\frac{\Gamma(\nu+\mu+1)}{\Gamma(\nu-\mu+1)}(z^2-1)^{\frac{1}{2}\mu}\int_0^\infty[z+(z^2-1)^{\frac{1}{2}}\cosh t]^{-\nu-\mu-1}(\sinh t)^{2\mu}dt$ $\qquad(\mathscr{R}(\nu\pm\mu+1)>0)$

8.8.3 $Q_n(z)=\frac{1}{2}\int_{-1}^1(z-t)^{-1}P_n(t)\,dt=(-1)^{n+1}Q_n(-z)$

(For other integral representations see [8.2].)

8.9. Summation Formulas

8.9.1 $(\xi-z)\sum_{m=0}^n(2m+1)P_m(z)P_m(\xi)=(n+1)[P_{n+1}(\xi)P_n(z)-P_n(\xi)P_{n+1}(z)]$

8.9.2 $(\xi-z)\sum_{m=0}^n(2m+1)P_m(z)Q_m(\xi)=1-(n+1)[P_{n+1}(z)Q_n(\xi)-P_n(z)Q_{n+1}(\xi)]$

8.10. Asymptotic Expansions

For fixed z and ν and $\mathscr{R}\mu\to\infty$, **8.10.1–8.10.3** are asymptotic expansions if z is not on the real axis between $-\infty$ and -1 and $+\infty$ and $+1$. (Upper or lower signs according as $\mathscr{I}z\gtrless0$.)

8.10.1 $P_\nu^\mu(z)=\frac{\Gamma(\nu+\mu+1)\Gamma(\mu-\nu)}{\pi\Gamma(\mu+1)}\left(\frac{z+1}{z-1}\right)^{\frac{1}{2}\mu}\sin\mu\pi\left[F(-\nu,\nu+1;1+\mu;\tfrac{1}{2}+\tfrac{1}{2}z)\right.$

$$\left.-\frac{\sin\nu\pi}{\sin\mu\pi}e^{\mp i\mu\pi}\left(\frac{z-1}{z+1}\right)^\mu F(-\nu,\nu+1;1+\mu;\tfrac{1}{2}-\tfrac{1}{2}z)\right]$$

8.10.2 $Q_\nu^\mu(z)=\frac{1}{2}e^{i\mu\pi}\frac{\Gamma(\nu+\mu+1)}{\Gamma(\mu+1)}\left(\frac{z+1}{z-1}\right)^{\frac{1}{2}\mu}\Gamma(\mu-\nu)\left[F(-\nu,\nu+1;1+\mu;\tfrac{1}{2}+\tfrac{1}{2}z)\right.$

$$\left.-e^{\mp i\nu\pi}\left(\frac{z-1}{z+1}\right)^\mu F(-\nu,\nu+1;1+\mu;\tfrac{1}{2}-\tfrac{1}{2}z)\right]$$

8.10.3 $$Q_\nu^{-\mu}(z)=\frac{e^{-i\mu\pi}\csc[\pi(\nu-\mu)]}{2\pi\Gamma(1+\mu)}\left[e^{\mp i\nu\pi}\left(\frac{z+1}{z-1}\right)^{-\frac{1}{2}\mu}F(-\nu,\nu+1;1+\mu;\tfrac{1}{2}-\tfrac{1}{2}z)\right.$$
$$\left.-\left(\frac{z-1}{z+1}\right)^{-\frac{1}{2}\mu}F(-\nu,\nu+1;1+\mu;\tfrac{1}{2}+\tfrac{1}{2}z)\right]$$

With μ replaced by $-\mu$, **8.1.2** is an asymptotic expansion for $P_\nu^{-\mu}(z)$ for fixed z and ν and $\mathscr{R}\,\mu\to\infty$ if z is not on the real axis between $-\infty$ and -1.

For fixed z and μ and $\mathscr{R}\nu\to\infty$, **8.10.4** and **8.10.6** are asymptotic expansions if z is not on the real axis between $-\infty$ and -1 and $+\infty$ and $+1$; **8.10.5** if z is not on the real axis between $-\infty$ and $+1$.

8.10.4 $$P_\nu^\mu(z)=(2\pi)^{-\frac{1}{2}}(z^2-1)^{-1/4}\frac{\Gamma(\nu+\mu+1)}{\Gamma(\nu+\frac{3}{2})}\left\{[z+(z^2-1)^{\frac{1}{2}}]^{\nu+\frac{1}{2}}F(\tfrac{1}{2}+\mu,\tfrac{1}{2}-\mu;\tfrac{3}{2}+\nu;\frac{z+(z^2-1)^{\frac{1}{2}}}{2(z^2-1)^{\frac{1}{2}}})\right.$$
$$\left.+ie^{-i\mu\pi}[z-(z^2-1)^{\frac{1}{2}}]^{\nu+\frac{1}{2}}F(\tfrac{1}{2}+\mu,\tfrac{1}{2}-\mu;\tfrac{3}{2}+\nu;\frac{-z+(z^2-1)^{\frac{1}{2}}}{2(z^2-1)^{\frac{1}{2}}})\right\}$$

8.10.5 $$Q_\nu^\mu(z)=e^{i\mu\pi}(\tfrac{1}{2}\pi)^{\frac{1}{2}}(z^2-1)^{-1/4}\frac{\Gamma(\nu+\mu+1)}{\Gamma(\nu+\frac{3}{2})}[z-(z^2-1)^{\frac{1}{2}}]^{\nu+\frac{1}{2}}F(\tfrac{1}{2}+\mu,\tfrac{1}{2}-\mu;\tfrac{3}{2}+\nu;\frac{-z+(z^2-1)^{\frac{1}{2}}}{2(z^2-1)^{\frac{1}{2}}})$$

8.10.6 $$Q_{-\nu}^\mu(z)=\frac{e^{i\mu\pi}(\frac{1}{2}\pi)^{\frac{1}{2}}(z^2-1)^{-1/4}}{\sin[\pi(\mu-\nu)]}\frac{\Gamma(\mu+\nu)}{\Gamma(\frac{1}{2}-\mu)}\left\{\cos\nu\pi[z+(z^2-1)^{\frac{1}{2}}]^{\nu-\frac{1}{2}}F(\tfrac{1}{2}+\mu,\tfrac{1}{2}-\mu;\tfrac{1}{2}+\nu;\frac{z+(z^2-1)^{\frac{1}{2}}}{2(z^2-1)^{\frac{1}{2}}})\right.$$
$$\left.+ie^{i\nu\pi}\cos\mu\pi[z-(z^2-1)^{\frac{1}{2}}]^{\nu-\frac{1}{2}}F(\tfrac{1}{2}+\mu,\tfrac{1}{2}-\mu;\tfrac{1}{2}+\nu;\frac{-z+(z^2-1)^{\frac{1}{2}}}{2(z^2-1)^{\frac{1}{2}}})\right\}$$

The related asymptotic expansion for $P_{-\nu}^\mu(z)$ may be derived from **8.10.4** together with **8.2.1.**

8.10.7 $$P_\nu^\mu(\cos\theta)=\frac{\Gamma(\nu+\mu+1)}{\Gamma(\nu+\frac{3}{2})}(\tfrac{1}{2}\pi\sin\theta)^{-\frac{1}{2}}\cos[(\nu+\tfrac{1}{2})\theta-\frac{\pi}{4}+\frac{\mu\pi}{2}]+O(\nu^{-1})$$

8.10.8 $$Q_\nu^\mu(\cos\theta)=\frac{\Gamma(\nu+\mu+1)}{\Gamma(\nu+\frac{3}{2})}\left(\frac{\pi}{2\sin\theta}\right)^{\frac{1}{2}}\cos[(\nu+\tfrac{1}{2})\theta+\frac{\pi}{4}+\frac{\mu\pi}{2}]+O(\nu^{-1})\qquad(\epsilon<\theta<\pi-\epsilon,\ \epsilon>0)$$

For other asymptotic expansions, see [8.7] and [8.9].

8.11. Toroidal Functions (or Ring Functions)

(Only special properties are given; other properties and representations follow from the earlier sections.)

8.11.1 $$P_{\nu-\frac{1}{2}}^\mu(\cosh\eta)=[\Gamma(1-\mu)]^{-1}2^{2\mu}(1-e^{-2\eta})^{-\mu}e^{-(\nu+\frac{1}{2})\eta}F(\tfrac{1}{2}-\mu,\tfrac{1}{2}+\nu-\mu;1-2\mu;1-e^{-2\eta})$$

8.11.2 $$P_{n-\frac{1}{2}}^m(\cosh\eta)=\frac{\Gamma(n+m+\frac{1}{2})(\sinh\eta)^m}{\Gamma(n-m+\frac{1}{2})2^m\sqrt{\pi}\Gamma(m+\frac{1}{2})}\int_0^\pi\frac{(\sin\varphi)^{2m}d\varphi}{(\cosh\eta+\cos\varphi\sinh\eta)^{n+m+\frac{1}{2}}}$$

8.11.3 $$Q_{\nu-\frac{1}{2}}^\mu(\cosh\eta)=[\Gamma(1+\nu)]^{-1}\sqrt{\pi}e^{i\mu\pi}\Gamma(\tfrac{1}{2}+\nu+\mu)(1-e^{-2\eta})^\mu e^{-(\nu+\frac{1}{2})\eta}F(\tfrac{1}{2}+\mu,\tfrac{1}{2}+\nu+\mu;1+\nu;e^{-2\eta})$$

8.11.4 $$Q_{n-\frac{1}{2}}^m(\cosh\eta)=\frac{(-1)^m\Gamma(n+\frac{1}{2})}{\Gamma(n-m+\frac{1}{2})}\int_0^\infty\frac{\cosh mt\,dt}{(\cosh\eta+\cosh t\sinh\eta)^{n+\frac{1}{2}}}\qquad(n>m)$$

8.12. Conical Functions

$$(P^{\mu}_{-\frac12+i\lambda}(\cos\theta),\ Q^{\mu}_{-\frac12+i\lambda}(\cos\theta))$$

(Only special properties are given as other properties and representations follow from earlier sections with $\nu=-\frac12+i\lambda$ (λ, a real parameter) and $=\cos\theta$.)

.12.1

$$P_{-\frac12+i\lambda}(\cos\theta)=1+\frac{4\lambda^2+1^2}{2^2}\sin^2\frac{\theta}{2}+\frac{(4\lambda^2+1^2)(4\lambda^2+3^2)}{2^2 4^2}\sin^4\frac{\theta}{2}+\dots \qquad (0\leq\theta<\pi)$$

.12.2 $$P_{-\frac12+i\lambda}(\cos\theta)=P_{-\frac12-i\lambda}(\cos\theta)$$

.12.3 $$P_{-\frac12+i\lambda}(\cos\theta)=\frac{2}{\pi}\int_0^\theta\frac{\cosh\lambda t\,dt}{\sqrt{2(\cos t-\cos\theta)}}$$

.12.4

$$P_{-\frac12\mp i\lambda}(\cos\theta)=\pm i\sinh\lambda\pi\int_0^\infty\frac{\cos\lambda t\,dt}{\sqrt{2(\cosh t+\cos\theta)}}+\int_0^\infty\frac{\cosh\lambda t\,dt}{\sqrt{2(\cosh t-\cos\theta)}}$$

.12.5

$$P_{-\frac12+i\lambda}(-\cos\theta)=\frac{\cosh\lambda\pi}{\pi}[Q_{-\frac12+i\lambda}(\cos\theta)+Q_{-\frac12-i\lambda}(\cos\theta)]$$

8.13. Relation to Elliptic Integrals (see chapter 17) ($\mathscr{R}\eta>0$)

.13.1 $$P_{-\frac12}(z)=\frac{2}{\pi}\sqrt{\frac{2}{z+1}}\,K\left(\sqrt{\frac{z-1}{z+1}}\right)$$

8.13.2 $$P_{-\frac12}(\cosh\eta)=\left[\frac{\pi}{2}\cosh\frac{\eta}{2}\right]^{-1}K\left(\tanh\frac{\eta}{2}\right)$$

8.13.3 $$Q_{-\frac12}(z)=\sqrt{\frac{2}{z+1}}\,K\left(\sqrt{\frac{2}{z+1}}\right)$$

8.13.4 $$Q_{-\frac12}(\cosh\eta)=2e^{-\eta/2}K(e^{-\eta})$$

8.13.5

$$P_{\frac12}(z)=\frac{2}{\pi}(z+\sqrt{z^2-1})^{\frac12}E\left(\sqrt{\frac{2(z^2-1)^{1/2}}{z+(z^2-1)^{1/2}}}\right)$$

8.13.6 $$P_{\frac12}(\cosh\eta)=\frac{2}{\pi}e^{\eta/2}E(\sqrt{1-e^{-2\eta}})$$

8.13.7

$$Q_{\frac12}(z)=z\sqrt{\frac{2}{z+1}}\,K\left(\sqrt{\frac{2}{z+1}}\right)-[2(z+1)]^{\frac12}E\left(\sqrt{\frac{2}{z+1}}\right)$$

$(-1<x<1)$

8.13.8 $$P_{-\frac12}(x)=\frac{2}{\pi}K\left(\sqrt{\frac{1-x}{2}}\right)$$

8.13.9 $$P_{-\frac12}(\cos\theta)=\frac{2}{\pi}K\left(\sin\frac{\theta}{2}\right)$$

8.13.10 $$Q_{-\frac12}(x)=K\left(\sqrt{\frac{1+x}{2}}\right)$$

8.13.11 $$P_{\frac12}(x)=\frac{2}{\pi}\left[2E\left(\sqrt{\frac{1-x}{2}}\right)-K\left(\sqrt{\frac{1-x}{2}}\right)\right]$$

8.13.12 $$Q_{\frac12}(x)=K\left(\sqrt{\frac{1+x}{2}}\right)-2E\left(\sqrt{\frac{1+x}{2}}\right)$$

8.14. Integrals

.14.1 $$\int_1^\infty P_\nu(x)Q_\rho(x)dx=[(\rho-\nu)(\rho+\nu+1)]^{-1} \qquad (\mathscr{R}\rho>\mathscr{R}\nu>0)$$

.14.2 $$\int_1^\infty Q_\nu(x)Q_\rho(x)dx=[(\rho-\nu)(\rho+\nu+1)]^{-1}[\psi(\rho+1)-\psi(\nu+1)]$$ $(\mathscr{R}(\rho+\nu)>-1,\ \rho+\nu+1\neq0;\ \nu,\ \rho\neq-1,\ -2,\ -3,\ \dots)$

.14.3 $$\int_1^\infty[Q_\nu(x)]^2dx=(2\nu+1)^{-1}\psi'(\nu+1) \qquad (\mathscr{R}\nu>-\tfrac12)$$

.14.4 $$\int_{-1}^1 P_\nu(x)P_\rho(x)dx=\frac{2}{\pi^2}[(\rho-\nu)(\rho+\nu+1)]^{-1}\{2\sin\pi\nu\sin\pi\rho[\psi(\nu+1)-\psi(\rho+1)]+\pi\sin(\pi\rho-\pi\nu)\}$$ $(\rho+\nu+1\neq0)$

.14.5 $$\int_{-1}^1[P_\nu(x)]^2dx=\frac{\pi^2-2(\sin\pi\nu)^2\psi'(\nu+1)}{\pi^2(\nu+\frac12)}$$

.14.6 $$\int_{-1}^1 Q_\nu(x)Q_\rho(x)dx=[(\rho-\nu)(\rho+\nu+1)]^{-1}\{[\psi(\nu+1)-\psi(\rho+1)][1+\cos\rho\pi\cos\nu\pi]-\tfrac12\pi\sin(\nu\pi-\rho\pi)\}$$ $(\rho+\nu+1\neq0;\ \nu,\ \rho\neq-1,\ -2,\ -3,\ \dots)$

.14.7 $$\int_{-1}^1[Q_\nu(x)]^2dx=(2\nu+1)^{-1}\{\tfrac12\pi^2-\psi'(\nu+1)[1+(\cos\nu\pi)^2]\} \qquad (\nu\neq-1,\ -2,\ -3,\ \dots)$$

8.14.8 $$\int_{-1}^{1} P_\nu(x) Q_\rho(x) dx = [(\nu-\rho)(\rho+\nu+1)]^{-1} \left\{ 1 - \cos(\rho\pi - \nu\pi) - \frac{2}{\pi} \sin \pi\nu \cos \pi\nu [\psi(\nu+1) - \psi(\rho+1)] \right\}$$
$(\mathscr{R}\nu > 0,\ \mathscr{R}\rho > 0,\ \rho \neq \nu)$

8.14.9 $$\int_{-1}^{1} P_\nu(x) Q_\nu(x) dx = -\frac{1}{\pi} (2\nu+1)^{-1} \sin 2\nu\pi \psi'(\nu+1)$$ $(\mathscr{R}\nu > 0)$

(m, n, l positive integers)

8.14.10
$$\int_{-1}^{1} Q_n^m(x) P_l^m(x) dx = (-1)^m \frac{1-(-1)^{l+n}(n+m)!}{(l-n)(l+n+1)(n-m)!}$$

8.14.11 $$\int_{-1}^{1} P_n^m(x) P_l^m(x) dx = 0 \qquad (l \neq n)$$

8.14.12 $$\int_{-1}^{1} P_n^m(x) P_n^l(x) (1-x^2)^{-1} dx = 0 \qquad (l \neq m)$$

8.14.13 $$\int_{-1}^{1} [P_n^m(x)]^2 dx = (n+\tfrac{1}{2})^{-1}(n+m)!/(n-m)!$$

8.14.14
$$\int_{-1}^{1} (1-x^2)^{-1} [P_n^m(x)]^2 dx = (n+m)!/m(n-m)!$$

8.14.15
$$\int_{0}^{1} P_\nu(x) x^\rho dx = \frac{\pi^{\frac{1}{2}} 2^{-\rho-1} \Gamma(1+\rho)}{\Gamma(1+\frac{1}{2}\rho - \frac{1}{2}\nu)\Gamma(\frac{1}{2}\rho + \frac{1}{2}\nu + \frac{3}{2})}$$
$(\mathscr{R}\rho > -1)$

8.14.16
$$\int_{0}^{\pi} (\sin t)^{\alpha-1} P_\nu^{-\mu}(\cos t) dt = \frac{2^{-\mu}\pi \Gamma(\frac{1}{2}\alpha + \frac{1}{2}\mu)\Gamma(\frac{1}{2}\alpha - \frac{1}{2}\mu)}{\Gamma(\frac{1}{2}+\frac{1}{2}\alpha+\frac{1}{2}\nu)\Gamma(\frac{1}{2}\alpha - \frac{1}{2}\nu)\Gamma(\frac{1}{2}\mu + \frac{1}{2}\nu + 1)\Gamma(\frac{1}{2}\mu - \frac{1}{2}\nu + \frac{1}{2})}$$ $(\mathscr{R}(\alpha \pm \mu) > 0)$

8.14.17
$$P_\nu^{-m}(z) = (z^2-1)^{-\frac{1}{2}m} \int_1^z \cdots \int_1^z P_\nu(z)(dz)^m$$

8.14.18
$$Q_\nu^{-m}(z) = (-1)^m (z^2-1)^{-\frac{1}{2}m} \int_z^\infty \cdots \int_z^\infty Q_\nu(z)(dz)^m$$

For other integrals, see [8.2], [8.4] and chapter **22.**

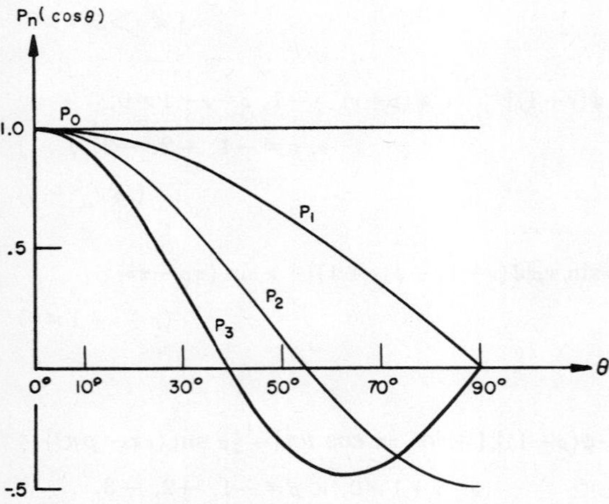

FIGURE 8.1. $P_n(\cos\theta)$. $n=0(1)3$.

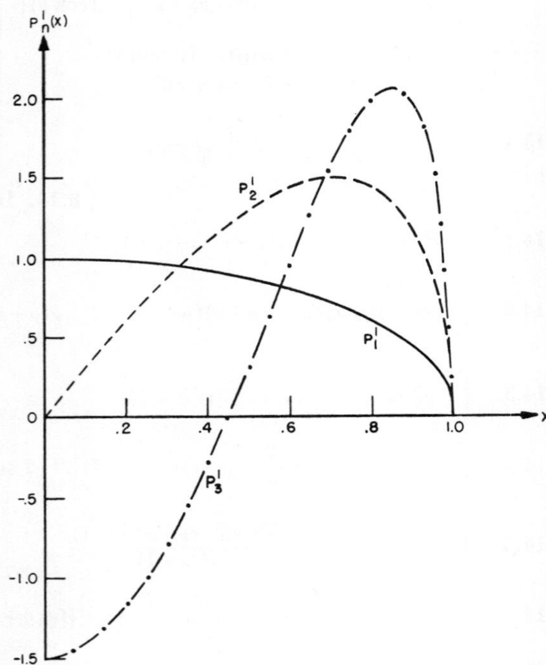

FIGURE 8.2. $P_n^1(x)$. $n=1(1)3$, $x \leq 1$.

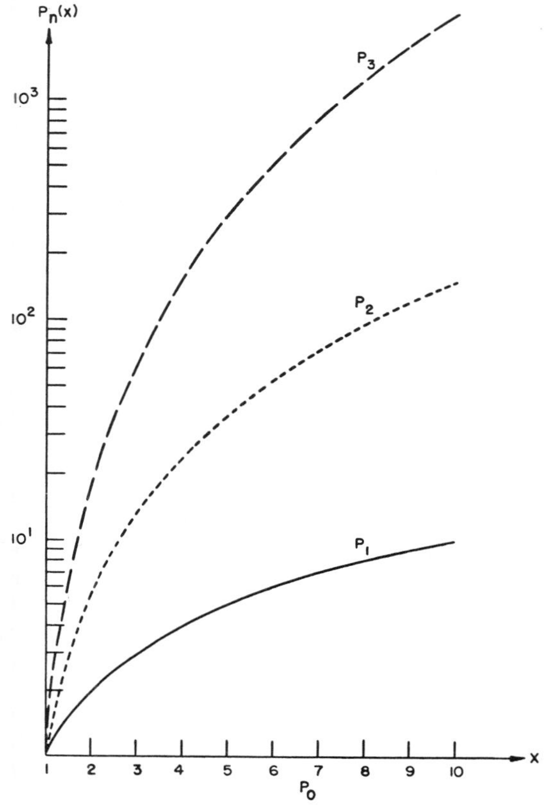

FIGURE 8.3. $P_n(x)$. $n=0(1)3, x \geq 1$.

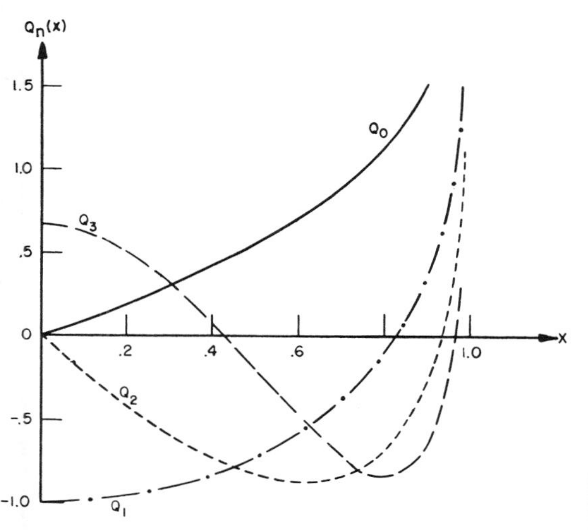

FIGURE 8.4. $Q_n(x)$. $n=0(1)3, x<1$.

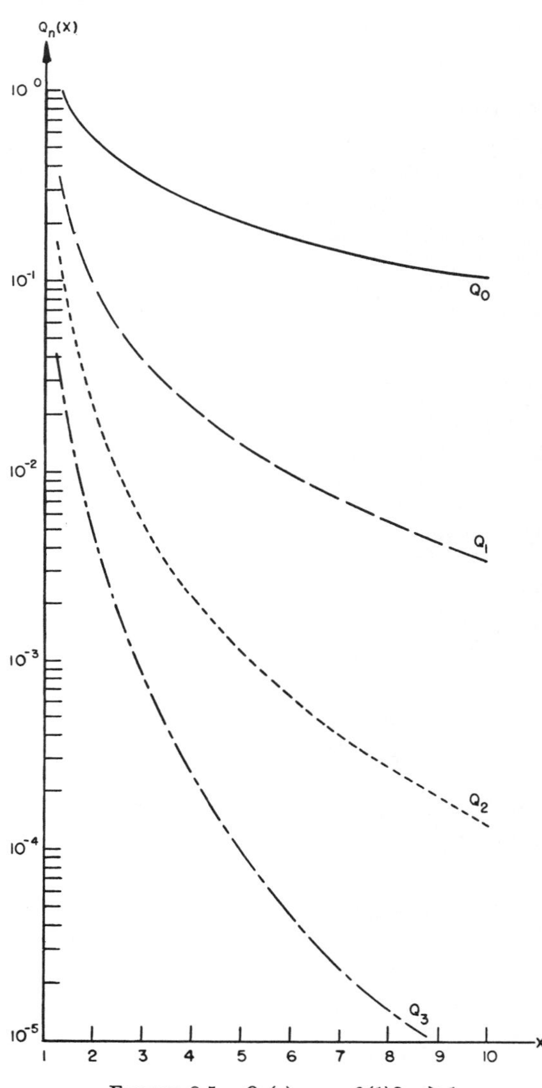

FIGURE 8.5. $Q_n(x)$. $n=0(1)3, x>1$.

Notation

The tables in this chapter are for Bessel functions of integer order; the text treats general orders. The conventions used are:

$z=x+iy;\ x,\ y$ real.

n is a positive integer or zero.

ν, μ are unrestricted except where otherwise indicated; ν is supposed real in the sections devoted to Kelvin functions **9.9, 9.10,** and **9.11.**

The notation used for the Bessel functions is that of Watson [9.15] and the British Association and Royal Society Mathematical Tables. The function $Y_\nu(z)$ is often denoted $N_\nu(z)$ by physicists and European workers.

Other notations are those of:

Aldis, Airey:

$$G_n(z) \text{ for } -\tfrac{1}{2}\pi Y_n(z), K_n(z) \text{ for } (-)^n K_n(z).$$

Clifford:

$$C_n(x) \text{ for } x^{-\frac{1}{2}n} J_n(2\sqrt{x}).$$

Gray, Mathews and MacRobert [9.9]:

$$Y_n(z) \text{ for } \tfrac{1}{2}\pi Y_n(z)+(\ln 2-\gamma)J_n(z),$$

$$\overline{Y}_\nu(z) \text{ for } \pi e^{\nu\pi i}\sec(\nu\pi)Y_\nu(z),$$

$$G_\nu(z) \text{ for } \tfrac{1}{2}\pi i H_\nu^{(1)}(z).$$

Jahnke, Emde and Lösch [9.32]:

$$\Lambda_\nu(z) \text{ for } \Gamma(\nu+1)(\tfrac{1}{2}z)^{-\nu}J_\nu(z).$$

Jeffreys:

$Hs_\nu(z)$ for $H_\nu^{(1)}(z)$, $Hi_\nu(z)$ for $H_\nu^{(2)}(z)$,

$Kh_\nu(z)$ for $(2/\pi)K_\nu(z)$.

Heine:

$$K_n(z) \text{ for} -\tfrac{1}{2}\pi Y_n(z).$$

Neumann:

$$Y^n(z) \text{ for } \tfrac{1}{2}\pi Y_n(z)+(\ln 2-\gamma)J_n(z).$$

Whittaker and Watson [9.18]:

$$K_\nu(z) \text{ for } \cos(\nu\pi)K_\nu(z).$$

Bessel Functions *J* and *Y*

9.1. Definitions and Elementary Properties

Differential Equation

9.1.1
$$z^2\frac{d^2w}{dz^2}+z\frac{dw}{dz}+(z^2-\nu^2)w=0$$

Solutions are the Bessel functions of the first kind $J_{\pm\nu}(z)$, of the second kind $Y_\nu(z)$ (also called Weber's function) and of the third kind $H_\nu^{(1)}(z)$, $H_\nu^{(2)}(z)$ (also called the Hankel functions). Each is a regular (holomorphic) function of z throughout the z-plane cut along the negative real axis, and for fixed $z(\neq 0)$ each is an entire (integral) function of ν. When $\nu=\pm n$, $J_\nu(z)$ has no branch point and is an entire (integral) function of z.

Important features of the various solutions are as follows: $J_\nu(z)(\mathscr{R}\nu\geq 0)$ is bounded as $z\rightarrow 0$ in any bounded range of arg z. $J_\nu(z)$ and $J_{-\nu}(z)$ are linearly independent except when ν is an integer. $J_\nu(z)$ and $Y_\nu(z)$ are linearly independent for all values of ν.

$H_\nu^{(1)}(z)$ tends to zero as $|z|\rightarrow\infty$ in the sector $0<\arg z<\pi$; $H_\nu^{(2)}(z)$ tends to zero as $|z|\rightarrow\infty$ in the sector $-\pi<\arg z<0$. For all values of ν, $H_\nu^{(1)}(z)$ and $H_\nu^{(2)}(z)$ are linearly independent.

Relations Between Solutions

9.1.2
$$Y_\nu(z)=\frac{J_\nu(z)\cos(\nu\pi)-J_{-\nu}(z)}{\sin(\nu\pi)}$$

The right of this equation is replaced by its limiting value if ν is an integer or zero.

9.1.3
$$H_\nu^{(1)}(z)=J_\nu(z)+iY_\nu(z)$$
$$=i\csc(\nu\pi)\{e^{-\nu\pi i}J_\nu(z)-J_{-\nu}(z)\}$$

9.1.4
$$H_\nu^{(2)}(z)=J_\nu(z)-iY_\nu(z)$$
$$=i\csc(\nu\pi)\{J_{-\nu}(z)-e^{\nu\pi i}J_\nu(z)\}$$

9.1.5 $\quad J_{-n}(z)=(-)^nJ_n(z) \qquad Y_{-n}(z)=(-)^nY_n(z)$

9.1.6 $\quad H_{-\nu}^{(1)}(z)=e^{\nu\pi i}H_\nu^{(1)}(z) \qquad H_{-\nu}^{(2)}(z)=e^{-\nu\pi i}H_\nu^{(2)}(z)$

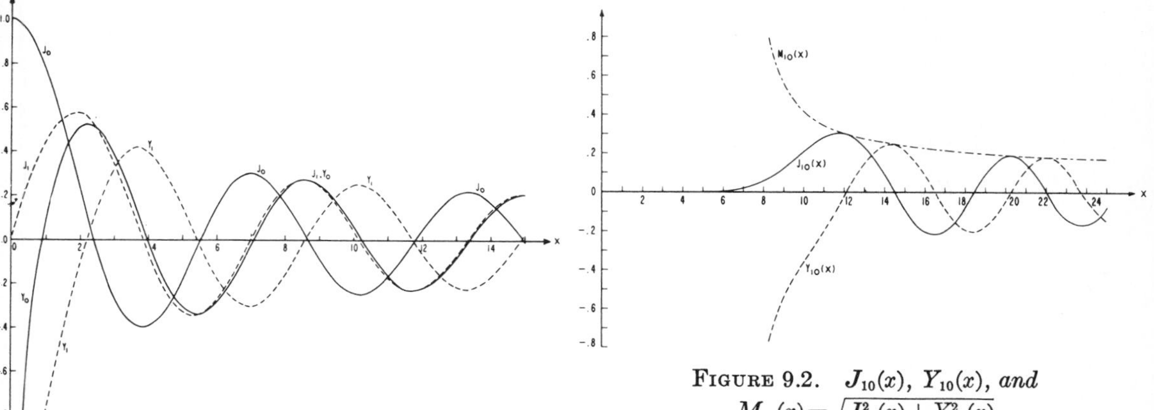

FIGURE 9.1. $J_0(x)$, $Y_0(x)$, $J_1(x)$, $Y_1(x)$.

FIGURE 9.2. $J_{10}(x)$, $Y_{10}(x)$, *and* $M_{10}(x)=\sqrt{J_{10}^2(x)+Y_{10}^2(x)}$.

FIGURE 9.3. $J_\nu(10)$ *and* $Y_\nu(10)$.

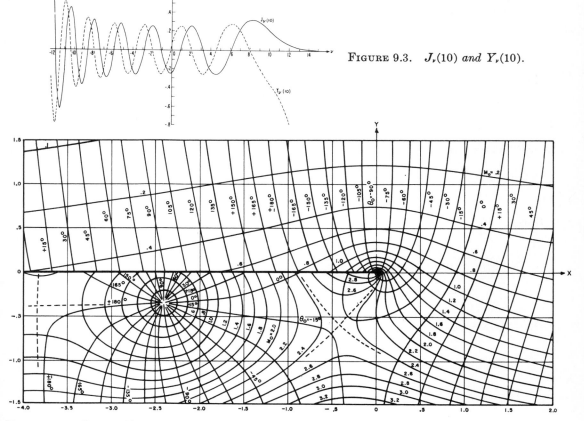

FIGURE 9.4. *Contour lines of the modulus and phase of the Hankel Function* $H_0^{(1)}(x+iy)=M_0e^{i\theta_0}$.

Limiting Forms for Small Arguments

When ν is fixed and $z \to 0$

9.1.7
$$J_\nu(z) \sim (\tfrac{1}{2}z)^\nu / \Gamma(\nu+1) \qquad (\nu \neq -1, -2, -3, \ldots)$$

9.1.8 $$Y_0(z) \sim -iH_0^{(1)}(z) \sim iH_0^{(2)}(z) \sim (2/\pi) \ln z$$

9.1.9
$$Y_\nu(z) \sim -iH_\nu^{(1)}(z) \sim iH_\nu^{(2)}(z) \sim -(1/\pi)\Gamma(\nu)(\tfrac{1}{2}z)^{-\nu} \qquad (\mathscr{R}\nu > 0)$$

Ascending Series

9.1.10 $$J_\nu(z) = (\tfrac{1}{2}z)^\nu \sum_{k=0}^{\infty} \frac{(-\frac{1}{4}z^2)^k}{k!\,\Gamma(\nu+k+1)}$$

9.1.11
$$Y_n(z) = -\frac{(\frac{1}{2}z)^{-n}}{\pi} \sum_{k=0}^{n-1} \frac{(n-k-1)!}{k!} (\tfrac{1}{4}z^2)^k + \frac{2}{\pi} \ln(\tfrac{1}{2}z) J_n(z) - \frac{(\frac{1}{2}z)^n}{\pi} \sum_{k=0}^{\infty} \{\psi(k+1) + \psi(n+k+1)\} \frac{(-\frac{1}{4}z^2)^k}{k!\,(n+k)!}$$

where $\psi(n)$ is given by **6.3.2.**

9.1.12 $$J_0(z) = 1 - \frac{\frac{1}{4}z^2}{(1!)^2} + \frac{(\frac{1}{4}z^2)^2}{(2!)^2} - \frac{(\frac{1}{4}z^2)^3}{(3!)^2} + \ldots$$

9.1.13
$$Y_0(z) = \frac{2}{\pi} \{\ln(\tfrac{1}{2}z) + \gamma\} J_0(z) + \frac{2}{\pi} \left\{ \frac{\frac{1}{4}z^2}{(1!)^2} - (1+\tfrac{1}{2}) \frac{(\frac{1}{4}z^2)^2}{(2!)^2} + (1+\tfrac{1}{2}+\tfrac{1}{3}) \frac{(\frac{1}{4}z^2)^3}{(3!)^2} - \ldots \right\}$$

9.1.14
$$J_\nu(z) J_\mu(z) = (\tfrac{1}{2}z)^{\nu+\mu} \sum_{k=0}^{\infty} \frac{(-)^k \Gamma(\nu+\mu+2k+1)(\frac{1}{4}z^2)^k}{\Gamma(\nu+k+1)\Gamma(\mu+k+1)\Gamma(\nu+\mu+k+1)\,k!}$$

Wronskians

9.1.15
$$W\{J_\nu(z), J_{-\nu}(z)\} = J_{\nu+1}(z)J_{-\nu}(z) + J_\nu(z)J_{-(\nu+1)}(z) = -2\sin(\nu\pi)/(\pi z)$$

9.1.16
$$W\{J_\nu(z), Y_\nu(z)\} = J_{\nu+1}(z)Y_\nu(z) - J_\nu(z)Y_{\nu+1}(z) = 2/(\pi z)$$

9.1.17
$$W\{H_\nu^{(1)}(z), H_\nu^{(2)}(z)\} = H_{\nu+1}^{(1)}(z)H_\nu^{(2)}(z) - H_\nu^{(1)}(z)H_{\nu+1}^{(2)}(z) = -4i/(\pi z)$$

Integral Representations

9.1.18
$$J_0(z) = \frac{1}{\pi}\int_0^\pi \cos(z\sin\theta)\,d\theta = \frac{1}{\pi}\int_0^\pi \cos(z\cos\theta)\,d\theta$$

9.1.19
$$Y_0(z) = \frac{4}{\pi^2}\int_0^{\frac{1}{2}\pi} \cos(z\cos\theta)\{\gamma + \ln(2z\sin^2\theta)\}\,d\theta$$

9.1.20
$$J_\nu(z) = \frac{(\frac{1}{2}z)^\nu}{\pi^{\frac{1}{2}}\Gamma(\nu+\frac{1}{2})}\int_0^\pi \cos(z\cos\theta)\sin^{2\nu}\theta\,d\theta = \frac{2(\frac{1}{2}z)^\nu}{\pi^{\frac{1}{2}}\Gamma(\nu+\frac{1}{2})}\int_0^1 (1-t^2)^{\nu-\frac{1}{2}}\cos(zt)\,dt \qquad (\mathscr{R}\nu > -\tfrac{1}{2})$$

9.1.21
$$J_n(z) = \frac{1}{\pi}\int_0^\pi \cos(z\sin\theta - n\theta)\,d\theta = \frac{i^{-n}}{\pi}\int_0^\pi e^{iz\cos\theta}\cos(n\theta)\,d\theta$$

9.1.22
$$J_\nu(z) = \frac{1}{\pi}\int_0^\pi \cos(z\sin\theta - \nu\theta)\,d\theta - \frac{\sin(\nu\pi)}{\pi}\int_0^\infty e^{-z\sinh t - \nu t}\,dt \qquad (|\arg z| < \tfrac{1}{2}\pi)$$

$$Y_\nu(z) = \frac{1}{\pi}\int_0^\pi \sin(z\sin\theta - \nu\theta)\,d\theta - \frac{1}{\pi}\int_0^\infty \{e^{\nu t} + e^{-\nu t}\cos(\nu\pi)\} e^{-z\sinh t}\,dt \qquad (|\arg z| < \tfrac{1}{2}\pi)$$

9.1.23
$$J_0(x) = \frac{2}{\pi}\int_0^\infty \sin(x\cosh t)\,dt \qquad (x > 0)$$

$$Y_0(x) = -\frac{2}{\pi}\int_0^\infty \cos(x\cosh t)\,dt \qquad (x > 0)$$

9.1.24
$$J_\nu(x) = \frac{2(\frac{1}{2}x)^{-\nu}}{\pi^{\frac{1}{2}}\Gamma(\frac{1}{2}-\nu)}\int_1^\infty \frac{\sin(xt)\,dt}{(t^2-1)^{\nu+\frac{1}{2}}} \qquad (|\mathscr{R}\nu| < \tfrac{1}{2}, x > 0)$$

$$Y_\nu(x) = -\frac{2(\frac{1}{2}x)^{-\nu}}{\pi^{\frac{1}{2}}\Gamma(\frac{1}{2}-\nu)}\int_1^\infty \frac{\cos(xt)\,dt}{(t^2-1)^{\nu+\frac{1}{2}}} \qquad (|\mathscr{R}\nu| < \tfrac{1}{2}, x > 0)$$

9.1.25
$$H_\nu^{(1)}(z) = \frac{1}{\pi i}\int_{-\infty}^{\infty+\pi i} e^{z\sinh t - \nu t}\,dt \qquad (|\arg z| < \tfrac{1}{2}\pi)$$

$$H_\nu^{(2)}(z) = -\frac{1}{\pi i}\int_{-\infty}^{\infty-\pi i} e^{z\sinh t - \nu t}\,dt \qquad (|\arg z| < \tfrac{1}{2}\pi)$$

9.1.26
$$J_\nu(x) = \frac{1}{2\pi i}\int_{-i\infty}^{i\infty} \frac{\Gamma(-t)(\frac{1}{2}x)^{\nu+2t}}{\Gamma(\nu+t+1)}\,dt \qquad (\mathscr{R}\nu > 0, x > 0)$$

In the last integral the path of integration must lie to the left of the points $t=0, 1, 2, \ldots$.

Recurrence Relations

9.1.27

$$\mathscr{C}_{\nu-1}(z)+\mathscr{C}_{\nu+1}(z)=\frac{2\nu}{z}\mathscr{C}_\nu(z)$$
$$\mathscr{C}_{\nu-1}(z)-\mathscr{C}_{\nu+1}(z)=2\mathscr{C}_\nu'(z)$$
$$\mathscr{C}_\nu'(z)=\mathscr{C}_{\nu-1}(z)-\frac{\nu}{z}\mathscr{C}_\nu(z)$$
$$\mathscr{C}_\nu'(z)=-\mathscr{C}_{\nu+1}(z)+\frac{\nu}{z}\mathscr{C}_\nu(z)$$

$\mathscr{C}$ denotes $J, Y, H^{(1)}, H^{(2)}$ or any linear combination of these functions, the coefficients in which are independent of z and ν.

9.1.28 $J_0'(z)=-J_1(z) \qquad Y_0'(z)=-Y_1(z)$

If $f_\nu(z)=z^p\mathscr{C}_\nu(\lambda z^q)$ where p, q, λ are independent of ν, then

9.1.29

$$f_{\nu-1}(z)+f_{\nu+1}(z)=(2\nu/\lambda)z^{-q}f_\nu(z)$$
$$(p+\nu q)f_{\nu-1}(z)+(p-\nu q)f_{\nu+1}(z)=(2\nu/\lambda)z^{1-q}f_\nu'(z)$$
$$zf_\nu'(z)=\lambda qz^qf_{\nu-1}(z)+(p-\nu q)f_\nu(z)$$
$$zf_\nu'(z)=-\lambda qz^qf_{\nu+1}(z)+(p+\nu q)f_\nu(z)$$

Formulas for Derivatives

9.1.30

$$\left(\frac{1}{z}\frac{d}{dz}\right)^k\{z^\nu\mathscr{C}_\nu(z)\}=z^{\nu-k}\mathscr{C}_{\nu-k}(z)$$
$$\left(\frac{1}{z}\frac{d}{dz}\right)^k\{z^{-\nu}\mathscr{C}_\nu(z)\}=(-)^kz^{-\nu-k}\mathscr{C}_{\nu+k}(z) \qquad (k=0,1,2,\ldots)$$

9.1.31

$$\mathscr{C}_\nu^{(k)}(z)=\frac{1}{2^k}\left\{\mathscr{C}_{\nu-k}(z)-\binom{k}{1}\mathscr{C}_{\nu-k+2}(z)+\binom{k}{2}\mathscr{C}_{\nu-k+4}(z)-\ldots+(-)^k\mathscr{C}_{\nu+k}(z)\right\} \qquad (k=0,1,2,\ldots)$$

Recurrence Relations for Cross-Products

If

9.1.32

$$p_\nu=J_\nu(a)Y_\nu(b)-J_\nu(b)Y_\nu(a)$$
$$q_\nu=J_\nu(a)Y_\nu'(b)-J_\nu'(b)Y_\nu(a)$$
$$r_\nu=J_\nu'(a)Y_\nu(b)-J_\nu(b)Y_\nu'(a)$$
$$s_\nu=J_\nu'(a)Y_\nu'(b)-J_\nu'(b)Y_\nu'(a)$$

then

9.1.33

$$p_{\nu+1}-p_{\nu-1}=-\frac{2\nu}{a}q_\nu-\frac{2\nu}{b}r_\nu$$
$$q_{\nu+1}+r_\nu=\frac{\nu}{a}p_\nu-\frac{\nu+1}{b}p_{\nu+1}$$
$$r_{\nu+1}+q_\nu=\frac{\nu}{b}p_\nu-\frac{\nu+1}{a}p_{\nu+1}$$
$$s_\nu=\frac{1}{2}p_{\nu+1}+\frac{1}{2}p_{\nu-1}-\frac{\nu^2}{ab}p_\nu$$

and

9.1.34 $$p_\nu s_\nu-q_\nu r_\nu=\frac{4}{\pi^2ab}$$

Analytic Continuation

In **9.1.35** to **9.1.38**, m is an integer.

9.1.35 $$J_\nu(ze^{m\pi i})=e^{m\nu\pi i}J_\nu(z)$$

9.1.36

$$Y_\nu(ze^{m\pi i})=e^{-m\nu\pi i}Y_\nu(z)+2i\sin(m\nu\pi)\cot(\nu\pi)J_\nu(z)$$

9.1.37

$$\sin(\nu\pi)H_\nu^{(1)}(ze^{m\pi i})=-\sin\{(m-1)\nu\pi\}H_\nu^{(1)}(z)-e^{-\nu\pi i}\sin(m\nu\pi)H_\nu^{(2)}(z)$$

9.1.38

$$\sin(\nu\pi)H_\nu^{(2)}(ze^{m\pi i})=\sin\{(m+1)\nu\pi\}H_\nu^{(2)}(z)+e^{\nu\pi i}\sin(m\nu\pi)H_\nu^{(1)}(z)$$

9.1.39

$$H_\nu^{(1)}(ze^{\pi i})=-e^{-\nu\pi i}H_\nu^{(2)}(z)$$
$$H_\nu^{(2)}(ze^{-\pi i})=-e^{\nu\pi i}H_\nu^{(1)}(z)$$

9.1.40

$$J_\nu(\bar{z})=\overline{J_\nu(z)} \qquad Y_\nu(\bar{z})=\overline{Y_\nu(z)}$$
$$H_\nu^{(1)}(\bar{z})=\overline{H_\nu^{(2)}(z)} \qquad H_\nu^{(2)}(\bar{z})=\overline{H_\nu^{(1)}(z)} \qquad (\nu \text{ real})$$

Generating Function and Associated Series

9.1.41 $$e^{\frac{1}{2}z(t-1/t)}=\sum_{k=-\infty}^{\infty}t^kJ_k(z) \qquad (t\neq 0)$$

9.1.42 $$\cos(z\sin\theta)=J_0(z)+2\sum_{k=1}^{\infty}J_{2k}(z)\cos(2k\theta)$$

9.1.43 $$\sin(z\sin\theta)=2\sum_{k=0}^{\infty}J_{2k+1}(z)\sin\{(2k+1)\theta\}$$

9.1.44

$$\cos(z\cos\theta)=J_0(z)+2\sum_{k=1}^{\infty}(-)^kJ_{2k}(z)\cos(2k\theta)$$

9.1.45

$$\sin(z\cos\theta)=2\sum_{k=0}^{\infty}(-)^kJ_{2k+1}(z)\cos\{(2k+1)\theta\}$$

9.1.46 $$1=J_0(z)+2J_2(z)+2J_4(z)+2J_6(z)+\ldots$$

9.1.47

$$\cos z=J_0(z)-2J_2(z)+2J_4(z)-2J_6(z)+\ldots$$

9.1.48 $$\sin z=2J_1(z)-2J_3(z)+2J_5(z)-\ldots$$

Other Differential Equations

9.1.49 $w''+\left(\lambda^2-\frac{\nu^2-\frac{1}{4}}{z^2}\right)w=0, \qquad w=z^{\frac{1}{2}}\mathscr{C}_\nu(\lambda z)$

9.1.50 $w''+\left(\frac{\lambda^2}{4z}-\frac{\nu^2-1}{4z^2}\right)w=0, \qquad w=z^{\frac{1}{2}}\mathscr{C}_\nu(\lambda z^{\frac{1}{2}})$

9.1.51 $w''+\lambda^2 z^{p-2}w=0, \qquad w=z^{\frac{1}{2}}\mathscr{C}_{1/p}(2\lambda z^{\frac{1}{2}p}/p)$

9.1.52

$$w''-\frac{2\nu-1}{z}w'+\lambda^2 w=0, \qquad w=z^\nu\mathscr{C}_\nu(\lambda z)$$

9.1.53

$$z^2w''+(1-2p)zw'+(\lambda^2q^2z^{2q}+p^2-\nu^2q^2)w=0, \qquad w=z^p\mathscr{C}_\nu(\lambda z^q)$$

9.1.54

$$w''+(\lambda^2e^{2z}-\nu^2)w=0, \qquad w=\mathscr{C}_\nu(\lambda e^z)$$

9.1.55

$$z^2(z^2-\nu^2)w''+z(z^2-3\nu^2)w' +\{(z^2-\nu^2)^2-(z^2+\nu^2)\}w=0, \qquad w=\mathscr{C}'_\nu(z)$$

9.1.56

$$w^{(2n)}=(-)^n\lambda^{2n}z^{-n}w, \qquad w=z^{\frac{1}{2}n}\mathscr{C}_n(2\lambda\alpha z^{\frac{1}{2}})$$

where α is any of the $2n$ roots of unity.

Differential Equations for Products

In the following $\vartheta\equiv z\frac{d}{dz}$ and $\mathscr{C}_\nu(z)$, $\mathscr{D}_\mu(z)$ are any cylinder functions of orders ν, μ respectively.

9.1.57

$$\{\vartheta^4-2(\nu^2+\mu^2)\vartheta^2+(\nu^2-\mu^2)^2\}w +4z^2(\vartheta+1)(\vartheta+2)w=0, \qquad w=\mathscr{C}_\nu(z)\mathscr{D}_\mu(z)$$

9.1.58

$$\vartheta(\vartheta^2-4\nu^2)w+4z^2(\vartheta+1)w=0, \qquad w=\mathscr{C}_\nu(z)\mathscr{D}_\nu(z)$$

9.1.59

$$z^3w'''+z(4z^2+1-4\nu^2)w'+(4\nu^2-1)w=0, \qquad w=z\mathscr{C}_\nu(z)\mathscr{D}_\nu(z)$$

Upper Bounds

9.1.60 $|J_\nu(x)|\leq 1 \; (\nu\geq 0), \; |J_\nu(x)|\leq 1/\sqrt{2} \qquad (\nu\geq 1)$

9.1.61 $0<J_\nu(\nu)<\frac{2^{\frac{1}{3}}}{3^{\frac{2}{3}}\Gamma(\frac{2}{3})\nu^{\frac{1}{3}}} \qquad (\nu>0)$

9.1.62 $|J_\nu(z)|\leq\frac{|\frac{1}{2}z|^\nu e^{|\mathscr{I}z|}}{\Gamma(\nu+1)} \qquad (\nu\geq -\frac{1}{2})$

9.1.63 $|J_n(nz)|\leq\left|\frac{z^n\exp\{n\sqrt{(1-z^2)}\}}{\{1+\sqrt{(1-z^2)}\}^n}\right|$

Derivatives With Respect to Order

9.1.64

$$\frac{\partial}{\partial\nu}J_\nu(z)=J_\nu(z)\ln(\tfrac{1}{2}z) -(\tfrac{1}{2}z)^\nu\sum_{k=0}^\infty(-)^k\frac{\psi(\nu+k+1)}{\Gamma(\nu+k+1)}\frac{(\frac{1}{4}z^2)^k}{k!}$$

9.1.65

$$\frac{\partial}{\partial\nu}Y_\nu(z)=\cot(\nu\pi)\left\{\frac{\partial}{\partial\nu}J_\nu(z)-\pi Y_\nu(z)\right\} -\csc(\nu\pi)\frac{\partial}{\partial\nu}J_{-\nu}(z)-\pi J_\nu(z) \qquad (\nu\neq 0,\pm 1,\pm 2,\ldots)$$

9.1.66

$$\left[\frac{\partial}{\partial\nu}J_\nu(z)\right]_{\nu=n}=\frac{\pi}{2}Y_n(z)+\frac{n!(\frac{1}{2}z)^{-n}}{2}\sum_{k=0}^{n-1}\frac{(\frac{1}{2}z)^kJ_k(z)}{(n-k)k!}$$

9.1.67

$$\left[\frac{\partial}{\partial\nu}Y_\nu(z)\right]_{\nu=n}=-\frac{\pi}{2}J_n(z)+\frac{n!(\frac{1}{2}z)^{-n}}{2}\sum_{k=0}^{n-1}\frac{(\frac{1}{2}z)^kY_k(z)}{(n-k)k!}$$

9.1.68

$$\left[\frac{\partial}{\partial\nu}J_\nu(z)\right]_{\nu=0}=\frac{\pi}{2}Y_0(z), \left[\frac{\partial}{\partial\nu}Y_\nu(z)\right]_{\nu=0}=-\frac{\pi}{2}J_0(z)$$

Expressions in Terms of Hypergeometric Functions

9.1.69

$$J_\nu(z)=\frac{(\frac{1}{2}z)^\nu}{\Gamma(\nu+1)}\,{}_0F_1(\nu+1;-\tfrac{1}{4}z^2) =\frac{(\frac{1}{2}z)^\nu e^{-iz}}{\Gamma(\nu+1)}M(\nu+\tfrac{1}{2},2\nu+1,2iz)$$

9.1.70

$$J_\nu(z)=\frac{(\frac{1}{2}z)^\nu}{\Gamma(\nu+1)}\lim F\left(\lambda,\mu;\nu+1;-\frac{z^2}{4\lambda\mu}\right)$$

as λ, $\mu\to\infty$ through real or complex values; z, ν being fixed.

(${}_0F_1$ is the generalized hypergeometric function. For $M(a, b, z)$ and $F(a, b; c; z)$ see chapters **13** and **15**.)

Connection With Legendre Functions

If μ and x are fixed and $\nu\to\infty$ through real positive values

9.1.71

$$\lim\left\{\nu^\mu P_\nu^{-\mu}\left(\cos\frac{x}{\nu}\right)\right\}=J_\mu(x) \qquad (x>0)$$

9.1.72

$$\lim\{\nu^{\mu}Q_{\nu}^{-\mu}\left(\cos\frac{x}{\nu}\right)\}=-\tfrac{1}{2}\pi Y_{\mu}(x)\qquad(x>0)$$

For $P_{\nu}^{-\mu}$ and $Q_{\nu}^{-\mu}$, see chapter **8.**

Continued Fractions

9.1.73

$$\frac{J_{\nu}(z)}{J_{\nu-1}(z)}=\frac{1}{2\nu z^{-1}-}\;\frac{1}{2(\nu+1)z^{-1}-}\;\frac{1}{2(\nu+2)z^{-1}-}\cdots$$

$$=\frac{\frac{1}{2}z/\nu}{1-}\;\frac{\frac{1}{4}z^2/\{\nu(\nu+1)\}}{1-}\;\frac{\frac{1}{4}z^2/\{(\nu+1)(\nu+2)\}}{1-}\cdots$$

Multiplication Theorem

9.1.74

$$\mathscr{C}_{\nu}(\lambda z)=\lambda^{\pm\nu}\sum_{k=0}^{\infty}\frac{(\mp)^k(\lambda^2-1)^k(\frac{1}{2}z)^k}{k!}\mathscr{C}_{\nu\pm k}(z)\qquad(|\lambda^2-1|<1)$$

If $\mathscr{C}=J$ and the upper signs are taken, the restriction on λ is unnecessary.

This theorem will furnish expansions of $\mathscr{C}_{\nu}(re^{i\theta})$ in terms of $\mathscr{C}_{\nu\pm k}(r)$.

Addition Theorems

Neumann's

9.1.75 $$\mathscr{C}_{\nu}(u\pm v)=\sum_{k=-\infty}^{\infty}\mathscr{C}_{\nu\mp k}(u)J_k(v)\qquad(|v|<|u|)$$

The restriction $|v|<|u|$ is unnecessary when $\mathscr{C}=J$ and ν is an integer or zero. Special cases are

9.1.76 $$1=J_0^2(z)+2\sum_{k=1}^{\infty}J_k^2(z)$$

9.1.77

$$0=\sum_{k=0}^{2n}(-)^kJ_k(z)J_{2n-k}(z)+2\sum_{k=1}^{\infty}J_k(z)J_{2n+k}(z)\quad(n\geq 1)$$

9.1.78

$$J_n(2z)=\sum_{k=0}^{n}J_k(z)J_{n-k}(z)+2\sum_{k=1}^{\infty}(-)^kJ_k(z)J_{n+k}(z)$$

Graf's

9.1.79

$$\mathscr{C}_{\nu}(w)\begin{matrix}\cos\\ \sin\end{matrix}\nu\chi=\sum_{k=-\infty}^{\infty}\mathscr{C}_{\nu+k}(u)J_k(v)\begin{matrix}\cos\\ \sin\end{matrix}k\alpha\,(|ve^{\pm i\alpha}|<|u|)$$

Gegenbauer's

9.1.80

$$\frac{\mathscr{C}_{\nu}(w)}{w^{\nu}}=2^{\nu}\Gamma(\nu)\sum_{k=0}^{\infty}(\nu+k)\frac{\mathscr{C}_{\nu+k}(u)}{u^{\nu}}\frac{J_{\nu+k}(v)}{v^{\nu}}C_k^{(\nu)}(\cos\alpha)$$

$$(\nu\neq 0,-1,\ldots,|ve^{\pm i\alpha}|<|u|)$$

In **9.1.79** and **9.1.80**,

$$w=\sqrt{(u^2+v^2-2uv\cos\alpha)},$$

$$u-v\cos\alpha=w\cos\chi,\ v\sin\alpha=w\sin\chi$$

the branches being chosen so that $w\to u$ and $\chi\to 0$ as $v\to 0$. $C_k^{(\nu)}(\cos\alpha)$ is Gegenbauer's polynomial (see chapter **22**).

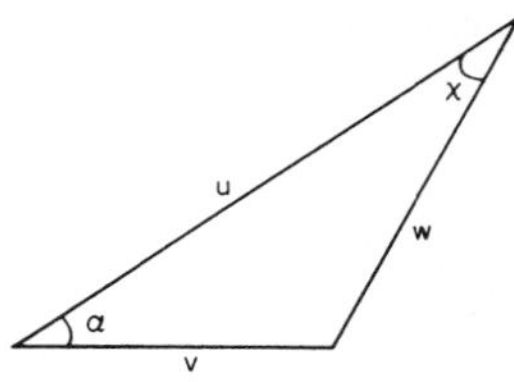

Gegenbauer's addition theorem.

If u, v are real and positive and $0\leq\alpha\leq\pi$, then w, χ are real and non-negative, and the geometrical relationship of the variables is shown in the diagram.

The restrictions $|ve^{\pm i\alpha}|<|u|$ are unnecessary in **9.1.79** when $\mathscr{C}=J$ and ν is an integer or zero, and in **9.1.80** when $\mathscr{C}=J$.

Degenerate Form ($u=\infty$):

9.1.81

$$e^{iv\cos\alpha}=\Gamma(\nu)(\tfrac{1}{2}v)^{-\nu}\sum_{k=0}^{\infty}(\nu+k)i^kJ_{\nu+k}(v)C_k^{(\nu)}(\cos\alpha)$$

$$(\nu\neq 0,-1,\ldots)$$

Neumann's Expansion of an Arbitrary Function in a Series of Bessel Functions

9.1.82 $$f(z)=a_0J_0(z)+2\sum_{k=1}^{\infty}a_kJ_k(z)\qquad(|z|<c)$$

where c is the distance of the nearest singularity of $f(z)$ from $z=0$,

9.1.83 $$a_k=\frac{1}{2\pi i}\int_{|z|=c'}f(t)O_k(t)dt\qquad(0<c'<c)$$

and $O_k(t)$ is Neumann's polynomial. The latter is defined by the generating function

9.1.84

$$\frac{1}{t-z}=J_0(z)O_0(t)+2\sum_{k=1}^{\infty}J_k(z)O_k(t)\qquad(|z|<|t|)$$

$O_n(t)$ is a polynomial of degree $n+1$ in $1/t$; $O_0(t)=1/t$,

9.1.85

$$O_n(t)=\frac{1}{4}\sum_{k=0}^{\leq\frac{1}{2}n}\frac{n(n-k-1)!}{k!}\left(\frac{2}{t}\right)^{n-2k+1}\qquad(n=1,2,\ldots)$$

The more general form of expansion

9.1.86 $$f(z)=a_0J_{\nu}(z)+2\sum_{k=1}^{\infty}a_kJ_{\nu+k}(z)$$

also called a Neumann expansion, is investigated in [9.7] and [9.15] together with further generalizations. Examples of Neumann expansions are **9.1.41** to **9.1.48** and the Addition Theorems. Other examples are

9.1.87

$$(\tfrac{1}{2}z)^\nu=\sum_{k=0}^{\infty}\frac{(\nu+2k)\Gamma(\nu+k)}{k!}J_{\nu+2k}(z) \qquad (\nu\neq 0,-1,-2,\ldots)$$

9.1.88

$$Y_n(z)=-\frac{n!(\tfrac{1}{2}z)^{-n}}{\pi}\sum_{k=0}^{n-1}\frac{(\tfrac{1}{2}z)^kJ_k(z)}{(n-k)k!}+\frac{2}{\pi}\{\ln(\tfrac{1}{2}z)-\psi(n+1)\}J_n(z)-\frac{2}{\pi}\sum_{k=1}^{\infty}(-)^k\frac{(n+2k)J_{n+2k}(z)}{k(n+k)}$$

where $\psi(n)$ is given by **6.3.2.**

9.1.89

$$Y_0(z)=\frac{2}{\pi}\{\ln(\tfrac{1}{2}z)+\gamma\}J_0(z)-\frac{4}{\pi}\sum_{k=1}^{\infty}(-)^k\frac{J_{2k}(z)}{k}$$

9.2. Asymptotic Expansions for Large Arguments

Principal Asymptotic Forms

When ν is fixed and $|z|\to\infty$

9.2.1

$$J_\nu(z)=\sqrt{2/(\pi z)}\{\cos(z-\tfrac{1}{2}\nu\pi-\tfrac{1}{4}\pi)+e^{|\mathscr{I}z|}O(|z|^{-1})\} \qquad (|\arg z|<\pi)$$

9.2.2

$$Y_\nu(z)=\sqrt{2/(\pi z)}\{\sin(z-\tfrac{1}{2}\nu\pi-\tfrac{1}{4}\pi)+e^{|\mathscr{I}z|}O(|z|^{-1})\} \qquad (|\arg z|<\pi)$$

9.2.3

$$H_\nu^{(1)}(z)\sim\sqrt{2/(\pi z)}e^{i(z-\frac{1}{2}\nu\pi-\frac{1}{4}\pi)} \qquad (-\pi<\arg z<2\pi)$$

9.2.4

$$H_\nu^{(2)}(z)\sim\sqrt{2/(\pi z)}e^{-i(z-\frac{1}{2}\nu\pi-\frac{1}{4}\pi)} \qquad (-2\pi<\arg z<\pi)$$

Hankel's Asymptotic Expansions

When ν is fixed and $|z|\to\infty$

9.2.5

$$J_\nu(z)=\sqrt{2/(\pi z)}\{P(\nu,z)\cos\chi-Q(\nu,z)\sin\chi\} \qquad (|\arg z|<\pi)$$

9.2.6

$$Y_\nu(z)=\sqrt{2/(\pi z)}\{P(\nu,z)\sin\chi+Q(\nu,z)\cos\chi\} \qquad (|\arg z|<\pi)$$

9.2.7

$$H_\nu^{(1)}(z)=\sqrt{2/(\pi z)}\{P(\nu,z)+iQ(\nu,z)\}e^{i\chi} \qquad (-\pi<\arg z<2\pi)$$

9.2.8

$$H_\nu^{(2)}(z)=\sqrt{2/(\pi z)}\{P(\nu,z)-iQ(\nu,z)\}e^{-i\chi} \qquad (-2\pi<\arg z<\pi)$$

where $\chi=z-(\tfrac{1}{2}\nu+\tfrac{1}{4})\pi$ and, with $4\nu^2$ denoted by μ,

9.2.9

$$P(\nu,z)\sim\sum_{k=0}^{\infty}(-)^k\frac{(\nu,2k)}{(2z)^{2k}}=1-\frac{(\mu-1)(\mu-9)}{2!(8z)^2}+\frac{(\mu-1)(\mu-9)(\mu-25)(\mu-49)}{4!(8z)^4}-\ldots$$

9.2.10

$$Q(\nu,z)\sim\sum_{k=0}^{\infty}(-)^k\frac{(\nu,2k+1)}{(2z)^{2k+1}}=\frac{\mu-1}{8z}-\frac{(\mu-1)(\mu-9)(\mu-25)}{3!(8z)^3}+\ldots$$

If ν is real and non-negative and z is positive, the remainder after k terms in the expansion of $P(\nu,z)$ does not exceed the $(k+1)$th term in absolute value and is of the same sign, provided that $k>\tfrac{1}{2}\nu-\tfrac{1}{4}$. The same is true of $Q(\nu,z)$ provided that $k>\tfrac{1}{2}\nu-\tfrac{3}{4}$.

Asymptotic Expansions of Derivatives

With the conditions and notation of the preceding subsection

9.2.11

$$J'_\nu(z)=\sqrt{2/(\pi z)}\{-R(\nu,z)\sin\chi-S(\nu,z)\cos\chi\} \qquad (|\arg z|<\pi)$$

9.2.12

$$Y'_\nu(z)=\sqrt{2/(\pi z)}\{R(\nu,z)\cos\chi-S(\nu,z)\sin\chi\} \qquad (|\arg z|<\pi)$$

9.2.13

$$H_\nu^{(1)\prime}(z)=\sqrt{2/(\pi z)}\{iR(\nu,z)-S(\nu,z)\}e^{i\chi} \qquad (-\pi<\arg z<2\pi)$$

9.2.14

$$H_\nu^{(2)\prime}(z)=\sqrt{2/(\pi z)}\{-iR(\nu,z)-S(\nu,z)\}e^{-i\chi} \qquad (-2\pi<\arg z<\pi)$$

9.2.15

$$R(\nu,z)\sim\sum_{k=0}^{\infty}(-)^k\frac{4\nu^2+16k^2-1}{4\nu^2-(4k-1)^2}\frac{(\nu,2k)}{(2z)^{2k}}$$

$$=1-\frac{(\mu-1)(\mu+15)}{2!(8z)^2}+\ldots$$

9.2.16

$$S(\nu,z)\sim\sum_{k=0}^{\infty}(-)^k\frac{4\nu^2+4(2k+1)^2-1}{4\nu^2-(4k+1)^2}\frac{(\nu,2k+1)}{(2z)^{2k+1}}$$

$$=\frac{\mu+3}{8z}-\frac{(\mu-1)(\mu-9)(\mu+35)}{3!(8z)^3}+\ldots$$

Modulus and Phase

For real ν and positive x

9.2.17

$$M_\nu=|H_\nu^{(1)}(x)|=\sqrt{\{J_\nu^2(x)+Y_\nu^2(x)\}}$$
$$\theta_\nu=\arg H_\nu^{(1)}(x)=\arctan\{Y_\nu(x)/J_\nu(x)\}$$

9.2.18

$$N_\nu=|H_\nu^{(1)\prime}(x)|=\sqrt{\{J_\nu'^2(x)+Y_\nu'^2(x)\}}$$
$$\varphi_\nu=\arg H_\nu^{(1)\prime}(x)=\arctan\{Y_\nu'(x)/J_\nu'(x)\}$$

9.2.19 $J_\nu(x)=M_\nu\cos\theta_\nu,\qquad Y_\nu(x)=M_\nu\sin\theta_\nu,$

9.2.20 $J_\nu'(x)=N_\nu\cos\varphi_\nu,\qquad Y_\nu'(x)=N_\nu\sin\varphi_\nu.$

In the following relations, primes denote differentiations with respect to x.

9.2.21 $M_\nu^2\theta_\nu'=2/(\pi x)\qquad N_\nu^2\varphi_\nu'=2(x^2-\nu^2)/(\pi x^3)$

9.2.22 $N_\nu^2=M_\nu'^2+M_\nu^2\theta_\nu'^2=M_\nu'^2+4/(\pi xM_\nu)^2$

9.2.23 $(x^2-\nu^2)M_\nu M_\nu'+x^2N_\nu N_\nu'+xN_\nu^2=0$

9.2.24

$$\tan(\varphi_\nu-\theta_\nu)=M_\nu\theta_\nu'/M_\nu'=2/(\pi xM_\nu M_\nu')$$
$$M_\nu N_\nu\sin(\varphi_\nu-\theta_\nu)=2/(\pi x)$$

9.2.25 $x^2M_\nu''+xM_\nu'+(x^2-\nu^2)M_\nu-4/(\pi^2M_\nu^3)=0$

9.2.26

$$x^3w'''+x(4x^2+1-4\nu^2)w'+(4\nu^2-1)w=0,\quad w=xM_\nu^2$$

9.2.27 $$\theta_\nu'^2+\frac{1}{2}\frac{\theta_\nu'''}{\theta_\nu'}-\frac{3}{4}\left(\frac{\theta_\nu''}{\theta_\nu'}\right)^2=1-\frac{\nu^2-\frac{1}{4}}{x^2}$$

Asymptotic Expansions of Modulus and Phase

When ν is fixed, x is large and positive, and $\mu=4\nu^2$

9.2.28

$$M_\nu^2\sim\frac{2}{\pi x}\left\{1+\frac{1}{2}\frac{\mu-1}{(2x)^2}+\frac{1\cdot3}{2\cdot4}\frac{(\mu-1)(\mu-9)}{(2x)^4}+\frac{1\cdot3\cdot5}{2\cdot4\cdot6}\frac{(\mu-1)(\mu-9)(\mu-25)}{(2x)^6}+\ldots\right\}$$

9.2.29

$$\theta_\nu\sim x-(\tfrac{1}{2}\nu+\tfrac{1}{4})\pi+\frac{\mu-1}{2(4x)}+\frac{(\mu-1)(\mu-25)}{6(4x)^3}+\frac{(\mu-1)(\mu^2-114\mu+1073)}{5(4x)^5}+\frac{(\mu-1)(5\mu^3-1535\mu^2+54703\mu-375733)}{14(4x)^7}+\ldots$$

9.2.30

$$N_\nu^2\sim\frac{2}{\pi x}\left\{1-\frac{1}{2}\frac{\mu-3}{(2x)^2}-\frac{1\cdot1}{2\cdot4}\frac{(\mu-1)(\mu-45)}{(2x)^4}-\ldots\right\}$$

The general term in the last expansion is given by

$$-\frac{1\cdot1\cdot3\ldots(2k-3)}{2\cdot4\cdot6\ldots(2k)}\times\frac{(\mu-1)(\mu-9)\ldots\{\mu-(2k-3)^2\}\{\mu-(2k+1)(2k-1)^2}{(2x)^{2k}}$$

9.2.31

$$\phi_\nu\sim x-(\tfrac{1}{2}\nu-\tfrac{1}{4})\pi+\frac{\mu+3}{2(4x)}+\frac{\mu^2+46\mu-63}{6(4x)^3}+\frac{\mu^3+185\mu^2-2053\mu+1899}{5(4x)^5}+\ldots$$

If $\nu\geq0$, the remainder after k terms in **9.2.28** does not exceed the $(k+1)$th term in absolute value and is of the same sign, provided that $k>\nu-\frac{1}{2}$.

9.3. Asymptotic Expansions for Large Orders

Principal Asymptotic Forms

In the following equations it is supposed that $\nu\to\infty$ through real positive values, the other variables being fixed.

9.3.1

$$J_\nu(z)\sim\frac{1}{\sqrt{2\pi\nu}}\left(\frac{ez}{2\nu}\right)^\nu$$

$$Y_\nu(z)\sim-\sqrt{\frac{2}{\pi\nu}}\left(\frac{ez}{2\nu}\right)^{-\nu}$$

9.3.2

$$J_\nu(\nu\operatorname{sech}\alpha)\sim\frac{e^{\nu(\tanh\alpha-\alpha)}}{\sqrt{2\pi\nu\tanh\alpha}}\qquad(\alpha>0)$$

$$Y_\nu(\nu\operatorname{sech}\alpha)\sim-\frac{e^{\nu(\alpha-\tanh\alpha)}}{\sqrt{\frac{1}{2}\pi\nu\tanh\alpha}}\qquad(\alpha>0)$$

9.3.3

$$J_\nu(\nu\sec\beta)=\sqrt{2/(\pi\nu\tan\beta)}\{\cos(\nu\tan\beta-\nu\beta-\tfrac{1}{4}\pi)+O(\nu^{-1})\}\qquad(0<\beta<\tfrac{1}{2}\pi)$$

$$Y_\nu(\nu\sec\beta)=\sqrt{2/(\pi\nu\tan\beta)}\{\sin(\nu\tan\beta-\nu\beta-\tfrac{1}{4}\pi)+O(\nu^{-1})\}\qquad(0<\beta<\tfrac{1}{2}\pi)$$

9.3.4

$$J_\nu(\nu+z\nu^{1/3})=2^{1/3}\nu^{-1/3}\,\mathrm{Ai}(-2^{1/3}z)+O(\nu^{-1})$$

$$Y_\nu(\nu+z\nu^{1/3})=-2^{1/3}\nu^{-1/3}\,\mathrm{Bi}(-2^{1/3}z)+O(\nu^{-1})$$

9.3.5
$$J_\nu(\nu)\sim\frac{2^{1/3}}{3^{2/3}\Gamma(\frac{2}{3})}\frac{1}{\nu^{1/3}}$$

$$Y_\nu(\nu)\sim-\frac{2^{1/3}}{3^{1/6}\Gamma(\frac{2}{3})}\frac{1}{\nu^{1/3}}$$

9.3.6

$$J_\nu(\nu z)=\left(\frac{4\zeta}{1-z^2}\right)^{1/4}\left\{\frac{\mathrm{Ai}(\nu^{2/3}\zeta)}{\nu^{1/3}}+\frac{\exp(-\frac{2}{3}\nu\zeta^{3/2})}{1+\nu^{1/6}|\zeta|^{1/4}}\,O\left(\frac{1}{\nu^{4/3}}\right)\right\}\qquad(|\arg z|<\pi)$$

$$Y_\nu(\nu z)=-\left(\frac{4\zeta}{1-z^2}\right)^{1/4}\left\{\frac{\mathrm{Bi}(\nu^{2/3}\zeta)}{\nu^{1/3}}+\frac{\exp|\mathscr{R}(\frac{2}{3}\nu\zeta^{3/2})|}{1+\nu^{1/6}|\zeta|^{1/4}}\,O\left(\frac{1}{\nu^{4/3}}\right)\right\}\qquad(|\arg z|<\pi)$$

In the last two equations ζ is given by **9.3.38** and **9.3.39** below.

Debye's Asymptotic Expansions

(i) If α is fixed and positive and ν is large and positive

9.3.7

$$J_\nu(\nu\,\mathrm{sech}\,\alpha)\sim\frac{e^{\nu(\tanh\alpha-\alpha)}}{\sqrt{2\pi\nu\tanh\alpha}}\left\{1+\sum_{k=1}^{\infty}\frac{u_k(\coth\alpha)}{\nu^k}\right\}$$

9.3.8

$$Y_\nu(\nu\,\mathrm{sech}\,\alpha)\sim-\frac{e^{\nu(\alpha-\tanh\alpha)}}{\sqrt{\frac{1}{2}\pi\nu\tanh\alpha}}\left\{1+\sum_{k=1}^{\infty}(-)^k\frac{u_k(\coth\alpha)}{\nu^k}\right\}$$

where

9.3.9

$$u_0(t)=1$$
$$u_1(t)=(3t-5t^3)/24$$
$$u_2(t)=(81t^2-462t^4+385t^6)/1152$$
$$u_3(t)=(30375t^3-3\,69603t^5+7\,65765t^7-4\,25425t^9)/4\,14720$$
$$u_4(t)=(44\,65125t^4-941\,21676t^6+3499\,22430t^8-4461\,85740t^{10}+1859\,10725t^{12})/398\,13120$$

For $u_5(t)$ and $u_6(t)$ see [9.4] or [9.21].

9.3.10

$$u_{k+1}(t)=\tfrac{1}{2}t^2(1-t^2)u_k'(t)+\frac{1}{8}\int_0^t(1-5t^2)u_k(t)dt\qquad(k=0,1,\ldots)$$

Also

9.3.11

$$J_\nu'(\nu\,\mathrm{sech}\,\alpha)\sim\sqrt{\frac{\sinh 2\alpha}{4\pi\nu}}\,e^{\nu(\tanh\alpha-\alpha)}\left\{1+\sum_{k=1}^{\infty}\frac{v_k(\coth\alpha)}{\nu^k}\right\}$$

9.3.12

$$Y_\nu'(\nu\,\mathrm{sech}\,\alpha)\sim\sqrt{\frac{\sinh 2\alpha}{\pi\nu}}\,e^{\nu(\alpha-\tanh\alpha)}\left\{1+\sum_{k=1}^{\infty}(-)^k\frac{v_k(\coth\alpha)}{\nu^k}\right\}$$

where

9.3.13

$$v_0(t)=1$$
$$v_1(t)=(-9t+7t^3)/24$$
$$v_2(t)=(-135t^2+594t^4-455t^6)/1152$$
$$v_3(t)=(-42525t^3+4\,51737t^5-8\,83575t^7+4\,75475t^9)/4\,14720$$

9.3.14

$$v_k(t)=u_k(t)+t(t^2-1)\{\tfrac{1}{2}u_{k-1}(t)+tu_{k-1}'(t)\}\qquad(k=1,2,\ldots)$$

(ii) If β is fixed, $0<\beta<\frac{1}{2}\pi$ and ν is large and positive

9.3.15

$$J_\nu(\nu\sec\beta)=\sqrt{2/(\pi\nu\tan\beta)}\{L(\nu,\beta)\cos\Psi+M(\nu,\beta)\sin\Psi\}$$

9.3.16

$$Y_\nu(\nu\sec\beta)=\sqrt{2/(\pi\nu\tan\beta)}\{L(\nu,\beta)\sin\Psi-M(\nu,\beta)\cos\Psi\}$$

where $\Psi=\nu(\tan\beta-\beta)-\frac{1}{4}\pi$

9.3.17

$$L(\nu,\beta)\sim\sum_{k=0}^{\infty}\frac{u_{2k}(i\cot\beta)}{\nu^{2k}}=1-\frac{81\cot^2\beta+462\cot^4\beta+385\cot^6\beta}{1152\nu^2}+\ldots$$

9.3.18

$$M(\nu,\beta)\sim -i\sum_{k=0}^{\infty}\frac{u_{2k+1}(i\cot\beta)}{\nu^{2k+1}}=\frac{3\cot\beta+5\cot^3\beta}{24\nu}-\ldots$$

Also

9.3.19

$$J'_\nu(\nu\sec\beta)=\sqrt{(\sin 2\beta)/(\pi\nu)}\{-N(\nu,\beta)\sin\Psi-O(\nu,\beta)\cos\Psi\}$$

9.3.20

$$Y'_\nu(\nu\sec\beta)=\sqrt{(\sin 2\beta)/(\pi\nu)}\{N(\nu,\beta)\cos\Psi-O(\nu,\beta)\sin\Psi\}$$

where

9.3.21

$$N(\nu,\beta)\sim\sum_{k=0}^{\infty}\frac{v_{2k}(i\cot\beta)}{\nu^{2k}}=1+\frac{135\cot^2\beta+594\cot^4\beta+455\cot^6\beta}{1152\nu^2}-\ldots$$

9.3.22

$$O(\nu,\beta)\sim i\sum_{k=0}^{\infty}\frac{v_{2k+1}(i\cot\beta)}{\nu^{2k+1}}=\frac{9\cot\beta+7\cot^3\beta}{24\nu}-\ldots$$

Asymptotic Expansions in the Transition Regions

When z is fixed, $|\nu|$ is large and $|\arg\nu|<\frac{1}{2}\pi$

9.3.23

$$J_\nu(\nu+z\nu^{1/3})\sim\frac{2^{1/3}}{\nu^{1/3}}\,\mathrm{Ai}\,(-2^{1/3}z)\{1+\sum_{k=1}^{\infty}\frac{f_k(z)}{\nu^{2k/3}}\}+\frac{2^{2/3}}{\nu}\,\mathrm{Ai}'\,(-2^{1/3}z)\sum_{k=0}^{\infty}\frac{g_k(z)}{\nu^{2k/3}}$$

9.3.24

$$Y_\nu(\nu+z\nu^{1/3})\sim-\frac{2^{1/3}}{\nu^{1/3}}\,\mathrm{Bi}\,(-2^{1/3}z)\{1+\sum_{k=1}^{\infty}\frac{f_k(z)}{\nu^{2k/3}}\}-\frac{2^{2/3}}{\nu}\,\mathrm{Bi}'\,(-2^{1/3}z)\sum_{k=0}^{\infty}\frac{g_k(z)}{\nu^{2k/3}}$$

where

9.3.25

$$f_1(z)=-\frac{1}{5}z$$

$$f_2(z)=-\frac{9}{100}z^5+\frac{3}{35}z^2$$

$$f_3(z)=\frac{957}{7000}z^6-\frac{173}{3150}z^3-\frac{1}{225}$$

$$f_4(z)=\frac{27}{20000}z^{10}-\frac{23573}{147000}z^7+\frac{5903}{138600}z^4+\frac{947}{346500}z$$

9.3.26

$$g_0(z)=\frac{3}{10}z^2$$

$$g_1(z)=-\frac{17}{70}z^3+\frac{1}{70}$$

$$g_2(z)=-\frac{9}{1000}z^7+\frac{611}{3150}z^4-\frac{37}{3150}z$$

$$g_3(z)=\frac{549}{28000}z^8-\frac{110767}{693000}z^5+\frac{79}{12375}z^2$$

The corresponding expansions for $H^{(1)}_\nu(\nu+z\nu^{1/3})$ and $H^{(2)}_\nu(\nu+z\nu^{1/3})$ are obtained by use of **9.1.3** and **9.1.4**; they are valid for $-\frac{1}{2}\pi<\arg\nu<\frac{3}{2}\pi$ and $-\frac{3}{2}\pi<\arg\nu<\frac{1}{2}\pi$, respectively.

9.3.27

$$J'_\nu(\nu+z\nu^{1/3})\sim-\frac{2^{2/3}}{\nu^{2/3}}\,\mathrm{Ai}'\,(-2^{1/3}z)\{1+\sum_{k=1}^{\infty}\frac{h_k(z)}{\nu^{2k/3}}\}+\frac{2^{1/3}}{\nu^{4/3}}\,\mathrm{Ai}\,(-2^{1/3}z)\sum_{k=0}^{\infty}\frac{l_k(z)}{\nu^{2k/3}}$$

9.3.28

$$Y'_\nu(\nu+z\nu^{1/3})\sim\frac{2^{2/3}}{\nu^{2/3}}\,\mathrm{Bi}'\,(-2^{1/3}z)\{1+\sum_{k=1}^{\infty}\frac{h_k(z)}{\nu^{2k/3}}\}-\frac{2^{1/3}}{\nu^{4/3}}\,\mathrm{Bi}\,(-2^{1/3}z)\sum_{k=0}^{\infty}\frac{l_k(z)}{\nu^{2k/3}}$$

where

9.3.29

$$h_1(z)=-\frac{4}{5}z$$

$$h_2(z)=-\frac{9}{100}z^5+\frac{57}{70}z^2$$

$$h_3(z)=\frac{699}{3500}z^6-\frac{2617}{3150}z^3+\frac{23}{3150}$$

$$h_4(z)=\frac{27}{20000}z^{10}-\frac{46631}{147000}z^7+\frac{3889}{4620}z^4-\frac{1159}{115500}z$$

9.3.30

$$l_0(z)=\frac{3}{5}z^3-\frac{1}{5}$$

$$l_1(z)=-\frac{131}{140}z^4+\frac{1}{5}z$$

$$l_2(z)=-\frac{9}{500}z^8+\frac{5437}{4500}z^5-\frac{593}{3150}z^2$$

$$l_3(z)=\frac{369}{7000}z^9-\frac{999443}{693000}z^6+\frac{31727}{173250}z^3+\frac{947}{346500}$$

9.3.31 $J_\nu(\nu)\sim\frac{a}{\nu^{1/3}}\{1+\sum_{k=1}^{\infty}\frac{\alpha_k}{\nu^{2k}}\}-\frac{b}{\nu^{5/3}}\sum_{k=0}^{\infty}\frac{\beta_k}{\nu^{2k}}$

9.3.32 $Y_\nu(\nu)\sim-\frac{3^{1/2}a}{\nu^{1/3}}\{1+\sum_{k=1}^{\infty}\frac{\alpha_k}{\nu^{2k}}\}-\frac{3^{1/2}b}{\nu^{5/3}}\sum_{k=0}^{\infty}\frac{\beta_k}{\nu^{2k}}$

9.3.33 $J_\nu'(\nu)\sim\frac{b}{\nu^{2/3}}\{1+\sum_{k=1}^{\infty}\frac{\gamma_k}{\nu^{2k}}\}-\frac{a}{\nu^{4/3}}\sum_{k=0}^{\infty}\frac{\delta_k}{\nu^{2k}}$

9.3.34 $Y_\nu'(\nu)\sim\frac{3^{1/2}b}{\nu^{2/3}}\{1+\sum_{k=1}^{\infty}\frac{\gamma_k}{\nu^{2k}}\}+\frac{3^{1/2}a}{\nu^{4/3}}\sum_{k=0}^{\infty}\frac{\delta_k}{\nu^{2k}}$

where

$a=\frac{2^{1/3}}{3^{2/3}\Gamma(\frac{2}{3})}=.44730\ 73184,\qquad 3^{\frac{1}{2}}a=.77475\ 90021$

$b=\frac{2^{2/3}}{3^{1/3}\Gamma(\frac{1}{3})}=.41085\ 01939,\qquad 3^{\frac{1}{2}}b=.71161\ 34101$

$\alpha_0=1,\qquad \alpha_1=-\frac{1}{225}=-.00\dot{4},$

$\alpha_2=.00069\ 3735\ldots,\qquad \alpha_3=-.00035\ 38\ldots$

$\beta_0=\frac{1}{70}=.01428\ 57143\ldots,$

$\beta_1=-\frac{1213}{10\ 23750}=-.00118\ 48596\ldots,$

$\beta_2=.00043\ 78\ldots,\qquad \beta_3=-.00038\ldots$

$\gamma_0=1,\qquad \gamma_1=\frac{23}{3150}=.00730\ 15873\ldots,$

$\gamma_2=-.00093\ 7300\ldots,\qquad \gamma_3=.00044\ 40\ldots$

$\delta_0=\frac{1}{5},\quad \delta_1=-\frac{947}{3\ 46500}=-.00273\ 30447\ldots,$

$\delta_2=.00060\ 47\ldots,\qquad \delta_3=-.00038\ldots$

Uniform Asymptotic Expansions

These are more powerful than the previous expansions of this section, save for **9.3.31** and **9.3.32,** but their coefficients are more complicated. They reduce to **9.3.31** and **9.3.32** when the argument equals the order.

9.3.35

$$J_\nu(\nu z)\sim\left(\frac{4\zeta}{1-z^2}\right)^{1/4}\left\{\frac{\mathrm{Ai}(\nu^{2/3}\zeta)}{\nu^{1/3}}\sum_{k=0}^{\infty}\frac{a_k(\zeta)}{\nu^{2k}}+\frac{\mathrm{Ai}'(\nu^{2/3}\zeta)}{\nu^{5/3}}\sum_{k=0}^{\infty}\frac{b_k(\zeta)}{\nu^{2k}}\right\}$$

9.3.36

$$Y_\nu(\nu z)\sim-\left(\frac{4\zeta}{1-z^2}\right)^{1/4}\left\{\frac{\mathrm{Bi}(\nu^{2/3}\zeta)}{\nu^{1/3}}\sum_{k=0}^{\infty}\frac{a_k(\zeta)}{\nu^{2k}}+\frac{\mathrm{Bi}'(\nu^{2/3}\zeta)}{\nu^{5/3}}\sum_{k=0}^{\infty}\frac{b_k(\zeta)}{\nu^{2k}}\right\}$$

9.3.37

$$H_\nu^{(1)}(\nu z)\sim2e^{-\pi i/3}\left(\frac{4\zeta}{1-z^2}\right)^{1/4}\left\{\frac{\mathrm{Ai}(e^{2\pi i/3}\nu^{2/3}\zeta)}{\nu^{1/3}}\sum_{k=0}^{\infty}\frac{a_k(\zeta)}{\nu^{2k}}+\frac{e^{2\pi i/3}\mathrm{Ai}'(e^{2\pi i/3}\nu^{2/3}\zeta)}{\nu^{5/3}}\sum_{k=0}^{\infty}\frac{b_k(\zeta)}{\nu^{2k}}\right\}$$

When $\nu\to+\infty$, these expansions hold uniformly with respect to z in the sector $|\arg z|\leq\pi-\epsilon$, where ϵ is an arbitrary positive number. The corresponding expansion for $H_\nu^{(2)}(\nu z)$ is obtained by changing the sign of i in **9.3.37.**

Here

9.3.38

$$\frac{2}{3}\zeta^{3/2}=\int_z^1\frac{\sqrt{1-t^2}}{t}dt=\ln\frac{1+\sqrt{1-z^2}}{z}-\sqrt{1-z^2}$$

equivalently,

9.3.39

$$\frac{2}{3}(-\zeta)^{3/2}=\int_1^z\frac{\sqrt{t^2-1}}{t}dt=\sqrt{z^2-1}-\arccos\left(\frac{1}{z}\right)$$

the branches being chosen so that ζ is real when z is positive. The coefficients are given by

9.3.40

$$a_k(\zeta)=\sum_{s=0}^{2k}\mu_s\zeta^{-3s/2}u_{2k-s}\{(1-z^2)^{-\frac{1}{2}}\}$$

$$b_k(\zeta)=-\zeta^{-\frac{1}{2}}\sum_{s=0}^{2k+1}\lambda_s\zeta^{-3s/2}u_{2k-s+1}\{(1-z^2)^{-\frac{1}{2}}\}$$

where u_k is given by **9.3.9** and **9.3.10,** $\lambda_0=\mu_0=1$ and

9.3.41

$$\lambda_s=\frac{(2s+1)(2s+3)\ldots(6s-1)}{s!(144)^s},\qquad \mu_s=-\frac{6s+1}{6s-1}\lambda_s$$

Thus $a_0(\zeta)=1$,

9.3.42

$$b_0(\zeta)=-\frac{5}{48\zeta^2}+\frac{1}{\zeta^{\frac{1}{2}}}\left\{\frac{5}{24(1-z^2)^{3/2}}-\frac{1}{8(1-z^2)^{\frac{1}{2}}}\right\}$$

$$=-\frac{5}{48\zeta^2}+\frac{1}{(-\zeta)^{\frac{1}{2}}}\left\{\frac{5}{24(z^2-1)^{3/2}}+\frac{1}{8(z^2-1)^{\frac{1}{2}}}\right\}$$

Tables of the early coefficients are given below. For more extensive tables of the coefficients and for bounds on the remainder terms in **9.3.35** and **9.3.36** see [9.38].

Uniform Expansions of the Derivatives

With the conditions of the preceding subsection

9.3.43

$$J'_\nu(\nu z)\sim-\frac{2}{z}\left(\frac{1-z^2}{4\zeta}\right)^{\frac{1}{4}}\left\{\frac{\mathrm{Ai}\,(\nu^{2/3}\zeta)}{\nu^{4/3}}\sum_{k=0}^{\infty}\frac{c_k(\zeta)}{\nu^{2k}}+\frac{\mathrm{Ai}'\,(\nu^{2/3}\zeta)}{\nu^{2/3}}\sum_{k=0}^{\infty}\frac{d_k(\zeta)}{\nu^{2k}}\right\}$$

9.3.44

$$Y'_\nu(\nu z)\sim\frac{2}{z}\left(\frac{1-z^2}{4\zeta}\right)^{\frac{1}{4}}\left\{\frac{\mathrm{Bi}\,(\nu^{2/3}\zeta)}{\nu^{4/3}}\sum_{k=0}^{\infty}\frac{c_k(\zeta)}{\nu^{2k}}+\frac{\mathrm{Bi}'\,(\nu^{2/3}\zeta)}{\nu^{2/3}}\sum_{k=0}^{\infty}\frac{d_k(\zeta)}{\nu^{2k}}\right\}$$

9.3.45

$$H^{(1)\prime}_\nu(\nu z)\sim\frac{4e^{2\pi i/3}}{z}\left(\frac{1-z^2}{4\zeta}\right)^{\frac{1}{4}}\left\{\frac{\mathrm{Ai}\,(e^{2\pi i/3}\nu^{2/3}\zeta)}{\nu^{4/3}}\sum_{k=0}^{\infty}\frac{c_k(\zeta)}{\nu^{2k}}+\frac{e^{2\pi i/3}\,\mathrm{Ai}'\,(e^{2\pi i/3}\nu^{2/3}\zeta)}{\nu^{2/3}}\sum_{k=0}^{\infty}\frac{d_k(\zeta)}{\nu^{2k}}\right\}$$

where

9.3.46

$$c_k(\zeta)=-\zeta^{\frac{1}{2}}\sum_{s=0}^{2k+1}\mu_s\zeta^{-3s/2}v_{2k-s+1}\{(1-z^2)^{-\frac{1}{2}}\}$$

$$d_k(\zeta)=\sum_{s=0}^{2k}\lambda_s\zeta^{-3s/2}v_{2k-s}\{(1-z^2)^{-\frac{1}{2}}\}$$

and v_k is given by **9.3.13** and **9.3.14**. For bounds on the remainder terms in **9.3.43** and **9.3.44** see [9.38].

ζ	$b_0(\zeta)$	$a_1(\zeta)$	$c_0(\zeta)$	$d_1(\zeta)$
0	0.0180	−0.004	0.1587	0.007
1	.0278	−.004	.1785	.009
2	.0351	−.001	.1862	.007
3	.0366	+.002	.1927	.005
4	.0352	.003	.2031	.004
5	.0331	.004	.2155	.003
6	.0311	.004	.2284	.003
7	.0294	.004	.2413	.003
8	.0278	.004	.2539	.003
9	.0265	.004	.2662	.003
10	.0253	.004	.2781	.003

$-\zeta$	$b_0(\zeta)$	$a_1(\zeta)$	$c_0(\zeta)$	$d_1(\zeta)$
0	0.0180	−0.004	0.1587	0.007
1	.0109	−.003	.1323	.004
2	.0067	−.002	.1087	.002
3	.0044	−.001	.0903	.001
4	.0031	−.001	.0764	.001
5	.0022	−.000	.0658	.000
6	.0017	−.000	.0576	.000
7	.0013	−.000	.0511	.000
8	.0011	−.000	.0459	.000
9	.0009	−.000	.0415	.000
10	.0007	−.000	.0379	.000

For $\zeta>10$ use

$$b_0(\zeta)\sim\frac{1}{12}\zeta^{-\frac{1}{2}}-.104\zeta^{-2},\qquad a_1(\zeta)=.003,$$

$$c_0(\zeta)\sim\frac{1}{12}\zeta^{\frac{1}{2}}+.146\zeta^{-1},\qquad d_1(\zeta)=.003.$$

For $\zeta<-10$ use

$$b_0(\zeta)\sim\frac{1}{12}\zeta^{-2},\qquad a_1(\zeta)=.000,$$

$$c_0(\zeta)\sim-\frac{5}{12}\zeta^{-1}-1.33(-\zeta)^{-5/2},\qquad d_1(\zeta)=.000.$$

Maximum values of higher coefficients:

$$|b_1(\zeta)|=.003,\qquad |a_2(\zeta)|=.0008,\qquad |d_2(\zeta)|=.001$$

$$|c_1(\zeta)|=.008\ (\zeta<10),\quad c_1(\zeta)\sim-.003\zeta^{\frac{1}{2}}\text{ as }\zeta\rightarrow+\infty.$$

9.4. Polynomial Approximations [2]

9.4.1 $\qquad -3\leq x\leq 3$

$$J_0(x)=1-2.24999\,97(x/3)^2+1.26562\,08(x/3)^4-.31638\,66(x/3)^6+.04444\,79(x/3)^8-.00394\,44(x/3)^{10}+.00021\,00(x/3)^{12}+\epsilon$$

$$|\epsilon|<5\times10^{-8}$$

9.4.2 $\qquad 0<x\leq 3$

$$Y_0(x)=(2/\pi)\ln(\tfrac{1}{2}x)J_0(x)+.36746\,691+.60559\,366(x/3)^2-.74350\,384(x/3)^4+.25300\,117(x/3)^6-.04261\,214(x/3)^8+.00427\,916(x/3)^{10}-.00024\,846(x/3)^{12}+\epsilon$$

$$|\epsilon|<1.4\times10^{-8}$$

9.4.3 $\qquad 3\leq x<\infty$

$$J_0(x)=x^{-\frac{1}{2}}f_0\cos\theta_0\qquad Y_0(x)=x^{-\frac{1}{2}}f_0\sin\theta_0$$

$$f_0=.79788\,456-.00000\,077(3/x)-.00552\,740(3/x)^2-.00009\,512(3/x)^3+.00137\,237(3/x)^4-.00072\,805(3/x)^5+.00014\,476(3/x)^6+\epsilon$$

$$|\epsilon|<1.6\times10^{-8}$$

[2] Equations **9.4.1** to **9.4.6** and **9.8.1** to **9.8.8** are taken from E. E. Allen, Analytical approximations, Math. Tables Aids Comp. **8**, 240–241 (1954), and Polynomial approximations to some modified Bessel functions, Math. Tables Aids Comp. **10**, 162–164 (1956)

$$\theta_0=x-.78539\ 816-.04166\ 397(3/x)$$
$$-.00003\ 954(3/x)^2+.00262\ 573(3/x)^3$$
$$-.00054\ 125(3/x)^4-.00029\ 333(3/x)^5$$
$$+.00013\ 558(3/x)^6+\epsilon$$
$$|\epsilon|<7\times10^{-8}$$

9.4.4 $$-3\leq x\leq 3$$

$$x^{-1}J_1(x)=\tfrac{1}{2}-.56249\ 985(x/3)^2+.21093\ 573(x/3)^4$$
$$-.03954\ 289(x/3)^6+.00443\ 319(x/3)^8$$
$$-.00031\ 761(x/3)^{10}+.00001\ 109(x/3)^{12}+\epsilon$$
$$|\epsilon|<1.3\times10^{-8}$$

9.4.5 $$0<x\leq 3$$

$$xY_1(x)=(2/\pi)x\ln(\tfrac{1}{2}x)J_1(x)-.63661\ 98$$
$$+.22120\ 91(x/3)^2+2.16827\ 09(x/3)^4$$
$$-1.31648\ 27(x/3)^6+.31239\ 51(x/3)^8$$
$$-.04009\ 76(x/3)^{10}+.00278\ 73(x/3)^{12}+\epsilon$$
$$|\epsilon|<1.1\times10^{-7}$$

9.4.6 $$3\leq x<\infty$$

$$J_1(x)=x^{-\frac{1}{2}}f_1\cos\theta_1,\qquad Y_1(x)=x^{-\frac{1}{2}}f_1\sin\theta_1$$

$$f_1=.79788\ 456+.00000\ 156(3/x)+.01659\ 667(3/x)^2$$
$$+.00017\ 105(3/x)^3-.00249\ 511(3/x)^4$$
$$+.00113\ 653(3/x)^5-.00020\ 033(3/x)^6+\epsilon$$
$$|\epsilon|<4\times10^{-8}$$

$$\theta_1=x-2.35619\ 449+.12499\ 612(3/x)$$
$$+.00005\ 650(3/x)^2-.00637\ 879(3/x)^3$$
$$+.00074\ 348(3/x)^4+.00079\ 824(3/x)^5$$
$$-.00029\ 166(3/x)^6+\epsilon$$
$$|\epsilon|<9\times10^{-8}$$

For expansions of $J_0(x)$, $Y_0(x)$, $J_1(x)$, and $Y_1(x)$ in series of Chebyshev polynomials for the ranges $0\leq x\leq 8$ and $0\leq 8/x\leq 1$, see [9.37].

9.5. Zeros

Real Zeros

When ν is real, the functions $J_\nu(z)$, $J'_\nu(z)$, $Y_\nu(z)$ and $Y'_\nu(z)$ each have an infinite number of real zeros, all of which are simple with the possible exception of $z=0$. For *non-negative* ν the sth positive zeros of these functions are denoted by $j_{\nu,s}$, $j'_{\nu,s}$, $y_{\nu,s}$ and $y'_{\nu,s}$ respectively, except that $z=0$ is counted as the first zero of $J'_0(z)$. Since $J'_0(z)=-J_1(z)$, it follows that

9.5.1 $$j'_{0,1}=0,\qquad j'_{0,s}=j_{1,s-1}\qquad(s=2,3,\ldots)$$

The zeros interlace according to the inequalities

9.5.2
$$j_{\nu,1}<j_{\nu+1,1}<j_{\nu,2}<j_{\nu+1,2}<j_{\nu,3}<\ldots$$
$$y_{\nu,1}<y_{\nu+1,1}<y_{\nu,2}<y_{\nu+1,2}<y_{\nu,3}<\ldots$$
$$\nu\leq j'_{\nu,1}<y_{\nu,1}<y'_{\nu,1}<j_{\nu,1}<j'_{\nu,2}$$
$$<y_{\nu,2}<y'_{\nu,2}<j_{\nu,2}<j'_{\nu,3}<\ldots$$

The positive zeros of any two real distinct cylinder functions of the same order are interlaced, as are the positive zeros of any real cylinder function $\mathscr{C}_\nu(z)$, defined as in **9.1.27,** and the contiguous function $\mathscr{C}_{\nu+1}(z)$.

If ρ_ν is a zero of the cylinder function

9.5.3 $$\mathscr{C}_\nu(z)=J_\nu(z)\cos(\pi t)+Y_\nu(z)\sin(\pi t)$$

where t is a parameter, then

9.5.4 $$\mathscr{C}'_\nu(\rho_\nu)=\mathscr{C}_{\nu-1}(\rho_\nu)=-\mathscr{C}_{\nu+1}(\rho_\nu)$$

If σ_ν is a zero of $\mathscr{C}'_\nu(z)$ then

9.5.5 $$\mathscr{C}_\nu(\sigma_\nu)=\frac{\sigma_\nu}{\nu}\mathscr{C}_{\nu-1}(\sigma_\nu)=\frac{\sigma_\nu}{\nu}\mathscr{C}_{\nu+1}(\sigma_\nu)$$

The parameter t may be regarded as a continuous variable and ρ_ν, σ_ν as functions $\rho_\nu(t)$, $\sigma_\nu(t)$ of t. If these functions are fixed by

9.5.6 $$\rho_\nu(0)=0,\qquad \sigma_\nu(0)=j'_{\nu,1}$$

then

9.5.7
$$j_{\nu,s}=\rho_\nu(s),\qquad y_{\nu,s}=\rho_\nu(s-\tfrac{1}{2})\qquad(s=1,2,\ldots)$$

9.5.8
$$j'_{\nu,s}=\sigma_\nu(s-1),\qquad y'_{\nu,s}=\sigma_\nu(s-\tfrac{1}{2})\qquad(s=1,2,\ldots)$$

9.5.9 $$\mathscr{C}'_\nu(\rho_\nu)=\left(\frac{\rho_\nu}{2}\frac{d\rho_\nu}{dt}\right)^{-\frac{1}{2}},\ \mathscr{C}_\nu(\sigma_\nu)=\left(\frac{\sigma_\nu^2-\nu^2}{2\sigma_\nu}\frac{d\sigma_\nu}{dt}\right)^{-\frac{1}{2}}$$

Infinite Products

9.5.10 $$J_\nu(z)=\frac{(\tfrac{1}{2}z)^\nu}{\Gamma(\nu+1)}\prod_{s=1}^{\infty}\left(1-\frac{z^2}{j_{\nu,s}^2}\right)$$

9.5.11 $$J'_\nu(z)=\frac{(\tfrac{1}{2}z)^{\nu-1}}{2\Gamma(\nu)}\prod_{s=1}^{\infty}\left(1-\frac{z^2}{j'^2_{\nu,s}}\right)\qquad(\nu>0)$$

McMahon's Expansions for Large Zeros

When ν is fixed, $s>>\nu$ and $\mu=4\nu^2$

9.5.12

$$j_{\nu,s}, y_{\nu,s} \sim \beta - \frac{\mu-1}{8\beta} - \frac{4(\mu-1)(7\mu-31)}{3(8\beta)^3} - \frac{32(\mu-1)(83\mu^2-982\mu+3779)}{15(8\beta)^5} - \frac{64(\mu-1)(6949\mu^3-1\ 53855\mu^2+15\ 85743\mu-62\ 77237)}{105(8\beta)^7} - \ldots$$

where $\beta=(s+\frac{1}{2}\nu-\frac{1}{4})\pi$ for $j_{\nu,s}$, $\beta=(s+\frac{1}{2}\nu-\frac{3}{4})\pi$ for $y_{\nu,s}$. With $\beta=(t+\frac{1}{2}\nu-\frac{1}{4})\pi$, the right of **9.5.12** is the asymptotic expansion of $\rho_\nu(t)$ for large t.

9.5.13

$$j'_{\nu,s}, y'_{\nu,s} \sim \beta' - \frac{\mu+3}{8\beta'} - \frac{4(7\mu^2+82\mu-9)}{3(8\beta')^3} - \frac{32(83\mu^3+2075\mu^2-3039\mu+3537)}{15(8\beta')^5} - \frac{64(6949\mu^4+2\ 96492\mu^3-12\ 48002\mu^2+74\ 14380\mu-58\ 53627)}{105(8\beta')^7} - \ldots$$

where $\beta'=(s+\frac{1}{2}\nu-\frac{3}{4})\pi$ for $j'_{\nu,s}$, $\beta'=(s+\frac{1}{2}\nu-\frac{1}{4})\pi$ for $y'_{\nu,s}$, $\beta'=(t+\frac{1}{2}\nu+\frac{1}{4})\pi$ for $\sigma_\nu(t)$. For higher terms in **9.5.12** and **9.5.13** see [9.4] or [9.40].

Asymptotic Expansions of Zeros and Associated Values for Large Orders

9.5.14

$$j_{\nu,1} \sim \nu+1.85575\ 71\nu^{1/3}+1.03315\ 0\nu^{-1/3} -.00397\nu^{-1}-.0908\nu^{-5/3}+.043\nu^{-7/3}+\ldots$$

9.5.15

$$y_{\nu,1} \sim \nu+.93157\ 68\nu^{1/3}+.26035\ 1\nu^{-1/3} +.01198\nu^{-1}-.0060\nu^{-5/3}-.001\nu^{-7/3}+\ldots$$

9.5.16

$$j'_{\nu,1} \sim \nu+.80861\ 65\nu^{1/3}+.07249\ 0\nu^{-1/3} -.05097\nu^{-1}+.0094\nu^{-5/3}+\ldots$$

9.5.17

$$y'_{\nu,1} \sim \nu+1.82109\ 80\nu^{1/3}+.94000\ 7\nu^{-1/3} -.05808\nu^{-1}-.0540\nu^{-5/3}+\ldots$$

9.5.18

$$J'_\nu(j_{\nu,1}) \sim -1.11310\ 28\nu^{-2/3}/(1+1.48460\ 6\nu^{-2/3} +.43294\nu^{-4/3}-.1943\nu^{-2}+.019\nu^{-8/3}+\ldots)$$

9.5.19

$$Y'_\nu(y_{\nu,1}) \sim .95554\ 86\nu^{-2/3}/(1+.74526\ 1\nu^{-2/3} +.10910\nu^{-4/3}-.0185\nu^{-2}-.003\nu^{-8/3}+\ldots)$$

9.5.20

$$J_\nu(j'_{\nu,1}) \sim .67488\ 51\nu^{-1/3}(1-.16172\ 3\nu^{-2/3} +.02918\nu^{-4/3}-.0068\nu^{-2}+\ldots)$$

9.5.21

$$Y_\nu(y'_{\nu,1}) \sim .57319\ 40\nu^{-1/3}(1-.36422\ 0\nu^{-2/3} +.09077\nu^{-4/3}+.0237\nu^{-2}+\ldots)$$

Corresponding expansions for $s=2, 3$ are given in [9.40]. These expansions become progressively weaker as s increases; those which follow do not suffer from this defect.

Uniform Asymptotic Expansions of Zeros and Associated Values for Large Orders

9.5.22 $$j_{\nu,s} \sim \nu z(\zeta) + \sum_{k=1}^{\infty} \frac{f_k(\zeta)}{\nu^{2k-1}} \text{ with } \zeta=\nu^{-2/3}a_s$$

9.5.23

$$J'_\nu(j_{\nu,s}) \sim -\frac{2}{\nu^{2/3}} \frac{\mathrm{Ai}'(a_s)}{z(\zeta)h(\zeta)} \{1+\sum_{k=1}^{\infty} \frac{F_k(\zeta)}{\nu^{2k}}\} \quad \text{with } \zeta=\nu^{-2/3}a_s$$

9.5.24 $$j'_{\nu,s} \sim \nu z(\zeta) + \sum_{k=1}^{\infty} \frac{g_k(\zeta)}{\nu^{2k-1}} \text{ with } \zeta=\nu^{-2/3}a'_s$$

9.5.25

$$J_\nu(j'_{\nu,s}) \sim \mathrm{Ai}(a'_s) \frac{h(\zeta)}{\nu^{1/3}} \{1+\sum_{k=1}^{\infty} \frac{G_k(\zeta)}{\nu^{2k}}\} \text{ with } \zeta=\nu^{-2/3}a'_s$$

where a_s, a'_s are the sth negative zeros of $\mathrm{Ai}(z)$, $\mathrm{Ai}'(z)$ (see **10.4**), $z=z(\zeta)$ is the inverse function defined implicitly by **9.3.39**, and

9.5.26

$$h(\zeta)=\{4\zeta/(1-z^2)\}^{\frac{1}{4}}$$

$$f_1(\zeta)=\tfrac{1}{2}z(\zeta)\{h(\zeta)\}^2 b_0(\zeta)$$

$$g_1(\zeta)=\tfrac{1}{2}\zeta^{-1}z(\zeta)\{h(\zeta)\}^2 c_0(\zeta)$$

where $b_0(\zeta)$, $c_0(\zeta)$ appear in **9.3.42** and **9.3.46.** Tables of the leading coefficients follow. More extensive tables are given in [9.40].

The expansions of $y_{\nu,s}$, $Y'_\nu(y_{\nu,s})$, $y'_{\nu,s}$ and $Y_\nu(y'_{\nu,s})$ corresponding to **9.5.22** to **9.5.25** are obtained by changing the symbols j, J, Ai, Ai′, a_s and a'_s to y, Y, $-$Bi, $-$Bi′, b_s and b'_s respectively.

$-\zeta$	$z(\zeta)$	$h(\zeta)$	$f_1(\zeta)$	$F_1(\zeta)$	$(-\zeta)g_1(\zeta)$	$(-\zeta)^3g_2(\zeta)$	$(-\zeta)^2G_1(\zeta)$
0. 0	1. 000000	1. 25992	0. 0143	−0. 007	−0. 1260	−0. 010	0. 000
0. 2	1. 166284	1. 22076	. 0142	−. 005	−. 1335	−. 010	. 002
0. 4	1. 347557	1. 18337	. 0139	−. 004	−. 1399	−. 009	. 004
0. 6	1. 543615	1. 14780	. 0135	−. 003	−. 1453	−. 009	. 005
0. 8	1. 754187	1. 11409	. 0131	−. 003	−. 1498	−. 008	. 006
1. 0	1. 978963	1. 08220	0. 0126	−0. 002	−0. 1533	−0. 008	0. 006

$-\zeta$	$z(\zeta)$	$h(\zeta)$	$f_1(\zeta)$	$F_1(\zeta)$	$g_1(\zeta)$	$g_2(\zeta)$	$G_1(\zeta)$
1. 0	1. 978963	1. 08220	0. 0126	−0. 002	−0. 1533	−0. 008	0. 006
1. 2	2. 217607	1. 05208	. 0121	−. 002	−. 1301	−. 004	. 004
1. 4	2. 469770	1. 02367	. 0115	−. 001	−. 1130	−. 002	. 003
1. 6	2. 735103	0. 99687	. 0110	−. 001	−. 0998	−. 001	. 002
1. 8	3. 013256	. 97159	. 0105	−. 001	−. 0893	−. 001	. 002
2. 0	3. 303889	0. 94775	0. 0100	−0. 001	−0. 0807	−0. 001	0. 001
2. 2	3. 606673	. 92524	. 0095	−0. 001	−. 0734		. 001
2. 4	3. 921292	. 90397	. 0091		−. 0673		. 001
2. 6	4. 247441	. 88387	. 0086		−. 0619		. 001
2. 8	4. 584833	. 86484	. 0082		−. 0573		0. 001
3. 0	4. 933192	0. 84681	0. 0078		−0. 0533		
3. 2	5. 292257	. 82972	. 0075		−. 0497		
3. 4	5. 661780	. 81348	. 0071		−. 0464		
3. 6	6. 041525	. 79806	. 0068		−. 0436		
3. 8	6. 431269	. 78338	. 0065		−. 0410		
4. 0	6. 830800	0. 76939	0. 0062		−0. 0386		
4. 2	7. 239917	. 75605	. 0060		−. 0365		
4. 4	7. 658427	. 74332	. 0057		−. 0345		
4. 6	8. 086150	. 73115	. 0055		−. 0328		
4. 8	8. 522912	. 71951	. 0052		−. 0311		
5. 0	8. 968548	0. 70836	0. 0050		−0. 0296		
5. 2	9. 422900	. 69768	. 0048		−. 0282		
5. 4	9. 885820	. 68742	. 0047		−. 0270		
5. 6	10. 357162	. 67758	. 0045		−. 0258		
5. 8	10. 836791	. 66811	. 0043		−. 0246		
6. 0	11. 324575	0. 65901	0. 0042		−0. 0236		
6. 2	11. 820388	. 65024	. 0040		−. 0227		
6. 4	12. 324111	. 64180	. 0039		−. 0218		
6. 6	12. 835627	. 63366	. 0037		−. 0209		
6. 8	13. 354826	. 62580	. 0036		−. 0201		
7. 0	13. 881601	0. 61821	0. 0035		−0. 0194		

$(-\zeta)^{-\frac{1}{2}}$	$z(\zeta)-\frac{2}{3}(-\zeta)^{\frac{3}{2}}$	$(-\zeta)^{\frac{1}{2}}h(\zeta)$	$f_1(\zeta)$	$g_1(\zeta)$
0. 40	1. 528915	1. 62026	0. 0040	−0. 0224
. 35	1. 541532	1. 65351	. 0029	−. 0158
. 30	1. 551741	1. 68067	. 0020	−. 0104
. 25	1. 559490	1. 70146	. 0012	−. 0062
. 20	1. 564907	1. 71607	. 0006	−. 0033
0. 15	1. 568285	1. 72523	0. 0003	−0. 0014
. 10	1. 570048	1. 73002	. 0001	−. 0004
. 05	1. 570703	1. 73180	. 0000	−. 0001
. 00	1. 570796	1. 73205	. 0000	−. 0000

Maximum Values of Higher Coefficients

$|f_2(\zeta)|=.001,\ |F_2(\zeta)|=.0004 \qquad (0\leq-\zeta<\infty)$

$|g_3(\zeta)|=.001,\ |G_2(\zeta)|=.0007 \qquad (1\leq-\zeta<\infty)$

$|(-\zeta)^5g_3(\zeta)|=.002,\ |(-\zeta)^4G_2(\zeta)|=.0007 \qquad (0\leq-\zeta\leq1)$

Complex Zeros of $J_\nu(z)$

When $\nu\geq-1$ the zeros of $J_\nu(z)$ are all real. If $\nu<-1$ and ν is not an integer the number of complex zeros of $J_\nu(z)$ is twice the integer part of $(-\nu)$; if the integer part of $(-\nu)$ is odd two of these zeros lie on the imaginary axis.

If $\nu\geq0$, all zeros of $J'_\nu(z)$ are real.

Complex Zeros of $Y_\nu(z)$

When ν is real the pattern of the complex zeros of $Y_\nu(z)$ and $Y'_\nu(z)$ depends on the non-integer part of ν. Attention is confined here to the case $\nu=n$ a positive integer or zero.

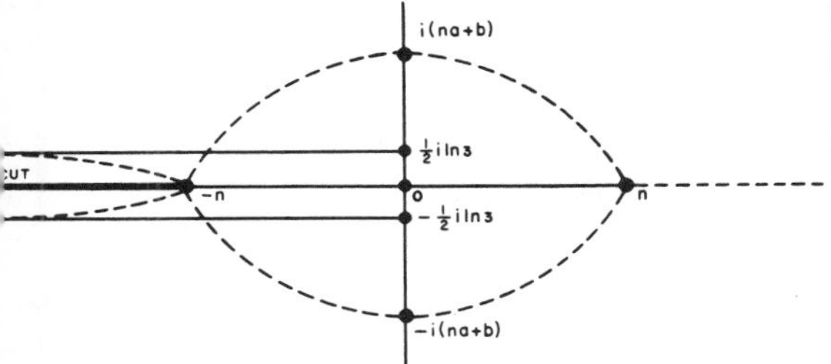

FIGURE 9.5. *Zeros of* $Y_n(z)$ *and* $Y_n'(z)$ . . . $|\arg z| \leq \pi$.

Figure 9.5 shows the approximate distribution of the complex zeros of $Y_n(z)$ in the region $|\arg z| \leq \pi$. The figure is symmetrical about the real axis. The two curves on the left extend to infinity, having the asymptotes

$$\mathscr{I} z = \pm \tfrac{1}{2} \ln 3 = \pm .54931 \ . \ . \ .$$

There are an infinite number of zeros near each of these curves.

The two curves extending from $z=-n$ to $z=n$ and bounding an eye-shaped domain intersect the imaginary axis at the points $\pm i(na+b)$, where

$$a = \sqrt{t_0^2 - 1} = .66274 \ . \ . \ .$$

$$b = \tfrac{1}{2}\sqrt{1 - t_0^{-2}} \ln 2 = .19146 \ . \ . \ .$$

and $t_0 = 1.19968$ . . . is the positive root of $\coth t = t$. There are n zeros near each of these curves. Asymptotic expansions of these zeros for large n are given by the right of **9.5.22** with $\nu = n$ and $\zeta = n^{-2/3}\beta_s$ or $n^{-2/3}\bar{\beta}_s$, where β_s, $\bar{\beta}_s$ are the complex zeros of $\mathrm{Bi}(z)$ (see **10.4**).

Figure 9.5 is also applicable to the zeros of $Y_n'(z)$. There are again an infinite number near the infinite curves, and n near each of the finite curves. Asymptotic expansions of the latter for large n are given by the right of **9.5.24** with $\nu = n$ and $\zeta = n^{-2/3}\beta_s'$ or $n^{-2/3}\bar{\beta}_s'$; where β_s' and $\bar{\beta}_s'$ are the complex zeros of $\mathrm{Bi}'(z)$.

Numerical values of the three smallest complex zeros of $Y_0(z)$, $Y_1(z)$ and $Y_1'(z)$ in the region $0 < \arg z < \pi$ are given below.

For further details see [9.36] and [9.13]. The latter reference includes tables to facilitate computation.

Complex Zeros of the Hankel Functions

The approximate distribution of the zeros of $H_n^{(1)}(z)$ and its derivative in the region $|\arg z| \leq \pi$ is indicated in a similar manner on **Figure 9.6.**

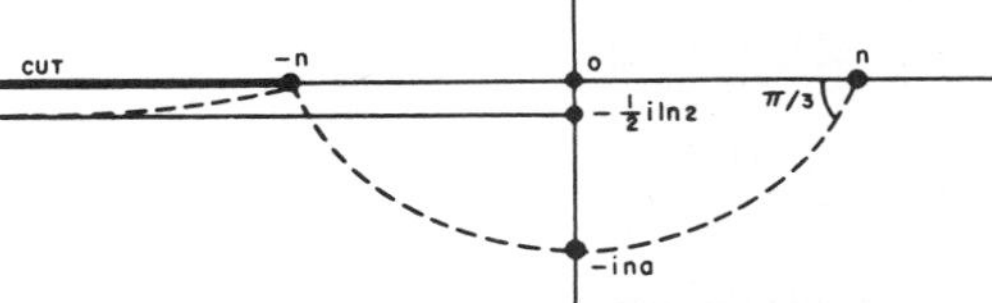

FIGURE 9.6. *Zeros of* $H_n^{(1)}(z)$ *and* $H_n^{(1)\prime}(z)$ . . . $|\arg z| \leq \pi$.

The asymptote of the solitary infinite curve is given by

$$\mathscr{I} z = -\tfrac{1}{2} \ln 2 = -.34657 \ . \ . \ .$$

Zeros of $Y_0(z)$ *and Values of* $Y_1(z)$ *at the Zeros*[3]

Zero		Y_1	
Real	*Imag.*	*Real*	*Imag.*
−2. 40301 6632	+. 53988 2313	+. 10074 7689	−. 88196 7710
−5. 51987 6702	+. 54718 0011	−. 02924 6418	+. 58716 9503
−8. 65367 2403	+. 54841 2067	+. 01490 8063	−. 46945 8752

Zeros of $Y_1(z)$ *and Values of* $Y_0(z)$ *at the Zeros*

Zero		Y_0	
Real	*Imag.*	*Real*	*Imag.*
−0. 50274 3273	+. 78624 3714	−. 45952 7684	+1. 31710 1937
−3. 83353 5193	+. 56235 6538	+. 04830 1909	−0. 69251 2884
−7. 01590 3683	+. 55339 3046	−. 02012 6949	+0. 51864 2833

Zeros of $Y_1'(z)$ *and Values of* $Y_1(z)$ *at the Zeros*

Zero		Y_1	
Real	*Imag.*	*Real*	*Imag.*
+0. 57678 5129	+. 90398 4792	−. 76349 7088	+. 58924 4865
−1. 94047 7342	+. 72118 5919	+. 16206 4006	−. 95202 7886
−5. 33347 8617	+. 56721 9637	−. 03179 4008	+. 59685 3673

[3] From National Bureau of Standards, Tables of the Bessel functions $Y_0(z)$ and $Y_1(z)$ for complex arguments.

There are n zeros of each function near the finite curve extending from $z=-n$ to $z=n$; the asymptotic expansions of these zeros for large n are given by the right side of **9.5.22** or **9.5.24** with $\nu=n$ and $\zeta=e^{-2\pi i/3}n^{-2/3}a_s$ or $\zeta=e^{-2\pi i/3}n^{-2/3}a_s'$.

Zeros of Cross-Products

If ν is real and λ is positive, the zeros of the function

9.5.27 $$J_\nu(z)Y_\nu(\lambda z)-J_\nu(\lambda z)Y_\nu(z)$$

are real and simple. If $\lambda>1$, the asymptotic expansion of the sth zero is

9.5.28 $$\beta+\frac{p}{\beta}+\frac{q-p^2}{\beta^3}+\frac{r-4pq+2p^3}{\beta^5}+\ldots$$

where with $4\nu^2$ denoted by μ,

9.5.29
$$\beta=s\pi/(\lambda-1)$$
$$p=\frac{\mu-1}{8\lambda},\qquad q=\frac{(\mu-1)(\mu-25)(\lambda^3-1)}{6(4\lambda)^3(\lambda-1)}$$
$$r=\frac{(\mu-1)(\mu^2-114\mu+1073)(\lambda^5-1)}{5(4\lambda)^5(\lambda-1)}$$

The asymptotic expansion of the large positive zeros (not necessarily the sth) of the function

9.5.30 $$J_\nu'(z)Y_\nu'(\lambda z)-J_\nu'(\lambda z)Y_\nu'(z)\qquad(\lambda>1)$$

is given by **9.5.28** with the same value of β, but instead of **9.5.29** we have

9.5.31
$$p=\frac{\mu+3}{8\lambda},\qquad q=\frac{(\mu^2+46\mu-63)(\lambda^3-1)}{6(4\lambda)^3(\lambda-1)}$$
$$r=\frac{(\mu^3+185\mu^2-2053\mu+1899)(\lambda^5-1)}{5(4\lambda)^5(\lambda-1)}$$

The asymptotic expansion of the large positive zeros of the function

9.5.32 $$J_\nu'(z)Y_\nu(\lambda z)-Y_\nu'(z)J_\nu(\lambda z)$$

is given by **9.5.28** with

9.5.33
$$\beta=(s-\tfrac{1}{2})\pi/(\lambda-1)$$
$$p=\frac{(\mu+3)\lambda-(\mu-1)}{8\lambda(\lambda-1)}$$
$$q=\frac{(\mu^2+46\mu-63)\lambda^3-(\mu-1)(\mu-25)}{6(4\lambda)^3(\lambda-1)}$$
$$5(4\lambda)^5(\lambda-1)r=(\mu^3+185\mu^2-2053\mu+1899)\lambda^5-(\mu-1)(\mu^2-114\mu+1073)$$

Modified Bessel Functions I and K

9.6. Definitions and Properties

Differential Equation

9.6.1 $$z^2\frac{d^2w}{dz^2}+z\frac{dw}{dz}-(z^2+\nu^2)w=0$$

Solutions are $I_{\pm\nu}(z)$ and $K_\nu(z)$. Each is a regular function of z throughout the z-plane cut along the negative real axis, and for fixed $z(\neq0)$ each is an entire function of ν. When $\nu=\pm n$, $I_\nu(z)$ is an entire function of z.

$I_\nu(z)$ $(\mathscr{R}\nu\geq0)$ is bounded as $z\rightarrow0$ in any bounded range of arg z. $I_\nu(z)$ and $I_{-\nu}(z)$ are linearly independent except when ν is an integer. $K_\nu(z)$ tends to zero as $|z|\rightarrow\infty$ in the sector $|\arg z|<\frac{1}{2}\pi$, and for all values of ν, $I_\nu(z)$ and $K_\nu(z)$ are linearly independent. $I_\nu(z)$, $K_\nu(z)$ are real and positive when $\nu>-1$ and $z>0$.

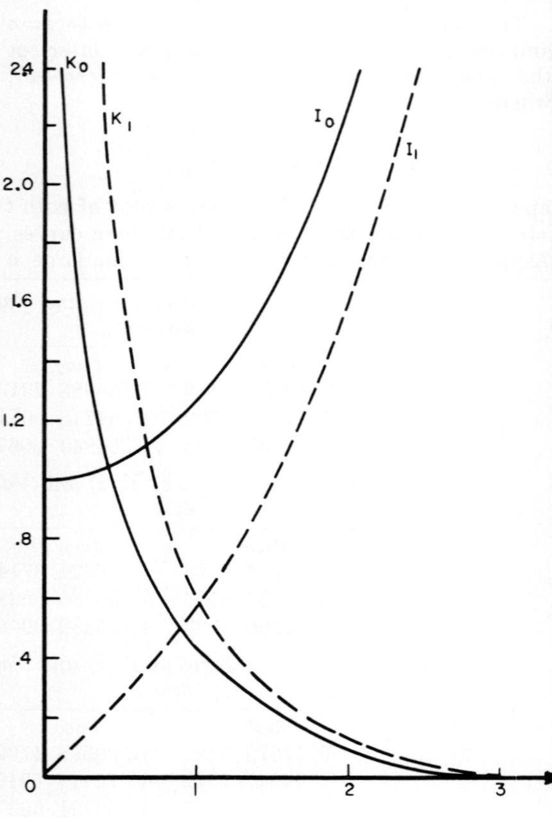

FIGURE 9.7. $I_0(x)$, $K_0(x)$, $I_1(x)$ and $K_1(x)$.

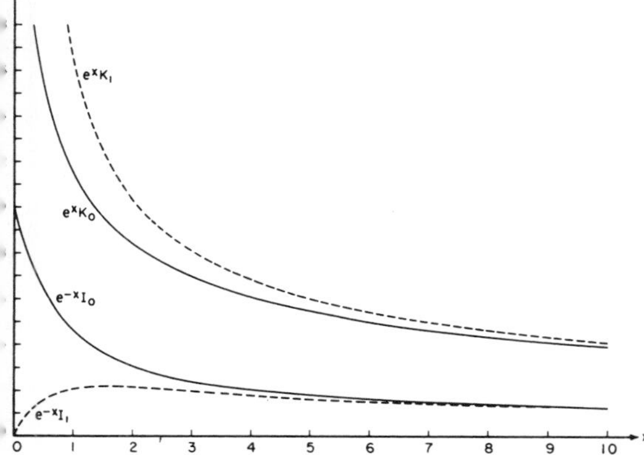

FIGURE 9.8. $e^{-x}I_0(x), e^{-x}I_1(x), e^{x}K_0(x)$ *and* $e^{x}K_1(x)$.

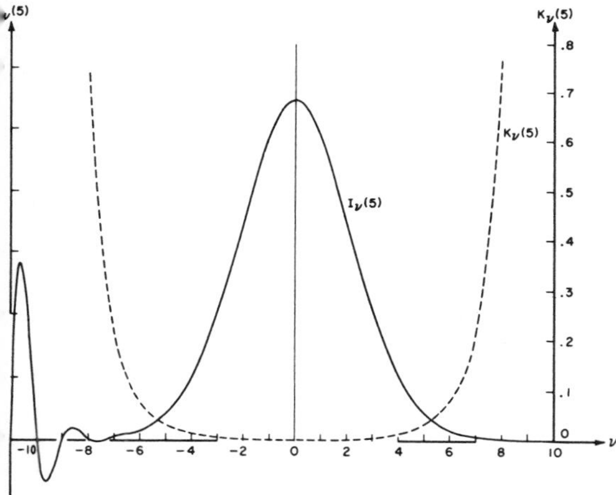

FIGURE 9.9. $I_\nu(5)$ *and* $K_\nu(5)$.

Relations Between Solutions

9.6.2 $$K_\nu(z)=\tfrac{1}{2}\pi\,\frac{I_{-\nu}(z)-I_\nu(z)}{\sin(\nu\pi)}$$

The right of this equation is replaced by its limiting value if ν is an integer or zero.

9.6.3

$$I_\nu(z)=e^{-\frac{1}{2}\nu\pi i}J_\nu(ze^{\frac{1}{2}\pi i})\qquad(-\pi<\arg z\leq\tfrac{1}{2}\pi)$$

$$I_\nu(z)=e^{3\nu\pi i/2}J_\nu(ze^{-3\pi i/2})\qquad(\tfrac{1}{2}\pi<\arg z\leq\pi)$$

9.6.4

$$K_\nu(z)=\tfrac{1}{2}\pi i e^{\frac{1}{2}\nu\pi i}H_\nu^{(1)}(ze^{\frac{1}{2}\pi i})\qquad(-\pi<\arg z\leq\tfrac{1}{2}\pi)$$

$$K_\nu(z)=-\tfrac{1}{2}\pi i e^{-\frac{1}{2}\nu\pi i}H_\nu^{(2)}(ze^{-\frac{1}{2}\pi i})\qquad(-\tfrac{1}{2}\pi<\arg z\leq\pi)$$

9.6.5

$$Y_\nu(ze^{\frac{1}{2}\pi i})=e^{\frac{1}{2}(\nu+1)\pi i}I_\nu(z)-(2/\pi)e^{-\frac{1}{2}\nu\pi i}K_\nu(z)\qquad(-\pi<\arg z\leq\tfrac{1}{2}\pi)$$

9.6.6 $$I_{-n}(z)=I_n(z),\quad K_{-\nu}(z)=K_\nu(z)$$

Most of the properties of modified Bessel functions can be deduced immediately from those of ordinary Bessel functions by application of these relations.

Limiting Forms for Small Arguments

When ν is fixed and $z\rightarrow0$

9.6.7

$$I_\nu(z)\sim(\tfrac{1}{2}z)^\nu/\Gamma(\nu+1)\qquad(\nu\neq-1,-2,\ldots)$$

9.6.8 $$K_0(z)\sim-\ln z$$

9.6.9 $$K_\nu(z)\sim\tfrac{1}{2}\Gamma(\nu)(\tfrac{1}{2}z)^{-\nu}\qquad(\mathscr{R}\nu>0)$$

Ascending Series

9.6.10 $$I_\nu(z)=(\tfrac{1}{2}z)^\nu\sum_{k=0}^{\infty}\frac{(\frac{1}{4}z^2)^k}{k!\,\Gamma(\nu+k+1)}$$

9.6.11

$$K_n(z)=\tfrac{1}{2}(\tfrac{1}{2}z)^{-n}\sum_{k=0}^{n-1}\frac{(n-k-1)!}{k!}(-\tfrac{1}{4}z^2)^k+(-)^{n+1}\ln(\tfrac{1}{2}z)I_n(z)$$
$$+(-)^n\tfrac{1}{2}(\tfrac{1}{2}z)^n\sum_{k=0}^{\infty}\{\psi(k+1)+\psi(n+k+1)\}\frac{(\frac{1}{4}z^2)^k}{k!(n+k)!}$$

where $\psi(n)$ is given by **6.3.2.**

9.6.12 $$I_0(z)=1+\frac{\frac{1}{4}z^2}{(1!)^2}+\frac{(\frac{1}{4}z^2)^2}{(2!)^2}+\frac{(\frac{1}{4}z^2)^3}{(3!)^2}+\ldots$$

9.6.13

$$K_0(z)=-\{\ln(\tfrac{1}{2}z)+\gamma\}I_0(z)+\frac{\frac{1}{4}z^2}{(1!)^2}+(1+\tfrac{1}{2})\frac{(\frac{1}{4}z^2)^2}{(2!)^2}+(1+\tfrac{1}{2}+\tfrac{1}{3})\frac{(\frac{1}{4}z^2)^3}{(3!)^2}+\ldots$$

Wronskians

9.6.14

$$W\{I_\nu(z),I_{-\nu}(z)\}=I_\nu(z)I_{-(\nu+1)}(z)-I_{\nu+1}(z)I_{-\nu}(z)=-2\sin(\nu\pi)/(\pi z)$$

9.6.15

$$W\{K_\nu(z),I_\nu(z)\}=I_\nu(z)K_{\nu+1}(z)+I_{\nu+1}(z)K_\nu(z)=1/z$$

Integral Representations

9.6.16
$$I_0(z)=\frac{1}{\pi}\int_0^\pi e^{\pm z\cos\theta}d\theta=\frac{1}{\pi}\int_0^\pi \cosh(z\cos\theta)d\theta$$

9.6.17 $$K_0(z)=-\frac{1}{\pi}\int_0^\pi e^{\pm z\cos\theta}\{\gamma+\ln(2z\sin^2\theta)\}d\theta$$

9.6.18
$$I_\nu(z)=\frac{(\frac{1}{2}z)^\nu}{\pi^{\frac{1}{2}}\Gamma(\nu+\frac{1}{2})}\int_0^\pi e^{\pm z\cos\theta}\sin^{2\nu}\theta\,d\theta$$
$$=\frac{(\frac{1}{2}z)^\nu}{\pi^{\frac{1}{2}}\Gamma(\nu+\frac{1}{2})}\int_{-1}^1 (1-t^2)^{\nu-\frac{1}{2}}e^{\pm zt}dt \qquad (\mathscr{R}\nu>-\tfrac{1}{2})$$

9.6.19 $$I_n(z)=\frac{1}{\pi}\int_0^\pi e^{z\cos\theta}\cos(n\theta)d\theta$$

9.6.20
$$I_\nu(z)=\frac{1}{\pi}\int_0^\pi e^{z\cos\theta}\cos(\nu\theta)d\theta$$
$$-\frac{\sin(\nu\pi)}{\pi}\int_0^\infty e^{-z\cosh t-\nu t}dt \qquad (|\arg z|<\tfrac{1}{2}\pi)$$

9.6.21
$$K_0(x)=\int_0^\infty \cos(x\sinh t)dt=\int_0^\infty \frac{\cos(xt)}{\sqrt{t^2+1}}dt \qquad (x>0)$$

9.6.22
$$K_\nu(x)=\sec(\tfrac{1}{2}\nu\pi)\int_0^\infty \cos(x\sinh t)\cosh(\nu t)dt$$
$$=\csc(\tfrac{1}{2}\nu\pi)\int_0^\infty \sin(x\sinh t)\sinh(\nu t)dt \qquad (|\mathscr{R}\nu|<1,\ x>0)$$

9.6.23
$$K_\nu(z)=\frac{\pi^{\frac{1}{2}}(\frac{1}{2}z)^\nu}{\Gamma(\nu+\frac{1}{2})}\int_0^\infty e^{-z\cosh t}\sinh^{2\nu}t\,dt$$
$$=\frac{\pi^{\frac{1}{2}}(\frac{1}{2}z)^\nu}{\Gamma(\nu+\frac{1}{2})}\int_1^\infty e^{-zt}(t^2-1)^{\nu-\frac{1}{2}}\,dt \qquad (\mathscr{R}\nu>-\tfrac{1}{2},\ |\arg z|<\tfrac{1}{2}\pi)$$

9.6.24 $$K_\nu(z)=\int_0^\infty e^{-z\cosh t}\cosh(\nu t)\,dt \quad (|\arg z|<\tfrac{1}{2}\pi)$$

9.6.25
$$K_\nu(xz)=\frac{\Gamma(\nu+\frac{1}{2})(2z)^\nu}{\pi^{\frac{1}{2}}x^\nu}\int_0^\infty \frac{\cos(xt)dt}{(t^2+z^2)^{\nu+\frac{1}{2}}} \qquad (\mathscr{R}\nu>-\tfrac{1}{2},\ x>0,\ |\arg z|<\tfrac{1}{2}\pi)$$

Recurrence Relations

9.6.26
$$\mathscr{Z}_{\nu-1}(z)-\mathscr{Z}_{\nu+1}(z)=\frac{2\nu}{z}\mathscr{Z}_\nu(z)$$
$$\mathscr{Z}'_\nu(z)=\mathscr{Z}_{\nu-1}(z)-\frac{\nu}{z}\mathscr{Z}_\nu(z)$$
$$\mathscr{Z}_{\nu-1}(z)+\mathscr{Z}_{\nu+1}(z)=2\mathscr{Z}'_\nu(z)$$
$$\mathscr{Z}'_\nu(z)=\mathscr{Z}_{\nu+1}(z)+\frac{\nu}{z}\mathscr{Z}_\nu(z)$$

$\mathscr{Z}_\nu$ denotes I_ν, $e^{\nu\pi i}K_\nu$ or any linear combination of these functions, the coefficients in which are independent of z and ν.

9.6.27 $$I'_0(z)=I_1(z), \qquad K'_0(z)=-K_1(z)$$

Formulas for Derivatives

9.6.28
$$\left(\frac{1}{z}\frac{d}{dz}\right)^k\{z^\nu\mathscr{Z}_\nu(z)\}=z^{\nu-k}\mathscr{Z}_{\nu-k}(z)$$
$$\left(\frac{1}{z}\frac{d}{dz}\right)^k\{z^{-\nu}\mathscr{Z}_\nu(z)\}=z^{-\nu-k}\mathscr{Z}_{\nu+k}(z) \qquad (k=0,1,2,\ldots)$$

9.6.29
$$\mathscr{Z}_\nu^{(k)}(z)=\frac{1}{2^k}\left\{\mathscr{Z}_{\nu-k}(z)+\binom{k}{1}\mathscr{Z}_{\nu-k+2}(z)+\binom{k}{2}\mathscr{Z}_{\nu-k+4}(z)+\ldots+\mathscr{Z}_{\nu+k}(z)\right\} \qquad (k=0,1,2,\ldots)$$

Analytic Continuation

9.6.30 $$I_\nu(ze^{m\pi i})=e^{m\nu\pi i}I_\nu(z) \qquad (m \text{ an integer})$$

9.6.31
$$K_\nu(ze^{m\pi i})=e^{-m\nu\pi i}K_\nu(z)-\pi i\sin(m\nu\pi)\csc(\nu\pi)I_\nu(z) \qquad (m \text{ an integer})$$

9.6.32 $$I_\nu(\bar{z})=\overline{I_\nu(z)}, \qquad K_\nu(\bar{z})=\overline{K_\nu(z)} \qquad (\nu \text{ real})$$

Generating Function and Associated Series

9.6.33 $$e^{\frac{1}{2}z(t+1/t)}=\sum_{k=-\infty}^{\infty} t^kI_k(z) \qquad (t\neq 0)$$

9.6.34 $$e^{z\cos\theta}=I_0(z)+2\sum_{k=1}^{\infty} I_k(z)\cos(k\theta)$$

9.6.35
$$e^{z\sin\theta}=I_0(z)+2\sum_{k=0}^{\infty}(-)^kI_{2k+1}(z)\sin\{(2k+1)\theta\}+2\sum_{k=1}^{\infty}(-)^kI_{2k}(z)\cos(2k\theta)$$

9.6.36 $$1=I_0(z)-2I_2(z)+2I_4(z)-2I_6(z)+\ldots$$

9.6.37 $$e^z=I_0(z)+2I_1(z)+2I_2(z)+2I_3(z)+\ldots$$

9.6.38 $$e^{-z}=I_0(z)-2I_1(z)+2I_2(z)-2I_3(z)+\ldots$$

9.6.39
$$\cosh z=I_0(z)+2I_2(z)+2I_4(z)+2I_6(z)+\ldots$$

9.6.40 $$\sinh z=2I_1(z)+2I_3(z)+2I_5(z)+\ldots$$

Other Differential Equations

The quantity λ^2 in equations **9.1.49** to **9.1.54** and **9.1.56** can be replaced by $-\lambda^2$ if at the same time the symbol $\mathscr{C}$ in the given solutions is replaced by $\mathscr{Z}$.

9.6.41

$$z^2w''+z(1\pm 2z)w'+(\pm z-\nu^2)w=0, \qquad w=e^{\mp z}\mathscr{Z}_\nu(z)$$

Differential equations for products may be obtained from **9.1.57** to **9.1.59** by replacing z by iz.

Derivatives With Respect to Order

9.6.42

$$\frac{\partial}{\partial\nu}I_\nu(z)=I_\nu(z)\ln(\tfrac{1}{2}z)-(\tfrac{1}{2}z)^\nu\sum_{k=0}^{\infty}\frac{\psi(\nu+k+1)}{\Gamma(\nu+k+1)}\frac{(\frac{1}{4}z^2)^k}{k!}$$

9.6.43

$$\frac{\partial}{\partial\nu}K_\nu(z)=\tfrac{1}{2}\pi\csc(\nu\pi)\left\{\frac{\partial}{\partial\nu}I_{-\nu}(z)-\frac{\partial}{\partial\nu}I_\nu(z)\right\}-\pi\cot(\nu\pi)K_\nu(z) \qquad (\nu\neq 0,\pm 1,\pm 2,\ldots)$$

9.6.44

$$(-)^n\left[\frac{\partial}{\partial\nu}I_\nu(z)\right]_{\nu=n}=-K_n(z)+\frac{n!(\frac{1}{2}z)^{-n}}{2}\sum_{k=0}^{n-1}(-)^k\frac{(\frac{1}{2}z)^kI_k(z)}{(n-k)k!}$$

9.6.45

$$\left[\frac{\partial}{\partial\nu}K_\nu(z)\right]_{\nu=n}=\frac{n!(\frac{1}{2}z)^{-n}}{2}\sum_{k=0}^{n-1}\frac{(\frac{1}{2}z)^kK_k(z)}{(n-k)k!}$$

9.6.46

$$\left[\frac{\partial}{\partial\nu}I_\nu(z)\right]_{\nu=0}=-K_0(z), \qquad \left[\frac{\partial}{\partial\nu}K_\nu(z)\right]_{\nu=0}=0$$

Expressions in Terms of Hypergeometric Functions

9.6.47

$$I_\nu(z)=\frac{(\frac{1}{2}z)^\nu}{\Gamma(\nu+1)}\,{}_0F_1(\nu+1;\tfrac{1}{4}z^2)=\frac{(\frac{1}{2}z)^\nu e^{-z}}{\Gamma(\nu+1)}M(\nu+\tfrac{1}{2},2\nu+1,2z)=\frac{z^{-\frac{1}{2}}M_{0,\nu}(2z)}{2^{2\nu+\frac{1}{2}}\Gamma(\nu+1)}$$

9.6.48 $$K_\nu(z)=\left(\frac{\pi}{2z}\right)^{\frac{1}{2}}W_{0,\nu}(2z)$$

(${}_0F_1$ is the generalized hypergeometric function. For $M(a,b,z)$, $M_{0,\nu}(z)$ and $W_{0,\nu}(z)$ see chapter **13**.)

Connection With Legendre Functions

If μ and z are fixed, $\mathscr{R}z>0$, and $\nu\to\infty$ through real positive values

9.6.49 $$\lim\left\{\nu^\mu P_\nu^{-\mu}\left(\cosh\frac{z}{\nu}\right)\right\}=I_\mu(z)$$

9.6.50 $$\lim\left\{\nu^{-\mu}e^{-\mu\pi i}Q_\nu^\mu\left(\cosh\frac{z}{\nu}\right)\right\}=K_\mu(z)$$

For the definition of $P_\nu^{-\mu}$ and Q_ν^μ, see chapter **8.**

Multiplication Theorems

9.6.51

$$\mathscr{Z}_\nu(\lambda z)=\lambda^{\pm\nu}\sum_{k=0}^{\infty}\frac{(\lambda^2-1)^k(\frac{1}{2}z)^k}{k!}\mathscr{Z}_{\nu\pm k}(z) \qquad (|\lambda^2-1|<1)$$

If $\mathscr{Z}=I$ and the upper signs are taken, the restriction on λ is unnecessary.

9.6.52

$$I_\nu(z)=\sum_{k=0}^{\infty}\frac{z^k}{k!}J_{\nu+k}(z), \qquad J_\nu(z)=\sum_{k=0}^{\infty}(-)^k\frac{z^k}{k!}I_{\nu+k}(z)$$

Neumann Series for $K_n(z)$

9.6.53

$$K_n(z)=(-)^{n-1}\{\ln(\tfrac{1}{2}z)-\psi(n+1)\}I_n(z)+\frac{n!(\frac{1}{2}z)^{-n}}{2}\sum_{k=0}^{n-1}(-)^k\frac{(\frac{1}{2}z)^kI_k(z)}{(n-k)k!}+(-)^n\sum_{k=1}^{\infty}\frac{(n+2k)I_{n+2k}(z)}{k(n+k)}$$

9.6.54 $$K_0(z)=-\{\ln(\tfrac{1}{2}z)+\gamma\}I_0(z)+2\sum_{k=1}^{\infty}\frac{I_{2k}(z)}{k}$$

Zeros

Properties of the zeros of $I_\nu(z)$ and $K_\nu(z)$ may be deduced from those of $J_\nu(z)$ and $H_\nu^{(1)}(z)$ respectively, by application of the transformations **9.6.3** and **9.6.4.**

For example, if ν is real the zeros of $I_\nu(z)$ are all complex unless $-2k<\nu<-(2k-1)$ for some positive integer k, in which event $I_\nu(z)$ has two real zeros.

The approximate distribution of the zeros of $K_n(z)$ in the region $-\frac{3}{2}\pi\leq\arg z\leq\frac{1}{2}\pi$ is obtained on rotating **Figure 9.6** through an angle $-\frac{1}{2}\pi$ so that the cut lies along the positive imaginary axis. The zeros in the region $-\frac{1}{2}\pi\leq\arg z\leq\frac{3}{2}\pi$ are their conjugates. $K_n(z)$ has no zeros in the region $|\arg z|\leq\frac{1}{2}\pi$; this result remains true when n is replaced by any real number ν.

9.7. Asymptotic Expansions

Asymptotic Expansions for Large Arguments

When ν is fixed, $|z|$ is large and $\mu=4\nu^2$

9.7.1

$$I_\nu(z)\sim\frac{e^z}{\sqrt{2\pi z}}\left\{1-\frac{\mu-1}{8z}+\frac{(\mu-1)(\mu-9)}{2!(8z)^2}-\frac{(\mu-1)(\mu-9)(\mu-25)}{3!(8z)^3}+\ldots\right\} \qquad (|\arg z|<\tfrac{1}{2}\pi)$$

9.7.2

$$K_\nu(z)\sim\sqrt{\frac{\pi}{2z}}\,e^{-z}\{1+\frac{\mu-1}{8z}+\frac{(\mu-1)(\mu-9)}{2!(8z)^2}+\frac{(\mu-1)(\mu-9)(\mu-25)}{3!(8z)^3}+\ldots\}\qquad(|\arg z|<\tfrac{3}{2}\pi)$$

9.7.3

$$I'_\nu(z)\sim\frac{e^z}{\sqrt{2\pi z}}\{1-\frac{\mu+3}{8z}+\frac{(\mu-1)(\mu+15)}{2!(8z)^2}-\frac{(\mu-1)(\mu-9)(\mu+35)}{3!(8z)^3}+\ldots\}\qquad(|\arg z|<\tfrac{1}{2}\pi)$$

9.7.4

$$K'_\nu(z)\sim-\sqrt{\frac{\pi}{2z}}e^{-z}\{1+\frac{\mu+3}{8z}+\frac{(\mu-1)(\mu+15)}{2!(8z)^2}+\frac{(\mu-1)(\mu-9)(\mu+35)}{3!(8z)^3}+\ldots\}\qquad(|\arg z|<\tfrac{3}{2}\pi)$$

The general terms in the last two expansions can be written down by inspection of **9.2.15** and **9.2.16.**

If ν is real and non-negative and z is positive the remainder after k terms in the expansion **9.7.2** does not exceed the $(k+1)$th term in absolute value and is of the same sign, provided that $k\geq\nu-\frac{1}{2}$.

9.7.5

$$I_\nu(z)K_\nu(z)\sim\frac{1}{2z}\{1-\frac{1}{2}\frac{\mu-1}{(2z)^2}+\frac{1\cdot3}{2\cdot4}\frac{(\mu-1)(\mu-9)}{(2z)^4}-\ldots\}\qquad(|\arg z|<\tfrac{1}{2}\pi)$$

9.7.6

$$I'_\nu(z)K'_\nu(z)\sim-\frac{1}{2z}\{1+\frac{1}{2}\frac{\mu-3}{(2z)^2}-\frac{1\cdot1}{2\cdot4}\frac{(\mu-1)(\mu-45)}{(2z)^4}+\ldots\}\qquad(|\arg z|<\tfrac{1}{2}\pi)$$

The general terms can be written down by inspection of **9.2.28** and **9.2.30.**

Uniform Asymptotic Expansions for Large Orders

9.7.7 $$I_\nu(\nu z)\sim\frac{1}{\sqrt{2\pi\nu}}\frac{e^{\nu\eta}}{(1+z^2)^{1/4}}\{1+\sum_{k=1}^{\infty}\frac{u_k(t)}{\nu^k}\}$$

9.7.8

$$K_\nu(\nu z)\sim\sqrt{\frac{\pi}{2\nu}}\frac{e^{-\nu\eta}}{(1+z^2)^{1/4}}\{1+\sum_{k=1}^{\infty}(-)^k\frac{u_k(t)}{\nu^k}\}$$

9.7.9 $$I'_\nu(\nu z)\sim\frac{1}{\sqrt{2\pi\nu}}\frac{(1+z^2)^{1/4}}{z}e^{\nu\eta}\{1+\sum_{k=1}^{\infty}\frac{v_k(t)}{\nu^k}\}$$

9.7.10

$$K'_\nu(\nu z)\sim-\sqrt{\frac{\pi}{2\nu}}\frac{(1+z^2)^{1/4}}{z}e^{-\nu\eta}\{1+\sum_{k=1}^{\infty}(-)^k\frac{v_k(t)}{\nu^k}\}$$

When $\nu\to+\infty$, these expansions hold uniformly with respect to z in the sector $|\arg z|\leq\frac{1}{2}\pi-\epsilon$, where ϵ is an arbitrary positive number. Here

9.7.11 $$t=1/\sqrt{1+z^2},\qquad\eta=\sqrt{1+z^2}+\ln\frac{z}{1+\sqrt{1+z^2}}$$

and $u_k(t)$, $v_k(t)$ are given by **9.3.9, 9.3.10, 9.3.13** and **9.3.14**. See [9.38] for tables of η, $u_k(t)$, $v_k(t)$, and also for bounds on the remainder terms in **9.7.7** to **9.7.10**.

9.8. Polynomial Approximations [4]

In equations **9.8.1** to **9.8.4**, $t=x/3.75$.

9.8.1 $$-3.75\leq x\leq3.75$$

$$I_0(x)=1+3.51562\,29t^2+3.08994\,24t^4+1.20674\,92t^6+.26597\,32t^8+.03607\,68t^{10}+.00458\,13t^{12}+\epsilon$$

$$|\epsilon|<1.6\times10^{-7}$$

9.8.2 $$3.75\leq x<\infty$$

$$x^{\frac{1}{2}}e^{-x}I_0(x)=.39894\,228+.01328\,592t^{-1}+.00225\,319t^{-2}-.00157\,565t^{-3}+.00916\,281t^{-4}-.02057\,706t^{-5}+.02635\,537t^{-6}-.01647\,633t^{-7}+.00392\,377t^{-8}+\epsilon$$

$$|\epsilon|<1.9\times10^{-7}$$

9.8.3 $$-3.75\leq x\leq3.75$$

$$x^{-1}I_1(x)=\tfrac{1}{2}+.87890\,594t^2+.51498\,869t^4+.15084\,934t^6+.02658\,733t^8+.00301\,532t^{10}+.00032\,411t^{12}+\epsilon$$

$$|\epsilon|<8\times10^{-9}$$

9.8.4 $$3.75\leq x<\infty$$

$$x^{\frac{1}{2}}e^{-x}I_1(x)=.39894\,228-.03988\,024t^{-1}-.00362\,018t^{-2}+.00163\,801t^{-3}-.01031\,555t^{-4}+.02282\,967t^{-5}-.02895\,312t^{-6}+.01787\,654t^{-7}-.00420\,059t^{-8}+\epsilon$$

$$|\epsilon|<2.2\times10^{-7}$$

[4] See footnote 2, section **9.4**.

.8.5 $\qquad 0<x\leq 2$

$$K_0(x)=-\ln(x/2)I_0(x)-.57721\ 566$$
$$+.42278\ 420(x/2)^2+.23069\ 756(x/2)^4$$
$$+.03488\ 590(x/2)^6+.00262\ 698(x/2)^8$$
$$+.00010\ 750(x/2)^{10}+.00000\ 740(x/2)^{12}+\epsilon$$
$$|\epsilon|<1\times 10^{-8}$$

.8.6 $\qquad 2\leq x<\infty$

$$x^{\frac{1}{2}}e^xK_0(x)=1.25331\ 414-.07832\ 358(2/x)$$
$$+.02189\ 568(2/x)^2-.01062\ 446(2/x)^3$$
$$+.00587\ 872(2/x)^4-.00251\ 540(2/x)^5$$
$$+.00053\ 208(2/x)^6+\epsilon$$
$$|\epsilon|<1.9\times 10^{-7}$$

.8.7 $\qquad 0<x\leq 2$

$$xK_1(x)=x\ln(x/2)I_1(x)+1+.15443\ 144(x/2)^2$$
$$-.67278\ 579(x/2)^4-.18156\ 897(x/2)^6$$
$$-.01919\ 402(x/2)^8-.00110\ 404(x/2)^{10}$$
$$-.00004\ 686(x/2)^{12}+\epsilon$$
$$|\epsilon|<8\times 10^{-9}$$

.8.8 $\qquad 2\leq x<\infty$

$$x^{\frac{1}{2}}e^xK_1(x)=1.25331\ 414+.23498\ 619(2/x)$$
$$-.03655\ 620(2/x)^2+.01504\ 268(2/x)^3$$
$$-.00780\ 353(2/x)^4+.00325\ 614(2/x)^5$$
$$-.00068\ 245(2/x)^6+\epsilon$$
$$|\epsilon|<2.2\times 10^{-7}$$

For expansions of $I_0(x)$, $K_0(x)$, $I_1(x)$, and $K_1(x)$ in series of Chebyshev polynomials for the ranges $0\leq x\leq 8$ and $0\leq 8/x\leq 1$, see [9.37].

Kelvin Functions

9.9. Definitions and Properties

In this and the following section ν is real, x is real and non-negative, and n is again a positive integer or zero.

Definitions

9.9.1

$$\mathrm{ber}_\nu x+i\,\mathrm{bei}_\nu x=J_\nu(xe^{3\pi i/4})=e^{\nu\pi i}J_\nu(xe^{-\pi i/4})$$
$$=e^{\frac{1}{2}\nu\pi i}I_\nu(xe^{\pi i/4})=e^{3\nu\pi i/2}I_\nu(xe^{-3\pi i/4})$$

9.9.2

$$\mathrm{ker}_\nu x+i\,\mathrm{kei}_\nu x=e^{-\frac{1}{2}\nu\pi i}K_\nu(xe^{\pi i/4})$$
$$=\tfrac{1}{2}\pi iH_\nu^{(1)}(xe^{3\pi i/4})=-\tfrac{1}{2}\pi ie^{-\nu\pi i}H_\nu^{(2)}(xe^{-\pi i/4})$$

When $\nu=0$, suffices are usually suppressed.

Differential Equations

9.9.3

$$x^2w''+xw'-(ix^2+\nu^2)w=0,$$
$$w=\mathrm{ber}_\nu x+i\,\mathrm{bei}_\nu x,\quad \mathrm{ber}_{-\nu} x+i\,\mathrm{bei}_{-\nu} x,$$
$$\mathrm{ker}_\nu x+i\,\mathrm{kei}_\nu x,\quad \mathrm{ker}_{-\nu} x+i\,\mathrm{kei}_{-\nu} x$$

9.9.4

$$x^4w^{iv}+2x^3w'''-(1+2\nu^2)(x^2w''-xw')$$
$$+(\nu^4-4\nu^2+x^4)w=0,$$
$$w=\mathrm{ber}_{\pm\nu} x,\ \mathrm{bei}_{\pm\nu} x,\ \mathrm{ker}_{\pm\nu} x,\ \mathrm{kei}_{\pm\nu} x$$

Relations Between Solutions

9.9.5

$$\mathrm{ber}_{-\nu} x=\cos(\nu\pi)\,\mathrm{ber}_\nu x+\sin(\nu\pi)\,\mathrm{bei}_\nu x$$
$$+(2/\pi)\sin(\nu\pi)\,\mathrm{ker}_\nu x$$

$$\mathrm{bei}_{-\nu} x=-\sin(\nu\pi)\,\mathrm{ber}_\nu x+\cos(\nu\pi)\,\mathrm{bei}_\nu x$$
$$+(2/\pi)\sin(\nu\pi)\,\mathrm{kei}_\nu x$$

9.9.6

$$\mathrm{ker}_{-\nu} x=\cos(\nu\pi)\,\mathrm{ker}_\nu x-\sin(\nu\pi)\,\mathrm{kei}_\nu x$$
$$\mathrm{kei}_{-\nu} x=\sin(\nu\pi)\,\mathrm{ker}_\nu x+\cos(\nu\pi)\,\mathrm{kei}_\nu x$$

9.9.7 $\quad \mathrm{ber}_{-n} x=(-)^n\,\mathrm{ber}_n x,\quad \mathrm{bei}_{-n} x=(-)^n\,\mathrm{bei}_n x$

9.9.8 $\quad \mathrm{ker}_{-n} x=(-)^n\,\mathrm{ker}_n x,\quad \mathrm{kei}_{-n} x=(-)^n\,\mathrm{kei}_n x$

Ascending Series

9.9.9

$$\mathrm{ber}_\nu x=(\tfrac{1}{2}x)^\nu\sum_{k=0}^{\infty}\frac{\cos\{(\frac{3}{4}\nu+\frac{1}{2}k)\pi\}}{k!\Gamma(\nu+k+1)}(\tfrac{1}{4}x^2)^k$$

$$\mathrm{bei}_\nu x=(\tfrac{1}{2}x)^\nu\sum_{k=0}^{\infty}\frac{\sin\{(\frac{3}{4}\nu+\frac{1}{2}k)\pi\}}{k!\Gamma(\nu+k+1)}(\tfrac{1}{4}x^2)^k$$

9.9.10

$$\mathrm{ber}\,x=1-\frac{(\frac{1}{4}x^2)^2}{(2!)^2}+\frac{(\frac{1}{4}x^2)^4}{(4!)^2}-\cdots$$

$$\mathrm{bei}\,x=\tfrac{1}{4}x^2-\frac{(\frac{1}{4}x^2)^3}{(3!)^2}+\frac{(\frac{1}{4}x^2)^5}{(5!)^2}-\cdots$$

9.9.11

$$\mathrm{ker}_n x=\tfrac{1}{2}(\tfrac{1}{2}x)^{-n}\sum_{k=0}^{n-1}\cos\{(\tfrac{3}{4}n+\tfrac{1}{2}k)\pi\}$$
$$\times\frac{(n-k-1)!}{k!}(\tfrac{1}{4}x^2)^k-\ln(\tfrac{1}{2}x)\,\mathrm{ber}_n x+\tfrac{1}{4}\pi\,\mathrm{bei}_n x$$
$$+\tfrac{1}{2}(\tfrac{1}{2}x)^n\sum_{k=0}^{\infty}\cos\{(\tfrac{3}{4}n+\tfrac{1}{2}k)\pi\}$$
$$\times\frac{\{\psi(k+1)+\psi(n+k+1)\}}{k!(n+k)!}(\tfrac{1}{4}x^2)^k$$

$$\operatorname{kei}_n x = -\tfrac{1}{2}(\tfrac{1}{2}x)^{-n}\sum_{k=0}^{n-1}\sin\{(\tfrac{3}{4}n+\tfrac{1}{2}k)\pi\}$$
$$\times\frac{(n-k-1)!}{k!}(\tfrac{1}{4}x^2)^k - \ln(\tfrac{1}{2}x)\operatorname{bei}_n x - \tfrac{1}{4}\pi\operatorname{ber}_n x$$
$$+\tfrac{1}{2}(\tfrac{1}{2}x)^n\sum_{k=0}^{\infty}\sin\{(\tfrac{3}{4}n+\tfrac{1}{2}k)\pi\}$$
$$\times\frac{\{\psi(k+1)+\psi(n+k+1)\}}{k!(n+k)!}(\tfrac{1}{4}x^2)^k$$

where $\psi(n)$ is given by **6.3.2.**

9.9.12

$$\ker x = -\ln(\tfrac{1}{2}x)\operatorname{ber} x + \tfrac{1}{4}\pi\operatorname{bei} x + \sum_{k=0}^{\infty}(-)^k\frac{\psi(2k+1)}{\{(2k)!\}^2}(\tfrac{1}{4}x^2)^{2k}$$

$$\operatorname{kei} x = -\ln(\tfrac{1}{2}x)\operatorname{bei} x - \tfrac{1}{4}\pi\operatorname{ber} x + \sum_{k=0}^{\infty}(-)^k\frac{\psi(2k+2)}{\{(2k+1)!\}^2}(\tfrac{1}{4}x^2)^{2k+1}$$

Functions of Negative Argument

In general Kelvin functions have a branch point at $x=0$ and individual functions with arguments $xe^{\pm\pi i}$ are complex. The branch point is absent however in the case of ber_ν and bei_ν when ν is an integer, and

9.9.13

$$\operatorname{ber}_n(-x) = (-)^n\operatorname{ber}_n x, \qquad \operatorname{bei}_n(-x) = (-)^n\operatorname{bei}_n x$$

Recurrence Relations

9.9.14

$$f_{\nu+1}+f_{\nu-1} = -\frac{\nu\sqrt{2}}{x}(f_\nu - g_\nu)$$
$$f'_\nu = \frac{1}{2\sqrt{2}}(f_{\nu+1}+g_{\nu+1}-f_{\nu-1}-g_{\nu-1})$$
$$f'_\nu - \frac{\nu}{x}f_\nu = \frac{1}{\sqrt{2}}(f_{\nu+1}+g_{\nu+1})$$
$$f'_\nu + \frac{\nu}{x}f_\nu = -\frac{1}{\sqrt{2}}(f_{\nu-1}+g_{\nu-1})$$

where

9.9.15

$$\left.\begin{aligned}f_\nu&=\operatorname{ber}_\nu x\\ g_\nu&=\operatorname{bei}_\nu x\end{aligned}\right\}\qquad \left.\begin{aligned}f_\nu&=\operatorname{bei}_\nu x\\ g_\nu&=-\operatorname{ber}_\nu x\end{aligned}\right\}$$
$$\left.\begin{aligned}f_\nu&=\ker_\nu x\\ g_\nu&=\operatorname{kei}_\nu x\end{aligned}\right\}\qquad \left.\begin{aligned}f_\nu&=\operatorname{kei}_\nu x\\ g_\nu&=-\ker_\nu x\end{aligned}\right\}$$

9.9.16

$$\sqrt{2}\operatorname{ber}' x = \operatorname{ber}_1 x + \operatorname{bei}_1 x$$
$$\sqrt{2}\operatorname{bei}' x = -\operatorname{ber}_1 x + \operatorname{bei}_1 x$$

9.9.17

$$\sqrt{2}\ker' x = \ker_1 x + \operatorname{kei}_1 x$$
$$\sqrt{2}\operatorname{kei}' x = -\ker_1 x + \operatorname{kei}_1 x$$

Recurrence Relations for Cross-Products

If

9.9.18

$$p_\nu = \operatorname{ber}_\nu^2 x + \operatorname{bei}_\nu^2 x$$
$$q_\nu = \operatorname{ber}_\nu x\operatorname{bei}'_\nu x - \operatorname{ber}'_\nu x\operatorname{bei}_\nu x$$
$$r_\nu = \operatorname{ber}_\nu x\operatorname{ber}'_\nu x + \operatorname{bei}_\nu x\operatorname{bei}'_\nu x$$
$$s_\nu = \operatorname{ber}'^2_\nu x + \operatorname{bei}'^2_\nu x$$

then

9.9.19

$$p_{\nu+1} = p_{\nu-1} - \frac{4\nu}{x}r_\nu$$
$$q_{\nu+1} = -\frac{\nu}{x}p_\nu + r_\nu = -q_{\nu-1} + 2r_\nu$$
$$r_{\nu+1} = -\frac{(\nu+1)}{x}p_{\nu+1} + q_\nu$$
$$s_\nu = \frac{1}{2}p_{\nu+1} + \frac{1}{2}p_{\nu-1} - \frac{\nu^2}{x^2}p_\nu$$

and

9.9.20 $$p_\nu s_\nu = r_\nu^2 + q_\nu^2$$

The same relations hold with ber, bei replaced throughout by ker, kei, respectively.

Indefinite Integrals

In the following f_ν, g_ν are any one of the pairs given by equations **9.9.15** and f_ν^*, g_ν^* are either the same pair or any other pair.

9.9.21

$$\int x^{1+\nu}f_\nu dx = -\frac{x^{1+\nu}}{\sqrt{2}}(f_{\nu+1}-g_{\nu+1}) = -x^{1+\nu}\left(\frac{\nu}{x}g_\nu - g'_\nu\right)$$

9.9.22

$$\int x^{1-\nu}f_\nu dx = \frac{x^{1-\nu}}{\sqrt{2}}(f_{\nu-1}-g_{\nu-1}) = x^{1-\nu}\left(\frac{\nu}{x}g_\nu + g'_\nu\right)$$

9.9.23

$$\int x(f_\nu g_\nu^* - g_\nu f_\nu^*)dx = \frac{x}{2\sqrt{2}}\{f_\nu^*(f_{\nu+1}+g_{\nu+1})$$
$$-g_\nu^*(f_{\nu+1}-g_{\nu+1}) - f_\nu(f_{\nu+1}^*+g_{\nu+1}^*) + g_\nu(f_{\nu+1}^*-g_{\nu+1}^*)\}$$
$$=\frac{1}{2}x(f'_\nu f_\nu^* - f_\nu f_\nu^{*\prime} + g'_\nu g_\nu^* - g_\nu g_\nu^{*\prime})$$

9.9.24

$$\int x(f_\nu g_\nu^* + g_\nu f_\nu^*)dx = \frac{1}{4} x^2(2f_\nu g_\nu^* - f_{\nu-1}g_{\nu+1}^* - f_{\nu+1}g_{\nu-1}^* + 2g_\nu f_\nu^* - g_{\nu-1}f_{\nu+1}^* - g_{\nu+1}f_{\nu-1}^*)$$

9.9.25

$$\int x(f_\nu^2 + g_\nu^2)dx = x(f_\nu g_\nu' - f_\nu' g_\nu) = -(x/\sqrt{2})(f_\nu f_{\nu+1} + g_\nu g_{\nu+1} - f_\nu g_{\nu+1} + f_{\nu+1} g_\nu)$$

9.9.26

$$\int x f_\nu g_\nu dx = \frac{1}{4} x^2(2f_\nu g_\nu - f_{\nu-1}g_{\nu+1} - f_{\nu+1}g_{\nu-1})$$

9.9.27

$$\int x(f_\nu^2 - g_\nu^2)dx = \frac{1}{2} x^2(f_\nu^2 - f_{\nu-1}f_{\nu+1} - g_\nu^2 + g_{\nu-1}g_{\nu+1})$$

Ascending Series for Cross-Products

9.9.28

$$\mathrm{ber}_\nu^2 x + \mathrm{bei}_\nu^2 x = (\tfrac{1}{2}x)^{2\nu} \sum_{k=0}^\infty \frac{1}{\Gamma(\nu+k+1)\Gamma(\nu+2k+1)} \frac{(\frac{1}{4}x^2)^{2k}}{k!}$$

9.9.29

$$\mathrm{ber}_\nu x \, \mathrm{bei}_\nu' x - \mathrm{ber}_\nu' x \, \mathrm{bei}_\nu x = (\tfrac{1}{2}x)^{2\nu+1} \sum_{k=0}^\infty \frac{1}{\Gamma(\nu+k+1)\Gamma(\nu+2k+2)} \frac{(\frac{1}{4}x^2)^{2k}}{k!}$$

9.9.30

$$\mathrm{ber}_\nu x \, \mathrm{ber}_\nu' x + \mathrm{bei}_\nu x \, \mathrm{bei}_\nu' x = \tfrac{1}{2}(\tfrac{1}{2}x)^{2\nu-1} \sum_{k=0}^\infty \frac{1}{\Gamma(\nu+k+1)\Gamma(\nu+2k)} \frac{(\frac{1}{4}x^2)^{2k}}{k!}$$

9.9.31

$$\mathrm{ber}_\nu'^2 x + \mathrm{bei}_\nu'^2 x = (\tfrac{1}{2}x)^{2\nu-2} \sum_{k=0}^\infty \frac{(2k^2+2\nu k+\frac{1}{4}\nu^2)}{\Gamma(\nu+k+1)\Gamma(\nu+2k+1)} \frac{(\frac{1}{4}x^2)^{2k}}{k!}$$

Expansions in Series of Bessel Functions

9.9.32

$$\mathrm{ber}_\nu x + i \, \mathrm{bei}_\nu x = \sum_{k=0}^\infty \frac{e^{(3\nu+k)\pi i/4} x^k J_{\nu+k}(x)}{2^{\frac{1}{2}k} \, k!} = \sum_{k=0}^\infty \frac{e^{(3\nu+3k)\pi i/4} x^k I_{\nu+k}(x)}{2^{\frac{1}{2}k} \, k!}$$

9.9.33

$$\mathrm{ber}_n(x\sqrt{2}) = \sum_{k=-\infty}^\infty (-)^{n+k} J_{n+2k}(x) I_{2k}(x)$$

$$\mathrm{bei}_n(x\sqrt{2}) = \sum_{k=-\infty}^\infty (-)^{n+k} J_{n+2k+1}(x) I_{2k+1}(x)$$

Zeros of Functions of Order Zero [5]

	ber x	bei x	ker x	kei x
1st zero	2. 84892	5. 02622	1. 71854	3. 91467
2nd zero	7. 23883	9. 45541	6. 12728	8. 34422
3rd zero	11. 67396	13. 89349	10. 56294	12. 78256
4th zero	16. 11356	18. 33398	15. 00269	17. 22314
5th zero	20. 55463	22. 77544	19. 44381	21. 66464

	ber′ x	bei′ x	ker′ x	kei′ x
1st zero	6. 03871	3. 77320	2. 66584	4. 93181
2nd zero	10. 51364	8. 28099	7. 17212	9. 40405
3rd zero	14. 96844	12. 74215	11. 63218	13. 85827
4th zero	19. 41758	17. 19343	16. 08312	18. 30717
5th zero	23. 86430	21. 64114	20. 53068	22. 75379

9.10. Asymptotic Expansions

Asymptotic Expansions for Large Arguments

When ν is fixed and x is large

9.10.1

$$\mathrm{ber}_\nu x = \frac{e^{x/\sqrt{2}}}{\sqrt{2\pi x}} \{f_\nu(x) \cos\alpha + g_\nu(x) \sin\alpha\} - \frac{1}{\pi} \{\sin(2\nu\pi) \, \mathrm{ker}_\nu x + \cos(2\nu\pi) \, \mathrm{kei}_\nu x\}$$

9.10.2

$$\mathrm{bei}_\nu x = \frac{e^{x/\sqrt{2}}}{\sqrt{2\pi x}} \{f_\nu(x) \sin\alpha - g_\nu(x) \cos\alpha\} + \frac{1}{\pi} \{\cos(2\nu\pi) \, \mathrm{ker}_\nu x - \sin(2\nu\pi) \, \mathrm{kei}_\nu x\}$$

9.10.3

$$\mathrm{ker}_\nu x = \sqrt{\pi/(2x)} \, e^{-x/\sqrt{2}} \{f_\nu(-x) \cos\beta - g_\nu(-x) \sin\beta\}$$

9.10.4

$$\mathrm{kei}_\nu x = \sqrt{\pi/(2x)} \, e^{-x/\sqrt{2}} \{-f_\nu(-x) \sin\beta - g_\nu(-x) \cos\beta\}$$

where

9.10.5

$$\alpha = (x/\sqrt{2}) + (\tfrac{1}{2}\nu - \tfrac{1}{8})\pi, \qquad \beta = (x/\sqrt{2}) + (\tfrac{1}{2}\nu + \tfrac{1}{8})\pi = \alpha + \tfrac{1}{4}\pi$$

and, with $4\nu^2$ denoted by μ,

9.10.6

$$f_\nu(\pm x) \sim 1 + \sum_{k=1}^\infty (\mp)^k \frac{(\mu-1)(\mu-9)\ldots\{\mu-(2k-1)^2\}}{k!(8x)^k} \cos\left(\frac{k\pi}{4}\right)$$

[5] From British Association for the Advancement of Science, Annual Report (J. R. Airey), 254 (1927)

9.10.7

$$g_\nu(\pm x) \sim \sum_{k=1}^{\infty} (\mp)^k \frac{(\mu-1)(\mu-9)\ldots\{\mu-(2k-1)^2\}}{k!(8x)^k} \sin\left(\frac{k\pi}{4}\right)$$

The terms in $\ker_\nu x$ and $\mathrm{kei}_\nu x$ in equations **9.10.1** and **9.10.2** are asymptotically negligible compared with the other terms, but their inclusion in numerical calculations yields improved accuracy.

The corresponding series for $\mathrm{ber}'_\nu x$, $\mathrm{bei}'_\nu x$, $\ker'_\nu x$ and $\mathrm{kei}'_\nu x$ can be derived from **9.2.11** and **9.2.13** with $z=xe^{3\pi i/4}$; the extra terms in the expansions of $\mathrm{ber}'_\nu x$ and $\mathrm{bei}'_\nu x$ are respectively

$$-(1/\pi)\{\sin(2\nu\pi)\ker'_\nu x+\cos(2\nu\pi)\mathrm{kei}'_\nu x\}$$

and

$$(1/\pi)\{\cos(2\nu\pi)\ker'_\nu x-\sin(2\nu\pi)\mathrm{kei}'_\nu x\}.$$

Modulus and Phase

9.10.8

$$M_\nu=\sqrt{(\mathrm{ber}_\nu^2 x+\mathrm{bei}_\nu^2 x)},\qquad \theta_\nu=\arctan\,(\mathrm{bei}_\nu x/\mathrm{ber}_\nu x)$$

9.10.9 $\quad \mathrm{ber}_\nu x=M_\nu \cos\theta_\nu,\qquad \mathrm{bei}_\nu x=M_\nu \sin\theta_\nu$

9.10.10 $\quad M_{-n}=M_n,\qquad \theta_{-n}=\theta_n-n\pi$

9.10.11

$$\begin{aligned}\mathrm{ber}'_\nu x&=\tfrac{1}{2}M_{\nu+1}\cos(\theta_{\nu+1}-\tfrac{1}{4}\pi)-\tfrac{1}{2}M_{\nu-1}\cos(\theta_{\nu-1}-\tfrac{1}{4}\pi)\\&=(\nu/x)M_\nu\cos\theta_\nu+M_{\nu+1}\cos(\theta_{\nu+1}-\tfrac{1}{4}\pi)\\&=-(\nu/x)M_\nu\cos\theta_\nu-M_{\nu-1}\cos(\theta_{\nu-1}-\tfrac{1}{4}\pi)\end{aligned}$$

9.10.12

$$\begin{aligned}\mathrm{bei}'_\nu x&=\tfrac{1}{2}M_{\nu+1}\sin(\theta_{\nu+1}-\tfrac{1}{4}\pi)-\tfrac{1}{2}M_{\nu-1}\sin(\theta_{\nu-1}-\tfrac{1}{4}\pi)\\&=(\nu/x)M_\nu\sin\theta_\nu+M_{\nu+1}\sin(\theta_{\nu+1}-\tfrac{1}{4}\pi)\\&=-(\nu/x)M_\nu\sin\theta_\nu-M_{\nu-1}\sin(\theta_{\nu-1}-\tfrac{1}{4}\pi)\end{aligned}$$

9.10.13

$$\mathrm{ber}'\,x=M_1\cos(\theta_1-\tfrac{1}{4}\pi),\qquad \mathrm{bei}'\,x=M_1\sin(\theta_1-\tfrac{1}{4}\pi)$$

9.10.14

$$\begin{aligned}M'_\nu&=(\nu/x)M_\nu+M_{\nu+1}\cos(\theta_{\nu+1}-\theta_\nu-\tfrac{1}{4}\pi)\\&=-(\nu/x)M_\nu-M_{\nu-1}\cos(\theta_{\nu-1}-\theta_\nu-\tfrac{1}{4}\pi)\end{aligned}$$

9.10.15

$$\begin{aligned}\theta'_\nu&=(M_{\nu+1}/M_\nu)\sin(\theta_{\nu+1}-\theta_\nu-\tfrac{1}{4}\pi)\\&=-(M_{\nu-1}/M_\nu)\sin(\theta_{\nu-1}-\theta_\nu-\tfrac{1}{4}\pi)\end{aligned}$$

9.10.16

$$\begin{aligned}M'_0&=M_1\cos(\theta_1-\theta_0-\tfrac{1}{4}\pi)\\\theta'_0&=(M_1/M_0)\sin(\theta_1-\theta_0-\tfrac{1}{4}\pi)\end{aligned}$$

9.10.17

$$d(xM_\nu^2\theta'_\nu)/dx=xM_\nu^2,\qquad x^2M''_\nu+xM'_\nu-\nu^2M_\nu=x^2M_\nu\theta'^2_\nu$$

9.10.18

$$N_\nu=\sqrt{(\ker_\nu^2 x+\mathrm{kei}_\nu^2 x)},\qquad \phi_\nu=\arctan\,(\mathrm{kei}_\nu x/\ker_\nu x)$$

9.10.19 $\quad \ker_\nu x=N_\nu\cos\phi_\nu,\qquad \mathrm{kei}_\nu x=N_\nu\sin\phi_\nu$

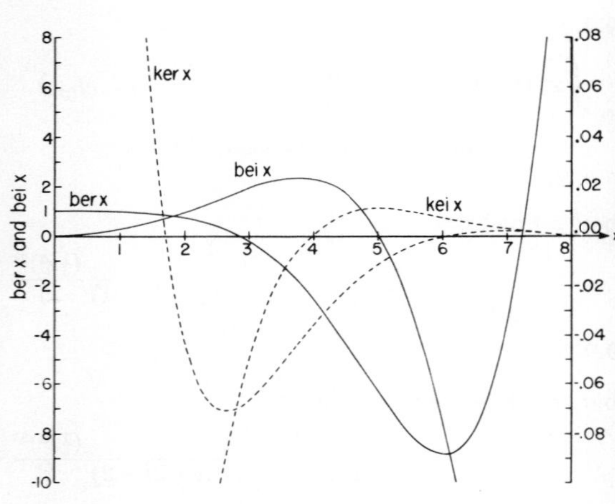

FIGURE 9.10. ber x, bei x, ker x *and* kei x.

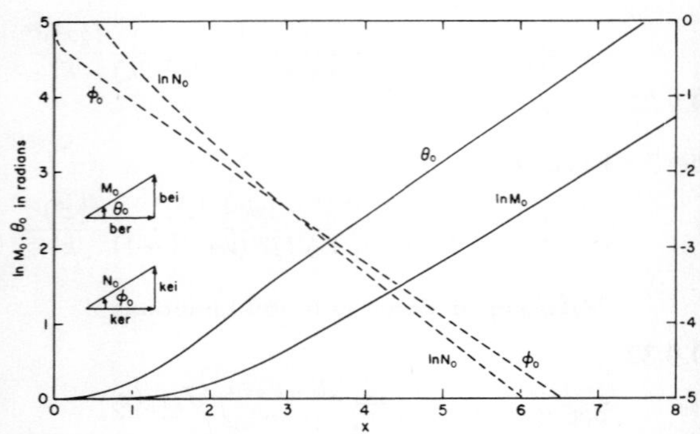

FIGURE 9.11. ln $M_0(x)$, $\theta_0(x)$, ln $N_0(x)$ *and* $\phi_0(x)$.

Equations **9.10.11** to **9.10.17** hold with the symbols b, M, θ replaced throughout by k, N, ϕ, respectively. In place of **9.10.10**

9.10.20 $\quad N_{-\nu}=N_\nu,\qquad \phi_{-\nu}=\phi_\nu+\nu\pi$

Asymptotic Expansions of Modulus and Phase

When ν is fixed, x is large and $\mu=4\nu^2$

9.10.21

$$M_\nu=\frac{e^{x/\sqrt{2}}}{\sqrt{2\pi x}}\left\{1-\frac{\mu-1}{8\sqrt{2}}\frac{1}{x}+\frac{(\mu-1)^2}{256}\frac{1}{x^2}-\frac{(\mu-1)(\mu^2+14\mu-399)}{6144\sqrt{2}}\frac{1}{x^3}+O\left(\frac{1}{x^4}\right)\right\}$$

9.10.22

$$\ln M_\nu=\frac{x}{\sqrt{2}}-\tfrac{1}{2}\ln(2\pi x)-\frac{\mu-1}{8\sqrt{2}}\frac{1}{x}-\frac{(\mu-1)(\mu-25)}{384\sqrt{2}}\frac{1}{x^3}-\frac{(\mu-1)(\mu-13)}{128}\frac{1}{x^4}+O\left(\frac{1}{x^5}\right)$$

9.10.23

$$\theta_\nu=\frac{x}{\sqrt{2}}+\left(\frac{1}{2}\nu-\frac{1}{8}\right)\pi+\frac{\mu-1}{8\sqrt{2}}\frac{1}{x}+\frac{\mu-1}{16}\frac{1}{x^2}-\frac{(\mu-1)(\mu-25)}{384\sqrt{2}}\frac{1}{x^3}+O\left(\frac{1}{x^5}\right)$$

9.10.24

$$N_\nu=\sqrt{\frac{\pi}{2x}}\,e^{-x/\sqrt{2}}\left\{1+\frac{\mu-1}{8\sqrt{2}}\frac{1}{x}+\frac{(\mu-1)^2}{256}\frac{1}{x^2}+\frac{(\mu-1)(\mu^2+14\mu-399)}{6144\sqrt{2}}\frac{1}{x^3}+O\left(\frac{1}{x^4}\right)\right\}$$

9.10.25

$$\ln N_\nu=-\frac{x}{\sqrt{2}}+\tfrac{1}{2}\ln\left(\frac{\pi}{2x}\right)+\frac{\mu-1}{8\sqrt{2}}\frac{1}{x}+\frac{(\mu-1)(\mu-25)}{384\sqrt{2}}\frac{1}{x^3}-\frac{(\mu-1)(\mu-13)}{128}\frac{1}{x^4}+O\left(\frac{1}{x^5}\right)$$

9.10.26

$$\phi_\nu=-\frac{x}{\sqrt{2}}-\left(\frac{1}{2}\nu+\frac{1}{8}\right)\pi-\frac{\mu-1}{8\sqrt{2}}\frac{1}{x}+\frac{\mu-1}{16}\frac{1}{x^2}+\frac{(\mu-1)(\mu-25)}{384\sqrt{2}}\frac{1}{x^3}+O\left(\frac{1}{x^5}\right)$$

Asymptotic Expansions of Cross-Products

If x is large

9.10.27

$$\mathrm{ber}^2\,x+\mathrm{bei}^2\,x\sim\frac{e^{x\sqrt{2}}}{2\pi x}\left(1+\frac{1}{4\sqrt{2}}\frac{1}{x}+\frac{1}{64}\frac{1}{x^2}-\frac{33}{256\sqrt{2}}\frac{1}{x^3}-\frac{1797}{8192}\frac{1}{x^4}+\ldots\right)$$

9.10.28

$$\mathrm{ber}\,x\,\mathrm{bei}'\,x-\mathrm{ber}'\,x\,\mathrm{bei}\,x\sim\frac{e^{x\sqrt{2}}}{2\pi x}\left(\frac{1}{\sqrt{2}}+\frac{1}{8}\frac{1}{x}+\frac{9}{64\sqrt{2}}\frac{1}{x^2}+\frac{39}{512}\frac{1}{x^3}+\frac{75}{8192\sqrt{2}}\frac{1}{x^4}+\ldots\right)$$

9.10.29

$$\mathrm{ber}\,x\,\mathrm{ber}'\,x+\mathrm{bei}\,x\,\mathrm{bei}'\,x\sim\frac{e^{x\sqrt{2}}}{2\pi x}\left(\frac{1}{\sqrt{2}}-\frac{3}{8}\frac{1}{x}-\frac{15}{64\sqrt{2}}\frac{1}{x^2}-\frac{45}{512}\frac{1}{x^3}+\frac{315}{8192\sqrt{2}}\frac{1}{x^4}+\ldots\right)$$

9.10.30

$$\mathrm{ber}'^2\,x+\mathrm{bei}'^2\,x\sim\frac{e^{x\sqrt{2}}}{2\pi x}\left(1-\frac{3}{4\sqrt{2}}\frac{1}{x}+\frac{9}{64}\frac{1}{x^2}+\frac{75}{256\sqrt{2}}\frac{1}{x^3}+\frac{2475}{8192}\frac{1}{x^4}+\ldots\right)$$

9.10.31

$$\mathrm{ker}^2\,x+\mathrm{kei}^2\,x\sim\frac{\pi}{2x}e^{-x\sqrt{2}}\left(1-\frac{1}{4\sqrt{2}}\frac{1}{x}+\frac{1}{64}\frac{1}{x^2}+\frac{33}{256\sqrt{2}}\frac{1}{x^3}-\frac{1797}{8192}\frac{1}{x^4}+\ldots\right)$$

9.10.32

$$\mathrm{ker}\,x\,\mathrm{kei}'\,x-\mathrm{ker}'\,x\,\mathrm{kei}\,x\sim-\frac{\pi}{2x}e^{-x\sqrt{2}}\left(\frac{1}{\sqrt{2}}-\frac{1}{8}\frac{1}{x}+\frac{9}{64\sqrt{2}}\frac{1}{x^2}-\frac{39}{512}\frac{1}{x^3}+\frac{75}{8192\sqrt{2}}\frac{1}{x^4}+\ldots\right)$$

9.10.33

$$\mathrm{ker}\,x\,\mathrm{ker}'\,x+\mathrm{kei}\,x\,\mathrm{kei}'\,x\sim-\frac{\pi}{2x}e^{-x\sqrt{2}}\left(\frac{1}{\sqrt{2}}+\frac{3}{8}\frac{1}{x}-\frac{15}{64\sqrt{2}}\frac{1}{x^2}+\frac{45}{512}\frac{1}{x^3}+\frac{315}{8192\sqrt{2}}\frac{1}{x^4}+\ldots\right)$$

9.10.34

$$\mathrm{ker}'^2\,x+\mathrm{kei}'^2\,x\sim\frac{\pi}{2x}e^{-x\sqrt{2}}\left(1+\frac{3}{4\sqrt{2}}\frac{1}{x}+\frac{9}{64}\frac{1}{x^2}-\frac{75}{256\sqrt{2}}\frac{1}{x^3}+\frac{2475}{8192}\frac{1}{x^4}+\cdots\right)$$

Asymptotic Expansions of Large Zeros

Let

9.10.35

$$f(\delta)=\frac{\mu-1}{16\delta}+\frac{\mu-1}{32\delta^2}+\frac{(\mu-1)(5\mu+19)}{1536\delta^3}+\frac{3(\mu-1)^2}{512\delta^4}+\cdots$$

where $\mu=4\nu^2$. Then if s is a large positive integer

9.10.36

Zeros of $\mathrm{ber}_\nu\,x\sim\sqrt{2}\{\delta-f(\delta)\}$, $\quad\delta=(s-\tfrac{1}{2}\nu-\tfrac{3}{8})\pi$

Zeros of $\mathrm{bei}_\nu\,x\sim\sqrt{2}\{\delta-f(\delta)\}$, $\quad\delta=(s-\tfrac{1}{2}\nu+\tfrac{1}{8})\pi$

Zeros of $\mathrm{ker}_\nu\,x\sim\sqrt{2}\{\delta+f(-\delta)\}$, $\quad\delta=(s-\tfrac{1}{2}\nu-\tfrac{5}{8})\pi$

Zeros of $\mathrm{kei}_\nu\,x\sim\sqrt{2}\{\delta+f(-\delta)\}$, $\quad\delta=(s-\tfrac{1}{2}\nu-\tfrac{1}{8})\pi$

For $\nu=0$ these expressions give the sth zero of each function; for other values of ν the zeros represented may not be the sth.

Uniform Asymptotic Expansions for Large Orders

When ν is large and positive

9.10.37

$$\operatorname{ber}_\nu(\nu x)+i\operatorname{bei}_\nu(\nu x)\sim \frac{e^{\nu\xi}}{\sqrt{2\pi\nu\xi}}\left(\frac{xe^{3\pi i/4}}{1+\xi}\right)^\nu\{1+\sum_{k=1}^\infty \frac{u_k(\xi^{-1})}{\nu^k}\}$$

9.10.38

$$\operatorname{ker}_\nu(\nu x)+i\operatorname{kei}_\nu(\nu x)\sim\sqrt{\frac{\pi}{2\nu\xi}}\,e^{-\nu\xi}\left(\frac{xe^{3\pi i/4}}{1+\xi}\right)^{-\nu}\{1+\sum_{k=1}^\infty(-)^k\frac{u_k(\xi^{-1})}{\nu^k}\}$$

9.10.39

$$\operatorname{ber}'_\nu(\nu x)+i\operatorname{bei}'_\nu(\nu x)\sim\sqrt{\frac{\xi}{2\pi\nu}}\,\frac{e^{\nu\xi}}{x}\left(\frac{xe^{3\pi i/4}}{1+\xi}\right)^\nu\{1+\sum_{k=1}^\infty\frac{v_k(\xi^{-1})}{\nu^k}\}$$

9.10.40

$$\operatorname{ker}'_\nu(\nu x)+i\operatorname{kei}'_\nu(\nu x)\sim-\sqrt{\frac{\pi\xi}{2\nu}}\,\frac{e^{-\nu\xi}}{x}\left(\frac{xe^{3\pi i/4}}{1+\xi}\right)^{-\nu}\{1+\sum_{k=1}^\infty(-)^k\frac{v_k(\xi^{-1})}{\nu^k}\}$$

where

9.10.41 $\xi=\sqrt{1+ix^2}$

and $u_k(t)$, $v_k(t)$ are given by **9.3.9** and **9.3.13.** All fractional powers take their principal values.

9.11. Polynomial Approximations

9.11.1 $-8\leq x\leq 8$

$$\begin{aligned}\operatorname{ber} x=1&-64(x/8)^4+113.77777\ 774(x/8)^8\\&-32.36345\ 652(x/8)^{12}+2.64191\ 397(x/8)^{16}\\&-.08349\ 609(x/8)^{20}+.00122\ 552(x/8)^{24}\\&-.00000\ 901(x/8)^{28}+\epsilon\end{aligned}$$

$$|\epsilon|<1\times10^{-9}$$

9.11.2 $-8\leq x\leq 8$

$$\begin{aligned}\operatorname{bei} x=16(x/8)^2&-113.77777\ 774(x/8)^6\\&+72.81777\ 742(x/8)^{10}-10.56765\ 779(x/8)^{14}\\&+.52185\ 615(x/8)^{18}-.01103\ 667(x/8)^{22}\\&+.00011\ 346(x/8)^{26}+\epsilon\end{aligned}$$

$$|\epsilon|<6\times10^{-9}$$

9.11.3 $0<x\leq 8$

$$\begin{aligned}\operatorname{ker} x=-\ln(\tfrac12 x)\operatorname{ber} x+\tfrac14\pi\operatorname{bei} x-.57721\ 566\\-59.05819\ 744(x/8)^4+171.36272\ 133(x/8)^8\\-60.60977\ 451(x/8)^{12}+5.65539\ 121(x/8)^{16}\\-.19636\ 347(x/8)^{20}+.00309\ 699(x/8)^{24}\\-.00002\ 458(x/8)^{28}+\epsilon\end{aligned}$$

$$|\epsilon|<1\times10^{-8}$$

9.11.4 $0<x\leq 8$

$$\begin{aligned}\operatorname{kei} x=-\ln(\tfrac12 x)\operatorname{bei} x-\tfrac14\pi\operatorname{ber} x+6.76454\ 936(x/8)^2\\-142.91827\ 687(x/8)^6+124.23569\ 650(x/8)^{10}\\-21.30060\ 904(x/8)^{14}+1.17509\ 064(x/8)^{18}\\-.02695\ 875(x/8)^{22}+.00029\ 532(x/8)^{26}+\epsilon\end{aligned}$$

$$|\epsilon|<3\times10^{-9}$$

9.11.5 $-8\leq x\leq 8$

$$\begin{aligned}\operatorname{ber}' x=x[-4(x/8)^2+14.22222\ 222(x/8)^6\\-6.06814\ 810(x/8)^{10}+.66047\ 849(x/8)^{14}\\-.02609\ 253(x/8)^{18}+.00045\ 957(x/8)^{22}\\-.00000\ 394(x/8)^{26}]+\epsilon\end{aligned}$$

$$|\epsilon|<2.1\times10^{-8}$$

9.11.6 $-8\leq x\leq 8$

$$\begin{aligned}\operatorname{bei}' x=x[\tfrac12-10.66666\ 666(x/8)^4\\+11.37777\ 772(x/8)^8-2.31167\ 514(x/8)^{12}\\+.14677\ 204(x/8)^{16}-.00379\ 386(x/8)^{20}\\+.00004\ 609(x/8)^{24}]+\epsilon\end{aligned}$$

$$|\epsilon|<7\times10^{-8}$$

9.11.7 $0<x\leq 8$

$$\begin{aligned}\operatorname{ker}' x=-\ln(\tfrac12 x)\operatorname{ber}' x-x^{-1}\operatorname{ber} x+\tfrac14\pi\operatorname{bei}' x\\+x[-3.69113\ 734(x/8)^2+21.42034\ 017(x/8)^6\\-11.36433\ 272(x/8)^{10}+1.41384\ 780(x/8)^{14}\\-.06136\ 358(x/8)^{18}+.00116\ 137(x/8)^{22}\\-.00001\ 075(x/8)^{26}]+\epsilon\end{aligned}$$

$$|\epsilon|<8\times10^{-8}$$

9.11.8 $0<x\leq 8$

$$\mathrm{kei}'\,x=-\ln\left(\tfrac{1}{2}x\right)\mathrm{bei}'\,x-x^{-1}\,\mathrm{bei}\,x-\tfrac{1}{4}\pi\,\mathrm{ber}'\,x$$
$$+x[.21139\ 217-13.39858\ 846(x/8)^4$$
$$+19.41182\ 758(x/8)^8-4.65950\ 823(x/8)^{12}$$
$$+.33049\ 424(x/8)^{16}-.00926\ 707(x/8)^{20}$$
$$+.00011\ 997(x/8)^{24}]+\epsilon$$
$$|\epsilon|<7\times 10^{-8}$$

9.11.9 $8\leq x<\infty$

$$\mathrm{ker}\,x+i\,\mathrm{kei}\,x=f(x)(1+\epsilon_1)$$
$$f(x)=\sqrt{\frac{\pi}{2x}}\exp\left[-\frac{1+i}{\sqrt{2}}\,x+\theta(-x)\right]$$
$$|\epsilon_1|<1\times 10^{-7}$$

9.11.10 $8\leq x<\infty$

$$\mathrm{ber}\,x+i\,\mathrm{bei}\,x-\frac{i}{\pi}\left(\mathrm{ker}\,x+i\,\mathrm{kei}\,x\right)=g(x)(1+\epsilon_2)$$
$$g(x)=\frac{1}{\sqrt{2\pi x}}\exp\left[\frac{1+i}{\sqrt{2}}\,x+\theta(x)\right]$$
$$|\epsilon_2|<3\times 10^{-7}$$

where

9.11.11

$$\theta(x)=(.00000\ 00-.39269\ 91i)$$
$$+(.01104\ 86-.01104\ 85i)(8/x)$$
$$+(.00000\ 00-.00097\ 65i)(8/x)^2$$
$$+(-.00009\ 06-.00009\ 01i)(8/x)^3$$
$$+(-.00002\ 52+.00000\ 00i)(8/x)^4$$
$$+(-.00000\ 34+.00000\ 51i)(8/x)^5$$
$$+(.00000\ 06+.00000\ 19i)(8/x)^6$$

9.11.12 $8\leq x<\infty$

$$\mathrm{ker}'\,x+i\,\mathrm{kei}'\,x=-f(x)\phi(-x)(1+\epsilon_3)$$
$$|\epsilon_3|<2\times 10^{-7}$$

9.11.13 $8\leq x<\infty$

$$\mathrm{ber}'\,x+i\,\mathrm{bei}'\,x-\frac{i}{\pi}\left(\mathrm{ker}'\,x+i\,\mathrm{kei}'\,x\right)=g(x)\phi(x)(1+\epsilon_4)$$
$$|\epsilon_4|<3\times 10^{-7}$$

where

9.11.14

$$\phi(x)=(.70710\ 68+.70710\ 68i)$$
$$+(-.06250\ 01-.00000\ 01i)(8/x)$$
$$+(-.00138\ 13+.00138\ 11i)(8/x)^2$$
$$+(.00000\ 05+.00024\ 52i)(8/x)^3$$
$$+(.00003\ 46+.00003\ 38i)(8/x)^4$$
$$+(.00001\ 17-.00000\ 24i)(8/x)^5$$
$$+(.00000\ 16-.00000\ 32i)(8/x)^6$$

Table 9.1 BESSEL FUNCTIONS—ORDERS 0, 1 AND 2

x	$J_0(x)$	$J_1(x)$	$J_2(x)$
0.0	1.00000 00000 00000	0.00000 00000	0.00000 00000
0.1	0.99750 15620 66040	0.04993 75260	0.00124 89587
0.2	0.99002 49722 39576	0.09950 08326	0.00498 33542
0.3	0.97762 62465 38296	0.14831 88163	0.01116 58619
0.4	0.96039 82266 59563	0.19602 65780	0.01973 46631
0.5	0.93846 98072 40813	0.24226 84577	0.03060 40235
0.6	0.91200 48634 97211	0.28670 09881	0.04366 50967
0.7	0.88120 08886 07405	0.32899 57415	0.05878 69444
0.8	0.84628 73527 50480	0.36884 20461	0.07581 77625
0.9	0.80752 37981 22545	0.40594 95461	0.09458 63043
1.0	0.76519 76865 57967	0.44005 05857	0.11490 34849
1.1	0.71962 20185 27511	0.47090 23949	0.13656 41540
1.2	0.67113 27442 64363	0.49828 90576	0.15934 90183
1.3	0.62008 59895 61509	0.52202 32474	0.18302 66988
1.4	0.56685 51203 74289	0.54194 77139	0.20735 58995
1.5	0.51182 76717 35918	0.55793 65079	0.23208 76721
1.6	0.45540 21676 39381	0.56989 59353	0.25696 77514
1.7	0.39798 48594 46109	0.57776 52315	0.28173 89424
1.8	0.33998 64110 42558	0.58151 69517	0.30614 35353
1.9	0.28181 85593 74385	0.58115 70727	0.32992 57277
2.0	0.22389 07791 41236	0.57672 48078	0.35283 40286
2.1	0.16660 69803 31990	0.56829 21358	0.37462 36252
2.2	0.11036 22669 22174	0.55596 30498	0.39505 86875
2.3	0.05553 97844 45602	0.53987 25326	0.41391 45917
2.4	+0.00250 76832 97244	0.52018 52682	0.43098 00402
2.5	−0.04838 37764 68198	0.49709 41025	0.44605 90584
2.6	−0.09680 49543 97038	0.47081 82665	0.45897 28517
2.7	−0.14244 93700 46012	0.44160 13791	0.46956 15027
2.8	−0.18503 60333 64387	0.40970 92469	0.47768 54954
2.9	−0.22431 15457 91968	0.37542 74818	0.48322 70505
3.0	−0.26005 19549 01933	0.33905 89585	0.48609 12606
3.1	−0.29206 43476 50698	0.30092 11331	0.48620 70142
3.2	−0.32018 81696 57123	0.26134 32488	0.48352 77001
3.3	−0.34429 62603 98885	0.22066 34530	0.47803 16865
3.4	−0.36429 55967 62000	0.17922 58517	0.46972 25683
3.5	−0.38012 77399 87263	0.13737 75274	0.45862 91842
3.6	−0.39176 89837 00798	0.09546 55472	0.44480 53988
3.7	−0.39923 02033 71191	0.05383 39877	0.42832 96562
3.8	−0.40255 64101 78564	+0.01282 10029	0.40930 43065
3.9	−0.40182 60148 87640	−0.02724 40396	0.38785 47125
4.0	−0.39714 98098 63847	−0.06604 33280	0.36412 81459
4.1	−0.38866 96798 35854	−0.10327 32577	0.33829 24809
4.2	−0.37655 70543 67568	−0.13864 69421	0.31053 47010
4.3	−0.36101 11172 36535	−0.17189 65602	0.28105 92288
4.4	−0.34225 67900 03886	−0.20277 55219	0.25008 60982
4.5	−0.32054 25089 85121	−0.23106 04319	0.21784 89837
4.6	−0.29613 78165 74141	−0.25655 28361	0.18459 31052
4.7	−0.26933 07894 19753	−0.27908 07358	0.15057 30295
4.8	−0.24042 53272 91183	−0.29849 98581	0.11605 03864
4.9	−0.20973 83275 85326	−0.31469 46710	0.08129 15231
5.0	−0.17759 67713 14338	−0.32757 91376	0.04656 51163

$$J_{n+1}(x)=\frac{2n}{x}J_n(x)-J_{n-1}(x)$$

BESSEL FUNCTIONS—ORDERS 0, 1 AND 2 Table 9.1

x	$Y_0(x)$	$Y_1(x)$	$Y_2(x)$
0.0	$-\infty$	$-\infty$	$-\infty$
0.1	-1.53423 86514	-6.45895 10947	-127.64478 324
0.2	-1.08110 53224	-3.32382 49881	- 32.15714 456
0.3	-0.80727 35778	-2.29310 51384	- 14.48009 401
0.4	-0.60602 45684	-1.78087 20443	- 8.29833 565
0.5	-0.44451 87335	-1.47147 23927	- 5.44137 084
0.6	-0.30850 98701	-1.26039 13472	- 3.89279 462
0.7	-0.19066 49293	-1.10324 98719	- 2.96147 756
0.8	-0.08680 22797	-0.97814 41767	- 2.35855 816
0.9	+0.00562 83066	-0.87312 65825	- 1.94590 960
1.0	0.08825 69642	-0.78121 28213	- 1.65068 261
1.1	0.16216 32029	-0.69811 95601	- 1.43147 149
1.2	0.22808 35032	-0.62113 63797	- 1.26331 080
1.3	0.28653 53572	-0.54851 97300	- 1.13041 186
1.4	0.33789 51297	-0.47914 69742	- 1.02239 081
1.5	0.38244 89238	-0.41230 86270	- 0.93219 376
1.6	0.42042 68964	-0.34757 80083	- 0.85489 941
1.7	0.45202 70002	-0.28472 62451	- 0.78699 905
1.8	0.47743 17149	-0.22366 48682	- 0.72594 824
1.9	0.49681 99713	-0.16440 57723	- 0.66987 868
2.0	0.51037 56726	-0.10703 24315	- 0.61740 810
2.1	0.51829 37375	-0.05167 86121	- 0.56751 146
2.2	0.52078 42854	+0.00148 77893	- 0.51943 175
2.3	0.51807 53962	0.05227 73158	- 0.47261 686
2.4	0.51041 47487	0.10048 89383	- 0.42667 397
2.5	0.49807 03596	0.14591 81380	- 0.38133 585
2.6	0.48133 05906	0.18836 35444	- 0.33643 556
2.7	0.46050 35491	0.22763 24459	- 0.29188 692
2.8	0.43591 59856	0.26354 53936	- 0.24766 928
2.9	0.40791 17692	0.29594 00546	- 0.20381 518
3.0	0.37685 00100	0.32467 44248	- 0.16040 039
3.1	0.34310 28894	0.34962 94823	- 0.11753 548
3.2	0.30705 32501	0.37071 13384	- 0.07535 866
3.3	0.26909 19951	0.38785 29310	- 0.03402 961
3.4	0.22961 53372	0.40101 52921	+ 0.00627 601
3.5	0.18902 19439	0.41018 84179	0.04537 144
3.6	0.14771 00126	0.41539 17621	0.08306 319
3.7	0.10607 43153	0.41667 43727	0.11915 508
3.8	0.06450 32467	0.41411 46893	0.15345 185
3.9	+0.02337 59082	0.40782 00193	0.18576 256
4.0	-0.01694 07393	0.39792 57106	0.21590 359
4.1	-0.05609 46266	0.38459 40348	0.24370 147
4.2	-0.09375 12013	0.36801 28079	0.26899 540
4.3	-0.12959 59029	0.34839 37583	0.29163 951
4.4	-0.16333 64628	0.32597 06708	0.31150 495
4.5	-0.19470 50086	0.30099 73231	0.32848 160
4.6	-0.22345 99526	0.27374 52415	0.34247 962
4.7	-0.24938 76472	0.24450 12968	0.35343 075
4.8	-0.27230 37945	0.21356 51673	0.36128 928
4.9	-0.29205 45942	0.18124 66920	0.36603 284
5.0	-0.30851 76252	0.14786 31434	0.36766 288

$$Y_{n+1}(x)=\frac{2n}{x}Y_n(x)-Y_{n-1}(x)$$

Table 9.1 BESSEL FUNCTIONS—ORDERS 0, 1 AND 2

x	$J_0(x)$	$J_1(x)$	$J_2(x)$
5.0	−0.17759 67713 14338	−0.32757 91376	0.04656 51163
5.1	−0.14433 47470 60501	−0.33709 72020	+0.01213 97659
5.2	−0.11029 04397 90987	−0.34322 30059	−0.02171 84086
5.3	−0.07580 31115 85584	−0.34596 08338	−0.05474 81465
5.4	−0.04121 01012 44991	−0.34534 47908	−0.08669 53768
5.5	−0.00684 38694 17819	−0.34143 82154	−0.11731 54816
5.6	+0.02697 08846 85114	−0.33433 28363	−0.14637 54691
5.7	0.05992 00097 24037	−0.32414 76802	−0.17365 60379
5.8	0.09170 25675 74816	−0.31102 77443	−0.19895 35139
5.9	0.12203 33545 92823	−0.29514 24447	−0.22208 16409
6.0	0.15064 52572 50997	−0.27668 38581	−0.24287 32100
6.1	0.17729 14222 42744	−0.25586 47726	−0.26118 15116
6.2	0.20174 72229 48904	−0.23291 65671	−0.27688 15994
6.3	0.22381 20061 32191	−0.20808 69402	−0.28987 13522
6.4	0.24331 06048 23407	−0.18163 75090	−0.30007 23264
6.5	0.26009 46055 81606	−0.15384 13014	−0.30743 03906
6.6	0.27404 33606 24146	−0.12498 01652	−0.31191 61379
6.7	0.28506 47377 10576	−0.09534 21180	−0.31352 50715
6.8	0.29309 56031 04273	−0.06521 86634	−0.31227 75629
6.9	0.29810 20354 04820	−0.03490 20961	−0.30821 85850
7.0	0.30007 92705 19556	−0.00468 28235	−0.30141 72201
7.1	0.29905 13805 01550	+0.02515 32743	−0.29196 59511
7.2	0.29507 06914 00958	0.05432 74202	−0.27997 97413
7.3	0.28821 69476 35014	0.08257 04305	−0.26559 49119
7.4	0.27859 62326 57478	0.10962 50949	−0.24896 78286
7.5	0.26633 96578 80378	0.13524 84276	−0.23027 34105
7.6	0.25160 18338 49976	0.15921 37684	−0.20970 34737
7.7	0.23455 91395 86464	0.18131 27153	−0.18746 49278
7.8	0.21540 78077 46263	0.20135 68728	−0.16377 78404
7.9	0.19436 18448 41278	0.21917 93999	−0.13887 33892
8.0	0.17165 08071 37554	0.23463 63469	−0.11299 17204
8.1	0.14751 74540 44378	0.24760 77670	−0.08637 97338
8.2	0.12221 53017 84138	0.25799 85976	−0.05928 88146
8.3	0.09600 61008 95010	0.26573 93020	−0.03197 25341
8.4	0.06915 72616 56985	0.27078 62683	−0.00468 43406
8.5	0.04193 92518 42935	0.27312 19637	+0.02232 47396
8.6	+0.01462 29912 78741	0.27275 48445	0.04880 83679
8.7	−0.01252 27324 49665	0.26971 90241	0.07452 71058
8.8	−0.03923 38031 76542	0.26407 37032	0.09925 05539
8.9	−0.06525 32468 51244	0.25590 23714	0.12275 93977
9.0	−0.09033 36111 82876	0.24531 17866	0.14484 73415
9.1	−0.11423 92326 83199	0.23243 07450	0.16532 29129
9.2	−0.13674 83707 64864	0.21740 86550	0.18401 11218
9.3	−0.15765 51899 43403	0.20041 39278	0.20075 49594
9.4	−0.17677 15727 51508	0.18163 22040	0.21541 67225
9.5	−0.19392 87476 87422	0.16126 44308	0.22787 91542
9.6	−0.20897 87183 68872	0.13952 48117	0.23804 63875
9.7	−0.22179 54820 31723	0.11663 86479	0.24584 46878
9.8	−0.23227 60275 79367	0.09284 00911	0.25122 29849
9.9	−0.24034 11055 34760	0.06836 98323	0.25415 31929
10.0	−0.24593 57644 51348	0.04347 27462	0.25463 03137

$$J_{n+1}(x)=\frac{2n}{x}J_n(x)-J_{n-1}(x)$$

BESSEL FUNCTIONS—ORDERS 0, 1 AND 2 **Table 9.1**

x	$Y_0(x)$	$Y_1(x)$	$Y_2(x)$
5.0	-0.30851 76252	0.14786 31434	0.36766 288
5.1	-0.32160 24491	0.11373 64420	0.36620 498
5.2	-0.33125 09348	0.07919 03430	0.36170 876
5.3	-0.33743 73011	0.04454 76191	0.35424 772
5.4	-0.34016 78783	+0.01012 72667	0.34391 872
5.5	-0.33948 05929	-0.02375 82390	0.33084 123
5.6	-0.33544 41812	-0.05680 56144	0.31515 646
5.7	-0.32815 71408	-0.08872 33405	0.29702 614
5.8	-0.31774 64300	-0.11923 41135	0.27663 122
5.9	-0.30436 59300	-0.14807 71525	0.25417 029
6.0	-0.28819 46840	-0.17501 03443	0.22985 790
6.1	-0.26943 49304	-0.19981 22045	0.20392 273
6.2	-0.24830 99505	-0.22228 36406	0.17660 555
6.3	-0.22506 17496	-0.24224 95005	0.14815 715
6.4	-0.19994 85953	-0.25955 98934	0.11883 613
6.5	-0.17324 24349	-0.27409 12740	0.08890 666
6.6	-0.14522 62172	-0.28574 72791	0.05863 613
6.7	-0.11619 11427	-0.29445 93130	+0.02829 284
6.8	-0.08643 38683	-0.30018 68758	-0.00185 639
6.9	-0.05625 36922	-0.30291 76343	-0.03154 852
7.0	-0.02594 97440	-0.30266 72370	-0.06052 661
7.1	+0.00418 17932	-0.29947 88746	-0.08854 204
7.2	0.03385 04048	-0.29342 25939	-0.11535 668
7.3	0.06277 38864	-0.28459 43719	-0.14074 495
7.4	0.09068 08802	-0.27311 49598	-0.16449 573
7.5	0.11731 32861	-0.25912 85105	-0.18641 422
7.6	0.14242 85247	-0.24280 10021	-0.20632 353
7.7	0.16580 16324	-0.22431 84743	-0.22406 617
7.8	0.18722 71733	-0.20388 50954	-0.23950 540
7.9	0.20652 09481	-0.18172 10773	-0.25252 628
8.0	0.22352 14894	-0.15806 04617	-0.26303 660
8.1	0.23809 13287	-0.13314 87960	-0.27096 757
8.2	0.25011 80276	-0.10724 07223	-0.27627 430
8.3	0.25951 49638	-0.08059 75035	-0.27893 605
8.4	0.26622 18674	-0.05348 45084	-0.27895 627
8.5	0.27020 51054	-0.02616 86794	-0.27636 244
8.6	0.27145 77123	+0.00108 39918	-0.27120 562
8.7	0.26999 91703	0.02801 09592	-0.26355 987
8.8	0.26587 49418	0.05435 55633	-0.25352 140
8.9	0.25915 57617	0.07986 93974	-0.24120 758
9.0	0.24993 66983	0.10431 45752	-0.22675 568
9.1	0.23833 59921	0.12746 58820	-0.21032 151
9.2	0.22449 36870	0.14911 27879	-0.19207 786
9.3	0.20857 00676	0.16906 13071	-0.17221 280
9.4	0.19074 39189	0.18713 56847	-0.15092 782
9.5	0.17121 06262	0.20317 98994	-0.12843 591
9.6	0.15018 01353	0.21705 89660	-0.10495 952
9.7	0.12787 47920	0.22866 00298	-0.08072 839
9.8	0.10452 70840	0.23789 32421	-0.05597 744
9.9	0.08037 73052	0.24469 24113	-0.03094 449
10.0	0.05567 11673	0.24901 54242	-0.00586 808

$$Y_{n+1}(x)=\frac{2n}{x}Y_n(x)-Y_{n-1}(x)$$

Table 9.1 **BESSEL FUNCTIONS—ORDERS 0, 1 AND 2**

x	$J_0(x)$	$J_1(x)$	$J_2(x)$
10.0	−0.24593 57644 51348	0.04347 27462	0.25463 03137
10.1	−0.24902 96505 80910	+0.01839 55155	0.25267 23269
10.2	−0.24961 70698 54127	−0.00661 57433	0.24831 98653
10.3	−0.24771 68134 82244	−0.03131 78295	0.24163 56815
10.4	−0.24337 17507 14207	−0.05547 27618	0.23270 39119
10.5	−0.23664 81944 62347	−0.07885 00142	0.22162 91441
10.6	−0.22763 50476 20693	−0.10122 86626	0.20853 53000
10.7	−0.21644 27399 23818	−0.12239 94239	0.19356 43429
10.8	−0.20320 19671 12039	−0.14216 65683	0.17687 48248
10.9	−0.18806 22459 63342	−0.16034 96867	0.15864 02851
11.0	−0.17119 03004 07196	−0.17678 52990	0.13904 75188
11.1	−0.15276 82954 35677	−0.19132 82878	0.11829 47301
11.2	−0.13299 19368 59575	−0.20385 31459	0.09658 95894
11.3	−0.11206 84561 09807	−0.21425 50262	0.07414 72125
11.4	−0.09021 45002 47520	−0.22245 05864	0.05118 80816
11.5	−0.06765 39481 11665	−0.22837 86207	0.02793 59271
11.6	−0.04461 56740 94438	−0.23200 04746	+0.00461 55923
11.7	−0.02133 12813 88500	−0.23330 02408	−0.01854 91017
11.8	+0.00196 71733 06740	−0.23228 47343	−0.04133 74673
11.9	0.02504 94416 99590	−0.22898 32497	−0.06353 40215
12.0	0.04768 93107 96834	−0.22344 71045	−0.08493 04949
12.1	0.06966 67736 06807	−0.21574 89734	−0.10532 77609
12.2	0.09077 01231 70505	−0.20598 20217	−0.12453 76677
12.3	0.11079 79503 07585	−0.19425 88480	−0.14238 47549
12.4	0.12956 10265 17502	−0.18071 02469	−0.15870 78405
12.5	0.14688 40547 00421	−0.16548 38046	−0.17336 14634
12.6	0.16260 72717 45511	−0.14874 23434	−0.18621 71675
12.7	0.17658 78885 61499	−0.13066 22290	−0.19716 46175
12.8	0.18870 13547 80683	−0.11143 15593	−0.20611 25359
12.9	0.19884 24371 36331	−0.09124 82522	−0.21298 94530
13.0	0.20692 61023 77068	−0.07031 80521	−0.21774 42642
13.1	0.21288 81975 22060	−0.04885 24733	−0.22034 65904
13.2	0.21668 59222 58564	−0.02706 67028	−0.22078 69378
13.3	0.21829 80903 19277	−0.00517 74806	−0.21907 66588
13.4	0.21772 51787 31184	+0.01659 90199	−0.21524 77131
13.5	0.21498 91658 80401	0.03804 92921	−0.20935 22337
13.6	0.21013 31613 69248	0.05896 45572	−0.20146 19030
13.7	0.20322 08326 33007	0.07914 27651	−0.19166 71443
13.8	0.19433 56352 15629	0.09839 05167	−0.18007 61400
13.9	0.18357 98554 57870	0.11652 48904	−0.16681 36842
14.0	0.17107 34761 10459	0.13337 51547	−0.15201 98826
14.1	0.15695 28770 32601	0.14878 43513	−0.13584 87137
14.2	0.14136 93846 57129	0.16261 07342	−0.11846 64643
14.3	0.12448 76852 83919	0.17472 90520	−0.10005 00556
14.4	0.10648 41184 90342	0.18503 16616	−0.08078 52766
14.5	0.08754 48680 10376	0.19342 94636	−0.06086 49420
14.6	0.06786 40683 23379	0.19985 26514	−0.04048 69928
14.7	0.04764 18459 01522	0.20425 12683	−0.01985 25577
14.8	0.02708 23145 85872	0.20659 55672	+0.00083 60053
14.9	+0.00639 15448 90853	0.20687 61718	0.02137 70688
15.0	−0.01422 44728 26781	0.20510 40386	0.04157 16780

$$J_{n+1}(x)=\frac{2n}{x}J_n(x)-J_{n-1}(x)$$

BESSEL FUNCTIONS—ORDERS 0, 1 AND 2 Table 9.1

x	$Y_0(x)$	$Y_1(x)$	$Y_2(x)$
10.0	0.05567 11673	0.24901 54242	-0.00586 808
10.1	0.03065 73806	0.25084 44363	+0.01901 478
10.2	+0.00558 52273	0.25018 58292	0.04347 082
10.3	-0.01929 78497	0.24706 99395	0.06727 260
10.4	-0.04374 86190	0.24155 05610	0.09020 065
10.5	-0.06753 03725	0.23370 42284	0.11204 546
10.6	-0.09041 51548	0.22362 92892	0.13260 936
10.7	-0.11218 58897	0.21144 47763	0.15170 828
10.8	-0.13263 83844	0.19728 90905	0.16917 340
10.9	-0.15158 31932	0.18131 85097	0.18485 264
11.0	-0.16884 73239	0.16370 55374	0.19861 197
11.1	-0.18427 57716	0.14463 71102	0.21033 651
11.2	-0.19773 28675	0.12431 26795	0.21993 156
11.3	-0.20910 34295	0.10294 21889	0.22732 329
11.4	-0.21829 37073	0.08074 39654	0.23245 932
11.5	-0.22523 21117	0.05794 25471	0.23530 908
11.6	-0.22986 97260	0.03476 64663	0.23586 394
11.7	-0.23218 05930	+0.01144 60113	0.23413 718
11.8	-0.23216 17790	-0.01178 90120	0.23016 364
11.9	-0.22983 32139	-0.03471 14983	0.22399 935
12.0	-0.22523 73126	-0.05709 92183	0.21572 078
12.1	-0.21843 83806	-0.07873 69315	0.20542 401
12.2	-0.20952 18128	-0.09941 84171	0.19322 371
12.3	-0.19859 30946	-0.11894 84033	0.17925 189
12.4	-0.18577 66153	-0.13714 43766	0.16365 655
12.5	-0.17121 43068	-0.15383 82565	0.14660 019
12.6	-0.15506 41238	-0.16887 79186	0.12825 810
12.7	-0.13749 83780	-0.18212 85528	0.10881 672
12.8	-0.11870 19463	-0.19347 38454	0.08847 166
12.9	-0.09887 03702	-0.20281 69743	0.06742 588
13.0	-0.07820 78645	-0.21008 14084	0.04588 765
13.1	-0.05692 52568	-0.21521 15060	0.02406 854
13.2	-0.03523 78771	-0.21817 29066	+0.00218 138
13.3	-0.01336 34191	-0.21895 27145	-0.01956 180
13.4	+0.00848 02072	-0.21755 94728	-0.04095 177
13.5	0.03007 70090	-0.21402 29303	-0.06178 411
13.6	0.05121 50115	-0.20839 36044	-0.08186 113
13.7	0.07168 83040	-0.20074 21453	-0.10099 373
13.8	0.09129 90143	-0.19115 85095	-0.11900 315
13.9	0.10985 91895	-0.17975 09511	-0.13572 264
14.0	0.12719 25686	-0.16664 48419	-0.15099 897
14.1	0.14313 62286	-0.15198 13335	-0.16469 386
14.2	0.15754 20895	-0.13591 58742	-0.17668 517
14.3	0.17027 82640	-0.11861 65967	-0.18686 800
14.4	0.18123 02411	-0.10026 25924	-0.19515 560
14.5	0.19030 18912	-0.08104 20909	-0.20148 011
14.6	0.19741 62858	-0.06115 05609	-0.20579 307
14.7	0.20251 63238	-0.04078 87536	-0.20806 581
14.8	0.20556 51604	-0.02016 07059	-0.20828 958
14.9	0.20654 64347	+0.00052 82751	-0.20647 553
15.0	0.20546 42960	0.02107 36280	-0.20265 448

$$Y_{n+1}(x)=\frac{2n}{x}Y_n(x)-Y_{n-1}(x)$$

Table 9.2 **BESSEL FUNCTIONS—ORDERS 3–9**

x	$J_3(x)$	$J_4(x)$	$J_5(x)$	$J_6(x)$	$J_7(x)$	$J_8(x)$	$J_9(x)$
0.0	0.0000	0.0000	0.0000	0.0000	0.0000	0.0000	0.0000
0.2	(-4)1.6625	(-6)4.1583	(-8)8.3195	(-9)1.3869	(-11)1.9816	(-13)2.4774	(-15)2.7530
0.4	(-3)1.3201	(-5)6.6135	(-6)2.6489	(-8)8.8382	(- 9)2.5270	(-11)6.3210	(-12)1.4053
0.6	(-3)4.3997	(-4)3.3147	(-5)1.9948	(-7)9.9956	(- 8)4.2907	(- 9)1.6110	(-11)5.3755
0.8	(-2)1.0247	(-3)1.0330	(-5)8.3084	(-6)5.5601	(- 7)3.1864	(- 8)1.5967	(-10)7.1092
1.0	(-2)1.9563	(-3)2.4766	(-4)2.4976	(-5)2.0938	(- 6)1.5023	(- 8)9.4223	(- 9)5.2493
1.2	(-2)3.2874	(-3)5.0227	(-4)6.1010	(-5)6.1541	(- 6)5.3093	(- 7)4.0021	(- 8)2.6788
1.4	(-2)5.0498	(-3)9.0629	(-3)1.2901	(-4)1.5231	(- 5)1.5366	(- 6)1.3538	(- 7)1.0587
1.6	(-2)7.2523	(-2)1.4995	(-3)2.4524	(-4)3.3210	(- 5)3.8397	(- 6)3.8744	(- 7)3.4687
1.8	(-2)9.8802	(-2)2.3197	(-3)4.2936	(-4)6.5690	(- 5)8.5712	(- 6)9.7534	(- 7)9.8426
2.0	0.12894	(-2)3.3996	(-3)7.0396	(-3)1.2024	(- 4)1.7494	(- 5)2.2180	(- 6)2.4923
2.2	0.16233	(-2)4.7647	(-2)1.0937	(-3)2.0660	(- 4)3.3195	(- 5)4.6434	(- 6)5.7535
2.4	0.19811	(-2)6.4307	(-2)1.6242	(-3)3.3669	(- 4)5.9274	(- 5)9.0756	(- 5)1.2300
2.6	0.23529	(-2)8.4013	(-2)2.3207	(-3)5.2461	(- 3)1.0054	(- 4)1.6738	(- 5)2.4647
2.8	0.27270	(-1)1.0667	(-2)3.2069	(-3)7.8634	(- 3)1.6314	(- 4)2.9367	(- 5)4.6719
3.0	0.30906	0.13203	(-2)4.3028	(-2)1.1394	(- 3)2.5473	(- 4)4.9344	(- 5)8.4395
3.2	0.34307	0.15972	(-2)5.6238	(-2)1.6022	(- 3)3.8446	(- 4)7.9815	(- 4)1.4615
3.4	0.37339	0.18920	(-2)7.1785	(-2)2.1934	(- 3)5.6301	(- 3)1.2482	(- 4)2.4382
3.6	0.39876	0.21980	(-2)8.9680	(-2)2.9311	(- 3)8.0242	(- 3)1.8940	(- 4)3.9339
3.8	0.41803	0.25074	(-1)1.0984	(-2)3.8316	(- 2)1.1159	(- 3)2.7966	(- 4)6.1597
4.0	0.43017	0.28113	0.13209	(-2)4.9088	(- 2)1.5176	(- 3)4.0287	(- 4)9.3860
4.2	0.43439	0.31003	0.15614	(-2)6.1725	(- 2)2.0220	(- 3)5.6739	(- 3)1.3952
4.4	0.43013	0.33645	0.18160	(-2)7.6279	(- 2)2.6433	(- 3)7.8267	(- 3)2.0275
4.6	0.41707	0.35941	0.20799	(-2)9.2745	(- 2)3.3953	(- 2)1.0591	(- 3)2.8852
4.8	0.39521	0.37796	0.23473	(-1)1.1105	(- 2)4.2901	(- 2)1.4079	(- 3)4.0270
5.0	0.36483	0.39123	0.26114	0.13105	(- 2)5.3376	(- 2)1.8405	(- 3)5.5203
5.2	0.32652	0.39847	0.28651	0.15252	(- 2)6.5447	(- 2)2.3689	(- 3)7.4411
5.4	0.28113	0.39906	0.31007	0.17515	(- 2)7.9145	(- 2)3.0044	(- 3)9.8734
5.6	0.22978	0.39257	0.33103	0.19856	(- 2)9.4455	(- 2)3.7577	(- 2)1.2907
5.8	0.17382	0.37877	0.34862	0.22230	(- 1)1.1131	(- 2)4.6381	(- 2)1.6639
6.0	0.11477	0.35764	0.36209	0.24584	0.12959	(- 2)5.6532	(- 2)2.1165
6.2	+0.05428	0.32941	0.37077	0.26860	0.14910	(- 2)6.8077	(- 2)2.6585
6.4	-0.00591	0.29453	0.37408	0.28996	0.16960	(- 2)8.1035	(- 2)3.2990
6.6	-0.06406	0.25368	0.37155	0.30928	0.19077	(- 2)9.5385	(- 2)4.0468
6.8	-0.11847	0.20774	0.36288	0.32590	0.21224	(- 1)1.1107	(- 2)4.9093
7.0	-0.16756	0.15780	0.34790	0.33920	0.23358	0.12797	(- 2)5.8921
7.2	-0.20987	0.10509	0.32663	0.34857	0.25432	0.14594	(- 2)6.9987
7.4	-0.24420	+0.05097	0.29930	0.35349	0.27393	0.16476	(- 2)8.2300
7.6	-0.26958	-0.00313	0.26629	0.35351	0.29188	0.18417	(- 2)9.5839
7.8	-0.28535	-0.05572	0.22820	0.34828	0.30762	0.20385	(- 1)1.1054
8.0	-0.29113	-0.10536	0.18577	0.33758	0.32059	0.22345	0.12632
8.2	-0.28692	-0.15065	0.13994	0.32131	0.33027	0.24257	0.14303
8.4	-0.27302	-0.19033	0.09175	0.29956	0.33619	0.26075	0.16049
8.6	-0.25005	-0.22326	+0.04237	0.27253	0.33790	0.27755	0.17847
8.8	-0.21896	-0.24854	-0.00699	0.24060	0.33508	0.29248	0.19670
9.0	-0.18094	-0.26547	-0.05504	0.20432	0.32746	0.30507	0.21488
9.2	-0.13740	-0.27362	-0.10053	0.16435	0.31490	0.31484	0.23266
9.4	-0.08997	-0.27284	-0.14224	0.12152	0.29737	0.32138	0.24965
9.6	-0.04034	-0.26326	-0.17904	0.07676	0.27499	0.32427	0.26546
9.8	+0.00970	-0.24528	-0.20993	+0.03107	0.24797	0.32318	0.27967
10.0	0.05838	-0.21960	-0.23406	-0.01446	0.21671	0.31785	0.29186

BESSEL FUNCTIONS—ORDERS 3–9

Table 9.2

x	$Y_3(x)$	$Y_4(x)$	$Y_5(x)$	$Y_6(x)$	$Y_7(x)$	$Y_8(x)$	$Y_9(x)$
0.0	$-\infty$	$-\infty$	$-\infty$	$-\infty$	$-\infty$	$-\infty$	$-\infty$
0.2	(2)-6.3982	(4)-1.9162	(5)-7.6586	(7)-3.8274	(9)-2.2957	(11)-1.6066	(13)-1.2850
0.4	(1)-8.1202	(3)-1.2097	(4)-2.4114	(5)-6.0163	(7)-1.8025	(8)-6.3027	(10)-2.5193
0.6	(1)-2.4692	(2)-2.4302	(3)-3.2156	(4)-5.3351	(6)-1.0638	(7)-2.4769	(8)-6.5943
0.8	(1)-1.0815	(1)-7.8751	(2)-7.7670	(3)-9.6300	(5)-1.4367	(6)-2.5046	(7)-4.9949
1.0	-5.8215	(1)-3.3278	(2)-2.6041	(3)-2.5708	(4)-3.0589	(5)-4.2567	(6)-6.7802
1.2	-3.5899	(1)-1.6686	(2)-1.0765	(2)-8.8041	(3)-8.6964	(5)-1.0058	(6)-1.3323
1.4	-2.4420	-9.4432	(1)-5.1519	(2)-3.5855	(3)-3.0218	(4)-2.9859	(5)-3.3823
1.6	-1.7897	-5.8564	(1)-2.7492	(2)-1.6597	(3)-1.2173	(4)-1.0485	(5)-1.0364
1.8	-1.3896	-3.9059	(1)-1.5970	(1)-8.4816	(2)-5.4947	(3)-4.1889	(4)-3.6685
2.0	-1.1278	-2.7659	-9.9360	(1)-4.6914	(2)-2.7155	(3)-1.8539	(4)-1.4560
2.2	-0.94591	-2.0603	-6.5462	(1)-2.7695	(2)-1.4452	(2)-8.9196	(3)-6.3425
2.4	-0.81161	-1.6024	-4.5296	(1)-1.7271	(1)-8.1825	(2)-4.6004	(3)-2.9851
2.6	-0.70596	-1.2927	-3.2716	(1)-1.1290	(1)-4.8837	(2)-2.5168	(3)-1.5000
2.8	-0.61736	-1.0752	-2.4548	-7.6918	(1)-3.0510	(2)-1.4486	(2)-7.9725
3.0	-0.53854	-0.91668	-1.9059	-5.4365	(1)-1.9840	(1)-8.7150	(2)-4.4496
3.2	-0.46491	-0.79635	-1.5260	-3.9723	(1)-1.3370	(1)-5.4522	(2)-2.5924
3.4	-0.39363	-0.70092	-1.2556	-2.9920	-9.3044	(1)-3.5320	(2)-1.5691
3.6	-0.32310	-0.62156	-1.0581	-2.3177	-6.6677	(1)-2.3612	(1)-9.8275
3.8	-0.25259	-0.55227	-0.91009	-1.8427	-4.9090	(1)-1.6243	(1)-6.3483
4.0	-0.18202	-0.48894	-0.79585	-1.5007	-3.7062	(1)-1.1471	(1)-4.2178
4.2	-0.11183	-0.42875	-0.70484	-1.2494	-2.8650	-8.3005	(1)-2.8756
4.4	-0.04278	-0.36985	-0.62967	-1.0612	-2.2645	-6.1442	(1)-2.0078
4.6	+0.02406	-0.31109	-0.56509	-0.91737	-1.8281	-4.6463	(1)-1.4333
4.8	0.08751	-0.25190	-0.50735	-0.80507	-1.5053	-3.5855	(1)-1.0446
5.0	0.14627	-0.19214	-0.45369	-0.71525	-1.2629	-2.8209	-7.7639
5.2	0.19905	-0.13204	-0.40218	-0.64139	-1.0780	-2.2608	-5.8783
5.4	0.24463	-0.07211	-0.35146	-0.57874	-0.93462	-1.8444	-4.5302
5.6	0.28192	-0.01310	-0.30063	-0.52375	-0.82168	-1.5304	-3.5510
5.8	0.31001	+0.04407	-0.24922	-0.47377	-0.73099	-1.2907	-2.8295
6.0	0.32825	0.09839	-0.19706	-0.42683	-0.65659	-1.1052	-2.2907
6.2	0.33622	0.14877	-0.14426	-0.38145	-0.59403	-0.95990	-1.8831
6.4	0.33383	0.19413	-0.09117	-0.33658	-0.53992	-0.84450	-1.5713
6.6	0.32128	0.23344	-0.03833	-0.29151	-0.49169	-0.75147	-1.3301
6.8	0.29909	0.26576	+0.01357	-0.24581	-0.44735	-0.67521	-1.1414
7.0	0.26808	0.29031	0.06370	-0.19931	-0.40537	-0.61144	-0.99220
7.2	0.22934	0.30647	0.11119	-0.15204	-0.36459	-0.55689	-0.87293
7.4	0.18420	0.31385	0.15509	-0.10426	-0.32416	-0.50902	-0.77643
7.6	0.13421	0.31228	0.19450	-0.05635	-0.28348	-0.46585	-0.69726
7.8	0.08106	0.30186	0.22854	-0.00886	-0.24217	-0.42581	-0.63128
8.0	+0.02654	0.28294	0.25640	+0.03756	-0.20006	-0.38767	-0.57528
8.2	-0.02753	0.25613	0.27741	0.08218	-0.15716	-0.35049	-0.52673
8.4	-0.07935	0.22228	0.29104	0.12420	-0.11361	-0.31355	-0.48363
8.6	-0.12723	0.18244	0.29694	0.16284	-0.06973	-0.27635	-0.44440
8.8	-0.16959	0.13789	0.29495	0.19728	-0.02593	-0.23853	-0.40777
9.0	-0.20509	0.09003	0.28512	0.22677	+0.01724	-0.19995	-0.37271
9.2	-0.23262	+0.04037	0.26773	0.25064	0.05920	-0.16056	-0.33843
9.4	-0.25136	-0.00951	0.24326	0.26830	0.09925	-0.12048	-0.30433
9.6	-0.26079	-0.05804	0.21243	0.27932	0.13672	-0.07994	-0.26995
9.8	-0.26074	-0.10366	0.17612	0.28338	0.17087	-0.03928	-0.23499
10.0	-0.25136	-0.14495	0.13540	0.28035	0.20102	+0.00108	-0.19930

Table 9.2 **BESSEL FUNCTIONS—ORDERS 3–9**

x	$J_3(x)$	$J_4(x)$	$J_5(x)$	$J_6(x)$	$J_7(x)$	$J_8(x)$	$J_9(x)$
10.0	0.05838	-0.21960	-0.23406	-0.01446	0.21671	0.31785	0.29186
10.2	0.10400	-0.18715	-0.25078	-0.05871	0.18170	0.30811	0.30161
10.4	0.14497	-0.14906	-0.25964	-0.10059	0.14358	0.29386	0.30852
10.6	0.17992	-0.10669	-0.26044	-0.13901	0.10308	0.27515	0.31224
10.8	0.20768	-0.06150	-0.25323	-0.17297	0.06104	0.25210	0.31244
11.0	0.22735	-0.01504	-0.23829	-0.20158	+0.01838	0.22497	0.30886
11.2	0.23835	+0.03110	-0.21614	-0.22408	-0.02395	0.19414	0.30130
11.4	0.24041	0.07534	-0.18754	-0.23985	-0.06494	0.16010	0.28964
11.6	0.23359	0.11621	-0.15345	-0.24849	-0.10361	0.12344	0.27388
11.8	0.21827	0.15232	-0.11500	-0.24978	-0.13901	0.08485	0.25407
12.0	0.19514	0.18250	-0.07347	-0.24372	-0.17025	0.04510	0.23038
12.2	0.16515	0.20576	-0.03023	-0.23053	-0.19653	+0.00501	0.20310
12.4	0.12951	0.22138	+0.01331	-0.21064	-0.21716	-0.03453	0.17260
12.6	0.08963	0.22890	0.05571	-0.18469	-0.23160	-0.07264	0.13935
12.8	0.04702	0.22815	0.09557	-0.15349	-0.23947	-0.10843	0.10393
13.0	+0.00332	0.21928	0.13162	-0.11803	-0.24057	-0.14105	0.06698
13.2	-0.03984	0.20268	0.16267	-0.07944	-0.23489	-0.16969	+0.02921
13.4	-0.08085	0.17905	0.18774	-0.03894	-0.22261	-0.19364	-0.00860
13.6	-0.11822	0.14931	0.20605	+0.00220	-0.20411	-0.21231	-0.04567
13.8	-0.15059	0.11460	0.21702	0.04266	-0.17993	-0.22520	-0.08117
14.0	-0.17681	0.07624	0.22038	0.08117	-0.15080	-0.23197	-0.11431
14.2	-0.19598	+0.03566	0.21607	0.11650	-0.11762	-0.23246	-0.14432
14.4	-0.20747	-0.00566	0.20433	0.14756	-0.08136	-0.22666	-0.17048
14.6	-0.21094	-0.04620	0.18563	0.17335	-0.04315	-0.21472	-0.19216
14.8	-0.20637	-0.08450	0.16069	0.19308	-0.00415	-0.19700	-0.20883
15.0	-0.19402	-0.11918	0.13046	0.20615	+0.03446	-0.17398	-0.22005
15.2	-0.17445	-0.14901	0.09603	0.21219	0.07149	-0.14634	-0.22553
15.4	-0.14850	-0.17296	0.05865	0.21105	0.10580	-0.11487	-0.22514
15.6	-0.11723	-0.19021	+0.01968	0.20283	0.13634	-0.08047	-0.21888
15.8	-0.08188	-0.20020	-0.01949	0.18787	0.16217	-0.04417	-0.20690
16.0	-0.04385	-0.20264	-0.05747	0.16672	0.18251	-0.00702	-0.18953
16.2	-0.00461	-0.19752	-0.09293	0.14016	0.19675	+0.02987	-0.16725
16.4	+0.03432	-0.18511	-0.12462	0.10913	0.20447	0.06542	-0.14065
16.6	0.07146	-0.16596	-0.15144	0.07473	0.20546	0.09855	-0.11047
16.8	0.10542	-0.14083	-0.17248	0.03817	0.19974	0.12829	-0.07756
17.0	0.13493	-0.11074	-0.18704	+0.00072	0.18755	0.15374	-0.04286
17.2	0.15891	-0.07685	-0.19466	-0.03632	0.16932	0.17414	-0.00733
17.4	0.17651	-0.04048	-0.19512	-0.07166	0.14570	0.18889	+0.02799
17.6	0.18712	-0.00300	-0.18848	-0.10410	0.11751	0.19757	0.06210
17.8	0.19041	+0.03417	-0.17505	-0.13251	0.08571	0.19993	0.09400
18.0	0.18632	0.06964	-0.15537	-0.15596	0.05140	0.19593	0.12276
18.2	0.17510	0.10209	-0.13022	-0.17364	+0.01573	0.18574	0.14756
18.4	0.15724	0.13033	-0.10058	-0.18499	-0.02007	0.16972	0.16766
18.6	0.13351	0.15334	-0.06756	-0.18966	-0.05481	0.14841	0.18247
18.8	0.10487	0.17031	-0.03240	-0.18755	-0.08731	0.12253	0.19159
19.0	0.07249	0.18065	+0.00357	-0.17877	-0.11648	0.09294	0.19474
19.2	0.03764	0.18403	0.03904	-0.16370	-0.14135	0.06063	0.19187
19.4	+0.00170	0.18039	0.07269	-0.14292	-0.16110	+0.02667	0.18309
19.6	-0.03395	0.16994	0.10331	-0.11723	-0.17508	-0.00783	0.16869
19.8	-0.06791	0.15313	0.12978	-0.08759	-0.18287	-0.04171	0.14916
20.0	-0.09890	0.13067	0.15117	-0.05509	-0.18422	-0.07387	0.12513

BESSEL FUNCTIONS—ORDERS 3–9 Table 9.2

x	$Y_3(x)$	$Y_4(x)$	$Y_5(x)$	$Y_6(x)$	$Y_7(x)$	$Y_8(x)$	$Y_9(x)$
10.0	−0.25136	−0.14495	0.13540	0.28035	0.20102	0.00108	−0.19930
10.2	−0.23314	−0.18061	0.09148	0.27030	0.22652	0.04061	−0.16282
10.4	−0.20686	−0.20954	+0.04567	0.25346	0.24678	0.07874	−0.12563
10.6	−0.17359	−0.23087	−0.00065	0.23025	0.26131	0.11488	−0.08791
10.8	−0.13463	−0.24397	−0.04609	0.20130	0.26975	0.14838	−0.04993
11.0	−0.09148	−0.24851	−0.08925	0.16737	0.27184	0.17861	−0.01205
11.2	−0.04577	−0.24445	−0.12884	0.12941	0.26750	0.20496	+0.02530
11.4	+0.00082	−0.23203	−0.16365	0.08848	0.25678	0.22687	0.06163
11.6	0.04657	−0.21178	−0.19262	0.04573	0.23992	0.24384	0.09640
11.8	0.08981	−0.18450	−0.21489	+0.00238	0.21732	0.25545	0.12906
12.0	0.12901	−0.15122	−0.22982	−0.04030	0.18952	0.26140	0.15902
12.2	0.16277	−0.11317	−0.23698	−0.08107	0.15724	0.26151	0.18573
12.4	0.18994	−0.07175	−0.23623	−0.11875	0.12130	0.25571	0.20865
12.6	0.20959	−0.02845	−0.22766	−0.15223	0.08268	0.24409	0.22728
12.8	0.22112	+0.01518	−0.21163	−0.18052	0.04240	0.22689	0.24122
13.0	0.22420	0.05759	−0.18876	−0.20279	+0.00157	0.20448	0.25010
13.2	0.21883	0.09729	−0.15987	−0.21840	−0.03868	0.17738	0.25369
13.4	0.20534	0.13289	−0.12600	−0.22692	−0.07722	0.14625	0.25184
13.6	0.18432	0.16318	−0.08833	−0.22813	−0.11296	0.11185	0.24454
13.8	0.15666	0.18712	−0.04819	−0.22204	−0.14489	0.07505	0.23190
14.0	0.12350	0.20393	−0.00697	−0.20891	−0.17209	+0.03682	0.21417
14.2	0.08615	0.21308	+0.03390	−0.18921	−0.19380	−0.00186	0.19170
14.4	0.04605	0.21434	0.07303	−0.16363	−0.20939	−0.03994	0.16501
14.6	+0.00477	0.20775	0.10907	−0.13305	−0.21842	−0.07640	0.13470
14.8	−0.03613	0.19364	0.14080	−0.09850	−0.22067	−0.11024	0.10149
15.0	−0.07511	0.17261	0.16717	−0.06116	−0.21610	−0.14053	0.06620
15.2	−0.11072	0.14550	0.18730	−0.02228	−0.20489	−0.16644	+0.02969
15.4	−0.14165	0.11339	0.20055	+0.01684	−0.18743	−0.18723	−0.00710
15.6	−0.16678	0.07750	0.20652	0.05489	−0.16430	−0.20234	−0.04322
15.8	−0.18523	+0.03920	0.20507	0.09059	−0.13627	−0.21134	−0.07775
16.0	−0.19637	−0.00007	0.19633	0.12278	−0.10425	−0.21399	−0.10975
16.2	−0.19986	−0.03885	0.18067	0.15038	−0.06928	−0.21025	−0.13838
16.4	−0.19566	−0.07571	0.15873	0.17250	−0.03251	−0.20025	−0.16286
16.6	−0.18402	−0.10930	0.13135	0.18843	+0.00487	−0.18432	−0.18253
16.8	−0.16547	−0.13841	0.09956	0.19767	0.04164	−0.16297	−0.19685
17.0	−0.14078	−0.16200	0.06455	0.19996	0.07660	−0.13688	−0.20543
17.2	−0.11098	−0.17924	+0.02761	0.19529	0.10864	−0.10686	−0.20805
17.4	−0.07725	−0.18956	−0.00990	0.18387	0.13671	−0.07387	−0.20464
17.6	−0.04094	−0.19265	−0.04663	0.16616	0.15991	−0.03895	−0.19533
17.8	−0.00347	−0.18846	−0.08123	0.14282	0.17752	−0.00320	−0.18039
18.0	+0.03372	−0.17722	−0.11249	0.11472	0.18897	+0.03225	−0.16030
18.2	0.06920	−0.15942	−0.13928	0.08289	0.19393	0.06629	−0.13566
18.4	0.10163	−0.13580	−0.16067	0.04848	0.19229	0.09782	−0.10722
18.6	0.12977	−0.10731	−0.17593	+0.01272	0.18414	0.12587	−0.07586
18.8	0.15261	−0.07506	−0.18455	−0.02310	0.16980	0.14955	−0.04252
19.0	0.16930	−0.04031	−0.18628	−0.05773	0.14982	0.16812	−0.00824
19.2	0.17927	−0.00440	−0.18111	−0.08993	0.12490	0.18100	+0.02593
19.4	0.18221	+0.03131	−0.16930	−0.11857	0.09595	0.18782	0.05895
19.6	0.17805	0.06546	−0.15134	−0.14267	0.06399	0.18838	0.08979
19.8	0.16705	0.09678	−0.12794	−0.16139	+0.03013	0.18270	0.11750
20.0	0.14967	0.12409	−0.10004	−0.17411	−0.00443	0.17101	0.14124

Table 9.5

ZEROS AND ASSOCIATED VALUES OF BESSEL FUNCTIONS AND THEIR DERIVATIVES

s	$j_{0,s}$	$J'_0(j_{0,s})$	$j_{1,s}$	$J'_1(j_{1,s})$	$j_{2,s}$	$J'_2(j_{2,s})$
1	2.40482 55577	−0.51914 74973	3.83171	−0.40276	5.13562	−0.33967
2	5.52007 81103	+0.34026 48065	7.01559	+0.30012	8.41724	+0.27138
3	8.65372 79129	−0.27145 22999	10.17347	−0.24970	11.61984	−0.23244
4	11.79153 44391	+0.23245 98314	13.32369	+0.21836	14.79595	+0.20654
5	14.93091 77086	−0.20654 64331	16.47063	−0.19647	17.95982	−0.18773
6	18.07106 39679	+0.18772 88030	19.61586	+0.18006	21.11700	+0.17326
7	21.21163 66299	−0.17326 58942	22.76008	−0.16718	24.27011	−0.16170
8	24.35247 15308	+0.16170 15507	25.90367	+0.15672	27.42057	+0.15218
9	27.49347 91320	−0.15218 12138	29.04683	−0.14801	30.56920	−0.14417
10	30.63460 64684	+0.14416 59777	32.18968	+0.14061	33.71652	+0.13730
11	33.77582 02136	−0.13729 69434	35.33231	−0.13421	36.86286	−0.13132
12	36.91709 83537	+0.13132 46267	38.47477	+0.12862	40.00845	+0.12607
13	40.05842 57646	−0.12606 94971	41.61709	−0.12367	43.15345	−0.12140
14	43.19979 17132	+0.12139 86248	44.75932	+0.11925	46.29800	+0.11721
15	46.34118 83717	−0.11721 11989	47.90146	−0.11527	49.44216	−0.11343
16	49.48260 98974	+0.11342 91926	51.04354	+0.11167	52.58602	+0.10999
17	52.62405 18411	−0.10999 11430	54.18555	−0.10839	55.72963	−0.10685
18	55.76551 07550	+0.10684 78883	57.32753	+0.10537	58.87302	+0.10396
19	58.90698 39261	−0.10395 95729	60.46946	−0.10260	62.01622	−0.10129
20	62.04846 91902	+0.10129 34989	63.61136	+0.10004	65.15927	+0.09882

s	$j_{3,s}$	$J'_3(j_{3,s})$	$j_{4,s}$	$J'_4(j_{4,s})$	$j_{5,s}$	$J'_5(j_{5,s})$
1	6.38016	−0.29827	7.58834	−0.26836	8.77148	−0.24543
2	9.76102	+0.24942	11.06471	+0.23188	12.33860	+0.21743
3	13.01520	−0.21828	14.37254	−0.20636	15.70017	−0.19615
4	16.22347	+0.19644	17.61597	+0.18766	18.98013	+0.17993
5	19.40942	−0.18005	20.82693	−0.17323	22.21780	−0.16712
6	22.58273	+0.16718	24.01902	+0.16168	25.43034	+0.15669
7	25.74817	−0.15672	27.19909	−0.15217	28.62662	−0.14799
8	28.90835	+0.14801	30.37101	+0.14416	31.81172	+0.14059
9	32.06485	−0.14060	33.53714	−0.13729	34.98878	−0.13420
10	35.21867	+0.13421	36.69900	+0.13132	38.15987	+0.12861
11	38.37047	−0.12862	39.85763	−0.12607	41.32638	−0.12366
12	41.52072	+0.12367	43.01374	+0.12140	44.48932	+0.11925
13	44.66974	−0.11925	46.16785	−0.11721	47.64940	−0.11527
14	47.81779	+0.11527	49.32036	+0.11343	50.80717	+0.11167
15	50.96503	−0.11167	52.47155	−0.10999	53.96303	−0.10838
16	54.11162	+0.10839	55.62165	+0.10685	57.11730	+0.10537
17	57.25765	−0.10537	58.77084	−0.10396	60.27025	−0.10260
18	60.40322	+0.10260	61.91925	+0.10129	63.42205	+0.10003
19	63.54840	−0.10004	65.06700	−0.09882	66.57289	−0.09765
20	66.69324	+0.09765	68.21417	+0.09652	69.72289	+0.09543

s	$j_{6,s}$	$J'_6(j_{6,s})$	$j_{7,s}$	$J'_7(j_{7,s})$	$j_{8,s}$	$J'_8(j_{8,s})$
1	9.93611	−0.22713	11.08637	−0.21209	12.22509	−0.19944
2	13.58929	+0.20525	14.82127	+0.19479	16.03777	+0.18569
3	17.00382	−0.18726	18.28758	−0.17942	19.55454	−0.17244
4	20.32079	+0.17305	21.64154	+0.16688	22.94517	+0.16130
5	23.58608	−0.16159	24.93493	−0.15657	26.26681	−0.15196
6	26.82015	+0.15212	28.19119	+0.14792	29.54566	+0.14404
7	30.03372	−0.14413	31.42279	−0.14055	32.79580	−0.13722
8	33.23304	+0.13727	34.63709	+0.13418	36.02562	+0.13127
9	36.42202	−0.13131	37.83872	−0.12859	39.24045	−0.12603
10	39.60324	+0.12606	41.03077	+0.12365	42.44389	+0.12137
11	42.77848	−0.12139	44.21541	−0.11924	45.63844	−0.11719
12	45.94902	+0.11721	47.39417	+0.11526	48.82593	+0.11342
13	49.11577	−0.11343	50.56818	−0.11166	52.00769	−0.10998
14	52.27945	+0.10999	53.73833	+0.10838	55.18475	+0.10684
15	55.44059	−0.10685	56.90525	−0.10537	58.35789	−0.10395
16	58.59961	+0.10396	60.06948	+0.10260	61.52774	+0.10129
17	61.75682	−0.10129	63.23142	−0.10003	64.69478	−0.09882
18	64.91251	+0.09882	66.39141	+0.09765	67.85943	+0.09652
19	68.06689	−0.09652	69.54971	−0.09543	71.02200	−0.09438
20	71.22013	+0.09438	72.70655	+0.09336	74.18277	+0.09237

Table 9.5
ZEROS AND ASSOCIATED VALUES OF BESSEL FUNCTIONS AND THEIR DERIVATIVES

s	$y_{0,s}$	$Y'_0(y_{0,s})$	$y_{1,s}$	$Y'_1(y_{1,s})$	$y_{2,s}$	$Y'_2(y_{2,s})$
1	0.89357 697	+0.87942 080	2.19714	+0.52079	3.38424	+0.39921
2	3.95767 842	-0.40254 267	5.42968	-0.34032	6.79381	-0.29992
3	7.08605 106	+0.30009 761	8.59601	+0.27146	10.02348	+0.24967
4	10.22234 504	-0.24970 124	11.74915	-0.23246	13.20999	-0.21835
5	13.36109 747	+0.21835 830	14.89744	+0.20655	16.37897	+0.19646
6	16.50092 244	-0.19646 494	18.04340	-0.18773	19.53904	-0.18006
7	19.64130 970	+0.18006 318	21.18807	+0.17327	22.69396	+0.16718
8	22.78202 805	-0.16718 450	24.33194	-0.16170	25.84561	-0.15672
9	25.92295 765	+0.15672 493	27.47529	+0.15218	28.99508	+0.14801
10	29.06403 025	-0.14801 108	30.61829	-0.14417	32.14300	-0.14061
11	32.20520 412	+0.14060 578	33.76102	+0.13730	35.28979	+0.13421
12	35.34645 231	-0.13421 123	36.90356	-0.13132	38.43573	-0.12862
13	38.48775 665	+0.12861 661	40.04594	+0.12607	41.58101	+0.12367
14	41.62910 447	-0.12366 795	43.18822	-0.12140	44.72578	-0.11925
15	44.77048 661	+0.11924 981	46.33040	+0.11721	47.87012	+0.11527
16	47.91189 633	-0.11527 369	49.47251	-0.11343	51.01413	-0.11167
17	51.05332 855	+0.11167 049	52.61455	+0.10999	54.15785	+0.10839
18	54.19477 936	-0.10838 535	55.75654	-0.10685	57.30135	-0.10537
19	57.33624 570	+0.10537 405	58.89850	+0.10396	60.44464	+0.10260
20	60.47772 516	-0.10260 057	62.04041	-0.10129	63.58777	-0.10004

s	$y_{3,s}$	$Y'_3(y_{3,s})$	$y_{4,s}$	$Y'_4(y_{4,s})$	$y_{5,s}$	$Y'_5(y_{5,s})$
1	4.52702	+0.33256	5.64515	+0.28909	6.74718	+0.25795
2	8.09755	-0.27080	9.36162	-0.24848	10.59718	-0.23062
3	11.39647	+0.23232	12.73014	+0.21805	14.03380	+0.20602
4	14.62308	-0.20650	15.99963	-0.19635	17.34709	-0.18753
5	17.81846	+0.18771	19.22443	+0.18001	20.60290	+0.17317
6	20.99728	-0.17326	22.42481	-0.16716	23.82654	-0.16165
7	24.16624	+0.16170	25.61027	+0.15671	27.03013	+0.15215
8	27.32880	-0.15218	28.78589	-0.14800	30.22034	-0.14415
9	30.48699	+0.14416	31.95469	+0.14060	33.40111	+0.13729
10	33.64205	-0.13730	35.11853	-0.13421	36.57497	-0.13132
11	36.79479	+0.13132	38.27867	+0.12861	39.74363	+0.12606
12	39.94577	-0.12607	41.43596	-0.12367	42.90825	-0.12140
13	43.09537	+0.12140	44.59102	+0.11925	46.06968	+0.11721
14	46.24387	-0.11721	47.74429	-0.11527	49.22854	-0.11343
15	49.39150	+0.11343	50.89611	+0.11167	52.38531	+0.10999
16	52.53840	-0.10999	54.04673	-0.10838	55.54035	-0.10685
17	55.68470	+0.10685	57.19635	+0.10537	58.69393	+0.10396
18	58.83049	-0.10396	60.34513	-0.10260	61.84628	-0.10129
19	61.97586	+0.10129	63.49320	+0.10003	64.99759	+0.09882
20	65.12086	-0.09882	66.64065	-0.09765	68.14799	-0.09652

s	$y_{6,s}$	$Y'_6(y_{6,s})$	$y_{7,s}$	$Y'_7(y_{7,s})$	$y_{8,s}$	$Y'_8(y_{8,s})$
1	7.83774	+0.23429	8.91961	+0.21556	9.99463	+0.20027
2	11.81104	-0.21591	13.00771	-0.20352	14.19036	-0.19289
3	15.31362	+0.19571	16.57392	+0.18672	17.81789	+0.17880
4	18.67070	-0.17975	19.97434	-0.17283	21.26093	-0.16662
5	21.95829	+0.16703	23.29397	+0.16148	24.61258	+0.15643
6	25.20621	-0.15664	26.56676	-0.15206	27.91052	-0.14785
7	28.42904	+0.14796	29.80953	+0.14409	31.17370	+0.14051
8	31.63488	-0.14058	33.03177	-0.13725	34.41286	-0.13415
9	34.82864	+0.13419	36.23927	+0.13130	37.63465	+0.12857
10	38.01347	-0.12860	39.43579	-0.12605	40.84342	-0.12364
11	41.19152	+0.12366	42.62391	+0.12138	44.04215	+0.11923
12	44.36427	-0.11924	45.80544	-0.11720	47.23298	-0.11526
13	47.53282	+0.11527	48.98171	+0.11342	50.41746	+0.11166
14	50.69796	-0.11167	52.15369	-0.10999	53.59675	-0.10838
15	53.86031	+0.10838	55.32215	+0.10684	56.77177	+0.10537
16	57.02034	-0.10537	58.48767	-0.10396	59.94319	-0.10260
17	60.17842	+0.10260	61.65071	+0.10129	63.11158	+0.10003
18	63.33485	-0.10003	64.81164	-0.09882	66.27738	-0.09765
19	66.48986	+0.09765	67.97075	+0.09652	69.44095	+0.09543
20	69.64364	-0.09543	71.12830	-0.09438	72.60259	-0.09336

Table 9.5

ZEROS AND ASSOCIATED VALUES OF BESSEL FUNCTIONS AND THEIR DERIVATIVES

s	$j'_{0,s}$	$J_0(j'_{0,s})$	$j'_{1,s}$	$J_1(j'_{1,s})$	$j'_{2,s}$	$J_2(j'_{2,s})$
1	0.00000 00000	+1.00000 00000	1.84118	+0.58187	3.05424	+0.48650
2	3.83170 59702	−0.40275 93957	5.33144	−0.34613	6.70613	−0.31353
3	7.01558 66698	+0.30011 57525	8.53632	+0.27330	9.96947	+0.25474
4	10.17346 81351	−0.24970 48771	11.70600	−0.23330	13.17037	−0.22088
5	13.32369 19363	+0.21835 94072	14.86359	+0.20701	16.34752	+0.19794
6	16.47063 00509	−0.19646 53715	18.01553	−0.18802	19.51291	−0.18101
7	19.61585 85105	+0.18006 33753	21.16437	+0.17346	22.67158	+0.16784
8	22.76008 43806	−0.16718 46005	24.31133	−0.16184	25.82604	−0.15720
9	25.90367 20876	+0.15672 49863	27.45705	+0.15228	28.97767	+0.14836
10	29.04682 85349	−0.14801 11100	30.60192	−0.14424	32.12733	−0.14088
11	32.18967 99110	+0.14060 57982	33.74618	+0.13736	35.27554	+0.13443
12	35.33230 75501	−0.13421 12403	36.88999	−0.13137	38.42265	−0.12879
13	38.47476 62348	+0.12861 66221	40.03344	+0.12611	41.56893	+0.12381
14	41.61709 42128	−0.12366 79608	43.17663	−0.12143	44.71455	−0.11937
15	44.75931 89977	+0.11924 98120	46.31960	+0.11724	47.85964	+0.11537
16	47.90146 08872	−0.11527 36941	49.46239	−0.11345	51.00430	−0.11176
17	51.04353 51836	+0.11167 04969	52.60504	+0.11001	54.14860	+0.10846
18	54.18555 36411	−0.10838 53489	55.74757	−0.10687	57.29260	−0.10544
19	57.32752 54379	+0.10537 40554	58.89000	+0.10397	60.43635	+0.10266
20	60.46945 78453	−0.10260 05671	62.03235	−0.10131	63.57989	−0.10008

s	$j'_{3,s}$	$J_3(j'_{3,s})$	$j'_{4,s}$	$J_4(j'_{4,s})$	$j'_{5,s}$	$J_5(j'_{5,s})$
1	4.20119	+0.43439	5.31755	+0.39965	6.41562	+0.37409
2	8.01524	−0.29116	9.28240	−0.27438	10.51986	−0.26109
3	11.34592	+0.24074	12.68191	+0.22959	13.98719	+0.22039
4	14.58585	−0.21097	15.96411	−0.20276	17.31284	−0.19580
5	17.78875	+0.19042	19.19603	+0.18403	20.57551	+0.17849
6	20.97248	−0.17505	22.40103	−0.16988	23.80358	−0.16533
7	24.14490	+0.16295	25.58976	+0.15866	27.01031	+0.15482
8	27.31006	−0.15310	28.76784	−0.14945	30.20285	−0.14616
9	30.47027	+0.14487	31.93854	+0.14171	33.38544	+0.13885
10	33.62695	−0.13784	35.10392	−0.13509	36.56078	−0.13256
11	36.78102	+0.13176	38.26532	+0.12932	39.73064	+0.12707
12	39.93311	−0.12643	41.42367	−0.12425	42.89627	−0.12223
13	43.08365	+0.12169	44.57962	+0.11973	46.05857	+0.11790
14	46.23297	−0.11746	47.73367	−0.11568	49.21817	−0.11402
15	49.38130	+0.11364	50.88616	+0.11202	52.37559	+0.11049
16	52.52882	−0.11017	54.03737	−0.10868	55.53120	−0.10728
17	55.67567	+0.10700	57.18752	+0.10563	58.68528	+0.10434
18	58.82195	−0.10409	60.33677	−0.10283	61.83809	−0.10163
19	61.96775	+0.10141	63.48526	+0.10023	64.98980	+0.09912
20	65.11315	−0.09893	66.63309	−0.09783	68.14057	−0.09678

s	$j'_{6,s}$	$J_6(j'_{6,s})$	$j'_{7,s}$	$J_7(j'_{7,s})$	$j'_{8,s}$	$J_8(j'_{8,s})$
1	7.50127	+0.35414	8.57784	+0.33793	9.64742	+0.32438
2	11.73494	−0.25017	12.93239	−0.24096	14.11552	−0.23303
3	15.26818	+0.21261	16.52937	+0.20588	17.77401	+0.19998
4	18.63744	−0.18978	19.94185	−0.18449	21.22906	−0.17979
5	21.93172	+0.17363	23.26805	+0.16929	24.58720	+0.16539
6	25.18393	−0.16127	26.54503	−0.15762	27.88927	−0.15431
7	28.40978	+0.15137	29.79075	+0.14823	31.15533	+0.14537
8	31.61788	−0.14317	33.01518	−0.14044	34.39663	−0.13792
9	34.81339	+0.13623	36.22438	+0.13381	37.62008	+0.13158
10	37.99964	−0.13024	39.42227	−0.12808	40.83018	−0.12608
11	41.17885	+0.12499	42.61152	+0.12305	44.03001	+0.12124
12	44.35258	−0.12035	45.79400	−0.11859	47.22176	−0.11695
13	47.52196	+0.11620	48.97107	+0.11460	50.40702	+0.11309
14	50.68782	−0.11246	52.14375	−0.11099	53.58700	−0.10960
15	53.85079	+0.10906	55.31282	+0.10771	56.76260	+0.10643
16	57.01138	−0.10596	58.47887	−0.10471	59.93454	−0.10352
17	60.16995	+0.10311	61.64239	+0.10195	63.10340	+0.10084
18	63.32681	−0.10049	64.80374	−0.09940	66.26961	−0.09837
19	66.48221	+0.09805	67.96324	+0.09704	69.43356	+0.09607
20	69.63635	−0.09579	71.12113	−0.09484	72.59554	−0.09393

Table 9.5

ZEROS AND ASSOCIATED VALUES OF BESSEL FUNCTIONS AND THEIR DERIVATIVES

s	$y'_{0,s}$	$Y_0(y'_{0,s})$	$y'_{1,s}$	$Y_1(y'_{1,s})$	$y'_{2,s}$	$Y_2(y'_{2,s})$
1	2.19714 133	+0.52078 641	3.68302	+0.41673	5.00258	+0.36766
2	5.42968 104	-0.34031 805	6.94150	-0.30317	8.35072	-0.27928
3	8.59600 587	+0.27145 988	10.12340	+0.25091	11.57420	+0.23594
4	11.74915 483	-0.23246 177	13.28576	-0.21897	14.76091	-0.20845
5	14.89744 213	+0.20654 711	16.44006	+0.19683	17.93129	+0.18890
6	18.04340 228	-0.18772 909	19.59024	-0.18030	21.09289	-0.17405
7	21.18806 893	+0.17326 604	22.73803	+0.16735	24.24923	+0.16225
8	24.33194 257	-0.16170 163	25.88431	-0.15684	27.40215	-0.15259
9	27.47529 498	+0.15218 126	29.02958	+0.14810	30.55271	+0.14448
10	30.61828 649	-0.14416 600	32.17412	-0.14067	33.70159	-0.13754
11	33.76101 780	+0.13729 696	35.31813	+0.13427	36.84921	+0.13152
12	36.90355 532	-0.13132 464	38.46175	-0.12866	39.99589	-0.12623
13	40.04594 464	+0.12606 951	41.60507	+0.12370	43.14182	+0.12153
14	43.18821 810	-0.12139 863	44.74814	-0.11928	46.28716	-0.11732
15	46.33039 925	+0.11721 120	47.89101	+0.11530	49.43202	+0.11352
16	49.47250 568	-0.11342 920	51.03373	-0.11169	52.57649	-0.11007
17	52.61455 077	+0.10999 115	54.17632	+0.10840	55.72063	+0.10692
18	55.75654 488	-0.10684 789	57.31880	-0.10539	58.86450	-0.10402
19	58.89849 617	+0.10395 957	60.46118	+0.10261	62.00814	+0.10135
20	62.04041 115	-0.10129 350	63.60349	-0.10005	65.15159	-0.09887

s	$y'_{3,s}$	$Y_3(y'_{3,s})$	$y'_{4,s}$	$Y_4(y'_{4,s})$	$y'_{5,s}$	$Y_5(y'_{5,s})$
1	6.25363	+0.33660	7.46492	+0.31432	8.64956	+0.29718
2	9.69879	-0.26195	11.00517	-0.24851	12.28087	-0.23763
3	12.97241	+0.22428	14.33172	+0.21481	15.66080	+0.20687
4	16.19045	-0.19987	17.58444	-0.19267	18.94974	-0.18650
5	19.38239	+0.18223	20.80106	+0.17651	22.19284	+0.17151
6	22.55979	-0.16867	23.99700	-0.16397	25.40907	-0.15980
7	25.72821	+0.15779	27.17989	+0.15384	28.60804	+0.15030
8	28.89068	-0.14881	30.35396	-0.14543	31.79520	-0.14236
9	32.04898	+0.14122	33.52180	+0.13828	34.97389	+0.13559
10	35.20427	-0.13470	36.68505	-0.13211	38.14631	-0.12973
11	38.35728	+0.12901	39.84483	+0.12671	41.31392	+0.12458
12	41.50855	-0.12399	43.00191	-0.12193	44.47779	-0.12001
13	44.65845	+0.11952	46.15686	+0.11765	47.63867	+0.11591
14	47.80725	-0.11550	49.31009	-0.11380	50.79713	-0.11221
15	50.95515	+0.11186	52.46191	+0.11031	53.95360	+0.10885
16	54.10232	-0.10855	55.61257	-0.10712	57.10841	-0.10578
17	57.24887	+0.10552	58.76225	+0.10420	60.26183	+0.10295
18	60.39491	-0.10273	61.91110	-0.10151	63.41407	-0.10035
19	63.54050	+0.10015	65.05925	+0.09901	66.56530	+0.09793
20	66.68571	-0.09775	68.20679	-0.09669	69.71565	-0.09568

s	$y'_{6,s}$	$Y_6(y'_{6,s})$	$y'_{7,s}$	$Y_7(y'_{7,s})$	$y'_{8,s}$	$Y_8(y'_{8,s})$
1	9.81480	+0.28339	10.96515	+0.27194	12.10364	+0.26220
2	13.53281	-0.22854	14.76569	-0.22077	15.98284	-0.21402
3	16.96553	+0.20007	18.25012	+0.19414	19.51773	+0.18891
4	20.29129	-0.18111	21.61275	-0.17634	22.91696	-0.17207
5	23.56186	+0.16708	24.91131	+0.16311	26.24370	+0.15953
6	26.79950	-0.15607	28.17105	-0.15269	29.52596	-0.14962
7	30.01567	+0.14709	31.40518	+0.14417	32.77857	+0.14149
8	33.21697	-0.13957	34.62140	-0.13700	36.01026	-0.13463
9	36.40752	+0.13313	37.82455	+0.13085	39.22658	+0.12874
10	39.59002	-0.12753	41.01785	-0.12549	42.43122	-0.12359
11	42.76632	+0.12260	44.20351	+0.12076	45.62678	+0.11904
12	45.93775	-0.11822	47.38314	-0.11654	48.81512	-0.11497
13	49.10528	+0.11428	50.55791	+0.11275	51.99761	+0.11131
14	52.26963	-0.11072	53.72870	-0.10931	55.17529	-0.10798
15	55.43136	+0.10748	56.89619	+0.10618	58.34899	+0.10494
16	58.59089	-0.10451	60.06092	-0.10330	61.51933	-0.10216
17	61.74857	+0.10177	63.22331	+0.10065	64.68681	+0.09958
18	64.90468	-0.09925	66.38370	-0.09820	67.85185	-0.09720
19	68.05943	+0.09690	69.54237	+0.09592	71.01478	+0.09498
20	71.21301	-0.09471	72.69955	-0.09379	74.17587	-0.09291

Table 9.8 MODIFIED BESSEL FUNCTIONS—ORDERS 0, 1 AND 2

x	$e^{-x}I_0(x)$	$e^{-x}I_1(x)$	$x^{-2}I_2(x)$
0.0	1.00000 00000	0.00000 00000	0.12500 00000
0.1	0.90710 09258	0.04529 84468	0.12510 41992
0.2	0.82693 85516	0.08228 31235	0.12541 71878
0.3	0.75758 06252	0.11237 75606	0.12594 01407
0.4	0.69740 21705	0.13676 32243	0.12667 50222
0.5	0.64503 52706	0.15642 08032	0.12762 45967
0.6	0.59932 72031	0.17216 44195	0.12879 24416
0.7	0.55930 55265	0.18466 99828	0.13018 29658
0.8	0.52414 89420	0.19449 86933	0.13180 14318
0.9	0.49316 29662	0.20211 65309	0.13365 39819
1.0	0.46575 96077	0.20791 04154	0.13574 76698
1.1	0.44144 03776	0.21220 16132	0.13809 04952
1.2	0.41978 20789	0.21525 68594	0.14069 14455
1.3	0.40042 49127	0.21729 75878	0.14356 05405
1.4	0.38306 25154	0.21850 75923	0.14670 88837
1.5	0.36743 36090	0.21903 93874	0.15014 87192
1.6	0.35331 49978	0.21901 94899	0.15389 34944
1.7	0.34051 56880	0.21855 28066	0.15795 79288
1.8	0.32887 19497	0.21772 62788	0.16235 80900
1.9	0.31824 31629	0.21661 19112	0.16711 14772
2.0	0.30850 83225	0.21526 92892	0.17223 71119
2.1	0.29956 30945	0.21374 76721	0.17775 56370
2.2	0.29131 73331	0.21208 77328	0.18368 94251
2.3	0.28369 29857	0.21032 30051	0.19006 26964
2.4	0.27662 23231	0.20848 10887	0.19690 16460
2.5	0.27004 64416	0.20658 46495	0.20423 45837
2.6	0.26391 39957	0.20465 22544	0.21209 20841
2.7	0.25818 01238	0.20269 90640	0.22050 71509
2.8	0.25280 55337	0.20073 74113	0.22951 53938
2.9	0.24775 57304	0.19877 72816	0.23915 52213
3.0	0.24300 03542	0.19682 67133	0.24946 80490
3.1	0.23851 26187	0.19489 21309	0.26049 85252
3.2	0.23426 88316	0.19297 86229	0.27229 47757
3.3	0.23024 79845	0.19109 01727	0.28490 86686
3.4	0.22643 14011	0.18922 98511	0.29839 61010
3.5	0.22280 24380	0.18739 99766	0.31281 73100
3.6	0.21934 62245	0.18560 22484	0.32823 72078
3.7	0.21604 94417	0.18383 78580	0.34472 57467
3.8	0.21290 01308	0.18210 75810	0.36235 83128
3.9	0.20988 75279	0.18041 18543	0.38121 61528
4.0	0.20700 19211	0.17875 08394	0.40138 68359
4.1	0.20423 45274	0.17712 44763	0.42296 47539
4.2	0.20157 73840	0.17553 25260	0.44605 16629
4.3	0.19902 32571	0.17397 46091	0.47075 72701
4.4	0.19656 55589	0.17245 02337	0.49719 98689
4.5	0.19419 82777	0.17095 88223	0.52550 70272
4.6	0.19191 59151	0.16949 97311	0.55581 63319
4.7	0.18971 34330	0.16807 22681	0.58827 61978
4.8	0.18758 62042	0.16667 57058	0.62304 67409
4.9	0.18552 99721	0.16530 92936	0.66030 07270
5.0	0.18354 08126	0.16397 22669	0.70022 45988

$$I_{n+1}(x) = -\frac{2n}{x} I_n(x) + I_{n-1}(x)$$

MODIFIED BESSEL FUNCTIONS—ORDERS 0, 1 AND 2 Table 9.8

x	$e^x K_0(x)$	$e^x K_1(x)$	$x^2 K_2(x)$
0.0	∞	∞	2.00000 0000
0.1	2.68232 61023	10.89018 2683	1.99503 9646
0.2	2.14075 73233	5.83338 6037	1.98049 7172
0.3	1.85262 73007	4.12515 7762	1.95711 6625
0.4	1.66268 20891	3.25867 3880	1.92580 8202
0.5	1.52410 93857	2.73100 97082	1.88754 5888
0.6	1.41673 76214	2.37392 00376	1.84330 9881
0.7	1.33012 36562	2.11501 13128	1.79405 1681
0.8	1.25820 31216	1.91793 02990	1.74067 2762
0.9	1.19716 33803	1.76238 82197	1.68401 1992
1.0	1.14446 30797	1.63615 34863	1.62483 8899
1.1	1.09833 02828	1.53140 37541	1.56385 0953
1.2	1.05748 45322	1.44289 75522	1.50167 3576
1.3	1.02097 31613	1.36698 72841	1.43886 2011
1.4	0.98806 99961	1.30105 37400	1.37590 4446
1.5	0.95821 00533	1.24316 58736	1.31322 5917
1.6	0.93094 59808	1.19186 75654	1.25119 2681
1.7	0.90591 81386	1.14603 92462	1.19011 6819
1.8	0.88283 35270	1.10480 53726	1.13026 0897
1.9	0.86145 06168	1.06747 09298	1.07184 2567
2.0	0.84156 82151	1.03347 68471	1.01503 9018
2.1	0.82301 71525	1.00236 80527	0.95999 1226
2.2	0.80565 39812	0.97377 01679	0.90680 7952
2.3	0.78935 61312	0.94737 22250	0.85556 9487
2.4	0.77401 81407	0.92291 36650	0.80633 1113
2.5	0.75954 86903	0.90017 44239	0.75912 6289
2.6	0.74586 82430	0.87896 72806	0.71396 9565
2.7	0.73290 71515	0.85913 18867	0.67085 9227
2.8	0.72060 41251	0.84053 00604	0.62977 9698
2.9	0.70890 49774	0.82304 20403	0.59070 3688
3.0	0.69776 15980	0.80656 34800	0.55359 4126
3.1	0.68713 11010	0.79100 30157	0.51840 5885
3.2	0.67697 51139	0.77628 02824	0.48508 7306
3.3	0.66725 91831	0.76232 42864	0.45358 1550
3.4	0.65795 22725	0.74907 20613	0.42382 7789
3.5	0.64902 63377	0.73646 75480	0.39576 2241
3.6	0.64045 59647	0.72446 06608	0.36931 9074
3.7	0.63221 80591	0.71300 65010	0.34443 1194
3.8	0.62429 15812	0.70206 46931	0.32103 0914
3.9	0.61665 73147	0.69159 88206	0.29905 0529
4.0	0.60929 76693	0.68157 59452	0.27842 2808
4.1	0.60219 65064	0.67196 61952	0.25908 1398
4.2	0.59533 89889	0.66274 24110	0.24096 1165
4.3	0.58871 14486	0.65387 98395	0.22399 8474
4.4	0.58230 12704	0.64535 58689	0.20813 1411
4.5	0.57609 67897	0.63714 97988	0.19329 9963
4.6	0.57008 72022	0.62924 26383	0.17944 6150
4.7	0.56426 24840	0.62161 69312	0.16651 4127
4.8	0.55861 33194	0.61425 66003	0.15445 0249
4.9	0.55313 10397	0.60714 68131	0.14320 3117
5.0	0.54780 75643	0.60027 38587	0.13272 3593

$$K_{n+1}(x)=\frac{2n}{x}K_n(x)+K_{n-1}(x)$$

Table 9.8 MODIFIED BESSEL FUNCTIONS—ORDERS 0, 1 AND 2

x	$e^{-x}I_0(x)$	$e^{-x}I_1(x)$	$e^{-x}I_2(x)$
5.0	0.18354 08126	0.16397 22669	0.11795 1906
5.1	0.18161 51021	0.16266 38546	0.11782 5355
5.2	0.17974 94883	0.16138 32850	0.11767 8994
5.3	0.17794 08646	0.16012 97913	0.11751 4528
5.4	0.17618 63475	0.15890 26150	0.11733 3527
5.5	0.17448 32564	0.15770 10090	0.11713 7435
5.6	0.17282 90951	0.15652 42405	0.11692 7581
5.7	0.17122 15362	0.15537 15922	0.11670 5188
5.8	0.16965 84061	0.15424 23641	0.11647 1384
5.9	0.16813 76726	0.15313 58742	0.11622 7207
6.0	0.16665 74327	0.15205 14593	0.11597 3613
6.1	0.16521 59021	0.15098 84754	0.11571 1484
6.2	0.16381 14064	0.14994 62978	0.11544 1633
6.3	0.16244 23718	0.14892 43212	0.11516 4809
6.4	0.16110 73175	0.14792 19595	0.11488 1705
6.5	0.15980 48490	0.14693 86457	0.11459 2958
6.6	0.15853 36513	0.14597 38314	0.11429 9157
6.7	0.15729 24831	0.14502 69866	0.11400 0845
6.8	0.15608 01720	0.14409 75991	0.11369 8525
6.9	0.15489 56090	0.14318 51745	0.11339 2660
7.0	0.15373 77447	0.14228 92347	0.11308 3678
7.1	0.15260 55844	0.14140 93186	0.11277 1974
7.2	0.15149 81855	0.14054 49809	0.11245 7913
7.3	0.15041 46530	0.13969 57915	0.11214 1833
7.4	0.14935 41371	0.13886 13353	0.11182 4046
7.5	0.14831 58301	0.13804 12115	0.11150 4840
7.6	0.14729 89636	0.13723 50333	0.11118 4481
7.7	0.14630 28062	0.13644 24270	0.11086 3215
7.8	0.14532 66611	0.13566 30318	0.11054 1268
7.9	0.14436 98642	0.13489 64995	0.11021 8852
8.0	0.14343 17818	0.13414 24933	0.10989 6158
8.1	0.14251 18095	0.13340 06883	0.10957 3368
8.2	0.14160 93695	0.13267 07705	0.10925 0645
8.3	0.14072 39098	0.13195 24362	0.10892 8142
8.4	0.13985 49027	0.13124 53923	0.10860 6000
8.5	0.13900 18430	0.13054 93551	0.10828 4348
8.6	0.13816 42474	0.12986 40505	0.10796 3305
8.7	0.13734 16526	0.12918 92134	0.10764 2983
8.8	0.13653 36147	0.12852 45873	0.10732 3481
8.9	0.13573 97082	0.12786 99242	0.10700 4894
9.0	0.13495 95247	0.12722 49839	0.10668 7306
9.1	0.13419 26720	0.12658 95342	0.10637 0796
9.2	0.13343 87740	0.12596 33501	0.10605 5437
9.3	0.13269 74691	0.12534 62139	0.10574 1294
9.4	0.13196 84094	0.12473 79145	0.10542 8428
9.5	0.13125 12609	0.12413 82477	0.10511 6893
9.6	0.13054 57016	0.12354 70154	0.10480 6740
9.7	0.12985 14223	0.12296 40258	0.10449 8015
9.8	0.12916 81248	0.12238 90929	0.10419 0759
9.9	0.12849 55220	0.12182 20364	0.10388 5010
10.0	0.12783 33371	0.12126 26814	0.10358 0801

MODIFIED BESSEL FUNCTIONS—ORDERS 0, 1 AND 2 Table 9.8

x	$e^xK_0(x)$	$e^xK_1(x)$	$e^xK_2(x)$
5.0	0.54780 75643	0.60027 38587	0.78791 711
5.1	0.54263 53519	0.59362 50463	0.77542 949
5.2	0.53760 73540	0.58718 86062	0.76344 913
5.3	0.53271 69744	0.58095 36085	0.75194 475
5.4	0.52795 80329	0.57490 98871	0.74088 762
5.5	0.52332 47316	0.56904 79741	0.73025 127
5.6	0.51881 16252	0.56335 90393	0.72001 128
5.7	0.51441 35938	0.55783 48348	0.71014 511
5.8	0.51012 58183	0.55246 76495	0.70063 190
5.9	0.50594 37583	0.54725 02639	0.69145 232
6.0	0.50186 31309	0.54217 59104	0.68258 843
6.1	0.49787 98929	0.53723 82386	0.67402 358
6.2	0.49399 02237	0.53243 12833	0.66574 225
6.3	0.49019 05093	0.52774 94344	0.65773 001
6.4	0.48647 73291	0.52318 74101	0.64997 339
6.5	0.48284 74413	0.51874 02336	0.64245 982
6.6	0.47929 77729	0.51440 32108	0.63517 753
6.7	0.47582 54066	0.51017 19097	0.62811 553
6.8	0.47242 75723	0.50604 21421	0.62126 350
6.9	0.46910 16370	0.50200 99471	0.61461 177
7.0	0.46584 50959	0.49807 15749	0.60815 126
7.1	0.46265 55657	0.49422 34737	0.60187 345
7.2	0.45953 07756	0.49046 22755	0.59577 030
7.3	0.45646 85618	0.48678 47842	0.58983 426
7.4	0.45346 68594	0.48318 79648	0.58405 820
7.5	0.45052 36991	0.47966 89336	0.57843 541
7.6	0.44763 71996	0.47622 49486	0.57295 955
7.7	0.44480 55636	0.47285 33995	0.56762 463
7.8	0.44202 70724	0.46955 18010	0.56242 497
7.9	0.43930 00819	0.46631 77847	0.55735 522
8.0	0.43662 30185	0.46314 90928	0.55241 029
8.1	0.43399 43754	0.46004 35709	0.54758 538
8.2	0.43141 27084	0.45699 91615	0.54287 592
8.3	0.42887 66329	0.45401 39001	0.53827 757
8.4	0.42638 48214	0.45108 59089	0.53378 623
8.5	0.42393 59993	0.44821 33915	0.52939 797
8.6	0.42152 89433	0.44539 46295	0.52510 909
8.7	0.41916 24781	0.44262 79775	0.52091 604
8.8	0.41683 54743	0.43991 18594	0.51681 544
8.9	0.41454 68462	0.43724 47648	0.51280 410
9.0	0.41229 55493	0.43462 52454	0.50887 894
9.1	0.41008 05783	0.43205 19116	0.50503 704
9.2	0.40790 09662	0.42952 34301	0.50127 562
9.3	0.40575 57809	0.42703 85204	0.49759 202
9.4	0.40364 41245	0.42459 59520	0.49398 369
9.5	0.40156 51322	0.42219 45430	0.49044 819
9.6	0.39951 79693	0.41983 31565	0.48698 321
9.7	0.39750 18313	0.41751 06989	0.48358 651
9.8	0.39551 59416	0.41522 61179	0.48025 597
9.9	0.39355 95506	0.41297 84003	0.47698 953
10.0	0.39163 19344	0.41076 65704	0.47378 525

MODIFIED BESSEL FUNCTIONS—ORDERS 3–9 Table 9.9

x	$e^{-x}I_3(x)$	$e^{-x}I_4(x)$	$e^{-x}I_5(x)$	$e^{-x}I_6(x)$	$e^{-x}I_7(x)$	$e^{-x}I_8(x)$	$e^{-x}I_9(x)$
0.0	0.0000	0.0000	0.0000	0.0000	0.0000	0.0000	0.0000
0.2	(-4) 1.3680	(-6) 3.4182	(-8) 6.8341	(-9) 1.1388	(-11) 1.6265	(-13) 2.0328	(-15) 2.2585
0.4	(-4) 9.0273	(-5) 4.5047	(-6) 1.7995	(-8) 5.9925	(- 9) 1.7109	(-11) 4.2750	(-13) 9.4957
0.6	(-3) 2.5257	(-4) 1.8858	(-5) 1.1281	(-7) 5.6286	(- 8) 2.4084	(-10) 9.0201	(-11) 3.0037
0.8	(-3) 4.9877	(-4) 4.9483	(-5) 3.9377	(-6) 2.6152	(- 7) 1.4902	(- 9) 7.4343	(-10) 3.2983
1.0	(-3) 8.1553	(-3) 1.0069	(-5) 9.9866	(-6) 8.2731	(- 7) 5.8832	(- 8) 3.6643	(- 9) 2.0301
1.2	(-2) 1.1855	(-3) 1.7471	(-4) 2.0719	(-5) 2.0544	(- 6) 1.7497	(- 7) 1.3058	(- 9) 8.6707
1.4	(-2) 1.5911	(-3) 2.7189	(-4) 3.7459	(-5) 4.3203	(- 6) 4.2831	(- 7) 3.7225	(- 8) 2.8797
1.6	(-2) 2.0168	(-3) 3.9110	(-4) 6.1288	(-5) 8.0504	(- 6) 9.0974	(- 7) 9.0178	(- 8) 7.9596
1.8	(-2) 2.4495	(-3) 5.3023	(-4) 9.2978	(-4) 1.3686	(- 5) 1.7349	(- 6) 1.9302	(- 7) 1.9131
2.0	(-2) 2.8791	(-3) 6.8654	(-3) 1.3298	(-4) 2.1656	(- 5) 3.0402	(- 6) 3.7487	(- 7) 4.1199
2.2	(-2) 3.2978	(-3) 8.5701	(-3) 1.8142	(-4) 3.2349	(- 5) 4.9776	(- 6) 6.7325	(- 7) 8.1206
2.4	(-2) 3.7001	(-2) 1.0386	(-3) 2.3819	(-4) 4.6097	(- 5) 7.7080	(- 5) 1.1339	(- 6) 1.4883
2.6	(-2) 4.0823	(-2) 1.2283	(-3) 3.0293	(-4) 6.3166	(- 4) 1.1395	(- 5) 1.8099	(- 6) 2.5669
2.8	(-2) 4.4421	(-2) 1.4234	(-3) 3.7511	(-4) 8.3747	(- 4) 1.6197	(- 5) 2.7609	(- 6) 4.2048
3.0	(-2) 4.7783	(-2) 1.6216	(-3) 4.5409	(-3) 1.0796	(- 4) 2.2265	(- 5) 4.0512	(- 6) 6.5905
3.2	(-2) 5.0907	(-2) 1.8206	(-3) 5.3913	(-3) 1.3584	(- 4) 2.9735	(- 5) 5.7482	(- 6) 9.9425
3.4	(-2) 5.3795	(-2) 2.0188	(-3) 6.2947	(-3) 1.6738	(- 4) 3.8725	(- 5) 7.9208	(- 5) 1.4507
3.6	(-2) 5.6454	(-2) 2.2145	(-3) 7.2431	(-3) 2.0249	(- 4) 4.9334	(- 4) 1.0638	(- 5) 2.0556
3.8	(-2) 5.8893	(-2) 2.4065	(-3) 8.2288	(-3) 2.4106	(- 4) 6.1640	(- 4) 1.3965	(- 5) 2.8380
4.0	(-2) 6.1124	(-2) 2.5940	(-3) 9.2443	(-3) 2.8291	(- 4) 7.5698	(- 4) 1.7968	(- 5) 3.8284
4.2	(-2) 6.3161	(-2) 2.7761	(-2) 1.0283	(-3) 3.2785	(- 4) 9.1545	(- 4) 2.2703	(- 5) 5.0587
4.4	(-2) 6.5015	(-2) 2.9523	(-2) 1.1337	(-3) 3.7566	(- 3) 1.0919	(- 4) 2.8224	(- 5) 6.5607
4.6	(-2) 6.6699	(-2) 3.1221	(-2) 1.2402	(-3) 4.2609	(- 3) 1.2864	(- 4) 3.4578	(- 5) 8.3667
4.8	(-2) 6.8227	(-2) 3.2854	(-2) 1.3471	(-3) 4.7890	(- 3) 1.4986	(- 4) 4.1806	(- 4) 1.0508
5.0	(-2) 6.9611	(-2) 3.4419	(-2) 1.4540	(-3) 5.3384	(- 3) 1.7282	(- 4) 4.9939	(- 4) 1.3015
5.2	(-2) 7.0861	(-2) 3.5916	(-2) 1.5605	(-3) 5.9065	(- 3) 1.9747	(- 4) 5.9005	(- 4) 1.5916
5.4	(-2) 7.1989	(-2) 3.7346	(-2) 1.6662	(-3) 6.4909	(- 3) 2.2374	(- 4) 6.9020	(- 4) 1.9240
5.6	(-2) 7.3005	(-2) 3.8708	(-2) 1.7707	(-3) 7.0892	(- 3) 2.5157	(- 4) 7.9996	(- 4) 2.3010
5.8	(-2) 7.3917	(-2) 4.0005	(-2) 1.8738	(-3) 7.6990	(- 3) 2.8087	(- 4) 9.1937	(- 4) 2.7249
6.0	(-2) 7.4736	(-2) 4.1238	(-2) 1.9752	(-3) 8.3181	(- 3) 3.1156	(- 3) 1.0484	(- 4) 3.1978
6.2	(-2) 7.5468	(-2) 4.2408	(-2) 2.0747	(-3) 8.9445	(- 3) 3.4355	(- 3) 1.1870	(- 4) 3.7214
6.4	(-2) 7.6121	(-2) 4.3518	(-2) 2.1723	(-3) 9.5763	(- 3) 3.7674	(- 3) 1.3351	(- 4) 4.2971
6.6	(-2) 7.6702	(-2) 4.4570	(-2) 2.2677	(-2) 1.0212	(- 3) 4.1105	(- 3) 1.4924	(- 4) 4.9261
6.8	(-2) 7.7216	(-2) 4.5567	(-2) 2.3608	(-2) 1.0849	(- 3) 4.4637	(- 3) 1.6587	(- 4) 5.6094
7.0	(-2) 7.7670	(-2) 4.6509	(-2) 2.4516	(-2) 1.1486	(- 3) 4.8261	(- 3) 1.8337	(- 4) 6.3475
7.2	(-2) 7.8068	(-2) 4.7401	(-2) 2.5401	(-2) 1.2122	(- 3) 5.1969	(- 3) 2.0172	(- 4) 7.1409
7.4	(-2) 7.8416	(-2) 4.8244	(-2) 2.6261	(-2) 1.2756	(- 3) 5.5750	(- 3) 2.2089	(- 4) 7.9897
7.6	(-2) 7.8717	(-2) 4.9040	(-2) 2.7096	(-2) 1.3387	(- 3) 5.9596	(- 3) 2.4084	(- 4) 8.8937
7.8	(-2) 7.8975	(-2) 4.9791	(-2) 2.7907	(-2) 1.4012	(- 3) 6.3499	(- 3) 2.6152	(- 4) 9.8527
8.0	(-2) 7.9194	(-2) 5.0500	(-2) 2.8694	(-2) 1.4633	(- 3) 6.7449	(- 3) 2.8292	(- 3) 1.0866
8.2	(-2) 7.9378	(-2) 5.1169	(-2) 2.9456	(-2) 1.5247	(- 3) 7.1440	(- 3) 3.0497	(- 3) 1.1933
8.4	(-2) 7.9528	(-2) 5.1800	(-2) 3.0195	(-2) 1.5854	(- 3) 7.5464	(- 3) 3.2766	(- 3) 1.3053
8.6	(-2) 7.9649	(-2) 5.2395	(-2) 3.0909	(-2) 1.6453	(- 3) 7.9513	(- 3) 3.5093	(- 3) 1.4224
8.8	(-2) 7.9741	(-2) 5.2954	(-2) 3.1601	(-2) 1.7045	(- 3) 8.3582	(- 3) 3.7475	(- 3) 1.5446
9.0	(-2) 7.9808	(-2) 5.3482	(-2) 3.2269	(-2) 1.7627	(- 3) 8.7663	(- 3) 3.9907	(- 3) 1.6716
9.2	(-2) 7.9852	(-2) 5.3978	(-2) 3.2915	(-2) 1.8201	(- 3) 9.1750	(- 3) 4.2386	(- 3) 1.8035
9.4	(-2) 7.9875	(-2) 5.4445	(-2) 3.3539	(-2) 1.8765	(- 3) 9.5839	(- 3) 4.4908	(- 3) 1.9399
9.6	(-2) 7.9878	(-2) 5.4883	(-2) 3.4141	(-2) 1.9319	(- 3) 9.9924	(- 3) 4.7470	(- 3) 2.0808
9.8	(-2) 7.9862	(-2) 5.5296	(-2) 3.4723	(-2) 1.9864	(- 2) 1.0400	(- 3) 5.0066	(- 3) 2.2260
10.0	(-2) 7.9830	(-2) 5.5683	(-2) 3.5284	(-2) 2.0398	(- 2) 1.0806	(- 3) 5.2694	(- 3) 2.3753

Table 9.9 MODIFIED BESSEL FUNCTIONS—ORDERS 3–9

x	$e^xK_3(x)$	$e^xK_4(x)$	$e^xK_5(x)$	$e^xK_6(x)$	$e^xK_7(x)$	$e^xK_8(x)$	$e^xK_9(x)$
0.0	∞	∞	∞	∞	∞	∞	∞
0.2	(3)1.2153	(4)3.6520	(6)1.4620	(7)7.3138	(9)4.3897	(11)3.0735	(13)2.4593
0.4	(2)1.8282	(3)2.7602	(4)5.5388	(6)1.3875	(7)4.1679	(9)1.4602	(10)5.8448
0.6	(1)6.4573	(2)6.5506	(3)8.7987	(5)1.4730	(6)2.9548	(7)6.9092	(9)1.8454
0.8	(1)3.2183	(2)2.4743	(3)2.5064	(4)3.1578	(5)4.7618	(6)8.3647	(8)1.6777
1.0	(1)1.9303	(2)1.2024	(2)9.8119	(3)9.9322	(5)1.2017	(6)1.6923	(7)2.7197
1.2	(1)1.2984	(1)6.8382	(2)4.6886	(3)3.9756	(4)4.0225	(5)4.7326	(6)6.3504
1.4	(0)9.4345	(1)4.3280	(2)2.5675	(3)1.8772	(4)1.6347	(5)1.6535	(6)1.9061
1.6	(0)7.2438	(1)2.9585	(2)1.5517	(2)9.9939	(3)7.6506	(4)6.7942	(5)6.8707
1.8	(0)5.7946	(1)2.1426	(2)1.0102	(2)5.8265	(3)3.9853	(4)3.1580	(5)2.8469
2.0	(0)4.7836	(1)1.6226	(1)6.9687	(2)3.6466	(3)2.2576	(4)1.6168	(5)1.3160
2.2	(0)4.0481	(1)1.2731	(1)5.0344	(2)2.4157	(3)1.3680	(3)8.9469	(4)6.6436
2.4	(0)3.4948	(1)1.0280	(1)3.7762	(2)1.6762	(2)8.7586	(3)5.2768	(4)3.6055
2.6	(0)3.0667	(0)8.4989	(1)2.9217	(2)1.2087	(2)5.8709	(3)3.2821	(4)2.0785
2.8	(0)2.7276	(0)7.1659	(1)2.3202	(1)9.0029	(2)4.0904	(3)2.1352	(4)1.2610
3.0	(0)2.4539	(0)6.1432	(1)1.8836	(1)6.8929	(2)2.9455	(3)1.4435	(3)7.9932
3.2	(0)2.2290	(0)5.3415	(1)1.5583	(1)5.4037	(2)2.1822	(3)1.0088	(3)5.2620
3.4	(0)2.0415	(0)4.7013	(1)1.3103	(1)4.3240	(2)1.6572	(2)7.2560	(3)3.5803
3.6	(0)1.8833	(0)4.1817	(1)1.1176	(1)3.5226	(2)1.2860	(2)5.3532	(3)2.5078
3.8	(0)1.7482	(0)3.7541	(0)9.6515	(1)2.9153	(2)1.0171	(2)4.0388	(3)1.8023
4.0	(0)1.6317	(0)3.3976	(0)8.4268	(1)2.4465	(1)8.1821	(2)3.1084	(3)1.3252
4.2	(0)1.5303	(0)3.0971	(0)7.4295	(1)2.0786	(1)6.6819	(2)2.4352	(2)9.9450
4.4	(0)1.4414	(0)2.8412	(0)6.6072	(1)1.7858	(1)5.5310	(2)1.9384	(2)7.6019
4.6	(0)1.3629	(0)2.6213	(0)5.9217	(1)1.5495	(1)4.6342	(2)1.5654	(2)5.9082
4.8	(0)1.2931	(0)2.4309	(0)5.3445	(1)1.3565	(1)3.9258	(2)1.2807	(2)4.6615
5.0	(0)1.2306	(0)2.2646	(0)4.8540	(1)1.1973	(1)3.3589	(2)1.0602	(2)3.7285
5.2	(0)1.1745	(0)2.1186	(0)4.4338	(1)1.0645	(1)2.9000	(1)8.8721	(2)3.0199
5.4	(0)1.1237	(0)1.9895	(0)4.0711	(0)9.5285	(1)2.5245	(1)7.4980	(2)2.4741
5.6	(0)1.0777	(0)1.8746	(0)3.7557	(0)8.5813	(1)2.2144	(1)6.3942	(2)2.0483
5.8	(0)1.0357	(0)1.7720	(0)3.4798	(0)7.7717	(1)1.9559	(1)5.4983	(2)1.7124
6.0	(-1)9.9723	(0)1.6798	(0)3.2370	(0)7.0748	(1)1.7387	(1)4.7644	(2)1.4444
6.2	(-1)9.6194	(0)1.5967	(0)3.0221	(0)6.4711	(1)1.5547	(1)4.1577	(2)1.2284
6.4	(-1)9.2942	(0)1.5213	(0)2.8311	(0)5.9448	(1)1.3978	(1)3.6521	(2)1.0528
6.6	(-1)8.9936	(0)1.4528	(0)2.6603	(0)5.4835	(1)1.2630	(1)3.2275	(1)9.0873
6.8	(-1)8.7149	(0)1.3902	(0)2.5071	(0)5.0771	(1)1.1467	(1)2.8685	(1)7.8960
7.0	(-1)8.4559	(0)1.3329	(0)2.3689	(0)4.7171	(1)1.0455	(1)2.5628	(1)6.9034
7.2	(-1)8.2145	(0)1.2803	(0)2.2440	(0)4.3970	(0)9.5723	(1)2.3010	(1)6.0705
7.4	(-1)7.9890	(0)1.2318	(0)2.1306	(0)4.1110	(0)8.7970	(1)2.0754	(1)5.3671
7.6	(-1)7.7778	(0)1.1870	(0)2.0273	(0)3.8544	(0)8.1132	(1)1.8800	(1)4.7692
7.8	(-1)7.5797	(0)1.1455	(0)1.9328	(0)3.6235	(0)7.5074	(1)1.7098	(1)4.2581
8.0	(-1)7.3935	(0)1.1069	(0)1.8463	(0)3.4148	(0)6.9684	(1)1.5610	(1)3.8188
8.2	(-1)7.2182	(0)1.0710	(0)1.7667	(0)3.2256	(0)6.4871	(1)1.4301	(1)3.4392
8.4	(-1)7.0527	(0)1.0376	(0)1.6934	(0)3.0535	(0)6.0556	(1)1.3146	(1)3.1096
8.6	(-1)6.8963	(0)1.0062	(0)1.6257	(0)2.8966	(0)5.6674	(1)1.2123	(1)2.8221
8.8	(-1)6.7483	(-1)9.7693	(0)1.5629	(0)2.7530	(0)5.3170	(1)1.1212	(1)2.5702
9.0	(-1)6.6079	(-1)9.4941	(0)1.5047	(0)2.6213	(0)4.9998	(1)1.0399	(1)2.3486
9.2	(-1)6.4746	(-1)9.2354	(0)1.4505	(0)2.5002	(0)4.7117	(0)9.6702	(1)2.1529
9.4	(-1)6.3480	(-1)8.9918	(0)1.4001	(0)2.3886	(0)4.4493	(0)9.0153	(1)1.9794
9.6	(-1)6.2274	(-1)8.7620	(0)1.3529	(0)2.2855	(0)4.2098	(0)8.4247	(1)1.8251
9.8	(-1)6.1125	(-1)8.5449	(0)1.3088	(0)2.1900	(0)3.9904	(0)7.8906	(1)1.6873
10.0	(-1)6.0028	(-1)8.3395	(0)1.2674	(0)2.1014	(0)3.7891	(0)7.4062	(1)1.5639

Table 9.12 KELVIN FUNCTIONS—ORDERS 0 AND 1

x	ber x	bei x	$\mathrm{ber}_1\, x$	$\mathrm{bei}_1\, x$
0.0	1.00000 00000	0.00000 00000	0.00000 00000	0.00000 00000
0.1	0.99999 84375	0.00249 99996	-0.03539 95148	0.03531 11265
0.2	0.99997 50000	0.00999 99722	-0.07106 36418	0.07035 65360
0.3	0.99987 34379	0.02249 96836	-0.10725 47768	0.10486 83082
0.4	0.99960 00044	0.03999 82222	-0.14423 08645	0.13857 41359
0.5	0.99902 34640	0.06249 32184	-0.18224 31238	0.17119 51797
0.6	0.99797 51139	0.08997 97504	-0.22153 37177	0.20244 39824
0.7	0.99624 88284	0.12244 89390	-0.26233 33470	0.23202 24623
0.8	0.99360 11377	0.15988 62295	-0.30485 87511	0.25962 00070
0.9	0.98975 13567	0.20226 93635	-0.34931 01000	0.28491 16898
1.0	0.98438 17812	0.24956 60400	-0.39586 82610	0.30755 66314
1.1	0.97713 79732	0.30173 12692	-0.44469 19268	0.32719 65305
1.2	0.96762 91558	0.35870 44199	-0.49591 45913	0.34345 43903
1.3	0.95542 87468	0.42040 59656	-0.54964 13636	0.35593 34649
1.4	0.94007 50567	0.48673 39336	-0.60594 56099	0.36421 64560
1.5	0.92107 21835	0.55756 00623	-0.66486 54180	0.36786 49890
1.6	0.89789 11386	0.63272 56770	-0.72639 98786	0.36641 93986
1.7	0.86997 12370	0.71203 72924	-0.79050 51846	0.35939 88584
1.8	0.83672 17942	0.79526 19548	-0.85709 05470	0.34630 18876
1.9	0.79752 41670	0.88212 23406	-0.92601 39357	0.32660 72722
2.0	0.75173 41827	0.97229 16273	-0.99707 76519	0.29977 54370
2.1	0.69868 50014	1.06538 81608	-1.07002 37462	0.26525 03092
2.2	0.63769 04571	1.16096 99438	-1.14452 92997	0.22246 17120
2.3	0.56804 89261	1.25852 89751	-1.22020 15903	0.17082 83322
2.4	0.48904 77721	1.35748 54765	-1.29657 31717	0.10976 13027
2.5	0.39996 84171	1.45718 20442	-1.37309 68976	+0.03866 84440
2.6	0.30009 20903	1.55687 77737	-1.44914 09315	-0.04304 07916
2.7	0.18870 63040	1.65574 24073	-1.52398 37854	-0.13594 96285
2.8	+0.06511 21084	1.75285 05638	-1.59680 94413	-0.24062 74875
2.9	-0.07136 78258	1.84717 61157	-1.66670 26139	-0.35762 26713
3.0	-0.22138 02496	1.93758 67853	-1.73264 42211	-0.48745 41770
3.1	-0.38553 14550	2.02283 90420	-1.79350 71373	-0.63060 25952
3.2	-0.56437 64305	2.10157 33881	-1.84805 23125	-0.78750 00586
3.3	-0.75840 70121	2.17231 01315	-1.89492 53482	-0.95851 92089
3.4	-0.96803 89953	2.23344 57503	-1.93265 36306	-1.14396 11510
3.5	-1.19359 81796	2.28324 99669	-1.95964 41313	-1.34404 23731
3.6	-1.43530 53217	2.31986 36548	-1.97418 19924	-1.55888 06139
3.7	-1.69325 99843	2.34129 77145	-1.97443 00262	-1.78847 96677
3.8	-1.96742 32727	2.34543 30614	-1.95842 92665	-2.03271 31257
3.9	-2.25759 94661	2.33002 18823	-1.92410 07174	-2.29130 70630
4.0	-2.56341 65573	2.29269 03227	-1.86924 84590	-2.56382 16886
4.1	-2.88430 57320	2.23094 27803	-1.79156 42730	-2.84963 19932
4.2	-3.21947 98323	2.14216 79867	-1.68863 39648	-3.14790 74393
4.3	-3.56791 08628	2.02364 70694	-1.55794 55649	-3.45759 07560
4.4	-3.92830 66215	1.87256 37958	-1.39689 95997	-3.77737 59182
4.5	-4.29908 65516	1.68601 72036	-1.20282 16315	-4.10568 54084
4.6	-4.67835 69372	1.46103 68359	-0.97297 72697	-4.44064 68813
4.7	-5.06388 55867	1.19460 07968	-0.70458 98649	-4.78006 93721
4.8	-5.45307 61749	0.88365 68537	-0.39486 10961	-5.12141 92170
4.9	-5.84294 24419	0.52514 68109	-0.04099 46681	-5.46179 58790
5.0	-6.23008 24787	0.11603 43816	+0.35977 66668	-5.79790 79018

KELVIN FUNCTIONS—ORDERS 0 AND 1 Table 9.12

x	ker x	kei x	$\text{ker}_1\, x$	$\text{kei}_1\, x$
0.0	∞	-0.78539 8163	−∞	−∞
0.1	2.42047 3980	-0.77685 0646	-7.14668 1711	-6.94024 2153
0.2	1.73314 2752	-0.75812 4933	-3.63868 3342	-3.32341 7218
0.3	1.33721 8637	-0.73310 1912	-2.47074 2357	-2.08283 4751
0.4	1.06262 3902	-0.70380 0212	-1.88202 4050	-1.44430 5150
0.5	0.85590 5872	-0.67158 1695	-1.52240 3406	-1.05118 2085
0.6	0.69312 0695	-0.63744 9494	-1.27611 7712	-0.78373 8860
0.7	0.56137 8274	-0.60217 5451	-1.09407 2943	-0.59017 5251
0.8	0.45288 2093	-0.56636 7650	-0.95203 2751	-0.44426 9985
0.9	0.36251 4812	-0.53051 1122	-0.83672 7829	-0.33122 6820
1.0	0.28670 6208	-0.49499 4636	-0.74032 2276	-0.24199 5966
1.1	0.22284 4513	-0.46012 9528	-0.65791 0729	-0.17068 4462
1.2	0.16894 5592	-0.42616 3604	-0.58627 4386	-0.11325 6800
1.3	0.12345 5395	-0.39329 1826	-0.52321 5989	-0.06683 2622
1.4	0.08512 6048	-0.36166 4781	-0.46718 3076	-0.02928 3749
1.5	0.05293 4915	-0.33139 5562	-0.41704 4285	+0.00100 8681
1.6	0.02602 9861	-0.30256 5474	-0.37195 1238	0.02530 6776
1.7	+0.00369 1104	-0.27522 8834	-0.33125 0485	0.04461 5190
1.8	-0.01469 6087	-0.24941 7069	-0.29442 5803	0.05974 7779
1.9	-0.02966 1407	-0.22514 2235	-0.26105 9495	0.07137 3592
2.0	-0.04166 4514	-0.20240 0068	-0.23080 5929	0.08004 9398
2.1	-0.05110 6500	-0.18117 2644	-0.20337 3135	0.08624 3202
2.2	-0.05833 8834	-0.16143 0701	-0.17850 9812	0.09035 1619
2.3	-0.06367 0454	-0.14313 5677	-0.15599 6054	0.09271 2940
2.4	-0.06737 3493	-0.12624 1488	-0.13563 6638	0.09361 7161
2.5	-0.06968 7972	-0.11069 6099	-0.11725 6136	0.09331 3788
2.6	-0.07082 5700	-0.09644 2891	-0.10069 5314	0.09201 8037
2.7	-0.07097 3560	-0.08342 1858	-0.08580 8451	0.08991 5810
2.8	-0.07029 6321	-0.07157 0648	-0.07246 1339	0.08716 7762
2.9	-0.06893 9052	-0.06082 5473	-0.06052 9755	0.08391 2666
3.0	-0.06702 9233	-0.05112 1884	-0.04989 8308	0.08027 0223
3.1	-0.06467 8610	-0.04239 5446	-0.04045 9533	0.07634 3451
3.2	-0.06198 4833	-0.03458 2313	-0.03211 3183	0.07222 0724
3.3	-0.05903 2916	-0.02761 9697	-0.02476 5662	0.06797 7529
3.4	-0.05589 6550	-0.02144 6287	-0.01832 9556	0.06367 7999
3.5	-0.05263 9277	-0.01600 2568	-0.01272 3249	0.05937 6256
3.6	-0.04931 5556	-0.01123 1096	-0.00787 0585	0.05511 7592
3.7	-0.04597 1723	-0.00707 6704	-0.00370 0576	0.05093 9514
3.8	-0.04264 6864	-0.00348 6665	-0.00014 7138	0.04687 2681
3.9	-0.03937 3608	-0.00041 0809	+0.00285 1155	0.04294 1728
4.0	-0.03617 8848	+0.00219 8399	0.00535 1296	0.03916 6011
4.1	-0.03308 4395	0.00438 5818	0.00740 6063	0.03556 0272
4.2	-0.03010 7574	0.00619 3613	0.00906 4226	0.03213 5235
4.3	-0.02726 1764	0.00766 1269	0.01037 0752	0.02889 8142
4.4	-0.02455 6892	0.00882 5624	0.01136 6998	0.02585 3229
4.5	-0.02199 9875	0.00972 0918	0.01209 0904	0.02300 2160
4.6	-0.01959 5024	0.01037 8865	0.01257 7182	0.02034 4409
4.7	-0.01734 4409	0.01082 8725	0.01285 7498	0.01787 7607
4.8	-0.01524 8188	0.01109 7399	0.01296 0651	0.01559 7847
4.9	-0.01330 4899	0.01120 9526	0.01291 2753	0.01349 9960
5.0	-0.01151 1727	0.01118 7587	0.01273 7390	0.01157 7754

Table 9.12 KELVIN FUNCTIONS—MODULUS AND PHASE

$\text{ber}\, x = M_0(x) \cos \theta_0(x)$ $\quad \text{ber}_1\, x = M_1(x) \cos \theta_1(x)$

$\text{bei}\, x = M_0(x) \sin \theta_0(x)$ $\quad \text{bei}_1\, x = M_1(x) \sin \theta_1(x)$

x	$M_0(x)$	$\theta_0(x)$	$M_1(x)$	$\theta_1(x)$
0.0	1.000000	0.000000	0.000000	2.356194
0.2	1.000025	0.010000	0.100000	2.361194
0.4	1.000400	0.039993	0.200013	2.376194
0.6	1.002023	0.089919	0.300101	2.401189
0.8	1.006383	0.159548	0.400427	2.436166
1.0	1.015525	0.248294	0.501301	2.481086
1.2	1.031976	0.354999	0.603235	2.535872
1.4	1.058608	0.477755	0.706982	2.600386
1.6	1.098431	0.613860	0.813585	2.674406
1.8	1.154359	0.759999	0.924407	2.757605
2.0	1.229006	0.912639	1.041167	2.849536
2.2	1.324576	1.068511	1.165949	2.949617
2.4	1.442891	1.225011	1.301211	3.057139
2.6	1.585536	1.380379	1.449780	3.171285
2.8	1.754059	1.533667	1.614838	3.291160
3.0	1.950193	1.684559	1.799908	3.415839
3.2	2.176036	1.833156	2.008844	3.544415
3.4	2.434210	1.979784	2.245840	3.676044
3.6	2.727979	2.124854	2.515453	3.809981
3.8	3.061341	2.268771	2.822653	3.945601
4.0	3.439118	2.411887	3.172896	4.082407
4.2	3.867032	2.554483	3.572227	4.220023
4.4	4.351791	2.696771	4.027393	4.358179
4.6	4.901189	2.838893	4.545990	4.496691
4.8	5.524209	2.980942	5.136619	4.635441
5.0	6.231163	3.122970	5.809060	4.774362
5.2	7.033841	3.265002	6.574474	4.913417
5.4	7.945700	3.407044	7.445618	5.052589
5.6	8.982083	3.549094	8.437083	5.191872
5.8	10.160473	3.691142	9.565568	5.331267
6.0	11.500794	3.833179	10.850182	5.470772
6.2	13.025757	3.975197	12.312791	5.610390
6.4	14.761257	4.117190	13.978402	5.750117
6.6	16.736836	4.259152	15.875614	5.889950
6.8	18.986208	4.401083	18.037122	6.029884
7.0	21.547863	4.542982	20.500302	6.169913

KELVIN FUNCTIONS—MODULUS AND PHASE Table 9.12

$\mathrm{ker}\, x = N_0(x) \cos \phi_0(x)$ $\mathrm{ker}_1\, x = N_1(x) \cos \phi_1(x)$

$\mathrm{kei}\, x = N_0(x) \sin \phi_0(x)$ $\mathrm{kei}_1\, x = N_1(x) \sin \phi_1(x)$

x	$N_0(x)$	$\phi_0(x)$	$N_1(x)$	$\phi_1(x)$
0.0	∞	0.000000	∞	-2.356194
0.2	1.891702	-0.412350	4.927993	-2.401447
0.4	1.274560	-0.584989	2.372347	-2.487035
0.6	0.941678	-0.743582	1.497572	-2.590827
0.8	0.725172	-0.896284	1.050591	-2.704976
1.0	0.572032	-1.045803	0.778870	-2.825662
1.2	0.458430	-1.193368	0.597114	-2.950763
1.4	0.371548	-1.339631	0.468100	-3.078993
1.6	0.303683	-1.484977	0.372811	-3.209526
1.8	0.249850	-1.629650	0.300427	-3.341804
2.0	0.206644	-1.773813	0.244293	-3.475437
2.2	0.171649	-1.917579	0.200073	-3.610143
2.4	0.143095	-2.061029	0.164807	-3.745715
2.6	0.119656	-2.204225	0.136407	-3.881994
2.8	0.100319	-2.347212	0.113353	-4.018860
3.0	0.084299	-2.490025	0.094515	-4.156217
3.2	0.070979	-2.632692	0.079039	-4.293990
3.4	0.059870	-2.775236	0.066264	-4.432118
3.6	0.050578	-2.917672	0.055677	-4.570551
3.8	0.042789	-3.060017	0.046873	-4.709250
4.0	0.036246	-3.202283	0.039530	-4.848179
4.2	0.030738	-3.344478	0.033389	-4.987312
4.4	0.026095	-3.486612	0.028242	-5.126623
4.6	0.022174	-3.628692	0.023918	-5.266093
4.8	0.018859	-3.770724	0.020280	-5.405705
5.0	0.016052	-3.912712	0.017213	-5.545443
5.2	0.013674	-4.054662	0.014624	-5.685295
5.4	0.011656	-4.196576	0.012435	-5.825250
5.6	0.009942	-4.338460	0.010583	-5.965298
5.8	0.008485	-4.480314	0.009013	-6.105430
6.0	0.007246	-4.622142	0.007682	-6.245638
6.2	0.006191	-4.763947	0.006551	-6.385917
6.4	0.005292	-4.905730	0.005590	-6.526260
6.6	0.004526	-5.047493	0.004773	-6.666662
6.8	0.003872	-5.189238	0.004077	-6.807119
7.0	0.003315	-5.330966	0.003485	-6.947625

10.1. Spherical Bessel Functions

Definitions

Differential Equation

10.1.1

$$z^2w''+2zw'+[z^2-n(n+1)]w=0 \qquad (n=0, \pm 1, \pm 2, \ldots)$$

Particular solutions are the *Spherical Bessel functions of the first kind*

$$j_n(z)=\sqrt{\tfrac{1}{2}\pi/z}J_{n+\frac{1}{2}}(z),$$

the *Spherical Bessel functions of the second kind*

$$y_n(z)=\sqrt{\tfrac{1}{2}\pi/z}Y_{n+\frac{1}{2}}(z),$$

and the *Spherical Bessel functions of the third kind*

$$h_n^{(1)}(z)=j_n(z)+iy_n(z)=\sqrt{\tfrac{1}{2}\pi/z}H^{(1)}_{n+\frac{1}{2}}(z),$$

$$h_n^{(2)}(z)=j_n(z)-iy_n(z)=\sqrt{\tfrac{1}{2}\pi/z}H^{(2)}_{n+\frac{1}{2}}(z).$$

The pairs $j_n(z)$, $y_n(z)$ and $h_n^{(1)}(z)$, $h_n^{(2)}(z)$ are linearly independent solutions for every n. For general properties see the remarks after **9.1.1.**

Ascending Series (See 9.1.2, 9.1.10)

10.1.2

$$j_n(z)=\frac{z^n}{1\cdot 3\cdot 5\ldots(2n+1)}\left\{1-\frac{\frac{1}{2}z^2}{1!(2n+3)}+\frac{(\frac{1}{2}z^2)^2}{2!(2n+3)(2n+5)}-\ldots\right\}$$

10.1.3

$$y_n(z)=-\frac{1\cdot 3\cdot 5\ldots(2n-1)}{z^{n+1}}\left\{1-\frac{\frac{1}{2}z^2}{1!(1-2n)}+\frac{(\frac{1}{2}z^2)^2}{2!(1-2n)(3-2n)}-\ldots\right\}$$

$$(n=0, 1, 2, \ldots)$$

Limiting Values as $z\to 0$

10.1.4 $$z^{-n}j_n(z)\to\frac{1}{1\cdot 3\cdot 5\ldots(2n+1)}$$

10.1.5

$$z^{n+1}y_n(z)\to -1\cdot 3\cdot 5\ldots(2n-1) \qquad (n=0, 1, 2, \ldots)$$

Wronskians

10.1.6 $$W\{j_n(z), y_n(z)\}=z^{-2}$$

10.1.7

$$W\{h_n^{(1)}(z), h_n^{(2)}(z)\}=-2iz^{-2} \qquad (n=0, 1, 2, \ldots)$$

Representations by Elementary Functions

10.1.8

$$j_n(z)=z^{-1}[P(n+\tfrac{1}{2}, z)\sin(z-\tfrac{1}{2}n\pi)+Q(n+\tfrac{1}{2}, z)\cos(z-\tfrac{1}{2}n\pi)]$$

10.1.9

$$y_n(z)=(-1)^{n+1}z^{-1}[P(n+\tfrac{1}{2}, z)\cos(z+\tfrac{1}{2}n\pi)-Q(n+\tfrac{1}{2}, z)\sin(z+\tfrac{1}{2}n\pi)]$$

$$P(n+\tfrac{1}{2}, z)=1-\frac{(n+2)!}{2!\Gamma(n-1)}(2z)^{-2}+\frac{(n+4)!}{4!\Gamma(n-3)}(2z)^{-4}-\ldots$$

$$=\sum_0^{[\frac{1}{2}n]}(-1)^k(n+\tfrac{1}{2}, 2k)(2z)^{-2k}$$

$$Q(n+\tfrac{1}{2}, z)=\frac{(n+1)!}{1!\Gamma(n)}(2z)^{-1}-\frac{(n+3)!}{3!\Gamma(n-2)}(2z)^{-3}+\frac{(n+5)!}{5!\Gamma(n-4)}(2z)^{-5}-\ldots$$

$$=\sum_0^{[\frac{1}{2}(n-1)]}(-1)^k(n+\tfrac{1}{2}, 2k+1)(2z)^{-2k-1}$$

$$(n=0, 1, 2, \ldots)$$

$$(n+\tfrac{1}{2}, k)=\frac{(n+k)!}{k!\Gamma(n-k+1)}$$

n \ k	1	2	3	4	5
1	2				
2	6	12			
3	12	60	120		
4	20	180	840	1680	
5	30	420	3360	15120	30240

10.1.10

$$j_n(z)=f_n(z)\sin z+(-1)^{n+1}f_{-n-1}(z)\cos z$$

$$f_0(z)=z^{-1},\qquad f_1(z)=z^{-2}$$

$$f_{n-1}(z)+f_{n+1}(z)=(2n+1)z^{-1}f_n(z)$$

$$(n=0,\ \pm1,\ \pm2,\ \ldots)$$

The Functions $j_n(z)$, $y_n(z)$ for $n=0, 1, 2$

10.1.11 $$j_0(z)=\frac{\sin z}{z}$$

$$j_1(z)=\frac{\sin z}{z^2}-\frac{\cos z}{z}$$

$$j_2(z)=\left(\frac{3}{z^3}-\frac{1}{z}\right)\sin z-\frac{3}{z^2}\cos z$$

10.1.12

$$y_0(z)=-j_{-1}(z)=-\frac{\cos z}{z}$$

$$y_1(z)=j_{-2}(z)=-\frac{\cos z}{z^2}-\frac{\sin z}{z}$$

$$y_2(z)=-j_{-3}(z)=\left(-\frac{3}{z^3}+\frac{1}{z}\right)\cos z-\frac{3}{z^2}\sin z$$

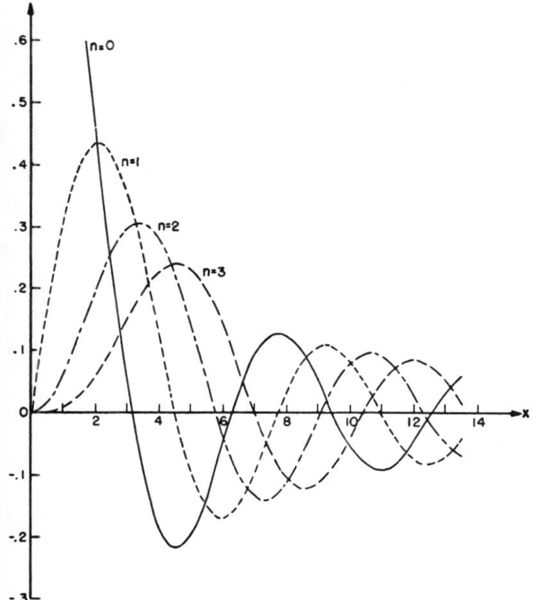

FIGURE 10.1. $j_n(x)$. $n=0(1)3$.

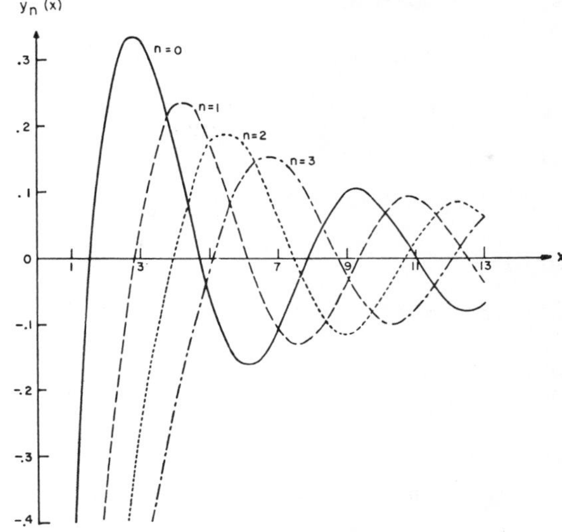

FIGURE 10.2. $y_n(x)$. $n=0(1)3$.

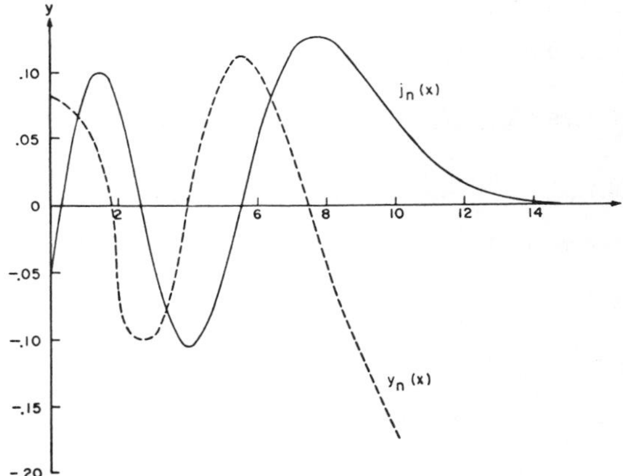

FIGURE 10.3. $j_n(x)$, $y_n(x)$. $x=10$.

Poisson's Integral and Gegenbauer's Generalization

10.1.13 $$j_n(z)=\frac{z^n}{2^{n+1}n!}\int_0^\pi \cos(z\cos\theta)\sin^{2n+1}\theta\,d\theta$$

(See **9.1.20.**)

10.1.14

$$=\frac{1}{2}(-i)^n\int_0^\pi e^{iz\cos\theta}P_n(\cos\theta)\sin\theta\,d\theta$$

$$(n=0,\ 1,\ 2,\ \ldots)$$

Spherical Bessel Functions of the Second and Third Kind

10.1.15

$$y_n(z)=(-1)^{n+1}j_{-n-1}(z) \qquad (n=0, \pm 1, \pm 2, \ldots)$$

10.1.16

$$h_n^{(1)}(z)=i^{-n-1}z^{-1}e^{iz}\sum_0^n (n+\tfrac{1}{2}, k)(-2iz)^{-k}$$

10.1.17

$$h_n^{(2)}(z)=i^{n+1}z^{-1}e^{-iz}\sum_0^n (n+\tfrac{1}{2}, k)\ (2iz)^{-k}$$

10.1.18

$$h_{-n-1}^{(1)}(z)=i(-1)^n h_n^{(1)}(z)$$
$$h_{-n-1}^{(2)}(z)=-i(-1)^n h_n^{(2)}(z) \qquad (n=0, 1, 2, \ldots)$$

Elementary Properties

Recurrence Relations

$f_n(z): j_n(z), y_n(z), h_n^{(1)}(z), h_n^{(2)}(z)$

$(n=0, \pm 1, \pm 2, \ldots)$

10.1.19 $$f_{n-1}(z)+f_{n+1}(z)=(2n+1)z^{-1}f_n(z)$$

10.1.20 $$nf_{n-1}(z)-(n+1)f_{n+1}(z)=(2n+1)\frac{d}{dz}f_n(z)$$

10.1.21 $$\frac{n+1}{z}f_n(z)+\frac{d}{dz}f_n(z)=f_{n-1}(z)$$

(See **10.1.23.**)

10.1.22 $$\frac{n}{z}f_n(z)-\frac{d}{dz}f_n(z)=f_{n+1}(z)$$

(See **10.1.24.**)

Differentiation Formulas

$f_n(z): j_n(z), y_n(z), h_n^{(1)}(z), h_n^{(2)}(z)$

$(n=0, \pm 1, \pm 2, \ldots)$

10.1.23 $$\left(\frac{1}{z}\frac{d}{dz}\right)^m [z^{n+1}f_n(z)]=z^{n-m+1}f_{n-m}(z)$$

10.1.24 $$\left(\frac{1}{z}\frac{d}{dz}\right)^m [z^{-n}f_n(z)]=(-1)^m z^{-n-m}f_{n+m}(z)$$

$(m=1, 2, 3, \ldots)$

Rayleigh's Formulas

10.1.25

$$j_n(z)=z^n\left(-\frac{1}{z}\frac{d}{dz}\right)^n\frac{\sin z}{z}$$

10.1.26

$$y_n(z)=-z^n\left(-\frac{1}{z}\frac{d}{dz}\right)^n\frac{\cos z}{z} \qquad (n=0, 1, 2, \ldots)$$

Modulus and Phase

$$j_n(z)=\sqrt{\tfrac{1}{2}\pi/z}\,M_{n+\frac{1}{2}}(z)\cos\theta_{n+\frac{1}{2}}(z),$$
$$y_n(z)=\sqrt{\tfrac{1}{2}\pi/z}\,M_{n+\frac{1}{2}}(z)\sin\theta_{n+\frac{1}{2}}(z)$$

(See **9.2.17.**)

10.1.27

$$(\tfrac{1}{2}\pi/z)\,M_{n+\frac{1}{2}}^2(z)=\frac{1}{z^2}\sum_0^n\frac{(2n-k)!(2n-2k)!}{k![(n-k)!]^2}(2z)^{2k-2n}$$

(See **9.2.28.**)

10.1.28 $$(\tfrac{1}{2}\pi/z)M_{1/2}^2(z)=j_0^2(z)+y_0^2(z)=z^{-2}$$

10.1.29

$$(\tfrac{1}{2}\pi/z)M_{3/2}^2(z)=j_1^2(z)+y_1^2(z)=z^{-2}+z^{-4}$$

10.1.30

$$(\tfrac{1}{2}\pi/z)M_{5/2}^2(z)=j_2^2(z)+y_2^2(z)=z^{-2}+3z^{-4}+9z^{-6}$$

Cross Products

10.1.31 $$j_n(z)y_{n-1}(z)-j_{n-1}(z)y_n(z)=z^{-2}$$

10.1.32

$$j_{n+1}(z)y_{n-1}(z)-j_{n-1}(z)y_{n+1}(z)=(2n+1)z^{-3}$$

10.1.33

$$j_0(z)j_n(z)+y_0(z)y_n(z)$$
$$=z^{-2}\sum_0^{[\frac{1}{2}n]}(-1)^k 2^{n-2k}\left(k+\tfrac{1}{2}\right)_{n-2k}\binom{n-k}{k}z^{2k-n}$$

$(n=0, 1, 2, \ldots)$

Analytic Continuation

10.1.34 $$j_n(ze^{m\pi i})=e^{mn\pi i}j_n(z)$$

10.1.35 $$y_n(ze^{m\pi i})=(-1)^m e^{mn\pi i}y_n(z)$$

10.1.36 $$h_n^{(1)}(ze^{(2m+1)\pi i})=(-1)^n h_n^{(2)}(z)$$

10.1.37 $$h_n^{(2)}(ze^{(2m+1)\pi i})=(-1)^n h_n^{(1)}(z)$$

10.1.38 $$h_n^{(l)}(ze^{2m\pi i})=h_n^{(l)}(z)$$

$(l=1, 2;\ m, n=0, 1, 2, \ldots)$

Generating Functions

10.1.39

$$\frac{1}{z}\sin\sqrt{z^2+2zt}=\sum_0^\infty\frac{(-t)^n}{n!}y_{n-1}(z) \qquad (2|t|<|z|)$$

10.1.40 $$\frac{1}{z}\cos\sqrt{z^2-2zt}=\sum_0^\infty\frac{t^n}{n!}j_{n-1}(z)$$

Derivatives With Respect to Order

10.1.41

$$\left[\frac{\partial}{\partial\nu}j_\nu(x)\right]_{\nu=0}=(\tfrac{1}{2}\pi/x)\{\mathrm{Ci}(2x)\sin x-\mathrm{Si}(2x)\cos x\}$$

10.1.42

$$\left[\frac{\partial}{\partial\nu}j_\nu(x)\right]_{\nu=-1}=(\tfrac{1}{2}\pi/x)\{\mathrm{Ci}(2x)\cos x+\mathrm{Si}(2x)\sin x\}$$

10.1.43

$$\left[\frac{\partial}{\partial\nu}y_\nu(x)\right]_{\nu=0}=(\tfrac{1}{2}\pi/x)\{\mathrm{Ci}(2x)\cos x+[\mathrm{Si}(2x)-\pi]\sin x\}$$

10.1.44

$$\left[\frac{\partial}{\partial\nu}y_\nu(x)\right]_{\nu=-1}=(\tfrac{1}{2}\pi/x)\{\mathrm{Ci}(2x)\sin x-[\mathrm{Si}(2x)-\pi]\cos x\}$$

Addition Theorems and Degenerate Forms

r, ρ, θ, λ arbitrary complex; $R=\sqrt{(r^2+\rho^2-2r\rho\cos\theta)}$

10.1.45 $$\frac{\sin\lambda R}{\lambda R}=\sum_0^\infty(2n+1)j_n(\lambda r)j_n(\lambda\rho)P_n(\cos\theta)$$

10.1.46 $$-\frac{\cos\lambda R}{\lambda R}=\sum_0^\infty(2n+1)j_n(\lambda r)y_n(\lambda\rho)P_n(\cos\theta)\qquad |re^{\pm i\theta}|<|\rho|$$

10.1.47 $$e^{iz\cos\theta}=\sum_0^\infty(2n+1)e^{\frac{1}{2}n\pi i}j_n(z)P_n(\cos\theta)$$

10.1.48

$$J_0(z\sin\theta)=\sum_0^\infty(4n+1)\frac{(2n)!}{2^{2n}(n!)^2}j_{2n}(z)P_{2n}(\cos\theta)$$

Duplication Formula

10.1.49

$$j_n(2z)=-n!z^{n+1}\sum_0^n\frac{2n-2k+1}{k!(2n-k+1)!}j_{n-k}(z)y_{n-k}(z)$$

Some Infinite Series Involving $j_n^2(z)$

10.1.50 $$\sum_0^\infty(2n+1)j_n^2(z)=1$$

10.1.51 $$\sum_0^\infty(-1)^n(2n+1)j_n^2(z)=\frac{\sin 2z}{2z}$$

10.1.52 $$\sum_0^\infty j_n^2(z)=\frac{\mathrm{Si}(2z)}{2z}$$

Fresnel Integrals

10.1.53

$$C(\sqrt{2x/\pi})=\frac{1}{2}\int_0^x J_{-\frac{1}{2}}(t)dt$$
$$=\sqrt{2}[\cos\tfrac{1}{2}x\sum_0^\infty(-1)^nJ_{2n+\frac{1}{2}}(\tfrac{1}{2}x)+\sin\tfrac{1}{2}x\sum_0^\infty(-1)^nJ_{2n+3/2}(\tfrac{1}{2}x)]$$

10.1.54

$$S(\sqrt{2x/\pi})=\frac{1}{2}\int_0^x J_{\frac{1}{2}}(t)dt$$
$$=\sqrt{2}[\sin\tfrac{1}{2}x\sum_0^\infty(-1)^nJ_{2n+\frac{1}{2}}(\tfrac{1}{2}x)-\cos\tfrac{1}{2}x\sum_0^\infty(-1)^nJ_{2n+3/2}(\tfrac{1}{2}x)].$$

(See also **11.1.1, 11.1.2.**)

Zeros and Their Asymptotic Expansions

The zeros of $j_n(x)$ and $y_n(x)$ are the same as the zeros of $J_{n+\frac{1}{2}}(x)$ and $Y_{n+\frac{1}{2}}(x)$ and the formulas for $j_{\nu,s}$ and $y_{\nu,s}$ given in **9.5** are applicable with $\nu=n+\frac{1}{2}$. There are, however, no simple relations connecting the zeros of the derivatives. Accordingly, we now give formulas for $a'_{n,s}$, $b'_{n,s}$, the s-th positive zero of $j'_n(z)$, $y'_n(z)$, respectively; $z=0$ is counted as the first zero of $j'_0(z)$.

(Tables of $a'_{n,s}$, $b'_{n,s}$, $j_n(a'_{n,s})$, $y_n(b'_{n,s})$ are given in [10.31].)

Elementary Relations

$$f_n(z)=j_n(z)\cos\pi t+y_n(z)\sin\pi t$$

(t a real parameter, $0\le t\le 1$)

If τ_n is a zero of $f'_n(z)$ then

10.1.55 $f_n(\tau_n)=[\tau_n/(n+1)]f_{n-1}(\tau_n)$
(See **10.1.21.**)

10.1.56 $=(\tau_n/n)f_{n+1}(\tau_n)$
(See **10.1.22.**)

10.1.57 $$=\left\{\frac{1}{\pi}[\tau_n^2-n(n+1)]\frac{d\tau_n}{d\tau}\right\}^{-\frac{1}{2}}$$

McMahon's Expansions for n Fixed and s Large

10.1.58

$$a'_{n,s},\ b'_{n,s}\sim\beta-(\mu+7)(8\beta)^{-1}-\frac{4}{3}(7\mu^2+154\mu+95)(8\beta)^{-3}-\frac{32}{15}(85\mu^3+3535\mu^2+3561\mu+6133)(8\beta)^{-5}-\frac{64}{105}(6949\mu^4+474908\mu^3+330638\mu^2+9046780\mu-5075147)(8\beta)^{-7}-\ldots$$

$\beta=\pi(s+\frac{1}{2}n-\frac{1}{2})$ for $a'_{n,s}$, $\beta=\pi(s+\frac{1}{2}n)$ for $b'_{n,s}$; $\mu=(2n+1)^2$

Asymptotic Expansions of Zeros and Associated Values for n Large

10.1.59

$$a'_{n,1}\sim(n+\tfrac{1}{2})+.8086165(n+\tfrac{1}{2})^{1/3}-.236680(n+\tfrac{1}{2})^{-1/3}-.20736(n+\tfrac{1}{2})^{-1}+.0233(n+\tfrac{1}{2})^{-5/3}+\ldots$$

10.1.60

$$b'_{n,1}\sim(n+\tfrac{1}{2})+1.8210980(n+\tfrac{1}{2})^{1/3}+.802728(n+\tfrac{1}{2})^{-1/3}-.11740(n+\tfrac{1}{2})^{-1}+.0249(n+\tfrac{1}{2})^{-5/3}+\cdots$$

10.1.61

$$j_n(a'_{n,1})\sim.8458430(n+\tfrac{1}{2})^{-5/6}\{1-.566032(n+\tfrac{1}{2})^{-2/3}+.38081(n+\tfrac{1}{2})^{-4/3}-.2203(n+\tfrac{1}{2})^{-2}+\ldots\}$$

10.1.62

$$y_n(b'_{n,1})\sim.7183921(n+\tfrac{1}{2})^{-5/6}\{1-1.274769(n+\tfrac{1}{2})^{-2/3}+1.23038(n+\tfrac{1}{2})^{-4/3}-1.0070(n+\tfrac{1}{2})^{-2}+\ldots\}$$

See [10.31] for corresponding expansions for $s=2, 3$.

Uniform Asymptotic Expansions of Zeros and Associated Values for n Large

10.1.63

$$a'_{n,s}\sim(n+\tfrac{1}{2})\{z[(n+\tfrac{1}{2})^{-2/3}a'_s]+\sum_{k=1}^{\infty}h_k[(n+\tfrac{1}{2})^{-2/3}a'_s](n+\tfrac{1}{2})^{-2k}\}$$

10.1.64

$$b'_{n,s}\sim(n+\tfrac{1}{2})\{z[(n+\tfrac{1}{2})^{-2/3}b'_s]+\sum_{k=1}^{\infty}h_k[(n+\tfrac{1}{2})^{-2/3}b'_s](n+\tfrac{1}{2})^{-2k}\}$$

10.1.65

$$j_n(a'_{n,s})\sim\sqrt{\tfrac{1}{2}\pi}\,\mathrm{Ai}(a'_s)(n+\tfrac{1}{2})^{-5/6}\,h[(n+\tfrac{1}{2})^{-2/3}a'_s]\,(z[(n+\tfrac{1}{2})^{-2/3}a'_s])^{-1/2}\{1+\sum_{k=1}^{\infty}H_k[(n+\tfrac{1}{2})^{-2/3}a'_s](n+\tfrac{1}{2})^{-2k}\}$$

10.1.66

$$y_n(b'_{n,s})\sim-\sqrt{\tfrac{1}{2}\pi}\,\mathrm{Bi}(b'_s)(n+\tfrac{1}{2})^{-5/6}\,h[(n+\tfrac{1}{2})^{-2/3}b'_s]\,(z[(n+\tfrac{1}{2})^{-2/3}b'_s])^{-1/2}\{1+\sum_{k=1}^{\infty}H_k[(n+\tfrac{1}{2})^{-2/3}b'_s](n+\tfrac{1}{2})^{-2k}\}$$

$h(\xi)$, $z(\xi)$ are defined as in **9.5.26, 9.3.38, 9.3.39.** a'_s, b'_s s-th (negative) real zero of $\mathrm{Ai}'(z)$, $\mathrm{Bi}'(z)$ (see **10.4.95, 10.4.99.**)

Complex Zeros of $h_n^{(1)}(z)$, $h_n^{(1)\prime}(z)$

$h_n^{(1)}(z)$ and $h_n^{(1)}(ze^{2m\pi i})$, m any integer, have the same zeros.

$h_n^{(1)}(z)$ has n zeros, symmetrically distributed with respect to the imaginary axis and lying approximately on the finite arc joining $z=-n$ and $z=n$ shown in **Figure 9.6.** If n is odd, one zero lies on the imaginary axis.

$h_n^{(1)\prime}(z)$ has $n+1$ zeros lying approximately on the same curve. If n is even, one zero lies on the imaginary axis.

10.2. Modified Spherical Bessel Functions

Definitions

Differential Equation

10.2.1

$$z^2w''+2zw'-[z^2+n(n+1)]w=0 \qquad (n=0, \pm 1, \pm 2, \ldots)$$

Particular solutions are the *Modified Spherical Bessel functions of the first kind,*

10.2.2

$$\sqrt{\tfrac{1}{2}\pi/z}\,I_{n+\frac{1}{2}}(z)=e^{-n\pi i/2}j_n(ze^{\pi i/2}) \qquad (-\pi<\arg z\leq\tfrac{1}{2}\pi)$$
$$=e^{3n\pi i/2}j_n(ze^{-3\pi i/2}) \qquad (\tfrac{1}{2}\pi<\arg z\leq\pi)$$

of the second kind,

10.2.3

$$\sqrt{\tfrac{1}{2}\pi/z}\,I_{-n-\frac{1}{2}}(z)=e^{3(n+1)\pi i/2}y_n(ze^{\pi i/2}) \qquad (-\pi<\arg z\leq\tfrac{1}{2}\pi)$$
$$=e^{-(n+1)\pi i/2}y_n(ze^{-3\pi i/2}) \qquad (\tfrac{1}{2}\pi<\arg z\leq\pi)$$

of the third kind,

10.2.4

$$\sqrt{\tfrac{1}{2}\pi/z}\,K_{n+\frac{1}{2}}(z)=\tfrac{1}{2}\pi(-1)^{n+1}\sqrt{\tfrac{1}{2}\pi/z}[I_{n+\frac{1}{2}}(z)-I_{-n-\frac{1}{2}}(z)]$$

The pairs

$$\sqrt{\tfrac{1}{2}\pi/z}\,I_{n+\frac{1}{2}}(z),\ \sqrt{\tfrac{1}{2}\pi/z}\,I_{-n-\frac{1}{2}}(z)$$

and

$$\sqrt{\tfrac{1}{2}\pi/z}\,I_{n+\frac{1}{2}}(z),\ \sqrt{\tfrac{1}{2}\pi/z}\,K_{n+\frac{1}{2}}(z)$$

are linearly independent solutions for every n.

Most properties of the Modified Spherical Bessel functions can be derived from those of the Spherical Bessel functions by use of the above relations.

Ascending Series

10.2.5

$$\sqrt{\tfrac{1}{2}\pi/z}\,I_{n+\frac{1}{2}}(z)=\frac{z^n}{1\cdot 3\cdot 5\ldots(2n+1)}\left\{1+\frac{\frac{1}{2}z^2}{1!(2n+3)}+\frac{(\frac{1}{2}z^2)^2}{2!(2n+3)(2n+5)}+\ldots\right\}$$

10.2.6

$$\sqrt{\tfrac{1}{2}\pi/z}\,I_{-n-\frac{1}{2}}(z)=\frac{1\cdot 3\cdot 5\ldots(2n-1)}{(-1)^nz^{n+1}}\left\{1+\frac{\frac{1}{2}z^2}{1!(1-2n)}+\frac{(\frac{1}{2}z^2)^2}{2!(1-2n)(3-2n)}+\ldots\right\}$$
$$(n=0, 1, 2, \ldots)$$

Wronskians

10.2.7

$$W\{\sqrt{\tfrac{1}{2}\pi/z}\,I_{n+\frac{1}{2}}(z),\ \sqrt{\tfrac{1}{2}\pi/z}\,I_{-n-\frac{1}{2}}(z)\}=(-1)^{n+1}z^{-2}$$

10.2.8

$$W\{\sqrt{\tfrac{1}{2}\pi/z}\,I_{n+\frac{1}{2}}(z),\ \sqrt{\tfrac{1}{2}\pi/z}\,K_{n+\frac{1}{2}}(z)\}=-\tfrac{1}{2}\pi z^{-2}$$

Representations by Elementary Functions

10.2.9

$$\sqrt{\tfrac{1}{2}\pi/z}\,I_{n+\frac{1}{2}}(z)=(2z)^{-1}[R(n+\tfrac{1}{2},-z)e^z-(-1)^nR(n+\tfrac{1}{2},z)e^{-z}]$$

10.2.10

$$\sqrt{\tfrac{1}{2}\pi/z}\,I_{-n-\frac{1}{2}}(z)=(2z)^{-1}[R(n+\tfrac{1}{2},-z)e^z+(-1)^nR(n+\tfrac{1}{2},z)e^{-z}]$$

10.2.11

$$R(n+\tfrac{1}{2}, z)=1+\frac{(n+1)!}{1!\Gamma(n)}(2z)^{-1}+\frac{(n+2)!}{2!\Gamma(n-1)}(2z)^{-2}+\ldots$$
$$=\sum_0^n (n+\tfrac{1}{2}, k)(2z)^{-k} \qquad (n=0, 1, 2, \ldots)$$

(See **10.1.9.**)

10.2.12

$$\sqrt{\tfrac{1}{2}\pi/z}\,I_{n+\frac{1}{2}}(z)=g_n(z)\sinh z+g_{-n-1}(z)\cosh z$$
$$g_0(z)=z^{-1},\ g_1(z)=-z^{-2}$$
$$g_{n-1}(z)-g_{n+1}(z)=(2n+1)z^{-1}g_n(z) \qquad (n=0, \pm 1, \pm 2, \ldots)$$

The Functions $\sqrt{\frac{1}{2}\pi/z}\,I_{\pm(n+\frac{1}{2})}(z)$, $n=0, 1, 2$

10.2.13

$$\sqrt{\tfrac{1}{2}\pi/z}\,I_{1/2}(z)=\frac{\sinh z}{z}$$

$$\sqrt{\tfrac{1}{2}\pi/z}\,I_{3/2}(z)=-\frac{\sinh z}{z^2}+\frac{\cosh z}{z}$$

$$\sqrt{\tfrac{1}{2}\pi/z}\,I_{5/2}(z)=\left(\frac{3}{z^3}+\frac{1}{z}\right)\sinh z-\frac{3}{z^2}\cosh z$$

10.2.14

$$\sqrt{\tfrac{1}{2}\pi/z}\,I_{-1/2}(z)=\frac{\cosh z}{z}$$

$$\sqrt{\tfrac{1}{2}\pi/z}\,I_{-3/2}(z)=\frac{\sinh z}{z}-\frac{\cosh z}{z^2}$$

$$\sqrt{\tfrac{1}{2}\pi/z}\,I_{-5/2}(z)=-\frac{3}{z^2}\sinh z+\left(\frac{3}{z^3}+\frac{1}{z}\right)\cosh z$$

Modified Spherical Bessel Functions of the Third Kind

10.2.15

$$\sqrt{\tfrac{1}{2}\pi/z}K_{n+\frac{1}{2}}(z)=\tfrac{1}{2}\pi i e^{(n+1)\pi i/2}h_n^{(1)}(ze^{\frac{1}{2}\pi i}) \qquad (-\pi<\arg z\leq\tfrac{1}{2}\pi)$$

$$=-\tfrac{1}{2}\pi i e^{-(n+1)\pi i/2}h_n^{(2)}(ze^{-\frac{1}{2}\pi i}) \qquad (\tfrac{1}{2}\pi<\arg z\leq\pi)$$

$$=(\tfrac{1}{2}\pi/z)e^{-z}\sum_0^n (n+\tfrac{1}{2}, k)(2z)^{-k}$$

10.2.16

$$K_{n+\frac{1}{2}}(z)=K_{-n-\frac{1}{2}}(z) \qquad (n=0, 1, 2, \ldots)$$

The Functions $\sqrt{\frac{1}{2}\pi/z}K_{n+\frac{1}{2}}(z), n=0, 1, 2$

10.2.17 $\sqrt{\tfrac{1}{2}\pi/z}K_{1/2}(z)=(\tfrac{1}{2}\pi/z)e^{-z}$

$\sqrt{\tfrac{1}{2}\pi/z}K_{3/2}(z)=(\tfrac{1}{2}\pi/z)e^{-z}(1+z^{-1})$

$\sqrt{\tfrac{1}{2}\pi/z}K_{5/2}(z)=(\tfrac{1}{2}\pi/z)e^{-z}(1+3z^{-1}+3z^{-2})$

Elementary Properties

Recurrence Relations

$f_n(z)$: $\sqrt{\tfrac{1}{2}\pi/z}I_{n+\frac{1}{2}}(z)$, $(-1)^{n+1}\sqrt{\tfrac{1}{2}\pi/z}K_{n+\frac{1}{2}}(z)$ $\qquad (n=0, \pm1, \pm2, \ldots)$

10.2.18 $f_{n-1}(z)-f_{n+1}(z)=(2n+1)z^{-1}f_n(z)$

10.2.19 $nf_{n-1}(z)+(n+1)f_{n+1}(z)=(2n+1)\dfrac{d}{dz}f_n(z)$

10.2.20 $\dfrac{n+1}{z}f_n(z)+\dfrac{d}{dz}f_n(z)=f_{n-1}(z)$

(See **10.2.22.**)

10.2.21 $-\dfrac{n}{z}f_n(z)+\dfrac{d}{dz}f_n(z)=f_{n+1}(z)$

(See **10.2.23.**)

Differentiation Formulas

$f_n(z)$: $\sqrt{\tfrac{1}{2}\pi/z}I_{n+\frac{1}{2}}(z)$, $(-1)^{n+1}\sqrt{\tfrac{1}{2}\pi/z}K_{n+\frac{1}{2}}(z)$ $\qquad (n=0, \pm1, \pm2, \ldots)$

10.2.22 $\left(\dfrac{1}{z}\dfrac{d}{dz}\right)^m[z^{n+1}f_n(z)]=z^{n-m+1}f_{n-m}(z)$

10.2.23 $\left(\dfrac{1}{z}\dfrac{d}{dz}\right)^m[z^{-n}f_n(z)]=z^{-n-m}f_{n+m}(z)$ $\qquad (m=1, 2, 3, \ldots)$

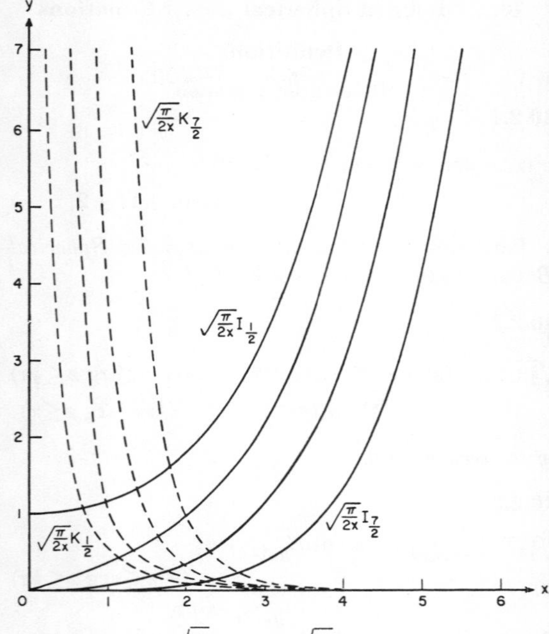

FIGURE 10.4. $\sqrt{\frac{\pi}{2x}}I_{n+\frac{1}{2}}(x)$, $\sqrt{\frac{\pi}{2x}}K_{n+\frac{1}{2}}(x)$. $n=0(1)3$.

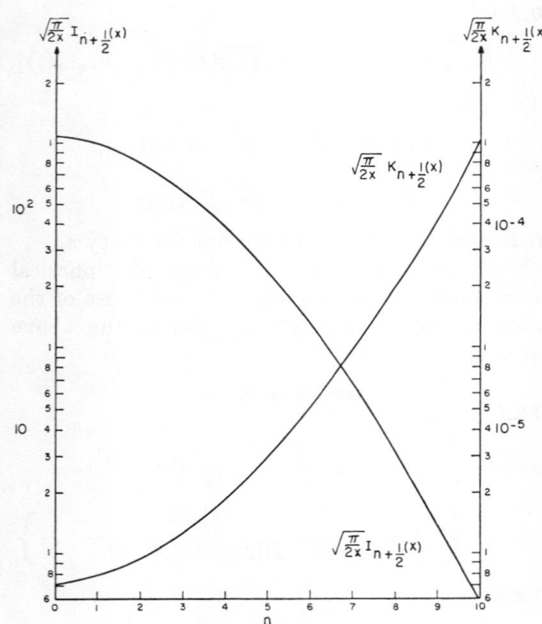

FIGURE 10.5. $\sqrt{\frac{\pi}{2x}}I_{n+\frac{1}{2}}(x)$, $\sqrt{\frac{\pi}{2x}}K_{n+\frac{1}{2}}(x)$. $x=10$.

Formulas of Rayleigh's Type

10.2.24 $\sqrt{\tfrac{1}{2}\pi/z}\,I_{n+\frac{1}{2}}(z)=z^n\left(\frac{1}{z}\frac{d}{dz}\right)^n\frac{\sinh z}{z}$

10.2.25

$$\sqrt{\tfrac{1}{2}\pi/z}\,I_{-n-\frac{1}{2}}(z)=z^n\left(\frac{1}{z}\frac{d}{dz}\right)^n\frac{\cosh z}{z}\qquad(n=0,1,2,\ldots)$$

Formulas for $I^2_{n+\frac{1}{2}}(z)-I^2_{-n-\frac{1}{2}}(z)$

10.2.26

$$(\tfrac{1}{2}\pi/z)[I^2_{n+\frac{1}{2}}(z)-I^2_{-n-\frac{1}{2}}(z)]=\frac{1}{z^2}\sum_0^n(-1)^{k+1}\frac{(2n-k)!(2n-2k)!}{k![(n-k)!]^2}(2z)^{2k-2n}\qquad(n=0,1,2,\ldots)$$

10.2.27 $(\tfrac{1}{2}\pi/z)[I^2_{1/2}(z)-I^2_{-1/2}(z)]=-z^{-2}$

10.2.28 $(\tfrac{1}{2}\pi/z)[I^2_{3/2}(z)-I^2_{-3/2}(z)]=z^{-2}-z^{-4}$

10.2.29

$$(\tfrac{1}{2}\pi/z)[I^2_{5/2}(z)-I^2_{-5/2}(z)]=-z^{-2}+3z^{-4}-9z^{-6}$$

Generating Functions

10.2.30

$$\frac{1}{z}\sinh\sqrt{z^2-2izt}=\sum_0^\infty\frac{(-it)^n}{n!}[\sqrt{\tfrac{1}{2}\pi/z}\,I_{-n+\frac{1}{2}}(z)]\qquad(2|t|<|z|)$$

10.2.31

$$\frac{1}{z}\cosh\sqrt{z^2+2izt}=\sum_0^\infty\frac{(it)^n}{n!}[\sqrt{\tfrac{1}{2}\pi/z}\,I_{n-\frac{1}{2}}(z)]$$

Derivatives With Respect to Order

10.2.32

$$\left[\frac{\partial}{\partial\nu}I_\nu(x)\right]_{\nu=\frac{1}{2}}=-\frac{1}{2\pi x}[\mathrm{Ei}(2x)e^{-x}-E_1(-2x)e^x]$$

10.2.33

$$\left[\frac{\partial}{\partial\nu}I_\nu(x)\right]_{\nu=-\frac{1}{2}}=\frac{1}{2\pi x}[\mathrm{Ei}(2x)e^{-x}+E_1(-2x)e^x]$$

10.2.34 $\left[\frac{\partial}{\partial\nu}K_\nu(x)\right]_{\nu=\pm\frac{1}{2}}=\mp\sqrt{\pi/2x}\,\mathrm{Ei}(-2x)e^x$

For $E_1(x)$ and $\mathrm{Ei}(x)$, see **5.1.1, 5.1.2.**

Addition Theorems and Degenerate Forms

$r<\rho$; θ, λ arbitrary complex; $R=\sqrt{r^2+\rho^2-2r\rho\cos\theta}$

10.2.35

$$\frac{e^{-\lambda R}}{\lambda R}=\frac{2}{\pi}\sum_0^\infty(2n+1)[\sqrt{\tfrac{1}{2}\pi/\lambda r}\,I_{n+\frac{1}{2}}(\lambda r)][\sqrt{\tfrac{1}{2}\pi/\lambda\rho}\,K_{n+\frac{1}{2}}(\lambda\rho)]P_n(\cos\theta)$$

10.2.36

$$e^{z\cos\theta}=\sum_0^\infty(2n+1)[\sqrt{\tfrac{1}{2}\pi/z}\,I_{n+\frac{1}{2}}(z)]P_n(\cos\theta)$$

10.2.37

$$e^{-z\cos\theta}=\sum_0^\infty(-1)^n(2n+1)[\sqrt{\tfrac{1}{2}\pi/z}\,I_{n+\frac{1}{2}}(z)]P_n(\cos\theta)$$

Duplication Formula

10.2.38

$$K_{n+\frac{1}{2}}(2z)=n!\pi^{-\frac{1}{2}}z^{n+\frac{1}{2}}\sum_0^n\frac{(-1)^k(2n-2k+1)}{k!(2n-k+1)!}K^2_{n-k+\frac{1}{2}}(z)$$

10.3. Riccati-Bessel Functions

Differential Equation

10.3.1

$$z^2w''+[z^2-n(n+1)]w=0\qquad(n=0,\pm1,\pm2,\ldots)$$

Pairs of linearly independent solutions are

$$zj_n(z),\ zy_n(z)$$
$$zh_n^{(1)}(z),\ zh_n^{(2)}(z)$$

All properties of these functions follow directly from those of the Spherical Bessel functions.

The Functions $zj_n(z)$, $zy_n(z)$, $n=0, 1, 2$

10.3.2

$zj_0(z)=\sin z,\qquad zj_1(z)=z^{-1}\sin z-\cos z$

$zj_2(z)=(3z^{-2}-1)\sin z-3z^{-1}\cos z$

10.3.3

$zy_0(z)=-\cos z,\qquad zy_1(z)=-\sin z-z^{-1}\cos z$

$zy_2(z)=-3z^{-1}\sin z-(3z^{-2}-1)\cos z$

Wronskians

10.3.4 $W\{zj_n(z),zy_n(z)\}=1$

10.3.5 $W\{zh_n^{(1)}(z),zh_n^{(2)}(z)\}=-2i\qquad(n=0,1,2,\ldots)$

10.4. Airy Functions

Definitions and Elementary Properties

Differential Equation

10.4.1 $$w''-zw=0$$

Pairs of linearly independent solutions are

$$\text{Ai}(z),\ \text{Bi}(z),$$
$$\text{Ai}(z),\ \text{Ai}(ze^{2\pi i/3}),$$
$$\text{Ai}(z),\ \text{Ai}(ze^{-2\pi i/3}).$$

Ascending Series

10.4.2 $$\text{Ai}(z)=c_1 f(z)-c_2 g(z)$$

10.4.3 $$\text{Bi}(z)=\sqrt{3}\,[c_1 f(z)+c_2 g(z)]$$

$$f(z)=1+\frac{1}{3!}z^3+\frac{1\cdot 4}{6!}z^6+\frac{1\cdot 4\cdot 7}{9!}z^9+\ldots$$
$$=\sum_0^\infty 3^k\left(\frac{1}{3}\right)_k\frac{z^{3k}}{(3k)!}$$

$$g(z)=z+\frac{2}{4!}z^4+\frac{2\cdot 5}{7!}z^7+\frac{2\cdot 5\cdot 8}{10!}z^{10}+\ldots$$
$$=\sum_0^\infty 3^k\left(\frac{2}{3}\right)_k\frac{z^{3k+1}}{(3k+1)!}$$

$$\left(\alpha+\frac{1}{3}\right)_0=1$$

$$3^k\left(\alpha+\frac{1}{3}\right)_k=(3\alpha+1)(3\alpha+4)\ldots(3\alpha+3k-2)$$
(α arbitrary; $k=1, 2, 3, \ldots$)

(See **6.1.22.**)

10.4.4

$$c_1=\text{Ai}(0)=\text{Bi}(0)/\sqrt{3}=3^{-2/3}/\Gamma(2/3)$$
$$=.35502\ 80538\ 87817$$

10.4.5

$$c_2=-\text{Ai}'(0)=\text{Bi}'(0)/\sqrt{3}=3^{-1/3}/\Gamma(1/3)$$
$$=.25881\ 94037\ 92807$$

Relations Between Solutions

10.4.6 $$\text{Bi}(z)=e^{\pi i/6}\,\text{Ai}(ze^{2\pi i/3})+e^{-\pi i/6}\,\text{Ai}(ze^{-2\pi i/3})$$

10.4.7

$$\text{Ai}(z)+e^{2\pi i/3}\,\text{Ai}(ze^{2\pi i/3})+e^{-2\pi i/3}\,\text{Ai}(ze^{-2\pi i/3})=0$$

10.4.8

$$\text{Bi}(z)+e^{2\pi i/3}\,\text{Bi}(ze^{2\pi i/3})+e^{-2\pi i/3}\,\text{Bi}(ze^{-2\pi i/3})=0$$

10.4.9 $$\text{Ai}(ze^{\pm 2\pi i/3})=\tfrac{1}{2}e^{\pm\pi i/3}[\text{Ai}(z)\mp i\,\text{Bi}(z)]$$

Wronskians

10.4.10 $$W\{\text{Ai}(z),\ \text{Bi}(z)\}=\pi^{-1}$$

10.4.11 $$W\{\text{Ai}(z),\ \text{Ai}(ze^{2\pi i/3})\}=\tfrac{1}{2}\pi^{-1}e^{-\pi i/6}$$

10.4.12 $$W\{\text{Ai}(z),\ \text{Ai}(ze^{-2\pi i/3})\}=\tfrac{1}{2}\pi^{-1}e^{\pi i/6}$$

10.4.13 $$W\{\text{Ai}(ze^{2\pi i/3}),\ \text{Ai}(ze^{-2\pi i/3})\}=\tfrac{1}{2}i\pi^{-1}$$

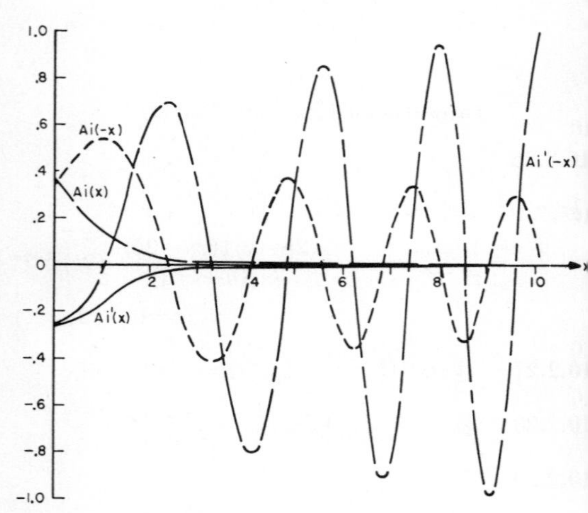

FIGURE 10.6. Ai ($\pm x$), Ai$'$ ($\pm x$).

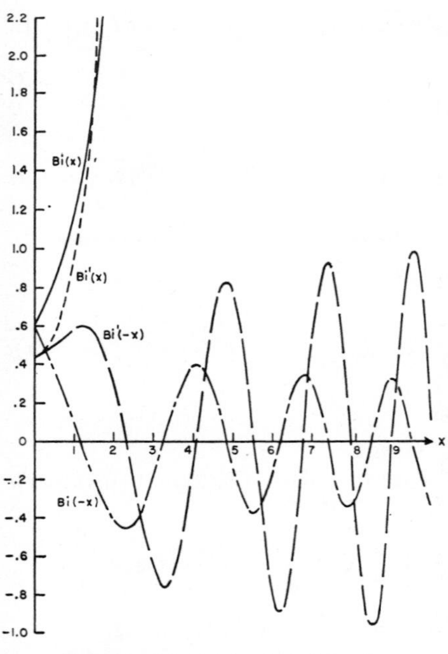

FIGURE 10.7. Bi ($\pm x$), Bi$'$ ($\pm x$).

Representations in Terms of Bessel Functions

$$\zeta=\tfrac{2}{3}z^{3/2}$$

10.4.14

$$\mathrm{Ai}\,(z)=\tfrac{1}{3}\sqrt{z}[I_{-1/3}(\zeta)-I_{1/3}(\zeta)]=\pi^{-1}\sqrt{z/3}K_{1/3}(\zeta)$$

10.4.15

$$\begin{aligned}\mathrm{Ai}\,(-z)&=\tfrac{1}{3}\sqrt{z}[J_{1/3}(\zeta)+J_{-1/3}(\zeta)]\\&=\tfrac{1}{2}\sqrt{z/3}[e^{\pi i/6}H^{(1)}_{1/3}(\zeta)+e^{-\pi i/6}H^{(2)}_{1/3}(\zeta)]\end{aligned}$$

10.4.16

$$-\mathrm{Ai}'(z)=\tfrac{1}{3}z[I_{-2/3}(\zeta)-I_{2/3}(\zeta)]=\pi^{-1}(z/\sqrt{3})K_{2/3}(\zeta)$$

10.4.17

$$\begin{aligned}\mathrm{Ai}'\,(-z)&=-\tfrac{1}{3}z[J_{-2/3}(\zeta)-J_{2/3}(\zeta)]\\&=\tfrac{1}{2}(z/\sqrt{3})[e^{-\pi i/6}H^{(1)}_{2/3}(\zeta)+e^{\pi i/6}H^{(2)}_{2/3}(\zeta)]\end{aligned}$$

10.4.18 $$\mathrm{Bi}\,(z)=\sqrt{z/3}[I_{-1/3}(\zeta)+I_{1/3}(\zeta)]$$

10.4.19

$$\begin{aligned}\mathrm{Bi}\,(-z)&=\sqrt{z/3}[J_{-1/3}(\zeta)-J_{1/3}(\zeta)]\\&=\tfrac{1}{2}i\sqrt{z/3}[e^{\pi i/6}H^{(1)}_{1/3}(\zeta)-e^{-\pi i/6}H^{(2)}_{1/3}(\zeta)]\end{aligned}$$

10.4.20 $$\mathrm{Bi}'\,(z)=(z/\sqrt{3})[I_{-2/3}(\zeta)+I_{2/3}(\zeta)]$$

10.4.21

$$\begin{aligned}\mathrm{Bi}'\,(-z)&=(z/\sqrt{3})[J_{-2/3}(\zeta)+J_{2/3}(\zeta)]\\&=\tfrac{1}{2}i(z/\sqrt{3})[e^{-\pi i/6}H^{(1)}_{2/3}(\zeta)-e^{\pi i/6}H^{(2)}_{2/3}(\zeta)]\end{aligned}$$

Representations of Bessel Functions in Terms of Airy Functions

$$z=\left(\frac{3}{2}\zeta\right)^{2/3}$$

10.4.22 $$J_{\pm1/3}(\zeta)=\tfrac{1}{2}\sqrt{3/z}[\sqrt{3}\,\mathrm{Ai}\,(-z)\mp\mathrm{Bi}\,(-z)]$$

10.4.23 $$H^{(1)}_{\pm1/3}(\zeta)=e^{\mp\pi i/6}\sqrt{3/z}[\mathrm{Ai}\,(-z)-i\,\mathrm{Bi}\,(-z)]$$

10.4.24 $$H^{(2)}_{\pm1/3}(\zeta)=e^{\pm\pi i/6}\sqrt{3/z}[\mathrm{Ai}\,(-z)+i\,\mathrm{Bi}\,(-z)]$$

10.4.25 $$I_{\pm1/3}(\zeta)=\tfrac{1}{2}\sqrt{3/z}[\mp\sqrt{3}\,\mathrm{Ai}\,(z)+\mathrm{Bi}\,(z)]$$

10.4.26 $$K_{\pm1/3}(\zeta)=\pi\sqrt{3/z}\,\mathrm{Ai}\,(z)$$

10.4.27 $$J_{\pm2/3}(\zeta)=(\sqrt{3}/2z)[\pm\sqrt{3}\,\mathrm{Ai}'\,(-z)+\mathrm{Bi}'\,(-z)]$$

10.4.28

$$\begin{aligned}H^{(1)}_{2/3}(\zeta)&=e^{-2\pi i/3}H^{(1)}_{-2/3}(\zeta)\\&=e^{\pi i/6}(\sqrt{3}/z)[\mathrm{Ai}'\,(-z)-i\,\mathrm{Bi}'\,(-z)]\end{aligned}$$

10.4.29

$$\begin{aligned}H^{(2)}_{2/3}(\zeta)&=e^{2\pi i/3}H^{(2)}_{-2/3}(\zeta)\\&=e^{-\pi i/6}(\sqrt{3}/z)[\mathrm{Ai}'\,(-z)+i\,\mathrm{Bi}'\,(-z)]\end{aligned}$$

10.4.30 $$I_{\pm2/3}(\zeta)=(\sqrt{3}/2z)[\pm\sqrt{3}\,\mathrm{Ai}'\,(z)+\mathrm{Bi}'\,(z)]$$

10.4.31 $$K_{\pm2/3}(\zeta)=-\pi(\sqrt{3}/z)\,\mathrm{Ai}'\,(z)$$

Integral Representations

10.4.32

$$(3a)^{-1/3}\pi\,\mathrm{Ai}\,[\pm(3a)^{-1/3}x]=\int_0^\infty\cos\,(at^3\pm xt)dt$$

10.4.33

$$\begin{aligned}&(3a)^{-1/3}\pi\,\mathrm{Bi}\,[\pm(3a)^{-1/3}x]\\&\qquad=\int_0^\infty[\exp\,(-at^3\pm xt)+\sin\,(at^3\pm xt)]dt\end{aligned}$$

The Integrals $\int_0^z\mathrm{Ai}\,(\pm t)dt,\ \int_0^z\mathrm{Bi}\,(\pm t)dt$

$$\zeta=\tfrac{2}{3}z^{3/2}$$

10.4.34 $$\int_0^z\mathrm{Ai}\,(t)dt=\frac{1}{3}\int_0^\zeta[I_{-1/3}(t)-I_{1/3}(t)]dt$$

10.4.35 $$\int_0^z\mathrm{Ai}\,(-t)dt=\frac{1}{3}\int_0^\zeta[J_{-1/3}(t)+J_{1/3}(t)]dt$$

10.4.36 $$\int_0^z\mathrm{Bi}\,(t)dt=\frac{1}{\sqrt{3}}\int_0^\zeta[I_{-1/3}(t)+I_{1/3}(t)]dt$$

10.4.37 $$\int_0^z\mathrm{Bi}\,(-t)dt=\frac{1}{\sqrt{3}}\int_0^\zeta[J_{-1/3}(t)-J_{1/3}(t)]dt$$

Ascending Series for $\int_0^z\mathrm{Ai}\,(\pm t)dt,\ \int_0^z\mathrm{Bi}\,(\pm t)dt$

10.4.38 $$\int_0^z\mathrm{Ai}\,(t)dt=c_1F(z)-c_2G(z)$$

(See **10.4.2.**)

10.4.39 $$\int_0^z\mathrm{Ai}\,(-t)dt=-c_1F(-z)+c_2G(-z)$$

10.4.40 $$\int_0^z\mathrm{Bi}\,(t)dt=\sqrt{3}[c_1F(z)+c_2G(z)]$$

(See **10.4.3.**)

10.4.41

$$\int_0^z\mathrm{Bi}\,(-t)dt=-\sqrt{3}[c_1F(-z)+c_2G(-z)]$$

$$\begin{aligned}F(z)&=z+\frac{1}{4!}z^4+\frac{1\cdot4}{7!}z^7+\frac{1\cdot4\cdot7}{10!}z^{10}+\ldots\\&=\sum_0^\infty 3^k\left(\frac{1}{3}\right)_k\frac{z^{3k+1}}{(3k+1)!}\end{aligned}$$

$$\begin{aligned}G(z)&=\frac{1}{2!}z^2+\frac{2}{5!}z^5+\frac{2\cdot5}{8!}z^8+\frac{2\cdot5\cdot8}{11!}z^{11}+\ldots\\&=\sum_0^\infty 3^k\left(\frac{2}{3}\right)_k\frac{z^{3k+2}}{(3k+2)!}\end{aligned}$$

The constants c_1, c_2 are given in **10.4.4, 10.4.5.**

The Functions Gi(z), Hi(z)

10.4.42

$$\mathrm{Gi}\,(z)=\pi^{-1}\int_0^\infty \sin\left(\frac{1}{3}t^3+zt\right)dt$$

$$=\frac{1}{3}\,\mathrm{Bi}\,(z)+\int_0^z[\mathrm{Ai}\,(z)\,\mathrm{Bi}\,(t)-\mathrm{Ai}\,(t)\,\mathrm{Bi}\,(z)]dt$$

10.4.43

$$\mathrm{Gi}'\,(z)=\frac{1}{3}\mathrm{Bi}'\,(z)+\int_0^z[\mathrm{Ai}'(z)\,\mathrm{Bi}\,(t)-\mathrm{Ai}\,(t)\,\mathrm{Bi}'(z)]dt$$

10.4.44

$$\mathrm{Hi}(z)=\pi^{-1}\int_0^\infty \exp\left(-\frac{1}{3}t^3+zt\right)dt$$

$$=\frac{2}{3}\mathrm{Bi}\,(z)+\int_0^z[\mathrm{Ai}\,(t)\,\mathrm{Bi}\,(z)-\mathrm{Ai}(z)\,\mathrm{Bi}\,(t)]dt$$

10.4.45

$$\mathrm{Hi}'\,(z)=\frac{2}{3}\mathrm{Bi}'\,(z)+\int_0^z[\mathrm{Ai}\,(t)\,\mathrm{Bi}'(z)-\mathrm{Ai}'(z)\,\mathrm{Bi}\,(t)]dt$$

10.4.46 $$\mathrm{Gi}\,(z)+\mathrm{Hi}\,(z)=\mathrm{Bi}\,(z)$$

Representations of $\int_0^z \mathrm{Ai}(\pm t)dt$, $\int_0^z \mathrm{Bi}(\pm t)dt$ by Gi $(\pm z)$, Hi $(\pm z)$

10.4.47

$$\int_0^z \mathrm{Ai}\,(t)dt=\frac{1}{3}+\pi[\mathrm{Ai}'\,(z)\mathrm{Gi}(z)-\mathrm{Ai}\,(z)\mathrm{Gi}'(z)]$$

10.4.48

$$=-\frac{2}{3}-\pi[\mathrm{Ai}'\,(z)\,\mathrm{Hi}\,(z)-\mathrm{Ai}\,(z)\,\mathrm{Hi}'\,(z)]$$

10.4.49

$$\int_0^z \mathrm{Ai}\,(-t)dt=-\frac{1}{3}-\pi[\mathrm{Ai}'\,(-z)\,\mathrm{Gi}\,(-z)-\mathrm{Ai}\,(-z)\,\mathrm{Gi}'\,(-z)]$$

10.4.50

$$=\frac{2}{3}+\pi[\mathrm{Ai}'\,(-z)\,\mathrm{Hi}\,(-z)-\mathrm{Ai}\,(-z)\mathrm{Hi}'(-z)]$$

10.4.51

$$\int_0^z \mathrm{Bi}\,(t)dt=\pi[\mathrm{Bi}'\,(z)\,\mathrm{Gi}\,(z)-\mathrm{Bi}\,(z)\,\mathrm{Gi}'\,(z)]$$

10.4.52 $$=-\pi[\mathrm{Bi}'\,(z)\,\mathrm{Hi}\,(z)-\mathrm{Bi}\,(z)\,\mathrm{Hi}'(z)]$$

10.4.53

$$\int_0^z \mathrm{Bi}\,(-t)dt=-\pi[\mathrm{Bi}'\,(-z)\,\mathrm{Gi}\,(-z)-\mathrm{Bi}\,(-z)\,\mathrm{Gi}'\,(-z)]$$

10.4.54 $$=\pi[\mathrm{Bi}'\,(-z)\,\mathrm{Hi}\,(-z)-\mathrm{Bi}\,(-z)\,\mathrm{Hi}'\,(-z)]$$

Differential Equations for Gi (z), Hi (z)

10.4.55 $$w''-zw=-\pi^{-1}$$

$$w(0)=\frac{1}{3}\,\mathrm{Bi}\,(0)=\frac{1}{\sqrt{3}}\,\mathrm{Ai}\,(0)=.20497\;55424\;78$$

$$w'(0)=\frac{1}{3}\,\mathrm{Bi}'\,(0)=-\frac{1}{\sqrt{3}}\,\mathrm{Ai}'\,(0)=.14942\;94524\;49$$

$$w(z)=\mathrm{Gi}(z)$$

10.4.56 $$w''-zw=\pi^{-1}$$

$$w(0)=\frac{2}{3}\,\mathrm{Bi}\,(0)=\frac{2}{\sqrt{3}}\,\mathrm{Ai}\,(0)=.40995\;10849\;56$$

$$w'(0)=\frac{2}{3}\,\mathrm{Bi}'\,(0)=-\frac{2}{\sqrt{3}}\,\mathrm{Ai}'\,(0)=.29885\;89048\;98$$

$$w(z)=\mathrm{Hi}\,(z)$$

Differential Equation for Products of Airy Function

10.4.57 $$w'''-4zw'-2w=0$$

Linearly independent solutions are $\mathrm{Ai}^2\,(z)$, $\mathrm{Ai}\,(z)\,\mathrm{Bi}\,(z)$, $\mathrm{Bi}^2\,(z)$.

Wronskian for Products of Airy Functions

10.4.58 $$W\{\mathrm{Ai}^2\,(z),\,\mathrm{Ai}\,(z)\,\mathrm{Bi}\,(z),\,\mathrm{Bi}^2\,(z)\}=2\pi^{-3}$$

Asymptotic Expansions for |z| Large

$$c_0=1,\;c_k=\frac{\Gamma(3k+\frac{1}{2})}{54^k k!\,\Gamma(k+\frac{1}{2})}=\frac{(2k+1)(2k+3)\ldots(6k-1)}{216^k k!}$$

$$d_0=1,\,d_k=-\frac{6k+1}{6k-1}\,c_k\qquad(k=1,2,3,\ldots)$$

$$\zeta=\frac{2}{3}\,z^{3/2}$$

10.4.59

$$\mathrm{Ai}\,(z)\sim\frac{1}{2}\,\pi^{-1/2}z^{-1/4}e^{-\zeta}\sum_0^\infty(-1)^k c_k\zeta^{-k}\qquad(|\arg z|<\pi$$

10.4.60

$$\mathrm{Ai}\,(-z)\sim\pi^{-1/2}z^{-1/4}\left[\sin\left(\zeta+\frac{\pi}{4}\right)\sum_0^\infty(-1)^k c_{2k}\zeta^{-2k}-\cos\left(\zeta+\frac{\pi}{4}\right)\sum_0^\infty(-1)^k c_{2k+1}\zeta^{-2k-1}\right.$$

$$(|\arg z|<\tfrac{2}{3}\pi$$

10.4.61

$$\mathrm{Ai}'\,(z)\sim-\tfrac{1}{2}\pi^{-1/2}z^{1/4}e^{-\zeta}\sum_0^\infty(-1)^k d_k\zeta^{-k}$$

$$(|\arg z|<\pi$$

10.4.62

$$\mathrm{Ai}'(-z)\sim-\pi^{-\frac{1}{2}}z^{\frac{1}{4}}\left[\cos\left(\zeta+\frac{\pi}{4}\right)\sum_0^\infty(-1)^k d_{2k}\zeta^{-2k}+\sin\left(\zeta+\frac{\pi}{4}\right)\sum_0^\infty(-1)^k d_{2k+1}\zeta^{-2k-1}\right]\qquad(|\arg z|<\tfrac{2}{3}\pi)$$

10.4.63

$$\mathrm{Bi}(z)\sim\pi^{-\frac{1}{2}}z^{-\frac{1}{4}}e^{\zeta}\sum_0^\infty c_k\zeta^{-k}\qquad(|\arg z|<\tfrac{1}{3}\pi)$$

10.4.64

$$\mathrm{Bi}(-z)\sim\pi^{-\frac{1}{2}}z^{-\frac{1}{4}}\left[\cos\left(\zeta+\frac{\pi}{4}\right)\sum_0^\infty(-1)^k c_{2k}\zeta^{-2k}+\sin\left(\zeta+\frac{\pi}{4}\right)\sum_0^\infty(-1)^k c_{2k+1}\zeta^{-2k-1}\right]\qquad(|\arg z|<\tfrac{2}{3}\pi)$$

10.4.65

$$\mathrm{Bi}(ze^{\pm\pi i/3})\sim\sqrt{2/\pi}\,e^{\pm\pi i/6}z^{-\frac{1}{4}}\left[\sin\left(\zeta+\frac{\pi}{4}\mp\frac{i}{2}\ln 2\right)\sum_0^\infty(-1)^k c_{2k}\zeta^{-2k}-\cos\left(\zeta+\frac{\pi}{4}\mp\frac{i}{2}\ln 2\right)\sum_0^\infty(-1)^k c_{2k+1}\zeta^{-2k-1}\right]\qquad(|\arg z|<\tfrac{2}{3}\pi)$$

10.4.66

$$\mathrm{Bi}'(z)\sim\pi^{-\frac{1}{2}}z^{\frac{1}{4}}e^{\zeta}\sum_0^\infty d_k\zeta^{-k}\quad(|\arg z|<\tfrac{1}{3}\pi)$$

10.4.67

$$\mathrm{Bi}'(-z)\sim\pi^{-\frac{1}{2}}z^{\frac{1}{4}}\left[\sin\left(\zeta+\frac{\pi}{4}\right)\sum_0^\infty(-1)^k d_{2k}\zeta^{-2k}-\cos\left(\zeta+\frac{\pi}{4}\right)\sum_0^\infty(-1)^k d_{2k+1}\zeta^{-2k-1}\right]\qquad(|\arg z|<\tfrac{2}{3}\pi)$$

10.4.68

$$\mathrm{Bi}'(ze^{\pm\pi i/3})\sim\sqrt{2/\pi}\,e^{\mp\pi i/6}z^{\frac{1}{4}}\left[\cos\left(\zeta+\frac{\pi}{4}\mp\frac{i}{2}\ln 2\right)\sum_0^\infty(-1)^k d_{2k}\zeta^{-2k}+\sin\left(\zeta+\frac{\pi}{4}\mp\frac{i}{2}\ln 2\right)\sum_0^\infty(-1)^k d_{2k+1}\zeta^{-2k-1}\right]\qquad(|\arg z|<\tfrac{2}{3}\pi)$$

Modulus and Phase

10.4.69

$$\mathrm{Ai}(-x)=M(x)\cos\theta(x),\ \mathrm{Bi}(-x)=M(x)\sin\theta(x)$$

$$M(x)=\sqrt{[\mathrm{Ai}^2(-x)+\mathrm{Bi}^2(-x)]},\qquad \theta(x)=\arctan[\mathrm{Bi}(-x)/\mathrm{Ai}(-x)]$$

10.4.70

$$\mathrm{Ai}'(-x)=N(x)\cos\phi(x),\ \mathrm{Bi}'(-x)=N(x)\sin\phi(x)$$

$$N(x)=\sqrt{[\mathrm{Ai}'^2(-x)+\mathrm{Bi}'^2(-x)]},\qquad \phi(x)=\arctan[\mathrm{Bi}'(-x)/\mathrm{Ai}'(-x)]$$

Differential Equations for Modulus and Phase

Primes denote differentiation with respect to x

10.4.71 $$M^2\theta'=-\pi^{-1},\ N^2\phi'=-\pi^{-1}x$$

10.4.72 $$N^2=M'^2+M^2\theta'^2=M'^2+\pi^{-2}M^{-2}$$

10.4.73 $$NN'=-xMM'$$

10.4.74

$$\tan(\phi-\theta)=M\theta'/M'=-(\pi MM')^{-1},\qquad MN\sin(\phi-\theta)=\pi^{-1}$$

10.4.75 $$M''+xM-\pi^{-2}M^{-3}=0$$

10.4.76 $$(M^2)'''+4x(M^2)'-2M^2=0$$

10.4.77 $$\theta'^2+\tfrac{1}{2}(\theta'''/\theta')-\tfrac{3}{4}(\theta''/\theta')^2=x$$

Asymptotic Expansions of Modulus and Phase for Large x

10.4.78 $$M^2(x)\sim\frac{1}{\pi}x^{-1/2}\sum_0^\infty\frac{(-1)^k}{12^k k!}2^{3k}\left(\frac{1}{2}\right)_{3k}(2x)^{-3k}$$

10.4.79

$$\theta(x)\sim\frac{1}{4}\pi-\frac{2}{3}x^{3/2}\left[1-\frac{5}{4}(2x)^{-3}+\frac{1105}{96}(2x)^{-6}-\frac{82825}{128}(2x)^{-9}+\frac{12820\,31525}{14336}(2x)^{-12}-\dots\right]$$

10.4.80

$$N^2(x)\sim\frac{1}{\pi}x^{\frac{1}{2}}\sum_0^\infty\frac{(-1)^{k+1}}{12^k k!}\frac{6k+1}{6k-1}2^{3k}\left(\frac{1}{2}\right)_{3k}(2x)^{-3k}$$

10.4.81

$$\phi(x)\sim\frac{3}{4}\pi-\frac{2}{3}x^{3/2}\left[1+\frac{7}{4}(2x)^{-3}-\frac{1463}{96}(2x)^{-6}+\frac{495271}{640}(2x)^{-9}-\frac{2065\;30429}{2048}(2x)^{-12}+\dots\right]$$

Asymptotic Forms of $\int_0^x \mathrm{Ai}(\pm t)dt$, $\int_0^x \mathrm{Bi}(\pm t)dt$ for Large x

10.4.82 $$\int_0^x\mathrm{Ai}(t)dt\sim\frac{1}{3}-\frac{1}{2}\pi^{-1/2}x^{-3/4}\exp\left(-\frac{2}{3}x^{3/2}\right)$$

10.4.83

$$\int_0^x\mathrm{Ai}(-t)dt\sim\frac{2}{3}-\pi^{-1/2}x^{-3/4}\cos\left(\frac{2}{3}x^{3/2}+\frac{\pi}{4}\right)$$

10.4.84 $\int_0^x \text{Bi}(t)dt \sim \pi^{-1/2} x^{-3/4} \exp\left(\frac{2}{3} x^{3/2}\right)$

10.4.85 $\int_0^x \text{Bi}(-t)dt \sim \pi^{-1/2} x^{-3/4} \sin\left(\frac{2}{3} x^{3/2} + \frac{\pi}{4}\right)$

Asymptotic Forms of Gi $(\pm x)$, Gi′ $(\pm x)$, Hi $(\pm x)$, Hi′ $(\pm x)$ for Large x

10.4.86 $\text{Gi}(x) \sim \pi^{-1} x^{-1}$

10.4.87 $\text{Gi}(-x) \sim \pi^{-1/2} x^{-1/4} \cos\left(\frac{2}{3} x^{3/2} + \frac{\pi}{4}\right)$

10.4.88 $\text{Gi}'(x) \sim \frac{7}{96} \pi^{-1} x^{-2}$

10.4.89 $\text{Gi}'(-x) \sim \pi^{-1/2} x^{1/4} \sin\left(\frac{2}{3} x^{3/2} + \frac{\pi}{4}\right)$

10.4.90 $\text{Hi}(x) \sim \pi^{-1/2} x^{-1/4} \exp\left(\tfrac{2}{3} x^{3/2}\right)$

10.4.91 $\text{Hi}(-x) \sim \pi^{-1} x^{-1}$

10.4.92 $\text{Hi}'(x) \sim \pi^{-1/2} x^{1/4} \exp\left(\tfrac{2}{3} x^{3/2}\right)$

10.4.93 $\text{Hi}'(-x) \sim -\frac{3}{2} \pi^{-1} x^{-2}$

Zeros and Their Asymptotic Expansions

Ai (z), Ai′ (z) have zeros on the negative real axis only. Bi (z), Bi′ (z) have zeros on the negative real axis and in the sector $\frac{1}{3}\pi < |\arg z| < \frac{1}{2}\pi$. a_s, a'_s; b_s, b'_s s-th (real) negative zero of Ai (z), Ai′ (z); Bi (z), Bi′ (z), respectively. β_s, β'_s; $\overline{\beta}_s$, $\overline{\beta}'_s$ s-th complex zero of Bi (z), Bi′ (z) in the sectors $\frac{1}{3}\pi < \arg z < \frac{1}{2}\pi$, $-\frac{1}{2}\pi < \arg z < -\frac{1}{3}\pi$, respectively.

10.4.94 $a_s = -f[3\pi(4s-1)/8]$

10.4.95 $a'_s = -g[3\pi(4s-3)/8]$

10.4.96 $\text{Ai}'(a_s) = (-1)^{s-1} f_1[3\pi(4s-1)/8]$

10.4.97 $\text{Ai}(a'_s) = (-1)^{s-1} g_1[3\pi(4s-3)/8]$

10.4.98 $b_s = -f[3\pi(4s-3)/8]$

10.4.99 $b'_s = -g[3\pi(4s-1)/8]$

10.4.100 $\text{Bi}'(b_s) = (-1)^{s-1} f_1[3\pi(4s-3)/8]$

10.4.101 $\text{Bi}(b'_s) = (-1)^{s} g_1[3\pi(4s-1)/8]$

10.4.102 $\beta_s = e^{\pi i/3} f\left[\frac{3\pi}{8}(4s-1) + \frac{3i}{4} \ln 2\right]$

10.4.103 $\beta'_s = e^{\pi i/3} g\left[\frac{3\pi}{8}(4s-3) + \frac{3i}{4} \ln 2\right]$

10.4.104

$$\text{Bi}'(\beta_s) = (-1)^s \sqrt{2} e^{-\pi i/6} f_1\left[\frac{3\pi}{8}(4s-1) + \frac{3i}{4} \ln 2\right]$$

10.4.105

$$\text{Bi}(\beta'_s) = (-1)^{s-1} \sqrt{2} e^{\pi i/6} g_1\left[\frac{3\pi}{8}(4s-3) + \frac{3i}{4} \ln 2\right]$$

$|z|$ sufficiently large

$$f(z) \sim z^{2/3}\left(1 + \frac{5}{48} z^{-2} - \frac{5}{36} z^{-4} + \frac{77125}{82944} z^{-6} - \frac{1080\,56875}{69\,67296} z^{-8} + \frac{16\,23755\,96875}{3344\,30208} z^{-10} - \ldots\right)$$

$$g(z) \sim z^{2/3}\left(1 - \frac{7}{48} z^{-2} + \frac{35}{288} z^{-4} - \frac{181223}{207360} z^{-6} + \frac{186\,83371}{12\,44160} z^{-8} - \frac{9\,11458\,84361}{1911\,02976} z^{-10} + \ldots\right)$$

$$f_1(z) \sim \pi^{-1/2} z^{1/6}\left(1 + \frac{5}{48} z^{-2} - \frac{1525}{4608} z^{-4} + \frac{23\,97875}{6\,63552} z^{-6} - \ldots\right)$$

$$g_1(z) \sim \pi^{-1/2} z^{-1/6}\left(1 - \frac{7}{96} z^{-2} + \frac{1673}{6144} z^{-4} - \frac{843\,94709}{265\,42080} z^{-6} + \ldots\right)$$

Formal and Asymptotic Solutions of Ordinary Differential Equations of Second Order With Turning Points

An equation

10.4.106 $W'' + a(z, \lambda)W' + b(z, \lambda)W = 0$

in which λ is a real or complex parameter and, for fixed λ, $a(z, \lambda)$ is analytic in z and $b(z, \lambda)$ is continuous in z in some region of the z-plane, may be reduced by the transformation

10.4.107 $W(z) = w(z) \exp\left(-\frac{1}{2}\int^z a(t, \lambda)dt\right)$

to the equation

10.4.108

$$w'' + \varphi(z, \lambda)w = 0$$

$$\varphi(z, \lambda) = b(z, \lambda) - \frac{1}{4} a^2(z, \lambda) - \frac{1}{2} \frac{d}{dz} a(z, \lambda).$$

If $\varphi(z, \lambda)$ can be written in the form

10.4.109 $$\varphi(z, \lambda)=\lambda^2 p(z)+q(z, \lambda)$$

where $q(z, \lambda)$ is bounded in a region R of the z-plane, then the zeros of $p(z)$ in R are said to be turning points of the equation **10.4.108.**

The Special Case $w''+[\lambda^2 z+q(z, \lambda)]w=0$

Let $\lambda=|\lambda|e^{i\omega}$ vary over a sectorial domain S: $|\lambda|\geq\lambda_0(>0)$, $\omega_1\leq\omega\leq\omega_2$, and suppose that $q(z, \lambda)$ is continuous in z for $|z|<r$ and λ in S, and $q(z, \lambda)$ $\sim\sum_0^\infty q_n(z)\lambda^{-n}$ as $\lambda\to\infty$ in S.

Formal Series Solution

10.4.110
$$w(z)=u(z)\sum_0^\infty \varphi_n(z)\lambda^{-n}+\lambda^{-1}u'(z)\sum_0^\infty \psi_n(z)\lambda^{-n}$$
$$u''+\lambda^2 zu=0$$

$$\varphi_0(z)=c_0,\qquad \psi_0(z)=z^{-\frac{1}{2}}c_1,\qquad c_0,\ c_1 \text{ constants}$$

$$\varphi_{n+1}(z)=-\frac{1}{2}\psi_n'(z)-\frac{1}{2}\int_0^z \sum_0^n q_{n-k}(t)\psi_k(t)dt$$

$$\psi_n(z)=\frac{1}{2}z^{-\frac{1}{2}}\int_0^z t^{-\frac{1}{2}}\left[\varphi_n''(t)+\sum_0^n q_{n-k}(t)\varphi_k(t)\right]dt$$
$$(n=0, 1, 2, \ldots)$$

Uniform Asymptotic Expansions of Solutions

For z real, i.e. for the equation

10.4.111 $$y''+[\lambda^2 x+q(x, \lambda)]y=0$$

where x varies in a bounded interval $a\leq x\leq b$ that includes the origin and where, for each fixed λ in S, $q(x, \lambda)$ is continuous in x for $a\leq x\leq b$, the following asymptotic representations hold.

(i) If λ is real and positive, there are solutions $y_0(x)$, $y_1(x)$ such that, uniformly in x on $a\leq x\leq 0$,

10.4.112
$$y_0(x)=\text{Ai}\,(-\lambda^{2/3}x)[1+O(\lambda^{-1})]\qquad(\lambda\to\infty)$$
$$y_1(x)=\text{Bi}\,(-\lambda^{2/3}x)[1+O(\lambda^{-1})]$$

and, uniformly in x on $0\leq x\leq b$

10.4.113
$$y_0(x)=\text{Ai}\,(-\lambda^{2/3}x)[1+O(\lambda^{-1})]+\text{Bi}\,(-\lambda^{2/3}x)O(\lambda^{-1}),$$
$$y_1(x)=\text{Bi}\,(-\lambda^{2/3}x)[1+O(\lambda^{-1})]+\text{Ai}\,(-\lambda^{2/3}x)O(\lambda^{-1})$$
$$(\lambda\to\infty)$$

(ii) If $\mathscr{R}\lambda\geq 0$, $\mathscr{I}\lambda\neq 0$, there are solutions $y_0(x)$, $y_1(x)$ such that, uniformly in x on $a\leq x\leq b$,

10.4.114
$$y_0(x)=\text{Ai}\,(-\lambda^{2/3}x)[1+O(\lambda^{-1})]$$
$$y_1(x)=\text{Bi}\,(-\lambda^{2/3}x)[1+O(\lambda^{-1})]\qquad(|\lambda|\to\infty)$$

For further representations and details, we refer to [10.4].

When z is complex (bounded or unbounded), conditions under which the formal series **10.4.110** yields a uniform asymptotic expansion of a solution are given in [10.12] if $q(z, \lambda)$ is independent of λ and $|\lambda|\to\infty$ with fixed ω, and in [10.14] if λ lies in any region of the complex plane. Further references are [10.2; 10.9; 10.10].

The General Case $w''+[\lambda^2 p(z)+q(z, \lambda)]w=0$

Let $\lambda=|\lambda|e^{i\omega}$ where $|\lambda|\geq\lambda_0(>0)$ and $-\pi\leq\omega\leq\pi$; suppose that $p(z)$ is analytic in a region R and has a zero $z=z_0$ in R, and that, for fixed λ, $q(z, \lambda)$ is analytic in z for z in R. The transformation $\xi=\xi(z)$, $v=[p(z)/\xi]^{1/4}w(z)$, where ξ is defined as the (unique) solution of the equation

10.4.115 $$\xi\left(\frac{d\xi}{dz}\right)^2=p(z),$$

yields the special case

10.4.116 $$\frac{d^2v}{d\xi^2}+[\lambda^2\xi+f(\xi, \lambda)]v=0,$$

$$f(\xi, \lambda)=\left(\frac{d\xi}{dz}\right)^{-2}q(z, \lambda)-\left(\frac{d\xi}{dz}\right)^{-\frac{1}{2}}\frac{d^2}{d\xi^2}\left[\left(\frac{d\xi}{dz}\right)^{\frac{1}{2}}\right].$$

Example:

Consider the equation

10.4.117 $$y''+[\lambda^2-(\lambda^2-\tfrac{1}{4})\,x^{-2}]y=0$$

for which the points $x=0$, ∞ are singular points and $x=1$ is a turning point. It has the functions $x^{\frac{1}{2}}J_\lambda(\lambda x)$, $x^{\frac{1}{2}}Y_\lambda(\lambda x)$ as particular solutions (see **9.1.49**).

The equation **10.4.115** becomes

$$\xi\left(\frac{d\xi}{dx}\right)^2=\frac{x^2-1}{x^2}$$

whence

$$\tfrac{2}{3}(-\xi)^{3/2}=-\sqrt{1-x^2}+\ln x^{-1}(1+\sqrt{1-x^2})\qquad(0<x\leq 1)$$

$$\tfrac{2}{3}\xi^{3/2}=\sqrt{x^2-1}-\arccos x^{-1}\qquad(1\leq x<\infty).$$

Thus

10.4.118 $$v(\xi)=\left(\frac{x^2-1}{x^2\xi}\right)^{1/4}y(x)$$

satisfies the equation

10.4.119 $$\frac{d^2v}{d\xi^2}+\left[\lambda^2\xi-\frac{5}{16\xi^2}+\frac{\xi^2}{4}\frac{x^2(x^2+4)}{(x^2-1)^3}\right]v=0$$

which is of the form **10.4.111** with x replaced by ξ and $q(\xi, \lambda)$ independent of λ.

Suppose $\mathscr{R}\lambda\geq 0$, $\mathscr{I}\lambda\neq 0$. By the first equation of **10.4.114** there is a solution $v_0(\xi)$ of **10.4.119**, i.e., a solution $y_0(x)$ of **10.4.117** for which the representation

10.4.120
$$v_0(\xi)=\left(\frac{x^2-1}{x^2\xi}\right)^{1/4} y_0(x)=\mathrm{Ai}(-\lambda^{2/3}\xi)[1+O(\lambda^{-1})]$$

holds uniformly in x on $0<x<\infty$ as $|\lambda|\to\infty$.

To identify $y_0(x)$ in terms of $x^{\frac{1}{2}}J_\lambda(\lambda x)$, $x^{\frac{1}{2}}Y_\lambda(\lambda x)$, restrict x to $0<x\leq b<1$ so that by **10.4.118** ξ is negative, and replace the Airy function by its asymptotic representation **10.4.59.** This yields

10.4.121
$$y_0(x)$$
$$=\left(\frac{x^2-1}{x^2\xi}\right)^{-1/4}\frac{1}{2}\pi^{-1/2}\lambda^{-1/6}(-\xi)^{1/4}\exp\left(\frac{2}{3}\lambda(-\xi)^{3/2}\right)[1+O(\lambda^{-1})]$$
$$=\frac{1}{2}\pi^{-1/2}\lambda^{-1/6}\left(\frac{1-x^2}{x^2}\right)^{-1/4}\exp\left(\frac{2}{3}\lambda(-\xi)^{3/2}\right)[1+O(\lambda^{-1})]$$

Let now λ be fixed and $x\to 0$ in **10.4.121.** There results

10.4.122 $$y_0(x)\sim\tfrac{1}{2}\pi^{-1/2}\lambda^{-1/6}x^{1/2}\left(\tfrac{1}{2}x\right)^{\lambda}e^{\lambda}.$$

On the other hand, $y_0(x)$ is a solution of **10.4.117** and therefore it can be written in the form

10.4.123 $$y_0(x)=x^{1/2}[c_1J_\lambda(\lambda x)+c_2Y_\lambda(\lambda x)]$$

where, from **9.1.7** for λ fixed and $x\to 0$

$$J_\lambda(\lambda x)\sim\frac{(\frac{1}{2}\lambda x)^\lambda}{\Gamma(\lambda+1)},$$

$$Y_\lambda(\lambda x)\sim\frac{(\frac{1}{2}\lambda x)^\lambda}{\Gamma(\lambda+1)}\cot\lambda\pi-\frac{(\frac{1}{2}\lambda x)^{-\lambda}}{\Gamma(1-\lambda)}\csc\lambda\pi.$$

Thus, letting $x\to 0$ in **10.4.123** and comparing the resulting relation with **10.4.122** one finds that $c_2=0$ and

10.4.124 $$y_0(x)=\tfrac{1}{2}\pi^{-1/2}\lambda^{-\lambda-1/6}e^{\lambda}\Gamma(\lambda+1)x^{1/2}J_\lambda(\lambda x).$$

It follows from **10.4.120** that uniformly in x on $0<x<\infty$

10.4.125

$$J_\lambda(\lambda x)$$
$$=\frac{2\pi^{1/2}}{\Gamma(\lambda+1)}\lambda^{\lambda+1/6}e^{-\lambda}\left(\frac{x^2-1}{\xi}\right)^{-1/4}\mathrm{Ai}\,(-\lambda^{2/3}\xi)[1+O(\lambda^{-1})]$$
$$(|\lambda|\to\infty)$$

AIRY FUNCTIONS

Table 10.11

x	$\mathrm{Ai}(x)$	$\mathrm{Ai}'(x)$	$\mathrm{Bi}(x)$	$\mathrm{Bi}'(x)$	x	$\mathrm{Ai}(x)$	$\mathrm{Ai}'(x)$	$\mathrm{Bi}(x)$	$\mathrm{Bi}'(x)$
0.00	0.35502 805	-0.25881 940	0.61492 663	0.44828 836	0.50	0.23169 361	-0.22491 053	0.85427 704	0.54457 256
0.01	0.35243 992	-0.25880 174	0.61940 962	0.44831 926	0.51	0.22945 031	-0.22374 617	0.85974 431	0.54890 049
0.02	0.34985 214	-0.25874 909	0.62389 322	0.44841 254	0.52	0.22721 872	-0.22257 027	0.86525 543	0.55334 239
0.03	0.34726 505	-0.25866 197	0.62837 808	0.44856 911	0.53	0.22499 894	-0.22138 322	0.87081 154	0.55789 959
0.04	0.34467 901	-0.25854 090	0.63286 482	0.44878 987	0.54	0.22279 109	-0.22018 541	0.87641 381	0.56257 345
0.05	0.34209 435	-0.25838 640	0.63735 409	0.44907 570	0.55	0.22059 527	-0.21897 720	0.88206 341	0.56736 532
0.06	0.33951 139	-0.25819 898	0.64184 655	0.44942 752	0.56	0.21841 158	-0.21775 898	0.88776 152	0.57227 662
0.07	0.33693 047	-0.25797 916	0.64634 286	0.44984 622	0.57	0.21624 012	-0.21653 112	0.89350 934	0.57730 873
0.08	0.33435 191	-0.25772 745	0.65084 370	0.45033 270	0.58	0.21408 099	-0.21529 397	0.89930 810	0.58246 311
0.09	0.33177 603	-0.25744 437	0.65534 975	0.45088 787	0.59	0.21193 427	-0.21404 790	0.90515 902	0.58774 120
0.10	0.32920 313	-0.25713 042	0.65986 169	0.45151 263	0.60	0.20980 006	-0.21279 326	0.91106 334	0.59314 448
0.11	0.32663 352	-0.25678 613	0.66438 023	0.45220 789	0.61	0.20767 844	-0.21153 041	0.91702 233	0.59867 447
0.12	0.32406 751	-0.25641 200	0.66890 609	0.45297 457	0.62	0.20556 948	-0.21025 970	0.92303 726	0.60433 267
0.13	0.32150 538	-0.25600 854	0.67343 997	0.45381 357	0.63	0.20347 327	-0.20898 146	0.92910 941	0.61012 064
0.14	0.31894 743	-0.25557 625	0.67798 260	0.45472 582	0.64	0.20138 987	-0.20769 605	0.93524 011	0.61603 997
0.15	0.31639 395	-0.25511 565	0.68253 473	0.45571 223	0.65	0.19931 937	-0.20640 378	0.94143 066	0.62209 226
0.16	0.31384 521	-0.25462 724	0.68709 709	0.45677 373	0.66	0.19726 182	-0.20510 500	0.94768 241	0.62827 912
0.17	0.31130 150	-0.25411 151	0.69167 046	0.45791 125	0.67	0.19521 729	-0.20380 004	0.95399 670	0.63460 222
0.18	0.30876 307	-0.25356 898	0.69625 558	0.45912 572	0.68	0.19318 584	-0.20248 920	0.96037 491	0.64106 324
0.19	0.30623 020	-0.25300 013	0.70085 323	0.46041 808	0.69	0.19116 752	-0.20117 281	0.96681 843	0.64766 389
0.20	0.30370 315	-0.25240 547	0.70546 420	0.46178 928	0.70	0.18916 240	-0.19985 119	0.97332 866	0.65440 592
0.21	0.30118 218	-0.25178 548	0.71008 928	0.46324 026	0.71	0.18717 052	-0.19852 464	0.97990 703	0.66129 109
0.22	0.29866 753	-0.25114 067	0.71472 927	0.46477 197	0.72	0.18519 192	-0.19719 347	0.98655 496	0.66832 121
0.23	0.29615 945	-0.25047 151	0.71938 499	0.46638 539	0.73	0.18322 666	-0.19585 798	0.99327 394	0.67549 810
0.24	0.29365 818	-0.24977 850	0.72405 726	0.46808 147	0.74	0.18127 478	-0.19451 846	1.00006 542	0.68282 363
0.25	0.29116 395	-0.24906 211	0.72874 690	0.46986 119	0.75	0.17933 631	-0.19317 521	1.00693 091	0.69029 970
0.26	0.28867 701	-0.24832 284	0.73345 477	0.47172 554	0.76	0.17741 128	-0.19182 851	1.01387 192	0.69792 824
0.27	0.28619 757	-0.24756 115	0.73818 170	0.47367 549	0.77	0.17549 975	-0.19047 865	1.02088 999	0.70571 121
0.28	0.28372 586	-0.24677 753	0.74292 857	0.47571 205	0.78	0.17360 172	-0.18912 591	1.02798 667	0.71365 062
0.29	0.28126 209	-0.24597 244	0.74769 624	0.47783 623	0.79	0.17171 724	-0.18777 055	1.03516 353	0.72174 849
0.30	0.27880 648	-0.24514 636	0.75248 559	0.48004 903	0.80	0.16984 632	-0.18641 286	1.04242 217	0.73000 690
0.31	0.27635 923	-0.24429 976	0.75729 752	0.48235 148	0.81	0.16798 899	-0.18505 310	1.04976 421	0.73842 795
0.32	0.27392 055	-0.24343 309	0.76213 292	0.48474 462	0.82	0.16614 526	-0.18369 153	1.05719 128	0.74701 380
0.33	0.27149 064	-0.24254 682	0.76699 272	0.48722 948	0.83	0.16431 516	-0.18232 840	1.06470 504	0.75576 663
0.34	0.26906 968	-0.24164 140	0.77187 782	0.48980 713	0.84	0.16249 870	-0.18096 398	1.07230 717	0.76468 865
0.35	0.26665 787	-0.24071 730	0.77678 917	0.49247 861	0.85	0.16069 588	-0.17959 851	1.07999 939	0.77378 215
0.36	0.26425 540	-0.23977 495	0.78172 770	0.49524 501	0.86	0.15890 673	-0.17823 223	1.08778 340	0.78304 942
0.37	0.26186 243	-0.23881 481	0.78669 439	0.49810 741	0.87	0.15713 124	-0.17686 539	1.09566 096	0.79249 282
0.38	0.25947 916	-0.23783 731	0.79169 018	0.50106 692	0.88	0.15536 942	-0.17549 823	1.10363 385	0.80211 473
0.39	0.25710 574	-0.23684 291	0.79671 605	0.50412 463	0.89	0.15362 128	-0.17413 097	1.11170 386	0.81191 759
0.40	0.25474 235	-0.23583 203	0.80177 300	0.50728 168	0.90	0.15188 680	-0.17276 384	1.11987 281	0.82190 389
0.41	0.25238 916	-0.23480 512	0.80686 202	0.51053 920	0.91	0.15016 600	-0.17139 708	1.12814 255	0.83207 615
0.42	0.25004 630	-0.23376 259	0.81198 412	0.51389 833	0.92	0.14845 886	-0.17003 090	1.13651 496	0.84243 695
0.43	0.24771 395	-0.23270 487	0.81714 033	0.51736 025	0.93	0.14676 538	-0.16866 551	1.14499 193	0.85298 891
0.44	0.24539 226	-0.23163 239	0.82233 167	0.52092 614	0.94	0.14508 555	-0.16730 113	1.15357 539	0.86373 470
0.45	0.24308 135	-0.23054 556	0.82755 920	0.52459 717	0.95	0.14341 935	-0.16593 797	1.16226 728	0.87467 704
0.46	0.24078 139	-0.22944 479	0.83282 397	0.52837 457	0.96	0.14176 678	-0.16457 623	1.17106 959	0.88581 871
0.47	0.23849 250	-0.22833 050	0.83812 705	0.53225 956	0.97	0.14012 782	-0.16321 611	1.17998 433	0.89716 253
0.48	0.23621 482	-0.22720 310	0.84346 952	0.53625 338	0.98	0.13850 245	-0.16185 781	1.18901 352	0.90871 137
0.49	0.23394 848	-0.22606 297	0.84885 248	0.54035 729	0.99	0.13689 066	-0.16050 153	1.19815 925	0.92046 818
0.50	0.23169 361	-0.22491 053	0.85427 704	0.54457 256	1.00	0.13529 242	-0.15914 744	1.20742 359	0.93243 593

Table 10.11 **AIRY FUNCTIONS**

x	$\mathrm{Ai}(-x)$	$\mathrm{Ai}'(-x)$	$\mathrm{Bi}(-x)$	$\mathrm{Bi}'(-x)$	x	$\mathrm{Ai}(-x)$	$\mathrm{Ai}'(-x)$	$\mathrm{Bi}(-x)$	$\mathrm{Bi}'(-x)$
0.00	0.35502 805	-0.25881 940	0.61492 663	0.44828 836	0.50	0.47572 809	-0.20408 167	0.38035 266	0.50593 371
0.01	0.35761 619	-0.25880 157	0.61044 364	0.44831 896	0.51	0.47775 692	-0.20167 409	0.37528 379	0.50784 166
0.02	0.36020 397	-0.25874 771	0.60596 005	0.44841 015	0.52	0.47976 138	-0.19920 846	0.37019 579	0.50976 123
0.03	0.36279 102	-0.25865 731	0.60147 524	0.44856 104	0.53	0.48174 089	-0.19668 449	0.36508 853	0.51169 132
0.04	0.36537 699	-0.25852 986	0.59698 863	0.44877 074	0.54	0.48369 487	-0.19410 192	0.35996 193	0.51363 080
0.05	0.36796 149	-0.25836 484	0.59249 963	0.44903 833	0.55	0.48562 274	-0.19146 050	0.35481 589	0.51557 853
0.06	0.37054 416	-0.25816 173	0.58800 767	0.44936 293	0.56	0.48752 389	-0.18875 999	0.34965 033	0.51753 339
0.07	0.37312 460	-0.25792 001	0.58351 218	0.44974 364	0.57	0.48939 774	-0.18600 016	0.34446 520	0.51949 424
0.08	0.37570 243	-0.25763 918	0.57901 261	0.45017 955	0.58	0.49124 369	-0.18318 078	0.33926 043	0.52145 991
0.09	0.37827 725	-0.25731 872	0.57450 841	0.45066 976	0.59	0.49306 115	-0.18030 166	0.33403 599	0.52342 927
0.10	0.38084 867	-0.25695 811	0.56999 904	0.45121 336	0.60	0.49484 953	-0.17736 260	0.32879 184	0.52540 115
0.11	0.38341 628	-0.25655 685	0.56548 397	0.45180 945	0.61	0.49660 821	-0.17436 341	0.32352 796	0.52737 438
0.12	0.38597 967	-0.25611 443	0.56096 268	0.45245 712	0.62	0.49833 659	-0.17130 392	0.31824 435	0.52934 780
0.13	0.38853 843	-0.25563 033	0.55643 466	0.45315 546	0.63	0.50003 408	-0.16818 399	0.31294 101	0.53132 022
0.14	0.39109 213	-0.25510 406	0.55189 940	0.45390 355	0.64	0.50170 007	-0.16500 345	0.30761 795	0.53329 046
0.15	0.39364 037	-0.25453 511	0.54735 642	0.45470 047	0.65	0.50333 395	-0.16176 218	0.30227 521	0.53525 733
0.16	0.39618 269	-0.25392 297	0.54280 523	0.45554 530	0.66	0.50493 511	-0.15846 007	0.29691 282	0.53721 964
0.17	0.39871 868	-0.25326 716	0.53824 536	0.45643 713	0.67	0.50650 295	-0.15509 701	0.29153 084	0.53917 618
0.18	0.40124 789	-0.25256 716	0.53367 634	0.45737 503	0.68	0.50803 685	-0.15167 290	0.28612 932	0.54112 575
0.19	0.40376 987	-0.25182 250	0.52909 771	0.45835 806	0.69	0.50953 620	-0.14818 768	0.28070 835	0.54306 714
0.20	0.40628 419	-0.25103 267	0.52450 903	0.45938 529	0.70	0.51100 040	-0.14464 129	0.27526 801	0.54499 912
0.21	0.40879 038	-0.25019 720	0.51990 986	0.46045 578	0.71	0.51242 882	-0.14103 366	0.26980 840	0.54692 048
0.22	0.41128 798	-0.24931 559	0.51529 977	0.46156 860	0.72	0.51382 087	-0.13736 479	0.26432 964	0.54883 000
0.23	0.41377 653	-0.24838 737	0.51067 835	0.46272 279	0.73	0.51517 591	-0.13363 464	0.25883 185	0.55072 642
0.24	0.41625 557	-0.24741 206	0.50604 518	0.46391 740	0.74	0.51649 336	-0.12984 322	0.25331 516	0.55260 852
0.25	0.41872 461	-0.24638 919	0.50139 987	0.46515 148	0.75	0.51777 258	-0.12599 055	0.24777 973	0.55447 506
0.26	0.42118 319	-0.24531 828	0.49674 203	0.46642 408	0.76	0.51901 296	-0.12207 665	0.24222 571	0.55632 480
0.27	0.42363 082	-0.24419 888	0.49207 127	0.46773 423	0.77	0.52021 390	-0.11810 157	0.23665 329	0.55815 647
0.28	0.42606 701	-0.24303 053	0.48738 722	0.46908 095	0.78	0.52137 479	-0.11406 538	0.23106 265	0.55996 884
0.29	0.42849 126	-0.24181 276	0.48268 953	0.47046 327	0.79	0.52249 501	-0.10996 815	0.22545 398	0.56176 063
0.30	0.43090 310	-0.24054 513	0.47797 784	0.47188 022	0.80	0.52357 395	-0.10580 999	0.21982 751	0.56353 059
0.31	0.43330 200	-0.23922 719	0.47325 181	0.47333 081	0.81	0.52461 101	-0.10159 101	0.21418 345	0.56527 745
0.32	0.43568 747	-0.23785 851	0.46851 112	0.47481 405	0.82	0.52560 557	-0.09731 134	0.20852 204	0.56699 994
0.33	0.43805 900	-0.23643 865	0.46375 543	0.47632 895	0.83	0.52655 703	-0.09297 113	0.20284 354	0.56869 679
0.34	0.44041 607	-0.23496 718	0.45898 443	0.47787 450	0.84	0.52746 479	-0.08857 055	0.19714 820	0.57036 671
0.35	0.44275 817	-0.23344 368	0.45419 784	0.47944 970	0.85	0.52832 824	-0.08410 979	0.19143 630	0.57200 845
0.36	0.44508 477	-0.23186 773	0.44939 534	0.48105 354	0.86	0.52914 678	-0.07958 904	0.18570 813	0.57362 071
0.37	0.44739 535	-0.23023 893	0.44457 667	0.48268 500	0.87	0.52991 982	-0.07500 854	0.17996 399	0.57520 220
0.38	0.44968 937	-0.22855 687	0.43974 156	0.48434 307	0.88	0.53064 676	-0.07036 852	0.17420 419	0.57675 165
0.39	0.45196 631	-0.22682 116	0.43488 973	0.48602 670	0.89	0.53132 700	-0.06566 925	0.16842 906	0.57826 777
0.40	0.45422 561	-0.22503 141	0.43002 094	0.48773 486	0.90	0.53195 995	-0.06091 100	0.16263 895	0.57974 926
0.41	0.45646 675	-0.22318 723	0.42513 495	0.48946 652	0.91	0.53254 502	-0.05609 407	0.15683 420	0.58119 484
0.42	0.45868 918	-0.22128 826	0.42023 153	0.49122 062	0.92	0.53308 163	-0.05121 879	0.15101 518	0.58260 321
0.43	0.46089 233	-0.21933 412	0.41531 047	0.49299 611	0.93	0.53356 920	-0.04628 549	0.14518 226	0.58397 309
0.44	0.46307 567	-0.21732 447	0.41037 154	0.49479 193	0.94	0.53400 715	-0.04129 452	0.13933 585	0.58530 317
0.45	0.46523 864	-0.21525 894	0.40541 457	0.49660 702	0.95	0.53439 490	-0.03624 628	0.13347 634	0.58659 217
0.46	0.46738 066	-0.21313 721	0.40043 934	0.49844 031	0.96	0.53473 189	-0.03114 116	0.12760 415	0.58783 879
0.47	0.46950 119	-0.21095 893	0.39544 570	0.50029 070	0.97	0.53501 754	-0.02597 957	0.12171 971	0.58904 174
0.48	0.47159 965	-0.20872 379	0.39043 348	0.50215 713	0.98	0.53525 129	-0.02076 197	0.11582 346	0.59019 973
0.49	0.47367 548	-0.20643 147	0.38540 251	0.50403 850	0.99	0.53543 259	-0.01548 880	0.10991 587	0.59131 145
0.50	0.47572 809	-0.20408 167	0.38035 266	0.50593 371	1.00	0.53556 088	-0.01016 057	0.10399 739	0.59237 563

AIRY FUNCTIONS

Table 10.11

x	$\mathrm{Ai}(-x)$	$\mathrm{Ai}'(-x)$	$\mathrm{Bi}(-x)$	$\mathrm{Bi}'(-x)$	x	$\mathrm{Ai}(-x)$	$\mathrm{Ai}'(-x)$	$\mathrm{Bi}(-x)$	$\mathrm{Bi}'(-x)$
1.0	0.53556 088	-0.01016 057	+0.10399 739	0.59237 563	5.5	+0.01778 154	0.86419 722	-0.36781 345	+0.02511 158
1.1	0.53381 051	+0.04602 915	+0.04432 659	0.60011 970	5.6	-0.06833 070	0.85003 256	-0.36017 223	-0.17783 760
1.2	0.52619 437	0.10703 157	-0.01582 137	0.60171 016	5.7	-0.15062 016	0.78781 722	-0.33245 825	-0.37440 903
1.3	0.51227 201	0.17199 181	-0.07576 964	0.59592 975	5.8	-0.22435 192	0.67943 152	-0.28589 021	-0.55300 203
1.4	0.49170 018	0.23981 912	-0.13472 406	0.58165 624	5.9	-0.28512 278	0.52962 857	-0.22282 969	-0.70247 952
1.5	0.46425 658	0.30918 697	-0.19178 486	0.55790 810	6.0	-0.32914 517	0.34593 549	-0.14669 838	-0.81289 879
1.6	0.42986 298	0.37854 219	-0.24596 320	0.52389 354	6.1	-0.35351 168	+0.13836 394	-0.06182 255	-0.87622 530
1.7	0.38860 704	0.44612 455	-0.29620 266	0.47906 134	6.2	-0.35642 107	-0.08106 856	+0.02679 081	-0.88697 896
1.8	0.34076 156	0.50999 763	-0.34140 583	0.42315 137	6.3	-0.33734 765	-0.29899 161	0.11373 701	-0.84276 110
1.9	0.28680 006	0.56809 172	-0.38046 588	0.35624 251	6.4	-0.29713 762	-0.50147 985	0.19354 136	-0.74461 387
2.0	0.22740 743	0.61825 902	-0.41230 259	0.27879 517	6.5	-0.23802 030	-0.67495 249	0.26101 266	-0.59717 067
2.1	0.16348 451	0.65834 069	-0.43590 235	0.19168 563	6.6	-0.16352 646	-0.80711 925	0.31159 995	-0.40856 734
2.2	0.09614 538	0.68624 482	-0.45036 098	+0.09622 919	6.7	-0.07831 247	-0.88790 797	0.34172 774	-0.19009 878
2.3	+0.02670 633	0.70003 366	-0.45492 823	-0.00581 106	6.8	+0.01210 452	-0.91030 401	0.34908 418	+0.04437 678
2.4	-0.04333 414	0.69801 760	-0.44905 228	-0.11223 237	6.9	0.10168 800	-0.87103 106	0.33283 784	0.27926 391
2.5	-0.11232 507	0.67885 273	-0.43242 247	-0.22042 015	7.0	0.18428 084	-0.77100 817	0.29376 207	0.49824 459
2.6	-0.17850 243	0.64163 799	-0.40500 828	-0.32739 717	7.1	0.25403 633	-0.61552 879	0.23425 088	0.68542 058
2.7	-0.24003 811	0.58600 720	-0.36709 211	-0.42989 534	7.2	0.30585 152	-0.41412 428	0.15821 739	0.82650 634
2.8	-0.29509 759	0.51221 098	-0.31929 389	-0.52445 040	7.3	0.33577 037	-0.18009 580	+0.07087 411	0.90998 427
2.9	-0.34190 510	0.42118 281	-0.26258 500	-0.60751 829	7.4	0.34132 375	+0.07027 632	-0.02159 652	0.92812 809
3.0	-0.37881 429	0.31458 377	-0.19828 963	-0.67561 122	7.5	0.32177 572	0.31880 951	-0.11246 349	0.87780 228
3.1	-0.40438 222	0.19482 045	-0.12807 165	-0.72544 957	7.6	0.27825 023	0.54671 882	-0.19493 376	0.76095 509
3.2	-0.41744 342	+0.06503 115	-0.05390 576	-0.75412 455	7.7	0.21372 037	0.73605 242	-0.26267 007	0.58474 045
3.3	-0.41718 094	-0.07096 362	+0.02196 800	-0.75926 518	7.8	0.13285 154	0.87115 540	-0.31030 057	0.36122 930
3.4	-0.40319 048	-0.20874 905	0.09710 619	-0.73920 163	7.9	+0.04170 188	0.94004 300	-0.33387 856	+0.10670 215
3.5	-0.37553 382	-0.34344 343	0.16893 984	-0.69311 628	8.0	-0.05270 505	0.93556 094	-0.33125 158	-0.15945 050
3.6	-0.33477 748	-0.46986 397	0.23486 631	-0.62117 283	8.1	-0.14290 815	0.85621 859	-0.30230 331	-0.41615 664
3.7	-0.28201 306	-0.58272 780	0.29235 261	-0.52461 361	8.2	-0.22159 945	0.70659 870	-0.24904 019	-0.64232 293
3.8	-0.21885 598	-0.67688 257	0.33904 647	-0.40581 592	8.3	-0.28223 176	0.49727 679	-0.17550 556	-0.81860 044
3.9	-0.14741 991	-0.74755 809	0.37289 058	-0.26829 836	8.4	-0.31959 219	+0.24422 089	-0.08751 798	-0.92910 958
4.0	-0.07026 553	-0.79062 858	0.39223 471	-0.11667 057	8.5	-0.33029 024	-0.03231 335	+0.00775 444	-0.96296 917
4.1	+0.00967 698	-0.80287 254	0.39593 974	+0.04347 872	8.6	-0.31311 245	-0.30933 027	0.10235 647	-0.91547 918
4.2	0.08921 076	-0.78221 561	0.38346 736	0.20575 691	8.7	-0.26920 454	-0.56297 685	0.18820 363	-0.78882 623
4.3	0.16499 781	-0.72794 081	0.35494 906	0.36320 468	8.8	-0.20205 445	-0.77061 301	0.25778 240	-0.59221 371
4.4	0.23370 326	-0.64085 018	0.31122 860	0.50858 932	8.9	-0.11726 631	-0.91289 276	0.30483 241	-0.34136 475
4.5	0.29215 278	-0.52336 253	0.25387 266	0.63474 477	9.0	-0.02213 372	-0.97566 398	0.32494 732	-0.05740 051
4.6	0.33749 598	-0.37953 391	0.18514 576	0.73494 444	9.1	+0.07495 989	-0.95149 682	0.31603 471	+0.23484 379
4.7	0.36736 748	-0.21499 018	0.10794 695	0.80328 926	9.2	0.16526 800	-0.84067 107	0.27858 425	0.50894 402
4.8	0.38003 668	-0.03676 510	+0.02570 779	0.83508 976	9.3	0.24047 380	-0.65149 241	0.21570 835	0.73928 028
4.9	0.37453 635	+0.14695 743	-0.05774 655	0.82721 903	9.4	0.29347 756	-0.39986 237	0.13293 876	0.90348 537
5.0	0.35076 101	0.32719 282	-0.13836 913	0.77841 177	9.5	0.31910 325	-0.10809 532	+0.03778 543	0.98471 407
5.1	0.30952 600	0.49458 600	-0.21208 913	0.68948 513	9.6	0.31465 158	+0.19695 044	-0.06091 293	0.97349 918
5.2	0.25258 034	0.63990 517	-0.27502 704	0.56345 898	9.7	0.28023 750	0.48628 629	-0.15379 421	0.86898 388
5.3	0.18256 793	0.75457 542	-0.32371 608	0.40555 694	9.8	0.21886 743	0.73154 486	-0.23186 331	0.67936 774
5.4	0.10293 460	0.83122 307	-0.35531 708	0.22307 496	9.9	0.13623 503	0.90781 333	-0.28738 356	0.42147 209
5.5	0.01778 154	0.86419 722	-0.36781 345	0.02511 158	10.0	0.04024 124	0.99626 504	-0.31467 983	0.11941 411

Table 10.12 INTEGRALS OF AIRY FUNCTIONS

x	$\int_0^x \mathrm{Ai}(t)\,dt$	$\int_0^x \mathrm{Ai}(-t)\,dt$	$\int_0^x \mathrm{Bi}(t)\,dt$	$\int_0^x \mathrm{Bi}(-t)\,dt$	x	$\int_0^x \mathrm{Ai}(t)\,dt$	$\int_0^x \mathrm{Ai}(-t)\,dt$	$\int_0^x \mathrm{Bi}(-t)\,dt$
0.0	0.00000 00	0.00000 00	0.00000 00	0.00000 00	5.0	0.33328 76	0.71788 22	0.15873 09
0.1	0.03421 01	0.03679 54	0.06373 67	0.05924 87	5.1	0.33329 73	0.75103 62	0.14113 39
0.2	0.06585 15	0.07615 70	0.13199 45	0.11398 10	5.2	0.33330 50	0.77926 27	0.11667 30
0.3	0.09497 09	0.11802 51	0.20487 68	0.16411 57	5.3	0.33331 11	0.80111 58	0.08660 41
0.4	0.12164 06	0.16229 44	0.28256 70	0.20952 89	5.4	0.33331 59	0.81545 49	0.05250 03
0.5	0.14595 33	0.20880 95	0.36533 85	0.25006 28	5.5	0.33331 97	0.82151 82	+0.01617 86
0.6	0.16801 79	0.25736 07	0.45356 50	0.28553 62	5.6	0.33332 27	0.81897 90	-0.02038 99
0.7	0.18795 52	0.30768 05	0.54773 36	0.31575 56	5.7	0.33332 50	0.80797 96	-0.05518 54
0.8	0.20589 45	0.35944 15	0.64845 82	0.34052 58	5.8	0.33332 69	0.78914 06	-0.08625 18
0.9	0.22196 97	0.41225 56	0.75649 64	0.35966 27	5.9	0.33332 83	0.76354 19	-0.11181 25
1.0	0.23631 73	0.46567 40	0.87276 91	0.37300 50	6.0	0.33332 95	0.73267 53	-0.13038 11
1.1	0.24907 33	0.51918 94	0.99838 41	0.38042 77	6.1	0.33333 03	0.69836 93	-0.14086 00
1.2	0.26037 12	0.57224 05	1.13466 38	0.38185 43	6.2	0.33333 10	0.66268 96	-0.14262 05
1.3	0.27034 09	0.62421 79	1.28318 00	0.37726 99	6.3	0.33333 16	0.62781 93	-0.13555 73
1.4	0.27910 66	0.67447 31	1.44579 42	0.36673 34	6.4	0.33333 20	0.59592 62	-0.12011 15
1.5	0.28678 67	0.72232 88	1.62470 81	0.35038 81	6.5	0.33333 23	0.56902 35	-0.09726 08
1.6	0.29349 24	0.76709 26	1.82252 33	0.32847 24	6.6	0.33333 25	0.54883 59	-0.06847 29
1.7	0.29932 75	0.80807 24	2.04231 52	0.30132 67	6.7	0.33333 27	0.53667 65	-0.03562 42
1.8	0.30438 82	0.84459 41	2.28772 12	0.26939 97	6.8	0.33333 29	0.53334 74	-0.00088 80
1.9	0.30876 29	0.87602 06	2.56304 90	0.23325 04	6.9	0.33333 30	0.53906 98	+0.03340 40
2.0	0.31253 28	0.90177 28	2.87340 83	0.19354 74	7.0	0.33333 31	0.55345 17	0.06491 67
2.1	0.31577 11	0.92135 09	.	0.15106 46	7.1	0.33333 31	0.57549 72	0.09147 36
2.2	0.31854 43	0.93435 56	.	0.10667 18	7.2	0.33333 32	0.60365 96	0.11121 47
2.3	0.32091 19	0.94050 97	.	0.06132 23	7.3	0.33333 32	0.63593 60	0.12273 90
2.4	0.32292 74	0.93967 67	.	+0.01603 45	7.4	0.33333 33	0.66999 96	0.12521 80
2.5	0.32463 80	0.93187 78	.	-0.02812 94	7.5	0.33333 33	0.70336 19	0.11847 31
2.6	0.32608 57	0.91730 54	.	-0.07009 01	7.6	.	0.73355 34	0.10300 57
2.7	0.32730 74	0.89633 20	.	-0.10878 06	7.7	.	0.75830 99	0.07997 85
2.8	0.32833 55	0.86951 37	.	-0.14317 88	7.8	.	0.77575 13	0.05114 35
2.9	0.32919 83	0.83758 77	.	-0.17234 20	7.9	.	0.78453 65	+0.01872 22
3.0	0.32992 04	0.80146 29	.	-0.19544 25	8.0	.	0.78398 26	-0.01475 64
3.1	0.33052 31	0.76220 32	.	-0.21180 21	8.1	.	0.77413 57	-0.04664 84
3.2	0.33102 49	0.72100 37	.	-0.22092 49	8.2	.	0.75578 55	-0.07440 43
3.3	0.33144 15	0.67915 91	.	-0.22252 61	8.3	.	0.73041 93	-0.09577 87
3.4	0.33178 65	0.63802 56	.	-0.21655 57	8.4	.	0.70011 70	-0.10902 22
3.5	0.33207 15	0.59897 71	.	-0.20321 50	8.5	.	0.66739 21	-0.11303 86
3.6	0.33230 63	0.56335 61	.	-0.18296 47	8.6	.	0.63499 08	-0.10749 35
3.7	0.33249 93	0.53242 25	.	-0.15652 33	8.7	.	0.60566 32	-0.09285 98
3.8	0.33265 76	0.50730 05	.	-0.12485 43	8.8	.	0.58192 70	-0.07039 64
3.9	0.33278 70	0.48892 77	.	-0.08914 28	8.9	.	0.56584 22	-0.04205 63
4.0	0.33289 27	0.47800 75	.	-0.05076 01	9.0	.	0.55881 97	-0.01033 04
4.1	0.33297 86	0.47496 79	.	-0.01121 78	9.1	.	0.56148 12	+0.02196 26
4.2	0.33304 84	0.47992 95	.	+0.02788 79	9.2	.	0.57358 51	0.05192 24
4.3	0.33310 50	0.49268 51	.	0.06494 00	9.3	.	0.59403 00	0.07682 93
4.4	0.33315 07	0.51269 28	.	0.09837 02	9.4	.	0.62093 76	0.09439 87
4.5	0.33318 76	0.53908 35	.	0.12673 04	9.5	.	0.65181 01	0.10300 27
4.6	0.33321 73	0.57068 59	.	0.14876 50	9.6	.	0.68375 25	0.10183 70
4.7	0.33324 11	0.60606 63	.	0.16347 66	9.7	.	0.71373 85	0.09101 44
4.8	0.33326 02	0.64358 51	.	0.17018 59	9.8	.	0.73889 84	0.07157 33
4.9	0.33327 54	0.68146 70	.	0.16857 74	9.9	.	0.75680 07	0.04539 57
5.0	0.33328 76	0.71788 22	.	0.15873 09	10.0	.	0.76569 84	0.01504 04

Table 10.13 ZEROS AND ASSOCIATED VALUES OF AIRY FUNCTIONS AND THEIR DERIVATIVES

s	a_s	$\mathrm{Ai}'(a_s)$	a'_s	$\mathrm{Ai}(a'_s)$	b_s	$\mathrm{Bi}'(b_s)$	b'_s	$\mathrm{Bi}(b'_s)$
1	- 2.33810 741	+0.70121 082	- 1.01879 297	+0.53565 666	- 1.17371 322	+0.60195 789	- 2.29443 968	-0.45494 438
2	- 4.08794 944	-0.80311 137	- 3.24819 758	-0.41901 548	- 3.27109 330	-0.76031 014	- 4.07315 509	+0.39652 284
3	- 5.52055 983	+0.86520 403	- 4.82009 921	+0.38040 647	- 4.83073 784	+0.83699 101	- 5.51239 573	-0.36796 916
4	- 6.78670 809	-0.91085 074	- 6.16330 736	-0.35790 794	- 6.16985 213	-0.88947 990	- 6.78129 445	+0.34949 912
5	- 7.94413 359	+0.94733 571	- 7.37217 726	+0.34230 124	- 7.37676 208	+0.92998 364	- 7.94017 869	-0.33602 624
6	- 9.02265 085	-0.97792 281	- 8.48848 673	-0.33047 623	- 8.49194 885	-0.96323 443	- 9.01958 336	+0.32550 974
7	-10.04017 434	+1.00437 012	- 9.53544 905	+0.32102 229	- 9.53819 438	+0.99158 637	-10.03769 633	-0.31693 465
8	-11.00852 430	-1.02773 869	-10.52766 040	-0.31318 539	-10.52991 351	-1.01638 966	-11.00646 267	+0.30972 594
9	-11.93601 556	+1.04872 065	-11.47505 663	+0.30651 729	-11.47695 355	+1.03849 429	-11.93426 165	-0.30352 766
10	-12.82877 675	-1.06779 386	-12.38478 837	-0.30073 083	-12.38641 714	-1.05847 184	-12.82725 831	+0.29810 491

AUXILIARY TABLE—COMPLEX ZEROS AND ASSOCIATED VALUES OF $\mathrm{Bi}(z)$ AND $\mathrm{Bi}'(z)$

	$e^{-\pi i/3}\beta_s$		$\mathrm{Bi}'(\beta_s)$		$e^{-\pi i/3}\beta'_s$		$\mathrm{Bi}(\beta'_s)$	
s	Modulus	Phase	Modulus	Phase	Modulus	Phase	Modulus	Phase
1	2.354	0.095	0.993	+2.641	1.121	0.331	0.750	+0.466
2	4.093	0.042	1.136	-0.513	3.257	0.059	0.592	-2.632
3	5.524	0.027	1.224	+2.625	4.824	0.033	0.538	+0.515
4	6.789	0.020	1.288	-0.519	6.166	0.023	0.506	-2.624
5	7.946	0.015	1.340	+2.622	7.374	0.017	0.484	+0.519

From J. C. P. Miller, The Airy integral, British Assoc. Adv. Sci. Mathematical Tables Part–vol. B. Cambridge Univ. Press, Cambridge, England, 1946 and F. W. J. Olver, The asymptotic expansion of Bessel functions of large order. Philos. Trans. Roy. Soc. London [A] **247**, 328–368, 1954

11.1. Simple Integrals of Bessel Functions

$$\int_0^z t^\mu J_\nu(t)dt$$

11.1.1

$$\int_0^z t^\mu J_\nu(t)dt=\frac{z^\mu\Gamma\left(\frac{\nu+\mu+1}{2}\right)}{\Gamma\left(\frac{\nu-\mu+1}{2}\right)}$$

$$\times\sum_{k=0}^\infty\frac{(\nu+2k+1)\Gamma\left(\frac{\nu-\mu+1}{2}+k\right)}{\Gamma\left(\frac{\nu+\mu+3}{2}+k\right)}J_{\nu+2k+1}(z)$$

$$(\mathscr{R}(\mu+\nu+1)>0)$$

11.1.2

$$\int_0^z J_\nu(t)dt=2\sum_{k=0}^\infty J_{\nu+2k+1}(z)\,(\mathscr{R}\nu>-1)$$

11.1.3 $$\int_0^z J_{2n}(t)dt=\int_0^z J_0(t)dt-2\sum_{k=0}^{n-1}J_{2k+1}(z)$$

11.1.4 $$\int_0^z J_{2n+1}(t)dt=1-J_0(z)-2\sum_{k=1}^{n}J_{2k}(z)$$

Recurrence Relations

11.1.5

$$\int_0^z J_{n+1}(t)dt=\int_0^z J_{n-1}(t)dt-2J_n(z)\qquad(n>0)$$

11.1.6 $$\int_0^z J_1(t)dt=1-J_0(z)$$

$$\int J_0(t)dt,\int Y_0(t)dt,\int I_0(t)dt,\int K_0(t)dt$$

11.1.7

$$\int_0^x \mathscr{C}_0(t)dt=x\mathscr{C}_0(x)+\frac{1}{2}\pi x\{\mathbf{H}_0(x)\mathscr{C}_1(x)-\mathbf{H}_1(x)\mathscr{C}_0(x)\}$$

$$\mathscr{C}_\nu(x)=AJ_\nu(x)+BY_\nu(x),\nu=0,1$$

A and B are constants.

11.1.8

$$\int_0^x Z_0(t)dt=xZ_0(x)+\frac{1}{2}\pi x\{-\mathbf{L}_0(x)Z_1(x)+\mathbf{L}_1(x)Z_0(x)\}$$

$$Z_\nu(x)=AI_\nu(x)+Be^{i\nu\pi}K_\nu(x),\nu=0,1$$

A and B are constants.

$\mathbf{H}_\nu(x)$ and $\mathbf{L}_\nu(x)$ are Struve functions (see chapter **12**).

11.1.9

$$\int_0^x K_0(t)dt=-\left(\gamma+\ln\frac{x}{2}\right)x\sum_{k=0}^\infty\frac{(x/2)^{2k}}{(k!)^2(2k+1)}$$

$$+x\sum_{k=0}^\infty\frac{(x/2)^{2k}}{(k!)^2(2k+1)^2}$$

$$+x\sum_{k=1}^\infty\frac{(x/2)^{2k}}{(k!)^2(2k+1)}\left(1+\frac{1}{2}+\ldots+\frac{1}{k}\right)$$

γ (Euler's constant) $=.57721\ 56649\ldots$

In this and all other integrals of **11.1**, x is real and positive although all the results remain valid for extended portions of the complex plane unless stated to the contrary.

11.1.10

$$\int_0^{-ix}K_0(t)dt=\frac{\pi}{2}\int_0^x J_0(t)dt+i\frac{\pi}{2}\int_0^x Y_0(t)dt$$

Asymptotic Expansions

11.1.11

$$\int_x^\infty[J_0(t)+iY_0(t)]dt\sim\left(\frac{2}{\pi x}\right)^{\frac{1}{2}}e^{i(x-\pi/4)}$$

$$\times\left[\sum_{k=0}^\infty(-)^k a_{2k+1}x^{-2k-1}+i\sum_{k=0}^\infty(-)^k a_{2k}x^{-2k}\right]$$

11.1.12 $$a_k=\frac{\Gamma(k+\frac{1}{2})}{\Gamma(\frac{1}{2})}\sum_{s=0}^k\frac{\Gamma(s+\frac{1}{2})}{2^s s!\Gamma(\frac{1}{2})}$$

11.1.13

$$2(k+1)a_{k+1}=3\left(k+\frac{1}{2}\right)\left(k+\frac{5}{6}\right)a_k$$

$$-\left(k+\frac{1}{2}\right)^2\left(k-\frac{1}{2}\right)a_{k-1}$$

11.1.14 $x^{\frac{1}{2}}e^{-x}\int_0^x I_0(t)dt\sim(2\pi)^{-\frac{1}{2}}\sum_{k=0}^{\infty}a_kx^{-k}$

where the a_k are defined as in **11.1.12.**

11.1.15 $x^{\frac{1}{2}}e^{x}\int_x^\infty K_0(t)dt\sim\left(\frac{\pi}{2}\right)^{\frac{1}{2}}\sum_{k=0}^{\infty}(-)^ka_kx^{-k}$

where the a_k are defined as in **11.1.12.**

Polynomial Approximations [2]

11.1.16 $8\leq x\leq\infty$

$$\int_x^\infty [J_0(t)+iY_0(t)]dt$$
$$=x^{-\frac{1}{2}}e^{i(x-\pi/4)}\left[\sum_{k=0}^{7}(-)^ka_k(x/8)^{-2k-1}+i\sum_{k=0}^{7}(-)^kb_k(x/8)^{-2k}+\epsilon(x)\right]$$

$$|\epsilon(x)|\leq 2\times10^{-9}$$

k	a_k	b_k
0	.06233 47304	.79788 45600
1	.00404 03539	.01256 42405
2	.00100 89872	.00178 70944
3	.00053 66169	.00067 40148
4	.00039 92825	.00041 00676
5	.00027 55037	.00025 43955
6	.00012 70039	.00011 07299
7	.00002 68482	.00002 26238

11.1.17 $8\leq x\leq\infty$

$$x^{\frac{1}{2}}e^{-x}\int_0^x I_0(t)\,dt=\sum_{k=0}^{6}d_k(x/8)^{-k}+\epsilon(x)$$

$$|\epsilon(x)|\leq 2\times10^{-6}$$

k	d_k
0	.39894 23
1	.03117 34
2	.00591 91
3	.00559 56
4	−.01148 58
5	.01774 40
6	−.00739 95

[2] Approximation **11.1.16** is from A. J. M. Hitchcock. Polynomial approximations to Bessel functions of order zero and one and to related functions, Math. Tables Aids Comp. **11**, 86–88 (1957)

11.1.18 $7\leq x\leq\infty$

$$x^{\frac{1}{2}}e^{x}\int_x^\infty K_0(t)dt=\sum_{k=0}^{6}(-)^ke_k(x/7)^{-k}+\epsilon(x)$$

$$|\epsilon(x)|\leq 2\times10^{-7}$$

k	e_k
0	1.25331 414
1	0.11190 289
2	.02576 646
3	.00933 994
4	.00417 454
5	.00163 271
6	.00033 934

$\int\frac{J_0(t)dt}{t}$, $\int\frac{Y_0(t)dt}{t}$, $\int\frac{K_0(t)dt}{t}$

11.1.19

$$\int_0^x\frac{1-J_0(t)}{t}\,dt$$
$$=2x^{-1}\sum_{k=0}^{\infty}(2k+3)[\psi(k+2)-\psi(1)]\,J_{2k+3}(x)$$
$$=1-2x^{-1}J_1(x)$$
$$+2x^{-1}\sum_{k=0}^{\infty}(2k+5)[\psi(k+3)-\psi(1)-1]J_{2k+5}(x)$$

For $\psi(z)$, see **6.3.**

11.1.20

$$\int_x^\infty\frac{J_0(t)dt}{t}+\gamma+\ln\frac{x}{2}=\int_0^x\frac{[1-J_0(t)]dt}{t}$$
$$=-\sum_{k=1}^{\infty}\frac{(-)^k\left(\frac{x}{2}\right)^{2k}}{2k(k!)^2}$$

11.1.21

$$\int_x^\infty\frac{Y_0(t)dt}{t}=-\frac{1}{\pi}\left(\ln\frac{x}{2}\right)^2-\frac{2\gamma}{\pi}\left(\ln\frac{x}{2}\right)+\frac{1}{\pi}\left(\frac{\pi^2}{6}-\gamma^2\right)$$
$$+\frac{2}{\pi}\sum_{k=1}^{\infty}\frac{(-)^k\left(\frac{x}{2}\right)^{2k}}{2k(k!)^2}\left\{\psi(k+1)+\frac{1}{2k}-\ln\frac{x}{2}\right\}$$

11.1.22

$$\int_x^\infty\frac{K_0(t)dt}{t}=\frac{1}{2}\left(\ln\frac{x}{2}\right)^2+\gamma\ln\frac{x}{2}+\frac{\pi^2}{24}+\frac{\gamma^2}{2}$$
$$-\sum_{k=1}^{\infty}\frac{\left(\frac{x}{2}\right)^{2k}}{2k(k!)^2}\left\{\psi(k+1)+\frac{1}{2k}-\ln\frac{x}{2}\right\}$$

11.1.23

$$\int_{-ix}^{-i\infty}\frac{K_0(t)dt}{t}=\frac{i\pi}{2}\int_x^\infty\frac{J_0(t)dt}{t}-\frac{\pi}{2}\int_x^\infty\frac{Y_0(t)dt}{t}$$

Asymptotic Expansions

11.1.24 $$\int_x^\infty \frac{\mathscr{C}_0(t)dt}{t}=\frac{2g_1(x)\mathscr{C}_0(x)}{x^2}-\frac{g_0(x)\mathscr{C}_1(x)}{x}$$

where

$$g_0(x)\sim\sum_{k=0}^\infty(-)^k\left(\frac{x}{2}\right)^{-2k}(k!)^2,$$

$$g_1(x)\sim\sum_{k=0}^\infty(-)^k\left(\frac{x}{2}\right)^{-2k}k!(k+1)!$$

11.1.25 $$g_0(x)=2x^2\int_x^\infty \frac{g_1(t)dt}{t^3}$$

11.1.26 $$x^{3/2}e^x\int_x^\infty \frac{K_0(t)dt}{t}\sim\left(\frac{\pi}{2}\right)^{\frac{1}{2}}\sum_{k=0}^\infty(-)^kc_kx^{-k}$$

where

11.1.27 $$c_0=1,\, c_1=\frac{13}{8}$$

$$2(k+1)c_{k+1}=\left[3(k+1)^2+\frac{1}{4}\right]c_k-\left(k+\frac{1}{2}\right)^3c_{k-1}$$

11.1.28 $$x^{3/2}e^{-x}\int_0^x \frac{[I_0(t)-1]dt}{t}\sim(2\pi)^{-\frac{1}{2}}\sum_{k=0}^\infty c_kx^{-k}$$

where c_k is defined as in **11.1.27.**

Polynomial Approximations

11.1.29 $$5\leq x\leq\infty$$

$$\int_x^\infty \frac{\mathscr{C}_0(t)dt}{t}=\frac{2g_1(x)\mathscr{C}_0(x)}{x^2}-\frac{g_0(x)\mathscr{C}_1(x)}{x}$$

where

$$g_0(x)=\sum_{k=0}^9 (-)^ka_k(x/5)^{-2k}+\epsilon(x),$$

$$g_1(x)=\sum_{k=0}^9 (-)^kb_k(x/5)^{-2k}+\epsilon(x)$$

$$|\epsilon(x)|\leq2\times10^{-7}$$

k	a_k	b_k
0	1. 0	1. 0
1	0. 15999 2815	0. 31998 5629
2	. 10161 9385	. 30485 8155
3	. 13081 1585	. 52324 6341
4	. 20740 4022	1. 03702 0112
5	. 28330 0508	1. 69980 3050
6	. 27902 9488	1. 95320 6413
7	. 17891 5710	1. 43132 5684
8	. 06622 8328	0. 59605 4956
9	. 01070 2234	. 10702 2336

11.1.30 $$4\leq x\leq\infty$$

$$x^{\frac{3}{2}}e^x\int_x^\infty \frac{K_0(t)dt}{t}=\sum_{k=0}^6(-)^kd_k\left(\frac{x}{4}\right)^{-k}+\epsilon(x)$$

$$|\epsilon(x)|\leq6\times10^{-6}$$

k	d_k
0	1. 25331 41
1	0. 50913 39
2	. 32191 84
3	. 26214 46
4	. 20601 26
5	. 11103 96
6	. 02724 00

11.1.31 $$5\leq x\leq\infty$$

$$x^{\frac{3}{2}}e^{-x}\int_0^x\frac{[I_0(t)-1]dt}{t}=\sum_{k=0}^{10}f_k\left(\frac{x}{5}\right)^{-k}+\epsilon(x)$$

$$|\epsilon(x)|\leq1.1\times10^{-5}$$

k	f_k
0	0. 39893 14
1	. 13320 55
2	—. 04938 43
3	1. 47800 44
4	—8. 65560 13
5	28. 12214 78
6	—48. 05241 15
7	40. 39473 40
8	—11. 90943 95
9	—3. 51950 09
10	2. 19454 64

11.2. Repeated Integrals of $J_n(z)$ and $K_0(z)$

Repeated Integrals of $J_n(z)$

Let

11.2.1

$$f_{0,n}(z)=J_n(z),$$

$$f_{1,n}(z)=\int_0^z J_n(t)dt,\ \ldots,\ f_{r,n}(z)=\int_0^z f_{r-1,n}(t)dt$$

11.2.2 $$f_{-r,n}(z)=\frac{d^r}{dz^r}J_n(z)$$

Then

11.2.3

$$f_{r,n}(z)=\frac{1}{\Gamma(r)}\int_0^z(z-t)^{r-1}J_n(t)dt\quad(\mathscr{R}r>0)$$

11.2.4 $$f_{r,n}(z)=\frac{2^r}{\Gamma(r)}\sum_{k=0}^\infty\frac{\Gamma(k+r)}{k!}J_{n+r+2k}(z)$$

Recurrence Relations

11.2.5

$$r(r-1)f_{r+1,n}(z)=2(r-1)zf_{r,n}(z)-[(1-r)^2-n^2+z^2]f_{r-1,n}(z)+(2r-3)zf_{r-2,n}(z)-z^2f_{r-3,n}(z)$$

11.2.6

$$rf_{r+1,0}(z)=zf_{r,0}(z)-(r-1)f_{r-1,0}(z)+zf_{r-2,0}(z)$$

11.2.7 $$f_{r+1,n+1}(z)=f_{r+1,n-1}(z)-2f_{r,n}(z)$$

Repeated Integrals of $K_0(z)$

Let

11.2.8

$$\mathrm{Ki}_0(z)=K_0(z),$$

$$\mathrm{Ki}_1(z)=\int_z^\infty K_0(t)dt,\ \ldots,\ \mathrm{Ki}_r(z)=\int_z^\infty \mathrm{Ki}_{r-1}(t)dt$$

11.2.9 $$\mathrm{Ki}_{-r}(z)=(-)^r\frac{d^r}{dz^r}K_0(z)$$

Then

11.2.10

$$\mathrm{Ki}_r(z)=\int_0^\infty \frac{e^{-z\cosh t}\,dt}{\cosh^r t}$$

$$(\mathscr{R}z\geq 0,\ \mathscr{R}r>0,\ \mathscr{R}z>0,\ r=0)$$

11.2.11

$$\mathrm{Ki}_r(z)=\frac{1}{\Gamma(r)}\int_z^\infty (t-z)^{r-1}K_0(t)dt$$

$$(\mathscr{R}z\geq 0,\ \mathscr{R}r>0)$$

11.2.12 $$\mathrm{Ki}_{2r}(0)=\frac{\Gamma(r)\Gamma(\frac{3}{2})}{\Gamma(r+\frac{1}{2})}\qquad(\mathscr{R}r>0)$$

11.2.13 $$\mathrm{Ki}_{2r+1}(0)=\frac{\frac{\pi}{2}\Gamma(r+\frac{1}{2})}{\Gamma(\frac{1}{2})\Gamma(r+1)}\qquad\left(\mathscr{R}r>-\frac{1}{2}\right)$$

11.2.14

$$r\mathrm{Ki}_{r+1}(z)=-z\mathrm{Ki}_r(z)+(r-1)\mathrm{Ki}_{r-1}(z)+z\mathrm{Ki}_{r-2}(z)$$

11.3. Reduction Formulas for Indefinite Integrals

Let

11.3.1 $$g_{\mu,\nu}(z)=\int^z e^{-pt}t^\mu Z_\nu(t)dt$$

where $Z_\nu(z)$ represents any of the Bessel functions of the first three kinds or the modified Bessel functions. The parameters a and b appearing in the reduction formulae are associated with the particular type of Bessel function as delineated in the following table.

11.3.2

$Z_\nu(z)$	a	b
$J_\nu(z),\ Y_\nu(z),\ H_\nu^{(1)}(z),\ H_\nu^{(2)}(z)$	1	1
$I_\nu(z)$	-1	1
$K_\nu(z)$	1	-1

11.3.3

$$pg_{\mu,\nu}(z)=-e^{-pz}z^\mu Z_\nu(z)+(\mu+\nu)g_{\mu-1,\nu}(z)-ag_{\mu,\nu+1}(z)$$

11.3.4

$$pg_{\mu,\nu+1}(z)=-e^{-pz}z^\mu Z_{\nu+1}(z)+(\mu-\nu-1)g_{\mu-1,\nu+1}(z)+bg_{\mu,\nu}(z)$$

11.3.5

$$(p^2+ab)g_{\mu,\nu}(z)=ae^{-pz}z^\mu Z_{\nu+1}(z)+(\mu-\nu-1)e^{-pz}z^{\mu-1}Z_\nu(z)-pe^{-pz}z^\mu Z_\nu(z)+p(2\mu-1)g_{\mu-1,\nu}(z)+[\nu^2-(\mu-1)^2]g_{\mu-2,\nu}(z)$$

11.3.6

$$a(\nu-\mu)g_{\mu,\nu+1}(z)=-2\nu e^{-pz}z^\mu Z_\nu(z)-2\nu pg_{\mu,\nu}(z)+b(\mu+\nu)g_{\mu,\nu-1}(z)$$

Case 1: $p^2+ab=0,\ \nu=\pm(\mu-1)$

11.3.7 $$g_{\nu,\nu}(z)=\frac{e^{-pz}z^{\nu+1}}{2\nu+1}\left\{Z_\nu(z)-\frac{a}{p}Z_{\nu+1}(z)\right\}$$

11.3.8 $$g_{-\nu,\nu}(z)=-\frac{e^{-pz}z^{-\nu+1}}{2\nu-1}\left\{Z_\nu(z)+\frac{b}{p}Z_{\nu-1}(z)\right\}$$

11.3.9

$$\int_0^z e^{it}t^\nu J_\nu(t)dt=\frac{e^{iz}z^{\nu+1}}{2\nu+1}[J_\nu(z)-iJ_{\nu+1}(z)]\qquad(\mathscr{R}\nu>-\tfrac{1}{2})$$

11.3.10

$$\int_0^z e^{it}t^{-\nu}J_\nu(t)dt=-\frac{e^{iz}z^{-\nu+1}}{2\nu-1}[J_\nu(z)+iJ_{\nu-1}(z)]+\frac{i}{2^{\nu-1}(2\nu-1)\Gamma(\nu)}\qquad(\nu\neq\tfrac{1}{2})$$

11.3.11

$$\int_0^z e^{it}t^\nu Y_\nu(t)dt=\frac{e^{iz}z^{\nu+1}}{2\nu+1}[Y_\nu(z)-iY_{\nu+1}(z)]-\frac{i2^{\nu+1}\Gamma(\nu+1)}{\pi(2\nu+1)}\qquad(\mathscr{R}\nu>-\tfrac{1}{2})$$

11.3.12

$$\int_0^z e^{\pm t}t^\nu I_\nu(t)dt=\frac{e^{\pm z}z^{\nu+1}}{2\nu+1}[I_\nu(z)\mp I_{\nu+1}(z)]\qquad(\mathscr{R}\nu>-\tfrac{1}{2})$$

11.3.13

$$\int_0^z e^{-t}I_n(t)dt=ze^{-z}[I_0(z)+I_1(z)]+n[e^{-z}I_0(z)-1]+2e^{-z}\sum_{k=1}^{n-1}(n-k)I_k(z)$$

11.3.14

$$\int_0^z e^{\pm t}t^{-\nu}I_\nu(t)dt=-\frac{e^{\pm z}z^{-\nu+1}}{2\nu-1}[I_\nu(z)\mp I_{\nu-1}(z)]\mp\frac{1}{2^{\nu-1}(2\nu-1)\Gamma(\nu)}\qquad (\nu\neq\tfrac{1}{2})$$

11.3.15

$$\int_0^z e^{\pm t}t^\nu K_\nu(t)dt=\frac{e^{\pm z}z^{\nu+1}}{2\nu+1}[K_\nu(z)\pm K_{\nu+1}(z)]\mp\frac{2^\nu\Gamma(\nu+1)}{2\nu+1}\qquad (\mathscr{R}\nu>-\tfrac{1}{2})$$

King's integral (see [11.5])

11.3.16 $$\int_0^z e^tK_0(t)dt=ze^z[K_0(z)+K_1(z)]-1$$

11.3.17

$$\int_z^\infty e^tt^{-\nu}K_\nu(t)dt=\frac{e^zz^{-\nu+1}}{2\nu-1}[K_\nu(z)+K_{\nu-1}(z)]\qquad (\mathscr{R}\nu>\tfrac{1}{2})$$

Case 2: $p=0,\ \mu=\pm\nu$

11.3.18 $$bg_{\nu,\nu-1}(z)=z^\nu Z_\nu(z)$$

11.3.19 $$ag_{-\nu,\nu+1}(z)=-z^{-\nu}Z_\nu(z)$$

11.3.20 $$\int_0^z t^\nu J_{\nu-1}(t)dt=z^\nu J_\nu(z)\qquad (\mathscr{R}\nu>0)$$

11.3.21 $$\int_0^z t^{-\nu}J_{\nu+1}(t)dt=\frac{1}{2^\nu\Gamma(\nu+1)}-z^{-\nu}J_\nu(z)$$

11.3.22

$$2n\int_0^z\frac{J_{2n}(t)dt}{t}=1-\frac{2}{z}\sum_{k=1}^n(2k-1)J_{2k-1}(z)=\frac{2}{z}\sum_{k=n+1}^\infty(2k-1)J_{2k-1}(z)\qquad (n>0)$$

11.3.23

$$(2n+1)\int_0^z\frac{J_{2n+1}(t)dt}{t}=\int_0^z J_0(t)dt-J_1(z)-\frac{4}{z}\sum_{k=1}^n kJ_{2k}(z)$$

11.3.24

$$\int_0^z t^\nu Y_{\nu-1}(t)dt=z^\nu Y_\nu(z)+\frac{2^\nu\Gamma(\nu)}{\pi}\qquad (\mathscr{R}\nu>0)$$

11.3.25 $$\int_0^z t^\nu I_{\nu-1}(t)dt=z^\nu I_\nu(z)\qquad (\mathscr{R}\nu>0)$$

11.3.26 $$\int_0^z t^{-\nu}I_{\nu+1}(t)dt=z^{-\nu}I_\nu(z)-\frac{1}{2^\nu\Gamma(\nu+1)}$$

11.3.27

$$\int_0^z t^\nu K_{\nu-1}(t)dt=-z^\nu K_\nu(z)+2^{\nu-1}\Gamma(\nu)\qquad (\mathscr{R}\nu>0)$$

11.3.28 $$\int_z^\infty t^{-\nu}K_{\nu+1}(t)dt=z^{-\nu}K_\nu(z)$$

Indefinite Integrals of Products of Bessel Functions

Let $\mathscr{C}_\mu(z)$ and $\mathscr{D}_\nu(z)$ denote any two cylinder functions of orders μ and ν respectively.

11.3.29

$$\int^z\left\{(k^2-l^2)t-\frac{(\mu^2-\nu^2)}{t}\right\}\mathscr{C}_\mu(kt)\mathscr{D}_\nu(lt)dt=z\{k\mathscr{C}_{\mu+1}(kz)\mathscr{D}_\nu(lz)-l\mathscr{C}_\mu(kz)\mathscr{D}_{\nu+1}(lz)\}-(\mu-\nu)\mathscr{C}_\mu(kz)\mathscr{D}_\nu(lz)$$

11.3.30

$$\int^z t^{-\mu-\nu-1}\mathscr{C}_{\mu+1}(t)\mathscr{D}_{\nu+1}(t)dt=-\frac{z^{-\mu-\nu}}{2(\mu+\nu+1)}\{\mathscr{C}_\mu(z)\mathscr{D}_\nu(z)+\mathscr{C}_{\mu+1}(z)\mathscr{D}_{\nu+1}(z)\}$$

11.3.31

$$\int^z t^{\mu+\nu+1}\mathscr{C}_\mu(t)\mathscr{D}_\nu(t)dt=\frac{z^{\mu+\nu+2}}{2(\mu+\nu+1)}\{\mathscr{C}_\mu(z)\mathscr{D}_\nu(z)+\mathscr{C}_{\mu+1}(z)\mathscr{D}_{\nu+1}(z)\}$$

11.3.32

$$\int_0^z tJ_{\nu-1}^2(t)dt=2\sum_{k=0}^\infty(\nu+2k)J_{\nu+2k}^2(z)\qquad (\mathscr{R}\nu>0)$$

11.3.33

$$\int_0^z t[J_{\nu-1}^2(t)-J_{\nu+1}^2(t)]dt=2\nu J_\nu^2(z)\qquad (\mathscr{R}\nu>0)$$

11.3.34 $$\int_0^z tJ_0^2(t)dt=\frac{z^2}{2}[J_0^2(z)+J_1^2(z)]$$

11.3.35

$$\int_0^z J_n(t)J_{n+1}(t)dt=\frac{1}{2}[1-J_0^2(z)]-\sum_{k=1}^n J_k^2(z)=\sum_{k=n+1}^\infty J_k^2(z)$$

11.3.36

$$(\mu+\nu)\int^z t^{-1}\mathscr{C}_\mu(t)\mathscr{D}_\nu(t)dt-(\mu+\nu+2n)\int^z t^{-1}\mathscr{C}_{\mu+n}(t)\mathscr{D}_{\nu+n}(t)dt$$
$$=\mathscr{C}_\mu(z)\mathscr{D}_\nu(z)+\mathscr{C}_{\mu+n}(z)\mathscr{D}_{\nu+n}(z)+2\sum_{k=1}^{n-1}\mathscr{C}_{\mu+k}(z)\mathscr{D}_{\nu+k}(z)$$

Convolution Type Integrals

11.3.37

$$\int_0^z J_\mu(t)J_\nu(z-t)dt=2\sum_{k=0}^\infty(-)^k J_{\mu+\nu+2k+1}(z)\qquad(\mathscr{R}\mu>-1,\mathscr{R}\nu>-1)$$

11.3.38

$$\int_0^z J_\nu(t)J_{1-\nu}(z-t)dt=J_0(z)-\cos z\qquad(-1<\mathscr{R}\nu<2)$$

11.3.39

$$\int_0^z J_\nu(t)J_{-\nu}(z-t)\,dt=\sin z\qquad(|\mathscr{R}\nu|<1)$$

11.3.40

$$\int_0^z t^{-1}J_\mu(t)J_\nu(z-t)dt=\frac{J_{\mu+\nu}(z)}{\mu}\qquad(\mathscr{R}\mu>0,\mathscr{R}\nu>-1)$$

11.3.41

$$\int_0^z\frac{J_\mu(t)J_\nu(z-t)dt}{t(z-t)}=\frac{(\mu+\nu)J_{\mu+\nu}(z)}{\mu\nu z}\qquad(\mathscr{R}\mu>0,\ \mathscr{R}\nu>0)$$

11.4. Definite Integrals

Orthogonality Properties of Bessel Functions

Let $\mathscr{C}_\nu(z)$ be a cylinder function of order ν. In particular, let

11.4.1 $$\mathscr{C}_\nu(z)=AJ_\nu(z)+BY_\nu(z)$$

where A and B are real constants. Then

11.4.2

$$\int_a^b t\mathscr{C}_\nu(\lambda_m t)\mathscr{C}_\nu(\lambda_n t)dt=0\ (m\neq n)$$
$$=\left[\frac{1}{2}t^2\left\{\left(1-\frac{\nu^2}{\lambda_n^2t^2}\right)\mathscr{C}_\nu^2(\lambda_n t)+\mathscr{C}_\nu'^2(\lambda_n t)\right\}\right]_a^b\qquad(m=n)(0<a<b)$$

provided the following two conditions hold:

1. λ_n is a real zero of

11.4.3 $$h_1\lambda\mathscr{C}_{\nu+1}(\lambda b)-h_2\mathscr{C}_\nu(\lambda b)=0$$

2. There must exist numbers k_1 and k_2 (both not zero) so that for all n

11.4.4 $$k_1\lambda_n\mathscr{C}_{\nu+1}(\lambda_n a)-k_2\mathscr{C}_\nu(\lambda_n a)=0$$

In connection with these formulae, see **11.3.29.** If $a=0$, the above is valid provided $B=0$. This case is covered by the following result.

11.4.5

$$\int_0^1 tJ_\nu(\alpha_m t)J_\nu(\alpha_n t)dt=0\qquad(m\neq n,\nu>-1)$$
$$=\tfrac{1}{2}[J_\nu'(\alpha_n)]^2\qquad(m=n,b=0,\nu>-1)$$
$$=\frac{1}{2\alpha_n^2}\left[\frac{a^2}{b^2}+\alpha_n^2-\nu^2\right][J_\nu(\alpha_n)]^2\qquad(m=n,\ b\neq0,\ \nu\geq-1)$$

$\alpha_1,\alpha_2,\ldots$ are the positive zeros of $aJ_\nu(x)+bxJ_\nu'(x)=0$, where a and b are real constants.

11.4.6

$$\int_0^\infty t^{-1}J_{\nu+2n+1}(t)J_{\nu+2m+1}(t)dt=0\qquad(m\neq n)$$
$$=\frac{1}{2(2n+\nu+1)}\qquad(m=n)(\nu+n+m>-1)$$

Definite Integrals Over a Finite Range

11.4.7 $$\int_0^{\frac{\pi}{2}}J_{2n}(2z\sin t)dt=\frac{\pi}{2}J_n^2(z)$$

11.4.8 $$\int_0^\pi J_0(2z\sin t)\cos 2nt\,dt=\pi J_n^2(z)$$

11.4.9 $$\int_0^{\frac{\pi}{2}}Y_0(2z\sin t)\cos 2nt\,dt=\frac{\pi}{2}J_n(z)Y_n(z)$$

11.4.10

$$\int_0^{\frac{\pi}{2}}J_\mu(z\sin t)\sin^{\mu+1}t\cos^{2\nu+1}t\,dt=\frac{2^\nu\Gamma(\nu+1)}{z^{\nu+1}}J_{\mu+\nu+1}(z)\qquad(\mathscr{R}\mu>-1,\mathscr{R}\nu>-1)$$

11.4.11

$$\int_0^{\frac{\pi}{2}}J_\mu(z\sin^2t)J_\nu(z\cos^2t)\csc 2t\,dt=\frac{(\mu+\nu)}{4\mu\nu}J_{\mu+\nu}(z)\qquad(\mathscr{R}\mu>0,\mathscr{R}\nu>0)$$

Infinite Integrals

Integrals of the Form $\int_0^\infty e^{-pt}t^\mu Z_\nu(t)dt$

11.4.12

$$\int_0^\infty e^{it}t^{\mu-1}J_\nu(t)dt=\frac{e^{\frac{1}{2}i\pi(\mu+\nu)}\Gamma(\mu+\nu)\Gamma(\frac{1}{2}-\mu)}{\Gamma(\frac{1}{2})2^\mu\Gamma(\nu-\mu+1)} \qquad \left(\mathscr{R}\mu<\frac{1}{2}, \mathscr{R}(\mu+\nu)>0\right)$$

11.4.13

$$\int_0^\infty e^{-t}t^{\mu-1}I_\nu(t)dt=\frac{\Gamma(\mu+\nu)\Gamma(\frac{1}{2}-\mu)}{\Gamma(\frac{1}{2})2^\mu\Gamma(\nu-\mu+1)} \qquad \left(\mathscr{R}\mu<\frac{1}{2}, \mathscr{R}(\mu+\nu)>0\right)$$

11.4.14

$$\int_0^\infty \cos bt\, K_0(t)\,dt=\frac{\frac{1}{2}\pi}{(1+b^2)^{\frac{1}{2}}} \qquad (|\mathscr{I}b|<1)$$

11.4.15

$$\int_0^\infty \sin bt\, K_0(t)dt=\frac{\text{arc sinh } b}{(1+b^2)^{\frac{1}{2}}} \qquad (|\mathscr{I}b|<1)$$

11.4.16 $$\int_0^\infty t^\mu J_\nu(t)dt=\frac{2^\mu\Gamma\left(\frac{\nu+\mu+1}{2}\right)}{\Gamma\left(\frac{\nu-\mu+1}{2}\right)} \qquad \left(\mathscr{R}(\mu+\nu)>-1, \mathscr{R}\mu<\frac{1}{2}\right)$$

11.4.17 $$\int_0^\infty J_\nu(t)dt=1 \qquad (\mathscr{R}\nu>-1)$$

11.4.18

$$\int_0^\infty \frac{[1-J_0(t)]dt}{t^\mu}=\frac{\Gamma\left(\frac{\mu-1}{2}\right)\Gamma\left(\frac{3-\mu}{2}\right)}{2^\mu\left\{\Gamma\left(\frac{\mu+1}{2}\right)\right\}^2} \qquad (1<\mathscr{R}\mu<3)$$

11.4.19

$$\int_0^\infty t^\mu Y_\nu(t)dt=\frac{2^\mu}{\pi}\Gamma\left(\frac{\mu+\nu+1}{2}\right)\Gamma\left(\frac{\mu-\nu+1}{2}\right) \times \sin\frac{\pi}{2}(\mu-\nu) \qquad \left(\mathscr{R}(\mu\pm\nu)>-1, \mathscr{R}\mu<\frac{1}{2}\right)$$

11.4.20 $$\int_0^\infty Y_\nu(t)dt=-\tan\frac{\nu\pi}{2} \qquad (|\mathscr{R}\nu|<1)$$

11.4.21 $$\int_0^\infty Y_0(t)dt=0$$

11.4.22

$$\int_0^\infty t^\mu K_\nu(t)dt=2^{\mu-1}\Gamma\left(\frac{\mu+\nu+1}{2}\right)\Gamma\left(\frac{\mu-\nu+1}{2}\right) \qquad (\mathscr{R}(\mu\pm\nu)>-1)$$

11.4.23 $$\int_0^\infty K_0(t)dt=\frac{\pi}{2}$$

11.4.24 $$\int_{-\infty}^\infty e^{-i\omega t}J_n(t)dt=\frac{2(-i)^nT_n(\omega)}{(1-\omega^2)^{\frac{1}{2}}} \quad (\omega^2<1)$$
$$=0 \quad (\omega^2>1)$$

where $T_n(\omega)$ is the Chebyshev polynomial of the first kind (see chapter **22**).

11.4.25

$$\int_{-\infty}^\infty t^{-1}e^{-i\omega t}J_n(t)dt =\frac{2i}{n}(-i)^n(1-\omega^2)^{\frac{1}{2}}U_{n-1}(\omega) \quad (\omega^2<1)$$
$$=0 \quad (\omega^2>1)$$

where $U_n(\omega)$ is the Chebyshev polynomial of the second kind (see chapter **22**).

11.4.26

$$\int_{-\infty}^\infty t^{-\frac{1}{2}}e^{-i\omega t}J_{n+\frac{1}{2}}(t)dt=(-i)^n(2\pi)^{\frac{1}{2}}P_n(\omega) \quad (\omega^2<1)$$
$$=0 \quad (\omega^2>1)$$

where $P_n(\omega)$ is the Legendre polynomial (see chapter **22**).

11.4.27

$$\int_0^\infty e^{-t}t^{\frac{a}{2}-1}J_a[2(zt)^{\frac{1}{2}}]dt=\frac{\gamma(a,z)}{z^{a/2}} \qquad (\mathscr{R}a>0, \mathscr{R}z>0)$$

where $\gamma(a, z)$ is the incomplete gamma function (see chapter **6**).

Integrals of the Form $\int_0^\infty e^{-a^2t^2}t^\mu Z_\nu(bt)\,dt$

11.4.28

$$\int_0^\infty e^{-a^2t^2}t^{\mu-1}J_\nu(bt)dt =\frac{\Gamma\left(\frac{1}{2}\nu+\frac{1}{2}\mu\right)\left(\frac{1}{2}\frac{b}{a}\right)^\nu}{2a^\mu\Gamma(\nu+1)}M\left(\frac{1}{2}\nu+\frac{1}{2}\mu, \nu+1, -\frac{b^2}{4a^2}\right) \qquad (\mathscr{R}(\mu+\nu)>0, \mathscr{R}a^2>0)$$

where the notation $M(a, b, z)$ stands for the confluent hypergeometric function (see chapter **13**).

11.4.29

$$\int_0^\infty e^{-a^2t^2}t^{\nu+1}J_\nu(bt)dt =\frac{b^\nu}{(2a^2)^{\nu+1}}e^{-\frac{b^2}{4a^2}} \qquad (\mathscr{R}\nu>-1, \mathscr{R}a^2>0)$$

11.4.30

$$\int_0^\infty e^{-a^2t^2}Y_{2\nu}(bt)dt=-\frac{\pi^{\frac{1}{2}}}{2a}e^{-\frac{b^2}{8a^2}}\left[I_\nu\left(\frac{b^2}{8a^2}\right)\tan\nu\pi+\frac{1}{\pi}K_\nu\left(\frac{b^2}{8a^2}\right)\sec\nu\pi\right]\qquad\left(|\mathscr{R}\nu|<\frac{1}{2},\mathscr{R}a^2>0\right)$$

11.4.31

$$\int_0^\infty e^{-a^2t^2}I_\nu(bt)dt=\frac{\pi^{\frac{1}{2}}}{2a}e^{\frac{b^2}{8a^2}}I_{\frac{1}{2}\nu}\left(\frac{b^2}{8a^2}\right)\qquad(\mathscr{R}\nu>-1,\mathscr{R}a^2>0)$$

11.4.32

$$\int_0^\infty e^{-a^2t^2}K_0(bt)dt=\frac{\pi^{\frac{1}{2}}}{4a}e^{\frac{b^2}{8a^2}}K_0\left(\frac{b^2}{8a^2}\right)\qquad(\mathscr{R}a^2>0)$$

Weber-Schafheitlin Type Integrals

11.4.33

$$\int_0^\infty\frac{J_\mu(at)J_\nu(bt)dt}{t^\lambda}=\frac{b^\nu\Gamma\left(\frac{\mu+\nu-\lambda+1}{2}\right)}{2^\lambda a^{\nu-\lambda+1}\Gamma(\nu+1)\Gamma\left(\frac{\mu-\nu+\lambda+1}{2}\right)}\times{}_2F_1\left(\frac{\mu+\nu-\lambda+1}{2},\frac{\nu-\mu-\lambda+1}{2};\nu+1;\frac{b^2}{a^2}\right)$$

$$(\mathscr{R}(\mu+\nu-\lambda+1)>0,\mathscr{R}\lambda>-1,0<b<a)$$

11.4.34

$$\int_0^\infty\frac{J_\mu(at)J_\nu(bt)dt}{t^\lambda}=\frac{a^\mu\Gamma\left(\frac{\mu+\nu-\lambda+1}{2}\right)}{2^\lambda b^{\mu-\lambda+1}\Gamma(\mu+1)\Gamma\left(\frac{\nu-\mu+\lambda+1}{2}\right)}\times{}_2F_1\left(\frac{\mu+\nu-\lambda+1}{2},\frac{\mu-\nu-\lambda+1}{2};\mu+1;\frac{a^2}{b^2}\right)$$

$$(\mathscr{R}(\mu+\nu-\lambda+1)>0,\mathscr{R}\lambda>-1,0<a<b)$$

For ${}_2F_1$, see chapter **15.**

Special Cases of the Discontinuous Weber-Schafheitlin Integral

11.4.35

$$\int_0^\infty\frac{J_\mu(at)\sin bt\,dt}{t}=\frac{1}{\mu}\sin\left[\mu\arcsin\frac{b}{a}\right]\qquad(0\le b\le a)$$

$$=\frac{a^\mu\sin\frac{\pi\mu}{2}}{\mu[b+(b^2-a^2)^{\frac{1}{2}}]^\mu}\qquad(b\ge a>0)$$

$$(\mathscr{R}\mu>-1)$$

11.4.36

$$\int_0^\infty\frac{J_\mu(at)\cos bt\,dt}{t}=\frac{1}{\mu}\cos\left[\mu\arcsin\frac{b}{a}\right]\qquad(0\le b\le a)$$

$$=\frac{a^\mu\cos\frac{\pi\mu}{2}}{\mu[b+(b^2-a^2)^{\frac{1}{2}}]^\mu}\qquad(b\ge a>0)$$

$$(\mathscr{R}\mu>0)$$

11.4.37

$$\int_0^\infty J_\mu(at)\cos bt\,dt=\frac{\cos\left[\mu\arcsin\frac{b}{a}\right]}{(a^2-b^2)^{\frac{1}{2}}}\qquad(0\le b<a)$$

$$=\frac{-a^\mu\sin\frac{\pi\mu}{2}}{(b^2-a^2)^{\frac{1}{2}}[b+(b^2-a^2)^{\frac{1}{2}}]^\mu}$$

$$(b>a>0)\qquad(\mathscr{R}\mu>-1)$$

11.4.38

$$\int_0^\infty J_\mu(at)\sin bt\,dt=\frac{\sin\left[\mu\arcsin\frac{b}{a}\right]}{(a^2-b^2)^{\frac{1}{2}}}\qquad(0\le b<a)$$

$$=\frac{a^\mu\cos\frac{\pi\mu}{2}}{(b^2-a^2)^{\frac{1}{2}}[b+(b^2-a^2)^{\frac{1}{2}}]^\mu}$$

$$(b>a>0)\qquad(\mathscr{R}\mu>-2)$$

11.4.39

$$\int_0^\infty e^{ibt}J_0(at)dt=\frac{1}{(a^2-b^2)^{\frac{1}{2}}}\qquad(0\le b<a)$$

$$=\frac{i}{(b^2-a^2)^{\frac{1}{2}}}\qquad(0<a<b)$$

11.4.40

$$\int_0^\infty e^{ibt}Y_0(at)dt=\frac{2i}{\pi(a^2-b^2)^{\frac{1}{2}}}\arcsin\frac{b}{a}\qquad(0\le b<a)$$

$$=\frac{-1}{(b^2-a^2)^{\frac{1}{2}}}+\frac{2i}{\pi(b^2-a^2)^{\frac{1}{2}}}\times\ln\left\{\frac{b-(b^2-a^2)^{\frac{1}{2}}}{a}\right\}\qquad(0<a<b)$$

11.4.41

$$\int_0^\infty t^{\mu-\nu+1}J_\mu(at)J_\nu(bt)dt=0\qquad(0<b<a)$$

$$=\frac{2^{\mu-\nu+1}a^\mu(b^2-a^2)^{\nu-\mu-1}}{b^\nu\Gamma(\nu-\mu)}$$

$$(b>a>0)$$

$$(\mathscr{R}\nu>\mathscr{R}\mu>-1)$$

11.4.42

$$\int_0^\infty J_\mu(at)J_{\mu-1}(bt)dt=\frac{b^{\mu-1}}{a^\mu}\qquad(0<b<a)$$

$$=\frac{1}{2b}\qquad(0<b=a)$$

$$=0\qquad(b>a>0)$$

$$(\mathscr{R}\mu>0)$$

11.4.43

$$\int_0^\infty\frac{J_0(at)}{t}\{1-J_0(bt)\}dt=0\qquad(0<b\le a)$$

$$=\ln\frac{b}{a}\qquad(b\ge a>0)$$

Hankel-Nicholson Type Integrals

11.4.44

$$\int_0^\infty \frac{t^{\nu+1}J_\nu(at)dt}{(t^2+z^2)^{\mu+1}}=\frac{a^\mu z^{\nu-\mu}}{2^\mu\Gamma(\mu+1)}K_{\nu-\mu}(az)$$

$$\left(a>0,\ \mathscr{R}z>0, -1<\mathscr{R}\nu<2\mathscr{R}\mu+\frac{3}{2}\right)$$

11.4.45

$$\int_0^\infty \frac{J_\nu(at)dt}{t^\nu(t^2+z^2)}=\frac{\pi}{2z^{\nu+1}}[I_\nu(az)-\mathbf{L}_\nu(az)]$$

$$\left(a>0,\ \mathscr{R}z>0,\ \mathscr{R}\nu>-\frac{5}{2}\right)$$

11.4.46

$$\int_0^\infty \frac{Y_0(at)dt}{t^2+z^2}=-\frac{K_0(az)}{z} \qquad (a>0,\ \mathscr{R}z>0)$$

11.4.47

$$\int_0^\infty \frac{K_\nu(at)dt}{t^\nu(t^2+z^2)}=\frac{\pi^2}{4z^{\nu+1}\cos\nu\pi}[\mathbf{H}_\nu(az)-Y_\nu(az)]$$

$$(\mathscr{R}a>0,\ \mathscr{R}z>0,\ \mathscr{R}\nu<\tfrac{1}{2})$$

11.4.48

$$\int_0^\infty \frac{J_\nu(at)dt}{(t^2+z^2)^{\frac{1}{2}}}=I_{\frac{1}{2}\nu}(\tfrac{1}{2}az)K_{\frac{1}{2}\nu}(\tfrac{1}{2}az)$$

$$(a>0,\ \mathscr{R}z>0,\ \mathscr{R}\nu>-1)$$

11.4.49

$$\int_0^\infty \frac{J_\nu(at)dt}{t^\nu(t^2+z^2)^{\nu+\frac{1}{2}}}=\frac{\left(\frac{2a}{z^2}\right)^\nu\Gamma(\nu+1)}{\Gamma(2\nu+1)}I_\nu(\tfrac{1}{2}az)K_\nu(\tfrac{1}{2}az)$$

$$(a>0,\ \mathscr{R}z>0,\ \mathscr{R}\nu>-\tfrac{1}{2})$$

Table 11.1 **INTEGRALS OF BESSEL FUNCTIONS**

x	$\int_0^x J_0(t)\,dt$	$\int_0^x Y_0(t)\,dt$	$e^{-x}\int_0^x I_0(t)\,dt$	$e^x\int_x^\infty K_0(t)\,dt$
0.0	0.00000 00000	0.00000 00000	0.00000 00	1.57079 63
0.1	0.09991 66979	-0.21743 05666	0.09055 92	1.35784 82
0.2	0.19933 43325	-0.34570 88380	0.16429 28	1.25032 54
0.3	0.29775 75802	-0.43928 31758	0.22391 79	1.17280 09
0.4	0.39469 85653	-0.50952 48283	0.27172 46	1.11171 28
0.5	0.48968 05066	-0.56179 54559	0.30964 29	1.06127 17
0.6	0.58224 12719	-0.59927 15570	0.33929 99	1.01836 48
0.7	0.67193 68094	-0.62409 96341	0.36206 71	0.98109 70
0.8	0.75834 44308	-0.63786 88991	0.37910 05	0.94821 80
0.9	0.84106 59149	-0.64184 01770	0.39137 42	0.91885 56
1.0	0.91973 04101	-0.63706 93766	0.39970 88	0.89237 52
1.1	0.99399 71082	-0.62447 91607	0.40479 52	0.86829 97
1.2	1.06355 76711	-0.60490 26964	0.40721 52	0.84626 10
1.3	1.12813 83885	-0.57911 12548	0.40745 78	0.82596 89
1.4	1.18750 20495	-0.54783 19295	0.40593 39	0.80719 04
1.5	1.24144 95144	-0.51175 90340	0.40298 85	0.78973 57
1.6	1.28982 09734	-0.47156 13039	0.39891 09	0.77344 80
1.7	1.33249 68829	-0.42788 62338	0.39394 29	0.75819 62
1.8	1.36939 85727	-0.38136 24134	0.38828 68	0.74386 97
1.9	1.40048 85208	-0.33260 04453	0.38211 11	0.73037 44
2.0	1.42577 02932	-0.28219 28501	0.37555 57	0.71762 95
2.1	1.44528 81525	-0.23071 32490	0.36873 67	0.70556 50
2.2	1.45912 63387	-0.17871 50399	0.36174 98	0.69412 02
2.3	1.46740 80303	-0.12672 97284	0.35467 38	0.68324 16
2.4	1.47029 39949	-0.07526 50420	0.34757 29	0.67288 26
2.5	1.46798 09446	-0.02480 29261	0.34049 93	0.66300 15
2.6	1.46069 96081	+0.02420 24953	0.33349 48	0.65356 16
2.7	1.44871 25408	0.07132 69288	0.32659 30	0.64452 98
2.8	1.43231 16899	0.11617 78353	0.31981 99	0.63587 68
2.9	1.41181 57386	0.15839 62206	0.31319 59	0.62757 60
3.0	1.38756 72520	0.19765 82565	0.30673 62	0.61960 34
3.1	1.35992 96508	0.23367 66986	0.30045 18	0.61193 74
3.2	1.32928 40386	0.26620 20748	0.29435 04	0.60455 84
3.3	1.29602 59125	0.29502 36222	0.28843 67	0.59744 84
3.4	1.26056 17835	0.31996 99576	0.28271 31	0.59059 11
3.5	1.22330 57382	0.34090 94657	0.27718 02	0.58397 14
3.6	1.18467 59706	0.35775 03989	0.27183 70	0.57757 57
3.7	1.14509 13136	0.37044 06831	0.26668 11	0.57139 13
3.8	1.10496 78009	0.37896 74266	0.26170 94	0.56540 66
3.9	1.06471 52877	0.38335 61369	0.25691 78	0.55961 09
4.0	1.02473 41595	0.38366 96479	0.25230 18	0.55399 42
4.1	0.98541 21560	0.38000 67672	0.24785 61	0.54854 72
4.2	0.94712 13375	0.37250 06552	0.24357 56	0.54326 15
4.3	0.91021 52175	0.36131 69475	0.23945 46	0.53812 91
4.4	0.87502 60866	0.34665 16398	0.23548 74	0.53314 27
4.5	0.84186 25481	0.32872 87513	0.23166 83	0.52829 52
4.6	0.81100 72858	0.30779 77892	0.22799 15	0.52358 03
4.7	0.78271 50802	0.28413 10351	0.22445 13	0.51899 19
4.8	0.75721 10902	0.25802 06786	0.22104 21	0.51452 43
4.9	0.73468 94106	0.22977 58227	0.21775 83	0.51017 24
5.0	0.71531 19178	0.19971 93876	0.21459 46	0.50593 10

INTEGRALS OF BESSEL FUNCTIONS Table 11.1

x	$\int_0^x J_0(t)\,dt$	$\int_0^x Y_0(t)\,dt$	$e^{-x}\int_0^x I_0(t)\,dt$	$e^x\int_x^\infty K_0(t)\,dt$
5.0	0.71531 19178	0.19971 93876	0.21459 46	0.50593 10
5.1	0.69920 74098	0.16818 49405	0.21154 58	0.50179 55
5.2	0.68647 10457	0.13551 34784	0.20860 68	0.49776 16
5.3	0.67716 40870	0.10205 01932	0.20577 28	0.49382 50
5.4	0.67131 39407	0.06814 12463	0.20303 89	0.48998 19
5.5	0.66891 44989	0.03413 05806	0.20040 08	0.48622 86
5.6	0.66992 67724	+0.00035 67983	0.19785 40	0.48256 16
5.7	0.67427 98068	-0.03284 98697	0.19539 44	0.47897 75
5.8	0.68187 18713	-0.06517 04775	0.19301 81	0.47547 34
5.9	0.69257 19078	-0.09630 01348	0.19072 13	0.47204 60
6.0	0.70622 12236	-0.12595 06129	0.18850 02	0.46869 29
6.1	0.72263 54100	-0.15385 27646	0.18635 16	0.46541 11
6.2	0.74160 64692	-0.17975 87372	0.18427 20	0.46219 83
6.3	0.76290 51256	-0.20344 39625	0.18225 84	0.45905 20
6.4	0.78628 33012	-0.22470 89068	0.18030 78	0.45596 99
6.5	0.81147 67291	-0.24338 05692	0.17841 74	0.45294 98
6.6	0.83820 76824	-0.25931 37161	0.17658 44	0.44998 97
6.7	0.86618 77897	-0.27239 18447	0.17480 64	0.44708 76
6.8	0.89512 09137	-0.28252 78684	0.17308 09	0.44424 15
6.9	0.92470 60635	-0.28966 45218	0.17140 55	0.44144 97
7.0	0.95464 03155	-0.29377 44843	0.16977 82	0.43871 05
7.1	0.98462 17153	-0.29486 02239	0.16819 68	0.43602 22
7.2	1.01435 21344	-0.29295 35658	0.16665 93	0.43338 34
7.3	1.04354 00558	-0.28811 49927	0.16516 39	0.43079 23
7.4	1.07190 32638	-0.28043 26862	0.16370 89	0.42824 76
7.5	1.09917 14142	-0.27002 13202	0.16229 24	0.42574 81
7.6	1.12508 84628	-0.25702 06208	0.16091 30	0.42329 20
7.7	1.14941 49299	-0.24159 37080	0.15956 91	0.42087 86
7.8	1.17192 99830	-0.22392 52368	0.15825 93	0.41850 63
7.9	1.19243 33198	-0.20421 93575	0.15698 21	0.41617 40
8.0	1.21074 68348	-0.18269 75150	0.15573 64	0.41388 07
8.1	1.22671 60587	-0.15959 61109	0.15452 08	0.41162 52
8.2	1.24021 13565	-0.13516 40494	0.15333 42	0.40940 65
8.3	1.25112 88778	-0.10966 01934	0.15217 55	0.40722 37
8.4	1.25939 12520	-0.08335 07540	0.15104 36	0.40507 56
8.5	1.26494 80240	-0.05650 66385	0.14993 74	0.40296 15
8.6	1.26777 58297	-0.02940 07834	0.14885 61	0.40088 04
8.7	1.26787 83120	-0.00230 54965	0.14779 88	0.39883 15
8.8	1.26528 57796	+0.02451 01664	0.14676 44	0.39681 40
8.9	1.26005 46162	0.05078 29664	0.14575 23	0.39482 69
9.0	1.25226 64460	0.07625 79635	0.14476 16	0.39286 97
9.1	1.24202 70675	0.10069 08937	0.14379 16	0.39094 15
9.2	1.22946 51666	0.12385 04194	0.14284 16	0.38904 17
9.3	1.21473 08237	0.14552 02334	0.14191 08	0.38716 95
9.4	1.19799 38314	0.16550 09969	0.14099 87	0.38532 41
9.5	1.17944 18392	0.18361 20962	0.14010 46	0.38350 53
9.6	1.15927 83464	0.19969 32017	0.13922 78	0.38171 20
9.7	1.13772 05614	0.21360 56169	0.13836 79	0.37994 39
9.8	1.11499 71504	0.22523 34059	0.13752 43	0.37820 03
9.9	1.09134 58985	0.23448 42919	0.13669 65	0.37648 06
10.0	1.06701 13040	0.24129 03183	0.13588 40	0.37478 43

Table 11.2 **INTEGRALS OF BESSEL FUNCTIONS**

x	$\int_0^x \frac{1-J_0(t)}{t}\,dt$	$\int_x^\infty \frac{Y_0(t)}{t}\,dt$	$e^{-x}\int_0^x \frac{I_0(t)-1}{t}\,dt$	$xe^x\int_x^\infty \frac{K_0(t)}{t}\,dt$
0.0	0.00000 000	$-\infty$	0.00000 000	0.000000
0.1	0.00124 961	−1.34138 382	0.00113 140	0.368126
0.2	0.00499 375	−0.43423 067	0.00409 877	0.460111
0.3	0.01121 841	−0.05107 832	0.00835 768	0.506394
0.4	0.01990 030	+0.15238 037	0.01347 363	0.532910
0.5	0.03100 699	0.26968 854	0.01910 285	0.548819
0.6	0.04449 711	0.33839 213	0.02497 622	0.558366
0.7	0.06032 057	0.37689 807	0.03088 584	0.563828
0.8	0.07841 882	0.39543 866	0.03667 383	0.566545
0.9	0.09872 519	0.40022 301	0.04222 295	0.567355
1.0	0.12116 525	0.39527 290	0.04744 889	0.566811
1.1	0.14565 721	0.38332 909	0.05229 376	0.565291
1.2	0.17211 240	0.36633 694	0.05672 080	0.563058
1.3	0.20043 570	0.34572 398	0.06070 995	0.560302
1.4	0.23052 610	0.32256 701	0.06425 420	0.557163
1.5	0.26227 724	0.29769 696	0.06735 663	0.553745
1.6	0.29557 796	0.27176 713	0.07002 797	0.550126
1.7	0.33031 288	0.24529 896	0.07228 458	0.546364
1.8	0.36636 308	0.21871 360	0.07414 688	0.542506
1.9	0.40360 666	0.19235 409	0.07563 806	0.538587
2.0	0.44191 940	0.16650 135	0.07678 298	0.534635
2.1	0.48117 541	0.14138 594	0.07760 744	0.530670
2.2	0.52124 775	0.11719 681	0.07813 746	0.526711
2.3	0.56200 913	0.09408 798	0.07839 884	0.522768
2.4	0.60333 248	0.07218 365	0.07841 674	0.518854
2.5	0.64509 164	0.05158 229	0.07821 544	0.514976
2.6	0.68716 194	0.03235 987	0.07781 809	0.511139
2.7	0.72942 081	+0.01457 248	0.07724 664	0.507350
2.8	0.77174 836	−0.00174 144	0.07652 168	0.503610
2.9	0.81402 795	−0.01655 931	0.07566 245	0.499924
3.0	0.85614 669	−0.02987 272	0.07468 681	0.496292
3.1	0.89799 596	−0.04168 613	0.07361 124	0.492717
3.2	0.93947 188	−0.05201 554	0.07245 090	0.489198
3.3	0.98047 571	−0.06088 740	0.07121 963	0.485736
3.4	1.02091 428	−0.06833 756	0.06993 006	0.482332
3.5	1.06070 032	−0.07441 025	0.06859 360	0.478984
3.6	1.09975 277	−0.07915 722	0.06722 060	0.475694
3.7	1.13799 707	−0.08263 683	0.06582 033	0.472459
3.8	1.17536 536	−0.08491 323	0.06440 109	0.469280
3.9	1.21179 667	−0.08605 553	0.06297 029	0.466155
4.0	1.24723 707	−0.08613 706	0.06153 450	0.463085
4.1	1.28163 975	−0.08523 459	0.06009 952	0.460067
4.2	1.31496 504	−0.08342 762	0.05867 042	0.457100
4.3	1.34718 044	−0.08079 769	0.05725 166	0.454185
4.4	1.37826 060	−0.07742 769	0.05584 708	0.451320
4.5	1.40818 716	−0.07340 123	0.05446 000	0.448503
4.6	1.43694 870	−0.06880 199	0.05309 325	0.445734
4.7	1.46454 052	−0.06371 317	0.05174 921	0.443012
4.8	1.49096 446	−0.05821 690	0.05042 989	0.440335
4.9	1.51622 864	−0.05239 371	0.04913 691	0.437703
5.0	1.54034 722	−0.04632 205	0.04787 161	0.435114

12.1. Struve Function $\mathbf{H}_\nu(z)$

Differential Equation and General Solution

12.1.1
$$z^2\frac{d^2w}{dz^2}+z\frac{dw}{dz}+(z^2-\nu^2)w=\frac{4(\frac{1}{2}z)^{\nu+1}}{\sqrt{\pi}\Gamma(\nu+\frac{1}{2})}$$

The general solution is

12.1.2 $w=aJ_\nu(z)+bY_\nu(z)+\mathbf{H}_\nu(z)$ $(a,b,$ constants)

where $z^{-\nu}\mathbf{H}_\nu(z)$ is an entire function of z.

Power Series Expansion

12.1.3
$$\mathbf{H}_\nu(z)=(\tfrac{1}{2}z)^{\nu+1}\sum_{k=0}^{\infty}\frac{(-1)^k(\frac{1}{2}z)^{2k}}{\Gamma(k+\frac{3}{2})\Gamma(k+\nu+\frac{3}{2})}$$

12.1.4 $$\mathbf{H}_0(z)=\frac{2}{\pi}\left[z-\frac{z^3}{1^2\cdot 3^2}+\frac{z^5}{1^2\cdot 3^2\cdot 5^2}-\cdots\right]$$

12.1.5
$$\mathbf{H}_1(z)=\frac{2}{\pi}\left[\frac{z^2}{1^2\cdot 3}-\frac{z^4}{1^2\cdot 3^2\cdot 5}+\frac{z^6}{1^2\cdot 3^2\cdot 5^2\cdot 7}-\cdots\right]$$

Integral Representations

If $\mathscr{R}\nu>-\frac{1}{2}$,

12.1.6
$$\mathbf{H}_\nu(z)=\frac{2(\frac{1}{2}z)^\nu}{\sqrt{\pi}\,\Gamma(\nu+\frac{1}{2})}\int_0^1(1-t^2)^{\nu-\frac{1}{2}}\sin(zt)\,dt$$

12.1.7 $$=\frac{2(\frac{1}{2}z)^\nu}{\sqrt{\pi}\,\Gamma(\nu+\frac{1}{2})}\int_0^{\frac{\pi}{2}}\sin(z\cos\theta)\sin^{2\nu}\theta\,d\theta$$

12.1.8 $$=Y_\nu(z)+\frac{2(\frac{1}{2}z)^\nu}{\sqrt{\pi}\,\Gamma(\nu+\frac{1}{2})}\int_0^\infty e^{-zt}(1+t^2)^{\nu-\frac{1}{2}}dt\qquad\left(|\arg z|<\frac{\pi}{2}\right)$$

Recurrence Relations

12.1.9 $$\mathbf{H}_{\nu-1}+\mathbf{H}_{\nu+1}=\frac{2\nu}{z}\mathbf{H}_\nu+\frac{(\frac{1}{2}z)^\nu}{\sqrt{\pi}\,\Gamma(\nu+\frac{3}{2})}$$

12.1.10 $$\mathbf{H}_{\nu-1}-\mathbf{H}_{\nu+1}=2\mathbf{H}'_\nu-\frac{(\frac{1}{2}z)^\nu}{\sqrt{\pi}\,\Gamma(\nu+\frac{3}{2})}$$

12.1.11 $$\mathbf{H}'_0=(2/\pi)-\mathbf{H}_1$$

12.1.12 $$\frac{d}{dz}(z^\nu\mathbf{H}_\nu)=z^\nu\mathbf{H}_{\nu-1}$$

12.1.13 $$\frac{d}{dz}(z^{-\nu}\mathbf{H}_\nu)=\frac{1}{\sqrt{\pi}\,2^\nu\Gamma(\nu+\frac{3}{2})}-z^{-\nu}\mathbf{H}_{\nu+1}$$

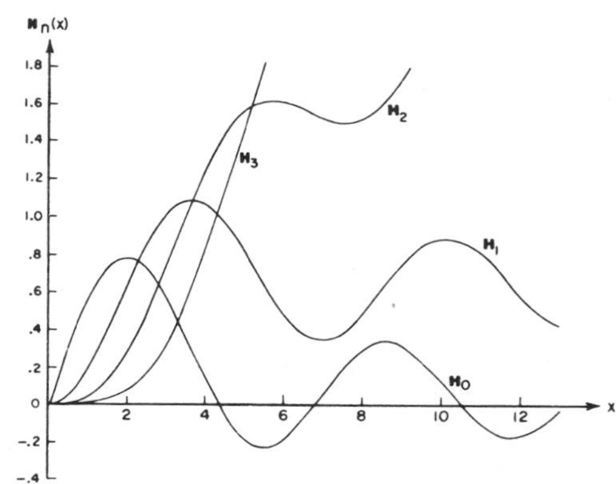

FIGURE 12.1. *Struve functions.*

$\mathbf{H}_n(x)$, $n=0(1)3$

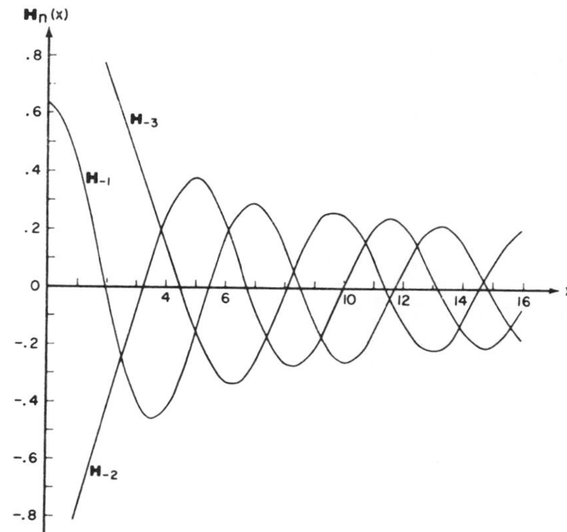

FIGURE 12.2. *Struve functions.*

$\mathbf{H}_n(x)$, $-n=1(1)3$

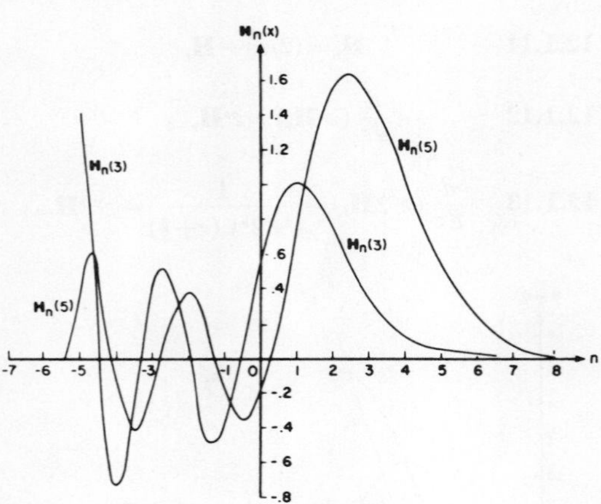

FIGURE 12.3. *Struve functions.*

$\mathbf{H}_n(x)$, $x=3, 5$

Special Properties

12.1.14 $\mathbf{H}_\nu(x)\geq 0 \qquad (x>0 \text{ and } \nu\geq\tfrac{1}{2})$

12.1.15

$$\mathbf{H}_{-(n+\frac{1}{2})}(z)=(-1)^n J_{n+\frac{1}{2}}(z) \quad (n \text{ an integer}\geq 0)$$

12.1.16

$$\mathbf{H}_{\frac{1}{2}}(z)=\left(\frac{2}{\pi z}\right)^{\frac{1}{2}}(1-\cos z)$$

12.1.17

$$\mathbf{H}_{\frac{3}{2}}(z)=\left(\frac{z}{2\pi}\right)^{\frac{1}{2}}\left(1+\frac{2}{z^2}\right)-\left(\frac{2}{\pi z}\right)^{\frac{1}{2}}\left(\sin z+\frac{\cos z}{z}\right)$$

12.1.18 $\mathbf{H}_\nu(ze^{m\pi i})=e^{m(\nu+1)\pi i}\,\mathbf{H}_\nu(z)$ (m an integer)

12.1.19

$$\mathbf{H}_0(z)=\frac{4}{\pi}\sum_{k=0}^{\infty}\frac{J_{2k+1}(z)}{2k+1}$$

12.1.20

$$\mathbf{H}_1(z)=\frac{2}{\pi}-\frac{2}{\pi}J_0(z)+\frac{4}{\pi}\sum_{k=1}^{\infty}\frac{J_{2k}(z)}{4k^2-1}$$

12.1.21

$$\mathbf{H}_\nu(z)=\frac{2(z/2)^{\nu+1}}{\sqrt{\pi}\,\Gamma(\nu+\frac{3}{2})}\,{}_1F_2\left(1;\frac{3}{2}+\nu,\frac{3}{2};-\frac{z^2}{4}\right)$$

Integrals (See chapter 11)

12.1.22

$$\int_0^\infty t^{-1}\,\mathbf{H}_0(t)dt=\frac{\pi}{2}$$

12.1.23

$$\int_0^z \mathbf{H}_0(t)dt=\frac{2}{\pi}\left[\frac{z^2}{2}-\frac{z^4}{1^2.3^2.4}+\frac{z^6}{1^2.3^2.5^2.6}-\ldots\right]$$

12.1.24

$$\int_0^z t^{-\nu}\,\mathbf{H}_{\nu+1}(t)dt=\frac{z}{2^\nu\sqrt{\pi}\,\Gamma(\nu+\frac{3}{2})}-z^{-\nu}\,\mathbf{H}_\nu(z)$$

Struve's Integral

12.1.25

$$\frac{4}{\pi}\int_z^\infty t^{-2}\,\mathbf{H}_1(t)dt=\frac{2}{\pi z}\,\mathbf{H}_1(z)+\frac{2}{\pi}\int_z^\infty t^{-1}\,\mathbf{H}_0(t)dt$$

12.1.26

$$\frac{2}{\pi}\int_z^\infty t^{-1}\,\mathbf{H}_0(t)dt=1-\frac{4}{\pi^2}\left[z-\frac{z^3}{1^2.3^2.3}+\frac{z^5}{1^2.3^2.5^2.5}-\ldots\right]$$

12.1.27

$$\int_0^\infty t^{\mu-\nu-1}\mathbf{H}_\nu(t)dt=\frac{\Gamma(\frac{1}{2}\mu)2^{\mu-\nu-1}\tan(\frac{1}{2}\pi\mu)}{\Gamma(\nu-\frac{1}{2}\mu+1)} \qquad (|\mathscr{R}\mu|<1,\ \mathscr{R}\nu>\mathscr{R}\mu-\tfrac{3}{2})$$

If $f_\nu(z)=\int_0^z \mathbf{H}_\nu(t)t^\nu dt$

12.1.28

$$f_{\nu+1}=(2\nu+1)f_\nu(z)-z^{\nu+1}\mathbf{H}_\nu(z)+\frac{z^{2\nu+2}}{(\nu+1)2^{\nu+1}\Gamma(\frac{1}{2})\Gamma(\nu+\frac{3}{2})} \qquad (\mathscr{R}\nu>-\tfrac{1}{2})$$

Asymptotic Expansions for Large $|z|$

12.1.29

$$\mathbf{H}_\nu(z)-Y_\nu(z)=\frac{1}{\pi}\sum_{k=0}^{m-1}\frac{\Gamma(k+\frac{1}{2})}{\Gamma(\nu+\frac{1}{2}-k)\left(\frac{z}{2}\right)^{2k-\nu+1}}+R_m \qquad (|\arg z|<\pi)$$

where $R_m=O(|z|^{\nu-2m-1})$. If ν is real, z positive and $m+\frac{1}{2}-\nu\geq 0$, the remainder after m terms is of the same sign and numerically less than the first term neglected.

12.1.30

$$\mathbf{H}_0(z)-Y_0(z)\sim\frac{2}{\pi}\left[\frac{1}{z}-\frac{1}{z^3}+\frac{1^2\cdot 3^2}{z^5}-\frac{1^2\cdot 3^2\cdot 5^2}{z^7}+\ldots\right] \qquad (|\arg z|<\pi)$$

12.1.31

$$\mathbf{H}_1(z)-Y_1(z)\sim\frac{2}{\pi}\left[1+\frac{1}{z^2}-\frac{1^2\cdot 3}{z^4}+\frac{1^2\cdot 3^2\cdot 5}{z^6}-\ldots\right] \qquad (|\arg z|<\pi)$$

12.1.32

$$\int_0^z [\mathbf{H}_0(t)-Y_0(t)]dt-\frac{2}{\pi}[\ln(2z)+\gamma]\sim\frac{2}{\pi}\sum_{k=1}^{\infty}\frac{(-1)^{k+1}(2k)!(2k-1)!}{(k!)^2(2z)^{2k}} \qquad (|\arg z|<\pi)$$

where $\gamma=.57721\ 56649\ldots$ is Euler's constant.

12.1.33

$$\int_z^\infty t^{-1}[\mathbf{H}_0(t)-Y_0(t)]dt\sim\frac{2}{\pi z}\sum_{k=0}^{\infty}\frac{(-1)^k[(2k)!]^2}{(k!)^2(2k+1)(2z)^{2k}} \qquad (|\arg z|<\pi)$$

Asymptotic Expansions for Large Orders

12.1.34

$$\mathbf{H}_\nu(z)-Y_\nu(z)\sim\frac{2(\frac{1}{2}z)^\nu}{\sqrt{\pi}\Gamma(\nu+\frac{1}{2})}\sum_{k=0}^\infty\frac{k!b_k}{z^{k+1}}$$

$$(|\arg z|<\tfrac{1}{2}\pi, |\nu|<|z|)$$

$b_0=1,\ b_1=2\nu/z,\ b_2=6(\nu/z)^2-\frac{1}{2},\ b_3=20(\nu/z)^3-4(\nu/z)$

12.1.35

$$\mathbf{H}_\nu(z)+iJ_\nu(z)\sim\frac{2(\frac{1}{2}z)^\nu}{\sqrt{\pi}\Gamma(\nu+\frac{1}{2})}\sum_{k=0}^\infty\frac{k!b_k}{z^{k+1}}\qquad(|\nu|>|z|)$$

12.2. Modified Struve Function $\mathbf{L}_\nu(z)$

Power Series Expansion

12.2.1 $$\mathbf{L}_\nu(z)=-ie^{-\frac{i\nu\pi}{2}}\mathbf{H}_\nu(iz)$$

$$=(\tfrac{1}{2}z)^{\nu+1}\sum_{k=0}^\infty\frac{(z/2)^{2k}}{\Gamma(k+\frac{3}{2})\Gamma(k+\nu+\frac{3}{2})}$$

Integral Representations

12.2.2 $$\mathbf{L}_\nu(z)=\frac{2(z/2)^\nu}{\sqrt{\pi}\Gamma(\nu+\frac{1}{2})}\int_0^{\frac{\pi}{2}}\sinh(z\cos\theta)\sin^{2\nu}\theta d\theta$$

$$(\mathscr{R}\nu>-\tfrac{1}{2})$$

12.2.3

$$I_{-\nu}(x)-\mathbf{L}_\nu(x)=\frac{2(x/2)^\nu}{\sqrt{\pi}\Gamma(\nu+\frac{1}{2})}\int_0^\infty\sin(tx)(1+t^2)^{\nu-\frac{1}{2}}dt$$

$$(\mathscr{R}\nu<\tfrac{1}{2}, x>0)$$

Recurrence Relations

12.2.4 $$\mathbf{L}_{\nu-1}-\mathbf{L}_{\nu+1}=\frac{2\nu}{z}\mathbf{L}_\nu+\frac{(z/2)^\nu}{\sqrt{\pi}\,\Gamma(\nu+\frac{3}{2})}$$

12.2.5 $$\mathbf{L}_{\nu-1}+\mathbf{L}_{\nu+1}=2\mathbf{L}'_\nu-\frac{(z/2)^\nu}{\sqrt{\pi}\,\Gamma(\nu+\frac{3}{2})}$$

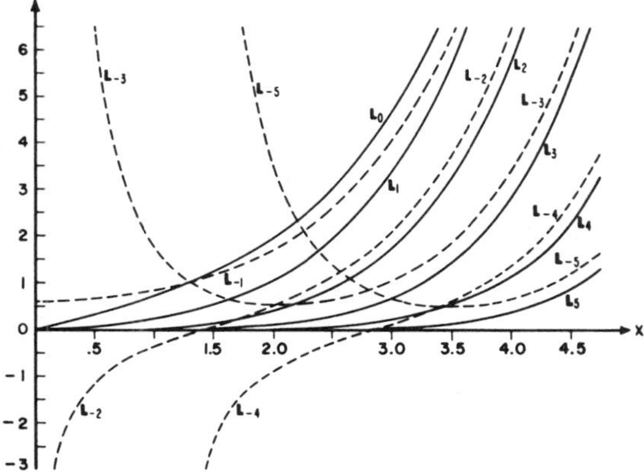

FIGURE 12.4. *Modified Struve functions.*

$\mathbf{L}_n(x),\ \pm n=0(1)5$

Asymptotic Expansion for Large $|z|$

12.2.6 $$\mathbf{L}_\nu(z)-I_{-\nu}(z)$$

$$\sim\frac{1}{\pi}\sum_{k=0}^\infty\frac{(-1)^{k+1}\Gamma(k+\frac{1}{2})}{\Gamma(\nu+\frac{1}{2}-k)\left(\frac{z}{2}\right)^{2k-\nu+1}}\quad(|\arg z|<\tfrac{1}{2}\pi)$$

Integrals

12.2.7

$$\int_0^z\mathbf{L}_0(t)dt=\frac{2}{\pi}\left[\frac{z^2}{2}+\frac{z^4}{1^2\cdot3^2\cdot4}+\frac{z^6}{1^2\cdot3^2\cdot5^2\cdot6}+\cdots\right]$$

12.2.8 $$\int_0^z[I_0(t)-\mathbf{L}_0(t)]dt-\frac{2}{\pi}[\ln(2z)+\gamma]$$

$$\sim-\frac{2}{\pi}\sum_{k=1}^\infty\frac{(2k)!\,(2k-1)!}{(k!)^2(2z)^{2k}}\quad(|\arg z|<\tfrac{1}{2}\pi)$$

12.2.9 $$\int_0^z\mathbf{L}_1(t)dt=\mathbf{L}_0(z)-\frac{2}{\pi}z$$

Relation to Modified Spherical Bessel Function

12.2.10 $$\mathbf{L}_{-(n+\frac{1}{2})}(z)=I_{(n+\frac{1}{2})}(z)\qquad(n\text{ an integer}\geq0)$$

12.3. Anger and Weber Functions

Anger's Function

12.3.1 $$\mathbf{J}_\nu(z)=\frac{1}{\pi}\int_0^\pi\cos(\nu\theta-z\sin\theta)\,d\theta$$

12.3.2 $$\mathbf{J}_n(z)=J_n(z)\qquad(n\text{ an integer})$$

Weber's Function

12.3.3 $$\mathbf{E}_\nu(z)=\frac{1}{\pi}\int_0^\pi\sin(\nu\theta-z\sin\theta)\,d\theta$$

Relations Between Anger's and Weber's Function

12.3.4 $$\sin(\nu\pi)\,\mathbf{J}_\nu(z)=\cos(\nu\pi)\,\mathbf{E}_\nu(z)-\mathbf{E}_{-\nu}(z)$$

12.3.5 $$\sin(\nu\pi)\,\mathbf{E}_\nu(z)=\mathbf{J}_{-\nu}(z)-\cos(\nu\pi)\,\mathbf{J}_\nu(z)$$

Relations Between Weber's Function and Struve's Function

If n is a positive integer or zero,

12.3.6 $$\mathbf{E}_n(z)=\frac{1}{\pi}\sum_{k=0}^{\left[\frac{n-1}{2}\right]}\frac{\Gamma(k+\frac{1}{2})(\frac{1}{2}z)^{n-2k-1}}{\Gamma(n+\frac{1}{2}-k)}-\mathbf{H}_n(z)$$

12.3.7

$$\mathbf{E}_{-n}(z)=\frac{(-1)^{n+1}}{\pi}\sum_{k=0}^{\left[\frac{n-1}{2}\right]}\frac{\Gamma(n-k-\frac{1}{2})(\frac{1}{2}z)^{-n+2k+1}}{\Gamma(k+\frac{3}{2})}-\mathbf{H}_{-n}(z)$$

12.3.8 $$\mathbf{E}_0(z)=-\mathbf{H}_0(z)$$

12.3.9 $$\mathbf{E}_1(z)=\frac{2}{\pi}-\mathbf{H}_1(z)$$

12.3.10 $$\mathbf{E}_2(z)=\frac{2z}{3\pi}-\mathbf{H}_2(z)$$

STRUVE FUNCTIONS

Table 12.1

x	$\mathbf{H}_0(x)$	$\mathbf{H}_1(x)$	$\int_0^x \mathbf{H}_0(t)dt$	$I_0(x)-\mathbf{L}_0(x)$	$I_1(x)-\mathbf{L}_1(x)$	$f_0(x)$	$\frac{2}{\pi}\int_x^\infty \frac{\mathbf{H}_0(t)}{t}dt$
0.0	0.00000 00	0.00000 00	0.000000	1.000000	0.000000	0.00000	1.000000
0.1	0.06359 13	0.00212 07	0.003181	0.938769	0.047939	0.09690	0.959487
0.2	0.12675 90	0.00846 57	0.012704	0.882134	0.091990	0.18791	0.919063
0.3	0.18908 29	0.01898 43	0.028505	0.829724	0.132480	0.27347	0.878819
0.4	0.25014 97	0.03359 25	0.050479	0.781198	0.169710	0.35398	0.838843
0.5	0.30955 59	0.05217 37	0.078480	0.736243	0.203952	0.42982	0.799223
0.6	0.36691 14	0.07457 97	0.112322	0.694573	0.235457	0.50134	0.760044
0.7	0.42184 24	0.10063 17	0.151781	0.655927	0.264454	0.56884	0.721389
0.8	0.47399 44	0.13012 25	0.196597	0.620063	0.291151	0.63262	0.683341
0.9	0.52303 50	0.16281 75	0.246476	0.586763	0.315740	0.69294	0.645976
1.0	0.56865 66	0.19845 73	0.301090	0.555823	0.338395	0.75005	0.609371
1.1	0.61057 87	0.23675 97	0.360084	0.527058	0.359276	0.80418	0.573596
1.2	0.64855 00	0.27742 18	0.423074	0.500300	0.378530	0.85553	0.538719
1.3	0.68235 03	0.32012 31	0.489655	0.475391	0.396290	0.90430	0.504803
1.4	0.71179 25	0.36452 80	0.559399	0.452188	0.412679	0.95066	0.471907
1.5	0.73672 35	0.41028 85	0.631863	0.430561	0.427810	0.99479	0.440086
1.6	0.75702 55	0.45704 72	0.706590	0.410388	0.441783	1.03682	0.409388
1.7	0.77261 68	0.50444 07	0.783111	0.391558	0.454694	1.07691	0.379857
1.8	0.78345 23	0.55210 21	0.860954	0.373970	0.466629	1.11518	0.351533
1.9	0.78952 36	0.59966 45	0.939643	0.357530	0.477666	1.15174	0.324450
2.0	0.79085 88	0.64676 37	1.018701	0.342152	0.487877	1.18672	0.298634
2.1	0.78752 22	0.69304 18	1.097659	0.327756	0.497329	1.22020	0.274109
2.2	0.77961 35	0.73814 96	1.176053	0.314270	0.506083	1.25230	0.250891
2.3	0.76726 65	0.78174 98	1.253434	0.301627	0.514194	1.28309	0.228992
2.4	0.75064 85	0.82351 98	1.329364	0.289765	0.521712	1.31265	0.208417
2.5	0.72995 77	0.86315 42	1.403427	0.278627	0.528685	1.34106	0.189168
2.6	0.70542 23	0.90036 74	1.475227	0.268162	0.535156	1.36840	0.171238
2.7	0.67729 77	0.93489 57	1.544392	0.258319	0.541164	1.39472	0.154618
2.8	0.64586 46	0.96649 98	1.610577	0.249056	0.546746	1.42008	0.139293
2.9	0.61142 64	0.99496 63	1.673465	0.240332	0.551933	1.44455	0.125242
3.0	0.57430 61	1.02010 96	1.732773	0.232107	0.556757	1.46816	0.112439
3.1	0.53484 44	1.04177 30	1.788248	0.224348	0.561246	1.49098	0.100857
3.2	0.49339 57	1.05983 03	1.839675	0.217022	0.565426	1.51305	0.090460
3.3	0.45032 57	1.07418 63	1.886873	0.210099	0.569319	1.53440	0.081212
3.4	0.40600 80	1.08477 74	1.929699	0.203553	0.572948	1.55508	0.073071
3.5	0.36082 08	1.09157 23	1.968046	0.197357	0.576333	1.57512	0.065992
3.6	0.31514 40	1.09457 16	2.001847	0.191488	0.579492	1.59456	0.059928
3.7	0.26935 59	1.09380 77	2.031071	0.185924	0.582442	1.61343	0.054829
3.8	0.22382 98	1.08934 44	2.055726	0.180646	0.585199	1.63176	0.050642
3.9	0.17893 12	1.08127 62	2.075858	0.175634	0.587776	1.64957	0.047311
4.0	0.13501 46	1.06972 67	2.091545	0.170872	0.590187	1.66689	0.044781
4.1	0.09242 08	1.05484 79	2.102905	0.166343	0.592445	1.68375	0.042994
4.2	0.05147 40	1.03681 86	2.110084	0.162032	0.594560	1.70017	0.041891
4.3	+0.01247 93	1.01584 22	2.113265	0.157926	0.596542	1.71616	0.041414
4.4	−0.02427 98	0.99214 51	2.112655	0.154012	0.598402	1.73176	0.041502
4.5	−0.05854 33	0.96597 44	2.108492	0.150279	0.600147	1.74697	0.042096
4.6	−0.09007 71	0.93759 56	2.101037	0.146714	0.601787	1.76182	0.043139
4.7	−0.11867 42	0.90729 01	2.090574	0.143309	0.603328	1.77632	0.044571
4.8	−0.14415 67	0.87535 28	2.077406	0.140053	0.604777	1.79049	0.046335
4.9	−0.16637 66	0.84208 90	2.061852	0.136938	0.606142	1.80434	0.048376
5.0	−0.18521 68	0.80781 19	2.044244	0.133955	0.607426	1.81788	0.050640

$$\int_0^x [I_0(t)-\mathbf{L}_0(t)]dt=f_0(x)$$

13.1. Definitions of Kummer and Whittaker Functions

Kummer's Equation

13.1.1 $$z\frac{d^2w}{dz^2}+(b-z)\frac{dw}{dz}-aw=0$$

It has a regular singularity at $z=0$ and an irregular singularity at ∞.

Independent solutions are

Kummer's Function

13.1.2

$$M(a,b,z)=1+\frac{az}{b}+\frac{(a)_2z^2}{(b)_22!}+\ldots+\frac{(a)_nz^n}{(b)_nn!}+\ldots$$

where

$$(a)_n=a(a+1)(a+2)\ldots(a+n-1),\ (a)_0=1,$$

and

13.1.3

$$U(a,b,z)=\frac{\pi}{\sin\pi b}\left\{\frac{M(a,b,z)}{\Gamma(1+a-b)\Gamma(b)}-z^{1-b}\frac{M(1+a-b,2-b,z)}{\Gamma(a)\Gamma(2-b)}\right\}$$

Parameters (m, n *positive integers*)		$M(a, b, z)$
$b\neq -n$	$a\neq -m$	a convergent series for all values of a, b and z
$b\neq -n$	$a=-m$	a polynomial of degree m in z
$b=-n$	$a\neq -m$	
$b=-n$	$a=-m$, $m>n$	a simple pole at $b=-n$
$b=-n$	$a=-m$, $m\leq n$	undefined

$U(a, b, z)$ is defined even when $b\to\pm n$

As $|z|\to\infty$,

13.1.4

$$M(a,b,z)=\frac{\Gamma(b)}{\Gamma(a)}e^zz^{a-b}[1+O(|z|^{-1})]\qquad(\mathscr{R}z>0)$$

and

13.1.5

$$M(a,b,z)=\frac{\Gamma(b)}{\Gamma(b-a)}(-z)^{-a}[1+O(|z|^{-1})]\qquad(\mathscr{R}z<0)$$

$U(a, b, z)$ is a many-valued function. Its principal branch is given by $-\pi<\arg z\leq\pi$.

Logarithmic Solution

13.1.6

$$U(a,n+1,z)=\frac{(-1)^{n+1}}{n!\Gamma(a-n)}\left[M(a,n+1,z)\ln z+\sum_{r=0}^{\infty}\frac{(a)_rz^r}{(n+1)_rr!}\{\psi(a+r)-\psi(1+r)-\psi(1+n+r)\}\right]+\frac{(n-1)!}{\Gamma(a)}z^{-n}M(a-n,1-n,z)_n$$

for $n=0, 1, 2, \ldots$, where the last function is the sum to n terms. It is to be interpreted as zero when $n=0$, and $\psi(a)=\Gamma'(a)/\Gamma(a)$.

13.1.7 $$U(a,1-n,z)=z^nU(a+n,1+n,z)$$

As $\mathscr{R}z\to\infty$

13.1.8 $$U(a,b,z)=z^{-a}[1+O(|z|^{-1})]$$

Analytic Continuation

13.1.9

$$U(a,b,ze^{\pm\pi i})=\frac{\pi}{\sin\pi b}e^{-z}\left\{\frac{M(b-a,b,z)}{\Gamma(1+a-b)\Gamma(b)}-\frac{e^{\pm\pi i(1-b)}z^{1-b}M(1-a,2-b,z)}{\Gamma(a)\Gamma(2-b)}\right\}$$

where either upper or lower signs are to be taken throughout.

13.1.10

$$U(a,b,ze^{2\pi in})=[1-e^{-2\pi ibn}]\frac{\Gamma(1-b)}{\Gamma(1+a-b)}M(a,b,z)+e^{-2\pi ibn}U(a,b,z)$$

Alternative Notations

${}_1F_1(a;\,b;\,z)$ or $\Phi(a;\,b;\,z)$ for $M(a, b, z)$

$z^{-a}{}_2F_0(a,1+a-b;\,;-1/z)$ or $\Psi(a;\,b;\,z)$ for $U(a, b, z)$

Complete Solution

13.1.11 $$y=AM(a,b,z)+BU(a,b,z)$$

where A and B are arbitrary constants, $b\neq -n$.

Eight Solutions

13.1.12 $$y_1=M(a,b,z)$$

13.1.13 $$y_2=z^{1-b}M(1+a-b,2-b,z)$$

13.1.14 $$y_3=e^zM(b-a,b,-z)$$

13.1.15 $y_4=z^{1-b}e^zM(1-a,\ 2-b,\ -z)$

13.1.16 $y_5=U(a,\ b,\ z)$

13.1.17 $y_6=z^{1-b}U(1+a-b,\ 2-b,\ z)$

13.1.18 $y_7=e^zU(b-a,\ b,\ -z)$

13.1.19 $y_8=z^{1-b}e^zU(1-a,\ 2-b,\ -z)$

Wronskians

If $W\{m,\ n\}=y_my_n'-y_ny_m'$ and

$$\epsilon=sgn\ (\mathscr{I}z)=1 \text{ if } \mathscr{I}z>0, \quad =-1 \text{ if } \mathscr{I}z\leq 0$$

13.1.20

$$W\{1,\ 2\}=W\{3,\ 4\}=W\{1,\ 4\}=-W\{2,\ 3\}=(1-b)z^{-b}e^z$$

13.1.21

$$W\{1,\ 3\}=W\{2,\ 4\}=W\{5,\ 6\}=W\{7,\ 8\}=0$$

13.1.22 $W\{1,\ 5\}=-\Gamma(b)z^{-b}e^z/\Gamma(a)$

13.1.23 $W\{1,\ 7\}=\Gamma(b)e^{\epsilon\pi ib}z^{-b}e^z/\Gamma(b-a)$

13.1.24 $W\{2,\ 5\}=-\Gamma(2-b)z^{-b}e^z/\Gamma(1+a-b)$

13.1.25 $W\{2,\ 7\}=-\Gamma(2-b)z^{-b}e^z/\Gamma(1-a)$

13.1.26 $W\{5,\ 7\}=e^{\epsilon\pi i(b-a)}z^{-b}e^z$

Kummer Transformations

13.1.27 $M(a,\ b,\ z)=e^zM(b-a,\ b,\ -z)$

13.1.28

$$z^{1-b}M(1+a-b,\ 2-b,\ z)=z^{1-b}e^zM(1-a,\ 2-b,\ -z)$$

13.1.29 $U(a,\ b,\ z)=z^{1-b}U(1+a-b,\ 2-b,\ z)$

13.1.30

$$e^zU(b-a,\ b,\ -z)=e^{\epsilon\pi i(1-b)}e^zz^{1-b}U(1-a,\ 2-b,\ -z)$$

Whittaker's Equation

13.1.31 $$\frac{d^2w}{dz^2}+[-\frac{1}{4}+\frac{\kappa}{z}+\frac{(\frac{1}{4}-\mu^2)}{z^2}]\ w=0$$

Solutions:

Whittaker's Functions

13.1.32 $M_{\kappa,\mu}(z)=e^{-\frac{1}{2}z}z^{\frac{1}{2}+\mu}M(\tfrac{1}{2}+\mu-\kappa,\ 1+2\mu,\ z)$

13.1.33

$$W_{\kappa,\mu}(z)=e^{-\frac{1}{2}z}z^{\frac{1}{2}+\mu}U(\tfrac{1}{2}+\mu-\kappa,\ 1+2\mu,\ z)$$
$$(-\pi<\arg z\leq\pi,\ \kappa=\tfrac{1}{2}b-a,\ \mu=\tfrac{1}{2}b-\tfrac{1}{2})$$

13.1.34

$$W_{\kappa,\mu}(z)=\frac{\Gamma(-2\mu)}{\Gamma(\frac{1}{2}-\mu-\kappa)}M_{\kappa,\mu}(z)+\frac{\Gamma(2\mu)}{\Gamma(\frac{1}{2}+\mu-\kappa)}M_{\kappa,-\mu}(z)$$

General Confluent Equation

13.1.35

$$w''+[\frac{2A}{Z}+2f'+\frac{bh'}{h}-h'-\frac{h''}{h'}]w'$$
$$+[\left(\frac{bh'}{h}-h'-\frac{h''}{h'}\right)\left(\frac{A}{Z}+f'\right)+\frac{A(A-1)}{Z^2}$$
$$+\frac{2Af'}{Z}+f''+f'^2-\frac{ah'^2}{h}]w=0$$

Solutions:

13.1.36 $Z^{-A}e^{-f(Z)}M(a,\ b,\ h(Z))$

13.1.37 $Z^{-A}e^{-f(Z)}U(a,\ b,\ h(Z))$

13.2. Integral Representations

$$\mathscr{R}b>\mathscr{R}a>0$$

13.2.1

$$\frac{\Gamma(b-a)\Gamma(a)}{\Gamma(b)}M(a,b,z)=\int_0^1 e^{zt}t^{a-1}(1-t)^{b-a-1}dt$$

13.2.2

$$=2^{1-b}e^{\frac{1}{2}z}\int_{-1}^{+1}e^{-\frac{1}{2}zt}(1+t)^{b-a-1}(1-t)^{a-1}dt$$

13.2.3

$$=2^{1-b}e^{\frac{1}{2}z}\int_0^{\pi}e^{-\frac{1}{2}z\cos\theta}\sin^{b-1}\theta\cot^{b-2a}(\tfrac{1}{2}\theta)d\theta$$

13.2.4

$$=e^{-Az}\int_A^B e^{zt}(t-A)^{a-1}(B-t)^{b-a-1}dt \qquad (A=B-1)$$

$$\mathscr{R}a>0,\ \mathscr{R}z>0$$

13.2.5

$$\Gamma(a)U(a,b,z)=\int_0^{\infty}e^{-zt}t^{a-1}(1+t)^{b-a-1}dt$$

13.2.6

$$=e^z\int_1^{\infty}e^{-zt}(t-1)^{a-1}t^{b-a-1}dt$$

13.2.7

$$=2^{1-b}e^{\frac{1}{2}z}\int_0^{\infty}e^{-\frac{1}{2}z\cosh\theta}\sinh^{b-1}\theta\coth^{b-2a}(\tfrac{1}{2}\theta)d\theta$$

13.2.8 $\Gamma(a)U(a, b, z)$

$$=e^{Az}\int_A^\infty e^{-zt}(t-A)^{a-1}(t+B)^{b-a-1}dt \quad (A=1-B)$$

Similar integrals for $M_{\kappa,\mu}(z)$ and $W_{\kappa,\mu}(z)$ can be deduced with the help of **13.1.32** and **13.1.33.**

Barnes-type Contour Integrals

13.2.9

$$\frac{\Gamma(a)}{\Gamma(b)}M(a, b, z)=\frac{1}{2\pi i}\int_{c-i\infty}^{c+i\infty}\frac{\Gamma(-s)\Gamma(a+s)}{\Gamma(b+s)}(-z)^s ds$$

for $|\arg(-z)|<\frac{1}{2}\pi$, $a, b\neq 0, -1, -2, \ldots$. The contour must separate the poles of $\Gamma(-s)$ from those of $\Gamma(a+s)$; c is finite.

13.2.10

$\Gamma(a)\Gamma(1+a-b)z^a U(a, b, z)$

$$=\frac{1}{2\pi i}\int_{c-i\infty}^{c+i\infty}\Gamma(-s)\Gamma(a+s)\Gamma(1+a-b+s)z^{-s}ds$$

for $|\arg z|<\frac{3\pi}{2}$, $a\neq 0, -1, -2, \ldots, b-a\neq 1, 2, 3, \ldots$. The contour must separate the poles of $\Gamma(-s)$ from those of $\Gamma(a+s)$ and $\Gamma(1+a-b+s)$.

13.3. Connections With Bessel Functions (see chapters 9 and 10)

Bessel Functions as Limiting Cases

If b and z are fixed,

13.3.1 $\lim_{a\to\infty}\{M(a, b, z/a)/\Gamma(b)\}=z^{\frac{1}{2}-\frac{1}{2}b}I_{b-1}(2\sqrt{z})$

13.3.2 $\lim_{a\to\infty}\{M(a, b, -z/a)/\Gamma(b)\}=z^{\frac{1}{2}-\frac{1}{2}b}J_{b-1}(2\sqrt{z})$

13.3.3

$$\lim_{a\to\infty}\{\Gamma(1+a-b)\,U(a, b, z/a)\}=2z^{\frac{1}{2}-\frac{1}{2}b}K_{b-1}(2\sqrt{z})$$

13.3.4

$$\lim_{a\to\infty}\{\Gamma(1+a-b)U(a, b, -z/a)\}$$
$$=-\pi i e^{\pi i b}z^{\frac{1}{2}-\frac{1}{2}b}H^{(1)}_{b-1}(2\sqrt{z}) \quad (\mathscr{I}z>0)$$

13.3.5 $$=\pi i e^{-\pi i b}z^{\frac{1}{2}-\frac{1}{2}b}H^{(2)}_{b-1}(2\sqrt{z}) \quad (\mathscr{I}z<0)$$

Expansions in Series

13.3.6

$$M(a, b, z)=e^{\frac{1}{2}z}\Gamma\left(b-a-\tfrac{1}{2}\right)\left(\tfrac{1}{4}z\right)^{a-b+\frac{1}{2}}$$
$$\cdot\sum_{n=0}^{\infty}\frac{(2b-2a-1)_n(b-2a)_n\left(b-a-\frac{1}{2}+n\right)}{n!(b)_n}(-1)^n I_{b-a-\frac{1}{2}+n}\left(\tfrac{1}{2}z\right) \quad (b\neq 0,-1,-2,\ldots)$$

13.3.7

$$\frac{M(a, b, z)}{\Gamma(b)}=e^{\frac{1}{2}z}\left(\tfrac{1}{2}bz-az\right)^{\frac{1}{2}-\frac{1}{2}b}$$
$$\cdot\sum_{n=0}^{\infty}A_n\left(\tfrac{1}{2}z\right)^{\frac{1}{2}n}(b-2a)^{-\frac{1}{2}n}J_{b-1+n}\left(\sqrt{(2zb-4za)}\right)$$

where

$A_0=1, A_1=0, A_2=\frac{1}{2}b,$

$$(n+1)A_{n+1}=(n+b-1)A_{n-1}+(2a-b)A_{n-2}, \quad (a \text{ real})$$

13.3.8

$$\frac{M(a, b, z)}{\Gamma(b)}$$
$$=e^{hz}\sum_{n=0}^{\infty}C_n z^n(-az)^{\frac{1}{2}(1-b-n)}J_{b-1+n}\left(2\sqrt{(-az)}\right)$$

where

$C_0=1,\ C_1=-bh,\ C_2=-\frac{1}{2}(2h-1)a+\frac{1}{2}b(b+1)h^2,$

$$(n+1)C_{n+1}=[(1-2h)n-bh]C_n$$
$$+[(1-2h)a-h(h-1)(b+n-1)]C_{n-1}$$
$$-h(h-1)aC_{n-2} \quad (h \text{ real})$$

13.3.9 $$M(a, b, z)=\sum_{n=0}^{\infty}C_n(a, b)I_n(z)$$

where

$C_0=1,\ C_1(a, b)=2a/b,$

$$C_{n+1}(a, b)=2aC_n(a+1, b+1)/b-C_{n-1}(a, b)$$

13.4. Recurrence Relations and Differential Properties

13.4.1

$$(b-a)M(a-1, b, z)+(2a-b+z)M(a, b, z)-aM(a+1, b, z)=0$$

13.4.2

$$b(b-1)M(a, b-1, z)+b(1-b-z)M(a, b, z)+z(b-a)M(a, b+1, z)=0$$

13.4.3

$$(1+a-b)M(a, b, z)-aM(a+1, b, z)+(b-1)M(a, b-1, z)=0$$

13.4.4

$$bM(a, b, z)-bM(a-1, b, z)-zM(a, b+1, z)=0$$

13.4.5

$$b(a+z)M(a, b, z)+z(a-b)M(a, b+1, z)-abM(a+1, b, z)=0$$

13.4.6

$$(a-1+z)M(a,b,z)+(b-a)M(a-1,b,z)+(1-b)M(a,b-1,z)=0$$

13.4.7

$$b(1-b+z)M(a,b,z)+b(b-1)M(a-1,b-1,z)-azM(a+1,b+1,z)=0$$

13.4.8 $M'(a,b,z)=\frac{a}{b}M(a+1,b+1,z)$

13.4.9 $\frac{d^n}{dz^n}\{M(a,b,z)\}=\frac{(a)_n}{(b)_n}M(a+n,b+n,z)$

13.4.10 $aM(a+1,b,z)=aM(a,b,z)+zM'(a,b,z)$

13.4.11

$$(b-a)M(a-1,b,z)=(b-a-z)M(a,b,z)+zM'(a,b,z)$$

13.4.12

$$(b-a)M(a,b+1,z)=bM(a,b,z)-bM'(a,b,z)$$

13.4.13

$$(b-1)M(a,b-1,z)=(b-1)M(a,b,z)+zM'(a,b,z)$$

13.4.14

$$(b-1)M(a-1,b-1,z)=(b-1-z)M(a,b,z)+zM'(a,b,z)$$

13.4.15

$$U(a-1,b,z)+(b-2a-z)U(a,b,z)+a(1+a-b)U(a+1,b,z)=0$$

13.4.16

$$(b-a-1)U(a,b-1,z)+(1-b-z)U(a,b,z)+zU(a,b+1,z)=0$$

13.4.17

$$U(a,b,z)-aU(a+1,b,z)-U(a,b-1,z)=0$$

13.4.18

$$(b-a)U(a,b,z)+U(a-1,b,z)-zU(a,b+1,z)=0$$

13.4.19

$$(a+z)U(a,b,z)-zU(a,b+1,z)+a(b-a-1)U(a+1,b,z)=0$$

13.4.20

$$(a+z-1)U(a,b,z)-U(a-1,b,z)+(1+a-b)U(a,b-1,z)=0$$

13.4.21 $U'(a,b,z)=-aU(a+1,b+1,z)$

13.4.22

$$\frac{d^n}{dz^n}\{U(a,b,z)\}=(-1)^n(a)_nU(a+n,b+n,z)$$

13.4.23

$$a(1+a-b)U(a+1,b,z)=aU(a,b,z)+zU'(a,b,z)$$

13.4.24

$$(1+a-b)U(a,b-1,z)=(1-b)U(a,b,z)-zU'(a,b,z)$$

13.4.25 $U(a,b+1,z)=U(a,b,z)-U'(a,b,z)$

13.4.26

$$U(a-1,b,z)=(a-b+z)U(a,b,z)-zU'(a,b,z)$$

13.4.27

$$U(a-1,b-1,z)=(1-b+z)U(a,b,z)-zU'(a,b,z)$$

13.4.28 $2\mu M_{\kappa-\frac{1}{2},\mu-\frac{1}{2}}(z)-z^{\frac{1}{2}}M_{\kappa,\mu}(z)=2\mu M_{\kappa+\frac{1}{2},\mu-\frac{1}{2}}(z)$

13.4.29

$$(1+2\mu+2\kappa)M_{\kappa+1,\mu}(z)-(1+2\mu-2\kappa)M_{\kappa-1,\mu}(z)=2(2\kappa-z)M_{\kappa,\mu}(z)$$

13.4.30

$$W_{\kappa+\frac{1}{2},\mu}(z)-z^{\frac{1}{2}}W_{\kappa,\mu+\frac{1}{2}}(z)+(\kappa+\mu)W_{\kappa-\frac{1}{2},\mu}(z)=0$$

13.4.31

$$(2\kappa-z)W_{\kappa,\mu}(z)+W_{\kappa+1,\mu}(z)=(\mu-\kappa+\tfrac{1}{2})(\mu+\kappa-\tfrac{1}{2})W_{\kappa-1,\mu}(z)$$

13.4.32

$$zM'_{\kappa,\mu}(z)=(\tfrac{1}{2}z-\kappa)M_{\kappa,\mu}(z)+(\tfrac{1}{2}+\mu+\kappa)M_{\kappa+1,\mu}(z)$$

13.4.33 $zW'_{\kappa,\mu}(z)=(\tfrac{1}{2}z-\kappa)W_{\kappa,\mu}(z)-W_{\kappa+1,\mu}(z)$

13.5. Asymptotic Expansions and Limiting Forms

For $|z|$ large, (a, b fixed)

13.5.1

$$\frac{M(a,b,z)}{\Gamma(b)}=$$

$$\frac{e^{\pm i\pi a}z^{-a}}{\Gamma(b-a)}\left\{\sum_{n=0}^{R-1}\frac{(a)_n(1+a-b)_n}{n!}(-z)^{-n}+O(|z|^{-R})\right\}$$

$$+\frac{e^{z}z^{a-b}}{\Gamma(a)}\left\{\sum_{n=0}^{S-1}\frac{(b-a)_n(1-a)_n}{n!}z^{-n}+O(|z|^{-S})\right\}$$

he upper sign being taken if $-\frac{1}{2}\pi<\arg z<\frac{3}{2}\pi$, the ower sign if $-\frac{3}{2}\pi<\arg z\leq-\frac{1}{2}\pi$.

13.5.2

$$U(a,b,z)=z^{-a}\left\{\sum_{n=0}^{R-1}\frac{(a)_n(1+a-b)_n}{n!}(-z)^{-n}\right.$$

$$\left.+O(|z|^{-R})\right\}\quad(-\tfrac{3}{2}\pi<\arg z<\tfrac{3}{2}\pi)$$

Converging Factors for the Remainders

13.5.3

$$O(|z|^{-R})=\frac{(a)_R(1+a-b)_R}{R!}(-z)^{-R}$$

$$\left[\tfrac{1}{2}+\frac{(\frac{1}{8}+\frac{1}{4}b-\frac{1}{2}a+\frac{1}{4}z-\frac{1}{4}R)}{z}+O(|z|^{-2})\right]$$

nd

13.5.4

$$O(|z|^{-S})=\frac{(b-a)_S(1-a)_S}{S!}z^{-S}$$

$$\left[\tfrac{2}{3}-b+2a+z-S+O(|z|^{-1})\right]$$

vhere the R'th and S'th terms are the smallest in he expansions **13.5.1** and **13.5.2.**

For small z (a, b fixed)

13.5.5 As $|z|\to 0$, $M(a,b,0)=1$, $b\neq -n$

13.5.6 $$U(a,b,z)=\frac{\Gamma(b-1)}{\Gamma(a)}z^{1-b}+O(|z|^{\mathscr{R}b-2})\qquad(\mathscr{R}b\geq 2,\ b\neq 2)$$

13.5.7 $$=\frac{\Gamma(b-1)}{\Gamma(a)}z^{1-b}+O(|\ln z|)\qquad(b=2)$$

13.5.8 $$=\frac{\Gamma(b-1)}{\Gamma(a)}z^{1-b}+O(1)\qquad(1<\mathscr{R}b<2)$$

13.5.9 $$=-\frac{1}{\Gamma(a)}[\ln z+\psi(a)+2\gamma]+O(|z\ln z|)\qquad(b=1)$$

13.5.10 $$U(a,b,z)=\frac{\Gamma(1-b)}{\Gamma(1+a-b)}+O(|z|^{1-\mathscr{R}b})\qquad(0<\mathscr{R}b<1)$$

13.5.11 $$=\frac{1}{\Gamma(1+a)}+O(|z\ln z|)\qquad(b=0)$$

13.5.12 $$=\frac{\Gamma(1-b)}{\Gamma(1+a-b)}+O(|z|)\qquad(\mathscr{R}b\leq 0,\ b\neq 0)$$

For large a (b, z fixed)

13.5.13

$$M(a,b,z)=$$

$$\Gamma(b)e^{\frac{1}{2}z}(\tfrac{1}{2}bz-az)^{\frac{1}{2}-\frac{1}{2}b}J_{b-1}(\sqrt{(2bz-4az)})$$

$$[1+O(|\tfrac{1}{2}b-a|^{-\sigma})]$$

where

$$|z|=\left|\tfrac{1}{2}b-a\right|^{\rho}\text{ and }\sigma=\min(1-\rho,\ \tfrac{1}{2}-\tfrac{3}{2}\rho),\ 0\leq\rho<\tfrac{1}{3}.$$

13.5.14

$$M(a,b,x)=\Gamma(b)e^{\frac{1}{2}x}(\tfrac{1}{2}bx-ax)^{\frac{1}{4}-\frac{1}{2}b}\pi^{-\frac{1}{2}}$$

$$\cos(\sqrt{(2bx-4ax)}-\tfrac{1}{2}b\pi+\tfrac{1}{4}\pi)$$

$$[1+O(|\tfrac{1}{2}b-a|^{-\frac{1}{2}})]$$

as $a\to-\infty$ for b bounded, x real.

13.5.15

$$U(a,b,z)=$$

$$\Gamma(\tfrac{1}{2}b-a+\tfrac{1}{2})e^{\frac{1}{2}z}z^{\frac{1}{2}-\frac{1}{2}b}[\cos(a\pi)J_{b-1}(\sqrt{(2bz-4az)})$$

$$-\sin(a\pi)Y_{b-1}(\sqrt{(2bz-4az)})]\ [1+O(|\tfrac{1}{2}b-a|^{-\sigma})]$$

where σ is defined in **13.5.13.**

13.5.16

$$U(a,b,x)=\Gamma(\tfrac{1}{2}b-a+\tfrac{1}{4})\pi^{-\frac{1}{2}}e^{\frac{1}{2}x}x^{\frac{1}{4}-\frac{1}{2}b}$$

$$\cos(\sqrt{(2bx-4ax)}-\tfrac{1}{2}b\pi+a\pi+\tfrac{1}{4}\pi)$$

$$[1+O(|\tfrac{1}{2}b-a|^{-\frac{1}{2}})]$$

as $a\to-\infty$ for b bounded, x real.

For large real a, b, x

If $\cosh^2\theta=x/(2b-4a)$ so that $x>2b-a>1$,

13.5.17

$$M(a,b,x)=\Gamma(b)\sin(a\pi)$$

$$\exp[(b-2a)(\tfrac{1}{4}\sinh 2\theta-\theta+\cosh^2\theta)]$$

$$[(b-2a)\cosh\theta]^{1-b}[\pi(\tfrac{1}{2}b-a)\sinh 2\theta]^{-\frac{1}{2}}$$

$$[1+O(|\tfrac{1}{2}b-a|^{-1})]$$

13.5.18

$$U(a,b,x)=\exp[(b-2a)(\tfrac{1}{4}\sinh 2\theta-\theta+\cosh^2\theta)]$$

$$[(b-2a)\cosh\theta]^{1-b}[(\tfrac{1}{2}b-a)\sinh 2\theta]^{-\frac{1}{2}}$$

$$[1+O(|\tfrac{1}{2}b-a|^{-1})]$$

If $x=(2b-4a)[1+t/(b-2a)^{\frac{2}{3}}]$, so that

$$x\sim 2b-4a$$

13.5.19

$$M(a, b, x)=e^{\frac{1}{2}x}(b-2a)^{\frac{1}{3}-b}\Gamma(b)[\mathrm{Ai}(t)\cos(a\pi)+\mathrm{Bi}(t)\sin(a\pi)+O(|\tfrac{1}{2}b-a|^{-\frac{2}{3}})]$$

13.5.20

$$U(a, b, x)=e^{\frac{1}{2}x+a-\frac{1}{2}b}\Gamma(\tfrac{1}{3})\pi^{-\frac{1}{2}}x6^{-\frac{1}{6}}\{1-t\Gamma(\tfrac{5}{6})(bx-2ax)^{-\frac{1}{3}}3^{\frac{1}{2}}\pi^{-\frac{1}{2}}+O(|\tfrac{1}{2}b-a|^{-\frac{2}{3}})\}$$

If $\cos^2\theta=x/(2b-4a)$ so that $2b-4a>x>0$,

13.5.21

$$M(a, b, x)=\Gamma(b)\exp\{(b-2a)\cos^2\theta\}[(b-2a)\cos\theta]^{1-b}[\pi(\tfrac{1}{2}b-a)\sin 2\theta]^{-\frac{1}{2}}[\sin(a\pi)+\sin\{(\tfrac{1}{2}b-a)(2\theta-\sin 2\theta)+\tfrac{1}{4}\pi\}+O(|\tfrac{1}{2}b-a|^{-1})]$$

13.5.22

$$U(a, b, x)=\exp[(b-2a)\cos^2\theta][(b-2a)\cos\theta]^{1-b}[(\tfrac{1}{2}b-a)\sin 2\theta]^{-\frac{1}{2}}\{\sin[(\tfrac{1}{2}b-a)(2\theta-\sin 2\theta)+\tfrac{1}{4}\pi]+O(|\tfrac{1}{2}b-a|^{-1})\}$$

13.6. Special Cases

	$M(a, b, z)$			Relation	Function
	a	b	z		
13.6.1	$\nu+\frac{1}{2}$	$2\nu+1$	$2iz$	$\Gamma(1+\nu)e^{iz}(\frac{1}{2}z)^{-\nu}J_\nu(z)$	Bessel
13.6.2	$-\nu+\frac{1}{2}$	$-2\nu+1$	$2iz$	$\Gamma(1-\nu)e^{iz}(\frac{1}{2}z)^{\nu}[\cos(\nu\pi)J_\nu(z)-\sin(\nu\pi)Y_\nu(z)]$	Bessel
13.6.3	$\nu+\frac{1}{2}$	$2\nu+1$	$2z$	$\Gamma(1+\nu)e^{z}(\frac{1}{2}z)^{-\nu}I_\nu(z)$	Modified Bessel
13.6.4	$n+1$	$2n+2$	$2iz$	$\Gamma(\frac{3}{2}+n)e^{iz}(\frac{1}{2}z)^{-n-\frac{1}{2}}J_{n+\frac{1}{2}}(z)$	Spherical Bessel
13.6.5	$-n$	$-2n$	$2iz$	$\Gamma(\frac{1}{2}-n)e^{iz}(\frac{1}{2}z)^{n+\frac{1}{2}}J_{-n-\frac{1}{2}}(z)$	Spherical Bessel
13.6.6	$n+1$	$2n+2$	$2z$	$\Gamma(\frac{3}{2}+n)e^{z}(\frac{1}{2}z)^{-n-\frac{1}{2}}I_{n+\frac{1}{2}}(z)$	Spherical Bessel
13.6.7	$n+\frac{1}{2}$	$2n+1$	$-2\sqrt{ix}$	$\Gamma(1+n)e^{-2x\pi}(\frac{1}{2}ix\pi)^{-n}(\mathrm{ber}_n\, x+i\,\mathrm{bei}_n\, x)$	Kelvin
13.6.8	$L+1-i\eta$	$2L+2$	$2ix$	$e^{ix}F_L(\eta, x)x^{-L-1}/C_L(\eta)$	Coulomb Wave
13.6.9	$-n$	$\alpha+1$	x	$\frac{n!}{(\alpha+1)_n}L_n^{(\alpha)}(x)$	Laguerre
13.6.10	a	$a+1$	$-x$	$ax^{-a}\gamma(a, x)$	Incomplete Gamma
13.6.11	$-n$	$1+\nu-n$	x	$\frac{(n!)^{\frac{1}{2}}x^{\frac{1}{2}n}}{(1+\nu-n)_n}\rho_n(\nu, x)$	Poisson-Charlier
13.6.12	a	a	z	e^{z}	Exponential
13.6.13	1	2	$-2iz$	$\frac{e^{-iz}}{z}\sin z$	Trigonometric
13.6.14	1	2	$2z$	$\frac{e^{z}}{z}\sinh z$	Hyperbolic
13.6.15	$-\frac{1}{2}\nu$	$\frac{1}{2}$	$\frac{1}{2}z^2$	$2^{-\frac{1}{2}}\exp(\frac{1}{4}z^2)E_\nu^{(0)}(z)$	Weber or Parabolic Cylinder
13.6.16	$\frac{1}{2}-\frac{1}{2}\nu$	$\frac{3}{2}$	$\frac{1}{2}z^2$	$\frac{\exp(\frac{1}{4}z^2)}{2z}E_\nu^{(1)}(z)$	
13.6.17	$-n$	$\frac{1}{2}$	$\frac{1}{2}x^2$	$\frac{n!}{(2n)!}(-\frac{1}{2})^{-n}He_{2n}(x)$	Hermite
13.6.18	$-n$	$\frac{3}{2}$	$\frac{1}{2}x^2$	$\frac{n!}{(2n+1)!}(-\frac{1}{2})^{-n}\frac{1}{x}He_{2n+1}(x)$	Hermite
13.6.19	$\frac{1}{2}$	$\frac{3}{2}$	$-x^2$	$\frac{\pi^{\frac{1}{2}}}{2x}\mathrm{erf}\, x$	Error Integral
13.6.20	$\frac{1}{2}m+\frac{1}{2}$	$1+n$	r^2	$\frac{n!r^{-2n+m-1}}{\Gamma(\frac{1}{2}m+\frac{1}{2})}e^{r^2}T(m, n, r)$	Toronto

13.6. Special Cases—Continued

	$U(a, b, z)$			Relation	Function
	a	b	z		
13.6.21	$\nu+\frac{1}{2}$	$2\nu+1$	$2z$	$\pi^{-\frac{1}{2}}e^{z}(2z)^{-\nu}K_{\nu}(z)$	Modified Bessel
13.6.22	$\nu+\frac{1}{2}$	$2\nu+1$	$-2iz$	$\frac{1}{2}\pi^{\frac{1}{2}}e^{i[\pi(\nu+\frac{1}{2})-z]}(2z)^{-\nu}H_{\nu}^{(1)}(z)$	Hankel
13.6.23	$\nu+\frac{1}{2}$	$2\nu+1$	$2iz$	$\frac{1}{2}\pi^{\frac{1}{2}}e^{-i[\pi(\nu+\frac{1}{2})-z]}(2z)^{-\nu}H_{\nu}^{(2)}(z)$	Hankel
13.6.24	$n+1$	$2n+2$	$2z$	$\pi^{-\frac{1}{2}}e^{z}(2z)^{-n-\frac{1}{2}}K_{n+\frac{1}{2}}(z)$	Spherical Bessel
13.6.25	$\frac{5}{6}$	$\frac{5}{3}$	$\frac{4}{3}z^{3/2}$	$\pi^{\frac{1}{2}}z^{-1}\exp(\frac{2}{3}z^{3/2})2^{-2/3}3^{5/6}\ \mathrm{Ai}\ (z)$	Airy
13.6.26	$n+\frac{1}{2}$	$2n+1$	$\sqrt{ix}$	$i^{n}\pi^{-\frac{1}{2}}e^{\sqrt{ix}}(2\sqrt{ix})^{-n}[\mathrm{ker}_n\,x+i\,\mathrm{kei}_n\,x]$	Kelvin
13.6.27	$-n$	$\alpha+1$	x	$(-1)^{n}n!L_{n}^{(\alpha)}(x)$	Laguerre
13.6.28	$1-a$	$1-a$	x	$e^{x}\Gamma(a, x)$	Incomplete Gamma
13.6.29	1	1	$-x$	$-e^{-x}\ \mathrm{Ei}\ (x)$	Exponential Integral
13.6.30	1	1	x	$e^{x}E_{1}(x)$	Exponential Integral
13.6.31	1	1	$-\ln x$	$-\frac{1}{x}\ \mathrm{li}\ (x)$	Logarithmic Integral
13.6.32	$\frac{1}{2}m-n$	$1+m$	x	$\Gamma(1+n-\frac{1}{2}m)e^{x-\pi i(\frac{1}{2}m-n)}\omega_{n,\,m}(x)$	Cunningham
13.6.33	$-\frac{1}{2}\nu$	0	$2x$	$\Gamma(1+\frac{1}{2}\nu)e^{x}k_{\nu}(x)$ for $x>0$	Bateman
13.6.34	1	1	ix	$e^{ix}[-\frac{1}{2}\pi i+i\ \mathrm{Si}\ (x)-\mathrm{Ci}\ (x)]$	Sine and Cosine Integral
13.6.35	1	1	$-ix$	$e^{-ix}[\frac{1}{2}\pi i-i\ \mathrm{Si}\ (x)-\mathrm{Ci}\ (x)]$	Sine and Cosine Integral
13.6.36	$-\frac{1}{2}\nu$	$\frac{1}{2}$	$\frac{1}{2}z^{2}$	$2^{-\frac{1}{2}\nu}e^{z^{2}/4}D_{\nu}(z)$	Weber or
13.6.37	$\frac{1}{2}-\frac{1}{2}\nu$	$\frac{3}{2}$	$\frac{1}{2}z^{2}$	$2^{\frac{1}{2}-\frac{1}{2}\nu}e^{z^{2}/4}D_{\nu}(z)/z$	Parabolic Cylinder
13.6.38	$\frac{1}{2}-\frac{1}{2}n$	$\frac{3}{2}$	x^{2}	$2^{-n}H_{n}(x)/x$	Hermite
13.6.39	$\frac{1}{2}$	$\frac{1}{2}$	x^{2}	$\sqrt{\pi}\ \exp\ (x^{2})\ \mathrm{erfc}\,x$	Error Integral

13.7. Zeros and Turning Values

If $j_{b-1,r}$ is the r'th positive zero of $J_{b-1}(x)$, then a first approximation X_0 to the r'th positive zero of $M(a, b, x)$ is

13.7.1 $$X_0=j_{b-1,r}^2\{1/(2b-4a)+O(1/(\tfrac{1}{2}b-a)^2)\}$$

13.7.2 $$X_0\approx\frac{\pi^2(r+\frac{1}{2}b-\frac{3}{4})^2}{2b-4a}$$

A closer approximation is given by

13.7.3 $$X_1=X_0-M(a, b, X_0)/M'(a, b, X_0)$$

For the derivative,

13.7.4 $$M'(a, b, X_1)=M'(a, b, X_0)\{1+(b-X_0)\frac{M(a, b, X_0)}{M'(a, b, X_0)}\}$$

If X_0' is the first approximation to a turning value of $M(a, b, x)$, that is, to a zero of $M'(a, b, x)$ then a better approximation is

13.7.5 $$X_1'=X_0'-\frac{X_0'M'(a, b, X_0')}{aM(a, b, X_0')}$$

The self-adjoint equation **13.1.1** can also be written

13.7.6 $$\frac{d}{dz}\left[z^{b}e^{-z}\frac{dw}{dz}\right]=az^{b-1}e^{-z}w$$

The Sonine-Polya Theorem

The maxima and minima of $|w|$ form an increasing or decreasing sequence according as

$$-ax^{2b-1}e^{-2x}$$

is an increasing or decreasing function of x, that is they form an increasing sequence for $M(a, b, x$ if $a>0$, $x<b-\frac{1}{2}$ or if $a<0$, $x>b-\frac{1}{2}$, and a decreasing sequence if $a>0$ and $x>b-\frac{1}{2}$ or if $a<0$ and $x<b-\frac{1}{2}$.

The turning values of $|w|$ lie near the curves

13.7.7

$$w=\pm\Gamma(b)\pi^{-1/2}e^{x/2}(\tfrac{1}{2}bx-ax)^{\frac{1}{4}-\frac{1}{2}b}\{1-x/(2b-4a)\}^{-1/}$$

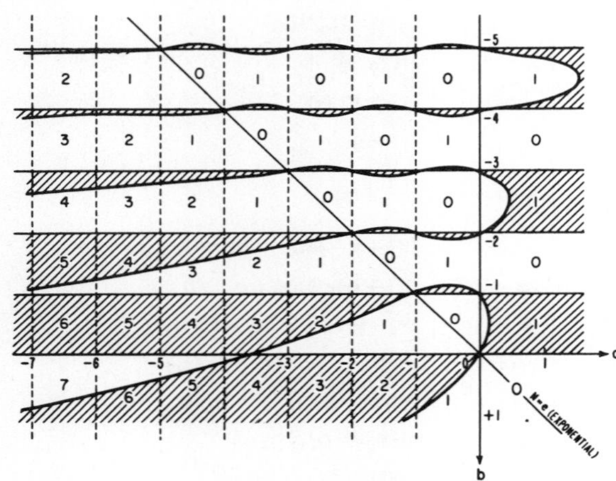

FIGURE 13.1.

Figure 13.1 shows the curves on which $M(a, b, x)=0$ in the a, b plane when $x=1$. The function is positive in the unshaded areas, and negative in the shaded areas. The number in each square gives the number of real positive zeros of $M(a, b, x)$ as a function of x in that square. The vertical boundaries to the left are to be included in each square.

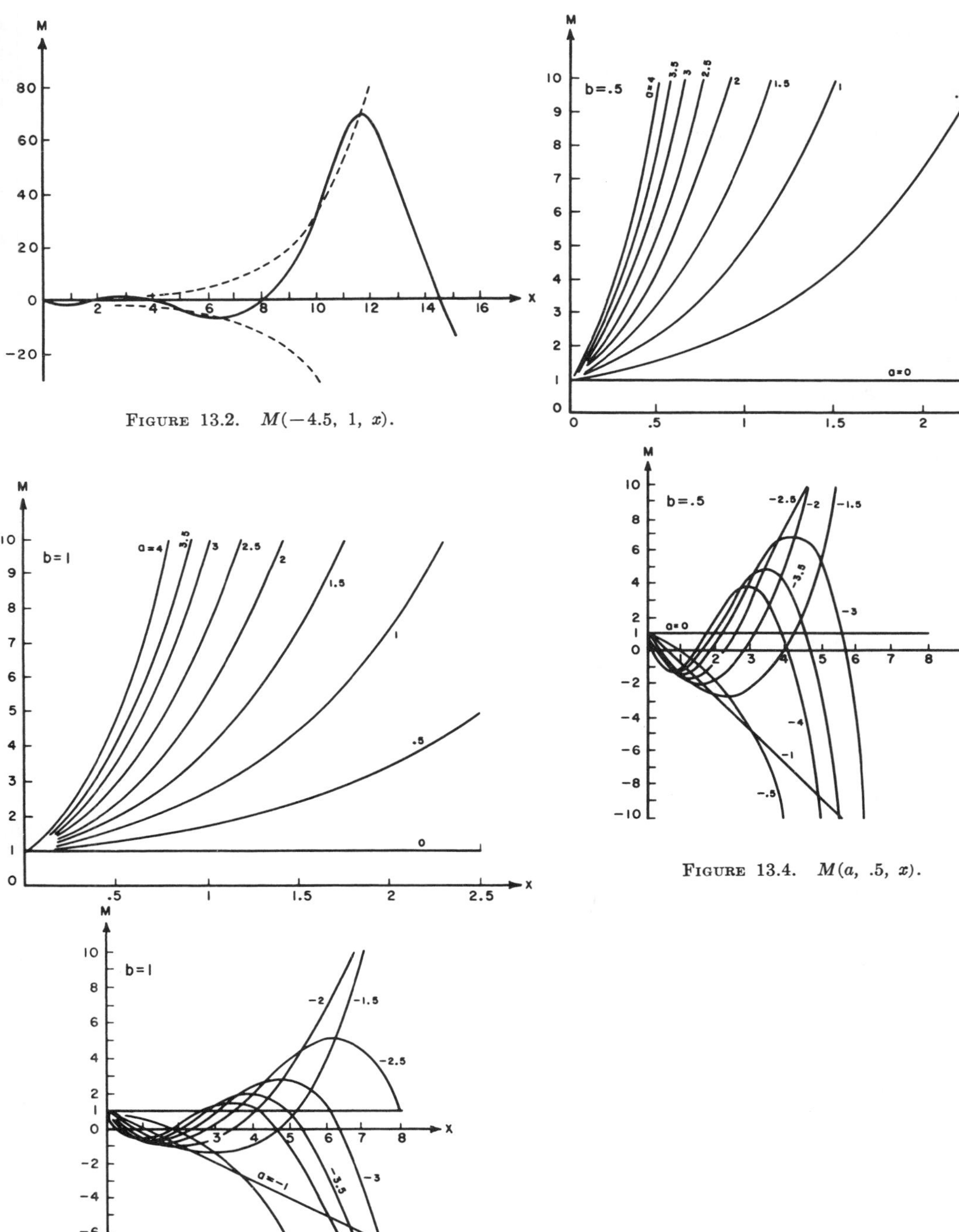

FIGURE 13.2. $M(-4.5, 1, x)$.

FIGURE 13.4. $M(a, .5, x)$.

FIGURE 13.3. $M(a, 1, x)$.

14. Coulomb Wave Functions

14.1. Differential Equation, Series Expansions

Differential Equation

14.1.1

$$\frac{d^2w}{d\rho^2}+\left[1-\frac{2\eta}{\rho}-\frac{L(L+1)}{\rho^2}\right]w=0$$

$(\rho>0,\ -\infty<\eta<\infty,\ L$ a non-negative integer)

The Coulomb wave equation has a regular singularity at $\rho=0$ with indices $L+1$ and $-L$; it has an irregular singularity at $\rho=\infty$.

General Solution

14.1.2

$$w=C_1F_L(\eta,\ \rho)+C_2G_L(\eta,\ \rho) \qquad (C_1,\ C_2 \text{ constants})$$

where $F_L(\eta,\ \rho)$ is the regular Coulomb wave function and $G_L(\eta,\ \rho)$ is the irregular (logarithmic) Coulomb wave function.

Regular Coulomb Wave Function $F_L(\eta, \rho)$

14.1.3

$$F_L(\eta,\rho)=C_L(\eta)\rho^{L+1}e^{-i\rho}M(L+1-i\eta,\ 2L+2,\ 2i\rho)$$

14.1.4

$$=C_L(\eta)\rho^{L+1}\Phi_L(\eta,\ \rho)$$

14.1.5 $$\Phi_L(\eta,\ \rho)=\sum_{k=L+1}^{\infty}A_k^L(\eta)\rho^{k-L-1}$$

14.1.6

$$A_{L+1}^L=1,\quad A_{L+2}^L=\frac{\eta}{L+1},$$

$$(k+L)(k-L-1)A_k^L=2\eta A_{k-1}^L-A_{k-2}^L \qquad (k>L+2)$$

14.1.7 $$C_L(\eta)=\frac{2^Le^{-\frac{\pi\eta}{2}}|\Gamma(L+1+i\eta)|}{\Gamma(2L+2)}$$

(See chapter **6**.)

14.1.8 $$C_0^2(\eta)=2\pi\eta(e^{2\pi\eta}-1)^{-1}$$

14.1.9 $$C_L^2(\eta)=\frac{p_L(\eta)C_0^2(\eta)}{2\eta(2L+1)}$$

14.1.10 $$C_L(\eta)=\frac{(L^2+\eta^2)^{\frac{1}{2}}}{L(2L+1)}C_{L-1}(\eta)$$

14.1.11 $$\frac{p_L(\eta)}{2\eta}=\frac{(1+\eta^2)(4+\eta^2)\ldots(L^2+\eta^2)2^{2L}}{(2L+1)[(2L)!]^2}$$

14.1.12 $$F_L'=\frac{d}{d\rho}F_L(\eta,\ \rho)=C_L(\eta)\rho^L\Phi_L^*(\eta,\ \rho)$$

14.1.13 $$\Phi_L^*(\eta,\ \rho)=\sum_{k=L+1}^{\infty}kA_k^L(\eta)\rho^{k-L-1}$$

Irregular Coulomb Wave Function $G_L(\eta, \rho)$

14.1.14

$$G_L(\eta,\ \rho)=\frac{2\eta}{C_0^2(\eta)}F_L(\eta,\ \rho)\left[\ln 2\rho+\frac{q_L(\eta)}{p_L(\eta)}\right]+\theta_L(\eta,\ \rho)$$

14.1.15 $$\theta_L(\eta,\ \rho)=D_L(\eta)\rho^{-L}\psi_L(\eta,\ \rho)$$

14.1.16 $$D_L(\eta)C_L(\eta)=\frac{1}{2L+1}$$

14.1.17 $$\psi_L(\eta,\ \rho)=\sum_{k=-L}^{\infty}a_k^L(\eta)\rho^{k+L}$$

14.1.18

$$a_{-L}^L=1,\quad a_{L+1}^L=0,$$

$$(k-L-1)(k+L)a_k^L=2\eta a_{k-1}^L-a_{k-2}^L-(2k-1)p_L(\eta)A_k^L$$

14.1.19

$$\frac{q_L(\eta)}{p_L(\eta)}=\sum_{s=1}^{L}\frac{s}{s^2+\eta^2}-\sum_{s=1}^{2L+1}\frac{1}{s}$$

$$+\mathscr{R}\left\{\frac{\Gamma'(1+i\eta)}{\Gamma(1+i\eta)}\right\}+2\gamma+\frac{r_L(\eta)}{p_L(\eta)}$$

(See **Table 6.8.**)

14.1.20

$$r_L(\eta)=\frac{(-1)^{L+1}}{(2L)!}\mathscr{I}\left\{\frac{1}{2L+1}+\frac{2(i\eta-L)}{2L(1!)}\right.$$

$$+\frac{2^2(i\eta-L)(i\eta-L+1)}{(2L-1)(2!)}+\ldots$$

$$\left.+\frac{2^{2L}(i\eta-L)(i\eta-L+1)\ldots(i\eta+L-1)}{(2L)!}\right\}$$

14.1.21

$$G_L'=\frac{dG_L}{d\rho}=\frac{2\eta}{C_0^2(\eta)}\left\{F_L'\left[\ln 2\rho+\frac{q_L(\eta)}{p_L(\eta)}\right]+\rho^{-1}F_L(\eta,\ \rho)\right\}$$

$$+\theta_L'(\eta,\ \rho)$$

14.1.22 $$\theta'_L=\frac{d}{d\rho}\theta_L(\eta,\rho)=D_L(\eta)\rho^{-L-1}\psi^*_L(\eta,\rho)$$

14.1.23 $$\psi^*_L(\eta,\rho)=\sum_{k=-L}^{\infty}ka^L_k(\eta)\rho^{k+L}$$

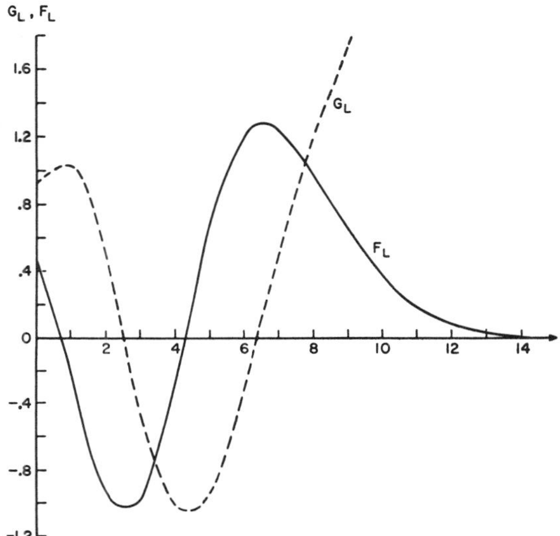

FIGURE 14.1. $F_L(\eta,\rho)$, $G_L(\eta,\rho)$.

$\eta=1$, $\rho=10$

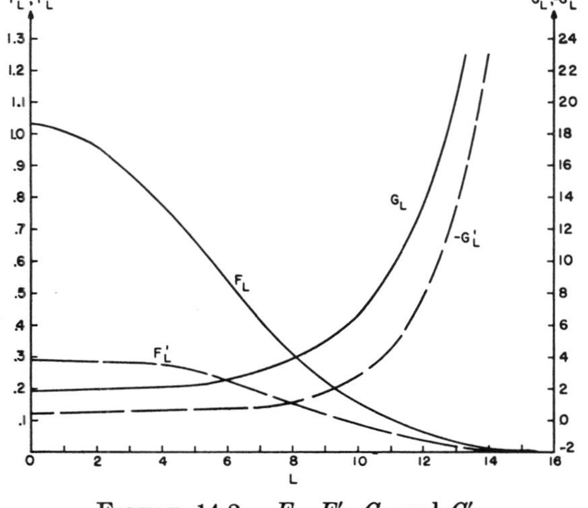

FIGURE 14.2. F_L, F'_L, G_L and G'_L.

$\eta=10$, $\rho=20$

14.2. Recurrence and Wronskian Relations

Recurrence Relations

If $u_L=F_L(\eta,\rho)$ or $G_L(\eta,\rho)$,

14.2.1 $$L\frac{du_L}{d\rho}=(L^2+\eta^2)^{\frac{1}{2}}u_{L-1}-\left(\frac{L^2}{\rho}+\eta\right)u_L$$

14.2.2

$$(L+1)\frac{du_L}{d\rho}=\left[\frac{(L+1)^2}{\rho}+\eta\right]u_L-[(L+1)^2+\eta^2]^{\frac{1}{2}}u_{L+1}$$

14.2.3

$$L[(L+1)^2+\eta^2]^{\frac{1}{2}}u_{L+1}=(2L+1)\left[\eta+\frac{L(L+1)}{\rho}\right]u_L-(L+1)[L^2+\eta^2]^{\frac{1}{2}}u_{L-1}$$

Wronskian Relations

14.2.4 $$F'_LG_L-F_LG'_L=1$$

14.2.5 $$F_{L-1}G_L-F_LG_{L-1}=L(L^2+\eta^2)^{-\frac{1}{2}}$$

14.3. Integral Representations

14.3.1

$$F_L+iG_L=\frac{ie^{-i\rho}\rho^{-L}}{(2L+1)!C_L(\eta)}\int_0^{\infty}e^{-t}t^{L-i\eta}(t+2i\rho)^{L+i\eta}dt$$

14.3.2

$$F_L-iG_L=\frac{e^{-\pi\eta}\rho^{L+1}}{(2L+1)!C_L(\eta)}\int_{-1}^{-i\infty}e^{-i\rho t}(1-t)^{L-i\eta}(1+t)^{L+i\eta}dt$$

14.3.3

$$F_L+iG_L=\frac{e^{-\pi\eta}\rho^{L+1}}{(2L+1)!C_L(\eta)}\cdot\int_0^{\infty}\{(1-\tanh^2 t)^{L+1}\exp[-i(\rho\tanh t-2\eta t)]+i(1+t^2)^L\exp[-\rho t+2\eta\arctan t]\}dt$$

14.4. Bessel Function Expansions

Expansion in Terms of Bessel-Clifford Functions

14.4.1

$$F_L(\eta,\rho)=C_L(\eta)\frac{(2L+1)!}{(2\eta)^{2L+1}}\rho^{-L}\sum_{k=2L+1}^{\infty}b_kt^{k/2}I_k(2\sqrt{t})$$

$$(t=2\eta\rho,\ \eta>0)$$

14.4.2

$$G_L(\eta,\rho)\sim D_L(\eta)\lambda_L(\eta)\rho^{-L}\sum_{k=2L+1}^{\infty}(-1)^kb_kt^{k/2}K_k(2\sqrt{t})$$

14.4.3

$$b_{2L+1}=1, \quad b_{2L+2}=0,$$

$$4\eta^2(k-2L)b_{k+1}+kb_{k-1}+b_{k-2}=0 \qquad (k\geq 2L+2)$$

14.4.4

$$\lambda_L(\eta) \sum_{k=2L+1}^{\infty} (-1)^k(k-1)!b_k=2$$

(See chapter **9**.)

Expansion in Terms of Spherical Bessel Functions

14.4.5

$$F_L(\eta,\rho)= 1\cdot 3\cdot 5 \ldots (2L+1)\rho C_L(\eta) \sum_{k=L}^{\infty} b_k\sqrt{\frac{\pi}{2\rho}}\, J_{k+\frac{1}{2}}(\rho)$$

14.4.6

$$b_L=1,\, b_{L+1}=\frac{2L+3}{L+1}\,\eta$$

$$b_k=\frac{(2k+1)}{k(k+1)-L(L+1)} \left\{2\eta b_{k-1}-\frac{(k-1)(k-2)-L(L+1)}{2k-3}\, b_{k-2}\right\} \qquad (k>L+1)$$

14.4.7

$$F'_L(\eta,\rho)=1\cdot 3\cdot 5 \ldots (2L+1)\rho C_L(\eta) \left\{\frac{(L+1)}{(2L+1)}\, b_L\sqrt{\frac{\pi}{2\rho}}\, J_{L-\frac{1}{2}}(\rho)+\frac{(L+2)}{(2L+3)}\cdot b_{L+1} \cdot\sqrt{\frac{\pi}{2\rho}}\, J_{L+\frac{3}{2}}(\rho)+\sum_{k=L+1}^{\infty} b'_k\sqrt{\frac{\pi}{2\rho}}\, J_{k+\frac{1}{2}}(\rho)\right\}$$

14.4.8 $$b'_k=\frac{(k+2)}{(2k+3)}\, b_{k+1}-\frac{(k-1)}{(2k-1)}\, b_{k-1}$$

Expansion in Terms of Airy Functions

$$x=(2\eta-\rho)/(2\eta)^{1/3} \qquad \mu=(2\eta)^{2/3},\ \eta>>0$$

$$|\rho-2\eta|<2\eta$$

14.4.9

$$\left.\begin{matrix}F_0(\eta,\rho)\\ G_0(\eta,\rho)\end{matrix}\right\}=\pi^{\frac{1}{2}}(2\eta)^{\frac{1}{6}}\left\{\begin{matrix}\mathrm{Ai}(x)\\ \mathrm{Bi}(x)\end{matrix}\left[1+\frac{g_1}{\mu}+\frac{g_2}{\mu^2}+\cdots\right] +\begin{matrix}\mathrm{Ai}'(x)\\ \mathrm{Bi}'(x)\end{matrix}\left[\frac{f_1}{\mu}+\frac{f_2}{\mu^2}+\cdots\right]\right\}$$

14.4.10

$$\left.\begin{matrix}F'_0(\eta,\rho)\\ G'_0(\eta,\rho)\end{matrix}\right\}=-\pi^{\frac{1}{2}}(2\eta)^{-\frac{1}{6}}\left\{\begin{matrix}\mathrm{Ai}(x)\\ \mathrm{Bi}(x)\end{matrix}\left[\frac{g'_1+xf_1}{\mu} +\frac{g'_2+xf_2}{\mu^2}+\cdots\right]+\begin{matrix}\mathrm{Ai}'(x)\\ \mathrm{Bi}'(x)\end{matrix}\left[1+\frac{(g_1+f'_1)}{\mu} +\frac{(g_2+f'_2)}{\mu^2}+\cdots\right]\right\}$$

$$f_1=(1/5)x^2$$

$$f_2=\frac{1}{35}\,(2x^3+6)$$

$$f_3=\frac{1}{63000}\,(84x^7+1480x^4+2320x)$$

$$g_1=-(1/5)x$$

$$g_2=\frac{1}{350}\,(7x^5-30x^2)$$

$$g_3=\frac{1}{63000}\,(1056x^6-1160x^3-2240)$$

(See chapter **10**.)

14.5. Asymptotic Expansions

Asymptotic Expansion for Large Values of ρ

14.5.1 $$F_L=g\cos\theta_L+f\sin\theta_L$$

14.5.2 $$G_L=f\cos\theta_L-g\sin\theta_L$$

14.5.3 $$F'_L=g^*\cos\theta_L+f^*\sin\theta_L$$

14.5.4 $$G'_L=f^*\cos\theta_L-g^*\sin\theta_L,\ gf^*-fg^*=1$$

14.5.5 $$\theta_L=\rho-\eta\ln 2\rho-L\frac{\pi}{2}+\sigma_L$$

14.5.6 $$\sigma_L=\arg\Gamma(L+1+i\eta)$$

(See **6.1.27, 6.1.44.**)

14.5.7 $$\sigma_{L+1}=\sigma_L+\arctan\frac{\eta}{L+1}$$

(See **Tables 4.14, 6.7.**)

14.5.8 $$f\sim\sum_{k=0}^{\infty} f_k,\ g\sim\sum_{k=0}^{\infty} g_k,\ f^*\sim\sum_{k=0}^{\infty} f^*_k,\ g^*\sim\sum_{k=0}^{\infty} g^*_k$$

where

$$f_0=1,\ g_0=0,\ f^*_0=0,\ g^*_0=1-\eta/\rho$$

$$f_{k+1}=a_kf_k-b_kg_k$$

$$g_{k+1}=a_kg_k+b_kf_k$$

$$f^*_{k+1}=a_kf^*_k-b_kg^*_k-f_{k+1}/\rho$$

$$g^*_{k+1}=a_kg^*_k+b_kf^*_k-g_{k+1}/\rho$$

$$a_k=\frac{(2k+1)\eta}{(2k+2)\rho}, \quad b_k=\frac{L(L+1)-k(k+1)+\eta^2}{(2k+2)\rho}$$

14.5.9

$$f+ig\sim 1+\frac{(i\eta-L)(i\eta+L+1)}{1!(2i\rho)}+\frac{(i\eta-L)(i\eta-L+1)(i\eta+L+1)(i\eta+L+2)}{2!(2i\rho)^2}$$
$$+\frac{(i\eta-L)(i\eta-L+1)(i\eta-L+2)(i\eta+L+1)(i\eta+L+2)(i\eta+L+3)}{3!(2i\rho)^3}+\ldots$$

Asymptotic Expansion for $L=0$, $\rho=2\eta>>0$

14.5.10
$$\begin{matrix}F_0(2\eta)\\ G_0(2\eta)/\sqrt{3}\end{matrix}\sim\frac{\Gamma(1/3)\beta^{1/2}}{2\sqrt{\pi}}\left\{1\mp\frac{2}{35}\frac{\Gamma(2/3)}{\Gamma(1/3)}\frac{1}{\beta^4}-\frac{32}{8100}\frac{1}{\beta^6}\mp\frac{92672}{7371\cdot 10^4}\frac{\Gamma(2/3)}{\Gamma(1/3)}\frac{1}{\beta^{10}}-\ldots\right\}$$

14.5.11
$$\begin{matrix}F_0'(2\eta)\\ G_0'(2\eta)/\sqrt{3}\end{matrix}\sim\frac{\Gamma(2/3)}{2\sqrt{\pi}\beta^{1/2}}\left\{\pm 1+\frac{1}{15}\frac{\Gamma(1/3)}{\Gamma(2/3)}\frac{1}{\beta^2}\pm\frac{8}{56700}\frac{1}{\beta^6}+\frac{11488}{18711\cdot 10^3}\frac{\Gamma(1/3)}{\Gamma(2/3)}\frac{1}{\beta^8}\pm\ldots\right\}$$

$\beta=(2\eta/3)^{1/3}$, $\Gamma(1/3)=2.6789\ 38534\ldots$, $\Gamma(2/3)=1.3541\ 17939\ldots$

14.5.12
$$\begin{matrix}F_0(2\eta)\\ G_0(2\eta)\end{matrix}\sim\left\{\begin{matrix}.70633\ 26373\\ 1.22340\ 4016\end{matrix}\right\}\eta^{1/6}\left\{1\mp\frac{.04959\ 570165}{\eta^{4/3}}-\frac{.00888\ 88888\ 89}{\eta^2}\right.$$
$$\left.\mp\frac{.00245\ 51991\ 81}{\eta^{10/3}}-\frac{.00091\ 08958\ 061}{\eta^4}\mp\frac{.00025\ 34684\ 115}{\eta^{16/3}}-\ldots\right\}$$

14.5.13
$$\begin{matrix}F_0'(2\eta)\\ G_0'(2\eta)\end{matrix}\sim\left\{\begin{matrix}.40869\ 57323\\ -.70788\ 17734\end{matrix}\right\}\eta^{-1/6}\left\{1\pm\frac{.17282\ 60369}{\eta^{2/3}}+\frac{.00031\ 74603\ 174}{\eta^2}\right.$$
$$\left.\pm\frac{.00358\ 12148\ 50}{\eta^{8/3}}+\frac{.00031\ 17824\ 680}{\eta^4}\pm\frac{.00090\ 73966\ 427}{\eta^{14/3}}+\ldots\right\}$$

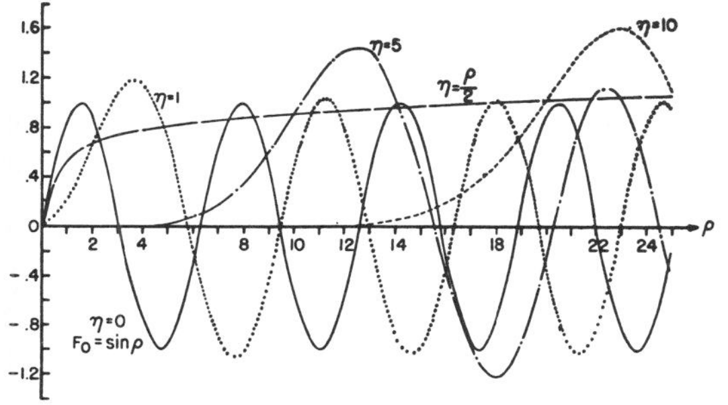

FIGURE 14.3. $F_0(\eta,\rho)$.
$\eta=0,\ 1,\ 5,\ 10,\ \rho/2$

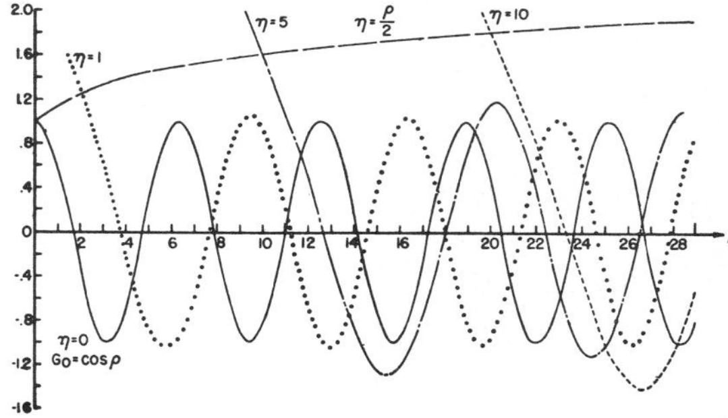

FIGURE 14.5. $G_0(\eta,\rho)$.
$\eta=0,\ 1,\ 5,\ 10,\ \rho/2$

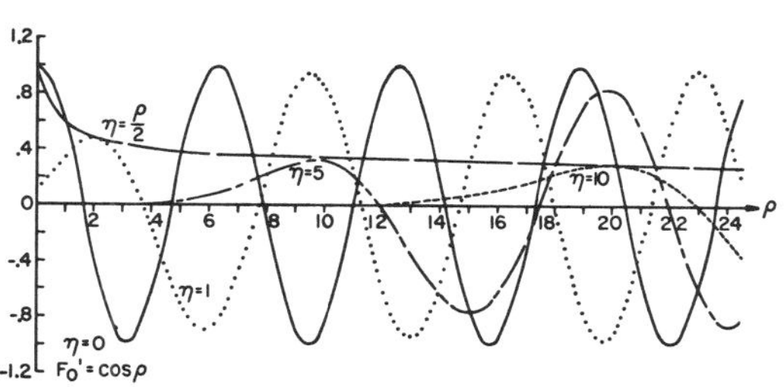

FIGURE 14.4. $F_0'(\eta,\rho)$.
$\eta=0,\ 1,\ 5,\ 10,\ \rho/2$

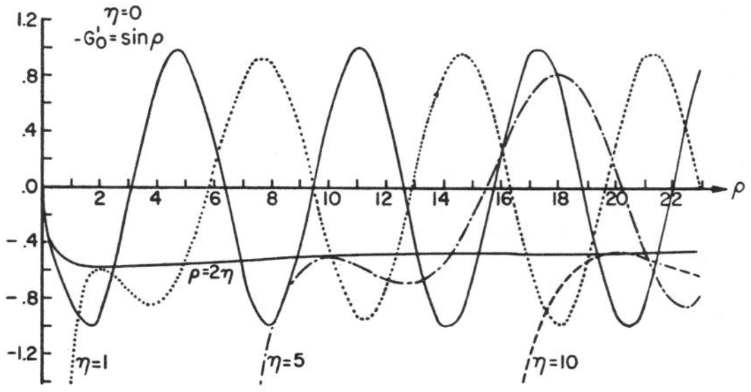

FIGURE 14.6. $G_0'(\eta,\rho)$.
$\eta=0,\ 1,\ 5,\ 10,\ \rho/2$

14.6. Special Values and Asymptotic Behavior

14.6.1 $L>0,\ \rho=0$

$$F_L=0,\ F'_L=0$$
$$G_L=\infty,\ G'_L=-\infty$$

14.6.2 $L=0,\ \rho=0$

$$F_0=0,\ F'_0=C_0(\eta)$$
$$G_0=1/C_0(\eta),\ G'_0=-\infty$$

14.6.3 $L\to\infty$

$$F_L\sim C_L(\eta)\rho^{L+1},\ G_L\sim D_L(\eta)\rho^{-L}$$

14.6.4 $L=0,\ \eta=0$

$$F_0=\sin\rho,\ F'_0=\cos\rho$$
$$G_0=\cos\rho,\ G'_0=-\sin\rho$$

14.6.5 $\rho\to\infty$

$$G_L+iF_L\sim\exp i[\rho-\eta\ln 2\rho-\frac{L\pi}{2}+\sigma_L]$$

14.6.6 $L\geq 0,\ \eta=0$

$$F_L=(\tfrac{1}{2}\pi\rho)^{\frac{1}{2}}\,J_{L+\frac{1}{2}}(\rho)$$
$$G_L=(-1)^L(\tfrac{1}{2}\pi\rho)^{\frac{1}{2}}\,J_{-(L+\frac{1}{2})}(\rho)$$

14.6.7 $L\geq 0,\ 2\eta>>\rho$

$$F_L\sim\frac{(2L+1)!C_L(\eta)}{(2\eta)^{L+1}}\,(2\eta\rho)^{\frac{1}{2}}I_{2L+1}[2(2\eta\rho)^{\frac{1}{2}}]$$

$$G_L\sim\frac{2(2\eta)^L}{(2L+1)!C_L(\eta)}\,(2\eta\rho)^{\frac{1}{2}}K_{2L+1}[2(2\eta\rho)^{\frac{1}{2}}]$$

14.6.8 $L=0,\ 2\eta>>\rho$

$$F_0\sim e^{-\pi\eta}(\pi\rho)^{\frac{1}{2}}I_1[2(2\eta\rho)^{\frac{1}{2}}]$$
$$F'_0\sim e^{-\pi\eta}(2\pi\eta)^{\frac{1}{2}}I_0[2(2\eta\rho)^{\frac{1}{2}}]$$
$$G_0\sim 2e^{\pi\eta}\left(\frac{\rho}{\pi}\right)^{\frac{1}{2}}K_1[2(2\eta\rho)^{\frac{1}{2}}]$$
$$G'_0\sim -2\left(\frac{2\eta}{\pi}\right)^{\frac{1}{2}}e^{\pi\eta}K_0[2(2\eta\rho)^{\frac{1}{2}}]$$

14.6.9 $L=0,\ 2\eta>>\rho$

$$F_0\sim\frac{1}{2}\,\beta e^{\alpha};\ F'_0\sim\frac{1}{2}\,\beta^{-1}e^{\alpha}$$
$$G_0\sim\beta e^{-\alpha};\ G'_0\sim-\beta^{-1}e^{-\alpha}$$
$$\alpha=2\sqrt{2\eta\rho}-\pi\eta$$
$$\beta=(\rho/2\eta)^{\frac{1}{4}}$$

14.6.10 $L=0,\ 2\eta>>\rho$

$$F_0\sim\frac{1}{2}\,\beta e^{\alpha};\ F'_0\sim\{\beta^{-2}+\frac{1}{8\eta}\,t^{-2}\beta^4\}F_0$$
$$G_0\sim\beta e^{-\alpha};\ G'_0\sim\{-\beta^{-2}+\frac{1}{8\eta}\,t^{-2}\beta^4\}G_0$$
$$t=\rho/2\eta$$
$$\alpha=2\eta\{[t(1-t)]^{\frac{1}{2}}+\arcsin t^{\frac{1}{2}}-\tfrac{1}{2}\pi\}$$
$$\beta=\{t/(1-t)\}^{\frac{1}{4}}$$

14.6.11 $L=0,\ \rho>>2\eta$

$$F_0=\alpha\sin\beta;\ F'_0=-t^2(bF_0-aG_0)$$
$$G_0=\alpha\cos\beta;\ G'_0=-t^2(aF_0+bG_0)$$
$$t=\frac{2\eta}{\rho}$$
$$\alpha=(\frac{1}{1-t})^{\frac{1}{4}}\exp\,[-\frac{8t^3-3t^4}{64(2\eta)^2(1-t)^3}]$$
$$\beta=\frac{\pi}{4}+2\eta\{\frac{(1-t)^{\frac{1}{2}}}{t}+\frac{1}{2}\ln\,[\frac{1-(1-t)^{\frac{1}{2}}}{1+(1-t)^{\frac{1}{2}}}]\}$$
$$a=t^{-2}(1-t)^{\frac{1}{2}},\ b=[8\eta(1-t)]^{-1}$$

14.6.12 $\eta>>0,\ 2\eta\sim\rho$

$$\begin{matrix}F_L(\eta,\rho)\\G_L(\eta,\rho)\end{matrix}\sim\sqrt{\pi}\left\{\frac{\rho_L}{1+\frac{L(L+1)}{\rho_L^2}}\right\}^{1/6}\left\{\begin{matrix}\mathrm{Ai}\,(x)\\\mathrm{Bi}\,(x)\end{matrix}\right\}$$
$$\rho_L=\eta+[\eta^2+L(L+1)]^{1/2}$$
$$x=(\rho_L-\rho)[\frac{1}{\rho_L}+\frac{L(L+1)}{\rho_L^3}]^{1/3}$$

14.6.13 $\eta>>0,\ 2\eta\sim\rho$

$$x=(2\eta-\rho)(2\eta)^{-1/3}$$
$$[G_0+iF_0]\sim\pi^{1/2}(2\eta)^{1/6}[\mathrm{Bi}(x)+i\mathrm{Ai}(x)]$$
$$[G'_0+iF'_0]\sim-\pi^{1/2}(2\eta)^{-1/6}[\mathrm{Bi}'(x)+i\mathrm{Ai}'(x)]$$

14.6.14 $\eta>>0$

$$\rho_L=\eta+[\eta^2+L(L+1)]^{1/2}$$
$$\begin{matrix}F_L(\rho_L)\\G_L(\rho_L)/\sqrt{3}\end{matrix}\sim\frac{\Gamma(1/3)}{2\sqrt{\pi}}\left(\frac{\rho_L}{3}\right)^{1/6}\left\{1+\frac{L(L+1)}{\rho_L^2}\right\}^{-1/6}$$
$$\begin{matrix}F'_L(\rho_L)\\G'_L(\rho_L)/\sqrt{3}\end{matrix}\sim\pm\frac{\Gamma(2/3)}{2\sqrt{\pi}}\left(\frac{\rho_L}{3}\right)^{-1/6}\left\{1+\frac{L(L+1)}{\rho_L^2}\right\}^{1/6}$$

14.6.15 $\rho=2\eta>>0$

$$\left.\begin{matrix}F_0\\ G_0/\sqrt{3}\end{matrix}\right.\sim\frac{\Gamma(1/3)}{2\sqrt{\pi}}\left(\frac{2\eta}{3}\right)^{1/6}$$

$$\left.\begin{matrix}F_0'\\ -G_0'/\sqrt{3}\end{matrix}\right.\sim\frac{\Gamma(2/3)}{2\sqrt{\pi}(2\eta/3)^{1/6}}$$

14.6.16 $\eta\to\infty$

$$\sigma_0(\eta)\sim[\frac{\pi}{4}+\eta(\ln\eta-1)]$$

$$C_0(\eta)\sim(2\pi\eta)^{1/2}e^{-\pi\eta},$$

(Equality to 8S for $\eta>3$.)

14.6.17 $\eta\to0$

$$\sigma_0(\eta)\sim-\gamma\eta\qquad(\gamma=\text{Euler's constant})$$

$$C_L(\eta)\sim\frac{2^LL!}{(2L+1)!}$$

14.6.18 $L\to\infty$

$$C_L(\eta)\sim\frac{2^LL!}{(2L+1)!}e^{-\pi\eta/2}$$

14.7. Use and Extension of the Tables

In general the tables as presented are not simply interpolable. However, values for $L>0$ may be obtained with the help of the recurrence relations. The values of $G_L(\eta,\rho)$ may be obtained by applying the recurrence relations in increasing order of L. Forward recurrence may be used for $F_L(\eta,\rho)$ as long as the instability does not produce errors in excess of the accuracy needed. In this case the backwards recurrence scheme (see **Example 1**) should be used.

Example 1. Compute $F_L(\eta,\rho)$ and $F_L'(\eta,\rho)$ for $\eta=2$, $\rho=5$, $L=0(1)5$. Starting with $F_{10}^*=1$, $F_{11}^*=0$, where $F_L^*=cF_L$, we compute from **14.2.3** in decreasing order of L:

L	(1) F_L^*	(2) F_L	(3) F_L	(4) F'_L
11	0.			
10	1.			
9	4.49284			
8	17.5225			
7	61.3603			
6	191.238			
5	523.472	.090791	.091	.1043
4	1238.53	.21481	.215	.2030
3	2486.72	.43130	.4313	.3205
2	4158.46	.72124	.72125	.3952
1	5727.97	.99346	.99347	.3709
0	6591.81	1.1433	1.1433	.29380

$F_0/F_0^*=1.7344\times10^{-4}=c^{-1}$.

The values in the second column are obtained from those in the first by multiplying by the normalization constant, F_0/F_0^* where F_0 is the known value obtained from **Table 14.1.**

Repetition starting with $F_{15}^*=1$ and $F_{16}^*=0$ yields the same results.

In column 3, the results have been given when **14.2.3** is used in increasing order of L.

F_L' (column 4) follows from **14.2.2.**

Example 2. Compute $G_L(\eta,\rho)$ and $G_L'(\eta,\rho)$ for $\eta=2$, $\rho=5$, $L=1(1)5$.

Using **14.2.2** and $G_0(2,5)=.79445$, $G_0'=-.67049$ from **Table 14.1** we find $G_1(2,5)=1.0815$. Then by forward recurrence using **14.2.3** we find:

L	G_L	$-G'_L$
1	1.0815	.60286
2	1.4969	.56619
3	2.0487	.79597
4	3.0941	1.7318
5	5.6298	4.5493

The values of G_L' are obtained with **14.2.1.**

Example 3. Compute $G_0(\eta,\rho)$ for $\eta=2$, $\rho=2.5$.

From **Table 14.1,** $G_0(2,2)=3.5124$, $G_0'(2,2)=-2.5554$. Successive differentiation of **14.1.1** for $L=0$ gives

$$\rho\frac{d^{k+2}w}{d\rho^{k+2}}=(2\eta-\rho)\frac{d^kw}{d\rho^k}-k\left\{\frac{d^{k+1}w}{d\rho^{k+1}}+\frac{d^{k-1}w}{d\rho^{k-1}}\right\}$$

Taylor's expansion is $w(\rho+\Delta\rho)=w(\rho)+(\Delta\rho)w'+\frac{(\Delta\rho)^2}{2!}w''+\ldots$. With $w=G_0(\eta,\rho)$ and $\Delta\rho=.5$ we get:

k	$\frac{d^kG_0}{d\rho^k}$	$\frac{(\Delta\rho)^k}{k!}\frac{d^kG_0}{d\rho^k}$
0	3.5124	3.5124
1	−2.5554	−1.2777
2	3.5124	.43905
3	−6.0678	−.12641
4	12.136	.03160
5	−29.540	−.00769
6	83.352	.00181
7	−268.26	−.00042

$G_0(2,2.5)=2.5726$

As a check the result is obtained with $\eta=2$, $\rho=3$, $\Delta\rho=-.5$. The derivative $G_0'(\eta,\rho)$ may be obtained using Taylor's formula with $w=G_0'(\eta,\rho)$.

Table 14.1 COULOMB WAVE FUNCTIONS OF ORDER ZERO

$F_0(\eta,\rho)$

$\eta \backslash \rho$	1	2	3	4	5
0.5	(- 1) 5.1660	(0) 1.0211	(0) 1.0432	(- 1) 4.1924	(- 1)-4.9046
1.0	(- 1) 2.2753	(- 1) 6.6178	(0) 1.0841	(0) 1.1571	(- 1)+6.8494
1.5	(- 2) 8.4815	(- 1) 3.3159	(- 1) 7.3013	(0) 1.1186	(0) 1.2327
2.0	(- 2) 2.8898	(- 1) 1.4445	(- 1) 3.9861	(- 1) 7.7520	(0) 1.1433
2.5	(- 3) 9.3008	(- 2) 5.7560	(- 1) 1.9162	(- 1) 4.4865	(- 1) 8.0955
3.0	(- 3) 2.8751	(- 2) 2.1538	(- 2) 8.4417	(- 1) 2.3093	(- 1) 4.8882
3.5	(- 4) 8.6200	(- 3) 7.6857	(- 2) 3.4863	(- 1) 1.0927	(- 1) 2.6473
4.0	(- 4) 2.5224	(- 3) 2.6417	(- 2) 1.3692	(- 2) 4.8493	(- 1) 1.3227
4.5	(- 5) 7.2358	(- 4) 8.8072	(- 3) 5.1636	(- 2) 2.0448	(- 2) 6.2060
5.0	(- 5) 2.0413	(- 4) 2.8622	(- 3) 1.8829	(- 3) 8.2690	(- 2) 2.7673
5.5	(- 6) 5.6770	(- 5) 9.1017	(- 4) 6.6735	(- 3) 3.2283	(- 2) 1.1829
6.0	(- 6) 1.5593	(- 5) 2.8403	(- 4) 2.3080	(- 3) 1.2230	(- 3) 4.8778
6.5	(- 7) 4.2367	(- 6) 8.7187	(- 5) 7.8131	(- 4) 4.5136	(- 3) 1.9502
7.0	(- 7) 1.1400	(- 6) 2.6375	(- 5) 2.5954	(- 4) 1.6280	(- 4) 7.5886
7.5	(- 8) 3.0407	(- 7) 7.8750	(- 6) 8.4780	(- 5) 5.7536	(- 4) 2.8831
8.0	(- 9) 8.0474	(- 7) 2.3238	(- 6) 2.7278	(- 5) 1.9966	(- 4) 1.0722
8.5	(- 9) 2.1146	(- 8) 6.7842	(- 7) 8.6573	(- 6) 6.8154	(- 5) 3.9115
9.0	(-10) 5.5203	(- 8) 1.9614	(- 7) 2.7136	(- 6) 2.2918	(- 5) 1.4023
9.5	(-10) 1.4325	(- 9) 5.6202	(- 8) 8.4089	(- 7) 7.6019	(- 6) 4.9481
10.0	(-11) 3.6966	(- 9) 1.5971	(- 8) 2.5785	(- 7) 2.4900	(- 6) 1.7207
10.5	(-12) 9.4903	(-10) 4.5043	(- 9) 7.8306	(- 8) 8.0621	(- 7) 5.9043
11.0	(-12) 2.4248	(-10) 1.2613	(- 9) 2.3567	(- 8) 2.5824	(- 7) 2.0009
11.5	(-13) 6.1679	(-11) 3.5086	(-10) 7.0332	(- 9) 8.1895	(- 8) 6.7032
12.0	(-13) 1.5623	(-12) 9.6998	(-10) 2.0826	(- 9) 2.5730	(- 8) 2.2216
12.5	(-14) 3.9419	(-12) 2.6660	(-11) 6.1216	(-10) 8.0134	(- 9) 7.2896
13.0	(-15) 9.9089	(-13) 7.2878	(-11) 1.7870	(-10) 2.4754	(- 9) 2.3694
13.5	(-15) 2.4822	(-13) 1.9819	(-12) 5.1827	(-11) 7.5877	(-10) 7.6337
14.0	(-16) 6.1972	(-14) 5.3636	(-12) 1.4939	(-11) 2.3090	(-10) 2.4390
14.5	(-16) 1.5424	(-14) 1.4449	(-13) 4.2812	(-12) 6.9781	(-11) 7.7314
15.0	(-17) 3.8274	(-15) 3.8752	(-13) 1.2201	(-12) 2.0952	(-11) 2.4326
15.5	(-18) 9.4708	(-15) 1.0350	(-14) 3.4592	(-13) 6.2521	(-12) 7.5998
16.0	(-18) 2.3372	(-16) 2.7536	(-15) 9.7586	(-13) 1.8547	(-12) 2.3584
16.5	(-19) 5.7529	(-17) 7.2980	(-15) 2.7399	(-14) 5.4712	(-13) 7.2719
17.0	(-19) 1.4126	(-17) 1.9272	(-16) 7.6580	(-14) 1.6053	(-13) 2.2286
17.5	(-20) 3.4602	(-18) 5.0719	(-16) 2.1311	(-15) 4.6864	(-14) 6.7904
18.0	(-21) 8.4571	(-18) 1.3304	(-17) 5.9063	(-15) 1.3614	(-14) 2.0575
18.5	(-21) 2.0625	(-19) 3.4785	(-17) 1.6304	(-16) 3.9364	(-15) 6.2009
19.0	(-22) 5.0197	(-20) 9.0677	(-18) 4.4834	(-16) 1.1331	(-15) 1.8594
19.5	(-22) 1.2192	(-20) 2.3568	(-18) 1.2284	(-17) 3.2476	(-16) 5.5480
20.0	(-23) 2.9556	(-21) 6.1087	(-19) 3.3538	(-18) 9.2696	(-16) 1.6477

$\frac{d}{d\rho}F_0(\eta,\rho)$

$\eta \backslash \rho$	1	2	3	4	5
0.5	(- 1) 5.9292	(- 1) 3.2960	(- 1)-3.1699	(- 1)-8.6672	(- 1)-8.3314
1.0	(- 1) 3.4873	(- 1) 4.8156	(- 1)+3.0192	(- 1)-1.9273	(- 1)-7.2364
1.5	(- 1) 1.5684	(- 1) 3.3631	(- 1) 4.3300	(- 1)+2.9671	(- 1)-1.0456
2.0	(- 2) 6.1308	(- 1) 1.7962	(- 1) 3.2695	(- 1) 4.0401	(- 1)+2.9380
2.5	(- 2) 2.1980	(- 2) 8.2804	(- 1) 1.9237	(- 1) 3.1922	(- 1) 3.8386
3.0	(- 3) 7.4239	(- 2) 3.4693	(- 2) 9.8019	(- 1) 2.0030	(- 1) 3.1264
3.5	(- 3) 2.3993	(- 2) 1.3575	(- 2) 4.5336	(- 1) 1.0945	(- 1) 2.0555
4.0	(- 4) 7.4933	(- 3) 5.0436	(- 2) 1.9532	(- 2) 5.4362	(- 1) 1.1839
4.5	(- 4) 2.2767	(- 3) 1.7984	(- 3) 7.9650	(- 2) 2.5140	(- 2) 6.2113
5.0	(- 5) 6.7615	(- 4) 6.2008	(- 3) 3.1077	(- 2) 1.0992	(- 2) 3.0360
5.5	(- 5) 1.9700	(- 4) 2.0789	(- 3) 1.1690	(- 3) 4.5914	(- 2) 1.4028
6.0	(- 6) 5.6457	(- 5) 6.8046	(- 4) 4.2638	(- 3) 1.8462	(- 3) 6.1885
6.5	(- 6) 1.5950	(- 5) 2.1817	(- 4) 1.5145	(- 4) 7.1867	(- 3) 2.6259
7.0	(- 7) 4.4497	(- 6) 6.8691	(- 5) 5.2563	(- 4) 2.7200	(- 3) 1.0777
7.5	(- 7) 1.2276	(- 6) 2.1283	(- 5) 1.7875	(- 4) 1.0045	(- 4) 4.2964
8.0	(- 8) 3.3527	(- 7) 6.5001	(- 6) 5.9696	(- 5) 3.6292	(- 4) 1.6695
8.5	(- 9) 9.0744	(- 7) 1.9597	(- 6) 1.9614	(- 5) 1.2859	(- 5) 6.3417
9.0	(- 9) 2.4359	(- 8) 5.8395	(- 7) 6.3501	(- 6) 4.4771	(- 5) 2.3601
9.5	(-10) 6.4900	(- 8) 1.7215	(- 7) 2.0285	(- 6) 1.5341	(- 6) 8.6225
10.0	(-10) 1.7173	(- 9) 5.0256	(- 8) 6.4011	(- 7) 5.1804	(- 6) 3.0976
10.5	(-11) 4.5150	(- 9) 1.4539	(- 8) 1.9973	(- 7) 1.7262	(- 6) 1.0958
11.0	(-11) 1.1801	(-10) 4.1713	(- 9) 6.1672	(- 8) 5.6813	(- 7) 3.8219
11.5	(-12) 3.0676	(-10) 1.1875	(- 9) 1.8860	(- 8) 1.8487	(- 7) 1.3157
12.0	(-13) 7.9334	(-11) 3.3562	(-10) 5.7160	(- 9) 5.9521	(- 8) 4.4743
12.5	(-13) 2.0420	(-12) 9.4217	(-10) 1.7179	(- 9) 1.8975	(- 8) 1.5045
13.0	(-14) 5.2322	(-12) 2.6282	(-11) 5.1227	(-10) 5.9935	(- 9) 5.0060
13.5	(-14) 1.3350	(-13) 7.2879	(-11) 1.5163	(-10) 1.8768	(- 9) 1.6492
14.0	(-15) 3.3929	(-13) 2.0096	(-12) 4.4571	(-11) 5.8291	(-10) 5.3830
14.5	(-16) 8.5905	(-14) 5.5121	(-12) 1.3016	(-11) 1.7966	(-10) 1.7417
15.0	(-16) 2.1673	(-14) 1.5043	(-13) 3.7774	(-12) 5.4972	(-11) 5.5888
15.5	(-17) 5.4495	(-15) 4.0861	(-13) 1.0899	(-12) 1.6705	(-11) 1.7794
16.0	(-17) 1.3659	(-15) 1.1049	(-14) 3.1270	(-13) 5.0433	(-12) 5.6234
16.5	(-18) 3.4129	(-16) 2.9747	(-15) 8.9243	(-13) 1.5132	(-12) 1.7647
17.0	(-19) 8.5032	(-17) 7.9764	(-15) 2.5341	(-14) 4.5133	(-13) 5.5009
17.5	(-19) 2.1127	(-17) 2.1304	(-16) 7.1612	(-14) 1.3386	(-13) 1.7038
18.0	(-20) 5.2352	(-18) 5.6690	(-16) 2.0144	(-15) 3.9490	(-14) 5.2453
18.5	(-20) 1.2940	(-18) 1.5031	(-17) 5.6414	(-15) 1.1590	(-14) 1.6054
19.0	(-21) 3.1905	(-19) 3.9718	(-17) 1.5733	(-16) 3.3848	(-15) 4.8863
19.5	(-22) 7.8484	(-19) 1.0461	(-18) 4.3698	(-17) 9.8388	(-15) 1.4793
20.0	(-22) 1.9263	(-20) 2.7464	(-18) 1.2090	(-17) 2.8470	(-16) 4.4556

For use of this table see **Examples 1–3**.

COULOMB WAVE FUNCTIONS OF ORDER ZERO Table 14.1

$G_0(\eta,\rho)$

$\eta \backslash \rho$	1	2	3	4	5
0.5	(0) 1.1975	(-1) 5.3221	(-1)-3.4105	(-1)-9.8570	(-1)-9.3493
1.0	(0) 2.0431	(0) 1.2758	(-1)+6.2704	(-1)-1.8901	(-1)-8.9841
1.5	(0) 4.0886	(0) 2.0276	(0) 1.3423	(-1)+7.1836	(-2)-5.3716
2.0	(0) 9.8003	(0) 3.5124	(0) 2.0405	(0) 1.3975	(-1)+7.9445
2.5	(1) 2.6401	(0) 7.1318	(0) 3.2733	(0) 2.0592	(0) 1.4442
3.0	(1) 7.6551	(1) 1.6390	(0) 6.0195	(0) 3.1445	(0) 2.0788
3.5	(2) 2.3355	(1) 4.0982	(1) 1.2493	(0) 5.4049	(0) 3.0657
4.0	(2) 7.4015	(2) 1.0878	(1) 2.8313	(1) 1.0423	(0) 5.0146
4.5	(3) 2.4167	(2) 3.0209	(1) 6.8403	(1) 2.1964	(0) 9.1424
5.0	(3) 8.0855	(2) 8.6969	(2) 1.7354	(1) 4.9434	(1) 1.8193
5.5	(4) 2.7606	(3) 2.5792	(2) 4.5790	(2) 1.1708	(1) 3.8704
6.0	(4) 9.5899	(3) 7.8428	(3) 1.2482	(2) 2.8891	(1) 8.6736
6.5	(5) 3.3815	(4) 2.4367	(3) 3.4980	(2) 7.3782	(2) 2.0275
7.0	(6) 1.2081	(4) 7.7137	(4) 1.0041	(3) 1.9403	(2) 4.9101
7.5	(6) 4.3664	(5) 2.4826	(4) 2.9432	(3) 5.2344	(3) 1.2258
8.0	(7) 1.5946	(5) 8.1086	(4) 8.7893	(4) 1.4441	(3) 3.1422
8.5	(7) 5.8778	(6) 2.6837	(5) 2.6689	(4) 4.0648	(3) 8.2458
9.0	(8) 2.1850	(6) 8.9891	(5) 8.2266	(5) 1.1648	(4) 2.2097
9.5	(8) 8.1855	(7) 3.0439	(6) 2.5706	(5) 3.3928	(4) 6.0344
10.0	(9) 3.0882	(8) 1.0411	(6) 8.1333	(6) 1.0029	(5) 1.6764
10.5	(10) 1.1727	(8) 3.5934	(7) 2.6029	(6) 3.0052	(5) 4.7305
11.0	(10) 4.4801	(9) 1.2509	(7) 8.4187	(6) 9.1181	(6) 1.3542
11.5	(11) 1.7211	(9) 4.3888	(8) 2.7496	(7) 2.7986	(6) 3.9285
12.0	(11) 6.6465	(10) 1.5511	(8) 9.0625	(7) 8.6825	(7) 1.1537
12.5	(12) 2.5793	(10) 5.5199	(9) 3.0124	(8) 2.7207	(7) 3.4272
13.0	(13) 1.0055	(11) 1.9769	(10) 1.0093	(8) 8.6053	(8) 1.0290
13.5	(13) 3.9366	(11) 7.1230	(10) 3.4069	(9) 2.7457	(8) 3.1205
14.0	(14) 1.5474	(12) 2.5811	(11) 1.1581	(9) 8.8331	(8) 9.5523
14.5	(14) 6.1061	(12) 9.4029	(11) 3.9629	(10) 2.8638	(9) 2.9500
15.0	(15) 2.4181	(13) 3.4429	(12) 1.3645	(10) 9.3530	(9) 9.1867
15.5	(15) 9.6091	(14) 1.2667	(12) 4.7264	(11) 3.0758	(10) 2.8835
16.0	(16) 3.8309	(14) 4.6814	(13) 1.6463	(12) 1.0182	(10) 9.1182
16.5	(17) 1.5320	(15) 1.7377	(13) 5.7652	(12) 3.3917	(11) 2.9039
17.0	(17) 6.1445	(15) 6.4769	(14) 2.0292	(13) 1.1365	(11) 9.3107
17.5	(18) 2.4714	(16) 2.4236	(14) 7.1771	(13) 3.8299	(12) 3.0045
18.0	(18) 9.9670	(16) 9.1034	(15) 2.5502	(14) 1.2976	(12) 9.7548
18.5	(19) 4.0300	(17) 3.4316	(15) 9.1019	(14) 4.4194	(13) 3.1857
19.0	(20) 1.6335	(18) 1.2981	(16) 3.2623	(15) 1.5126	(14) 1.0462
19.5	(20) 6.6365	(18) 4.9263	(17) 1.1741	(15) 5.2016	(14) 3.4544
20.0	(21) 2.7024	(19) 1.8756	(17) 4.2418	(16) 1.7969	(15) 1.1464

$\frac{d}{d\rho}G_0(\eta,\rho)$

$\eta \backslash \rho$	1	2	3	4	5
0.5	(-1)-5.6132	(-1)-8.0753	(-1)-8.5494	(-1)-3.4747	(-1)+4.5076
1.0	(0)-1.2636	(-1)-5.8273	(-1)-7.4783	(-1)-8.3273	(-1)-5.1080
1.5	(0)-4.2300	(-1)-9.5930	(-1)-5.7358	(-1)-7.0346	(-1)-8.0665
2.0	(1)-1.3813	(0)-2.5554	(-1)-8.3499	(-1)-5.6167	(-1)-6.7049
2.5	(1)-4.5128	(0)-7.1137	(0)-1.9326	(-1)-7.6379	(-1)-5.5046
3.0	(2)-1.5015	(1)-2.0029	(0)-4.8566	(0)-1.6029	(-1)-7.1618
3.5	(2)-5.1001	(1)-5.7725	(1)-1.2438	(0)-3.7375	(0)-1.3970
4.0	(3)-1.7657	(2)-1.7086	(1)-3.2646	(0)-8.9366	(0)-3.0719
4.5	(3)-6.2161	(2)-5.1859	(1)-8.8150	(1)-2.1901	(0)-6.9633
5.0	(4)-2.2206	(3)-1.6097	(2)-2.4467	(1)-5.5222	(1)-1.6176
5.5	(4)-8.0354	(3)-5.0961	(2)-6.9635	(2)-1.4325	(1)-3.8641
6.0	(5)-2.9409	(4)-1.6418	(3)-2.0268	(2)-3.8154	(1)-9.4968
6.5	(6)-1.0873	(4)-5.3723	(3)-6.0185	(3)-1.0408	(2)-2.3977
7.0	(6)-4.0566	(5)-1.7825	(4)-1.8195	(3)-2.9006	(2)-6.2044
7.5	(7)-1.5259	(5)-5.9890	(4)-5.5897	(3)-8.2422	(3)-1.6419
8.0	(7)-5.7831	(6)-2.0352	(5)-1.7425	(4)-2.3835	(3)-4.4339
8.5	(8)-2.2067	(6)-6.9879	(5)-5.5045	(4)-7.0031	(4)-1.2197
9.0	(8)-8.4732	(7)-2.4222	(6)-1.7601	(5)-2.0878	(4)-3.4122
9.5	(9)-3.2724	(7)-8.4693	(6)-5.6909	(5)-6.3080	(4)-9.6943
10.0	(10)-1.2706	(8)-2.9853	(7)-1.8591	(6)-1.9295	(5)-2.7937
10.5	(10)-4.9580	(9)-1.0602	(7)-6.1315	(6)-5.9693	(5)-8.1574
11.0	(11)-1.9437	(9)-3.7915	(8)-2.0402	(7)-1.8664	(6)-2.4111
11.5	(11)-7.6530	(10)-1.3647	(8)-6.8449	(7)-5.8932	(6)-7.2077
12.0	(12)-3.0256	(10)-4.9424	(9)-2.3143	(8)-1.8780	(7)-2.1776
12.5	(13)-1.2008	(11)-1.8002	(9)-7.8819	(8)-6.0367	(7)-6.6446
13.0	(13)-4.7827	(11)-6.5922	(10)-2.7027	(9)-1.9562	(8)-2.0464
13.5	(14)-1.9115	(12)-2.4263	(10)-9.3274	(9)-6.3878	(8)-6.3581
14.0	(14)-7.6643	(12)-8.9735	(11)-3.2386	(10)-2.1009	(9)-1.9918
14.5	(15)-3.0826	(13)-3.3339	(12)-1.1310	(10)-6.9573	(9)-6.2887
15.0	(16)-1.2434	(14)-1.2440	(12)-3.9713	(11)-2.3188	(10)-2.0003
15.5	(16)-5.0296	(14)-4.6610	(13)-1.4017	(11)-7.7763	(10)-6.4071
16.0	(17)-2.0399	(15)-1.7532	(13)-4.9720	(12)-2.6230	(11)-2.0660
16.5	(17)-8.2941	(15)-6.6194	(14)-1.7719	(12)-8.8973	(11)-6.7044
17.0	(18)-3.3805	(16)-2.5081	(14)-6.3433	(13)-3.0340	(12)-2.1889
17.5	(19)-1.3810	(16)-9.5361	(15)-2.2806	(14)-1.0399	(12)-7.1879
18.0	(19)-5.6545	(17)-3.6376	(15)-8.2334	(14)-3.5813	(13)-2.3735
18.5	(20)-2.3201	(18)-1.3919	(16)-2.9841	(15)-1.2392	(13)-7.8789
19.0	(20)-9.5394	(18)-5.3424	(17)-1.0857	(15)-4.3069	(14)-2.6288
19.5	(21)-3.9299	(19)-2.0564	(17)-3.9642	(16)-1.5033	(14)-8.8139
20.0	(22)-1.6221	(19)-7.9378	(18)-1.4526	(16)-5.2691	(15)-2.9690

Table 14.1 COULOMB WAVE FUNCTIONS OF ORDER ZERO

$F_0(\eta,\rho)$

$\eta \backslash \rho$	6	7	8	9	10
0.5	(0)-1.0286	(- 1)-7.6744	(- 1)+1.0351	(- 1)+8.8802	(- 1)+9.3919
1.0	(- 1)-1.6718	(- 1)-9.0632	(0)-1.0333	(- 1)-4.3441	(- 1)+4.7756
1.5	(- 1)+8.7682	(- 1)+1.1034	(- 1)-7.0763	(0)-1.1015	(- 1)-8.0125
2.0	(0) 1.2850	(0) 1.0148	(- 1)+3.3340	(- 1)-4.9930	(0)-1.0616
2.5	(0) 1.1633	(0) 1.3237	(0) 1.1181	(- 1)+5.1312	(- 1)-3.0351
3.0	(- 1) 8.3763	(0) 1.1803	(0) 1.3540	(0) 1.1984	(- 1)+6.6010
3.5	(- 1) 5.2251	(- 1) 8.6154	(0) 1.1952	(0) 1.3786	(0) 1.2627
4.0	(- 1) 2.9445	(- 1) 5.5158	(- 1) 8.8245	(0) 1.2085	(0) 1.3992
4.5	(- 1) 1.5362	(- 1) 3.2100	(- 1) 5.7720	(- 1) 9.0109	(0) 1.2207
5.0	(- 2) 7.5384	(- 1) 1.7351	(- 1) 3.4502	(- 1) 6.0014	(- 1) 9.1794
5.5	(- 2) 3.5181	(- 2) 8.8379	(- 1) 1.9214	(- 1) 3.6697	(- 1) 6.2092
6.0	(- 2) 1.5740	(- 2) 4.2849	(- 1) 1.0100	(- 1) 2.0964	(- 1) 3.8720
6.5	(- 3) 6.7927	(- 2) 1.9924	(- 2) 5.0593	(- 1) 1.1325	(- 1) 2.2615
7.0	(- 3) 2.8407	(- 3) 8.9366	(- 2) 2.4318	(- 2) 5.8352	(- 1) 1.2511
7.5	(- 3) 1.1557	(- 3) 3.8839	(- 2) 1.1277	(- 2) 2.8870	(- 2) 6.6087
8.0	(- 4) 4.5875	(- 3) 1.6415	(- 3) 5.0678	(- 2) 1.3786	(- 2) 3.3543
8.5	(- 4) 1.7814	(- 4) 6.7674	(- 3) 2.2145	(- 3) 6.3805	(- 2) 1.6440
9.0	(- 5) 6.7813	(- 4) 2.7281	(- 4) 9.4374	(- 3) 2.8716	(- 3) 7.8106
9.5	(- 5) 2.5352	(- 4) 1.0776	(- 4) 3.9317	(- 3) 1.2603	(- 3) 3.6091
10.0	(- 6) 9.3224	(- 5) 4.1786	(- 4) 1.6046	(- 4) 5.4065	(- 3) 1.6263
10.5	(- 6) 3.3763	(- 5) 1.5930	(- 5) 6.4260	(- 4) 2.2716	(- 4) 7.1627
11.0	(- 6) 1.2058	(- 6) 5.9782	(- 5) 2.5293	(- 5) 9.3643	(- 4) 3.0895
11.5	(- 7) 4.2504	(- 6) 2.2113	(- 6) 9.7972	(- 5) 3.7930	(- 4) 1.3072
12.0	(- 7) 1.4802	(- 7) 8.0697	(- 6) 3.7389	(- 5) 1.5115	(- 5) 5.4341
12.5	(- 8) 5.0971	(- 7) 2.9081	(- 6) 1.4073	(- 6) 5.9333	(- 5) 2.2220
13.0	(- 8) 1.7367	(- 7) 1.0358	(- 7) 5.2291	(- 6) 2.2964	(- 6) 8.9480
13.5	(- 9) 5.8586	(- 8) 3.6487	(- 7) 1.9195	(- 7) 8.7713	(- 6) 3.5521
14.0	(- 9) 1.9579	(- 8) 1.2720	(- 8) 6.9669	(- 7) 3.3091	(- 6) 1.3913
14.5	(-10) 6.4858	(- 9) 4.3915	(- 8) 2.5016	(- 7) 1.2340	(- 7) 5.3814
15.0	(-10) 2.1306	(- 9) 1.5022	(- 9) 8.8925	(- 8) 4.5511	(- 7) 2.0569
15.5	(-11) 6.9438	(-10) 5.0935	(- 9) 3.1309	(- 8) 1.6612	(- 8) 7.7746
16.0	(-11) 2.2461	(-10) 1.7129	(- 9) 1.0924	(- 9) 6.0045	(- 8) 2.9076
16.5	(-12) 7.2135	(-11) 5.7147	(-10) 3.7787	(- 9) 2.1502	(- 8) 1.0765
17.0	(-12) 2.3009	(-11) 1.8924	(-10) 1.2965	(-10) 7.6316	(- 9) 3.9479
17.5	(-13) 7.2918	(-12) 6.2217	(-11) 4.4135	(-10) 2.6859	(- 9) 1.4347
18.0	(-13) 2.2965	(-12) 2.0316	(-11) 1.4913	(-11) 9.3772	(-10) 5.1691
18.5	(-14) 7.1900	(-13) 6.5907	(-12) 5.0033	(-11) 3.2487	(-10) 1.8470
19.0	(-14) 2.2382	(-13) 2.1247	(-12) 1.6672	(-11) 1.1173	(-11) 6.5478
19.5	(-15) 6.9296	(-14) 6.8088	(-13) 5.5194	(-12) 3.8154	(-11) 2.3038
20.0	(-15) 2.1342	(-14) 2.1694	(-13) 1.8158	(-12) 1.2942	(-12) 8.0470

$\frac{d}{d\rho}F_0(\eta,\rho)$

$\eta \backslash \rho$	6	7	8	9	10
0.5	(- 1)-1.6439	(- 1)+6.5317	(- 1)+9.6217	(- 1)+4.8856	(- 1)-3.9577
1.0	(- 1)-8.9251	(- 1)-4.9515	(- 1)+2.6293	(- 1)+8.6117	(- 1)+8.4114
1.5	(- 1)-5.9833	(- 1)-8.7151	(- 1)-6.7918	(- 2)-5.9095	(- 1)+6.3051
2.0	(- 2)-4.4197	(- 1)-4.9758	(- 1)-8.2026	(- 1)-7.7036	(- 1)-2.9353
2.5	(- 1)+2.9104	(- 3)-1.2700	(- 1)-4.1714	(- 1)-7.6083	(- 1)-8.0858
3.0	(- 1) 3.6867	(- 1)+2.8830	(- 2)+3.0507	(- 1)-3.5216	(- 1)-7.0180
3.5	(- 1) 3.0694	(- 1) 3.5660	(- 1) 2.8559	(- 2)+5.4822	(- 1)-2.9887
4.0	(- 1) 2.0917	(- 1) 3.0193	(- 1) 3.4667	(- 1) 2.8296	(- 2)+7.3929
4.5	(- 1) 1.2557	(- 1) 2.1173	(- 1) 2.9748	(- 1) 3.3827	(- 1) 2.8044
5.0	(- 2) 6.8842	(- 1) 1.3148	(- 1) 2.1357	(- 1) 2.9346	(- 1) 3.3103
5.5	(- 2) 3.5199	(- 2) 7.4742	(- 1) 1.3640	(- 1) 2.1489	(- 1) 2.8982
6.0	(- 2) 1.7018	(- 2) 3.9680	(- 2) 7.9960	(- 1) 1.4058	(- 1) 2.1583
6.5	(- 3) 7.8549	(- 2) 1.9931	(- 2) 4.3832	(- 2) 8.4608	(- 1) 1.4416
7.0	(- 3) 3.4861	(- 3) 9.5595	(- 2) 2.2750	(- 2) 4.7685	(- 2) 8.8777
7.5	(- 3) 1.4956	(- 3) 4.4083	(- 2) 1.1280	(- 2) 2.5468	(- 2) 5.1268
8.0	(- 4) 6.2296	(- 3) 1.9647	(- 3) 5.3775	(- 2) 1.2999	(- 2) 2.8081
8.5	(- 4) 2.5276	(- 4) 8.4983	(- 3) 2.4777	(- 3) 6.3815	(- 2) 1.4707
9.0	(- 4) 1.0018	(- 4) 3.5795	(- 3) 1.1077	(- 3) 3.0279	(- 3) 7.4103
9.5	(- 5) 3.8880	(- 4) 1.4721	(- 4) 4.8216	(- 3) 1.3940	(- 3) 3.6095
10.0	(- 5) 1.4803	(- 5) 5.9256	(- 4) 2.0487	(- 4) 6.2477	(- 3) 1.7060
10.5	(- 6) 5.5384	(- 5) 2.3388	(- 5) 8.5166	(- 4) 2.7329	(- 4) 7.8494
11.0	(- 6) 2.0392	(- 6) 9.0675	(- 5) 3.4707	(- 4) 1.1694	(- 4) 3.5246
11.5	(- 7) 7.3981	(- 6) 3.4579	(- 5) 1.3887	(- 5) 4.9038	(- 4) 1.5479
12.0	(- 7) 2.6475	(- 6) 1.2988	(- 6) 5.4642	(- 5) 2.0187	(- 5) 6.6617
12.5	(- 8) 9.3549	(- 7) 4.8095	(- 6) 2.1167	(- 6) 8.1695	(- 5) 2.8139
13.0	(- 8) 3.2665	(- 7) 1.7578	(- 7) 8.0818	(- 6) 3.2541	(- 5) 1.1682
13.5	(- 8) 1.1280	(- 8) 6.3458	(- 7) 3.0443	(- 6) 1.2772	(- 6) 4.7727
14.0	(- 9) 3.8550	(- 8) 2.2647	(- 7) 1.1324	(- 7) 4.9445	(- 6) 1.9209
14.5	(- 9) 1.3046	(- 9) 7.9952	(- 8) 4.1623	(- 7) 1.8896	(- 7) 7.6241
15.0	(-10) 4.3743	(- 9) 2.7940	(- 8) 1.5130	(- 8) 7.1342	(- 7) 2.9865
15.5	(-10) 1.4540	(-10) 9.6701	(- 9) 5.4422	(- 8) 2.6629	(- 7) 1.1555
16.0	(-11) 4.7930	(-10) 3.3165	(- 9) 1.9382	(- 9) 9.8333	(- 8) 4.4191
16.5	(-11) 1.5677	(-10) 1.1277	(-10) 6.8378	(- 9) 3.5942	(- 8) 1.6715
17.0	(-12) 5.0893	(-11) 3.8030	(-10) 2.3909	(- 9) 1.3011	(- 9) 6.2571
17.5	(-12) 1.6405	(-11) 1.2726	(-11) 8.2893	(-10) 4.6667	(- 9) 2.3192
18.0	(-13) 5.2523	(-12) 4.2267	(-11) 2.8507	(-10) 1.6593	(-10) 8.5155
18.5	(-13) 1.6708	(-12) 1.3939	(-12) 9.7283	(-11) 5.8508	(-10) 3.0988
19.0	(-14) 5.2819	(-13) 4.5659	(-12) 3.2955	(-11) 2.0467	(-10) 1.1181
19.5	(-14) 1.6599	(-13) 1.4859	(-12) 1.1085	(-12) 7.1053	(-11) 4.0014
20.0	(-15) 5.1871	(-14) 4.8057	(-13) 3.7036	(-12) 2.4488	(-11) 1.4209

COULOMB WAVE FUNCTIONS OF ORDER ZERO Table 14.1

$G_0(\eta,\rho)$

$\eta\backslash\rho$	6	7	8	9	10
0.5	(- 1)-1.8864	(- 1)+7.0005	(0)+1.0284	(- 1)+5.2116	(- 1)-4.1435
1.0	(0)-1.0908	(- 1)-5.9842	(- 1)+2.9114	(- 1)+9.7148	(- 1)+9.4287
1.5	(- 1)-7.8946	(0)-1.1403	(- 1)-8.7095	(- 2)-9.0032	(- 1)+7.4235
2.0	(- 2)+5.7313	(- 1)-6.8409	(0)-1.1353	(0)-1.0415	(- 1)-3.9931
2.5	(- 1) 8.5834	(- 1)+1.4966	(- 1)-5.8782	(0)-1.1041	(0)-1.1456
3.0	(0) 1.4847	(- 1) 9.1321	(- 1)+2.2822	(- 1)-5.0095	(0)-1.0601
3.5	(0) 2.0980	(0) 1.5205	(- 1) 9.6127	(- 1)+2.9641	(- 1)-4.2253
4.0	(0) 3.0138	(0) 2.1165	(0) 1.5526	(0) 1.0040	(- 1)+3.5656
4.5	(0) 4.7449	(0) 2.9779	(0) 2.1340	(0) 1.5818	(0) 1.0426
5.0	(0) 8.2720	(0) 4.5475	(0) 2.9524	(0) 2.1507	(0) 1.6085
5.5	(1) 1.5713	(0) 7.6426	(0) 4.3971	(0) 2.9338	(0) 2.1665
6.0	(1) 3.1910	(1) 1.3964	(0) 7.1665	(0) 4.2789	(0) 2.9202
6.5	(1) 6.8300	(1) 2.7266	(1) 1.2667	(0) 6.7939	(0) 4.1837
7.0	(2) 1.5259	(1) 5.6125	(1) 2.3913	(1) 1.1669	(0) 6.4944
7.5	(2) 3.5340	(2) 1.2063	(1) 4.7587	(1) 2.1389	(1) 1.0879
8.0	(2) 8.4429	(2) 2.6887	(1) 9.8888	(1) 4.1320	(1) 1.9428
8.5	(3) 2.0726	(2) 6.1843	(2) 2.1316	(1) 8.3352	(1) 3.6553
9.0	(3) 5.2121	(3) 1.4623	(2) 4.7425	(2) 1.7442	(1) 7.1811
9.5	(4) 1.3393	(3) 3.5436	(3) 1.0850	(2) 3.7678	(2) 1.4634
10.0	(4) 3.5096	(3) 8.7792	(3) 2.5448	(2) 8.3709	(2) 3.0787
10.5	(4) 9.3615	(4) 2.2190	(3) 6.1041	(3) 1.9070	(2) 6.6618
11.0	(5) 2.5381	(4) 5.7119	(4) 1.4943	(3) 4.4437	(3) 1.4783
11.5	(5) 6.9851	(5) 1.4951	(4) 3.7266	(4) 1.0570	(3) 3.3559
12.0	(6) 1.9492	(5) 3.9745	(4) 9.4543	(4) 2.5623	(3) 7.7783
12.5	(6) 5.5096	(6) 1.0718	(5) 2.4367	(4) 6.3199	(4) 1.8375
13.0	(7) 1.5761	(6) 2.9290	(5) 6.3731	(5) 1.5841	(4) 4.4178
13.5	(7) 4.5596	(6) 8.1041	(6) 1.6898	(5) 4.0302	(5) 1.0796
14.0	(8) 1.3330	(7) 2.2686	(6) 4.5378	(6) 1.0398	(5) 2.6784
14.5	(8) 3.9356	(7) 6.4200	(7) 1.2333	(6) 2.7177	(5) 6.7399
15.0	(9) 1.1728	(8) 1.8356	(7) 3.3897	(6) 7.1908	(6) 1.7186
15.5	(9) 3.5260	(8) 5.2995	(7) 9.4158	(7) 1.9247	(6) 4.4374
16.0	(10) 1.0689	(9) 1.5441	(8) 2.6418	(7) 5.2078	(7) 1.1592
16.5	(10) 3.2661	(9) 4.5382	(8) 7.4830	(8) 1.4237	(7) 3.0621
17.0	(11) 1.0055	(10) 1.3449	(9) 2.1387	(8) 3.9301	(7) 8.1738
17.5	(11) 3.1176	(10) 4.0168	(9) 6.1650	(9) 1.0950	(8) 2.2037
18.0	(11) 9.7326	(11) 1.2087	(10) 1.7916	(9) 3.0778	(8) 5.9978
18.5	(12) 3.0582	(11) 3.6634	(10) 5.2473	(9) 8.7237	(9) 1.6472
19.0	(12) 9.6692	(12) 1.1179	(11) 1.5483	(10) 2.4925	(9) 4.5626
19.5	(13) 3.0754	(12) 3.4335	(11) 4.6007	(10) 7.1762	(10) 1.2742
20.0	(13) 9.8379	(13) 1.0612	(12) 1.3764	(11) 2.0813	(10) 3.5867

$\frac{d}{d\rho}G_0(\eta,\rho)$

$\eta\backslash\rho$	6	7	8	9	10
0.5	(- 1)+9.4204	(- 1)+7.0722	(- 1)-1.0134	(- 1)-8.3938	(- 1)-8.9014
1.0	(- 1)+1.5804	(- 1)+7.7643	(- 1)+8.9368	(- 1)+3.7613	(- 1)-4.3326
1.5	(- 1)-6.0177	(- 2)-5.6347	(- 1)+5.7724	(- 1)+9.0303	(- 1)+6.6389
2.0	(- 1)-7.8017	(- 1)-6.4998	(- 1)-2.0611	(- 1)+3.9589	(- 1)+8.3156
2.5	(- 1)-6.4488	(- 1)-7.5558	(- 1)-6.7507	(- 1)-3.1180	(- 1)+2.4273
3.0	(- 1)-5.4037	(- 1)-6.2420	(- 1)-7.3342	(- 1)-6.8725	(- 1)-3.8780
3.5	(- 1)-6.8137	(- 1)-5.3136	(- 1)-6.0700	(- 1)-7.1359	(- 1)-6.9193
4.0	(0)-1.2552	(- 1)-6.5441	(- 1)-5.2327	(- 1)-5.9237	(- 1)-6.9585
4.5	(0)-2.6310	(0)-1.1510	(- 1)-6.3266	(- 1)-5.1597	(- 1)-5.7969
5.0	(0)-5.7112	(0)-2.3175	(0)-1.0709	(- 1)-6.1460	(- 1)-5.0932
5.5	(1)-1.2704	(0)-4.8515	(0)-2.0829	(0)-1.0071	(- 1)-5.9925
6.0	(1)-2.9032	(1)-1.0407	(0)-4.2272	(0)-1.9007	(- 1)-9.5489
6.5	(1)-6.8237	(1)-2.2915	(0)-8.7913	(0)-3.7545	(0)-1.7550
7.0	(2)-1.6477	(1)-5.1862	(1)-1.8751	(0)-7.6010	(0)-3.3846
7.5	(2)-4.0793	(2)-1.2056	(1)-4.1077	(1)-1.5769	(0)-6.6920
8.0	(3)-1.0333	(2)-2.8738	(1)-9.2394	(1)-3.3574	(1)-1.3548
8.5	(3)-2.6728	(2)-7.0107	(2)-2.1308	(1)-7.3362	(1)-2.8128
9.0	(3)-7.0464	(3)-1.7469	(2)-5.0295	(2)-1.6432	(1)-5.9900
9.5	(4)-1.8904	(3)-4.4387	(3)-1.2129	(2)-3.7670	(2)-1.3072
10.0	(4)-5.1540	(4)-1.1482	(3)-2.9831	(2)-8.8229	(2)-2.9193
10.5	(5)-1.4262	(4)-3.0197	(3)-7.4717	(3)-2.1080	(2)-6.6607
11.0	(5)-4.0011	(4)-8.0639	(4)-1.9033	(3)-5.1298	(3)-1.5503
11.5	(6)-1.1369	(5)-2.1843	(4)-4.9246	(4)-1.2698	(3)-3.6759
12.0	(6)-3.2694	(5)-5.9953	(5)-1.2929	(4)-3.1937	(3)-8.8669
12.5	(6)-9.5069	(6)-1.6661	(5)-3.4407	(4)-8.1522	(4)-2.1734
13.0	(7)-2.7936	(6)-4.6839	(5)-9.2739	(5)-2.1099	(4)-5.4080
13.5	(7)-8.2899	(7)-1.3312	(6)-2.5296	(5)-5.5322	(5)-1.3647
14.0	(8)-2.4829	(7)-3.8226	(6)-6.9781	(6)-1.4684	(5)-3.4894
14.5	(8)-7.5021	(8)-1.1083	(7)-1.9454	(6)-3.9424	(5)-9.0337
15.0	(9)-2.2856	(8)-3.2430	(7)-5.4781	(7)-1.0701	(6)-2.3663
15.5	(9)-7.0183	(8)-9.5716	(8)-1.5573	(7)-2.9344	(6)-6.2673
16.0	(10)-2.1712	(9)-2.8485	(8)-4.4670	(7)-8.1256	(7)-1.6775
16.5	(10)-6.7650	(9)-8.5435	(9)-1.2923	(8)-2.2710	(7)-4.5347
17.0	(11)-2.1221	(10)-2.5817	(9)-3.7692	(8)-6.4031	(8)-1.2375
17.5	(11)-6.7001	(10)-7.8569	(10)-1.1079	(9)-1.8206	(8)-3.4078
18.0	(12)-2.1285	(11)-2.4075	(10)-3.2807	(9)-5.2180	(8)-9.4651
18.5	(12)-6.8019	(11)-7.4250	(10)-9.7840	(10)-1.5070	(9)-2.6506
19.0	(13)-2.1860	(12)-2.3043	(11)-2.9377	(10)-4.3845	(9)-7.4812
19.5	(13)-7.0638	(12)-7.1939	(11)-8.8779	(11)-1.2846	(10)-2.1275
20.0	(14)-2.2945	(13)-2.2589	(12)-2.6998	(11)-3.7889	(10)-6.0938

Table 14.1 COULOMB WAVE FUNCTIONS OF ORDER ZERO

$F_0(\eta,\rho)$

$\eta \backslash \rho$	11	12	13	14	15
0.5	(- 1)+2.0734	(- 1)-6.9792	(0)-1.0101	(- 1)-4.5964	(- 1)+4.8492
1.0	(0)+1.0298	(- 1)+7.9515	(- 2)-5.5932	(- 1)-8.6120	(- 1)-9.7879
1.5	(- 2)+2.4612	(- 1)+8.3008	(0)+1.0493	(- 1)+5.1243	(- 1)-3.9930
2.0	(0)-1.0170	(- 1)-3.6119	(- 1)+5.1844	(0)+1.0566	(- 1)+8.8343
2.5	(- 1)-9.6841	(0)-1.1262	(- 1)-6.5977	(- 1)+1.8869	(- 1)+9.1875
3.0	(- 1)-1.2613	(- 1)-8.5079	(0)-1.1642	(- 1)-8.7866	(- 1)-1.1758
3.5	(- 1)+7.8227	(- 2)+3.2549	(- 1)-7.2395	(0)-1.1551	(0)-1.0318
4.0	(0) 1.3156	(- 1) 8.8532	(- 1)+1.7404	(- 1)-5.9595	(0)-1.1153
4.5	(0) 1.4169	(0) 1.3600	(- 1) 9.7341	(- 1)+3.0035	(- 1)-4.7101
5.0	(0) 1.2318	(0) 1.4324	(0) 1.3978	(0) 1.0496	(- 1)+4.1342
5.5	(- 1) 9.3335	(0) 1.2422	(0) 1.4462	(0) 1.4305	(0) 1.1161
6.0	(- 1) 6.3994	(- 1) 9.4757	(0) 1.2519	(0) 1.4586	(0) 1.4592
6.5	(- 1) 4.0596	(- 1) 6.5749	(- 1) 9.6077	(0) 1.2610	(0) 1.4698
7.0	(- 1) 2.4178	(- 1) 4.2347	(- 1) 6.7378	(- 1) 9.7312	(0) 1.2697
7.5	(- 1) 1.3660	(- 1) 2.5662	(- 1) 4.3989	(- 1) 6.8900	(- 1) 9.8472
8.0	(- 2) 7.3768	(- 1) 1.4773	(- 1) 2.7074	(- 1) 4.5535	(- 1) 7.0328
8.5	(- 2) 3.8306	(- 2) 8.1375	(- 1) 1.5852	(- 1) 2.8422	(- 1) 4.6997
9.0	(- 2) 1.9215	(- 2) 4.3132	(- 2) 8.8895	(- 1) 1.6898	(- 1) 2.9711
9.5	(- 3) 9.3472	(- 2) 2.2096	(- 2) 4.8001	(- 2) 9.6316	(- 1) 1.7913
10.0	(- 3) 4.4228	(- 2) 1.0980	(- 2) 2.5064	(- 2) 5.2898	(- 1) 1.0363
10.5	(- 3) 2.0410	(- 3) 5.3087	(- 2) 1.2700	(- 2) 2.8108	(- 2) 5.7809
11.0	(- 4) 9.2064	(- 3) 2.5036	(- 3) 6.2624	(- 2) 1.4498	(- 2) 3.1214
11.5	(- 4) 4.0667	(- 3) 1.1541	(- 3) 3.0126	(- 3) 7.2798	(- 2) 1.6367
12.0	(- 4) 1.7621	(- 4) 5.2102	(- 3) 1.4168	(- 3) 3.5666	(- 3) 8.3567
12.5	(- 5) 7.5001	(- 4) 2.3072	(- 4) 6.5253	(- 3) 1.7085	(- 3) 4.1640
13.0	(- 5) 3.1398	(- 4) 1.0036	(- 4) 2.9480	(- 4) 8.0157	(- 3) 2.0290
13.5	(- 5) 1.2943	(- 5) 4.2931	(- 4) 1.3082	(- 4) 3.6890	(- 4) 9.6841
14.0	(- 6) 5.2587	(- 5) 1.8082	(- 5) 5.7090	(- 4) 1.6677	(- 4) 4.5343
14.5	(- 6) 2.1078	(- 6) 7.5055	(- 5) 2.4529	(- 5) 7.4139	(- 4) 2.0854
15.0	(- 7) 8.3417	(- 6) 3.0731	(- 5) 1.0386	(- 5) 3.2448	(- 5) 9.4326
15.5	(- 7) 3.2617	(- 6) 1.2422	(- 6) 4.3371	(- 5) 1.3994	(- 5) 4.2002
16.0	(- 7) 1.2609	(- 7) 4.9601	(- 6) 1.7878	(- 6) 5.9525	(- 5) 1.8429
16.5	(- 8) 4.8223	(- 7) 1.9580	(- 7) 7.2797	(- 6) 2.4990	(- 6) 7.9746
17.0	(- 8) 1.8255	(- 8) 7.6449	(- 7) 2.9299	(- 6) 1.0363	(- 6) 3.4058
17.5	(- 9) 6.8436	(- 8) 2.9542	(- 7) 1.1663	(- 7) 4.2471	(- 6) 1.4366
18.0	(- 9) 2.5420	(- 8) 1.1303	(- 8) 4.5940	(- 7) 1.7213	(- 7) 5.9886
18.5	(-10) 9.3587	(- 9) 4.2845	(- 8) 1.7916	(- 8) 6.9031	(- 7) 2.4686
19.0	(-10) 3.4166	(- 9) 1.6095	(- 9) 6.9206	(- 8) 2.7406	(- 7) 1.0068
19.5	(-10) 1.2373	(-10) 5.9943	(- 9) 2.6491	(- 8) 1.0776	(- 8) 4.0646
20.0	(-11) 4.4462	(-10) 2.2143	(- 9) 1.0052	(- 9) 4.1981	(- 8) 1.6250

$\frac{d}{d\rho}F_0(\eta,\rho)$

$\eta \backslash \rho$	11	12	13	14	15
0.5	(- 1)-9.5680	(- 1)-7.1349	(- 1)+1.3869	(- 1)+8.7670	(- 1)+8.6352
1.0	(- 1)+1.8546	(- 1)-6.2449	(- 1)-9.5769	(- 1)-5.3599	(- 1)+3.1951
1.5	(- 1)+9.2360	(- 1)+5.8520	(- 1)-1.7814	(- 1)-8.2728	(- 1)-8.7421
2.0	(- 1)+3.8476	(- 1)+8.5839	(- 1)+7.9972	(- 1)+2.0967	(- 1)-5.3804
2.5	(- 1)-4.5774	(- 1)+1.6399	(- 1)+7.2679	(- 1)+8.8132	(- 1)+4.9591
3.0	(- 1)-8.1670	(- 1)-5.7064	(- 2)-2.2037	(- 1)+5.7220	(- 1)+8.7738
3.5	(- 1)-6.4636	(- 1)-8.0763	(- 1)-6.4688	(- 1)-1.7427	(- 1)+4.1643
4.0	(- 1)-2.5453	(- 1)-5.9550	(- 1)-7.8882	(- 1)-6.9700	(- 1)-2.9695
4.5	(- 2)+8.9270	(- 1)-2.1713	(- 1)-5.4930	(- 1)-7.6466	(- 1)-7.2842
5.0	(- 1) 2.7803	(- 1)+1.0181	(- 1)-1.8523	(- 1)-5.0747	(- 1)-7.3777
5.5	(- 1) 3.2469	(- 1) 2.7572	(- 1)+1.1221	(- 1)-1.5772	(- 1)-4.6963
6.0	(- 1) 2.8649	(- 1) 3.1907	(- 1) 2.7353	(- 1)+1.2094	(- 1)-1.3378
6.5	(- 1) 2.1649	(- 1) 2.8342	(- 1) 3.1402	(- 1) 2.7144	(- 1)+1.2836
7.0	(- 1) 1.4725	(- 1) 2.1694	(- 1) 2.8059	(- 1) 3.0946	(- 1) 2.6945
7.5	(- 2) 9.2538	(- 1) 1.4994	(- 1) 2.1722	(- 1) 2.7794	(- 1) 3.0530
8.0	(- 2) 5.4607	(- 2) 9.5947	(- 1) 1.5231	(- 1) 2.1737	(- 1) 2.7548
8.5	(- 2) 3.0589	(- 2) 5.7724	(- 2) 9.9053	(- 1) 1.5440	(- 1) 2.1743
9.0	(- 2) 1.6394	(- 2) 3.2995	(- 2) 6.0640	(- 1) 1.0189	(- 1) 1.5625
9.5	(- 3) 8.4560	(- 2) 1.8054	(- 2) 3.5301	(- 2) 6.3375	(- 1) 1.0450
10.0	(- 3) 4.2172	(- 3) 9.5118	(- 2) 1.9685	(- 2) 3.7513	(- 2) 6.5943
10.5	(- 3) 2.0412	(- 3) 4.8467	(- 2) 1.0573	(- 2) 2.1282	(- 2) 3.9633
11.0	(- 4) 9.6175	(- 3) 2.3971	(- 3) 5.4937	(- 2) 1.1634	(- 2) 2.2844
11.5	(- 4) 4.4224	(- 3) 1.1542	(- 3) 2.7714	(- 3) 6.1551	(- 2) 1.2693
12.0	(- 4) 1.9888	(- 4) 5.4237	(- 3) 1.3612	(- 3) 3.1620	(- 3) 6.8276
12.5	(- 5) 8.7636	(- 4) 2.4927	(- 4) 6.5256	(- 3) 1.5818	(- 3) 3.5670
13.0	(- 5) 3.7897	(- 4) 1.1224	(- 4) 3.0596	(- 4) 7.7243	(- 3) 1.8150
13.5	(- 5) 1.6105	(- 5) 4.9597	(- 4) 1.4055	(- 4) 3.6892	(- 4) 9.0158
14.0	(- 6) 6.7342	(- 5) 2.1535	(- 5) 6.3355	(- 4) 1.7264	(- 4) 4.3806
14.5	(- 6) 2.7736	(- 6) 9.1993	(- 5) 2.8061	(- 5) 7.9271	(- 4) 2.0855
15.0	(- 6) 1.1263	(- 6) 3.8704	(- 5) 1.2227	(- 5) 3.5765	(- 5) 9.7427
15.5	(- 7) 4.5133	(- 6) 1.6053	(- 6) 5.2466	(- 5) 1.5873	(- 5) 4.4720
16.0	(- 7) 1.7861	(- 7) 6.5690	(- 6) 2.2191	(- 6) 6.9375	(- 5) 2.0192
16.5	(- 8) 6.9850	(- 7) 2.6544	(- 7) 9.2602	(- 6) 2.9885	(- 6) 8.9777
17.0	(- 8) 2.7014	(- 7) 1.0598	(- 7) 3.8151	(- 6) 1.2700	(- 6) 3.9341
17.5	(- 8) 1.0337	(- 8) 4.1839	(- 7) 1.5529	(- 7) 5.3278	(- 6) 1.7006
18.0	(- 9) 3.9159	(- 8) 1.6340	(- 8) 6.2491	(- 7) 2.2081	(- 7) 7.2565
18.5	(- 9) 1.4693	(- 9) 6.3169	(- 8) 2.4875	(- 8) 9.0465	(- 7) 3.0587
19.0	(-10) 5.4629	(- 9) 2.4184	(- 9) 9.8001	(- 8) 3.6658	(- 7) 1.2744
19.5	(-10) 2.0135	(-10) 9.1730	(- 9) 3.8231	(- 8) 1.4700	(- 8) 5.2514
20.0	(-11) 7.3598	(-10) 3.4487	(- 9) 1.4774	(- 9) 5.8367	(- 8) 2.1413

COULOMB WAVE FUNCTIONS OF ORDER ZERO

Table 14.1

$G_0(\eta,\rho)$

$\eta \backslash \rho$	11	12	13	14	15
0.5	(0)-1.0028	(- 1)-7.4645	(- 1)+1.4266	(- 1)+9.0905	(- 1)+8.9435
1.0	(- 1)+2.1054	(- 1)-6.8021	(0)-1.0410	(- 1)-5.8152	(- 1)+3.4046
1.5	(0)+1.0319	(- 1)+6.8165	(- 1)-1.9619	(- 1)-9.3005	(- 1)-9.7885
2.0	(- 1)+4.6526	(0)+1.0451	(- 1)+9.6524	(- 1)+2.5664	(- 1)-6.2172
2.5	(- 1)-6.4066	(- 1)+1.9303	(- 1)+9.1486	(0)+1.0999	(- 1)+6.1593
3.0	(0)-1.2065	(- 1)-8.2667	(- 2)-5.4999	(- 1)+7.4014	(0)+1.1292
3.5	(0)-1.0105	(0)-1.2387	(- 1)-9.6933	(- 1)-2.7342	(- 1)+5.4881
4.0	(- 1)-3.5145	(- 1)-9.5867	(0)-1.2515	(0)-1.0783	(- 1)-4.6254
4.5	(- 1)+4.1032	(- 1)-2.8667	(- 1)-9.0670	(0)-1.2510	(0)-1.1612
5.0	(0) 1.0777	(- 1)+4.5891	(- 1)-2.2730	(- 1)-8.5560	(0)-1.2413
5.5	(0) 1.6333	(0) 1.1100	(- 1)+5.0322	(- 1)-1.7259	(- 1)-8.0595
6.0	(0) 2.1816	(0) 1.6563	(0) 1.1399	(- 1)+5.4393	(- 1)-1.2194
6.5	(0) 2.9102	(0) 2.1960	(0) 1.6778	(0) 1.1677	(- 1)+5.8159
7.0	(0) 4.1056	(0) 2.9029	(0) 2.2097	(0) 1.6980	(0) 1.1937
7.5	(0) 6.2486	(0) 4.0404	(0) 2.8977	(0) 2.2229	(0) 1.7172
8.0	(1) 1.0238	(0) 6.0432	(0) 3.9853	(0) 2.8940	(0) 2.2355
8.5	(1) 1.7863	(0) 9.7072	(0) 5.8691	(0) 3.9383	(0) 2.8916
9.0	(1) 3.2824	(1) 1.6587	(0) 9.2614	(0) 5.7197	(0) 3.8977
9.5	(1) 6.2966	(1) 2.9836	(1) 1.5529	(0) 8.8817	(0) 5.5902
10.0	(2) 1.2529	(1) 5.6013	(1) 2.7395	(1) 1.4638	(0) 8.5544
10.5	(2) 2.5735	(2) 1.0906	(1) 5.0429	(1) 2.5369	(1) 1.3878
11.0	(2) 5.4370	(2) 2.1919	(1) 9.6258	(1) 4.5863	(1) 2.3662
11.5	(3) 1.1780	(2) 4.5309	(2) 1.8964	(1) 8.5960	(1) 4.2071
12.0	(3) 2.6115	(2) 9.6054	(2) 3.8424	(2) 1.6627	(1) 7.7536
12.5	(3) 5.9114	(3) 2.0835	(2) 7.9840	(2) 3.3072	(2) 1.4744
13.0	(4) 1.3640	(3) 4.6148	(3) 1.6974	(2) 6.7457	(2) 2.8830
13.5	(4) 3.2036	(4) 1.0421	(3) 3.6852	(3) 1.4078	(2) 5.7803
14.0	(4) 7.6488	(4) 2.3953	(3) 8.1567	(3) 3.0002	(3) 1.1857
14.5	(5) 1.8544	(4) 5.5978	(4) 1.8380	(3) 6.5186	(3) 2.4836
15.0	(5) 4.5606	(5) 1.3286	(4) 4.2110	(4) 1.4419	(3) 5.3038
15.5	(6) 1.1368	(5) 3.1990	(4) 9.7988	(4) 3.2432	(4) 1.1531
16.0	(6) 2.8697	(5) 7.8082	(5) 2.3136	(4) 7.4095	(4) 2.5494
16.5	(6) 7.3309	(6) 1.9303	(5) 5.5378	(5) 1.7177	(4) 5.7251
17.0	(7) 1.8940	(6) 4.8301	(6) 1.3427	(5) 4.0372	(5) 1.3047
17.5	(7) 4.9456	(7) 1.2225	(6) 3.2955	(5) 9.6130	(5) 3.0146
18.0	(8) 1.3046	(7) 3.1276	(6) 8.1823	(6) 2.3172	(5) 7.0570
18.5	(8) 3.4746	(7) 8.0845	(7) 2.0539	(6) 5.6510	(6) 1.6726
19.0	(8) 9.3396	(8) 2.1103	(7) 5.2096	(7) 1.3934	(6) 4.0107
19.5	(9) 2.5325	(8) 5.5602	(8) 1.3345	(7) 3.4722	(6) 9.7253
20.0	(9) 6.9249	(9) 1.4781	(8) 3.4512	(7) 8.7394	(7) 2.3833

$\frac{d}{d\rho}G_0(\eta,\rho)$

$\eta \backslash \rho$	11	12	13	14	15
0.5	(- 1)-1.9549	(- 1)+6.6972	(- 1)+9.7040	(- 1)+4.4173	(- 1)-4.6958
1.0	(- 1)-9.3312	(- 1)-7.2341	(- 2)+5.5060	(- 1)+7.9924	(- 1)+9.1053
1.5	(- 2)-3.0001	(- 1)-7.2415	(- 1)-9.1975	(- 1)-4.4998	(- 1)+3.6132
2.0	(- 1)+8.0730	(- 1)+2.8479	(- 1)-4.3994	(- 1)-8.9553	(- 1)-7.5330
2.5	(- 1)+7.2980	(- 1)+8.5982	(- 1)+5.0789	(- 1)-1.6218	(- 1)-7.5598
3.0	(- 1)+1.1621	(- 1)+6.2091	(- 1)+8.5795	(- 1)+6.5611	(- 2)+7.8968
3.5	(- 1)-4.4342	(- 2)+1.2156	(- 1)+5.1517	(- 1)+8.2450	(- 1)+7.4771
4.0	(- 1)-6.9211	(- 1)-4.8470	(- 2)-7.3596	(- 1)+4.1682	(- 1)+7.7350
4.5	(- 1)-6.7991	(- 1)-6.8955	(- 1)-5.1566	(- 1)-1.4460	(- 1)+3.2728
5.0	(- 1)-5.6855	(- 1)-6.6551	(- 1)-6.8530	(- 1)-5.3907	(- 1)-2.0374
5.5	(- 1)-5.0324	(- 1)-5.5863	(- 1)-6.5243	(- 1)-6.8002	(- 1)-5.5683
6.0	(- 1)-5.8597	(- 1)-4.9764	(- 1)-5.4972	(- 1)-6.4050	(- 1)-6.7414
6.5	(- 1)-9.1132	(- 1)-5.7431	(- 1)-4.9245	(- 1)-5.4165	(- 1)-6.2956
7.0	(0)-1.6356	(- 1)-8.7431	(- 1)-5.6396	(- 1)-4.8763	(- 1)-5.3428
7.5	(0)-3.0877	(0)-1.5360	(- 1)-8.4240	(- 1)-5.5466	(- 1)-4.8313
8.0	(0)-5.9776	(0)-2.8442	(0)-1.4516	(- 1)-8.1456	(- 1)-5.4626
8.5	(1)-1.1842	(0)-5.4029	(0)-2.6410	(0)-1.3790	(- 1)-7.9001
9.0	(1)-2.4038	(1)-1.0496	(0)-4.9315	(0)-2.4689	(0)-1.3159
9.5	(1)-5.0022	(1)-2.0879	(0)-9.4124	(0)-4.5385	(0)-2.3213
10.0	(2)-1.0663	(1)-4.2551	(1)-1.8382	(0)-8.5238	(0)-4.2061
10.5	(2)-2.3257	(1)-8.8802	(1)-3.6758	(1)-1.6369	(0)-7.7837
11.0	(2)-5.1822	(2)-1.8956	(1)-7.5239	(1)-3.2170	(1)-1.4720
11.5	(3)-1.1779	(2)-4.1335	(2)-1.5749	(1)-6.4688	(1)-2.8470
12.0	(3)-2.7275	(2)-9.1940	(2)-3.3666	(2)-1.3297	(1)-5.6316
12.5	(3)-6.4259	(3)-2.0833	(2)-7.3407	(2)-2.7912	(2)-1.1385
13.0	(4)-1.5386	(3)-4.8031	(3)-1.6305	(2)-5.9750	(2)-2.3496
13.5	(4)-3.7400	(4)-1.1255	(3)-3.6849	(3)-1.3029	(2)-4.9448
14.0	(4)-9.2211	(4)-2.6777	(3)-8.4644	(3)-2.8906	(3)-1.0599
14.5	(5)-2.3041	(4)-6.4624	(4)-1.9742	(3)-6.5183	(3)-2.3115
15.0	(5)-5.8301	(5)-1.5808	(4)-4.6712	(4)-1.4925	(3)-5.1233
15.5	(6)-1.4929	(5)-3.9163	(5)-1.1203	(4)-3.4670	(4)-1.1531
16.0	(6)-3.8658	(5)-9.8198	(5)-2.7217	(4)-8.1642	(4)-2.6329
16.5	(7)-1.0118	(6)-2.4904	(5)-6.6925	(5)-1.9474	(4)-6.0946
17.0	(7)-2.6753	(6)-6.3846	(6)-1.6647	(5)-4.7022	(5)-1.4291
17.5	(7)-7.1420	(7)-1.6537	(6)-4.1862	(6)-1.1486	(5)-3.3924
18.0	(8)-1.9243	(7)-4.3256	(7)-1.0637	(6)-2.8369	(5)-8.1473
18.5	(8)-5.2302	(8)-1.1421	(7)-2.7299	(6)-7.0806	(6)-1.9785
19.0	(9)-1.4335	(8)-3.0423	(7)-7.0724	(7)-1.7850	(6)-4.8557
19.5	(9)-3.9609	(8)-8.1738	(8)-1.8489	(7)-4.5433	(7)-1.2038
20.0	(10)-1.1028	(9)-2.2141	(8)-4.8757	(8)-1.1670	(7)-3.0133

Table 14.1 COULOMB WAVE FUNCTIONS OF ORDER ZERO

$F_0(\eta,\rho)$

$\eta\backslash\rho$	16	17	18	19	20
0.5	(0)+1.0105	(−1)+6.6039	(−1)−2.6356	(−1)−9.5714	(−1)−8.1320
1.0	(−1)−3.0813	(−1)+6.1193	(0)+1.0298	(−1)+5.9819	(−1)−3.2923
1.5	(0)−1.0106	(−1)−8.5450	(−2)−4.2659	(−1)+8.0098	(0)+1.0154
2.0	(−1)+1.0271	(−1)−7.4809	(0)−1.0610	(−1)−6.0110	(−1)+3.0159
2.5	(0)+1.0681	(−1)+5.2505	(−1)−3.6504	(0)−1.0050	(−1)−9.4813
3.0	(−1)+7.0689	(0)+1.1097	(−1)+8.3235	(−2)+3.2093	(−1)−7.8654
3.5	(−1)−3.8460	(−1)+4.6531	(0)+1.0517	(0)+1.0266	(−1)+3.8780
4.0	(0)−1.1328	(−1)−6.0877	(−1)+2.2016	(−1)+9.2908	(0)+1.1240
4.5	(0)−1.0557	(0)−1.1932	(−1)−7.9196	(−2)−1.3928	(−1)+7.6776
5.0	(−1)−3.5128	(−1)−9.8377	(0)−1.2226	(−1)−9.3827	(−1)−2.2935
5.5	(−1)+5.1503	(−1)−2.3772	(−1)−9.0447	(0)−1.2281	(0)−1.0524
6.0	(0) 1.1748	(−1)+6.0673	(−1)−1.3066	(−1)−8.2121	(0)−1.2155
6.5	(0) 1.4845	(0) 1.2270	(−1)+6.8982	(−2)−3.0049	(−1)−7.3630
7.0	(0) 1.4802	(0) 1.5072	(0) 1.2736	(−1)+7.6541	(−2)+6.4345
7.5	(0) 1.2778	(0) 1.4897	(0) 1.5276	(0) 1.3157	(−1) 8.3446
8.0	(−1) 9.9567	(0) 1.2856	(0) 1.4986	(0) 1.5461	(0) 1.3538
8.5	(−1) 7.1674	(0) 1.0060	(0) 1.2930	(0) 1.5069	(0) 1.5630
9.0	(−1) 4.8384	(−1) 7.2948	(0) 1.0159	(0) 1.3001	(0) 1.5147
9.5	(−1) 3.0947	(−1) 4.9703	(−1) 7.4157	(0) 1.0253	(0) 1.3070
10.0	(−1) 1.8899	(−1) 3.2134	(−1) 5.0960	(−1) 7.5308	(0) 1.0343
10.5	(−1) 1.1084	(−1) 1.9857	(−1) 3.3276	(−1) 5.2163	(−1) 7.6406
11.0	(−2) 6.2723	(−1) 1.1794	(−1) 2.0789	(−1) 3.4376	(−1) 5.3315
11.5	(−2) 3.4374	(−2) 6.7632	(−1) 1.2493	(−1) 2.1696	(−1) 3.5437
12.0	(−2) 1.8300	(−2) 3.7577	(−2) 7.2527	(−1) 1.3181	(−1) 2.2578
12.5	(−3) 9.4892	(−2) 2.0290	(−2) 4.0816	(−2) 7.7405	(−1) 1.3858
13.0	(−3) 4.8032	(−2) 1.0674	(−2) 2.2331	(−2) 4.4084	(−2) 8.2258
13.5	(−3) 2.3779	(−3) 5.4824	(−2) 1.1907	(−2) 2.4418	(−2) 4.7375
14.0	(−3) 1.1532	(−3) 2.7546	(−3) 6.2000	(−2) 1.3185	(−2) 2.6546
14.5	(−4) 5.4870	(−3) 1.3560	(−3) 3.1586	(−3) 6.9542	(−2) 1.4504
15.0	(−4) 2.5646	(−4) 6.5497	(−3) 1.5768	(−3) 3.5893	(−3) 7.7433
15.5	(−4) 1.1789	(−4) 3.1079	(−4) 7.7245	(−3) 1.8156	(−3) 4.0459
16.0	(−5) 5.3346	(−4) 1.4504	(−4) 3.7177	(−4) 9.0130	(−3) 2.0721
16.5	(−5) 2.3787	(−5) 6.6636	(−4) 1.7598	(−4) 4.3962	(−3) 1.0416
17.0	(−5) 1.0460	(−5) 3.0167	(−5) 8.2016	(−4) 2.1092	(−4) 5.1452
17.5	(−6) 4.5399	(−5) 1.3469	(−5) 3.7665	(−5) 9.9629	(−4) 2.5000
18.0	(−6) 1.9459	(−6) 5.9345	(−5) 1.7058	(−5) 4.6375	(−4) 1.1961
18.5	(−7) 8.2424	(−6) 2.5824	(−6) 7.6243	(−5) 2.1289	(−5) 5.6392
19.0	(−7) 3.4522	(−6) 1.1105	(−6) 3.3654	(−6) 9.6448	(−5) 2.6221
19.5	(−7) 1.4304	(−7) 4.7213	(−6) 1.4679	(−6) 4.3152	(−5) 1.2032
20.0	(−8) 5.8668	(−7) 1.9859	(−7) 6.3305	(−6) 1.9078	(−6) 5.4529

$\frac{d}{d\rho}F_0(\eta,\rho)$

$\eta\backslash\rho$	16	17	18	19	20
0.5	(−1)+1.0374	(−1)−7.4873	(−1)−9.5176	(−1)−3.2396	(−1)+5.8913
1.0	(−1)+9.2398	(−1)+7.7918	(−3)−6.9768	(−1)−7.9198	(−1)−9.2215
1.5	(−1)−2.6352	(−1)+5.5592	(−1)+9.5486	(−1)+6.1234	(−1)−2.1544
2.0	(−1)−9.2711	(−1)−6.6487	(−2)+8.1839	(−1)+7.7886	(−1)+9.0561
2.5	(−1)−2.1794	(−1)−8.0683	(−1)−8.6636	(−1)−3.3293	(−1)+4.4171
3.0	(−1)+6.8521	(−2)+7.3796	(−1)−6.0115	(−1)−9.0956	(−1)−6.3111
3.5	(−1)+8.2181	(−1)+7.9551	(−1)+3.1511	(−1)−3.6640	(−1)−8.4454
4.0	(−1)+2.6981	(−1)+7.3722	(−1)+8.4585	(−1)+5.0199	(−1)−1.3528
4.5	(−1)−3.9491	(−1)+1.3669	(−1)+6.3816	(−1)+8.5260	(−1)+6.3846
5.0	(−1)−7.4641	(−1)−4.7259	(−2)+1.8327	(−1)+5.3380	(−1)+8.2868
5.5	(−1)−7.0977	(−1)−7.5469	(−1)−5.3380	(−2)−8.5571	(−1)+4.2976
6.0	(−1)−4.3534	(−1)−6.8162	(−1)−7.5595	(−1)−5.8167	(−1)−1.7601
6.5	(−1)−1.1279	(−1)−4.0420	(−1)−6.5393	(−1)−7.5212	(−1)−6.1873
7.0	(−1)+1.3471	(−2)−9.4232	(−1)−3.7584	(−1)−6.2703	(−1)−7.4462
7.5	(−1) 2.6755	(−1)+1.4020	(−2)−7.7728	(−1)−3.4994	(−1)−6.0113
8.0	(−1) 3.0148	(−1) 2.6574	(−1)+1.4497	(−2)−6.2964	(−1)−3.2623
8.5	(−1) 2.7316	(−1) 2.9796	(−1) 2.6401	(−1)+1.4915	(−2)−4.9686
9.0	(−1) 2.1740	(−1) 2.7098	(−1) 2.9470	(−1) 2.6235	(−1)+1.5282
9.5	(−1) 1.5790	(−1) 2.1730	(−1) 2.6893	(−1) 2.9166	(−1) 2.6076
10.0	(−1) 1.0690	(−1) 1.5938	(−1) 2.1715	(−1) 2.6698	(−1) 2.8881
10.5	(−2) 6.8361	(−1) 1.0912	(−1) 1.6072	(−1) 2.1696	(−1) 2.6513
11.0	(−2) 4.1667	(−2) 7.0640	(−1) 1.1118	(−1) 1.6191	(−1) 2.1673
11.5	(−2) 2.4370	(−2) 4.3620	(−2) 7.2792	(−1) 1.1309	(−1) 1.6300
12.0	(−2) 1.3747	(−2) 2.5860	(−2) 4.5494	(−2) 7.4828	(−1) 1.1487
12.5	(−3) 7.5088	(−2) 1.4792	(−2) 2.7313	(−2) 4.7295	(−2) 7.6757
13.0	(−3) 3.9846	(−3) 8.1964	(−2) 1.5829	(−2) 2.8730	(−2) 4.9026
13.5	(−3) 2.0598	(−3) 4.4133	(−3) 8.8884	(−2) 1.6854	(−2) 3.0112
14.0	(−3) 1.0396	(−3) 2.3153	(−3) 4.8514	(−3) 9.5832	(−2) 1.7867
14.5	(−4) 5.1328	(−3) 1.1861	(−3) 2.5805	(−3) 5.2978	(−2) 1.0279
15.0	(−4) 2.4832	(−4) 5.9443	(−3) 1.3405	(−3) 2.8547	(−3) 5.7512
15.5	(−4) 1.1789	(−4) 2.9194	(−4) 6.8135	(−3) 1.5025	(−3) 3.1370
16.0	(−5) 5.4992	(−4) 1.4071	(−4) 3.3940	(−4) 7.7388	(−3) 1.6717
16.5	(−5) 2.5233	(−5) 6.6637	(−4) 1.6592	(−4) 3.9067	(−4) 8.7182
17.0	(−5) 1.1401	(−5) 3.1043	(−5) 7.9706	(−4) 1.9356	(−4) 4.4568
17.5	(−6) 5.0769	(−5) 1.4240	(−5) 3.7665	(−5) 9.4242	(−4) 2.2364
18.0	(−6) 2.2300	(−6) 6.4378	(−5) 1.7526	(−5) 4.5139	(−4) 1.1028
18.5	(−7) 9.6688	(−6) 2.8708	(−6) 8.0374	(−5) 2.1289	(−5) 5.3499
19.0	(−7) 4.1409	(−6) 1.2636	(−6) 3.6355	(−6) 9.8957	(−5) 2.5557
19.5	(−7) 1.7529	(−7) 5.4935	(−6) 1.6231	(−6) 4.5369	(−5) 1.2033
20.0	(−8) 7.3379	(−7) 2.3605	(−7) 7.1576	(−6) 2.0531	(−6) 5.5878

COULOMB WAVE FUNCTIONS OF ORDER ZERO Table 14.1

$G_0(\eta,\rho)$

$\eta \backslash \rho$	16	17	18	19	20
0.5	(- 1)+1.0821	(- 1)-7.7111	(- 1)-9.7953	(- 1)-3.3354	(- 1)+6.0387
1.0	(- 1)+9.8687	(- 1)+8.3065	(- 3)-5.5146	(- 1)-8.3622	(- 1)-9.7243
1.5	(- 1)-2.9626	(- 1)+6.0950	(0)+1.0457	(- 1)+6.6931	(- 1)-2.3123
2.0	(0)-1.0694	(- 1)-7.6383	(- 2)+8.8035	(- 1)+8.7398	(0)+1.0133
2.5	(- 1)-2.5363	(- 1)-9.5594	(0)-1.0212	(- 1)-3.9315	(- 1)+5.0534
3.0	(- 1)+8.7388	(- 1)+1.0254	(- 1)-7.2872	(0)-1.0987	(- 1)-7.5896
3.5	(0)+1.0876	(0)+1.0419	(- 1)+4.1434	(- 1)-4.5088	(0)-1.0436
4.0	(- 1)+3.5629	(0)+1.0004	(0)+1.1362	(- 1)+6.7042	(- 1)-1.6256
4.5	(- 1)-6.2482	(- 1)+1.7088	(- 1)+8.8526	(0)+1.1729	(- 1)+8.7013
5.0	(0)-1.2237	(- 1)-7.6338	(- 3)-3.2476	(- 1)+7.5425	(0)+1.1657
5.5	(0)-1.2251	(0)-1.2701	(- 1)-8.8135	(- 1)-1.6427	(- 1)+6.1562
6.0	(- 1)-7.5801	(0)-1.2045	(0)-1.3038	(- 1)-9.8158	(- 1)-3.1172
6.5	(- 2)-7.4816	(- 1)-7.1189	(0)-1.1808	(0)-1.3275	(0)-1.0666
7.0	(- 1)+6.1662	(- 2)-3.0805	(- 1)-6.6763	(0)-1.1549	(0)-1.3430
7.5	(0) 1.2182	(- 1)+6.4936	(- 2)+1.0458	(- 1)-6.2518	(0)-1.1277
8.0	(0) 1.7353	(0) 1.2413	(- 1) 6.8010	(- 2)+4.9276	(- 1)-5.8448
8.5	(0) 2.2476	(0) 1.7525	(0) 1.2631	(- 1) 7.0906	(- 2)+8.5910
9.0	(0) 2.8903	(0) 2.2593	(0) 1.7689	(0) 1.2839	(- 1) 7.3645
9.5	(0) 3.8625	(0) 2.8897	(0) 2.2705	(0) 1.7846	(0) 1.3037
10.0	(0) 5.4768	(0) 3.8316	(0) 2.8898	(0) 2.2814	(0) 1.7997
10.5	(0) 8.2695	(0) 5.3768	(0) 3.8044	(0) 2.8904	(0) 2.2919
11.0	(1) 1.3223	(0) 8.0193	(0) 5.2879	(0) 3.7803	(0) 2.8915
11.5	(1) 2.2207	(1) 1.2652	(0) 7.7978	(0) 5.2085	(0) 3.7589
12.0	(1) 3.8880	(1) 2.0953	(1) 1.2151	(0) 7.6004	(0) 5.1370
12.5	(1) 7.0544	(1) 3.6163	(1) 1.9863	(1) 1.1707	(0) 7.4234
13.0	(2) 1.3205	(1) 6.4666	(1) 3.3826	(1) 1.8906	(1) 1.1312
13.5	(2) 2.5411	(2) 1.1927	(1) 5.9669	(1) 3.1797	(1) 1.8061
14.0	(2) 5.0139	(2) 2.2615	(2) 1.0855	(1) 5.5380	(1) 3.0021
14.5	(3) 1.0121	(2) 4.3958	(2) 2.0297	(1) 9.9453	(1) 5.1664
15.0	(3) 2.0860	(2) 8.7404	(2) 3.8903	(2) 1.8354	(1) 9.1659
15.5	(3) 4.3833	(3) 1.7745	(2) 7.6267	(2) 3.4717	(2) 1.6708
16.0	(3) 9.3774	(3) 3.6727	(3) 1.5265	(2) 6.7162	(2) 3.1213
16.5	(4) 2.0400	(3) 7.7388	(3) 3.1148	(3) 1.3264	(2) 5.9630
17.0	(4) 4.5079	(4) 1.6582	(3) 6.4702	(3) 2.6703	(3) 1.1629
17.5	(5) 1.0109	(4) 3.6090	(4) 1.3667	(3) 5.4726	(3) 2.3115
18.0	(5) 2.2987	(4) 7.9717	(4) 2.9323	(4) 1.1404	(3) 4.6772
18.5	(5) 5.2957	(5) 1.7855	(4) 6.3851	(4) 2.4141	(3) 9.6229
19.0	(6) 1.2353	(5) 4.0519	(5) 1.4098	(4) 5.1860	(4) 2.0110
19.5	(6) 2.9156	(5) 9.3105	(5) 3.1542	(5) 1.1297	(4) 4.2650
20.0	(6) 6.9590	(6) 2.1648	(5) 7.1454	(5) 2.4935	(4) 9.1723

$\frac{d}{d\rho}G_0(\eta,\rho)$

$\eta \backslash \rho$	16	17	18	19	20
0.5	(- 1)-9.7855	(- 1)-6.4000	(- 1)+2.5695	(- 1)+9.3189	(- 1)+7.9224
1.0	(- 1)+2.8609	(- 1)-5.7650	(- 1)-9.7102	(- 1)-5.6460	(- 1)+3.1370
1.5	(- 1)+9.1227	(- 1)+7.7374	(- 2)+3.6067	(- 1)-7.3679	(- 1)-9.3578
2.0	(- 2)-8.3491	(- 1)+6.5787	(- 1)+9.3570	(- 1)+5.3119	(- 1)-2.7296
2.5	(- 1)-8.8452	(- 1)-4.3562	(- 1)+3.1578	(- 1)+8.6483	(- 1)+8.1928
3.0	(- 1)-5.6757	(- 1)-8.9431	(- 1)-6.7512	(- 2)-1.9960	(- 1)+6.6241
3.5	(- 1)+2.7609	(- 1)-3.6790	(- 1)-8.2667	(- 1)-8.1315	(- 1)-3.0592
4.0	(- 1)+7.9794	(- 1)+4.3113	(- 1)-1.7673	(- 1)-7.1410	(- 1)-8.7013
4.5	(- 1)+7.1352	(- 1)+8.1848	(- 1)+5.4934	(- 3)-3.4829	(- 1)-5.7890
5.0	(- 1)+2.4665	(- 1)+6.4978	(- 1)+8.1799	(- 1)+6.3669	(- 1)+1.4822
5.5	(- 1)-2.5327	(- 1)+1.7444	(- 1)+5.8546	(- 1)+8.0282	(- 1)+6.9880
6.0	(- 1)-5.7031	(- 1)-2.9499	(- 1)+1.0993	(- 1)+5.2246	(- 1)+7.7756
6.5	(- 1)-6.6792	(- 1)-5.8050	(- 1)-3.3031	(- 2)+5.2317	(- 1)+4.6186
7.0	(- 1)-6.1949	(- 1)-6.6155	(- 1)-5.8814	(- 1)-3.6035	(- 4)+8.3738
7.5	(- 1)-5.2752	(- 1)-6.1017	(- 1)-6.5515	(- 1)-5.9378	(- 1)-3.8601
8.0	(- 1)-4.7892	(- 1)-5.2127	(- 1)-6.0151	(- 1)-6.4880	(- 1)-5.9783
8.5	(- 1)-5.3860	(- 1)-4.7495	(- 1)-5.1547	(- 1)-5.9344	(- 1)-6.4254
9.0	(- 1)-7.6818	(- 1)-5.3157	(- 1)-4.7121	(- 1)-5.1007	(- 1)-5.8590
9.5	(0)-1.2605	(- 1)-7.4860	(- 1)-5.2509	(- 1)-4.6767	(- 1)-5.0502
10.0	(0)-2.1932	(0)-1.2115	(- 1)-7.3093	(- 1)-5.1908	(- 1)-4.6431
10.5	(0)-3.9217	(0)-2.0812	(0)-1.1677	(- 1)-7.1488	(- 1)-5.1349
11.0	(0)-7.1592	(0)-3.6757	(0)-1.9822	(0)-1.1284	(- 1)-7.0023
11.5	(1)-1.3348	(0)-6.6261	(0)-3.4609	(0)-1.8942	(0)-1.0929
12.0	(1)-2.5439	(1)-1.2193	(0)-6.1663	(0)-3.2719	(0)-1.8154
12.5	(1)-4.9562	(1)-2.2921	(1)-1.1209	(0)-5.7662	(0)-3.1044
13.0	(1)-9.8652	(1)-4.4031	(1)-2.0805	(1)-1.0363	(0)-5.4152
13.5	(2)-2.0042	(1)-8.6387	(1)-3.9443	(1)-1.9007	(0)-9.6285
14.0	(2)-4.1515	(2)-1.7295	(1)-7.6350	(1)-3.5594	(1)-1.7465
14.5	(2)-8.7576	(2)-3.5297	(2)-1.5077	(1)-6.8033	(1)-3.2330
15.0	(3)-1.8795	(2)-7.3354	(2)-3.0346	(2)-1.3263	(1)-6.1066
15.5	(3)-4.0993	(3)-1.5507	(2)-6.2186	(2)-2.6348	(2)-1.1761
16.0	(3)-9.0788	(3)-3.3317	(3)-1.2962	(2)-5.3284	(2)-2.3079
16.5	(4)-2.0399	(3)-7.2680	(3)-2.7456	(3)-1.0960	(2)-4.6095
17.0	(4)-4.6466	(4)-1.6085	(3)-5.9047	(3)-2.2906	(2)-9.3627
17.5	(5)-1.0722	(4)-3.6089	(4)-1.2883	(3)-4.8605	(3)-1.9322
18.0	(5)-2.5048	(4)-8.2028	(4)-2.8495	(4)-1.0463	(3)-4.0483
18.5	(5)-5.9202	(5)-1.8875	(4)-6.3850	(4)-2.2832	(3)-8.6039
19.0	(6)-1.4150	(5)-4.3947	(5)-1.4484	(4)-5.0474	(4)-1.8537
19.5	(6)-3.4181	(6)-1.0347	(5)-3.3247	(5)-1.1297	(4)-4.0457
20.0	(6)-8.3412	(6)-2.4624	(5)-7.7176	(5)-2.5583	(4)-8.9396

Table 14.2 $C_0(\eta)=e^{-\frac{1}{2}\pi\eta}|\Gamma(1+i\eta)|$

η	$C_0(\eta)$	η	$C_0(\eta)$	η	$C_0(\eta)$
0.00	1.000000	1.00	(-1)1.08423	2.00	(-3)6.61992
0.05	0.922568	1.05	(-2)9.49261	2.05	(-3)5.72791
0.10	0.847659	1.10	(-2)8.30211	2.10	(-3)4.95461
0.15	0.775700	1.15	(-2)7.25378	2.15	(-3)4.28450
0.20	0.707063	1.20	(-2)6.33205	2.20	(-3)3.70402
0.25	0.642052	1.25	(-2)5.52279	2.25	(-3)3.20136
0.30	0.580895	1.30	(-2)4.81320	2.30	(-3)2.76623
0.35	0.523742	1.35	(-2)4.19173	2.35	(-3)2.38968
0.40	0.470665	1.40	(-2)3.64804	2.40	(-3)2.06392
0.45	0.421667	1.45	(-2)3.17287	2.45	(-3)1.78218
0.50	0.376686	1.50	(-2)2.75796	2.50	(-3)1.53858
0.55	0.335605	1.55	(-2)2.39599	2.55	(-3)1.32801
0.60	0.298267	1.60	(-2)2.08045	2.60	(-3)1.14604
0.65	0.264478	1.65	(-2)1.80558	2.65	(-4)9.88816
0.70	0.234025	1.70	(-2)1.56632	2.70	(-4)8.53013
0.75	0.206680	1.75	(-2)1.35817	2.75	(-4)7.35735
0.80	0.182206	1.80	(-2)1.17720	2.80	(-4)6.34476
0.85	0.160370	1.85	(-2)1.01996	2.85	(-4)5.47066
0.90	0.140940	1.90	(-3)8.83391	2.90	(-4)4.71626
0.95	0.123694	1.95	(-3)7.64847	2.95	(-4)4.06528
1.00	0.108423	2.00	(-3)6.61992	3.00	(-4)3.50366

15.1. Gauss Series, Special Elementary Cases, Special Values of the Argument

Gauss Series

The circle of convergence of the Gauss hypergeometric series

15.1.1

$$F(a,b;c;z)={}_2F_1(a,b;c;z)$$

$$=F(b,a;c;z)=\sum_{n=0}^{\infty}\frac{(a)_n(b)_n}{(c)_n}\frac{z^n}{n!}$$

$$=\frac{\Gamma(c)}{\Gamma(a)\Gamma(b)}\sum_{n=0}^{\infty}\frac{\Gamma(a+n)\Gamma(b+n)}{\Gamma(c+n)}\frac{z^n}{n!}$$

is the unit circle $|z|=1$. The behavior of this series on its circle of convergence is:

(a) Divergence when $\mathscr{R}(c-a-b)\leqq -1$.

(b) Absolute convergence when $\mathscr{R}(c-a-b)>0$.

(c) Conditional convergence when $-1<\mathscr{R}(c-a-b)\leqq 0$; the point $z=1$ is excluded. The Gauss series reduces to a polynomial of degree n in z when a or b is equal to $-n$, $(n=0, 1, 2, \ldots)$. (For these cases see also **15.4.**) The series **15.1.1** is not defined when c is equal to $-m$, $(m=0, 1, 2, \ldots)$, provided a or b is not a negative integer n with $n<m$. For $c=-m$

15.1.2

$$\lim_{c\to -m}\frac{1}{\Gamma(c)}F(a,b;c;z)=$$

$$\frac{(a)_{m+1}(b)_{m+1}}{(m+1)!}z^{m+1}F(a+m+1,b+m+1;m+2;z)$$

Special Elementary Cases of Gauss Series

(For cases involving higher functions see **15.4.**)

15.1.3 $\quad F(1,1;2;z)=-z^{-1}\ln(1-z)$

15.1.4 $\quad F(\tfrac{1}{2},1;\tfrac{3}{2};z^2)=\tfrac{1}{2}z^{-1}\ln\left(\frac{1+z}{1-z}\right)$

15.1.5 $\quad F(\tfrac{1}{2},1;\tfrac{3}{2};-z^2)=z^{-1}\arctan z$

15.1.6

$$F(\tfrac{1}{2},\tfrac{1}{2};\tfrac{3}{2};z^2)=(1-z^2)^{\frac{1}{2}}F(1,1;\tfrac{3}{2};z^2)=z^{-1}\arcsin z$$

15.1.7

$$F(\tfrac{1}{2},\tfrac{1}{2};\tfrac{3}{2};-z^2)=(1+z^2)^{\frac{1}{2}}F(1,1;\tfrac{3}{2};-z^2)$$
$$=z^{-1}\ln[z+(1+z^2)^{\frac{1}{2}}]$$

15.1.8 $\quad F(a,b;b;z)=(1-z)^{-a}$

15.1.9 $\quad F(a,\tfrac{1}{2}+a;\tfrac{1}{2};z^2)=\tfrac{1}{2}[(1+z)^{-2a}+(1-z)^{-2a}]$

15.1.10

$$F(a,\tfrac{1}{2}+a;\tfrac{3}{2};z^2)=$$
$$\tfrac{1}{2}z^{-1}(1-2a)^{-1}[(1+z)^{1-2a}-(1-z)^{1-2a}]$$

15.1.11

$$F(-a,a;\tfrac{1}{2};-z^2)=\tfrac{1}{2}\{[(1+z^2)^{\frac{1}{2}}+z]^{2a}+[(1+z^2)^{\frac{1}{2}}-z]^{2a}\}$$

15.1.12

$$F(a,1-a;\tfrac{1}{2};-z^2)=$$
$$\tfrac{1}{2}(1+z^2)^{-\frac{1}{2}}\{[(1+z^2)^{\frac{1}{2}}+z]^{2a-1}+[(1+z^2)^{\frac{1}{2}}-z]^{2a-1}\}$$

15.1.13

$$F(a,\tfrac{1}{2}+a;1+2a;z)=2^{2a}[1+(1-z)^{\frac{1}{2}}]^{-2a}$$
$$=(1-z)^{\frac{1}{2}}F(1+a,\tfrac{1}{2}+a;1+2a;z)$$

15.1.14

$$F(a,\tfrac{1}{2}+a;2a;z)=2^{2a-1}(1-z)^{-\frac{1}{2}}[1+(1-z)^{\frac{1}{2}}]^{1-2a}$$

15.1.15 $\quad F(a,1-a;\tfrac{3}{2};\sin^2 z)=\dfrac{\sin[(2a-1)z]}{(2a-1)\sin z}$

15.1.16 $\quad F(a,2-a;\tfrac{3}{2};\sin^2 z)=\dfrac{\sin[(2a-2)z]}{(a-1)\sin(2z)}$

15.1.17 $\quad F(-a,a;\tfrac{1}{2};\sin^2 z)=\cos(2az)$

15.1.18 $\quad F(a,1-a;\tfrac{1}{2};\sin^2 z)=\dfrac{\cos[(2a-1)z]}{\cos z}$

15.1.19 $\quad F(a,\tfrac{1}{2}+a;\tfrac{1}{2};-\tan^2 z)=\cos^{2a}z\cos(2az)$

Special Values of the Argument

15.1.20

$$F(a,b;c;1)=\frac{\Gamma(c)\Gamma(c-a-b)}{\Gamma(c-a)\Gamma(c-b)}$$

$$(c\neq 0,-1,-2,\ldots,\ \mathscr{R}(c-a-b)>0)$$

15.1.21

$$F(a, b; a-b+1; -1)=2^{-a}\pi^{\frac{1}{2}}\frac{\Gamma(1+a-b)}{\Gamma(1+\frac{1}{2}a-b)\Gamma(\frac{1}{2}+\frac{1}{2}a)}$$

$$(1+a-b\neq 0, -1, -2, \ldots)$$

15.1.22

$$F(a, b; a-b+2; -1)=2^{-a}\pi^{1/2}(b-1)^{-1}\Gamma(a-b+2)$$

$$\left[\frac{1}{\Gamma(\frac{1}{2}a)\Gamma(\frac{3}{2}+\frac{1}{2}a-b)}-\frac{1}{\Gamma(\frac{1}{2}+\frac{1}{2}a)\Gamma(1+\frac{1}{2}a-b)}\right]$$

$$(a-b+2\neq 0, -1, -2, \ldots)$$

15.1.23 $F(1, a; a+1; -1)=\frac{1}{2}a[\psi(\frac{1}{2}+\frac{1}{2}a)-\psi(\frac{1}{2}a)]$

15.1.24

$$F(a, b; \tfrac{1}{2}a+\tfrac{1}{2}b+\tfrac{1}{2}; \tfrac{1}{2})=\pi^{\frac{1}{2}}\frac{\Gamma(\frac{1}{2}+\frac{1}{2}a+\frac{1}{2}b)}{\Gamma(\frac{1}{2}+\frac{1}{2}a)\Gamma(\frac{1}{2}+\frac{1}{2}b)}$$

$$(\tfrac{1}{2}a+\tfrac{1}{2}b+\tfrac{1}{2}\neq 0, -1, -2, \ldots)$$

15.1.25

$$F(a, b; \tfrac{1}{2}a+\tfrac{1}{2}b+1; \tfrac{1}{2})=2\pi^{\frac{1}{2}}(a-b)^{-1}\Gamma(1+\tfrac{1}{2}a+\tfrac{1}{2}b)$$

$$\{[\Gamma(\tfrac{1}{2}a)\Gamma(\tfrac{1}{2}+\tfrac{1}{2}b)]^{-1}-[\Gamma(\tfrac{1}{2}+\tfrac{1}{2}a)\Gamma(\tfrac{1}{2}b)]^{-1}\}$$

$$(\tfrac{1}{2}(a+b)+1\neq 0, -1, -2, \ldots)$$

15.1.26

$$F(a, 1-a; b; \tfrac{1}{2})=$$

$$2^{1-b}\pi^{\frac{1}{2}}\Gamma(b)\,[\Gamma(\tfrac{1}{2}a+\tfrac{1}{2}b)\,\Gamma(\tfrac{1}{2}+\tfrac{1}{2}b-\tfrac{1}{2}a)]^{-1}$$

$$(b\neq 0, -1, -2, \ldots)$$

15.1.27

$$F(1, 1; a+1; \tfrac{1}{2})=a[\psi(\tfrac{1}{2}+\tfrac{1}{2}a)-\psi(\tfrac{1}{2}a)]$$

$$(a\neq -1, -2, -3, \ldots)$$

15.1.28

$$F(a, a; a+1; \tfrac{1}{2})=2^{a-1}a[\psi(\tfrac{1}{2}+\tfrac{1}{2}a)-\psi(\tfrac{1}{2}a)]$$

$$(a\neq -1, -2, -3, \ldots)$$

15.1.29

$$F(a, \tfrac{1}{2}+a; \tfrac{3}{2}-2a; -\tfrac{1}{3})=(\tfrac{8}{9})^{-2a}\frac{\Gamma(\frac{4}{3})\Gamma(\frac{3}{2}-2a)}{\Gamma(\frac{3}{2})\Gamma(\frac{4}{3}-2a)}$$

$$(\tfrac{3}{2}-2a\neq 0, -1, -2, \ldots)$$

15.1.30

$$F(a, \tfrac{1}{2}+a; \tfrac{5}{6}+a; \tfrac{1}{9})=(\tfrac{3}{4})^{a}\pi^{\frac{1}{2}}\frac{\Gamma(\frac{5}{6}+\frac{2}{3}a)}{\Gamma(\frac{1}{2}+\frac{1}{3}a)\Gamma(\frac{5}{6}+\frac{1}{3}a)}$$

$$(\tfrac{5}{6}+\tfrac{2}{3}a\neq 0, -1, -2, \ldots)$$

15.1.31

$$F(a, \tfrac{1}{3}a+\tfrac{1}{3}; \tfrac{2}{3}a+\tfrac{2}{3}; e^{i\pi/3})$$

$$=2^{\frac{2}{3}a+\frac{2}{3}}\pi^{\frac{1}{2}}3^{-\frac{1}{2}(a+1)}e^{i\pi a/6}\frac{\Gamma(\frac{1}{3}a+\frac{5}{6})}{\Gamma(\frac{1}{3}a+\frac{2}{3})\Gamma(\frac{2}{3})}$$

$$(\tfrac{1}{3}a\neq -\tfrac{5}{6}, -\tfrac{11}{6}, -\tfrac{17}{6}, \ldots)$$

15.2. Differentiation Formulas and Gauss' Relations for Contiguous Functions

Differentiation Formulas

15.2.1 $\frac{d}{dz}F(a, b; c; z)=\frac{ab}{c}F(a+1, b+1; c+1; z)$

15.2.2

$$\frac{d^n}{dz^n}F(a, b; c; z)=\frac{(a)_n(b)_n}{(c)_n}F(a+n, b+n; c+n; z)$$

15.2.3

$$\frac{d^n}{dz^n}[z^{a+n-1}F(a, b; c; z)]=(a)_nz^{a-1}F(a+n, b; c; z)$$

15.2.4

$$\frac{d^n}{dz^n}[z^{c-1}F(a, b; c; z)]=(c-n)_nz^{c-n-1}F(a, b; c-n; z)$$

15.2.5

$$\frac{d^n}{dz^n}[z^{c-a+n-1}(1-z)^{a+b-c}F(a, b; c; z)]$$

$$=(c-a)_nz^{c-a-1}(1-z)^{a+b-c-n}F(a-n, b; c; z)$$

15.2.6

$$\frac{d^n}{dz^n}[(1-z)^{a+b-c}F(a, b; c; z)]$$

$$=\frac{(c-a)_n(c-b)_n}{(c)_n}(1-z)^{a+b-c-n}F(a, b; c+n; z)$$

15.2.7

$$\frac{d^n}{dz^n}[(1-z)^{a+n-1}F(a, b; c; z)]$$

$$=\frac{(-1)^n(a)_n(c-b)_n}{(c)_n}(1-z)^{a-1}F(a+n, b; c+n; z)$$

15.2.8

$$\frac{d^n}{dz^n}[z^{c-1}(1-z)^{b-c+n}F(a, b; c; z)]$$

$$=(c-n)_nz^{c-n-1}(1-z)^{b-c}F(a-n, b; c-n; z)$$

15.2.9

$$\frac{d^n}{dz^n}[z^{c-1}(1-z)^{a+b-c}F(a, b; c; z)]$$

$$=(c-n)_nz^{c-n-1}(1-z)^{a+b-c-n}F(a-n, b-n; c-n; z)$$

Gauss' Relations for Contiguous Functions

The six functions $F(a\pm 1, b; c; z)$, $F(a, b\pm 1; c; z)$, $F(a, b; c\pm 1; z)$ are called contiguous to $F(a, b; c; z)$. Relations between $F(a, b; c; z)$ and any two contiguous functions have been given by Gauss. By repeated application of these relations the function $F(a+m, b+n; c+l; z)$ with integral $m, n, l (c+l\neq 0, -1, -2, \ldots)$ can be expressed as a linear combination of $F(a, b; c; z)$ and one of its contiguous functions with coefficients which are rational functions of a, b, c, z.

15.2.10

$$(c-a)F(a-1, b; c; z)+(2a-c-az+bz)F(a, b; c; z) +a(z-1)F(a+1, b; c; z)=0$$

15.2.11

$$(c-b)F(a, b-1; c; z)+(2b-c-bz+az)F(a, b; c; z) +b(z-1)F(a, b+1; c; z)=0$$

15.2.12

$$c(c-1)(z-1)F(a, b; c-1; z) +c[c-1-(2c-a-b-1)z]F(a, b; c; z) +(c-a)(c-b)zF(a, b; c+1; z)=0$$

15.2.13

$$[c-2a-(b-a)z]F(a, b; c; z) +a(1-z)F(a+1, b; c; z) -(c-a)F(a-1, b; c; z)=0$$

15.2.14

$$(b-a)F(a, b; c; z)+aF(a+1, b; c; z) -bF(a, b+1; c; z)=0$$

15.2.15

$$(c-a-b)F(a, b; c; z)+a(1-z)F(a+1, b; c; z) -(c-b)F(a, b-1; c; z)=0$$

15.2.16

$$c[a-(c-b)z]F(a, b; c; z)-ac(1-z)F(a+1, b; c; z) +(c-a)(c-b)zF(a, b; c+1; z)=0$$

15.2.17

$$(c-a-1)F(a, b; c; z)+aF(a+1, b; c; z) -(c-1)F(a, b; c-1; z)=0$$

15.2.18

$$(c-a-b)F(a, b; c; z)-(c-a)F(a-1, b; c; z) +b(1-z)F(a, b+1; c; z)=0$$

15.2.19

$$(b-a)(1-z)F(a, b; c; z)-(c-a)F(a-1, b; c; z) +(c-b)F(a, b-1; c; z)=0$$

15.2.20

$$c(1-z)F(a, b; c; z)-cF(a-1, b; c; z) +(c-b)zF(a, b; c+1; z)=0$$

15.2.21

$$[a-1-(c-b-1)z]F(a, b; c; z) +(c-a)F(a-1, b; c; z) -(c-1)(1-z)F(a, b; c-1; z)=0$$

15.2.22

$$[c-2b+(b-a)z]F(a, b; c; z) +b(1-z)F(a, b+1; c; z) -(c-b)F(a, b-1; c; z)=0$$

15.2.23

$$c[b-(c-a)z]F(a, b; c; z)-bc(1-z)F(a, b+1; c; z) +(c-a)(c-b)zF(a, b; c+1; z)=0$$

15.2.24

$$(c-b-1)F(a, b; c; z)+bF(a, b+1; c; z) -(c-1)F(a, b; c-1; z)=0$$

15.2.25

$$c(1-z)F(a, b; c; z)-cF(a, b-1; c; z) +(c-a)zF(a, b; c+1; z)=0$$

15.2.26

$$[b-1-(c-a-1)z]F(a, b; c; z) +(c-b)F(a, b-1; c; z) -(c-1)(1-z)F(a, b; c-1; z)=0$$

15.2.27

$$c[c-1-(2c-a-b-1)z]F(a, b; c; z) +(c-a)(c-b)zF(a, b; c+1; z) -c(c-1)(1-z)F(a, b; c-1; z)=0$$

15.3. Integral Representations and Transformation Formulas

Integral Representations

15.3.1

$$F(a, b; c; z)=\frac{\Gamma(c)}{\Gamma(b)\Gamma(c-b)}\int_0^1 t^{b-1}(1-t)^{c-b-1}(1-tz)^{-a}dt \qquad (\mathscr{R}c>\mathscr{R}b>0)$$

The integral represents a one valued analytic function in the z-plane cut along the real axis from 1 to ∞ and hence **15.3.1** gives the analytic continuation of **15.1.1**, $F(a, b; c; z)$. Another integral representation is in the form of a Mellin-Barnes integral

15.3.2 $$F(a, b; c; z)=\frac{\Gamma(c)}{2\pi i\Gamma(a)\Gamma(b)}\int_{-i\infty}^{i\infty}\frac{\Gamma(a+s)\Gamma(b+s)\Gamma(-s)}{\Gamma(c+s)}(-z)^s ds$$

$$=\tfrac{1}{2}i\frac{\Gamma(c)}{\Gamma(a)\Gamma(b)}\int_{-i\infty}^{i\infty}\frac{\Gamma(a+s)\Gamma(b+s)}{\Gamma(1+s)\Gamma(c+s)}\csc(\pi s)(-z)^s ds$$

Here $-\pi<\arg(-z)<\pi$ and the path of integration is chosen such that the poles of $\Gamma(a+s)$ and $\Gamma(b+s)$ i.e. the points $s=-a-n$ and $s=-b-m (n, m=0, 1, 2, \ldots)$ respectively, are at its left side and the poles of $\csc(\pi s)$ or $\Gamma(-s)$ i.e. $s=0, 1, 2,$ are at its right side. The cases in which $-a$, $-b$ or $-c$ are non-negative integers or $a-b$ equal to an integer are excluded.

Linear Transformation Formulas

From **15.3.1** and **15.3.2** a number of transformation formulas for $F(a, b; c; z)$ can be derived.

15.3.3 $$F(a, b; c; z)=(1-z)^{c-a-b}F(c-a, c-b; c; z)$$

15.3.4 $$=(1-z)^{-a}F\left(a, c-b; c; \frac{z}{z-1}\right)$$

15.3.5 $$=(1-z)^{-b}F\left(b, c-a; c; \frac{z}{z-1}\right)$$

15.3.6 $$=\frac{\Gamma(c)\Gamma(c-a-b)}{\Gamma(c-a)\Gamma(c-b)}F(a, b; a+b-c+1; 1-z)$$

$$+(1-z)^{c-a-b}\frac{\Gamma(c)\Gamma(a+b-c)}{\Gamma(a)\Gamma(b)}F(c-a, c-b; c-a-b+1; 1-z)$$

$$(|\arg(1-z)|<\pi)$$

15.3.7 $$=\frac{\Gamma(c)\Gamma(b-a)}{\Gamma(b)\Gamma(c-a)}(-z)^{-a}F\left(a, 1-c+a; 1-b+a; \frac{1}{z}\right)$$

$$+\frac{\Gamma(c)\Gamma(a-b)}{\Gamma(a)\Gamma(c-b)}(-z)^{-b}F\left(b, 1-c+b; 1-a+b; \frac{1}{z}\right) \qquad (|\arg(-z)|<\pi)$$

15.3.8 $$=(1-z)^{-a}\frac{\Gamma(c)\Gamma(b-a)}{\Gamma(b)\Gamma(c-a)}F\left(a, c-b; a-b+1; \frac{1}{1-z}\right)$$

$$+(1-z)^{-b}\frac{\Gamma(c)\Gamma(a-b)}{\Gamma(a)\Gamma(c-b)}F\left(b, c-a; b-a+1; \frac{1}{1-z}\right) \qquad (|\arg(1-z)|<\pi)$$

15.3.9 $$=\frac{\Gamma(c)\Gamma(c-a-b)}{\Gamma(c-a)\Gamma(c-b)}z^{-a}F\left(a, a-c+1; a+b-c+1; 1-\frac{1}{z}\right)$$

$$+\frac{\Gamma(c)\Gamma(a+b-c)}{\Gamma(a)\Gamma(b)}(1-z)^{c-a-b}z^{a-c}F\left(c-a, 1-a; c-a-b+1; 1-\frac{1}{z}\right)$$

$$(|\arg z|<\pi, |\arg(1-z)|<\pi)$$

Each term of **15.3.6** has a pole when $c=a+b\pm m$, $(m=0, 1, 2, \ldots)$; this case is covered by

15.3.10 $$F(a, b; a+b; z)=\frac{\Gamma(a+b)}{\Gamma(a)\Gamma(b)}\sum_{n=0}^{\infty}\frac{(a)_n(b)_n}{(n!)^2}[2\psi(n+1)-\psi(a+n)-\psi(b+n)-\ln(1-z)](1-z)^n$$

$$(|\arg(1-z)|<\pi, |1-z|<1)$$

Furthermore for $m=1, 2, 3, \ldots$

15.3.11 $$F(a, b; a+b+m; z)=\frac{\Gamma(m)\Gamma(a+b+m)}{\Gamma(a+m)\Gamma(b+m)}\sum_{n=0}^{m-1}\frac{(a)_n(b)_n}{n!(1-m)_n}(1-z)^n$$

$$-\frac{\Gamma(a+b+m)}{\Gamma(a)\Gamma(b)}(z-1)^m\sum_{n=0}^{\infty}\frac{(a+m)_n(b+m)_n}{n!(n+m)!}(1-z)^n[\ln(1-z)-\psi(n+1)$$

$$-\psi(n+m+1)+\psi(a+n+m)+\psi(b+n+m)] \qquad (|\arg(1-z)|<\pi, |1-z|<1)$$

15.3.12 $$F(a,b;a+b-m;z)=\frac{\Gamma(m)\Gamma(a+b-m)}{\Gamma(a)\Gamma(b)}(1-z)^{-m}\sum_{n=0}^{m-1}\frac{(a-m)_n(b-m)_n}{n!(1-m)_n}(1-z)^n$$
$$-\frac{(-1)^m\Gamma(a+b-m)}{\Gamma(a-m)\Gamma(b-m)}\sum_{n=0}^{\infty}\frac{(a)_n(b)_n}{n!(n+m)!}(1-z)^n[\ln(1-z)-\psi(n+1)$$
$$-\psi(n+m+1)+\psi(a+n)+\psi(b+n)]$$
$$(|\arg(1-z)|<\pi, |1-z|<1)$$

Similarly each term of **15.3.7** has a pole when $b=a\pm m$ or $b-a=\pm m$ and the case is covered by

15.3.13 $$F(a,a;c;z)=\frac{\Gamma(c)}{\Gamma(a)\Gamma(c-a)}(-z)^{-a}\sum_{n=0}^{\infty}\frac{(a)_n(1-c+a)_n}{(n!)^2}z^{-n}[\ln(-z)+2\psi(n+1)-\psi(a+n)-\psi(c-a-n)]$$
$$(|\arg(-z)|<\pi, |z|>1, (c-a)\neq 0, \pm 1, \pm 2, \ldots)$$

The case $b-a=m$, $(m=1, 2, 3, \ldots)$ is covered by

15.3.14 $$F(a,a+m;c;z)=F(a+m,a;c;z)$$
$$=\frac{\Gamma(c)(-z)^{-a-m}}{\Gamma(a+m)\Gamma(c-a)}\sum_{n=0}^{\infty}\frac{(a)_{n+m}(1-c+a)_{n+m}}{n!(n+m)!}z^{-n}[\ln(-z)+\psi(1+m+n)+\psi(1+n)$$
$$-\psi(a+m+n)-\psi(c-a-m-n)]+(-z)^{-a}\frac{\Gamma(c)}{\Gamma(a+m)}\sum_{n=0}^{m-1}\frac{\Gamma(m-n)(a)_n}{n!\Gamma(c-a-n)}z^{-n}$$
$$(|\arg(-z)|<\pi, |z|>1, (c-a)\neq 0, \pm 1, \pm 2, \ldots)$$

The case $c-a=0, -1, -2, \ldots$ becomes elementary, **15.3.3**, and the case $c-a=1, 2, 3, \ldots$ can be obtained from **15.3.14**, by a limiting process (see [15.2]).

Quadratic Transformation Formulas

If, and only if the numbers $\pm(1-c)$, $\pm(a-b)$, $\pm(a+b-c)$ are such, that two of them are equal or one of them is equal to $\frac{1}{2}$, then there exists a quadratic transformation. The basic formulas are due to Kummer [15.7] and a complete list is due to Goursat [15.3]. See also [15.2].

15.3.15 $$F(a,b;2b;z)=(1-z)^{-\frac{1}{2}a}F\left(\tfrac{1}{2}a, b-\tfrac{1}{2}a; b+\tfrac{1}{2}; \frac{z^2}{4z-4}\right)$$

15.3.16 $$=(1-\tfrac{1}{2}z)^{-a}F(\tfrac{1}{2}a, \tfrac{1}{2}+\tfrac{1}{2}a; b+\tfrac{1}{2}; z^2(2-z)^{-2})$$

15.3.17 $$=(\tfrac{1}{2}+\tfrac{1}{2}\sqrt{1-z})^{-2a}F\left[a, a-b+\tfrac{1}{2}; b+\tfrac{1}{2}; \left(\frac{1-\sqrt{1-z}}{1+\sqrt{1-z}}\right)^2\right]$$

15.3.18 $$=(1-z)^{-\frac{1}{2}a}F\left(a, 2b-a; b+\tfrac{1}{2}; -\frac{(1-\sqrt{1-z})^2}{4\sqrt{1-z}}\right)$$

15.3.19 $$F(a,a+\tfrac{1}{2};c;z)=(\tfrac{1}{2}+\tfrac{1}{2}\sqrt{1-z})^{-2a}F\left(2a, 2a-c+1; c; \frac{1-\sqrt{1-z}}{1+\sqrt{1-z}}\right)$$

15.3.20 $$=(1\pm\sqrt{z})^{-2a}F\left(2a, c-\tfrac{1}{2}; 2c-1; \pm\frac{2\sqrt{z}}{1\pm\sqrt{z}}\right)$$

15.3.21 $$=(1-z)^{-a}F\left(2a, 2c-2a-1; c; \frac{\sqrt{1-z}-1}{2\sqrt{1-z}}\right)$$

15.3.22 $$F(a,b;a+b+\tfrac{1}{2};z)=F(2a, 2b; a+b+\tfrac{1}{2}; \tfrac{1}{2}-\tfrac{1}{2}\sqrt{1-z})$$

15.3.23 $$=(\tfrac{1}{2}+\tfrac{1}{2}\sqrt{1-z})^{-2a}F\left(2a, a-b+\tfrac{1}{2}; a+b+\tfrac{1}{2}; \frac{\sqrt{1-z}-1}{\sqrt{1-z}+1}\right)$$

15.3.24 $F(a, b; a+b-\tfrac{1}{2}; z)=(1-z)^{-\frac{1}{2}}F(2a-1, 2b-1; a+b-\tfrac{1}{2}; \tfrac{1}{2}-\tfrac{1}{2}\sqrt{1-z})$

15.3.25 $=(1-z)^{-\frac{1}{2}}\left(\tfrac{1}{2}+\tfrac{1}{2}\sqrt{1-z}\right)^{1-2a}F\left(2a-1, a-b+\tfrac{1}{2}; a+b-\tfrac{1}{2}; \frac{\sqrt{1-z}-1}{\sqrt{1-z}+1}\right)$

15.3.26 $F(a, b; a-b+1; z)=(1+z)^{-a}F\left(\tfrac{1}{2}a, \tfrac{1}{2}a+\tfrac{1}{2}; a-b+1; 4z(1+z)^{-2}\right)$

15.3.27 $=(1\pm\sqrt{z})^{-2a}F\left(a, a-b+\tfrac{1}{2}; 2a-2b+1; \pm 4\sqrt{z}(1\pm\sqrt{z})^{-2}\right)$

15.3.28 $=(1-z)^{-a}F\left(\tfrac{1}{2}a, \tfrac{1}{2}a-b+\tfrac{1}{2}; a-b+1; -4z(1-z)^{-2}\right)$

15.3.29 $F\left(a, b; \tfrac{1}{2}a+\tfrac{1}{2}b+\tfrac{1}{2}; z\right)=(1-2z)^{-a}F\left(\tfrac{1}{2}a, \tfrac{1}{2}a+\tfrac{1}{2}; \tfrac{1}{2}a+\tfrac{1}{2}b+\tfrac{1}{2}; \frac{4z^2-4z}{(1-2z)^2}\right)$

15.3.30 $=F\left(\tfrac{1}{2}a, \tfrac{1}{2}b; \tfrac{1}{2}a+\tfrac{1}{2}b+\tfrac{1}{2}; 4z-4z^2\right)$

15.3.31 $F(a, 1-a; c; z)=(1-z)^{c-1}F\left(\tfrac{1}{2}c-\tfrac{1}{2}a, \tfrac{1}{2}c+\tfrac{1}{2}a-\tfrac{1}{2}; c; 4z-4z^2\right)$

15.3.32 $=(1-z)^{c-1}(1-2z)^{a-c}F\left(\tfrac{1}{2}c-\tfrac{1}{2}a, \tfrac{1}{2}c-\tfrac{1}{2}a+\tfrac{1}{2}; c; (4z^2-4z)(1-2z)^{-2}\right)$

Cubic transformations are listed in [15.2] and [15.3].

In the formulas above, the square roots are defined so that their value is real and positive when $0\leqq z<1$. All formulas are valid in the neighborhood of $z=0$.

15.4. Special Cases of $F(a, b; c; z)$

Polynomials

When a or b is equal to a negative integer, then

15.4.1 $F(-m, b; c; z)=\sum_{n=0}^{m}\frac{(-m)_n(b)_n}{(c)_n}\frac{z^n}{n!}$

This formula is also valid when $c=-m-l$; $m, l=0, 1, 2, \ldots$

15.4.2 $F(-m, b; -m-l; z)=\sum_{n=0}^{m}\frac{(-m)_n(b)_n}{(-m-l)_n}\frac{z^n}{n!}$

Some particular cases are

15.4.3 $F(-n, n; \tfrac{1}{2}; x)=T_n(1-2x)$

15.4.4 $F(-n, n+1; 1; x)=P_n(1-2x)$

15.4.5 $F\left(-n, n+2\alpha; \alpha+\frac{1}{2}; x\right)=\frac{n!}{(2\alpha)_n}C_n^{(\alpha)}(1-2x)$

15.4.6 $F(-n, \alpha+1+\beta+n; \alpha+1; x)=\frac{n!}{(\alpha+1)_n}P_n^{(\alpha,\beta)}(1-2x)$

Here T_n, P_n, $C_n^{(\alpha)}$, $P_n^{(\alpha,\beta)}$ denote Chebyshev, Legendre's, Gegenbauer's and Jacobi's polynomials respectively (see chapter **22**).

Legendre Functions

Legendre functions are connected with those special cases of the hypergeometric function for which a quadratic transformation exists (see **15.3**).

15.4.7 $F(a, b; 2b; z)=2^{2b-1}\Gamma(\tfrac{1}{2}+b)z^{\frac{1}{2}-b}(1-z)^{\frac{1}{2}(b-a-\frac{1}{2})}P_{a-b-\frac{1}{2}}^{\frac{1}{2}-b}\left[\left(1-\frac{z}{2}\right)(1-z)^{-\frac{1}{2}}\right]$

15.4.8 $=2^{2b}\pi^{-\frac{1}{2}}\frac{\Gamma(\frac{1}{2}+b)}{\Gamma(2b-a)}z^{-b}(1-z)^{\frac{1}{2}(b-a)}e^{i\pi(a-b)}Q_{b-\frac{1}{2}}^{b-a}\left(\frac{2}{z}-1\right)$

15.4.9 $F(a, b; 2b; -z)=2^{2b}\pi^{-\frac{1}{2}}\frac{\Gamma(\frac{1}{2}+b)}{\Gamma(a)}z^{-b}(1+z)^{\frac{1}{2}(b-a)}e^{-i\pi(a-b)}Q_{b-\frac{1}{2}}^{a-b}\left(1+\frac{2}{z}\right)$ $(|\arg z|<\pi, |\arg(1\pm z)|<\pi)$

15.4.10 $F(a,a+\frac{1}{2};c;z)=2^{c-1}\Gamma(c)z^{\frac{1}{2}-\frac{1}{2}c}(1-z)^{\frac{1}{2}c-a-\frac{1}{2}}P^{1-c}_{2a-c}[(1-z)^{-\frac{1}{2}}]$

($|\arg z|<\pi$, $|\arg(1-z)|<\pi$, z not between 0 and $-\infty$)

15.4.11 $F(a,a+\frac{1}{2};c;x)=2^{c-1}\Gamma(c)(-x)^{\frac{1}{2}-\frac{1}{2}c}(1-x)^{\frac{1}{2}c-a-\frac{1}{2}}P^{1-c}_{2a-c}[(1-x)^{-\frac{1}{2}}]$ $(-\infty<x<0)$

15.4.12 $F(a,b;a+b+\frac{1}{2};z)=2^{a+b-\frac{1}{2}}\Gamma(\frac{1}{2}+a+b)(-z)^{\frac{1}{2}(\frac{1}{2}-a-b)}P^{\frac{1}{2}-a-b}_{a-b-\frac{1}{2}}[(1-z)^{\frac{1}{2}}]$

($|\arg(-z)|<\pi$, z not between 0 and 1)

15.4.13 $F(a,b;a+b+\frac{1}{2};x)=2^{a+b-\frac{1}{2}}\Gamma(\frac{1}{2}+a+b)x^{\frac{1}{2}(\frac{1}{2}-a-b)}P^{\frac{1}{2}-a-b}_{a-b-\frac{1}{2}}[(1-x)^{\frac{1}{2}}]$ $(0<x<1)$

15.4.14 $F(a,b;a-b+1;z)=\Gamma(a-b+1)z^{\frac{1}{2}b-\frac{1}{2}a}(1-z)^{-b}P^{b-a}_{-b}\left(\frac{1+z}{1-z}\right)$

($|\arg(1-z)|<\pi$, z not between 0 and $-\infty$)

15.4.15 $F(a,b;a-b+1;x)=\Gamma(a-b+1)(1-x)^{-b}(-x)^{\frac{1}{2}b-\frac{1}{2}a}P^{b-a}_{-b}\left(\frac{1+x}{1-x}\right)$ $(-\infty<x<0)$

15.4.16 $F(a,1-a;c;z)=\Gamma(c)(-z)^{\frac{1}{2}-\frac{1}{2}c}(1-z)^{\frac{1}{2}c-\frac{1}{2}}P^{1-c}_{-a}(1-2z)$

($|\arg(-z)|<\pi$, $|\arg(1-z)|<\pi$, z not between 0 and 1)

15.4.17 $F(a,1-a;c;x)=\Gamma(c)x^{\frac{1}{2}-\frac{1}{2}c}(1-x)^{\frac{1}{2}c-\frac{1}{2}}P^{1-c}_{-a}(1-2x)$ $(0<x<1)$

15.4.18 $F(a,b;\frac{1}{2}a+\frac{1}{2}b+\frac{1}{2};z)=\Gamma(\frac{1}{2}+\frac{1}{2}a+\frac{1}{2}b)[z(z-1)]^{\frac{1}{4}(1-a-b)}P^{\frac{1}{2}(1-a-b)}_{\frac{1}{2}(a-b-1)}(1-2z)$

($|\arg z|<\pi$, $|\arg(z-1)|<\pi$, z not between 0 and 1)

15.4.19 $F(a,b;\frac{1}{2}a+\frac{1}{2}b+\frac{1}{2};x)=\Gamma(\frac{1}{2}+\frac{1}{2}a+\frac{1}{2}b)(x-x^2)^{\frac{1}{4}(1-a-b)}P^{\frac{1}{2}(1-a-b)}_{\frac{1}{2}(a-b-1)}(1-2x)$ $(0<x<1)$

15.4.20 $F(a,b;a+b-\frac{1}{2};z)=2^{a+b-\frac{3}{2}}\Gamma(a+b-\frac{1}{2})(-z)^{\frac{1}{2}(\frac{3}{2}-a-b)}(1-z)^{-\frac{1}{2}}P^{\frac{3}{2}-a-b}_{b-a-\frac{1}{2}}[(1-z)^{\frac{1}{2}}]$

($|\arg(-z)|<\pi$, $|\arg(1-z)|<\pi$, $\mathscr{R}[(1-z)^{\frac{1}{2}}]>0$, z not between 0 and 1)

15.4.21 $F(a,b;a+b-\frac{1}{2};x)=2^{a+b-\frac{3}{2}}\Gamma(a+b-\frac{1}{2})x^{\frac{1}{2}(\frac{3}{2}-a-b)}(1-x)^{-\frac{1}{2}}P^{\frac{3}{2}-a-b}_{b-a-\frac{1}{2}}[(1-x)^{\frac{1}{2}}]$ $(0<x<1)$

15.4.22 $F(a,b;\frac{1}{2};z)=\pi^{-\frac{1}{2}}2^{a+b-\frac{3}{2}}\Gamma(\frac{1}{2}+a)\Gamma(\frac{1}{2}+b)(z-1)^{\frac{1}{2}(\frac{1}{2}-a-b)}[P^{\frac{1}{2}-a-b}_{a-b-\frac{1}{2}}(z^{\frac{1}{2}})+P^{\frac{1}{2}-a-b}_{a-b-\frac{1}{2}}(-z^{\frac{1}{2}})]$

($|\arg z|<\pi$, $|\arg(z-1)|<\pi$, z not between 0 and 1)

15.4.23 $F(a,b;\frac{1}{2};x)=\pi^{-\frac{1}{2}}2^{a+b-\frac{3}{2}}\Gamma(\frac{1}{2}+a)\Gamma(\frac{1}{2}+b)(1-x)^{\frac{1}{2}(\frac{1}{2}-a-b)}[P^{\frac{1}{2}-a-b}_{a-b-\frac{1}{2}}(x^{\frac{1}{2}})+P^{\frac{1}{2}-a-b}_{a-b-\frac{1}{2}}(-x^{\frac{1}{2}})]$ $(0<x<1)$

15.4.24 $F(a,b;\frac{1}{2};-z)=\pi^{-\frac{1}{2}}2^{a-b-1}\Gamma(\frac{1}{2}+a)\Gamma(1-b)(z+1)^{-\frac{1}{2}a-\frac{1}{2}b}e^{\pm i\frac{\pi}{2}(b-a)}\{P^{b-a}_{a+b-1}[z^{\frac{1}{2}}(1+z)^{-\frac{1}{2}}]$

$+P^{b-a}_{a+b-1}[-z^{\frac{1}{2}}(1+z)^{-\frac{1}{2}}]\}$

($\pm$ according as $\mathscr{I}z\gtrless 0$, z not between 0 and ∞)

15.4.25 $F(a,b;\frac{1}{2};-x)=\pi^{-\frac{1}{2}}2^{a-b-1}\Gamma(\frac{1}{2}+a)\Gamma(1-b)(1+x)^{-\frac{1}{2}a-\frac{1}{2}b}\{P^{b-a}_{a+b-1}[x^{\frac{1}{2}}(1+x)^{-\frac{1}{2}}]+P^{b-a}_{a+b-1}[-x^{1/2}(1+x)^{-\frac{1}{2}}]\}$

$(0<x<\infty)$

15.4.26 $F(a,b;\frac{3}{2};x)=-\pi^{-\frac{1}{2}}2^{a+b-\frac{5}{2}}\Gamma(a-\frac{1}{2})\Gamma(b-\frac{1}{2})x^{-\frac{1}{2}}(1-x)^{\frac{1}{2}(\frac{3}{2}-a-b)}\{P^{\frac{3}{2}-a-b}_{a-b-\frac{1}{2}}(x^{\frac{1}{2}})-P^{\frac{3}{2}-a-b}_{a-b-\frac{1}{2}}(-x^{\frac{1}{2}})\}$ $(0<x<1)$

15.5. The Hypergeometric Differential Equation

The hypergeometric differential equation

15.5.1 $$z(1-z)\frac{d^2w}{dz^2}+[c-(a+b+1)z]\frac{dw}{dz}-abw=0$$

has three (regular) singular points $z=0, 1, \infty$. The pairs of exponents at these points are

15.5.2 $\rho_{1,2}^{(0)}=0, 1-c, \qquad \rho_{1,2}^{(1)}=0, c-a-b, \qquad \rho_{1,2}^{(\infty)}=a, b$

respectively. The general theory of differential equations of the Fuchsian type distinguishes between the following cases.

A. None of the numbers c, $c-a-b$; $a-b$ is equal to an integer. Then two linearly independent solutions of **15.5.1** in the neighborhood of the singular points $0, 1, \infty$ are respectively

15.5.3 $w_{1(0)}=F(a, b; c; z)=(1-z)^{c-a-b}F(c-a, c-b; c; z)$

15.5.4 $w_{2(0)}=z^{1-c}F(a-c+1, b-c+1; 2-c; z)=z^{1-c}(1-z)^{c-a-b}F(1-a, 1-b; 2-c; z)$

15.5.5 $w_{1(1)}=F(a, b; a+b+1-c; 1-z)=z^{1-c}F(1+b-c, 1+a-c; a+b+1-c; 1-z)$

15.5.6 $w_{2(1)}=(1-z)^{c-a-b}F(c-b, c-a; c-a-b+1; 1-z)=z^{1-c}(1-z)^{c-a-b}F(1-a, 1-b; c-a-b+1; 1-z)$

15.5.7 $w_{1(\infty)}=z^{-a}F(a, a-c+1; a-b+1; z^{-1})=z^{b-c}(z-1)^{c-a-b}F(1-b, c-b; a-b+1; z^{-1})$

15.5.8 $w_{2(\infty)}=z^{-b}F(b, b-c+1; b-a+1; z^{-1})=z^{a-c}(z-1)^{c-a-b}F(1-a, c-a; b-a+1; z^{-1})$

The second set of the above expressions is obtained by applying **15.3.3** to the first set.

Another set of representations is obtained by applying **15.3.4** to **15.5.3** through **15.5.8.** This gives **15.5.9–15.5.14.**

15.5.9 $w_{1(0)}=(1-z)^{-a}F\left(a, c-b; c; \frac{z}{z-1}\right)=(1-z)^{-b}F\left(b, c-a; c; \frac{z}{z-1}\right)$

15.5.10 $w_{2(0)}=z^{1-c}(1-z)^{c-a-1}F\left(a-c+1, 1-b; 2-c; \frac{z}{z-1}\right)=z^{1-c}(1-z)^{c-b-1}F\left(b-c+1, 1-a; 2-c; \frac{z}{z-1}\right)$

15.5.11 $w_{1(1)}=z^{-a}F(a, a-c+1; a+b-c+1; 1-z^{-1})=z^{-b}F(b, b-c+1; a+b-c+1; 1-z^{-1})$

15.5.12

$w_{2(1)}=z^{a-c}(1-z)^{c-a-b}F(c-a, 1-a; c-a-b+1; 1-z^{-1})=z^{b-c}(1-z)^{c-a-b}F(c-b, 1-b; c-a-b+1; 1-z^{-1})$

15.5.13 $w_{1(\infty)}=(z-1)^{-a}F\left(a, c-b; a-b+1; \frac{1}{1-z}\right)=(z-1)^{-b}F\left(b, c-a; b-a+1; \frac{1}{1-z}\right)$

15.5.14

$w_{2(\infty)}=z^{1-c}(z-1)^{c-a-1}F\left(a-c+1, 1-b; a-b+1; \frac{1}{1-z}\right)=z^{1-c}(z-1)^{c-b-1}F\left(b-c+1, 1-a; b-a+1; \frac{1}{1-z}\right)$

15.5.3 to **15.5.14** constitute Kummer's 24 solutions of the hypergeometric equation. The analytic continuation of $w_{1,2(0)}(z)$ can then be obtained by means of **15.3.3** to **15.3.9.**

B. One of the numbers a, b, $c-a$, $c-b$ is an integer. Then one of the hypergeometric series for instance $w_{1,2(0)}$, **15.5.3, 15.5.4** terminates and the corresponding solution is of the form

15.5.15 $w=z^{\alpha}(1-z)^{\beta}p_n(z)$

where $p_n(z)$ is a polynomial in z of degree n. This case is referred to as the degenerate case of the hypergeometric differential equation and its solutions are listed and discussed in great detail in [15.2].

C. The number $c-a-b$ is an integer, c nonintegral. Then **15.3.10** to **15.3.12** give the analytic continuation of $w_{1,2(0)}$ into the neighborhood of $z=1$. Similarly **15.3.13** and **15.3.14** give the analytic continuation of $w_{1,2(0)}$ into the neighborhood of $z=\infty$ in case $a-b$ is an integer but not c, subject of course to the further restrictions $c-a=0, \pm1, \pm2 \ldots$ (For a detailed discussion of all possible cases, see [15.2]).

D. The number $c=1$. Then **15.5.3, 15.5.4** are replaced by

15.5.16 $w_{1(0)}=F(a, b; 1; z)$

15.5.17 $w_{2(0)}=F(a,b;1;z)\ln z+\sum_{n=1}^{\infty}\frac{(a)_n(b)_n}{(n!)^2}z^n[\psi(a+n)-\psi(a)+\psi(b+n)-\psi(b)-2\psi(n+1)+2\psi(1)]\qquad(|z|<1)$

E. The number $c=m+1$, $m=1, 2, 3, \ldots$. A fundamental system is

15.5.18 $w_{1(0)}=F(a, b; m+1; z)$

15.5.19
$$w_{2(0)}=F(a, b; m+1; z)\ln z+\sum_{n=1}^{\infty}\frac{(a)_n(b)_n}{(1+m)_n n!}z^n[\psi(a+n)-\psi(a)+\psi(b+n)-\psi(b)-\psi(m+1+n)$$
$$+\psi(m+1)-\psi(n+1)+\psi(1)]-\sum_{n=1}^{m}\frac{(n-1)!(-m)_n}{(1-a)_n(1-b)_n}z^{-n}\qquad(|z|<1 \text{ and } a, b\neq 0, 1, 2, \ldots (m-1))$$

F. The number $c=1-m$, $m=1, 2, 3, \ldots$. A fundamental system is

15.5.20 $w_{1(0)}=z^mF(a+m, b+m; 1+m; z)$

15.5.21
$$w_{2(0)}=z^mF(a+m, b+m; 1+m; z)\ln z+z^m\sum_{n=1}^{\infty}z^n\frac{(a+m)_n(b+m)_n}{(1+m)_n n!}[\psi(a+m+n)-\psi(a+m)+\psi(b+m+n)$$
$$-\psi(b+m)-\psi(m+1+n)+\psi(m+1)-\psi(n+1)+\psi(1)]-\sum_{n=1}^{m}\frac{(n-1)!(-m)_n}{(1-a-m)_n(1-b-m)_n}z^{m-n}$$
$$(|z|<1 \text{ and } a, b\neq 0, -1, -2, \ldots -(m-1))$$

15.6. Riemann's Differential Equation

The hypergeometric differential equation **15.5.1** with the (regular) singular points 0, 1, ∞ is a special case of Riemann's differential equation with three (regular) singular points a, b, c

15.6.1
$$\frac{d^2w}{dz^2}+\left[\frac{1-\alpha-\alpha'}{z-a}+\frac{1-\beta-\beta'}{z-b}+\frac{1-\gamma-\gamma'}{z-c}\right]\frac{dw}{dz}$$
$$+\left[\frac{\alpha\alpha'(a-b)(a-c)}{z-a}+\frac{\beta\beta'(b-c)(b-a)}{z-b}+\frac{\gamma\gamma'(c-a)(c-b)}{z-c}\right]\frac{w}{(z-a)(z-b)(z-c)}=0$$

The pairs of the exponents with respect to the singular points a; b; c are α, α'; β, β'; γ, γ' respectively subject to the condition

15.6.2 $\alpha+\alpha'+\beta+\beta'+\gamma+\gamma'=1$

The complete set of solutions of **15.6.1** is denoted by the symbol

15.6.3
$$w=P\begin{Bmatrix} a & b & c & \\ \alpha & \beta & \gamma & z \\ \alpha' & \beta' & \gamma' & \end{Bmatrix}$$

Special Cases of Riemann's *P* Function

(a) The generalized hypergeometric function

15.6.4
$$w=P\begin{Bmatrix} 0 & \infty & 1 & \\ \alpha & \beta & \gamma & z \\ \alpha' & \beta' & \gamma' & \end{Bmatrix}$$

(b) The hypergeometric function $F(a, b; c; z)$

15.6.5
$$w=P\begin{Bmatrix} 0 & \infty & 1 & \\ 0 & a & 0 & z \\ 1-c & b & c-a-b & \end{Bmatrix}$$

(c) The Legendre functions $P_\nu^\mu(z)$, $Q_\nu^\mu(z)$

15.6.6
$$w=P\begin{Bmatrix} 0 & \infty & 1 & \\ -\frac{1}{2}\nu & \frac{1}{2}\mu & 0 & (1-z^2)^{-1} \\ \frac{1}{2}+\frac{1}{2}\nu & -\frac{1}{2}\mu & \frac{1}{2} & \end{Bmatrix}$$

(d) The confluent hypergeometric function

15.6.7
$$w=P\begin{Bmatrix} 0 & \infty & c & \\ \frac{1}{2}+u & -c & c-k & z \\ \frac{1}{2}-u & 0 & k & \end{Bmatrix}$$

provided $\lim c\to\infty$.

Transformation Formulas for Riemann's *P* Function

15.6.8 $$\left(\frac{z-a}{z-b}\right)^k\left(\frac{z-c}{z-b}\right)^l P\left\{\begin{matrix} a & b & c & \\ \alpha & \beta & \gamma & z \\ \alpha' & \beta' & \gamma' & \end{matrix}\right\}=P\left\{\begin{matrix} a & b & c & \\ \alpha+k & \beta-k-l & \gamma+l & z \\ \alpha'+k & \beta'-k-l & \gamma'+l & \end{matrix}\right\}$$

15.6.9 $$P\left\{\begin{matrix} a & b & c & \\ \alpha & \beta & \gamma & z \\ \alpha' & \beta' & \gamma' & \end{matrix}\right\}=P\left\{\begin{matrix} a_1 & b_1 & c_1 & \\ \alpha & \beta & \gamma & z_1 \\ \alpha' & \beta' & \gamma' & \end{matrix}\right\}$$

where

15.6.10 $$z=\frac{Az_1+B}{Cz_1+D},\ a=\frac{Aa_1+B}{Ca_1+D},\ b=\frac{Ab_1+B}{Cb_1+D},\ c=\frac{Ac_1+B}{Cc_1+D}$$

and A, B, C, D are arbitrary constants such that $AD-BC\neq0$.

Riemann's P function reduced to the hypergeometric function is

15.6.11 $$P\left\{\begin{matrix} a & b & c & \\ \alpha & \beta & \gamma & z \\ \alpha' & \beta' & \gamma' & \end{matrix}\right\}=\left(\frac{z-a}{z-b}\right)^\alpha\left(\frac{z-c}{z-b}\right)^\gamma P\left\{\begin{matrix} 0 & \infty & 1 & \\ 0 & \alpha+\beta+\gamma & 0 & \frac{(z-a)(c-b)}{(z-b)(c-a)} \\ \alpha'-\alpha & \alpha+\beta'+\gamma & \gamma'-\gamma & \end{matrix}\right\}$$

The P function on the right hand side is Gauss' hypergeometric function (see **15.6.5**). If it is replaced by Kummer's 24 solutions **15.5.3** to **15.5.14** the complete set of 24 solutions for Riemann's differential equation **15.6.1** is obtained. The first of these solutions is for instance by **15.5.3** and **15.6.5**

15.6.12 $$w=\left(\frac{z-a}{z-b}\right)^\alpha\left(\frac{z-c}{z-b}\right)^\gamma F\left[\alpha+\beta+\gamma,\alpha+\beta'+\gamma;1+\alpha-\alpha';\frac{(z-a)\,(c-b)}{(z-b)\,(c-a)}\right]$$

15.7. Asymptotic Expansions

The behavior of $F(a, b; c; z)$ for large $|z|$ is described by the transformation formulas of **15.3.**

For fixed a, b, z and large $|c|$ one has [15.8]

15.7.1

$$F(a,b;c;z)=\sum_{n=0}^{m}\frac{(a)_n(b)_n}{(c)_n}\frac{z^n}{n!}+O(|c|^{-m-1})$$

For fixed a, c, z, ($c\neq0, -1, -2, \ldots, 0<|z|<1$) and large $|b|$ one has [15.2]

15.7.2

$$F(a,b;c;z)=e^{-i\pi a}[\Gamma(c)/\Gamma(c-a)]\,(bz)^{-a}[1+O(|bz|^{-1})]$$
$$+[\Gamma(c)/\Gamma(a)]\,e^{bz}(bz)^{a-c}[1+O(|bz|^{-1})]$$
$$\left(-\frac{3\pi}{2}<\arg(bz)<\tfrac{1}{2}\pi\right)$$

15.7.3

$$F(a,b;c;z)=e^{i\pi a}[\Gamma(c)/\Gamma(c-a)]\,(bz)^{-a}[1+O(|bz|^{-1})]$$
$$+[\Gamma(c)/\Gamma(a)]e^{bz}(bz)^{a-c}[1+O(|bz|^{-1})]$$
$$(-\tfrac{1}{2}\pi<\arg(bz)<\tfrac{3}{2}\pi)$$

For the case when more than one of the parameters are large consult [15.2].

Jacobian Elliptic Functions

16.1. Introduction

A doubly periodic meromorphic function is called an *elliptic function.*

Let m, m_1 be numbers such that

$$m+m_1=1.$$

We call m the *parameter*, m_1 the *complementary parameter*.

In what follows we shall assume that the parameter m is a real number. Without loss of generality we can then suppose that $0\leq m\leq 1$ (see **16.10, 16.11**).

We define *quarter-periods* K and iK' by

16.1.1

$$K(m)=K=\int_0^{\pi/2}\frac{d\theta}{(1-m\sin^2\theta)^{1/2}},$$

$$iK'(m)=iK'=i\int_0^{\pi/2}\frac{d\theta}{(1-m_1\sin^2\theta)^{1/2}}$$

so that K and K' are real numbers. K is called the real, iK' the imaginary quarter-period.

We note that

16.1.2 $\qquad K(m)=K'(m_1)=K'(1-m).$

We also note that if any *one* of the numbers m, m_1, $K(m)$, $K'(m)$, $K'(m)/K(m)$ is given, all the rest are determined. Thus K and K' can not both be chosen arbitrarily.

In the Argand diagram denote the points 0, K, $K+iK'$, iK' by s, c, d, n respectively. These points are at the vertices of a rectangle. The translations of this rectangle by λK, $\mu iK'$, where λ, μ are given all integral values positive or negative, will lead to the lattice

```
.s   .c   .s   .c
.n   .d   .n   .d
.s   .c   .s   .c
.n   .d   .n   .d
```

the pattern being repeated indefinitely on all sides.

Let p, q be any two of the letters s, c, d, n. Then p, q determine in the lattice a minimum rectangle whose sides are of length K and K' and whose vertices s, c, d, n are in counterclockwise order.

Definition

The Jacobian elliptic function pq u is defined by the following three properties.

(i) pq u has a simple zero at p and a simple pole at q.

(ii) The step from p to q is a half-period of pq u. Those of the numbers K, iK', $K+iK'$ which differ from this step are only quarter-periods.

(iii) The coefficient of the leading term in the expansion of pq u in ascending powers of u about $u=0$ is unity. With regard to (iii) the leading term is u, $1/u$, 1 according as $u=0$ is a zero, a pole, or an ordinary point.

Thus the functions with a pole or zero at the origin (i.e., the functions in which one letter is s) are odd, and the others are even.

Should we wish to call explicit attention to the value of the parameter, we write pq $(u|m)$ instead of pq u.

The Jacobian elliptic functions can also be defined with respect to certain integrals. Thus if

16.1.3
$$u=\int_0^{\varphi}\frac{d\theta}{(1-m\sin^2\theta)^{1/2}},$$

the angle φ is called the *amplitude*

16.1.4 $\quad \varphi=\text{am}\, u$

and we define

16.1.5

$$\text{sn}\, u=\sin\varphi,\ \text{cn}\, u=\cos\varphi,$$
$$\text{dn}\, u=(1-m\sin^2\varphi)^{1/2}=\Delta(\varphi).$$

Similarly all the functions pq u can be expressed in terms of φ. This second set of definitions, although seemingly different, is mathematically equivalent to the definition previously given in terms of a lattice. For further explanation of notations, including the interpretation, of such expressions as sn $(\varphi\backslash\alpha)$, cn $(u|m)$, dn (u, k), see **17.2.**

16.2. Classification of the Twelve Jacobian Elliptic Functions

According to Poles and Half-Periods

	Pole iK'	Pole $K+iK'$	Pole K	Pole 0	
Half period iK'	sn u	cd u	dc u	ns u	Periods $2iK'$, $4K+4iK'$, $4K$
Half period $K+iK'$	cn u	sd u	nc u	ds u	Periods $4iK'$, $2K+2iK'$, $4K$
Half period K	dn u	nd u	sc u	cs u	Periods $4iK'$, $4K+4iK'$, $2K$

The three functions in a vertical column are *copolar.*

The four functions in a horizontal line are *coperiodic.* Of the periods quoted in the last line of each row only two are independent.

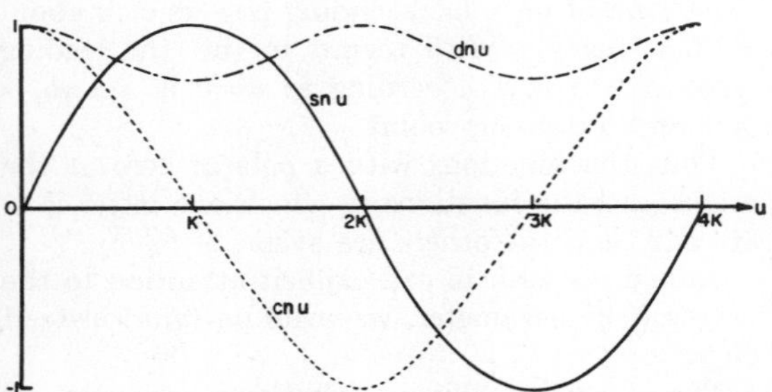

FIGURE 16.1. *Jacobian elliptic functions*

sn u, cn u, dn u

$$m=\frac{1}{2}$$

The curve for cn $(u|\frac{1}{2})$ is the boundary between those which have an inflexion and those which have not.

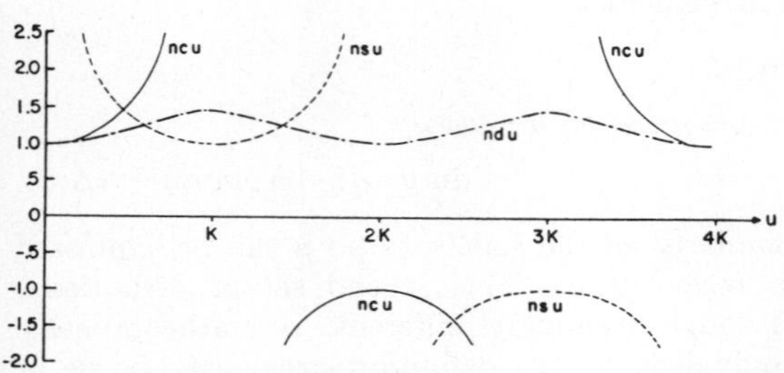

FIGURE 16.2. *Jacobian elliptic functions*

ns u, nc u, nd u

$$m=\frac{1}{2}$$

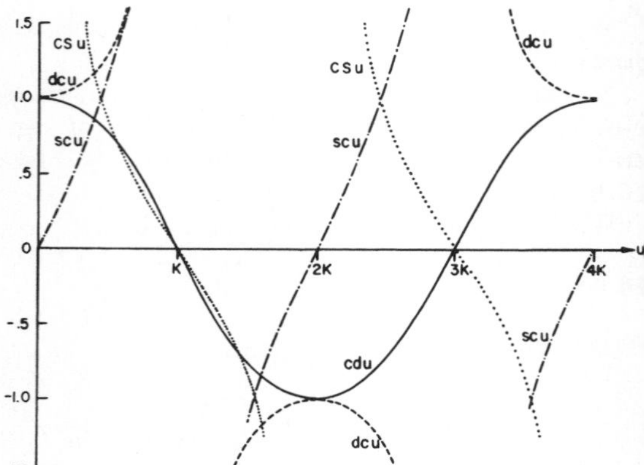

FIGURE 16.3. *Jacobian elliptic functions*

sc u, cs u, cd u, dc u

$$m=\frac{1}{2}$$

16.3. Relation of the Jacobian Functions to the Copolar Trio sn u, cn u, dn u

16.3.1 $\quad \text{cd}\, u=\frac{\text{cn}\, u}{\text{dn}\, u} \qquad \text{dc}\, u=\frac{\text{dn}\, u}{\text{cn}\, u} \qquad \text{ns}\, u=\frac{1}{\text{sn}\, u}$

16.3.2 $\quad \text{sd}\, u=\frac{\text{sn}\, u}{\text{dn}\, u} \qquad \text{nc}\, u=\frac{1}{\text{cn}\, u} \qquad \text{ds}\, u=\frac{\text{dn}\, u}{\text{sn}\, u}$

16.3.3 $\quad \text{nd}\, u=\frac{1}{\text{dn}\, u} \qquad \text{sc}\, u=\frac{\text{sn}\, u}{\text{cn}\, u} \qquad \text{cs}\, u=\frac{\text{cn}\, u}{\text{sn}\, u}$

And generally if p, q, r are any three of the letters s, c, d, n,

16.3.4 $$\text{pq}\, u=\frac{\text{pr}\, u}{\text{qr}\, u}$$

provided that when two letters are the same, e.g., pp u, the corresponding function is put equal to unity.

16.4. Calculation of the Jacobian Functions by Use of the Arithmetic-Geometric Mean (A.G.M.)

For the A.G.M. scale see **17.6.**

To calculate sn $(u|m)$, cn $(u|m)$, and dn $(u|m)$ form the A.G.M. scale starting with

16.4.1 $$a_0=1,\ b_0=\sqrt{m_1},\ c_0=\sqrt{m},$$

terminating at the step N when c_N is negligible to the accuracy required. Find φ_N in degrees where

16.4.2 $$\varphi_N=2^N a_N u\,\frac{180^\circ}{\pi}$$

and then compute successively φ_{N-1}, φ_{N-2}, . . ., φ_1, φ_0 from the recurrence relation

16.4.3 $$\sin\,(2\varphi_{n-1}-\varphi_n)=\frac{c_n}{a_n}\sin\varphi_n.$$

Then

16.4.4

$$\operatorname{sn}(u|m)=\sin\varphi_0,\quad \operatorname{cn}(u|m)=\cos\varphi_0$$

$$\operatorname{dn}(u|m)=\frac{\cos\varphi_0}{\cos\,(\varphi_1-\varphi_0)}.$$

From these all the other functions can be determined.

16.5. Special Arguments

	u	sn u	cn u	dn u
16.5.1	0	0	1	1
16.5.2	$\frac{1}{2}K$	$\frac{1}{(1+m_1^{1/2})^{1/2}}$	$\frac{m_1^{1/4}}{(1+m_1^{1/2})^{1/2}}$	$m_1^{1/4}$
16.5.3	K	1	0	$m_1^{1/2}$
16.5.4	$\frac{1}{2}(iK')$	$im^{-1/4}$	$\frac{(1+m^{1/2})^{1/2}}{m^{1/4}}$	$(1+m^{1/2})^{1/2}$
16.5.5	$\frac{1}{2}(K+iK')$	$2^{-1/2}m^{-1/4}[(1+m^{1/2})^{1/2}+i(1-m^{1/2})^{1/2}]$	$\left(\frac{m_1}{4m}\right)^{1/4}(1-i)$	$\left(\frac{m_1}{4}\right)^{1/4}[(1+m_1^{1/2})^{1/2}-i(1-m_1^{1/2})^{1/2}]$
16.5.6	$K+\frac{1}{2}(iK')$	$m^{-1/4}$	$-i\left(\frac{1-m^{1/2}}{m^{1/2}}\right)^{1/2}$	$(1-m^{1/2})^{1/2}$
16.5.7	iK'	∞	∞	∞
16.5.8	$\frac{1}{2}K+iK'$	$(1-m_1^{1/2})^{-1/2}$	$-i\left(\frac{m_1^{1/2}}{1-m_1^{1/2}}\right)^{1/2}$	$-im_1^{1/4}$
16.5.9	$K+iK'$	$m^{-1/2}$	$-i(m_1/m)^{1/2}$	0

16.6. Jacobian Functions when $m=0$ or 1

		$m=0$	$m=1$
16.6.1	sn $(u\|m)$	sin u	tanh u
16.6.2	cn $(u\|m)$	cos u	sech u
16.6.3	dn $(u\|m)$	1	sech u
16.6.4	cd $(u\|m)$	cos u	1
16.6.5	sd $(u\|m)$	sin u	sinh u
16.6.6	nd $(u\|m)$	1	cosh u
16.6.7	dc $(u\|m)$	sec u	1
16.6.8	nc $(u\|m)$	sec u	cosh u
16.6.9	sc $(u\|m)$	tan u	sinh u
16.6.10	ns $(u\|m)$	csc u	coth u
16.6.11	ds $(u\|m)$	csc u	csch u
16.6.12	cs $(u\|m)$	cot u	csch u
16.6.13	am $(u\|m)$	u	gd u

16.7. Principal Terms

When the elliptic function pq u is expanded in ascending powers of $(u-K_r)$, where K_r is one of $0, K, iK', K+iK'$, the first term of the expansion is called the principal term and has one of the forms A, $B\times(u-K_r)$, $C\div(u-K_r)$ according as K_r is an ordinary point, a zero, or a pole of pq u. The following list gives these forms, where $\times$ means that the factor $(u-K_r)$ has to be supplied and $\div$ means that the divisor $(u-K_r)$ has to be supplied.

	$K_r=$	0	K	iK'	$K+iK'$
16.7.1	sn u	$1\times$	1	$m^{-1/2}\div$	$m^{-1/2}$
16.7.2	cn u	1	$-m_1^{1/2}\times$	$-im^{-1/2}\div$	$-i\left(\frac{m_1}{m}\right)^{1/2}$
16.7.3	dn u	1	$m_1^{1/2}$	$-i\div$	$im_1^{1/2}\times$
16.7.4	cd u	1	$-1\times$	$m^{-1/2}$	$-m^{-1/2}\div$
16.7.5	sd u	$1\times$	$m_1^{-1/2}$	$im^{-1/2}$	$-i\frac{1}{(mm_1)^{1/2}}\div$
16.7.6	nd u	1	$m_1^{-1/2}$	$i\times$	$-im_1^{-1/2}\div$
16.7.7	dc u	1	$-1\div$	$m^{1/2}$	$-m^{1/2}\times$
16.7.8	nc u	1	$-m_1^{-1/2}\div$	$im^{1/2}\times$	$i\left(\frac{m}{m_1}\right)^{1/2}$
16.7.9	sc u	$1\times$	$-m_1^{-1/2}\div$	i	$im_1^{-1/2}$
16.7.10	ns u	$1\div$	1	$m^{1/2}\times$	$m^{1/2}$
16.7.11	ds u	$1\div$	$m_1^{1/2}$	$-im^{1/2}$	$i(mm_1)^{1/2}\times$
16.7.12	cs u	$1\div$	$-m_1^{1/2}\times$	$-i$	$-im_1^{1/2}$

16.8. Change of Argument

		u	$-u$	$u+K$	$u-K$	$K-u$	$u+2K$	$u-2K$	$2K-u$	$u+iK'$	$u+2iK'$	$u+K+iK'$	$u+2K+2iK'$
16.8.1	sn	sn u	$-$sn u	cd u	$-$cd u	cd u	$-$sn u	$-$sn u	sn u	$m^{-1/2}$ns u	sn u	$m^{-1/2}$dc u	$-$sn u
16.8.2	cn	cn u	cn u	$-m_1^{1/2}$sd u	$m_1^{1/2}$sd u	$m_1^{1/2}$sd u	$-$cn u	$-$cn u	$-$cn u	$-im^{-1/2}$ds u	$-$cn u	$-im_1^{1/2}m^{-1/2}$nc u	cn u
16.8.3	dn	dn u	dn u	$m_1^{1/2}$nd u	$m_1^{1/2}$nd u	$m_1^{1/2}$nd u	dn u	dn u	dn u	$-i$cs u	$-$dn u	$im_1^{1/2}$sc u	$-$dn u
16.8.4	cd	cd u	cd u	$-$sn u	sn u	sn u	$-$cd u	$-$cd u	$-$cd u	$m^{-1/2}$dc u	cd u	$-m^{-1/2}$ns u	$-$cd u
16.8.5	sd	sd u	$-$sd u	$m_1^{-1/2}$cn u	$-m_1^{-1/2}$cn u	$m_1^{-1/2}$cn u	$-$sd u	$-$sd u	sd u	$im^{-1/2}$nc u	$-$sd u	$-im_1^{-1/2}m^{-1/2}$ds u	sd u
16.8.6	nd	nd u	nd u	$m_1^{-1/2}$dn u	$m_1^{-1/2}$dn u	$m_1^{-1/2}$dn u	nd u	nd u	nd u	$i$sc u	$-$nd u	$-im_1^{-1/2}$cs u	$-$nd u
16.8.7	dc	dc u	dc u	$-$ns u	ns u	ns u	$-$dc u	$-$dc u	$-$dc u	$m^{1/2}$cd u	dc u	$-m^{1/2}$sn u	$-$dc u
16.8.8	nc	nc u	nc u	$-m_1^{-1/2}$ds u	$m_1^{-1/2}$ds u	$m_1^{-1/2}$ds u	$-$nc u	$-$nc u	$-$nc u	$im^{1/2}$sd u	$-$nc u	$im_1^{-1/2}m^{1/2}$cn u	nc u
16.8.9	sc	sc u	$-$sc u	$-m_1^{-1/2}$cs u	$-m_1^{-1/2}$cs u	$m_1^{-1/2}$cs u	sc u	sc u	$-$sc u	ind u	$-$sc u	$im_1^{-1/2}$dn u	$-$sc u
16.8.10	ns	ns u	$-$ns u	dc u	$-$dc u	dc u	$-$ns u	$-$ns u	ns u	$m^{1/2}$sn u	ns u	$m^{1/2}$cd u	$-$ns u
16.8.11	ds	ds u	$-$ds u	$m_1^{1/2}$nc u	$-m_1^{1/2}$nc u	$m_1^{1/2}$nc u	$-$ds u	$-$ds u	ds u	$-im^{1/2}$cn u	$-$ds u	$im_1^{1/2}m^{1/2}$sd u	ds u
16.8.12	cs	cs u	$-$cs u	$-m_1^{1/2}$sc u	$-m_1^{1/2}$sc u	$m_1^{1/2}$sc u	cs u	cs u	$-$cs u	$-i$dn u	$-$cs u	$-im_1^{1/2}$nd u	$-$cs u

16.9. Relations Between the Squares of the Functions

16.9.1 $-\text{dn}^2u+m_1=-m\,\text{cn}^2u=m\,\text{sn}^2u-m$

16.9.2 $-m_1\text{nd}^2u+m_1=-mm_1\text{sd}^2u=m\,\text{cd}^2u-m$

16.9.3 $m_1\text{sc}^2u+m_1=m_1\text{nc}^2u=\text{dc}^2u-m$

16.9.4 $\text{cs}^2u+m_1=\text{ds}^2u=\text{ns}^2u-m$

In using the above results remember that $m+m_1=1$.

If pq u, rt u are any two of the twelve functions, one entry expresses tq^2u in terms of pq^2u and another expresses qt^2u in terms of rt^2u. Since $\text{tq}^2u\cdot\text{qt}^2u=1$, we can obtain from the table the bilinear relation between pq^2u and rt^2u. Thus for the functions cd u, sn u we have

16.9.5 $$\text{nd}^2u=\frac{1-m\,\text{cd}^2u}{m_1},\ \text{dn}^2u=1-m\,\text{sn}^2u$$

and therefore

16.9.6 $$(1-m\,\text{cd}^2u)(1-m\,\text{sn}^2u)=m_1.$$

16.10. Change of Parameter

Negative Parameter

If m is a positive number, let

16.10.1 $$\mu=\frac{m}{1+m},\ \mu_1=\frac{1}{1+m},\ v=\frac{u}{\mu_1^{\frac{1}{2}}}\qquad(0<\mu<1)$$

16.10.2 $\text{sn}\,(u|-m)=\mu_1^{\frac{1}{2}}\text{sd}\,(v|\mu)$

16.10.3 $\text{cn}\,(u|-m)=\text{cd}\,(v|\mu)$

16.10.4 $\text{dn}\,(u|-m)=\text{nd}\,(v|\mu)$.

16.11. Reciprocal Parameter (Jacobi's Real Transformation)

16.11.1 $m>0,\ \mu=m^{-1},\ v=um^{1/2}$

16.11.2 $\text{sn}\,(u|m)=\mu^{1/2}\text{sn}\,(v|\mu)$

16.11.3 $\text{cn}\,(u|m)=\text{dn}\,(v|\mu)$

16.11.4 $\text{dn}\,(u|m)=\text{cn}\,(v|\mu)$

Here if $m>1$ then $m^{-1}=\mu<1$.

Thus elliptic functions whose parameter is real can be made to depend on elliptic functions whose parameter lies between 0 and 1.

16.12. Descending Landen Transformation (Gauss' Transformation)

To decrease the parameter, let

16.12.1 $$\mu=\left(\frac{1-m_1^{1/2}}{1+m_1^{1/2}}\right)^2,\ v=\frac{u}{1+\mu^{1/2}},$$

then

16.12.2 $$\text{sn}\,(u|m)=\frac{(1+\mu^{1/2})\,\text{sn}\,(v|\mu)}{1+\mu^{1/2}\,\text{sn}^2\,(v|\mu)}$$

16.12.3 $$\text{cn}\,(u|m)=\frac{\text{cn}\,(v|\mu)\,\text{dn}\,(v|\mu)}{1+\mu^{1/2}\,\text{sn}^2\,(v|\mu)}$$

16.12.4 $$\text{dn}\,(u|m)=\frac{\text{dn}^2(v|\mu)-(1-\mu^{1/2})}{(1+\mu^{1/2})-\text{dn}^2(v|\mu)}.$$

Note that successive applications can be made conveniently to find sn $(u|m)$ in terms of sn $(v|\mu)$ and dn $(u|m)$ in terms of dn $(v|\mu)$, but that the calculation of cn $(u|m)$ requires all three functions.

16.13. Approximation in Terms of Circular Functions

When the parameter m is so small that we may neglect m^2 and higher powers, we have the approximations

16.13.1
$$\text{sn}\,(u|m)\approx\sin u-\frac{1}{4}\,m(u-\sin u\cos u)\cos u$$

16.13.2
$$\text{cn}\,(u|m)\approx\cos u+\frac{1}{4}\,m(u-\sin u\cos u)\sin u$$

16.13.3 $$\text{dn}\,(u|m)\approx1-\frac{1}{2}\,m\sin^2 u$$

16.13.4 $$\text{am}\,(u|m)\approx u-\frac{1}{4}\,m(u-\sin u\cos u).$$

One way of calculating the Jacobian functions is to use Landen's descending transformation to reduce the parameter sufficiently for the above formulae to become applicable. See also **16.14.**

16.14. Ascending Landen Transformation

To increase the parameter, let

16.14.1 $$\mu=\frac{4m^{1/2}}{(1+m^{1/2})^2},\ \mu_1=\left(\frac{1-m^{1/2}}{1+m^{1/2}}\right)^2,\ v=\frac{u}{1+\mu_1^{1/2}}$$

16.14.2 $$\text{sn}\,(u|m)=(1+\mu_1^{1/2})\,\frac{\text{sn}\,(v|\mu)\,\text{cn}\,(v|\mu)}{\text{dn}\,(v|\mu)}$$

16.14.3 $$\text{cn}\,(u|m)=\frac{1+\mu_1^{1/2}}{\mu}\,\frac{\text{dn}^2(v|\mu)-\mu_1^{1/2}}{\text{dn}\,(v|\mu)}$$

16.14.4 $$\text{dn}\,(u|m)=\frac{1-\mu_1^{1/2}}{\mu}\,\frac{\text{dn}^2\,(v|\mu)+\mu_1^{1/2}}{\text{dn}\,(v|\mu)}$$

Note that, when successive applications are to be made, it is simplest to calculate dn $(u|m)$ since this is expressed always in terms of the same function. The calculation of cn $(u|m)$ leads to that of dn $(v|\mu)$.

The calculation of sn $(u|m)$ necessitates the evaluation of all three functions.

16.15. Approximation in Terms of Hyperbolic Functions

When the parameter m is so close to unity that m_1^2 and higher powers of m_1 can be neglected we have the approximations

16.15.1

$$\text{sn}\,(u|m)\approx\tanh u+\frac{1}{4}\,m_1\,(\sinh u\,\cosh u-u)\,\text{sech}^2\,u$$

16.15.2

$$\text{cn}\,(u|m)\approx\text{sech}\,u-\frac{1}{4}\,m_1\,(\sinh u\,\cosh u-u)\,\tanh u\,\text{sech}\,u$$

16.15.3

$$\text{dn}\,(u|m)\approx\text{sech}\,u+\frac{1}{4}\,m_1\,(\sinh u\,\cosh u+u)\,\tanh u\,\text{sech}\,u$$

16.15.4

$$\text{am}\,(u|m)\approx\text{gd}\,u+\frac{1}{4}\,m_1\,(\sinh u\,\cosh u-u)\,\text{sech}\,u.$$

Another way of calculating the Jacobian functions is to use Landen's ascending transformation to increase the parameter sufficiently for the above formulae to become applicable. See also **16.13.**

16.16. Derivatives

	Function	Derivative	
16.16.1	sn u	cn u dn u	Pole n
16.16.2	cn u	$-$sn u dn u	
16.16.3	dn u	$-m$ sn u cn u	
16.16.4	cd u	$-m_1$ sd u nd u	Pole d
16.16.5	sd u	cd u nd u	
16.16.6	nd u	m sd u cd u	
16.16.7	dc u	m_1 sc u nc u	Pole c
16.16.8	nc u	sc u dc u	
16.16.9	sc u	dc u nc u	
16.16.10	ns u	$-$ds u cs u	Pole s
16.16.11	ds u	$-$cs u ns u	
16.16.12	cs u	$-$ns u ds u	

Note that the derivative is proportional to the product of the two copolar functions.

16.17. Addition Theorems

16.17.1 sn$(u+v)$

$$=\frac{\text{sn}\,u\cdot\text{cn}\,v\cdot\text{dn}\,v+\text{sn}\,v\cdot\text{cn}\,u\cdot\text{dn}\,u}{1-m\,\text{sn}^2u\cdot\text{sn}^2v}$$

16.17.2 cn$(u+v)$

$$=\frac{\text{cn}\,u\cdot\text{cn}\,v-\text{sn}\,u\cdot\text{dn}\,u\cdot\text{sn}\,v\cdot\text{dn}\,v}{1-m\,\text{sn}^2u\,\text{sn}^2v}$$

16.17.3 $$\text{dn}(u+v)=\frac{\text{dn}\,u\cdot\text{dn}\,v-m\,\text{sn}\,u\cdot\text{cn}\,u\cdot\text{sn}\,v\cdot\text{cn}\,v}{1-m\,\text{sn}^2u\cdot\text{sn}^2v}$$

Addition theorems are derivable one from another and are expressible in a great variety of forms. Thus ns$(u+v)$ comes from $1/\text{sn}(u+v)$ in the form $(1-m\text{sn}^2u\,\text{sn}^2v)/(\text{sn}\,u\,\text{cn}\,v\,\text{dn}\,v+\text{sn}\,v\,\text{cn}\,u\,\text{dn}\,u)$ from **16.17.1.**

Alternatively $\text{ns}(u+v)=m^{1/2}\text{sn}\,\{(iK'-u)-v\}$ which again from **16.17.1** yields the form $(\text{ns}\,u\,\text{cs}\,v\,\text{ds}\,v-\text{ns}\,v\,\text{cs}\,u\,\text{ds}\,v)/(\text{ns}^2\,u-\text{ns}^2\,v)$.

The function pq$(u+v)$ is a rational function of the four functions pq u, pq v, pq$'u$, pq$'v$.

16.18. Double Arguments

16.18.1 sn $2u$

$$=\frac{2\text{sn}\,u\cdot\text{cn}\,u\cdot\text{dn}\,u}{1-m\text{sn}^4u}=\frac{2\text{sn}\,u\cdot\text{cn}\,u\cdot\text{dn}\,u}{\text{cn}^2u+\text{sn}^2u\cdot\text{dn}^2u}$$

16.18.2 cn $2u$

$$=\frac{\text{cn}^2u-\text{sn}^2u\cdot\text{dn}^2u}{1-m\text{sn}^4u}=\frac{\text{cn}^2u-\text{sn}^2u\cdot\text{dn}^2u}{\text{cn}^2u+\text{sn}^2u\cdot\text{dn}^2u}$$

16.18.3 dn $2u$

$$=\frac{\text{dn}^2u-m\text{sn}^2u\cdot\text{cn}^2\,u}{1-m\text{sn}^4u}=\frac{\text{dn}^2u+\text{cn}^2u(\text{dn}^2u-1)}{\text{dn}^2u-\text{cn}^2u(\text{dn}^2u-1)}$$

16.18.4 $$\frac{1-\text{cn}\,2u}{1+\text{cn}\,2u}=\frac{\text{sn}^2u\cdot\text{dn}^2u}{\text{cn}^2u}$$

16.18.5 $$\frac{1-\text{dn}\,2u}{1+\text{dn}\,2u}=\frac{m\text{sn}^2u\cdot\text{cn}^2u}{\text{dn}^2u}$$

16.19. Half Arguments

16.19.1 $$\text{sn}^2\tfrac{1}{2}u=\frac{1-\text{cn}\,u}{1+\text{dn}\,u}$$

16.19.2 $$\text{cn}^2\tfrac{1}{2}u=\frac{\text{dn}\,u+\text{cn}\,u}{1+\text{dn}\,u}$$

16.19.3 $$\text{dn}^2\tfrac{1}{2}\,u=\frac{m_1+\text{dn}\,u+m\text{cn}\,u}{1+\text{dn}\,u}$$

16.20. Jacobi's Imaginary Transformation

16.20.1 $\text{sn}(iu|m)=i\text{sc}(u|m_1)$

16.20.2 $\text{cn}(iu|m)=\text{nc}(u|m_1)$

16.20.3 $\text{dn}(iu|m)=\text{dc}(u|m_1)$

16.21. Complex Arguments

With the abbreviations

16.21.1

$$\mathrm{s}=\mathrm{sn}(x|m),\ \mathrm{c}=\mathrm{cn}(x|m),\ \mathrm{d}=\mathrm{dn}(x|m),\ \mathrm{s}_1=\mathrm{sn}(y|m_1),$$
$$\mathrm{c}_1=\mathrm{cn}(y|m_1),\ \mathrm{d}_1=\mathrm{dn}(y|m_1)$$

16.21.2 $$\mathrm{sn}(x+iy|m)=\frac{\mathrm{s}\cdot\mathrm{d}_1+i\mathrm{c}\cdot\mathrm{d}\cdot\mathrm{s}_1\cdot\mathrm{c}_1}{\mathrm{c}_1^2+m\mathrm{s}^2\cdot\mathrm{s}_1^2}$$

16.21.3 $$\mathrm{cn}(x+iy|m)=\frac{\mathrm{c}\cdot\mathrm{c}_1-i\mathrm{s}\cdot\mathrm{d}\cdot\mathrm{s}_1\cdot\mathrm{d}_1}{\mathrm{c}_1^2+m\mathrm{s}^2\cdot\mathrm{s}_1^2}$$

16.21.4 $$\mathrm{dn}(x+iy|m)=\frac{\mathrm{d}\cdot\mathrm{c}_1\cdot\mathrm{d}_1-im\mathrm{s}\cdot\mathrm{c}\cdot\mathrm{s}_1}{\mathrm{c}_1^2+m\mathrm{s}^2\cdot\mathrm{s}_1^2}$$

16.22. Leading Terms of the Series in Ascending Powers of u

16.22.1

$$\mathrm{sn}(u|m)=u-(1+m)\frac{u^3}{3!}+(1+14m+m^2)\frac{u^5}{5!}$$
$$-(1+135m+135m^2+m^3)\frac{u^7}{7!}+\ldots$$

16.22.2

$$\mathrm{cn}(u|m)=1-\frac{u^2}{2!}+(1+4m)\frac{u^4}{4!}$$
$$-(1+44m+16m^2)\frac{u^6}{6!}+\ldots$$

16.22.3

$$\mathrm{dn}(u|m)=1-m\frac{u^2}{2!}+m(4+m)\frac{u^4}{4!}$$
$$-m(16+44m+m^2)\frac{u^6}{6!}+\ldots$$

No formulae are known for the general coefficients in these series.

16.23. Series Expansions in Terms of the Nome $q=e^{-\pi K'/K}$ and the Argument $v=\pi u/(2K)$

16.23.1 $$\mathrm{sn}\ (u|m)=\frac{2\pi}{m^{1/2}K}\sum_{n=0}^{\infty}\frac{q^{n+1/2}}{1-q^{2n+1}}\sin\ (2n+1)v$$

16.23.2 $$\mathrm{cn}\ (u|m)=\frac{2\pi}{m^{1/2}K}\sum_{n=0}^{\infty}\frac{q^{n+1/2}}{1+q^{2n+1}}\cos\ (2n+1)v$$

16.23.3 $$\mathrm{dn}\ (u|m)=\frac{\pi}{2K}+\frac{2\pi}{K}\sum_{n=1}^{\infty}\frac{q^n}{1+q^{2n}}\cos 2nv$$

16.23.4

$$\mathrm{cd}\ (u|m)=\frac{2\pi}{m^{1/2}K}\sum_{n=0}^{\infty}\frac{(-1)^n q^{n+1/2}}{1-q^{2n+1}}\cos\ (2n+1)v$$

16.23.5

$$\mathrm{sd}\ (u|m)=\frac{2\pi}{(mm_1)^{1/2}K}\sum_{n=0}^{\infty}(-1)^n\frac{q^{n+1/2}}{1+q^{2n+1}}\sin\ (2n+1)v$$

16.23.6

$$\mathrm{nd}\ (u|m)=\frac{\pi}{2m_1^{1/2}K}+\frac{2\pi}{m_1^{1/2}K}\sum_{n=1}^{\infty}(-1)^n\frac{q^n}{1+q^{2n}}\cos 2nv$$

16.23.7

$$\mathrm{dc}\ (u|m)=\frac{\pi}{2K}\sec v$$
$$+\frac{2\pi}{K}\sum_{n=0}^{\infty}(-1)^n\frac{q^{2n+1}}{1-q^{2n+1}}\cos\ (2n+1)v$$

16.23.8

$$\mathrm{nc}\ (u|m)=\frac{\pi}{2m_1^{1/2}K}\sec v$$
$$-\frac{2\pi}{m_1^{1/2}K}\sum_{n=0}^{\infty}(-1)^n\frac{q^{2n+1}}{1+q^{2n+1}}\cos\ (2n+1)v$$

16.23.9

$$\mathrm{sc}\ (u|m)=\frac{\pi}{2m_1^{1/2}K}\tan v$$
$$+\frac{2\pi}{m_1^{1/2}K}\sum_{n=1}^{\infty}(-1)^n\frac{q^{2n}}{1+q^{2n}}\sin 2nv$$

16.23.10

$$\mathrm{ns}\ (u|m)=\frac{\pi}{2K}\csc v-\frac{2\pi}{K}\sum_{n=0}^{\infty}\frac{q^{2n+1}}{1-q^{2n+1}}\sin\ (2n+1)v$$

16.23.11

$$\mathrm{ds}\ (u|m)=\frac{\pi}{2K}\csc v-\frac{2\pi}{K}\sum_{n=0}^{\infty}\frac{q^{2n+1}}{1+q^{2n+1}}\sin\ (2n+1)v$$

16.23.12

$$\mathrm{cs}\ (u|m)=\frac{\pi}{2K}\cot v-\frac{2\pi}{K}\sum_{n=1}^{\infty}\frac{q^{2n}}{1+q^{2n}}\sin 2nv$$

16.24. Integrals of the Twelve Jacobian Elliptic Functions

16.24.1 $$\int\mathrm{sn}\ u\ du=m^{-1/2}\ln\ (\mathrm{dn}\ u-m^{1/2}\mathrm{cn}\ u)$$

16.24.2 $$\int\mathrm{cn}\ u\ du=m^{-1/2}\arccos\ (\mathrm{dn}\ u)$$

16.24.3 $$\int\mathrm{dn}\ u\ du=\arcsin\ (\mathrm{sn}\ u)$$

16.24.4 $$\int\mathrm{cd}\ u\ du=m^{-1/2}\ln\ (\mathrm{nd}\ u+m^{1/2}\mathrm{sd}\ u)$$

16.24.5 $$\int\mathrm{sd}\ u\ du=(mm_1)^{-1/2}\arcsin\ (-m^{1/2}\mathrm{cd}\ u)$$

16.24.6 $$\int\mathrm{nd}\ u\ du=m_1^{-1/2}\arccos\ (\mathrm{cd}\ u)$$

16.24.7 $$\int\mathrm{dc}\ u\ du=\ln\ (\mathrm{nc}\ u+\mathrm{sc}\ u)$$

16.24.8 $$\int\mathrm{nc}\ u\ du=m_1^{-1/2}\ln\ (\mathrm{dc}\ u+m_1^{1/2}\mathrm{sc}\ u)$$

16.24.9 $$\int\mathrm{sc}\ u\ du=m_1^{-1/2}\ln\ (\mathrm{dc}\ u+m_1^{1/2}\mathrm{nc}\ u)$$

16.24.10 $$\int\mathrm{ns}\ u\ du=\ln\ (\mathrm{ds}\ u-\mathrm{cs}\ u)$$

16.24.11 $$\int\mathrm{ds}\ u\ du=\ln\ (\mathrm{ns}\ u-\mathrm{cs}\ u)$$

16.24.12 $$\int\mathrm{cs}\ u\ du=\ln\ (\mathrm{ns}\ u-\mathrm{ds}\ u)$$

In numerical use of the above table certain restrictions must be put on u in order to keep the arguments of the logarithms positive and to avoid trouble with many-valued inverse circular functions.

16.25. Notation for the Integrals of the Squares of the Twelve Jacobian Elliptic Functions

16.25.1 $\mathrm{Pq}\, u = \int_0^u \mathrm{pq}^2 t \, dt$ when $\mathrm{q} \neq \mathrm{s}$

16.25.2 $\mathrm{Ps}\, u = \int_0^u \left(\mathrm{pq}^2 t - \frac{1}{t^2}\right) dt - \frac{1}{u}$

Examples

$$\mathrm{Cd}\, u = \int_0^u \mathrm{cd}^2 t \, dt, \quad \mathrm{Ns}\, u = \int_0^u \left(\mathrm{ns}^2 t - \frac{1}{t^2}\right) dt - \frac{1}{u}$$

16.26. Integrals in Terms of the Elliptic Integral of the Second Kind (see 17.4)

16.26.1 $m\mathrm{Sn}\, u = -E(u) + u$

16.26.2 $m\mathrm{Cn}\, u = E(u) - m_1 u$ Pole n

16.26.3 $\mathrm{Dn}\, u = E(u)$

16.26.4 $m\mathrm{Cd}\, u = -E(u) + u + m \mathrm{sn}\, u \,\mathrm{cd}\, u$

16.26.5

$mm_1\mathrm{Sd}\, u = E(u) - m_1 u - m \mathrm{sn}\, u \,\mathrm{cd}\, u$ Pole d

16.26.6 $m_1\mathrm{Nd}\, u = E(u) - m \mathrm{sn}\, u \,\mathrm{cd}\, u$

16.26.7 $\mathrm{Dc}\, u = -E(u) + u + \mathrm{sn}\, u \,\mathrm{dc}\, u$

16.26.8

$m_1\mathrm{Nc}\, u = -E(u) + m_1 u + \mathrm{sn}\, u \,\mathrm{dc}\, u$ Pole c

16.26.9 $m_1\mathrm{Sc}\, u = -E(u) + \mathrm{sn}\, u \,\mathrm{dc}\, u$

16.26.10 $\mathrm{Ns}\, u = -E(u) + u - \mathrm{cn}\, u \,\mathrm{ds}\, u$

16.26.11

$\mathrm{Ds}\, u = -E(u) + m_1 u - \mathrm{cn}\, u \,\mathrm{ds}\, u$ Pole s

16.26.12 $\mathrm{Cs}\, u = -E(u) - \mathrm{cn}\, u \,\mathrm{ds}\, u$

All the above may be expressed in terms of Jacobi's zeta function (see **17.4.27**).

$$Z(u) = E(u) - \frac{E}{K} u, \text{ where } E = E(K)$$

16.27. Theta Functions; Expansions in Terms of the Nome q

16.27.1

$$\vartheta_1(z, q) = \vartheta_1(z) = 2q^{1/4} \sum_{n=0}^{\infty} (-1)^n q^{n(n+1)} \sin (2n+1)z$$

16.27.2

$$\vartheta_2(z, q) = \vartheta_2(z) = 2q^{1/4} \sum_{n=0}^{\infty} q^{n(n+1)} \cos (2n+1)z$$

16.27.3 $\vartheta_3(z, q) = \vartheta_3(z) = 1 + 2 \sum_{n=1}^{\infty} q^{n^2} \cos 2nz$

16.27.4

$$\vartheta_4(z, q) = \vartheta_4(z) = 1 + 2 \sum_{n=1}^{\infty} (-1)^n q^{n^2} \cos 2nz$$

Theta functions are important because every one of the Jacobian elliptic functions can be expressed as the ratio of two theta functions. See **16.36.**

The notation shows these functions as depending on the variable z and the nome q, $|q| < 1$. In this case, here and elsewhere, the convergence is not dependent on the trigonometrical terms. In their relation to the Jacobian elliptic functions, we note that the nome q is given by

$$q = e^{-\pi K'/K},$$

where K and iK' are the quarter periods. Since $q = q(m)$ is determined when the parameter m is given, we can also regard the theta functions as dependent upon m and then we write

$$\vartheta_a(z, q) = \vartheta_a(z|m), \; a = 1, 2, 3, 4$$

but when no ambiguity is to be feared, we write $\vartheta_a(z)$ simply.

The above notations are those given in Modern Analysis [16.6].

There is a bewildering variety of notations, for example the function $\vartheta_4(z)$ above is sometimes denoted by $\vartheta_0(z)$ or $\vartheta(z)$; see the table given in Modern Analysis [16.6]. Further the argument $u = 2Kz/\pi$ is frequently used so that in consulting books caution should be exercised.

16.28. Relations Between the Squares of the Theta Functions

16.28.1 $\vartheta_1^2(z)\vartheta_4^2(0) = \vartheta_3^2(z)\vartheta_2^2(0) - \vartheta_2^2(z)\vartheta_3^2(0)$

16.28.2 $\vartheta_2^2(z)\vartheta_4^2(0) = \vartheta_4^2(z)\vartheta_2^2(0) - \vartheta_1^2(z)\vartheta_3^2(0)$

16.28.3 $\vartheta_3^2(z)\vartheta_4^2(0) = \vartheta_4^2(z)\vartheta_3^2(0) - \vartheta_1^2(z)\vartheta_2^2(0)$

16.28.4 $\vartheta_4^2(z)\vartheta_4^2(0) = \vartheta_3^2(z)\vartheta_3^2(0) - \vartheta_2^2(z)\vartheta_2^2(0)$

16.28.5 $\vartheta_2^4(0) + \vartheta_4^4(0) = \vartheta_3^4(0)$

Note also the important relation

16.28.6 $\vartheta_1'(0) = \vartheta_2(0)\vartheta_3(0)\vartheta_4(0)$ or $\vartheta_1' = \vartheta_2\vartheta_3\vartheta_4$

16.29. Logarithmic Derivatives of the Theta Functions

16.29.1 $\frac{\vartheta_1'(u)}{\vartheta_1(u)} = \cot u + 4 \sum_{n=1}^{\infty} \frac{q^{2n}}{1 - q^{2n}} \sin 2nu$

16.29.2

$$\frac{\vartheta_2'(u)}{\vartheta_2(u)}=-\tan u+4\sum_{n=1}^{\infty}(-1)^n\frac{q^{2n}}{1-q^{2n}}\sin 2nu$$

16.29.3 $$\frac{\vartheta_3'(u)}{\vartheta_3(u)}=4\sum_{n=1}^{\infty}(-1)^n\frac{q^n}{1-q^{2n}}\sin 2nu$$

16.29.4 $$\frac{\vartheta_4'(u)}{\vartheta_4(u)}=4\sum_{n=1}^{\infty}\frac{q^n}{1-q^{2n}}\sin 2nu$$

16.30. Logarithms of Theta Functions of Sum and Difference

16.30.1

$$\ln\frac{\vartheta_1(\alpha+\beta)}{\vartheta_1(\alpha-\beta)}=\ln\frac{\sin(\alpha+\beta)}{\sin(\alpha-\beta)}+4\sum_{n=1}^{\infty}\frac{1}{n}\frac{q^{2n}}{1-q^{2n}}\sin 2n\alpha\sin 2n\beta$$

16.30.2

$$\ln\frac{\vartheta_2(\alpha+\beta)}{\vartheta_2(\alpha-\beta)}=\ln\frac{\cos(\alpha+\beta)}{\cos(\alpha-\beta)}+4\sum_{n=1}^{\infty}\frac{(-1)^n}{n}\frac{q^{2n}}{1-q^{2n}}\sin 2n\alpha\sin 2n\beta$$

16.30.3

$$\ln\frac{\vartheta_3(\alpha+\beta)}{\vartheta_3(\alpha-\beta)}=4\sum_{n=1}^{\infty}\frac{(-1)^n}{n}\frac{q^n}{1-q^{2n}}\sin 2n\alpha\sin 2n\beta$$

16.30.4

$$\ln\frac{\vartheta_4(\alpha+\beta)}{\vartheta_4(\alpha-\beta)}=4\sum_{n=1}^{\infty}\frac{1}{n}\frac{q^n}{1-q^{2n}}\sin 2n\alpha\sin 2n\beta$$

The corresponding expressions when $\beta=i\gamma$ are easily deduced by use of the formulae **4.3.55** and **4.3.56.**

16.31. Jacobi's Notation for Theta Functions

16.31.1 $$\Theta(u|m)=\Theta(u)=\vartheta_4(v),\qquad v=\frac{\pi u}{2K}$$

16.31.2 $$\Theta_1(u|m)=\Theta_1(u)=\vartheta_3(v)=\Theta(u+K)$$

16.31.3 $$\mathrm{H}(u|m)=\mathrm{H}(u)=\vartheta_1(v)$$

16.31.4 $$\mathrm{H}_1(u|m)=\mathrm{H}_1(u)=\vartheta_2(v)=\mathrm{H}(u+K)$$

16.32. Calculation of Jacobi's Theta Function $\Theta(u|m)$ by Use of the Arithmetic-Geometric Mean

Form the A.G.M. scale starting with

16.32.1 $$a_0=1,\ b_0=\sqrt{m_1},\ c_0=\sqrt{m}$$

terminating with the Nth step when c_N is negligible to the accuracy required. Find φ_N in degrees, where

16.32.2 $$\varphi_N=2^N a_N u\,\frac{180^\circ}{\pi}$$

and then compute successively $\varphi_{N-1}, \varphi_{N-2}, \ldots, \varphi_1, \varphi_0$ from the recurrence relation

16.32.3 $$\sin(2\varphi_{n-1}-\varphi_n)=\frac{c_n}{a_n}\sin\varphi_n.$$

Then

16.32.4

$$\ln\Theta(u|m)=\frac{1}{2}\ln\frac{2m_1^{1/2}K(m)}{\pi}+\frac{1}{2}\ln\frac{\cos(\varphi_1-\varphi_0)}{\cos\varphi_0}+\frac{1}{4}\ln\sec(2\varphi_0-\varphi_1)+\frac{1}{8}\ln\sec(2\varphi_1-\varphi_2)+\ldots+\frac{1}{2^{N+1}}\ln\sec(2\varphi_{N-1}-\varphi_N)$$

16.33. Addition of Quarter-Periods to Jacobi's Eta and Theta Functions

u	$-u$	$u+K$	$u+2K$	$u+iK'$	$u+2iK'$	$u+K+iK'$	$u+2K+2iK'$
16.33.1 $\mathrm{H}(u)$	$-\mathrm{H}(u)$	$\mathrm{H}_1(u)$	$-\mathrm{H}(u)$	$iM(u)\Theta(u)$	$-N(u)\mathrm{H}(u)$	$M(u)\Theta_1(u)$	$N(u)\mathrm{H}(u)$
16.33.2 $\mathrm{H}_1(u)$	$\mathrm{H}_1(u)$	$-\mathrm{H}(u)$	$-\mathrm{H}_1(u)$	$M(u)\Theta_1(u)$	$N(u)\mathrm{H}_1(u)$	$-iM(u)\Theta(u)$	$-N(u)\mathrm{H}_1(u)$
16.33.3 $\Theta_1(u)$	$\Theta_1(u)$	$\Theta(u)$	$\Theta_1(u)$	$M(u)\mathrm{H}_1(u)$	$N(u)\Theta_1(u)$	$iM(u)\mathrm{H}(u)$	$N(u)\Theta_1(u)$
16.33.4 $\Theta(u)$	$\Theta(u)$	$\Theta_1(u)$	$\Theta(u)$	$iM(u)\mathrm{H}(u)$	$-N(u)\Theta(u)$	$M(u)\mathrm{H}_1(u)$	$-N(u)\Theta(u)$

where

$$M(u)=\left[\exp\left(-\frac{\pi iu}{2K}\right)\right]q^{-\frac{1}{4}},$$

$$N(u)=\left[\exp\left(-\frac{\pi iu}{K}\right)\right]q^{-1}$$

$\mathrm{H}(u)$ and $\mathrm{H}_1(u)$ have the period $4K$. $\Theta(u)$ and $\Theta_1(u)$ have the period $2K$.

$2iK'$ is a quasi-period for all four functions, that is to say, increase of the argument by $2iK'$ multiplies the function by a factor.

16.34. Relation of Jacobi's Zeta Function to the Theta Functions

$$Z(u)=\frac{\partial}{\partial u}\ln\Theta(u)$$

16.34.1 $$Z(u)=\frac{\pi}{2K}\frac{\vartheta_1'\left(\frac{\pi u}{2K}\right)}{\vartheta_1\left(\frac{\pi u}{2K}\right)}-\frac{\text{cn } u \text{ dn } u}{\text{sn } u}$$

16.34.2 $$=\frac{\pi}{2K}\frac{\vartheta_2'\left(\frac{\pi u}{2K}\right)}{\vartheta_2\left(\frac{\pi u}{2K}\right)}+\frac{\text{dn } u \text{ sn } u}{\text{cn } u}$$

16.34.3 $$=\frac{\pi}{2K}\frac{\vartheta_3'\left(\frac{\pi u}{2K}\right)}{\vartheta_3\left(\frac{\pi u}{2K}\right)}-m\frac{\text{sn } u \text{ cn } u}{\text{dn } u}$$

16.34.4 $$=\frac{\pi}{2K}\frac{\vartheta_4'\left(\frac{\pi u}{2K}\right)}{\vartheta_4\left(\frac{\pi u}{2K}\right)}$$

16.35. Calculation of Jacobi's Zeta Function *Z(u|m)* by Use of the Arithmetic-Geometric Mean

Form the A.G.M. scale **17.6** starting with

16.35.1 $$a_0=1,\ b_0=\sqrt{m_1},\ c_0=\sqrt{m}$$

terminating at the Nth step when c_N is negligible to the accuracy required. Find φ_N in degrees where

16.35.2 $$\varphi_N=2^N a_N u\,\frac{180°}{\pi}$$

and then compute successively $\varphi_{N-1}, \varphi_{N-2}, \ldots, \varphi_1, \varphi_0$ from the recurrence relation

16.35.3 $$\sin(2\varphi_{n-1}-\varphi_n)=\frac{c_n}{a_n}\sin\varphi_n.$$

Then

16.35.4

$$Z(u|m)=c_1\sin\varphi_1+c_2\sin\varphi_2+\ldots+c_N\sin\varphi_N.$$

16.36. Neville's Notation for Theta Functions

These functions are defined in terms of Jacobi's theta functions of **16.31** by

16.36.1 $$\vartheta_s(u)=\frac{\text{H}(u)}{\text{H}'(0)},\ \vartheta_c(u)=\frac{\text{H}(u+K)}{\text{H}(K)}$$

16.36.2 $$\vartheta_d(u)=\frac{\Theta(u+K)}{\Theta(K)},\ \vartheta_n(u)=\frac{\Theta(u)}{\Theta(0)}.$$

If λ, μ are any integers positive, negative, or zero the points $u_0+2\lambda K+2\mu iK'$ are said to be *congruent to* u_0.

$\vartheta_s(u)$ has zeros at the points congruent to 0
$\vartheta_c(u)$ has zeros at the points congruent to K
$\vartheta_n(u)$ has zeros at the points congruent to iK'
$\vartheta_d(u)$ has zeros at the points congruent to $K+iK'$

Thus the suffix secures that the function $\vartheta_p(u)$ has zeros at the points marked p in the introductory diagram in **16.1.2**, and the constant by which Jacobi's function is divided secures that the leading coefficient of $\vartheta_p(u)$ at the origin is unity. Therefore the functions have the fundamentally important property that if p, q are any two of the letters s, c, n, d, the Jacobian elliptic function pq u is given by

16.36.3 $$\text{pq } u=\frac{\vartheta_p(u)}{\vartheta_q(u)}.$$

These functions also have the property

16.36.4 $$m_1^{-1/4}\vartheta_c(K-u)=\vartheta_s(u)$$

16.36.5 $$m_1^{-1/4}\vartheta_d(K-u)=\vartheta_n(u),$$

for complementary arguments u and $K-u$.

In terms of the theta functions defined in **16.27**, let $v=\pi u/(2K)$, then

16.36.6 $$\vartheta_s(u)=\frac{2K\vartheta_1(v)}{\vartheta_1'(0)},\ \vartheta_c(u)=\frac{\vartheta_2(v)}{\vartheta_2(0)}$$

16.36.7 $$\vartheta_d(u)=\frac{\vartheta_3(v)}{\vartheta_3(0)},\ \vartheta_n(u)=\frac{\vartheta_4(v)}{\vartheta_4(0)}.$$

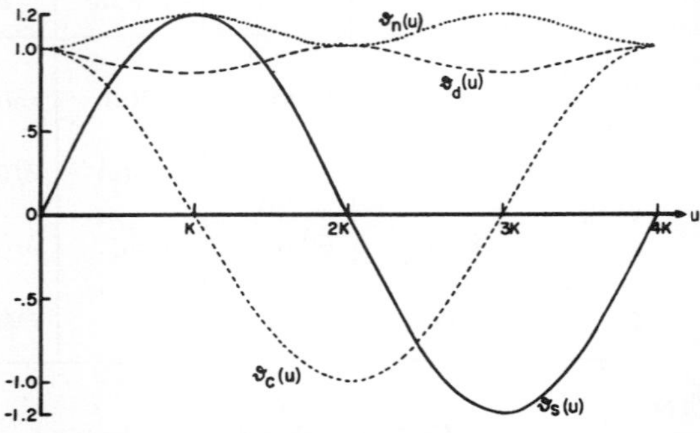

FIGURE 16.4. *Neville's theta functions* $\vartheta_s(u)$, $\vartheta_c(u)$, $\vartheta_d(u)$, $\vartheta_n(u)$ $m=\frac{1}{2}$

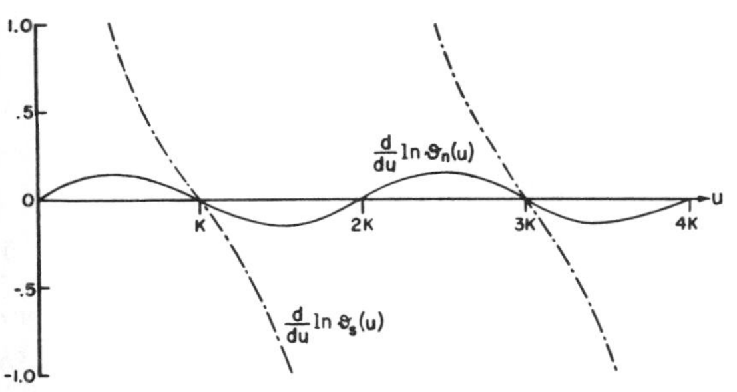

FIGURE 16.5. *Logarithmic derivatives of theta functions*

$$\frac{d}{du}\ln \vartheta_s(u),\ \frac{d}{du}\ln \vartheta_n(u)$$

$$m=\frac{1}{2}$$

16.37. Expression as Infinite Products

$$q=q(m),\ v=\pi u/(2K)$$

16.37.1

$$\vartheta_s(u)=\left(\frac{16q}{mm_1}\right)^{1/6}\sin v\prod_{n=1}^{\infty}(1-2q^{2n}\cos 2v+q^{4n})$$

16.37.2

$$\vartheta_c(u)=\left(\frac{16qm_1^{1/2}}{m}\right)^{1/6}\cos v\prod_{n=1}^{\infty}(1+2q^{2n}\cos 2v+q^{4n})$$

16.37.3

$$\vartheta_d(u)=\left(\frac{mm_1}{16q}\right)^{1/12}\prod_{n=1}^{\infty}(1+2q^{2n-1}\cos 2v+q^{4n-2})$$

16.37.4

$$\vartheta_n(u)=\left(\frac{m}{16qm_1^2}\right)^{1/12}\prod_{n=1}^{\infty}(1-2q^{2n-1}\cos 2v+q^{4n-2})$$

16.38. Expression as Infinite Series

Let $v=\pi u/(2K)$

16.38.1

$$\vartheta_s(u)=\left[\frac{2\pi q^{1/2}}{m^{1/2}m_1^{1/2}K}\right]^{1/2}\sum_{n=0}^{\infty}(-1)^n q^{n(n+1)}\sin(2n+1)v$$

16.38.2 $$\vartheta_c(u)=\left[\frac{2\pi q^{1/2}}{m^{1/2}K}\right]^{1/2}\sum_{n=0}^{\infty}q^{n(n+1)}\cos(2n+1)v$$

16.38.3 $$\vartheta_d(u)=\left[\frac{\pi}{2K}\right]^{1/2}\{1+2\sum_{n=1}^{\infty}q^{n^2}\cos 2nv\}$$

16.38.4

$$\vartheta_n(u)=\left[\frac{\pi}{2m_1^{1/2}K}\right]^{1/2}\{1+2\sum_{n=1}^{\infty}(-1)^n q^{n^2}\cos 2nv\}$$

16.38.5 $$(2K/\pi)^{1/2}=1+2q+2q^4+2q^9+\ldots=\vartheta_3(0,q)$$

16.38.6

$$(2K'/\pi)^{1/2}=1+2q_1+2q_1^4+2q_1^9+\ldots=\vartheta_3(0,q_1)$$

16.38.7

$$(2m^{1/2}K/\pi)^{1/2}=2q^{1/4}(1+q^2+q^6+q^{12}+q^{20}+\ldots)$$
$$=\vartheta_2(0,q)$$

16.38.8

$$(2m_1^{1/2}K/\pi)^{1/2}=1-2q+2q^4-2q^9+\ldots=\vartheta_4(0,q).$$

17. Elliptic Integrals

17.1. Definition of Elliptic Integrals

If $R(x, y)$ is a rational function of x and y, where y^2 is equal to a cubic or quartic polynomial in x, the integral

17.1.1
$$\int R(x,y)dx$$

is called an *elliptic integral.*

The elliptic integral just defined can not, in general, be expressed in terms of elementary functions.

Exceptions to this are

(i) when $R(x, y)$ contains no odd powers of y.

(ii) when the polynomial y^2 has a repeated factor.

We therefore exclude these cases.

By substituting for y^2 and denoting by $p_s(x)$ a polynomial in x we get [2]

$$R(x,y)=\frac{p_1(x)+yp_2(x)}{p_3(x)+yp_4(x)}$$
$$=\frac{[p_1(x)+yp_2(x)][p_3(x)-yp_4(x)]y}{\{[p_3(x)]^2-y^2[p_4(x)]^2\}y}$$
$$=\frac{p_5(x)+yp_6(x)}{yp_7(x)}=R_1(x)+\frac{R_2(x)}{y}$$

where $R_1(x)$ and $R_2(x)$ are rational functions of x. Hence, by expressing $R_2(x)$ as the sum of a polynomial and partial fractions

$$\int R(x,y)dx=\int R_1(x)dx+\Sigma_s A_s\int x^s y^{-1}dx$$
$$+\Sigma_s B_s\int [(x-c)^s y]^{-1}dx$$

Reduction Formulae

Let

17.1.2
$$y^2=a_0x^4+a_1x^3+a_2x^2+a_3x+a_4 \qquad (|a_0|+|a_1|\neq 0)$$
$$=b_0(x-c)^4+b_1(x-c)^3+b_2(x-c)^2+b_3(x-c)+b_4 \qquad (|b_0|+|b_1|\neq 0)$$

17.1.3 $$I_s=\int x^s y^{-1}dx,\; J_s=\int [y(x-c)^s]^{-1}dx$$

By integrating the derivatives of yx^s and $y(x-c)^{-s}$ we get the reduction formulae

17.1.4
$$(s+2)a_0I_{s+3}+\tfrac{1}{2}a_1(2s+3)I_{s+2}+a_2(s+1)I_{s+1}$$
$$+\tfrac{1}{2}a_3(2s+1)I_s+sa_4I_{s-1}=x^sy \quad (s=0, 1, 2, \ldots)$$

[2] See [17.7] 22.72.

17.1.5
$$(2-s)b_0J_{s-3}+\tfrac{1}{2}b_1(3-2s)J_{s-2}+b_2(1-s)J_{s-1}$$
$$+\tfrac{1}{2}b_3(1-2s)J_s-sb_4J_{s+1}=y(x-c)^{-s} \qquad (s=1, 2, 3, \ldots)$$

By means of these reduction formulae and certain transformations (see **Examples 1 and 2**) every elliptic integral can be brought to depend on the integral of a rational function and on three canonical forms for elliptic integrals.

17.2. Canonical Forms

Definitions

17.2.1
$m=\sin^2\alpha$; m is the parameter, α is the modular angle

17.2.2 $\quad x=\sin\varphi=\mathrm{sn}\, u$

17.2.3 $\quad \cos\varphi=\mathrm{cn}\, u$

17.2.4
$(1-m\sin^2\varphi)^{\frac{1}{2}}=\mathrm{dn}\, u=\Delta(\varphi)$, the delta amplitude

17.2.5 $\quad \varphi=\arcsin(\mathrm{sn}\, u)=\mathrm{am}\, u$, the amplitude

Elliptic Integral of the First Kind

17.2.6 $$F(\varphi\backslash\alpha)=F(\varphi|m)=\int_0^\varphi(1-\sin^2\alpha\sin^2\theta)^{-\frac{1}{2}}d\theta$$

17.2.7 $$=\int_0^x[(1-t^2)(1-mt^2)]^{-\frac{1}{2}}dt$$
$$=\int_0^u dw=u$$

Elliptic Integral of the Second Kind

17.2.8 $$E(\varphi\backslash\alpha)=E(u|m)=\int_0^x(1-t^2)^{-\frac{1}{2}}(1-mt^2)^{\frac{1}{2}}dt$$

17.2.9 $$=\int_0^\varphi(1-\sin^2\alpha\sin^2\theta)^{\frac{1}{2}}d\theta$$

17.2.10 $$=\int_0^u \mathrm{dn}^2 w\, dw$$

17.2.11 $$=m_1u+m\int_0^u \mathrm{cn}^2 w\, dw$$

17.2.12 $E(\varphi\backslash\alpha)=u-m\int_0^u \mathrm{sn}^2\, w\, dw$

17.2.13 $=\frac{\pi}{2K(m)}\frac{\vartheta_4'(\pi u/2K)}{\vartheta_4(\pi u/2K)}+\frac{E(m)u}{K(m)}$

(For theta functions, see chapter **16.**)

Elliptic Integral of the Third Kind

17.2.14

$$\Pi(n;\varphi\backslash\alpha)=\int_0^\varphi (1-n\sin^2\theta)^{-1}[1-\sin^2\alpha\sin^2\theta]^{-1/2}d\theta$$

If $x=\mathrm{sn}\,(u|m)$,

17.2.15

$$\Pi(n;u|m)=\int_0^x (1-nt^2)^{-1}[(1-t^2)(1-mt^2)]^{-1/2}dt$$

17.2.16 $=\int_0^u (1-n\,\mathrm{sn}^2\,(w|m))^{-1}dw$

The Amplitude φ

17.2.17 $\varphi=\mathrm{am}\, u=\arcsin\,(\mathrm{sn}\, u)=\arcsin\, x$

can be calculated from **Tables 17.5** and **4.14.**

The Parameter m

Dependence on the *parameter* m is denoted by a vertical stroke preceding the parameter, e.g., $F(\varphi|m)$.

Together with the parameter we define the *complementary parameter* m_1 by

17.2.18 $m+m_1=1$

When the parameter is real, it can always be arranged, see **17.4,** that $0\leq m\leq 1$.

The Modular Angle α

Dependence on the modular angle α, defined in terms of the parameter by **17.2.1,** is denoted by a backward stroke \ preceding the modular angle, thus $E(\varphi\backslash\alpha)$. The *complementary modular* angle is $\pi/2-\alpha$ or $90°-\alpha$ according to the unit and thus $m_1=\sin^2\,(90°-\alpha)=\cos^2\,\alpha$.

The Modulus k

In terms of Jacobian elliptic functions (chapter **16**), the modulus k and the complementary modulus are defined by

17.2.19 $k=\mathrm{ns}\,(K+iK'),\ k'=\mathrm{dn}\, K.$

They are related to the parameter by $k^2=m$, $k'^2=m_1$.

Dependence on the modulus is denoted by a comma preceding it, thus $\Pi(n;u,k)$.

In computation the modulus is of minimal importance, since it is the parameter and its complement which arise naturally. The parameter and the modular angle will be employed in this chapter to the exclusion of the modulus.

The Characteristic n

The elliptic integral of the third kind depends on three variables namely (i) the parameter, (ii) the amplitude, (iii) the characteristic n. When real, the characteristic may be any number in the interval $(-\infty,\infty)$. The properties of the integral depend upon the location of the characteristic in this interval, see **17.7.**

17.3. Complete Elliptic Integrals of the First and Second Kinds

Referred to the canonical forms of **17.2,** the elliptic integrals are said to be *complete* when the amplitude is $\frac{1}{2}\pi$ and so $x=1$. These complete integrals are designated as follows

17.3.1

$$[K(m)]=K=\int_0^1[(1-t^2)(1-mt^2)]^{-1/2}dt$$

$$=\int_0^{\pi/2}(1-m\sin^2\theta)^{-1/2}d\theta$$

17.3.2 $K=F(\frac{1}{2}\pi|m)=F(\frac{1}{2}\pi\backslash\alpha)$

17.3.3

$$E[K(m)]=E=\int_0^1(1-t^2)^{-1/2}(1-mt^2)^{1/2}dt$$

$$=\int_0^{\pi/2}(1-m\sin^2\theta)^{1/2}d\theta$$

17.3.4 $E=E[K(m)]=E(m)=E(\frac{1}{2}\pi\backslash\alpha)$

We also define

17.3.5

$$K'=K(m_1)=K(1-m)=\int_0^{\pi/2}(1-m_1\sin^2\theta)^{-1/2}d\theta$$

17.3.6 $K'=F(\frac{1}{2}\pi|m_1)=F(\frac{1}{2}\pi\backslash\frac{1}{2}\pi-\alpha)$

17.3.7

$$E'=E(m_1)=E(1-m)=\int_0^{\pi/2}(1-m_1\sin^2\theta)^{1/2}d\theta$$

17.3.8 $E'=E[K(m_1)]=E(m_1)=E(\frac{1}{2}\pi\backslash\frac{1}{2}\pi-\alpha)$

K and iK' are the "real" and "imaginary" *quarter-periods* of the corresponding Jacobian elliptic functions (see chapter **16**).

Relation to the Hypergeometric Function

(see chapter 15)

17.3.9 $K=\frac{1}{2}\pi F(\frac{1}{2},\frac{1}{2};1;m)$

17.3.10 $E=\frac{1}{2}\pi F(-\frac{1}{2},\frac{1}{2};1;m)$

Infinite Series

17.3.11

$$K(m)=\frac{1}{2}\pi\left[1+\left(\frac{1}{2}\right)^2 m+\left(\frac{1\cdot 3}{2\cdot 4}\right)^2 m^2+\left(\frac{1\cdot 3\cdot 5}{2\cdot 4\cdot 6}\right)^2 m^3+\ldots\right] \qquad (|m|<1)$$

17.3.12

$$E(m)=\frac{1}{2}\pi\left[1-\left(\frac{1}{2}\right)^2 \frac{m}{1}-\left(\frac{1\cdot 3}{2\cdot 4}\right)^2 \frac{m^2}{3}-\left(\frac{1\cdot 3\cdot 5}{2\cdot 4\cdot 6}\right)^2 \frac{m^3}{5}-\ldots\right] \qquad (|m|<1)$$

Legendre's Relation

17.3.13 $EK'+E'K-KK'=\frac{1}{2}\pi$

Auxiliary Function

17.3.14 $L(m)=\frac{K'(m)}{\pi}\ln\frac{16}{m_1}-K(m)$

17.3.15 $m=1-16\exp[-\pi(K(m)+L(m))/K'(m)]$

17.3.16 $m=16\exp[-\pi(K'(m)+L(m_1))/K(m)]$

The function $L(m)$ is tabulated in **Table 17.4.**

***q*-Series**

The Nome q and the Complementary Nome q_1

17.3.17 $q=q(m)=\exp[-\pi K'/K]$

17.3.18 $q_1=q(m_1)=\exp[-\pi K/K']$

17.3.19 $\ln\frac{1}{q}\ln\frac{1}{q_1}=\pi^2$

17.3.20

$$\log_{10}\frac{1}{q}\log_{10}\frac{1}{q_1}=(\pi\log_{10}e)^2=1.86152\ 28349 \text{ to 10D}$$

17.3.21

$$q=\exp[-\pi K'/K]=\frac{m}{16}+8\left(\frac{m}{16}\right)^2+84\left(\frac{m}{16}\right)^3+992\left(\frac{m}{16}\right)^4+\ldots \qquad (|m|<1)$$

17.3.22 $K=\frac{1}{2}\pi+2\pi\sum_{s=1}^{\infty}\frac{q^s}{1+q^{2s}}$

17.3.23

$$\frac{E}{K}=\frac{1}{3}(1+m_1)+(\pi/K)^2\left[1/12-2\sum_{s=1}^{\infty}q^{2s}(1-q^{2s})^{-2}\right]$$

17.3.24 $\operatorname{am} u=v+\sum_{s=1}^{\infty}\frac{2q^s\sin 2sv}{s(1+q^{2s})}$ where $v=\pi u/(2K)$

Limiting Values

17.3.25 $\lim_{m\to 0}K'(E-K)=0$

17.3.26 $\lim_{m\to 1}[K-\frac{1}{2}\ln(16/m_1)]=0$

17.3.27 $\lim_{m\to 0}m^{-1}(K-E)=\lim_{m\to 0}m^{-1}(E-m_1K)=\pi/4$

17.3.28 $\lim_{m\to 0}q/m=\lim_{m_1\to 1}q_1/m_1=1/16$

Alternative Evaluations of K and E (see also **17.5**)

17.3.29

$$K(m)=2[1+m_1^{1/2}]^{-1}K([(1-m_1^{1/2})/(1+m_1^{1/2})]^2)$$

17.3.30

$$E(m)=(1+m_1^{1/2})E([(1-m_1^{1/2})/(1+m_1^{1/2})]^2)-2m_1^{1/2}(1+m_1^{1/2})^{-1}K([(1-m_1^{1/2})/(1+m_1^{1/2})]^2)$$

17.3.31 $K(\alpha)=2F(\arctan(\sec^{1/2}\alpha)\backslash\alpha)$

17.3.32 $E(\alpha)=2E(\arctan(\sec^{1/2}\alpha)\backslash\alpha)-1+\cos\alpha$

Polynomial Approximations[3] ($0\leq m<1$)

17.3.33

$$K(m)=[a_0+a_1m_1+a_2m_1^2]+[b_0+b_1m_1+b_2m_1^2]\ln(1/m_1)+\epsilon(m)$$

$$|\epsilon(m)|\leq 3\times 10^{-5}$$

$a_0=1.38629\ 44$	$b_0=.5$
$a_1=\ .11197\ 23$	$b_1=.12134\ 78$
$a_2=\ .07252\ 96$	$b_2=.02887\ 29$

17.3.34

$$K(m)=[a_0+a_1m_1+\ldots+a_4m_1^4]+[b_0+b_1m_1+\ldots+b_4m_1^4]\ln(1/m_1)+\epsilon(m)$$

$$|\epsilon(m)|\leq 2\times 10^{-8}$$

$a_0=1.38629\ 436112$	$b_0=.5$
$a_1=\ .09666\ 344259$	$b_1=.12498\ 593597$
$a_2=\ .03590\ 092383$	$b_2=.06880\ 248576$
$a_3=\ .03742\ 563713$	$b_3=.03328\ 355346$
$a_4=\ .01451\ 196212$	$b_4=.00441\ 787012$

[3] The approximations **17.3.33–17.3.36** are from C. Hastings, Jr., Approximations for Digital Computers, Princeton Univ. Press, Princeton, N. J.

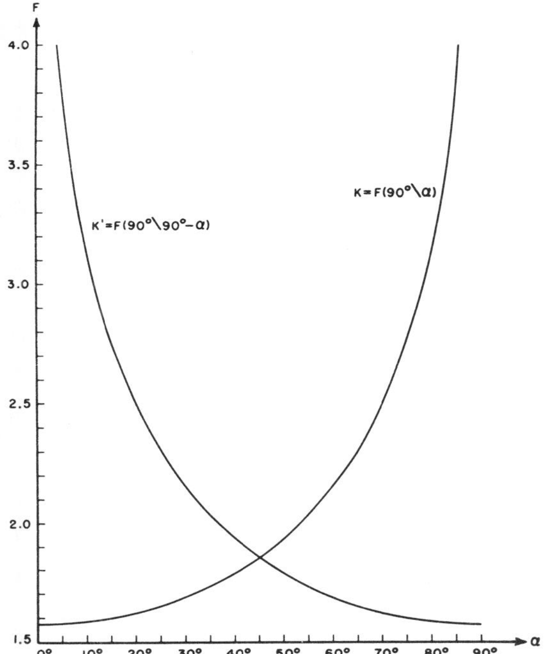

FIGURE 17.1. *Complete elliptic integral of the first kind.*

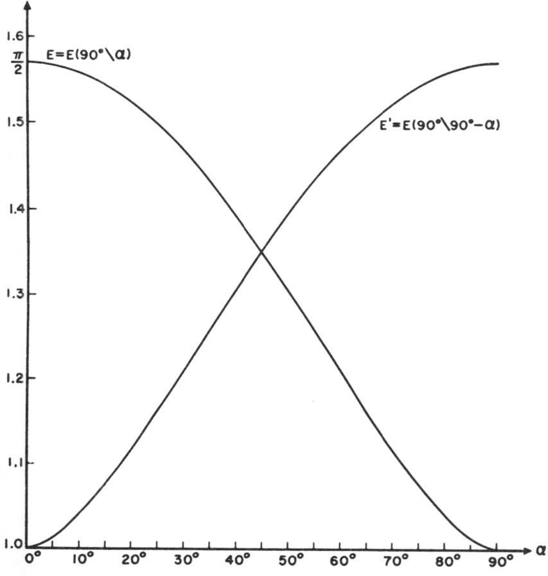

FIGURE 17.2. *Complete elliptic integral of the second kind.*

17.3.35

$$E(m)=[1+a_1m_1+a_2m_1^2]+[b_1m_1+b_2m_1^2]\ln(1/m_1)+\epsilon(m)$$

$$|\epsilon(m)|<4\times10^{-5}$$

$a_1=.46301\ 51$	$b_1=.24527\ 27$
$a_2=.10778\ 12$	$b_2=.04124\ 96$

17.3.36

$$E(m)=[1+a_1m_1+\ldots+a_4m_1^4]+[b_1m_1+\ldots+b_4m_1^4]\ln(1/m_1)+\epsilon(m)$$

$$|\epsilon(m)|<2\times10^{-8}$$

$a_1=.44325\ 141463$	$b_1=.24998\ 368310$
$a_2=.06260\ 601220$	$b_2=.09200\ 180037$
$a_3=.04757\ 383546$	$b_3=.04069\ 697526$
$a_4=.01736\ 506451$	$b_4=.00526\ 449639$

17.4. Incomplete Elliptic Integrals of the First and Second Kinds

Extension of the Tables

Negative Amplitude

17.4.1 $$F(-\varphi|m)=-F(\varphi|m)$$

17.4.2 $$E(-\varphi|m)=-E(\varphi|m)$$

Amplitude of Any Magnitude

17.4.3 $$F(s\pi\pm\varphi|m)=2sK\pm F(\varphi|m)$$

17.4.4 $$E(u+2K)=E(u)+2E$$

17.4.5 $$E(u+2iK')=E(u)+2i(K'-E')$$

17.4.6

$$E(u+2mK+2niK')=E(u)+2mE+2ni(K'-E')$$

17.4.7 $$E(K-u)=E-E(u)+m\,\mathrm{sn}\,u\,\mathrm{cd}\,u$$

Imaginary Amplitude

If $\tan\theta=\sinh\varphi$

17.4.8 $$F(i\varphi\backslash\alpha)=iF(\theta\backslash\tfrac{1}{2}\pi-\alpha)$$

17.4.9

$$E(i\varphi\backslash\alpha)=-iE(\theta\backslash\tfrac{1}{2}\pi-\alpha)+iF(\theta\backslash\tfrac{1}{2}\pi-\alpha)+i\tan\theta(1-\cos^2\alpha\sin^2\theta)^{\frac{1}{2}}$$

Jacobi's Imaginary Transformation

17.4.10

$$E(iu|m)=i[u+\mathrm{dn}(u|m_1)\mathrm{sc}(u|m_1)-E(u|m_1)]$$

Complex Amplitude

17.4.11 $$F(\varphi+i\psi|m)=F(\lambda|m)+iF(\mu|m_1)$$

where $\cot^2 \lambda$ is the positive root of the equation $x^2-[\cot^2 \varphi+m \sinh^2\psi \csc^2\varphi-m_1]x-m_1 \cot^2\varphi=0$ and $m \tan^2 \mu=\tan^2\varphi \cot^2\lambda-1$.

17.4.12

$$E(\varphi+i\psi\backslash\alpha)=E(\lambda\backslash\alpha)-iE(\mu\backslash 90^\circ-\alpha)+iF(\mu\backslash 90^\circ-\alpha)+\frac{b_1+ib_2}{b_3}$$

where

$$b_1=\sin^2 \alpha \sin \lambda \cos \lambda \sin^2 \mu(1-\sin^2 \alpha \sin^2 \lambda)^{\frac{1}{2}}$$

$$b_2=(1-\sin^2 \alpha \sin^2 \lambda)(1-\cos^2 \alpha \sin^2 \mu)^{\frac{1}{2}} \sin \mu \cos \mu$$

$$b_3=\cos^2 \mu+\sin^2 \alpha \sin^2 \lambda \sin^2 \mu$$

Amplitude Near to $\pi/2$ (see also 17.5)

If $\cos \alpha \tan \varphi \tan \psi=1$

17.4.13 $F(\varphi\backslash\alpha)+F(\psi\backslash\alpha)=F(\pi/2\backslash\alpha)=K$

17.4.14

$$E(\varphi\backslash\alpha)+E(\psi\backslash\alpha)=E(\pi/2\backslash\alpha)+\sin^2\alpha \sin\varphi \sin\psi$$

Values when φ is near to $\pi/2$ and m is near to unity can be calculated by these formulae.

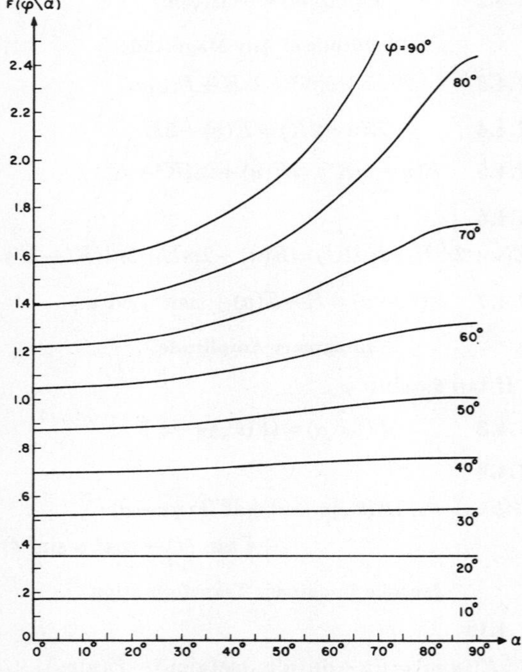

FIGURE 17.3. *Incomplete elliptic integral of the first kind.*

$F(\varphi\backslash\alpha)$, φ constant

Parameter Greater Than Unity

17.4.15 $F(\varphi|m)=m^{-\frac{1}{2}}F(\theta|m^{-1}),\ \sin\theta=m^{\frac{1}{2}}\sin\varphi$

17.4.16 $E(u|m)=m^{\frac{1}{2}}E(um^{\frac{1}{2}}|m^{-1})-(m-1)u$

by which a parameter greater than unity can be replaced by a parameter less than unity.

Negative Parameter

17.4.17

$$F(\varphi|-m)=(1+m)^{-\frac{1}{2}}K(m(1+m)^{-1})-(1+m)^{-\frac{1}{2}}F\left(\frac{\pi}{2}-\varphi\,|\,m(1+m)^{-1}\right)$$

17.4.18

$$E(u|-m)=(1+m)^{\frac{1}{2}}\{E(u(1+m)^{\frac{1}{2}}|m(m+1)^{-1})-m(1+m)^{-\frac{1}{2}}\mathrm{sn}(u(1+m)^{\frac{1}{2}}|m(1+m)^{-1})\,\mathrm{cd}(u(1+m)^{\frac{1}{2}}|m(1+m)^{-1})\}$$

whereby computations can be made for negative parameters, and therefore for pure imaginary modulus.

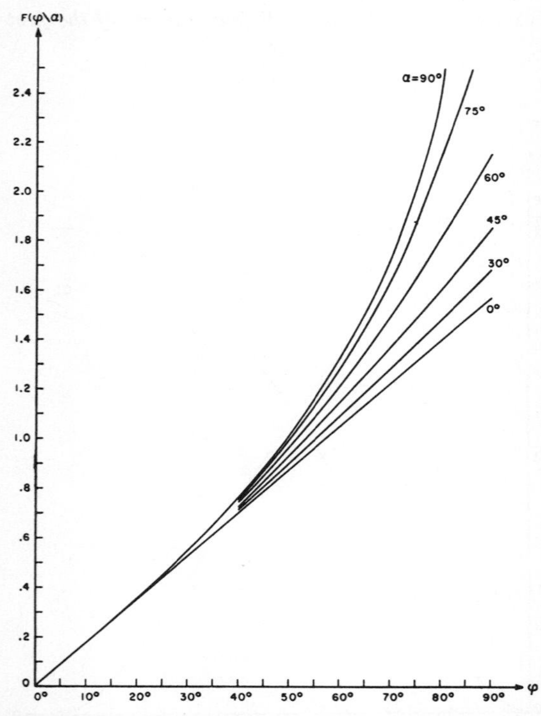

FIGURE 17.4. *Incomplete elliptic integral of the first kind.*

$F(\varphi\backslash\alpha)$, α constant

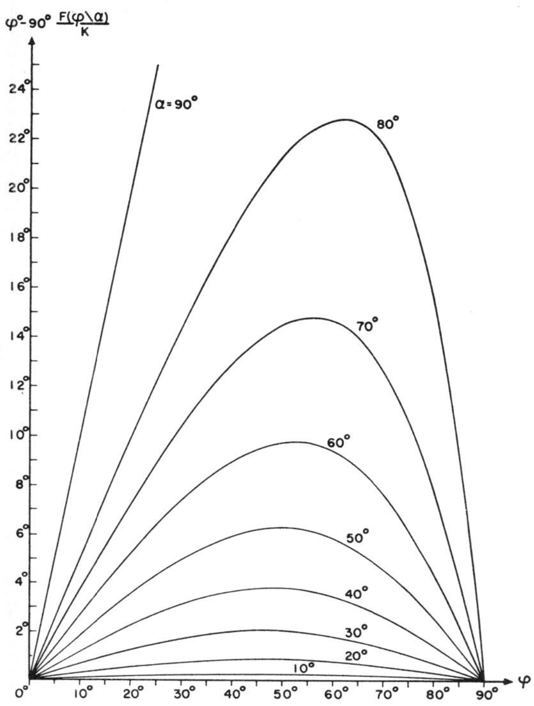

FIGURE 17.5. $\varphi - 90° \dfrac{F(\varphi\backslash\alpha)}{K}$, *α constant.*

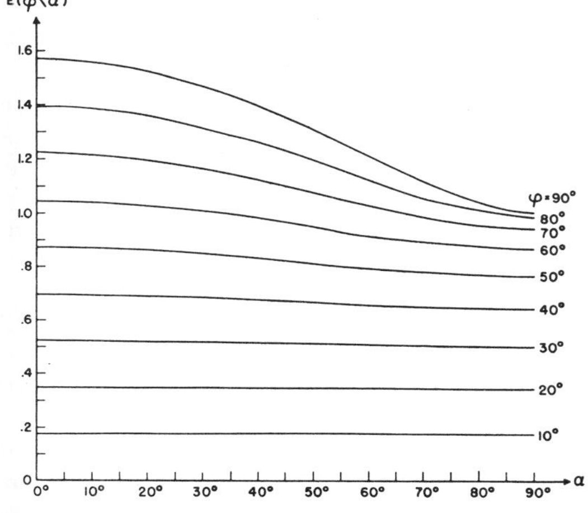

FIGURE 17.6. *Incomplete elliptic integral of the second kind.*

$E(\varphi\backslash\alpha)$, φ constant

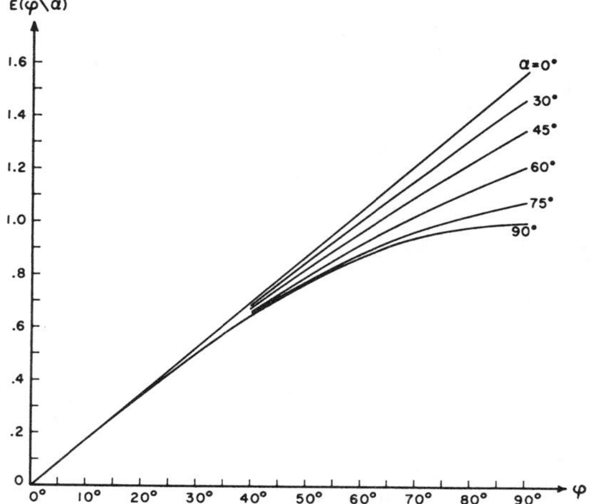

FIGURE 17.7. *Incomplete elliptic integral of the second kind.*

$E(\varphi\backslash\alpha)$, α constant

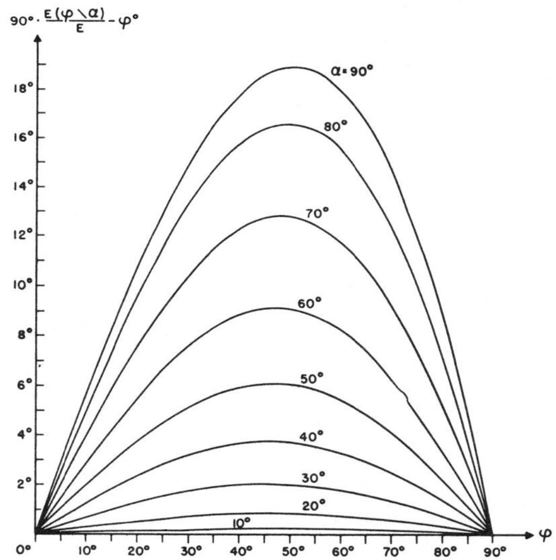

FIGURE 17.8. $90° \dfrac{E(\varphi\backslash\alpha)}{E} - \varphi$, *α constant.*

Special Cases

17.4.19 $$F(\varphi\backslash 0)=\varphi$$

17.4.20 $$F(i\varphi\backslash 0)=i\varphi$$

17.4.21

$$F(\varphi\backslash 90°)=\ln\,(\sec\varphi+\tan\varphi)=\ln\tan\left(\frac{\pi}{4}+\frac{\varphi}{2}\right)$$

17.4.22 $$F(i\varphi\backslash 90°)=i\arctan\,(\sinh\varphi)$$

17.4.23 $$E(\varphi\backslash 0)=\varphi$$

17.4.24 $$E(i\varphi\backslash 0)=i\varphi$$

17.4.25 $$E(\varphi\backslash 90°)=\sin\varphi$$

17.4.26 $$E(i\varphi\backslash 90°)=i\sinh\varphi$$

Jacobi's Zeta Function

17.4.27 $Z(\varphi\backslash\alpha)=E(\varphi\backslash\alpha)-E(\alpha)F(\varphi\backslash\alpha)/K(\alpha)$

17.4.28 $Z(u|m)=Z(u)=E(u)-uE(m)/K(m)$

17.4.29 $Z(-u)=-Z(u)$

17.4.30 $Z(u+2K)=Z(u)$

17.4.31 $Z(K-u)=-Z(K+u)$

17.4.32 $Z(u)=Z(u-K)-m\,\mathrm{sn}(u-K)\mathrm{cd}(u-K)$

Special Values

17.4.33 $Z(u|0)=0$

17.4.34 $Z(u|1)=\tanh u$

Addition Theorem

17.4.35

$$Z(u+v)=Z(u)+Z(v)-m\,\mathrm{sn}\,u\,\mathrm{sn}\,v\,\mathrm{sn}(u+v)$$

Jacobi's Imaginary Transformation

17.4.36

$$iZ(iu|m)=Z(u|m_1)+\frac{\pi u}{2KK'}-\mathrm{dn}(u|m_1)\mathrm{sc}(u|m_1)$$

Relation to Jacobi's Theta Function

17.4.37 $Z(u)=\Theta'(u)/\Theta(u)=\frac{d}{du}\ln\Theta(u)$

q-Series

17.4.38 $Z(u)=\frac{2\pi}{K}\sum_{s=1}^{\infty}q^s(1-q^{2s})^{-1}\sin(\pi su/K)$

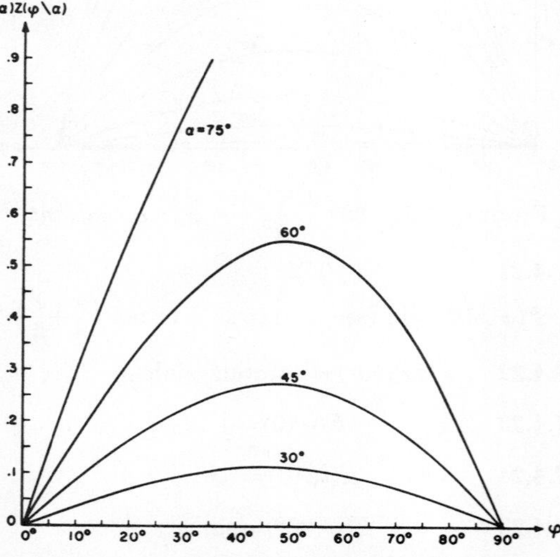

FIGURE 17.9. *Jacobian zeta function* $K(\alpha)Z(\varphi\backslash\alpha)$.

Heuman's Lambda Function

17.4.39

$$\Lambda_0(\varphi\backslash\alpha)=\frac{F(\varphi\backslash 90^\circ-\alpha)}{K'(\alpha)}+\frac{2}{\pi}K(\alpha)Z(\varphi\backslash 90^\circ-\alpha)$$

17.4.40

$$=\frac{2}{\pi}\{K(\alpha)E(\varphi\backslash 90^\circ-\alpha)-[K(\alpha)-E(\alpha)]F(\varphi\backslash 90^\circ-\alpha)\}$$

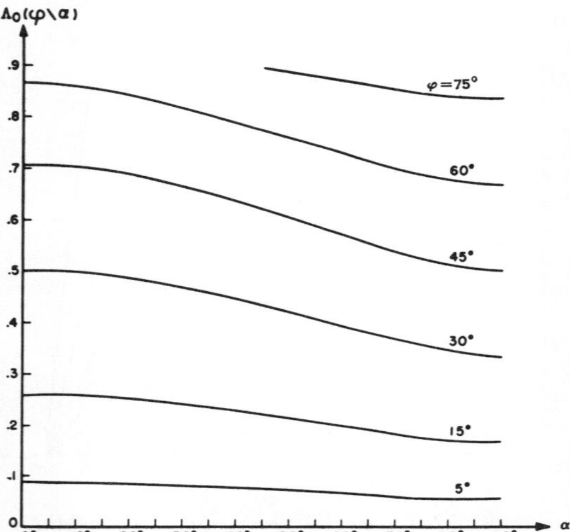

FIGURE 17.10. *Heuman's lambda function* $\Lambda_0(\varphi\backslash\alpha)$.

Numerical Evaluation of Incomplete Integrals of the First and Second Kinds

For the numerical evaluation of an elliptic integral the quartic (or cubic [4]) under the radical should first be expressed in terms of t^2, see **Examples 1 and 2.** In the resulting quartic there are only six possible sign patterns or combinations of the factors namely

$$(t^2+a^2)(t^2+b^2),\quad (a^2-t^2)(t^2-b^2),$$
$$(a^2-t^2)(b^2-t^2),\quad (t^2-a^2)(t^2-b^2),\quad (t^2+a^2)(t^2-b^2),$$
$$(t^2+a^2)(b^2-t^2).$$

The list which follows is then exhaustive for integrals which reduce to $F(\varphi\backslash\alpha)$ or $E(\varphi\backslash\alpha)$.

The value of the elliptic integral of the first kind is also expressed as an *inverse* Jacobian elliptic function. Here, for example, the notation $u=\mathrm{sn}^{-1}x$ means that $x=\mathrm{sn}\,u$.

The column headed "t substitution" gives the Jacobian elliptic function substitution which is appropriate to reduce every elliptic integral which contains the given quartic.

[4] For an alternate treatment of cubics see **17.4.61** and **17.4.70.**

	$F(\varphi\backslash\alpha)$	Equivalent Inverse Jacobian Elliptic Function	φ	t Substitution	$E(\varphi\backslash\alpha)$
$\cos\alpha=b/a$ $a>b$ $m=(a^2-b^2)/a^2$	**17.4.41** $a\int_0^x\frac{dt}{[(t^2+a^2)(t^2+b^2)]^{1/2}}$	$\mathrm{sc}^{-1}\left(\frac{x}{b}\middle\vert\frac{a^2-b^2}{a^2}\right)$	$\tan\varphi=\frac{x}{b}$	$t=b\ \mathrm{sc}\ v$	$\frac{b^2}{a}\int_0^x\left(\frac{t^2+a^2}{t^2+b^2}\right)\frac{dt}{[(t^2+a^2)(t^2+b^2)]^{1/2}}$
	17.4.42 $a\int_x^\infty\frac{dt}{[(t^2+a^2)(t^2+b^2)]^{1/2}}$	$\mathrm{cs}^{-1}\left(\frac{x}{a}\middle\vert\frac{a^2-b^2}{a^2}\right)$	$\tan\varphi=\frac{a}{x}$	$t=a\ \mathrm{cs}\ v$	$a\int_x^\infty\left(\frac{t^2+b^2}{t^2+a^2}\right)\frac{dt}{[(t^2+a^2)(t^2+b^2)]^{1/2}}$
	17.4.43 $a\int_b^x\frac{dt}{[(a^2-t^2)(t^2-b^2)]^{1/2}}$	$\mathrm{nd}^{-1}\left(\frac{x}{b}\middle\vert\frac{a^2-b^2}{a^2}\right)$	$\sin^2\varphi=\frac{a^2(x^2-b^2)}{x^2(a^2-b^2)}$	$t=b\ \mathrm{nd}\ v$	$ab^2\int_b^x\frac{1}{t^2}\frac{dt}{[(a^2-t^2)(t^2-b^2)]^{1/2}}$
	17.4.44 $a\int_x^a\frac{dt}{[(a^2-t^2)(t^2-b^2)]^{1/2}}$	$\mathrm{dn}^{-1}\left(\frac{x}{a}\middle\vert\frac{a^2-b^2}{a^2}\right)$	$\sin^2\varphi=\frac{a^2-x^2}{a^2-b^2}$	$t=a\ \mathrm{dn}\ v$	$\frac{1}{a}\int_x^a\frac{t^2dt}{[(a^2-t^2)(t^2-b^2)]^{1/2}}$
$\sin\alpha=b/a$ $a>b$ $m=b^2/a^2$	**17.4.45** $a\int_0^x\frac{dt}{[(a^2-t^2)(b^2-t^2)]^{1/2}}$	$\mathrm{sn}^{-1}\left(\frac{x}{b}\middle\vert\frac{b^2}{a^2}\right)$	$\sin\varphi=\frac{x}{b}$	$t=b\ \mathrm{sn}\ v$	$\frac{1}{a}\int_0^x\frac{(a^2-t^2)dt}{[(a^2-t^2)(b^2-t^2)]^{1/2}}$
	17.4.46 $a\int_x^b\frac{dt}{[(a^2-t^2)(b^2-t^2)]^{1/2}}$	$\mathrm{cd}^{-1}\left(\frac{x}{b}\middle\vert\frac{b^2}{a^2}\right)$	$\sin^2\varphi=\frac{a^2(b^2-x^2)}{b^2(a^2-x^2)}$	$t=b\ \mathrm{cd}\ v$	$a(a^2-b^2)\int_x^b\left(\frac{1}{a^2-t^2}\right)\frac{dt}{[(a^2-t^2)(b^2-t^2)]^{1/2}}$
	17.4.47 $a\int_a^x\frac{dt}{[(t^2-a^2)(t^2-b^2)]^{1/2}}$	$\mathrm{dc}^{-1}\left(\frac{x}{a}\middle\vert\frac{b^2}{a^2}\right)$	$\sin^2\varphi=\frac{x^2-a^2}{x^2-b^2}$	$t=a\ \mathrm{dc}\ v$	$\frac{a^2-b^2}{a}\int_a^x\left(\frac{t^2}{t^2-b^2}\right)\frac{dt}{[(t^2-a^2)(t^2-b^2)]^{1/2}}$
	17.4.48 $a\int_x^\infty\frac{dt}{[(t^2-a^2)(t^2-b^2)]^{1/2}}$	$\mathrm{ns}^{-1}\left(\frac{x}{a}\middle\vert\frac{b^2}{a^2}\right)$	$\sin\varphi=\frac{a}{x}$	$t=a\ \mathrm{ns}\ v$	$a\int_x^\infty\left(\frac{t^2-b^2}{t^2}\right)\frac{dt}{[(t^2-a^2)(t^2-b^2)]^{1/2}}$
$\cot\alpha=\frac{b}{a}$ $m=a^2/(a^2+b^2)$	**17.4.49** $(a^2+b^2)^{1/2}\int_b^x\frac{dt}{[(t^2+a^2)(t^2-b^2)]^{1/2}}$	$\mathrm{nc}^{-1}\left(\frac{x}{b}\middle\vert\frac{a^2}{a^2+b^2}\right)$	$\cos\varphi=\frac{b}{x}$	$t=b\ \mathrm{nc}\ v$	$\frac{b^2}{(a^2+b^2)^{1/2}}\int_b^x\frac{t^2+a^2}{t^2}\frac{dt}{[(t^2+a^2)(t^2-b^2)]^{1/2}}$
	17.4.50 $(a^2+b^2)^{1/2}\int_x^\infty\frac{dt}{[(t^2+a^2)(t^2-b^2)]^{1/2}}$	$\mathrm{ds}^{-1}\left(\frac{x}{(a^2+b^2)^{1/2}}\middle\vert\frac{a^2}{a^2+b^2}\right)$	$\sin^2\varphi=\frac{a^2+b^2}{a^2+x^2}$	$t=(a^2+b^2)^{1/2}\,\mathrm{ds}\,v$	$(a^2+b^2)^{1/2}\int_x^\infty\frac{t^2}{(t^2+a^2)}\frac{dt}{[(t^2+a^2)(t^2-b^2)]^{1/2}}$
$\tan\alpha=\frac{b}{a}$ $m=b^2/(a^2+b^2)$	**17.4.51** $(a^2+b^2)^{1/2}\int_0^x\frac{dt}{[(t^2+a^2)(b^2-t^2)]^{1/2}}$	$\mathrm{sd}^{-1}\left(\frac{x(a^2+b^2)^{1/2}}{ab}\middle\vert\frac{b^2}{a^2+b^2}\right)$	$\sin^2\varphi=\frac{x^2(a^2+b^2)}{b^2(a^2+x^2)}$	$t=\frac{ab}{(a^2+b^2)^{1/2}}\,\mathrm{sd}\,v$	$a^2(a^2+b^2)^{1/2}\int_0^x\frac{1}{(t^2+a^2)}\frac{dt}{[(t^2+a^2)(b^2-t^2)]^{1/2}}$
	17.4.52 $(a^2+b^2)^{1/2}\int_x^b\frac{dt}{[(t^2+a^2)(b^2-t^2)]^{1/2}}$	$\mathrm{cn}^{-1}\left(\frac{x}{b}\middle\vert\frac{b^2}{a^2+b^2}\right)$	$\cos\varphi=\frac{x}{b}$	$t=b\ \mathrm{cn}\ v$	$\frac{1}{(a^2+b^2)^{1/2}}\int_x^b\frac{(t^2+a^2)dt}{[(t^2+a^2)(b^2-t^2)]^{1/2}}$

Some Important Special Cases

$\frac{1}{2}F(\varphi\backslash\alpha)$	$\cos\varphi$	α
17.4.53 $\int_x^\infty \frac{dt}{(1+t^4)^{\frac{1}{2}}}$	$\frac{x^2-1}{x^2+1}$	45°
17.4.54 $\int_0^x \frac{dt}{(1+t^4)^{\frac{1}{2}}}$	$\frac{1-x^2}{1+x^2}$	45°
17.4.55 $\frac{1}{2^{\frac{1}{2}}}\int_1^x \frac{dt}{(t^4-1)^{\frac{1}{2}}}$	$\frac{1}{x}$	45°
17.4.56 $\frac{1}{2^{\frac{1}{2}}}\int_x^1 \frac{dt}{(1-t^4)^{\frac{1}{2}}}$	x	45°

$\frac{1}{3^{1/4}}F(\varphi\backslash\alpha)$	$\cos\varphi$	α
17.4.57 $\int_x^\infty \frac{dt}{(t^3-1)^{\frac{1}{2}}}$	$\frac{x-1-\sqrt{3}}{x-1+\sqrt{3}}$	15°
17.4.58 $\int_1^x \frac{dt}{(t^3-1)^{\frac{1}{2}}}$	$\frac{\sqrt{3}+1-x}{\sqrt{3}-1+x}$	15°
17.4.59 $\int_x^1 \frac{dt}{(1-t^3)^{\frac{1}{2}}}$	$\frac{\sqrt{3}-1+x}{\sqrt{3}+1-x}$	75°
17.4.60 $\int_{-\infty}^x \frac{dt}{(1-t^3)^{\frac{1}{2}}}$	$\frac{1-\sqrt{3}-x}{1+\sqrt{3}-x}$	75°

Reduction of $\int dt/\sqrt{P}$ where $P=P(t)$ is a cubic polynomial with three real factors $P=(t-\beta_1)(t-\beta_2)(t-\beta_3)$ where $\beta_1>\beta_2>\beta_3$. Write

17.4.61

$$\lambda=\frac{1}{2}(\beta_1-\beta_3)^{1/2},\ m=\sin^2\alpha=\frac{\beta_2-\beta_3}{\beta_1-\beta_3},$$

$$m_1=\cos^2\alpha=\frac{\beta_1-\beta_2}{\beta_1-\beta_3}$$

17.4.62 $\lambda\int_{\beta_3}^x \frac{dt}{\sqrt{P}}$	$F(\varphi\backslash\alpha)$	$\sin^2\varphi=\frac{x-\beta_3}{\beta_2-\beta_3}$
17.4.63 $\lambda\int_x^{\beta_2} \frac{dt}{\sqrt{P}}$	$F(\varphi\backslash\alpha)$	$\cos^2\varphi=\frac{(\beta_1-\beta_2)(x-\beta_3)}{(\beta_2-\beta_3)(\beta_1-x)}$
17.4.64 $\lambda\int_{\beta_1}^x \frac{dt}{\sqrt{P}}$	$F(\varphi\backslash\alpha)$	$\sin^2\varphi=\frac{x-\beta_1}{x-\beta_2}$
17.4.65 $\lambda\int_x^\infty \frac{dt}{\sqrt{P}}$	$F(\varphi\backslash\alpha)$	$\cos^2\varphi=\frac{x-\beta_1}{x-\beta_3}$
17.4.66 $\lambda\int_{-\infty}^x \frac{dt}{\sqrt{-P}}$	$F(\varphi\backslash(90°-\alpha°))$	$\sin^2\varphi=\frac{\beta_1-\beta_3}{\beta_1-x}$
17.4.67 $\lambda\int_x^{\beta_3} \frac{dt}{\sqrt{-P}}$	$F(\varphi\backslash(90°-\alpha°))$	$\cos^2\varphi=\frac{\beta_2-\beta_3}{\beta_2-x}$
17.4.68 $\lambda\int_{\beta_2}^x \frac{dt}{\sqrt{-P}}$	$F(\varphi\backslash(90°-\alpha°))$	$\sin^2\varphi=\frac{(\beta_1-\beta_3)(x-\beta_2)}{(\beta_1-\beta_2)(x-\beta_3)}$
17.4.69 $\lambda\int_x^{\beta_1} \frac{dt}{\sqrt{-P}}$	$F(\varphi\backslash(90°-\alpha°))$	$\cos^2\varphi=\frac{x-\beta_2}{\beta_1-\beta_2}$

Reduction of $\int dt/\sqrt{P}$ when $P=P(t)=t^3+a_1t^2+a_2t+a_3$ is a cubic polynomial with only one real root $t=\beta$. We form the first and second derivatives $P'(t)$, $P''(t)$ with respect to t and then write

17.4.70 $\lambda^2=[P'(\beta)]^{1/2},\ m=\sin^2\alpha=\frac{1}{2}-\frac{1}{8}\frac{P''(\beta)}{[P'(\beta)]^{1/2}}$

17.4.71 $\lambda\int_\beta^x \frac{dt}{\sqrt{P}}$	$F(\varphi\backslash\alpha)$	$\cos\varphi=\frac{\lambda^2-(x-\beta)}{\lambda^2+(x-\beta)}$
17.4.72 $\lambda\int_x^\infty \frac{dt}{\sqrt{P}}$	$F(\varphi\backslash\alpha)$	$\cos\varphi=\frac{(x-\beta)-\lambda^2}{(x-\beta)+\lambda^2}$
17.4.73 $\lambda\int_{-\infty}^x \frac{dt}{\sqrt{(-P)}}$	$F(\varphi\backslash(90°-\alpha°))$	$\cos\varphi=\frac{(\beta-x)-\lambda^2}{(\beta-x)+\lambda^2}$
17.4.74 $\lambda\int_x^\beta \frac{dt}{\sqrt{(-P)}}$	$F(\varphi\backslash(90°-\alpha°))$	$\cos\varphi=\frac{\lambda^2-(\beta-x)}{\lambda^2+(\beta-x)}$

17.5. Landen's Transformation

Descending Landen Transformation [5]

Let α_n, α_{n+1} be two modular angles such that

17.5.1 $(1+\sin\alpha_{n+1})(1+\cos\alpha_n)=2 \qquad (\alpha_{n+1}<\alpha_n)$

and let φ_n, φ_{n+1} be two corresponding amplitudes such that

17.5.2 $\tan(\varphi_{n+1}-\varphi_n)=\cos\alpha_n\tan\varphi_n \qquad (\varphi_{n+1}>\varphi_n)$

[5] The emphasis here is on the modular angle since this is an argument of the Tables. All formulae concerning Landen's transformation may also be expressed in terms of the modulus $k=m^{\frac{1}{2}}=\sin\alpha$ and its complement $k'=m_1^{\frac{1}{2}}=\cos\alpha$.

Thus the step from n to $n+1$ decreases the modular angle but increases the amplitude. By iterating the process we can descend from a given modular angle to one whose magnitude is negligible, when **17.4.19** becomes applicable.

With $\alpha_0=\alpha$ we have

17.5.3

$$F(\varphi\backslash\alpha)=(1+\cos\alpha)^{-1}F(\varphi_1\backslash\alpha_1)=\tfrac{1}{2}(1+\sin\alpha_1)F(\varphi_1\backslash\alpha_1)$$

17.5.4 $$F(\varphi\backslash\alpha)=2^{-n}\prod_{s=1}^{n}(1+\sin\alpha_s)F(\varphi_n\backslash\alpha_n)$$

17.5.5 $$F(\varphi\backslash\alpha)=\Phi\prod_{s=1}^{\infty}(1+\sin\alpha_s)$$

17.5.6 $$\Phi=\lim_{n\to\infty}\frac{1}{2^n}F(\varphi_n\backslash\alpha_n)=\lim_{n\to\infty}\frac{\varphi_n}{2^n}$$

17.5.7 $$K=F(\tfrac{1}{2}\pi\backslash\alpha)=\tfrac{1}{2}\pi\prod_{s=1}^{\infty}(1+\sin\alpha_s)$$

17.5.8 $$F(\varphi\backslash\alpha)=2\pi^{-1}K\Phi$$

17.5.9

$$E(\varphi\backslash\alpha)=F(\varphi\backslash\alpha)\left[1-\frac{1}{2}\sin^2\alpha\left(1+\frac{1}{2}\sin\alpha_1+\frac{1}{2^2}\sin\alpha_1\sin\alpha_2+\dots\right)\right]+\sin\alpha\left[\frac{1}{2}(\sin\alpha_1)^{1/2}\sin\varphi_1+\frac{1}{2^2}(\sin\alpha_1\sin\alpha_2)^{1/2}\sin\varphi_2+\dots\right]$$

17.5.10

$$E=K\left[1-\frac{1}{2}\sin^2\alpha\left(1+\frac{1}{2}\sin\alpha_1+\frac{1}{2^2}\sin\alpha_1\sin\alpha_2+\frac{1}{2^3}\sin\alpha_1\sin\alpha_2\sin\alpha_3+\dots\right)\right]$$

Ascending Landen Transformation

Let α_n, α_{n+1} be two modular angles such that

17.5.11 $$(1+\sin\alpha_n)(1+\cos\alpha_{n+1})=2\qquad(\alpha_{n+1}>\alpha_n)$$

and let φ_n, φ_{n+1} be two corresponding amplitudes such that

17.5.12 $$\sin(2\varphi_{n+1}-\varphi_n)=\sin\alpha_n\sin\varphi_n\qquad(\varphi_{n+1}<\varphi_n)$$

Thus the step from n to $n+1$ increases the modular angle but decreases the amplitude. By iterating the process we can ascend from a given modular angle to one whose difference from a right angle is so small that **17.4.21** becomes applicable.

With $\alpha_0=\alpha$ we have

17.5.13 $$F(\varphi\backslash\alpha)=2(1+\sin\alpha)^{-1}F(\varphi_1\backslash\alpha_1)$$

17.5.14 $$F(\varphi\backslash\alpha)=2^n\prod_{s=0}^{n-1}(1+\sin\alpha_s)^{-1}F(\varphi_n\backslash\alpha_n)$$

17.5.15 $$F(\varphi\backslash\alpha)=\prod_{s=1}^{n}(1+\cos\alpha_s)F(\varphi_n\backslash\alpha_n)$$

17.5.16 $$F(\varphi\backslash\alpha)=[\csc\alpha\prod_{s=1}^{\infty}\sin\alpha_s]^{\frac{1}{2}}\ln\tan(\tfrac{1}{4}\pi+\tfrac{1}{2}\Phi)$$

17.5.17 $$\Phi=\lim_{n\to\infty}\varphi_n$$

Neighborhood of a Right Angle (see also 17.4.13)

When both φ and α are near to a right angle, interpolation in the table $F(\varphi\backslash\alpha)$ is difficult. Either Landen's transformation can then be used with advantage to increase the modular angle and decrease the amplitude or vice-versa.

17.6. The Process of the Arithmetic-Geometric Mean

Starting with a given number triple (a_0, b_0, c_0) we proceed to determine number triples $(a_1, b_1, c_1,)$, (a_2, b_2, c_2), . . ., (a_N, b_N, c_N) according to the following scheme of arithmetic and geometric means

17.6.1

$$\begin{array}{ll} a_0 & b_0 \\ a_1=\tfrac{1}{2}(a_0+b_0) & b_1=(a_0b_0)^{\frac{1}{2}} \\ a_2=\tfrac{1}{2}(a_1+b_1) & b_2=(a_1b_1)^{\frac{1}{2}} \\ \vdots & \vdots \\ a_N=\tfrac{1}{2}(a_{N-1}+b_{N-1}) & b_N=(a_{N-1}b_{N-1})^{\frac{1}{2}} \end{array}$$

$$\begin{array}{l} c_0 \\ c_1=\tfrac{1}{2}(a_0-b_0) \\ c_2=\tfrac{1}{2}(a_1-b_1) \\ \vdots \\ c_N=\tfrac{1}{2}(a_{N-1}-b_{N-1}). \end{array}$$

We stop at the Nth step when $a_N=b_N$, i.e., when $c_N=0$ to the degree of accuracy to which the numbers are required.

To determine the complete elliptic integrals $K(\alpha)$, $E(\alpha)$ we start with

17.6.2 $$a_0=1,\ b_0=\cos\alpha,\ c_0=\sin\alpha$$

whence

17.6.3 $$K(\alpha)=\frac{\pi}{2a_N}$$

17.6.4 $$\frac{K(\alpha)-E(\alpha)}{K(\alpha)}=\frac{1}{2}\,[c_0^2+2c_1^2+2^2c_2^2+\ldots+2^Nc_N^2]$$

To determine $K'(\alpha)$, $E'(\alpha)$ we start with

17.6.5 $$a_0'=1,\ b_0'=\sin\alpha,\ c_0'=\cos\alpha$$

whence

17.6.6 $$K'(\alpha)=\frac{\pi}{2a_N'}$$

17.6.7

$$\frac{K'(\alpha)-E'(\alpha)}{K'(\alpha)}=\frac{1}{2}\,[c_0'^2+2c_1'^2+2^2c_2'^2+\ldots+2^Nc_N'^2]$$

To calculate $F(\varphi\backslash\alpha)$, $E(\varphi\backslash\alpha)$ start from **17.5.2** which corresponds to the descending Landen transformation and determine $\varphi_1,\ \varphi_2,\ \ldots,\ \varphi_N$ successively from the relation

17.6.8 $$\tan(\varphi_{n+1}-\varphi_n)=(b_n/a_n)\tan\varphi_n,\ \varphi_0=\varphi$$

Then to the prescribed accuracy

17.6.9 $$F(\varphi\backslash\alpha)=\varphi_N/(2^Na_N)$$

17.6.10

$$Z(\varphi\backslash\alpha)=E(\varphi\backslash\alpha)-(E/K)F(\varphi\backslash\alpha)$$
$$=c_1\sin\varphi_1+c_2\sin\varphi_2+\ldots+c_N\sin\varphi_N$$

17.7. Elliptic Integrals of the Third Kind

17.7.1

$$\Pi(n;\varphi\backslash\alpha)=\int_0^\varphi(1-n\sin^2\theta)^{-1}(1-\sin^2\alpha\sin^2\theta)^{-\frac{1}{2}}d\theta$$

17.7.2 $$\Pi(n;\tfrac{1}{2}\pi\backslash\alpha)=\Pi(n\backslash\alpha)$$

Case (i) Hyperbolic Case $0<n<\sin^2\alpha$

$$\epsilon=\arcsin(n/\sin^2\alpha)^{\frac{1}{2}},\qquad 0\le\epsilon\le\tfrac{1}{2}\pi$$

$$\beta=\tfrac{1}{2}\pi F(\epsilon\backslash\alpha)/K(\alpha)$$

$$q=q(\alpha)$$

$$v=\tfrac{1}{2}\pi F(\varphi\backslash\alpha)/K(\alpha),$$

$$\delta_1=[n(1-n)^{-1}(\sin^2\alpha-n)^{-1}]^{\frac{1}{2}}$$

17.7.3

$$\Pi(n;\varphi\backslash\alpha)=\delta_1\,[-\tfrac{1}{2}\ln[\vartheta_4(v+\beta)/\vartheta_4(v-\beta)]$$
$$+v\vartheta_1'(\beta)/\vartheta_1(\beta)]$$

17.7.4

$$\tfrac{1}{2}\ln\frac{\vartheta_4(v+\beta)}{\vartheta_4(v-\beta)}=2\sum_{s=1}^\infty s^{-1}q^s(1-q^{2s})^{-1}\sin 2sv\sin 2s\beta$$

17.7.5

$$\frac{\vartheta_1'(\beta)}{\vartheta_1(\beta)}=\cot\beta+4\sum_{s=1}^\infty q^{2s}(1-2q^{2s}\cos 2\beta+q^{4s})^{-1}\sin 2\beta$$

In the above we can also use Neville's theta functions **16.36.**

17.7.6 $$\Pi(n\backslash\alpha)=K(\alpha)+\delta_1K(\alpha)Z(\epsilon\backslash\alpha)$$

Case (ii) Hyperbolic Case $n>1$

The case $n>1$ can be reduced to the case $0<N<\sin^2\alpha$ by writing

17.7.7 $$N=n^{-1}\sin^2\alpha,\ p_1=[(n-1)(1-n^{-1}\sin^2\alpha)]^{\frac{1}{2}}$$

17.7.8

$$\Pi(n;\varphi\backslash\alpha)=-\Pi(N;\varphi\backslash\alpha)+F(\varphi\backslash\alpha)$$
$$+\frac{1}{2p_1}\ln[(\Delta(\varphi)+p_1\tan\varphi)(\Delta(\varphi)-p_1\tan\varphi)^{-1}]$$

where $\Delta(\varphi)$ is the delta amplitude, **17.2.4.**

17.7.9 $$\Pi(n\backslash\alpha)=K(\alpha)-\Pi(N\backslash\alpha)$$

Case (iii) Circular Case $\sin^2\alpha<n<1$

$$\epsilon=\arcsin[(1-n)/\cos^2\alpha]^{\frac{1}{2}}\qquad 0\le\epsilon\le\tfrac{1}{2}\pi$$

$$\beta=\tfrac{1}{2}\pi F(\epsilon\backslash 90^\circ-\alpha)/K(\alpha)$$

$$q=q(\alpha)$$

17.7.10

$$v=\tfrac{1}{2}\pi F(\varphi\backslash\alpha)/K(\alpha),\ \delta_2=[n(1-n)^{-1}(n-\sin^2\alpha)^{-1}]^{\frac{1}{2}}$$

17.7.11 $$\Pi(n;\varphi\backslash\alpha)=\delta_2(\lambda-4\mu v)$$

17.7.12

$$\lambda=\arctan(\tanh\beta\tan v)$$
$$+2\sum_{s=1}^\infty(-1)^{s-1}s^{-1}q^{2s}(1-q^{2s})^{-1}\sin 2sv\sinh 2s\beta$$

17.7.13

$$\mu=\left[\sum_{s=1}^\infty sq^{s^2}\sinh 2s\beta\right]\left[1+2\sum_{s=1}^\infty q^{s^2}\cosh 2s\beta\right]^{-1}$$

17.7.14 $$\Pi(n\backslash\alpha)=K(\alpha)+\tfrac{1}{2}\pi\delta_2[1-\Lambda_0(\epsilon\backslash\alpha)]$$

where Λ_0 is Heuman's Lambda function, **17.4.39.**

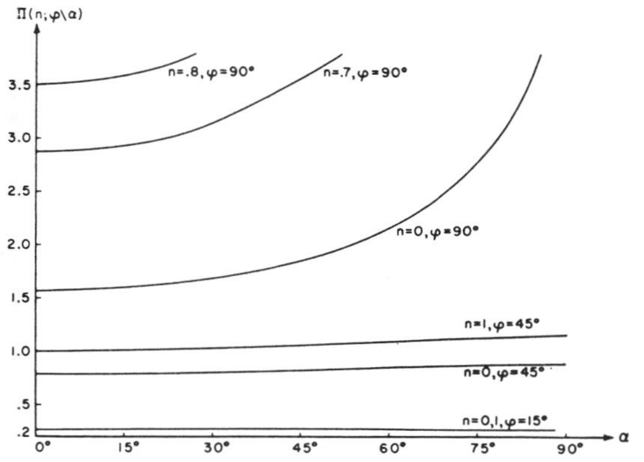

FIGURE 17.11. *Elliptic integral of the third kind* $\Pi(n;\varphi\backslash\alpha)$.

Case (iv) Circular Case $n<0$

The case $n<0$ can be reduced to the case $\sin^2\alpha<N<1$ by writing

17.7.15

$$N=(\sin^2\alpha-n)(1-n)^{-1}$$

$$p_2=[-n(1-n)^{-1}(\sin^2\alpha-n)]^{\frac{1}{2}}$$

17.7.16

$$[(1-n)(1-n^{-1}\sin^2\alpha)]^{\frac{1}{2}}\Pi(n;\varphi\backslash\alpha)$$
$$=[(1-N)(1-N^{-1}\sin^2\alpha)]^{\frac{1}{2}}\Pi(N;\varphi\backslash\alpha)$$
$$+p_2^{-1}\sin^2\alpha F(\varphi\backslash\alpha)+\arctan\,[\tfrac{1}{2}p_2\sin 2\varphi/\Delta(\varphi)]$$

17.7.17

$$\Pi(n\backslash\alpha)=(-n\cos^2\alpha)(1-n)^{-1}(\sin^2\alpha-n)^{-1}\Pi(N\backslash\alpha)$$
$$+\sin^2\alpha(\sin^2\alpha-n)^{-1}K(\alpha)$$

Special Cases

17.7.18 $n=0$

$$\Pi(0;\varphi\backslash\alpha)=F(\varphi\backslash\alpha)$$

17.7.19 $n=0,\ \alpha=0$

$$\Pi(0;\varphi\backslash 0)=\varphi$$

17.7.20 $\alpha=0$

$$\Pi(n;\varphi\backslash 0)=(1-n)^{-\frac{1}{2}}\arctan\,[(1-n)^{\frac{1}{2}}\tan\varphi],\qquad n<1$$
$$=(n-1)^{-\frac{1}{2}}\operatorname{arctanh}\,[(n-1)^{\frac{1}{2}}\tan\varphi],\qquad n>1$$
$$=\tan\varphi\qquad n=1$$

17.7.21 $\alpha=\pi/2$

$$\Pi(n;\varphi\backslash\pi/2)=(1-n)^{-1}[\ln\,(\tan\varphi+\sec\varphi)$$
$$-\tfrac{1}{2}n^{\frac{1}{2}}\ln\,(1+n^{\frac{1}{2}}\sin\varphi)(1-n^{\frac{1}{2}}\sin\varphi)^{-1}]\qquad n\neq 1$$

17.7.22 $n=\pm\sin\alpha$

$$(1\mp\sin\alpha)\{2\Pi(\pm\sin\alpha;\varphi\backslash\alpha)-F(\varphi\backslash\alpha)\}$$
$$=\arctan\,[(1\mp\sin\alpha)\tan\varphi/\Delta(\varphi)]$$

17.7.23 $n=1\pm\cos\alpha$

$$2\cos\alpha\Pi(1\pm\cos\alpha;\varphi\backslash\alpha)=\pm\tfrac{1}{2}\ln\,[(1+\tan\varphi$$
$$\cdot\Delta(\varphi))(1-\tan\varphi\cdot\Delta(\varphi))^{-1}]+\tfrac{1}{2}\ln\,[(\Delta(\varphi)$$
$$+\cos\alpha\cdot\tan\varphi)(\Delta(\varphi)-\cos\alpha\tan\varphi)^{-1}]$$
$$\mp(1\mp\cos\alpha)F(\varphi\backslash\alpha)$$

17.7.24 $n=\sin^2\alpha$

$$\Pi(\sin^2\alpha;\varphi\backslash\alpha)=\sec^2\alpha E(\varphi\backslash\alpha)-(\tan^2\alpha\sin 2\varphi)/(2\Delta(\varphi))$$

17.7.25 $n=1$

$$\Pi(1;\varphi\backslash\alpha)=F(\varphi\backslash\alpha)-\sec^2\alpha E(\varphi\backslash\alpha)+\sec^2\alpha\tan\varphi\Delta(\varphi)$$

18.1. Definitions, Symbolism, Restrictions and Conventions

An elliptic function is a single-valued doubly periodic function of a single complex variable which is analytic except at poles and whose only singularities in the finite plane are poles. If ω and ω' are a pair of (primitive) half-periods of such a function $f(z)$, then $f(z+2M\omega+2N\omega')=f(z)$, M and N being integers. Thus the study of any such function can be reduced to consideration of its behavior in a *fundamental period parallelogram* (FPP). An elliptic function has a finite number of poles (and the same number of zeros) in a FPP; the number of such poles (zeros) (an irreducible set) is the *order* of the function (poles and zeros are counted according to their multiplicity). All other poles (zeros) are called *congruent* to the irreducible set. The simplest (non-trivial) elliptic functions are of order two. One may choose as the standard function of order two either a function with two simple poles (Jacobi's choice) or one double pole (Weierstrass' choice) in a FPP.

Weierstrass' $\wp$-Function. Let ω, ω' denote a pair of complex numbers with $\mathscr{I}(\omega'/\omega)>0$. Then $\wp(z)=\wp(z|\omega, \omega')$ is an elliptic function of order two with periods 2ω, $2\omega'$ and having a double pole at $z=0$, whose principal part is z^{-2}; $\wp(z)-z^{-2}$ is analytic in a neighborhood of the origin and vanishes at $z=0$.

Weierstrass' ζ-Function $\zeta(z)=\zeta(z|\omega, \omega')$ satisfies the condition $\zeta'(z)=-\wp(z)$; further, $\zeta(z)$ has a simple pole at $z=0$ whose principal part is z^{-1}; $\zeta(z)-z^{-1}$ vanishes at $z=0$ and is analytic in a neighborhood of the origin. $\zeta(z)$ is *NOT* an elliptic function, since it is not periodic. However, it is quasi-periodic (see "period" relations), so reduction to FPP is possible.

Weierstrass' σ-Function $\sigma(z)=\sigma(z|\omega, \omega')$ satisfies the condition $\sigma'(z)/\sigma(z)=\zeta(z)$; further, $\sigma(z)$ is an entire function which vanishes at the origin. Like ζ, it is *NOT* an elliptic function, since it is not periodic. However, it is quasi-periodic (see "period" relations), so reduction to FPP is possible.

Invariants g_2 and g_3

Let $W=2M\omega+2N\omega'$, M and N being integers. Then

18.1.1 $\qquad g_2=60\Sigma' W^{-4}$ and $g_3=140\Sigma' W^{-6}$

are the INVARIANTS, summation being over all pairs M, N except $M=N=0$.

Alternate Symbolism Emphasizing Invariants

18.1.2 $\qquad \wp(z)=\wp(z; g_2, g_3)$

18.1.3 $\qquad \wp'(z)=\wp'(z; g_2, g_3)$

18.1.4 $\qquad \zeta(z)=\zeta(z; g_2, g_3)$

18.1.5 $\qquad \sigma(z)=\sigma(z; g_2, g_3)$

Fundamental Differential Equation, Discriminant and Related Quantities

18.1.6 $\qquad \wp'^2(z)=4\wp^3(z)-g_2\wp(z)-g_3$

18.1.7

$$=4(\wp(z)-e_1)(\wp(z)-e_2)(\wp(z)-e_3)$$

18.1.8

$$\Delta=g_2^3-27g_3^2=16(e_2-e_3)^2(e_3-e_1)^2(e_1-e_2)^2$$

18.1.9

$$g_2=-4(e_1e_2+e_1e_3+e_2e_3)=2(e_1^2+e_2^2+e_3^2)$$

18.1.10 $\qquad g_3=4e_1e_2e_3=\frac{4}{3}(e_1^3+e_2^3+e_3^3)$

18.1.11 $\qquad e_1+e_2+e_3=0$

18.1.12 $\qquad e_1^4+e_2^4+e_3^4=g_2^2/8$

18.1.13 $\qquad 4e_i^3-g_2e_i-g_3=0 (i=1, 2, 3)$

Agreement about Values of Invariants (and Discriminant)

We shall consider, in this chapter, only *real* g_2 and g_3 (this seems to cover most applications)—hence Δ is real. We shall dichotomize most of what follows (either $\Delta>0$ or $\Delta<0$). Homogeneity relations **18.2.1–18.2.15** enable a further restriction to non-negative g_3 (except for one case when $\Delta=0$).

Note on Symbolism for Roots of Complex Numbers and for Conjugate Complex Numbers

In this chapter, $z^{1/n}$ (n a positive integer) is used to denote the principal nth root of z, as in chapter 3; $\bar{z}$ is used to denote the complex conjugate of z.

FPP's, Symbols for Periods, etc.

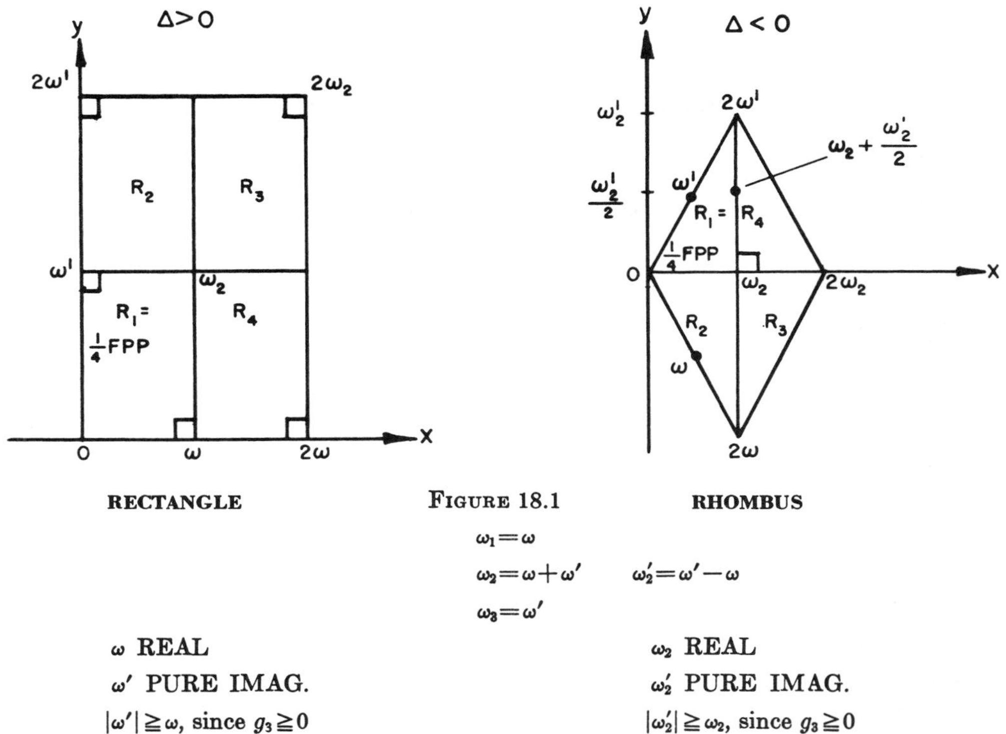

RECTANGLE FIGURE 18.1 RHOMBUS

$\omega_1 = \omega$

$\omega_2 = \omega + \omega'$ $\qquad \omega_2' = \omega' - \omega$

$\omega_3 = \omega'$

$\Delta>0$	$\Delta<0$
ω REAL	ω_2 REAL
ω' PURE IMAG.	ω_2' PURE IMAG.
$\lvert\omega'\rvert \geqq \omega$, since $g_3 \geqq 0$	$\lvert\omega_2'\rvert \geqq \omega_2$, since $g_3 \geqq 0$

Fundamental Rectangles

Study of all four functions ($\wp, \wp', \zeta, \sigma$) can be reduced to consideration of their values in a Fundamental Rectangle including the origin (see **18.2** on homogeneity relations, reduction formulas and processes).

$\Delta>0$

Fundamental Rectangle is $\frac{1}{4}$ FPP, which has vertices $0, \omega, \omega_2$ and ω'

$\Delta<0$

Fundamental Rectangle has vertices $0, \omega_2, \omega_2+\frac{\omega_2'}{2}, \frac{\omega_2'}{2}$.

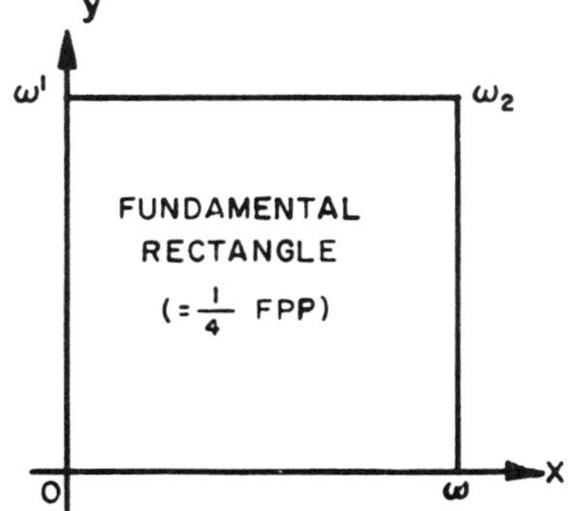

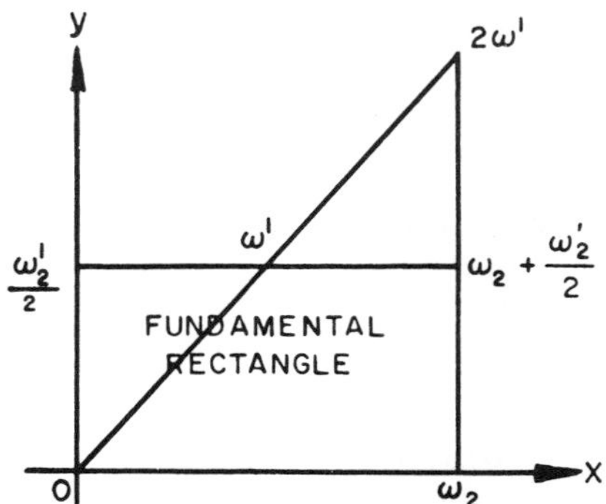

FIGURE 18.2

There is a point on the right boundary of Fundamental Rectangle where $\wp = 0$. Denote it by z_0.

18.2. Homogeneity Relations, Reduction Formulas and Processes

Homogeneity Relations (Suppose $t\neq 0$)

Note that Period Ratio is preserved.

18.2.1 $\wp'(tz|t\omega, t\omega')=t^{-3}\wp'(z|\omega, \omega')$

18.2.2 $\wp(tz|t\omega, t\omega')=t^{-2}\wp(z|\omega, \omega')$

18.2.3 $\zeta(tz|t\omega, t\omega')=t^{-1}\zeta(z|\omega, \omega')$

18.2.4 $\sigma(tz|t\omega, t\omega')=t\sigma(z|\omega, \omega')$

18.2.5 $g_2(t\omega, t\omega')=t^{-4}g_2(\omega, \omega')$

18.2.6 $g_3(t\omega, t\omega')=t^{-6}g_3(\omega, \omega')$

18.2.7 $e_i(t\omega, t\omega')=t^{-2}e_i(\omega, \omega'),\ i=1, 2, 3$

18.2.8 $\Delta(t\omega, t\omega')=t^{-12}\Delta(\omega, \omega')$

18.2.9 $H_i(t\omega, t\omega')=t^{-2}H_i(\omega, \omega'),\ i=1, 2, 3$ (See **18.3**)

18.2.10 $q(t\omega, t\omega')=q(\omega, \omega')$ (See **18.10**)

18.2.11 $m(t\omega, t\omega')=m(\omega, \omega')$ (See **18.9**)

18.2.12 $\wp'(tz; t^{-4}g_2, t^{-6}g_3)=t^{-3}\wp'(z; g_2, g_3)$

18.2.13 $\wp(tz; t^{-4}g_2, t^{-6}g_3)=t^{-2}\wp(z; g_2, g_3)$

18.2.14 $\zeta(tz; t^{-4}g_2, t^{-6}g_3)=t^{-1}\zeta(z; g_2, g_3)$

18.2.15 $\sigma(tz; t^{-4}g_2, t^{-6}g_3)=t\sigma(z; g_2, g_3)$

The Case $g_3<0$

Put $t=i$ and obtain, e.g.,

18.2.16 $\wp(z; g_2, g_3)=-\wp(iz; g_2, -g_3)$

Thus the case $g_3<0$ can be reduced to one where $g_3>0$.

"Period" Relations and Reduction to the FPP (M,N integers)

18.2.17 $\wp'(z+2M\omega+2N\omega')=\wp'(z)$

18.2.18 $\wp(z+2M\omega+2N\omega')=\wp(z)$

18.2.19

$$\zeta(z+2M\omega+2N\omega')=\zeta(z)+2M\eta+2N\eta'$$

18.2.20

$$\sigma(z+2M\omega+2N\omega')$$
$$=(-1)^{M+N+MN}\sigma(z)\exp[(z+M\omega+N\omega')(2M\eta+2N\eta')]$$

18.2.21 where $\eta=\zeta(\omega),\ \eta'=\zeta(\omega')$

"Conjugate" Values

$f(\bar{z})=\bar{f}(z)$, where f is any one of the functions $\wp$, $\wp'$, ζ, σ.

Reduction to ¼ FPP (See Figure 18.1)

($\bar{s}$ denotes conjugate of s)

	$\Delta>0$	$\Delta<0$
	Point z_4 in R_4	
18.2.22	$\wp'(z_4)=-\overline{\wp'}(\overline{2\omega-z_4})$	$\wp'(\bar{z}_4)=-\overline{\wp'}(\overline{2\omega_2-z_4})$
18.2.23	$\wp(z_4)=\overline{\wp}(2\omega-z_4)$	$\wp(z_4)=\overline{\wp}(\overline{2\omega_2-z_4})$
18.2.24	$\zeta(z_4)=-\zeta(\overline{2\omega-z_4})+2\eta$	$\zeta(z_4)=-\bar{\zeta}(\overline{2\omega_2-z_4})+2(\eta+\eta')$
18.2.25	$\sigma(z_4)=\bar{\sigma}(\overline{2\omega-z_4})\exp[2\eta(z_4-\omega)]$	$\sigma(z_4)=\bar{\sigma}(\overline{2\omega_2-z_4})\exp[2(\eta+\eta')(z_4-\omega_2)]$
	Point z_3 in R_3	
18.2.26	$\wp'(z_3)=-\wp'(2\omega_2-z_3)$	$\wp'(z_3)=-\wp'(2\omega_2-z_3)$
18.2.27	$\wp(z_3)=\wp(2\omega_2-z_3)$	$\wp(z_3)=\wp(2\omega_2-z_3)$
18.2.28	$\zeta(z_3)=-\zeta(2\omega_2-z_3)+2(\eta+\eta')$	$\zeta(z_3)=-\zeta(2\omega_2-z_3)+2(\eta+\eta')$
18.2.29	$\sigma(z_3)=\sigma(2\omega_2-z_3)\exp[2(\eta+\eta')(z_3-\omega_2)]$	$\sigma(z_3)=\sigma(2\omega_2-z_3)\exp[2(\eta+\eta')(z_3-\omega_2)]$
	Point z_2 in R_2	
18.2.30	$\wp'(z_2)=\overline{\wp'}(\overline{z_2-2\omega'})$	$\wp'(z_2)=\overline{\wp'}(\bar{z}_2)$
18.2.31	$\wp(z_2)=\overline{\wp}(\overline{z_2-2\omega'})$	$\wp(z_2)=\overline{\wp}(\bar{z}_2)$
18.2.32	$\zeta(z_2)=\bar{\zeta}(\overline{z_2-2\omega'})+2\eta'$	$\zeta(z_2)=\bar{\zeta}(\bar{z}_2)$
18.2.33	$\sigma(z_2)=-\bar{\sigma}(\overline{z_2-2\omega'})\exp[2\eta'(z_2-\omega')]$	$\sigma(z_2)=\bar{\sigma}(\bar{z}_2)$

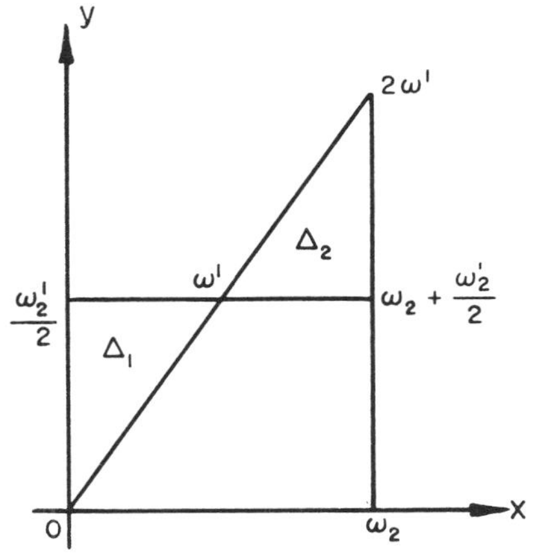

FIGURE 18.3

Reduction from ¼ FPP to Fundamental Rectangle in Case $\Delta<0$

We need only be concerned with the case when z is in triangle Δ_2 (therefore $2\omega'-z$ is in triangle Δ_1).

18.2.34 $$\wp(z)=\wp(2\omega'-z)$$

18.2.35 $$\wp'(z)=-\wp'(2\omega'-z)$$

18.2.36 $$\zeta(z)=2\eta'-\zeta(2\omega'-z)$$

18.2.37 $$\sigma(z)=\sigma(2\omega'-z)\exp[2\eta'(z-\omega')]$$

Reduction to Case where Real Half-Period is Unity

(preserving period ratio)

	$\Delta>0$	$\Delta<0$ ($\omega_2=\omega+\omega'$)
18.2.38	$\wp'(z\vert\omega,\omega')=\omega^{-3}\wp'\left(z\omega^{-1}\vert 1,\frac{\omega'}{\omega}\right)$	$\wp'(z\vert\omega,\omega')=\omega_2^{-3}\wp'\left(z\omega_2^{-1}\middle\vert\frac{\omega}{\omega_2},\frac{\omega'}{\omega_2}\right)$
18.2.39	$\wp(z\vert\omega,\omega')=\omega^{-2}\wp\left(z\omega^{-1}\vert 1,\frac{\omega'}{\omega}\right)$	$\wp(z\vert\omega,\omega')=\omega_2^{-2}\wp\left(z\omega_2^{-1}\middle\vert\frac{\omega}{\omega_2},\frac{\omega'}{\omega_2}\right)$
18.2.40	$\zeta(z\vert\omega,\omega')=\omega^{-1}\zeta\left(z\omega^{-1}\vert 1,\frac{\omega'}{\omega}\right)$	$\zeta(z\vert\omega,\omega')=\omega_2^{-1}\zeta\left(z\omega_2^{-1}\middle\vert\frac{\omega}{\omega_2},\frac{\omega'}{\omega_2}\right)$
18.2.41	$\sigma(z\vert\omega,\omega')=\omega\sigma\left(z\omega^{-1}\vert 1,\frac{\omega'}{\omega}\right)$	$\sigma(z\vert\omega,\omega')=\omega_2\sigma\left(z\omega_2^{-1}\middle\vert\frac{\omega}{\omega_2},\frac{\omega'}{\omega_2}\right)$
18.2.42	$g_2(\omega,\omega')=\omega^{-4}g_2\left(1,\frac{\omega'}{\omega}\right)$	$g_2(\omega,\omega')=\omega_2^{-4}g_2\left(\frac{\omega}{\omega_2},\frac{\omega'}{\omega_2}\right)$
18.2.43	$g_3(\omega,\omega')=\omega^{-6}g_3\left(1,\frac{\omega'}{\omega}\right)$	$g_3(\omega,\omega')=\omega_2^{-6}g_3\left(\frac{\omega}{\omega_2},\frac{\omega'}{\omega_2}\right)$
18.2.44	$e_i(\omega,\omega')=\omega^{-2}e_i\left(1,\frac{\omega'}{\omega}\right)$ $(i=1,2,3)$	$e_i(\omega,\omega')=\omega_2^{-2}e_i\left(\frac{\omega}{\omega_2},\frac{\omega'}{\omega_2}\right)$ $(i=1,2,3)$
18.2.45	$\Delta(\omega,\omega')=\omega^{-12}\Delta\left(1,\frac{\omega'}{\omega}\right)$	$\Delta(\omega,\omega')=\omega_2^{-12}\Delta\left(\frac{\omega}{\omega_2},\frac{\omega'}{\omega_2}\right)$

NOTE: New real half-period is

$$\frac{\omega}{\omega_2}+\frac{\omega'}{\omega_2}=\frac{\omega+\omega'}{\omega_2}=1$$

18.3. Special Values and Relations

Values at Periods

$\wp$, $\wp'$, and ζ are infinite, σ is zero at $z=2\omega_i$, $i=1,2,3$ and at $2\omega_2'(\Delta<0)$.

	$\Delta>0$	$\Delta<0$

Half-Periods

18.3.1	$\wp(\omega_i)=e_i (i=1,2,3)$	
18.3.2	$\wp'(\omega_i)=0 (i=1,2,3)$	
18.3.3	$\eta_i=\zeta(\omega_i) (i=1,2,3)$	
18.3.4	$\eta_1=\eta, \eta_2=\eta+\eta', \eta_3=\eta'$	
18.3.5	$H_i^2=2e_i^2+e_je_k$ $(i,j,k=1,2,3;\ i\neq j, i\neq k, j\neq k)$	
18.3.6	$=(e_i-e_j)(e_i-e_k)=2e_i^2+\frac{g_3}{4e_i}=3e_i^2-\frac{g_2}{4}$	

	$\Delta>0$	$\Delta<0$
18.3.7	e_i real	e_2 real and non-negative
18.3.8	$e_1>0\geq e_2>e_3$ (equality when $g_3=0$)	($e_2=0$ when $g_3=0$) $e_1=-\alpha+i\beta$, $e_3=\overline{e}_1$ where $\alpha\geq 0, \beta>0$ (equality when $g_3=0$)
18.3.9	$\eta>0$	$\eta_2'=\zeta(\omega_2')=\eta'-\eta$
18.3.10	$\eta'/i\lesseqgtr 0$ if	$\eta_2>0$
18.3.11	$\|\omega'\|/\omega\lesseqgtr 1.91014\ 050$ (approx.)	$\eta_2'/i\lesseqgtr 0$ if $\|\omega_2'\|/\omega_2\lesseqgtr 3.81915\ 447$ (approx.)
18.3.12	$H_1>0, H_3>0$	$H_2>0$
18.3.13	$H_2\equiv i\sqrt{-H_2^2}$	$\pi/4<\arg(H_3)\leq\pi/2$ (equality if $g_3=0$); $H_1=\overline{H}_3$
18.3.14	$\sigma(\omega)=e^{\eta\omega/2}/H_1^{1/2}$	$\sigma(\omega_2)=e^{\eta_2\omega_2/2}/H_2^{1/2}$
18.3.15	$\sigma(\omega')=ie^{\eta'\omega'/2}/H_3^{1/2}$	$\sigma(\omega_2')=ie^{\eta_2'\omega_2'/2}/H_2^{1/2}$
18.3.16	$\sigma^2(\omega_2)=e^{\eta_2\omega_2}/(-H_2)$	$\sigma^2(\omega')=e^{\eta'\omega'}/(-H_3)$
18.3.17	$\arg[\sigma(\omega_2)]=\frac{\eta'\omega}{i}+\frac{\pi}{2}$	$\arg[\sigma(\omega')]=\frac{\eta_2'\omega_2}{4i}+\frac{\pi}{2}-\frac{1}{2}\arg(e_2+H_2-e_i)$

Quarter Periods

18.3.18	$\wp(\omega/2)=e_1+H_1>e_1$	$\wp(\omega_2/2)=e_2+H_2>e_2$
18.3.19	$\wp'(\omega/2)=-2H_1\sqrt{2H_1+3e_1}$	$\wp'(\omega_2/2)=-2H_2\sqrt{2H_2+3e_2}$
18.3.20	$\zeta(\omega/2)=\frac{1}{2}[\eta+\sqrt{2H_1+3e_1}]$	$\zeta(\omega_2/2)=\frac{1}{2}[\eta_2+\sqrt{2H_2+3e_2}]$

	$\Delta>0$	$\Delta<0$
18.3.21	$\sigma(\omega/2)=\frac{e^{\eta\omega/8}}{2^{1/4}H_1^{3/8}(2H_1+3e_1)^{1/8}}$	$\sigma(\omega_2/2)=\frac{e^{\eta_2\omega_2/8}}{2^{1/4}H_2^{3/8}(2H_2+3e_2)^{1/8}}$
18.3.22	$\wp(\omega'/2)=e_3-H_3<e_3<0$	$\wp(\omega_2'/2)=e_2-H_2=\wp(\omega_2+\omega_2'/2)<e_2<0$
18.3.23	$\wp'(\omega'/2)=-2H_3 i\sqrt{2H_3-3e_3}$	$\wp'(\omega_2'/2)=-2H_2 i\sqrt{2H_2-3e_2}=\overline{\wp}'(\omega_2+\omega_2'/2)$
18.3.24	$\zeta(\omega'/2)=\frac{1}{2}[\eta'-i\sqrt{2H_3-3e_3}]$	$\zeta(\omega_2'/2)=\frac{1}{2}[\eta_2'-i\sqrt{2H_2-3e_2}]=-\zeta(\omega_2+\omega_2'/2)+2\eta'$
18.3.25	$\sigma(\omega'/2)=\frac{ie^{\eta'\omega'/8}}{2^{1/4}H_3^{3/8}(2H_3-3e_3)^{1/8}}$	$\sigma(\omega_2'/2)=\frac{ie^{\eta_2'\omega_2'/8}}{2^{1/4}H_2^{3/8}(2H_2-3e_2)^{1/8}}$ $=\sigma(\omega_2+\omega_2'/2)\exp[-\eta'\omega_2]$
18.3.26	$\wp(\omega_2/2)=e_2-H_2$	$\wp(\omega'/2)=e_3-H_3$
18.3.27	$\wp'(\omega_2/2)=-2H_2 i(2H_2-3e_2)^{\frac{1}{2}}$	$\wp'(\omega'/2)=-2iH_3(2H_3-3e_3)^{\frac{1}{2}}$
18.3.28	$\zeta(\omega_2/2)=\frac{1}{2}[\eta_2-i(2H_2-3e_2)^{\frac{1}{2}}]$	$\zeta(\omega'/2)=\frac{1}{2}[\eta'-i(2H_3-3e_3)^{\frac{1}{2}}]$
18.3.29	$\sigma(\omega_2/2)=\frac{e^{\eta_2\omega_2/8}e^{i\pi/4}}{[4H_2^3(2H_2-3e_2)]^{1/8}}$	$\sigma(\omega'/2)=\frac{e^{\eta'\omega'/8}e^{i\pi/4}}{[4H_3^3(2H_3-3e_3)]^{1/8}}$

One-Third Period Relations

At $z=2\omega_i/3\,(i=1,2,3)$ or $2\omega_2'/3$, $\wp''^2=12\wp\wp'^2$;

equivalently:

18.3.30 $$48\wp^4-24g_2\wp^2-48g_3\wp-g_2^2=0$$

	$\Delta>0$	$\Delta<0$
18.3.31	$\zeta(2\omega/3)=\frac{2\eta}{3}+\left[\frac{\wp(2\omega/3)}{3}\right]^{\frac{1}{2}}$	$\zeta(2\omega_2/3)=\frac{2\eta_2}{3}+\left[\frac{\wp(2\omega_2/3)}{3}\right]^{\frac{1}{2}}$
18.3.32	$\zeta(2\omega'/3)=\frac{2\eta'}{3}-\left[\frac{\wp(2\omega'/3)}{3}\right]^{\frac{1}{2}}$	$\zeta(2\omega_2'/3)=\frac{2\eta_2'}{3}-\left[\frac{\wp(2\omega_2'/3)}{3}\right]^{\frac{1}{2}}$
18.3.33	$\zeta(2\omega_2/3)=\frac{2\eta_2}{3}+\left[\frac{\wp(2\omega_2/3)}{3}\right]^{\frac{1}{2}}$	$\zeta(2\omega'/3)=\frac{2\eta'}{3}+\left[\frac{\wp(2\omega'/3)}{3}\right]^{\frac{1}{2}}$
18.3.34	$\sigma(2\omega/3)=\frac{-\exp[2\eta\omega/9]}{\sqrt[3]{\wp'(2\omega/3)}}$	$\sigma(2\omega_2/3)=\frac{-\exp[2\eta_2\omega_2/9]}{\sqrt[3]{\wp'(2\omega_2/3)}}$
18.3.35	$\sigma(2\omega'/3)=\frac{-\exp[2\eta'\omega'/9]}{[\wp'(2\omega'/3)]^{1/3}e^{2\pi i/3}}$	$\sigma(2\omega_2'/3)=\frac{-\exp[2\eta_2'\omega_2'/9]}{[\wp'(2\omega_2'/3)]^{1/3}e^{2\pi i/3}}$
18.3.36	$\sigma(2\omega_2/3)=\frac{-\exp[2\eta_2\omega_2/9]}{[\wp'(2\omega_2/3)]^{1/3}e^{2\pi i/3}}$	$\sigma(2\omega'/3)=\frac{-\exp[2\eta'\omega'/9]}{[\wp'(2\omega'/3)]^{1/3}e^{2\pi i/3}}$

Legendre's Relation

18.3.37	$\eta\omega'-\eta'\omega=\pi i/2$ (also valid for $\Delta<0$)	$\eta_2\omega_2'-\eta_2'\omega_2=\pi i$

Relations Among the H_i

18.3.38 $$H_1^2+H_2^2+H_3^2=3g_2/4$$

18.3.39 $$H_1^2H_2^2+H_2^2H_3^2+H_3^2H_1^2=0$$

18.3.40 $$H_1^2H_2^2H_3^2=-\Delta/16$$

18.3.41 $$16H_i^6-12g_2H_i^4+\Delta=0(i=1, 2, 3)$$

18.4. Addition and Multiplication Formulas

Addition Formulas[2] ($z_1\neq z_2$)

18.4.1 $$\wp(z_1+z_2)=\frac{1}{4}\left[\frac{\wp'(z_1)-\wp'(z_2)}{\wp(z_1)-\wp(z_2)}\right]^2-\wp(z_1)-\wp(z_2)$$

18.4.2 $$\wp'(z_1+z_2)=\frac{\wp(z_1+z_2)[\wp'(z_1)-\wp'(z_2)]+\wp(z_1)\wp'(z_2)-\wp'(z_1)\wp(z_2)}{\wp(z_2)-\wp(z_1)}$$

18.4.3 $$\zeta(z_1+z_2)=\zeta(z_1)+\zeta(z_2)+\frac{1}{2}\frac{\wp'(z_1)-\wp'(z_2)}{\wp(z_1)-\wp(z_2)}$$

18.4.4 $$\sigma(z_1+z_2)\sigma(z_1-z_2)=-\sigma^2(z_1)\sigma^2(z_2)[\wp(z_1)-\wp(z_2)]$$

Duplication and Triplication Formulas

$\left[\text{Note that } \wp''=6\wp^2(z)-\frac{g_2}{2},\ \wp'^2(z)=4\wp^3(z)-g_2\wp(z)-g_3 \text{ and } \wp'''(z)=12\wp(z)\wp'(z)\right]$

18.4.5 $$\wp(2z)=-2\wp(z)+\left[\frac{\wp''(z)}{2\wp'(z)}\right]^2$$

18.4.6 $$\wp'(2z)=\frac{-4\wp'^4(z)+12\wp(z)\wp'^2(z)\wp''(z)-\wp''^3(z)}{4\wp'^3(z)}$$

18.4.7 $$\zeta(2z)=2\zeta(z)+\wp''(z)/2\wp'(z)$$

18.4.8 $$\sigma(2z)=-\wp'(z)\sigma^4(z)$$

18.4.9 $$\zeta(3z)=3\zeta(z)+\frac{4\wp'^3(z)}{\wp'(z)\wp'''(z)-\wp''^2(z)}$$

18.4.10 $$\sigma(3z)=-\wp'^2(z)\sigma^9(z)[\wp(2z)-\wp(z)]$$

18.5. Series Expansions

Laurent Series

18.5.1 $$\wp(z)=z^{-2}+\sum_{k=2}^{\infty}c_kz^{2k-2}$$

18.5.2 where $$c_2=g_2/20,\ c_3=g_3/28$$

and

18.5.3 $$c_k=\frac{3}{(2k+1)(k-3)}\sum_{m=2}^{k-2}c_mc_{k-m},\ k\geqq 4$$

18.5.4 $$\wp'(z)=-2z^{-3}+\sum_{k=2}^{\infty}(2k-2)c_kz^{2k-3}$$

18.5.5 $$\zeta(z)=z^{-1}-\sum_{k=2}^{\infty}c_kz^{2k-1}/(2k-1)$$

18.5.6 $$\sigma(z)=\sum_{m,n=0}^{\infty}a_{m,n}(\tfrac{1}{2}g_2)^m(2g_3)^n\cdot\frac{z^{4m+6n+1}}{(4m+6n+1)!}$$

[2] Formulas for ζ and σ are *not* true algebraic addition formulas.

18.5.7 where $a_{0,0}=1$ and

18.5.8 $$a_{m,n}=3(m+1)a_{m+1,n-1}+\frac{16}{3}(n+1)a_{m-2,n+1}-\frac{1}{3}(2m+3n-1)(4m+6n-1)a_{m-1,n},$$

it being understood that $a_{m,n}=0$ if either subscript is negative.

(The radius of convergence of the above series for $\wp-z^{-2}$, $\wp'+2z^{-3}$ and $\zeta-z^{-1}$ is equal to the smallest of $|2\omega|$, $|2\omega'|$ and $|2\omega\pm 2\omega'|$; series for σ converges for all z.)

Values of Coefficients[3] c_k in Terms of c_2 and c_3

18.5.9 $$c_4=c_2^2/3$$

18.5.10 $$c_5=3c_2c_3/11$$

18.5.11 $$c_6=[2c_2^3+3c_3^2]/39$$

18.5.12 $$c_7=2c_2^2c_3/33$$

18.5.13 $$c_8=5c_2(11c_2^3+36c_3^2)/7293$$

18.5.14 $$c_9=c_3(29c_2^3+11c_3^2)/2717$$

18.5.15 $$c_{10}=(242c_2^5+1455c_2^2c_3^2)/240669$$

18.5.16 $$c_{11}=14c_2c_3(389c_2^3+369c_3^2)/3187041$$

18.5.17 $$c_{12}=(114950c_2^6+1080000c_2^3c_3^2+166617c_3^4)/891678645$$

18.5.18 $$c_{13}=10c_2^2c_3(297c_2^3+530c_3^2)/11685817$$

18.5.19 $$c_{14}=\frac{2c_2(528770c_2^6+7164675c_2^3c_3^2+2989602c_3^4)}{(306735)(215441)}$$

18.5.20 $$c_{15}=\frac{4c_3(62921815c_2^6+179865450c_2^3c_3^2+14051367c_3^4)}{(179685)(38920531)}$$

18.5.21 $$c_{16}=\frac{c_2^2(58957855c_2^6+1086511320c_2^3c_3^2+875341836c_3^4)}{(5909761)(5132565)}$$

18.5.22 $$c_{17}=\frac{c_2c_3(30171955c_2^6+126138075c_2^3c_3^2+28151739c_3^4)}{(920205)(6678671)}$$

18.5.23 $$c_{18}=\frac{1541470\cdot 949003c_2^9+30458088737\cdot 1155c_2^6c_3^2+122378650673\cdot 378c_2^3c_3^4+2348703\cdot 887777c_3^6}{(1342211013)(4695105713)}$$

18.5.24 $$c_{19}=\frac{2c_2^2c_3(3365544215c_2^6+429852433\cdot 45c_2^3c_3^2+8527743477c_3^4)}{(91100295)(113537407)}$$

[3] *NOTES:*

1. c_4–c_{16} were computed and checked independently by D. H. Lehmer; these were double-checked by substituting $g_2=20\ c_2$, $g_3=28\ c_3$ in values given in [18.10].

2. c_{17}–c_{18} were derived from values in [18.10] by the same substitution. These were checked (numerically) for particular values of g_2, g_3.

3. c_{19} is given incorrectly in [18.12] (factor 13 is missing in denominator of third term of bracket); this value was computed independently.

4. No factors of any of the above integers with more than ten digits are known to the author. This is not necessarily true of smaller integers, which have, in many instances, been arranged for convenient use with a desk calculator.

Value[4] of Coefficients $a_{m,n}$

$n \uparrow$ \ $m \rightarrow$	0	1	2	3	4	5	6	7	8	9	10	11	12
8	$-2^7\cdot3^{12}\cdot5\cdot59\cdot107895773$												
7	$-2^7\cdot3^{10}\cdot5\cdot23\cdot257\cdot18049$	$-2^7\cdot3^{11}\cdot5\cdot59\cdot107895773$											
6	$-2^6\cdot3^9\cdot5\cdot229\cdot2683$	$-2^7\cdot3^9\cdot5\cdot23\cdot257\cdot18049$	$-2^6\cdot3^{11}\cdot5\cdot7\cdot181\cdot1699\cdot2803$	$-2^8\cdot3^{10}\cdot5\cdot7\cdot41\cdot6047\cdot4922497$									
5	$2^3\cdot3^8\cdot5\cdot9103$	$-2^6\cdot3^8\cdot5\cdot229\cdot2683$	$-2^5\cdot3^{10}\cdot5\cdot40570423$	$-2^6\cdot3^9\cdot5\cdot7\cdot59\cdot179\cdot142231$	$-2^4\cdot3^{10}\cdot5\cdot7\cdot1321\cdot1415535763$								
4	$2^8\cdot3^5\cdot5^2\cdot31$	$2^3\cdot3^7\cdot5\cdot9103$	$-2^5\cdot3^8\cdot5\cdot7\cdot13\cdot37\cdot41$	$-2^5\cdot3^8\cdot5\cdot691\cdot83609$	$-2^4\cdot3^8\cdot5\cdot11\cdot31\cdot313\cdot190387$	$-2^4\cdot3^{10}\cdot5^2\cdot7\cdot23\cdot263\cdot4848953$	$-2^5\cdot3^9\cdot5\cdot7\cdot19\cdot1752686144977$						
3	$2^8\cdot3^4\cdot23$	$2^3\cdot3^4\cdot5^2\cdot31$	$2^3\cdot3^7\cdot5\cdot17\cdot109$	$-2^3\cdot3^6\cdot5\cdot83\cdot3911$	$-2^4\cdot3^6\cdot5\cdot503\cdot156217$	$-2^4\cdot3^8\cdot31\cdot315989669$	$-2^4\cdot3^7\cdot5\cdot7\cdot11\cdot29\cdot83\cdot1129\cdot9551$	$-2^4\cdot3^8\cdot5\cdot7\cdot613\cdot17605225081$					
2	$-2\cdot3^3$	$2^3\cdot3^3\cdot23$	$2^2\cdot3^5\cdot5\cdot53$	$2^3\cdot3^4\cdot5\cdot37\cdot167$	$-2\cdot3^6\cdot5\cdot17\cdot3037$	$-2^4\cdot3^7\cdot61\cdot151\cdot653$	$-2^3\cdot3^7\cdot2387260103$	$-2^4\cdot3^7\cdot5\cdot17\cdot53\cdot2957\cdot41189$	$-2\cdot3^9\cdot5\cdot7^2\cdot17\cdot67\cdot195651059$	$2^3\cdot3^7\cdot5\cdot7^2\cdot35866647631901$			
1	-3	$-2\cdot3^2$	$3^3\cdot19$	$2^2\cdot3^3\cdot311$	$3^3\cdot5\cdot20807$	$-2\cdot3^6\cdot11\cdot2609$	$-3^5\cdot17\cdot1578257$	$-2^3\cdot3^5\cdot7\cdot13\cdot2742587$	$-3^7\cdot248882935409$	$-2\cdot3^5\cdot5\cdot7^2\cdot193\cdot13679\cdot274973$	$3^6\cdot7\cdot89555603641079$		
0	1	-1	-3^2	$3\cdot23$	$3\cdot107$	$3^3\cdot7\cdot23\cdot37$	$3^2\cdot313\cdot503$	$-3^4\cdot7\cdot685973$	$3^5\cdot11\cdot37\cdot257981$	$-3^4\cdot7\cdot23\cdot14387\cdot40763$	$-3^4\cdot71\cdot176302760639$	$-3^6\cdot7\cdot11\cdot23^2\cdot383\cdot739\cdot18539$	$3^5\cdot7^2\cdot24733\cdot198922785511$

[4] Values of $a_{m,n}$ in unfactored form for $4m+6n+1\leq35$ are given in [18.25], p. 7; of $(a_{m,n})3^{-n}$ in factored form in [18.15], Vol. 4, p. 89 for $4m+6n+1\leq25$. Additional values were computed and checked on desk calculators; primality of large factors was established with the aid of SWAC (National Bureau of Standards Western Automatic Computer).

Reversed Series[5] for Large $|\wp|$

18.5.25

$$z=\frac{1}{2}\Big[2u+c_2u^5+c_3u^7+\frac{\alpha_2^2}{3}u^9+\frac{6\alpha_2\alpha_3}{11}u^{11}$$

$$+\frac{1}{13}(3\alpha_3^2+5\alpha_2^3)u^{13}+\alpha_2^2\alpha_3u^{15}+\frac{5\alpha_2}{68}(12\alpha_3^2+7\alpha_2^3)u^{17}$$

$$+\frac{5\alpha_3}{19}(\alpha_3^2+7\alpha_2^3)u^{19}+\frac{\alpha_2^2}{4}(3\alpha_2^3+10\alpha_3^2)u^{21}$$

$$+\frac{35\alpha_2\alpha_3}{92}(9\alpha_2^3+4\alpha_3^2)u^{23}$$

$$+\frac{7}{200}(33\alpha_2^6+180\alpha_2^3\alpha_3^2+10\alpha_3^4)u^{25}$$

$$+\frac{7\alpha_2^2\alpha_3}{12}(11\alpha_2^3+10\alpha_3^2)u^{27}$$

$$+\frac{3\alpha_2}{2^3\cdot 29}(143\alpha_2^6+1155\alpha_2^3\alpha_3^2+210\alpha_3^4)u^{29}$$

$$+\frac{21\alpha_3}{2^3\cdot 31}(143\alpha_2^6+220\alpha_2^3\alpha_3^2+6\alpha_3^4)u^{31}$$

$$+\frac{3\alpha_2^2}{2^6}(65\alpha_2^6+728\alpha_2^3\alpha_3^2+280\alpha_3^4)u^{33}$$

$$+\frac{33\alpha_2\alpha_3}{2^3\cdot 5\cdot 7}(195\alpha_2^6+455\alpha_2^3\alpha_3^2+42\alpha_3^4)u^{35}$$

$$+\frac{11}{2^6\cdot 37}(1105\alpha_2^9+16380\alpha_2^6\alpha_3^2+10920\alpha_2^3\alpha_3^4$$

$$+168\alpha_3^6)u^{37}+\frac{33\alpha_2^2\alpha_3}{2^6}(85\alpha_2^6+280\alpha_2^3\alpha_3^2+56\alpha_3^4)u^{39}$$

$$+\frac{143\alpha_2}{2^7\cdot 41}(323\alpha_2^9+6120\alpha_2^6\alpha_3^2+6300\alpha_2^3\alpha_3^4+336\alpha_3^6)u^{41}$$

$$+\frac{143\alpha_3}{2^6\cdot 43}(1615\alpha_2^9+7140\alpha_2^6\alpha_3^2+2520\alpha_2^3\alpha_3^4+24\alpha_3^6)u^{43}$$

$$+O(u^{45})\Big],$$

18.5.26 where $\alpha_2=g_2/8$

18.5.27 $\alpha_3=g_2/8$

18.5.28 $u=(\wp^{-1})^{\frac{1}{2}}$

[5] In this and other series a choice of the value of the root has been made so that z will be in the Fundamental Rectangle **(Figure 18.2)**, whenever the value of the given function is appropriate.

Reversed Series for Large $|\wp'|$

18.5.29 $z=A_1u+A_5u^5+A_7u^7+A_9u^9+\ldots$

18.5.30 where $u=(\wp'^{1/3})^{-1}e^{i\pi/3}$

18.5.31 $A_1=2^{1/3}$

18.5.32 $A_5=-\frac{a_2}{5}A_1^2$

18.5.33 $A_7=\frac{-4a_3A_1}{7}$

18.5.34 $A_9=0$

18.5.35 $A_{11}=8a_2a_3A_1^2/11$

18.5.36 $A_{13}=\frac{10A_1}{39}(a_2^3+6a_3^2)$

18.5.37 $A_{15}=-96a_2^2a_3/175$

18.5.38 $A_{17}=-\frac{14a_2A_1^2}{51}(a_2^3+12a_3^2)$

18.5.39 where $a_2=g_2/6$, $a_3=g_3/6$

Reversed Series for Large $|\zeta|$

18.5.40 $z=u+A_5u^5+A_7u^7+A_9u^9+\ldots$

18.5.41 where $u=\zeta^{-1}$

18.5.42 $A_5=-\delta_2/5$

18.5.43 $A_7=-\delta_3/7$

18.5.44 $A_9=\delta_2^2/7$

18.5.45 $A_{11}=3\delta_2\delta_3/11$

18.5.46 $A_{13}=\frac{17}{1001}(-8\delta_2^3+7\delta_3^2)$

18.5.47 $A_{15}=-41\delta_2^2\delta_3/91$

18.5.48 $A_{17}=\frac{\delta_2}{9163}(1349\delta_2^3-4116\delta_3^2)$

18.5.49 $A_{19}=\frac{2\delta_3}{323323}(115431\delta_2^3-22568\delta_3^2)$

18.5.50 where $\delta_2=g_2/12$

18.5.51 $\delta_3=g_3/20$

Other Series Involving $\wp$

Series near z_0 $[\wp(z_0)=0]$

18.5.52

$$\wp=\wp_0'u\left[1-3c_2u^4-4c_3u^6+\frac{10c_2^2}{3}u^8+\frac{114c_2c_3}{11}u^{10}+\frac{7(12c_3^2-5c_2^3)}{13}u^{12}-\frac{488c_2^2c_3}{33}u^{14}\right]+u^2\left[-5c_2-14c_3u^2+5c_2^2u^4+33c_2c_3u^6+\frac{84c_3^2-10c_2^3}{3}u^8-\frac{1363c_2^2c_3u^{10}}{33}+\frac{5c_2(55c_2^3-2316c_3^2)u^{12}}{143}\right]+\dots$$

18.5.53 where $u=(z-z_0)$, $\wp_0'\equiv\wp'(z_0)=i\sqrt{g_3}$

18.5.54

$$u=\wp_0'\Big[v+av^2+2a^2v^3+\left(\frac{g_3\wp_0'^2}{2}+5a^3\right)v^4+\frac{a}{5}(3\wp_0'^4+15g_3\wp_0'^2+70a^3)v^5+2a^2(2\wp_0'^4+7g_3\wp_0'^2+21a^3)v^6+\left(\frac{g_3\wp_0'^6}{7}+\{g_3^2+20a^3\}\wp_0'^4+15a^2g_3\wp_0'^2+132a^6\right)v^7+15a\left(\frac{g_3\wp_0'^6}{4}+\left\{\frac{3g_3^2}{4}+6a^3\right\}\wp_0'^4+\frac{33ag_3}{2}\wp_0'^2+\frac{143a^6}{5}\right)v^8+\frac{5a^2}{2}\left(\frac{2}{3}\wp_0'^8+15g_3\wp_0'^6+\{154a^3+33g_3^2\}\wp_0'^4+\frac{2002a^3g_3\wp_0'^2}{5}+572a^6\right)v^9+\frac{1}{4}\left(3\{28a^3+g_3^2\}\wp_0'^8+11g_3\{98a^3+g_3^2\}\wp_0'^6+2002a^3\left\{\frac{16}{5}a^3+g_3^2\right\}\wp_0'^4+16016\,a^6g_3\wp_0'^2+19448\,a^9\right)v^{10}\Big]+\dots$$

18.5.55 where $v=\wp/(\wp_0')^2$ and $a=g_2/4$

Series near ω_i

18.5.56

$$(\wp-e_i)=(3e_i^2-5c_2)u+(10c_2e_i+21c_3)u^2+(7c_2e_i^2+21c_3e_i+5c_2^2)u^3+(18c_3e_i^2+30c_2^2e_i+33c_2c_3)u^4+\left(22c_2^2e_i^2+92c_2c_3e_i+105c_3^2-\frac{10c_2^3}{3}\right)u^5+\left(\frac{728}{11}c_2c_3e_i^2+\frac{220}{3}c_2^3e_i+84c_3^2e_i+\frac{1214}{11}c_2^2c_3\right)u^6+\left(\frac{635}{13}c_2^3e_i^2+\frac{855}{13}c_3^2e_i^2+\frac{3405}{11}c_2^2c_3e_i+\frac{45750}{143}c_2c_3^2+\frac{25}{13}c_2^4\right)u^7+\dots,$$

18.5.57 where $u=(z-\omega_i)^2$

Other Series Involving $\wp'$

Series near z_0

18.5.58

$$(\wp'-\wp_0')=\left[-10c_2u-56c_3u^3+30c_2^2u^5+264c_2c_3u^7+\frac{(840c_3^2-100c_2^3)}{3}u^9-\frac{5452c_2^2c_3}{11}u^{11}+\frac{70c_2(55c_2^3-2316c_3^2)}{143}u^{13}\right]+\wp_0'\left[-15c_2u^4-28c_3u^6+30c_2^2u^8+114c_2c_3u^{10}+7(12c_3^2-5c_2^3)u^{12}-\frac{2440c_2^2c_3}{11}u^{14}\right]+\dots$$

18.5.59 where $u=(z-z_0)$

18.5.60

$$(z-z_0)=A-bA^3-\frac{3\wp_0'}{2}A^4+3(c_2+b^2)A^5+10b\wp_0'A^6-3[36c_3-3\wp_0'+4b^3]A^7-3\wp_0'\left(\frac{25}{2}c_2+21b^2\right)A^8+\frac{5}{12}\left(285b^2c_2+100c_2^2-279\wp_0'^2b+132b^4\right)A^9+\dots$$

18.5.61 where $A=(\wp'-\wp_0')/(-10c_2)$

18.5.62 and $b=4g_3/g_2$

Series near ω_i

18.5.63

$$\wp'=2(3e_i^2-5c_2)\alpha+4(10c_2e_i+21c_3)\alpha^3+6(7c_2e_i^2+21c_3e_i+5c_2^2)\alpha^5+24(6c_3e_i^2+10c_2^2e_i+11c_2c_3)\alpha^7+10\left(22c_2^2e_i^2+92c_2c_3e_i+105c_3^2-\frac{10c_2^3}{3}\right)\alpha^9+24\left(\frac{364}{11}c_2c_3e_i^2+\frac{110}{3}c_2^3e_i+42c_3^2e_i+\frac{607}{11}c_2^2c_3\right)\alpha^{11}+70\left(\frac{127}{13}c_2^3e_i^2+\frac{171}{13}c_3^2e_i^2+\frac{681}{11}c_2^2c_3e_i+\frac{9150}{143}c_2c_3^2+\frac{5}{13}c_2^4\right)\alpha^{13}+\dots,$$

18.5.64 where $\alpha=(z-\omega_i)$.

Other Series Involving ζ

Series near z_0 $[\wp(z_0)=0]$

18.5.65

$$\zeta-\zeta_0=\wp_0'\left[-\frac{u^2}{2}+\frac{c_2u^6}{2}+\frac{c_3u^8}{2}-\frac{c_2^2u^{10}}{3}-\frac{19c_2c_3u^{12}}{22}+\frac{(5c_2^3-12c_3^2)}{26}u^{14}+\frac{61c_2^2c_3u^{16}}{66}\right]+\left[\frac{5c_2u^3}{3}+\frac{7c_3u^5}{2}-\frac{5c_2^2u^7}{7}-\frac{11c_2c_3u^9}{3}+\frac{(10c_2^3-84c_3^2)}{33}u^{11}+\frac{1363c_2^2c_3}{429}u^{13}+\frac{c_2(2316c_3^2-55c_2^3)}{429}u^{15}\right]+\ldots,$$

18.5.66 where $u=(z-z_0)$,

18.5.67 $\zeta_0\equiv\zeta(z_0)$

Series near ω_i

18.5.68

$$(\zeta-\eta_i)=-e_i\alpha-\frac{(3e_i^2-5c_2)}{3}\alpha^3-\frac{(10c_2e_i+21c_3)\alpha^5}{5}-\frac{(7c_2e_i^2+21c_3e_i+5c_2^2)\alpha^7}{7}-\frac{(6c_3e_i^2+10c_2^2e_i+11c_2c_3)\alpha^9}{3}-\frac{\left(22c_2^2e_i^2+92c_2c_3e_i+105c_3^2-\frac{10}{3}c_2^3\right)\alpha^{11}}{11}-\frac{2}{13}\left(\frac{364}{11}c_2c_3e_i^2+\frac{110}{3}c_2^3e_i+42c_3^2e_i+\frac{607}{11}c_2^2c_3\right)\alpha^{13}-\frac{1}{3}\left(\frac{127}{13}c_2^3e_i^2+\frac{171}{13}c_3^2e_i^2+\frac{681}{11}c_2^2c_3e_i+\frac{9150}{143}c_2c_3^2+\frac{5}{13}c_2^4\right)\alpha^{15}-\ldots,$$

18.5.69 where $\alpha=(z-\omega_i)$

Reversed Series for Small $|\sigma|$

18.5.70

$$\zeta=\sigma+\frac{\gamma_2}{5}\sigma^5+\frac{\gamma_3}{7}\sigma^7+\frac{3\gamma_2^2}{14}\sigma^9+\frac{19\gamma_2\gamma_3}{55}\sigma^{11}+\frac{3842\gamma_2^3+861\gamma_3^2}{6006}\sigma^{13}+\ldots,$$

18.5.71 where $\gamma_2=g_2/48$

18.5.72 $\gamma_3=g_3/120$

For reversion of Maclaurin series, see **3.6.25** and 18.18].

18.6. Derivatives and Differential Equations

Ordinary $(c_2=g_2/20,\ c_3=g_3/28)$

18.6.1 $\zeta'(z)=-\wp(z)$

18.6.2 $\sigma'(z)/\sigma(z)=\zeta(z)$

18.6.3

$$\wp'^2(z)=4\wp^3(z)-g_2\wp(z)-g_3=4(\wp^3-5c_2\wp-7c_3)$$

18.6.4 $\wp''(z)=6\wp^2(z)-\frac{1}{2}g_2=6\wp^2-10c_2$

18.6.5 $\wp'''(z)=12\wp\wp'$

18.6.6

$$\wp^{(4)}(z)=12(\wp\wp''+\wp'\wp')=5!\left[\wp^3-3c_2\wp-\frac{14c_3}{5}\right]$$

18.6.7

$$\wp^{(5)}(z)=12(\wp\wp'''+2\wp'\wp''+\wp''\wp')=3\cdot5!\,\wp'[\wp^2-c_2]$$

18.6.8

$$\wp^{(6)}(z)=12(\wp\wp^{(4)}+3\wp'\wp'''+3\wp''\wp''+\wp'''\wp')$$

18.6.9 $=7![\wp^4-4c_2\wp^2-4c_3\wp+5c_2^2/7]$

18.6.10 $\wp^{(7)}(z)=4\cdot7!\,\wp'[\wp^3-2c_2\wp-c_3]$

18.6.11

$$\wp^{(8)}(z)=9![\wp^5-5c_2\wp^3-5c_3\wp^2+(10c_2^2\wp+11c_2c_3)/3]$$

18.6.12

$$\wp^{(9)}(z)=5\cdot9!\,\wp'[\wp^4-3c_2\wp^2-2c_3\wp+2c_2^2/3]$$

18.6.13

$$\wp^{(10)}(z)=11![\wp^6-6c_2\wp^4-6c_3\wp^3+7c_2^2\wp^2+(342c_2c_3\wp+84c_3^2-10c_2^3)/33]$$

18.6.14

$$\wp^{(11)}(z)=6\cdot11!\,\wp'[\wp^5-4c_2\wp^3-3c_3\wp^2+(77c_2^2\wp+57c_2c_3)/33]$$

18.6.15

$$\wp^{(12)}(z)=13![\wp^7-7c_2\wp^5-7c_3\wp^4+35c_2^2\wp^3/3+210c_2c_3\wp^2/11+(84c_3^2-35c_2^3)\wp/13-1363c_2^2c_3/429]$$

18.6.16

$$\wp^{(13)}(z)=7\cdot13!\,\wp'[\wp^6-5c_2\wp^4-4c_3\wp^3+5c_2^2\wp^2+60c_2c_3\wp/11+(12c_3^2-5c_2^3)/13]$$

18.6.17

$$\wp^{(14)}(z)=15![\wp^8-8c_2\wp^6-8c_3\wp^5+52c_2^2\wp^4/3+328c_2c_3\wp^3/11+(444c_3^2-328c_2^3)\wp^2/39-488c_2^2c_3\wp/33+c_2(55c_2^3-2316c_3^2)/429]$$

18.6.18

$$\wp^{(15)}(z)=8\cdot15!\,\wp'[\wp^7-6c_2\wp^5-5c_3\wp^4+26c_2^2\wp^3/3+123c_2c_3\wp^2/11+(111c_3^2-82c_2^3)\wp/39-61c_2^2c_3/33]$$

Partial Derivatives with Respect to Invariants

18.6.19

$$\Delta \frac{\partial \wp}{\partial g_3}=\wp'\left(3g_2\zeta-\frac{9}{2}g_3z\right)+6g_2\wp^2-9g_3\wp-g_2^2$$

18.6.20

$$\Delta \frac{\partial \wp}{\partial g_2}=\wp'\left(-\frac{9}{2}g_3\zeta+\frac{g_2^2z}{4}\right)-9g_3\wp^2+\frac{g_2^2}{2}\wp+\frac{3}{2}g_2g_3$$

18.6.21

$$\Delta \frac{\partial \zeta}{\partial g_3}=-3\zeta\left(g_2\wp+\frac{3}{2}g_3\right)+\frac{1}{2}z\left(9g_3\wp+\frac{1}{2}g_2^2\right)-\frac{3}{2}g_2\wp'$$

18.6.22

$$\Delta \frac{\partial \zeta}{\partial g_2}=\frac{1}{2}\zeta\left(9g_3\wp+\frac{1}{2}g_2^2\right)-\frac{1}{2}g_2z\left(\frac{1}{2}g_2\wp+\frac{3}{4}g_3\right)+\frac{9}{4}g_3\wp'$$

18.6.23 $$\Delta \frac{\partial \sigma}{\partial g_3}=\frac{3}{2}g_2\sigma''+\frac{9}{2}g_3\sigma+\frac{1}{8}g_2^2z^2\sigma-\frac{9}{2}g_2z\sigma'$$

18.6.24

$$\Delta \frac{\partial \sigma}{\partial g_2}=-\frac{9}{4}g_3\sigma''-\frac{1}{4}g_2^2\sigma-\frac{3}{16}g_2g_3z^2\sigma+\frac{1}{4}g_2^2z\sigma'$$

$$\left(\text{here } ' \text{ denotes } \frac{\partial}{\partial z}\right)$$

Differential Equations

18.6.25

Equation	*Solution*
$y'^3=y^2(y-a)^2$	$y=\frac{a}{2}+\frac{27}{16}\wp'\left(\frac{z}{2};0,-\frac{64a^2}{729}\right)$

18.6.26

$y'^3=(y^3-3ay^2+3y)^2$	$y=\frac{2}{a-3\wp'(z;0,g_3)}$, $g_3=\frac{4-3a^2}{27}$

18.6.27

$y'^4=\frac{128}{3}(y+a)^2(y+b)^3$	$y=6\wp^2(z;g_2,0)-b$, $g_2=-\frac{2}{3}(a-b)$

$y''=[a\wp(z)+b]y$ (Lamé's equation)—see [18.8] 2.26

For other (more specialized) equations (of orders 1–3) involving $\wp(z)$, see [18.8], nos. 1.49, 2.28, 2.72–3, 2.439–440, 3.9–12.

For the use of $\wp(z)$ in solving differential equations of the form $y'^m+A(z,y)=0$, where $A(z,y)$ is a polynomial in y of degree $2m$, with coefficients which are analytic functions of z, see [18.7], p. 312ff.

18.7. Integrals

Indefinite

18.7.1 $$\int\wp^2(z)dz=\frac{1}{6}\wp'(z)+\frac{1}{12}g_2z$$

18.7.2 $$\int\wp^3(z)dz=\frac{1}{120}\wp'''(z)-\frac{3}{20}g_2\zeta(z)+\frac{1}{10}g_3z$$

(formulas for higher powers may be derived by integration of formulas for $\wp^{(2k)}(z)$)

For $\int\wp^n(z)dz$, n any positive integer, see [18.15] vol. 4, pp. 108–9.

If $\wp'(a)\neq 0$

18.7.3

$$\wp'(a)\int\frac{dz}{\wp(z)-\wp(a)}=2z\zeta(a)+\ln\sigma(z-a)-\ln\sigma(z+a)$$

For $\int dz/[\wp(z)-\wp(a)]^n$, ($\wp'(a)\neq 0$) n any positive integer, see [18.15], vol. 4, pp. 109–110.

Definite

$\Delta>0$ $\Delta<0$

18.7.4

$$\omega=\int_{e_1}^{\infty}\frac{dt}{\sqrt{s(t)}}\qquad \omega_2=\int_{e_2}^{\infty}\frac{dt}{\sqrt{s(t)}}$$

18.7.5

$$\omega'=i\int_{-\infty}^{e_3}\frac{dt}{\sqrt{|s(t)|}}\qquad \omega_2'=i\int_{-\infty}^{e_2}\frac{dt}{\sqrt{|s(t)|}}$$

18.7.6 where t is real and

18.7.7 $$s(t)=4t^3-g_2t-g_3$$

18.8 Conformal Mapping

$w=u+iv$

$\Delta>0$

$w=\wp(z)$ maps the Fundamental Rectangle onto the half-plane $v\leq 0$; if $|\omega'|=\omega(g_3=0)$, the isosceles triangle $0\omega\omega_2$ is mapped onto $u\geq 0$, $v\leq 0$.

$w=\wp'(z)$ maps the Fundamental Rectangle onto the w-plane less quadrant III; if $|\omega'|=\omega$, the triangle $0\omega\omega_2$ is mapped onto $v\geq 0$, $v\geq u$.

$\Delta<0$

$w=\wp(z)$ maps the Fundamental Rectangle onto the half-plane $v\leq 0$; if $|\omega_2'|=\omega_2(g_3=0)$, the isosceles triangle $0\omega_2\omega'$ is mapped onto $u\geq 0$, $v\leq 0$.

$w=\wp'(z)$ maps the Fundamental Rectangle onto most of the w-plane less quadrant III; if $|\omega_2'|=\omega_2$, the triangle $0\omega_2\omega'$ is mapped onto $v\geq 0$, $v\geq u$.

(a=**period ratio**)

$\Delta>0$

$w=\zeta(z)$ maps the Fundamental Rectangle onto the half-plane $u\geq 0$. If $a\leq 1.9$ (approx.), $v\leq 0$; otherwise the image extends into quadrant I. For very large a, the image has a large area in quadrant I.

$w=\sigma(z)$ maps the Fundamental Rectangle onto quadrant I if $a<1.9$ (approx.), onto quadrants I and II if $1.9\leq a<3.8$ (approx.). For large a, $\arg[\sigma(\omega_2)]\approx\frac{\pi^2 a}{12}$; consequently the image winds around the origin for large a.

Other maps are described in [18.23] arts. 13.7 (square on circle), 13.11 (ring on plane with 2 slits in line) and in [18.24], p. 35 (double half equilateral triangle on half-plane).

$\Delta<0$

$w=\zeta(z)$ maps the Fundamental Rectangle onto the half-plane $u\geq 0$. The image is mostly in quadrant IV for small a, entirely so for (approx.) $1.3\leq a\leq 3.8$. For very large a, the image has a large area in quadrant I.

$w=\sigma(z)$ maps the Fundamental Rectangle onto quadrant I if $a<3.8$ (approx.), onto quadrants I and II if $3.8\leq a<7.6$ (approx.). For large a, $\arg\left[\sigma\left(\omega_2+\frac{\omega_2'}{2}\right)\right]\approx\frac{\pi^2 a}{24}$; consequently the image winds around the origin for large a.

Other maps are described in [18.23] arts. 13.8 (equilateral triangle on half-plane) and 13.9 (isosceles triangle on half-plane).

Obtaining $\wp'$ from $\wp'^2$

Fundamental Rectangle

$\Delta>0$

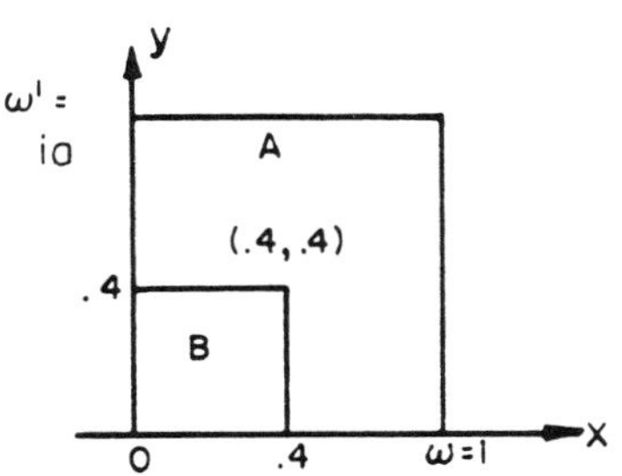

Fundamental Rectangle

$\Delta<0$

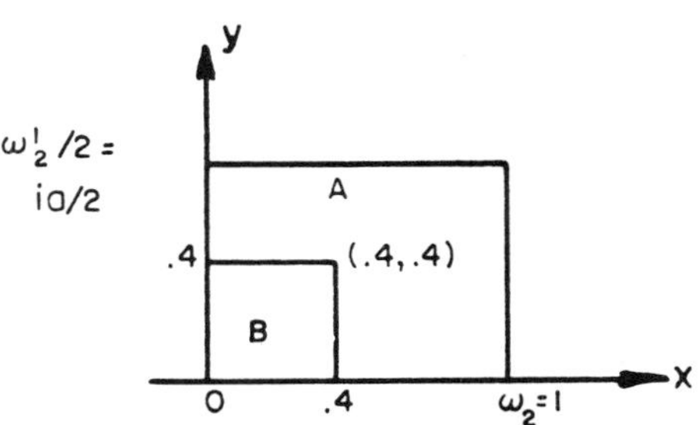

FIGURE 18.4

$\Delta>0$: In region A

$\mathscr{R}(\wp')\geq 0$ if $y\geq .4$ and $x\leq .5$; $\mathscr{I}(\wp')\geq 0$ elsewhere

$\Delta<0$: In region A

(1) If $a\geq 1.05$, use criterion for region A for $\Delta>0$.

(2) If $1\leq a<1.05$: $\mathscr{R}(\wp')\geq 0$ if $y\geq .4$ and $x\leq .4$, $-\pi/4<\arg(\wp')<3\pi/4$ if $.4<y\leq .5$ and $.4<x\leq .5$. $\mathscr{I}(\wp')\geq 0$ elsewhere

In region B

The sign (indeed, perhaps one or more significant digits) of $\wp'$ is obtainable from the first term, $-2/z^3$, of the Laurent series for $\wp'$.

In region B

Use the criterion for region B for $\Delta>0$.

(Precisely similar criteria apply when the real half-period $\neq 1$)

$\Delta>0 \qquad \omega=1$

Map: $\wp(z)=u+iv$

Near zero: $\wp(z)=\frac{1}{z^2}+\epsilon_1$

$\wp(z)=\frac{1}{z^2}+c_2z^2+\epsilon_2$

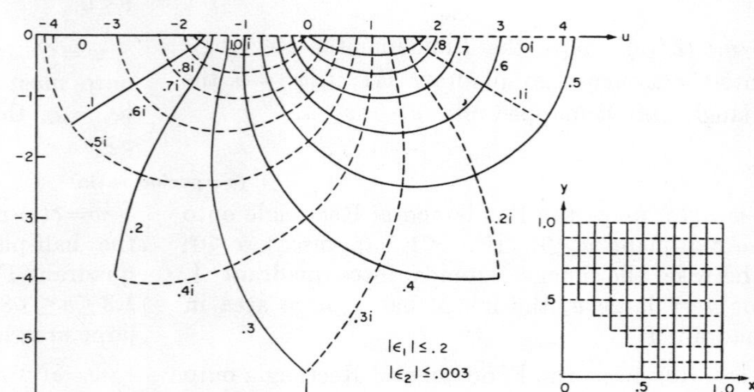

$\omega'=i$

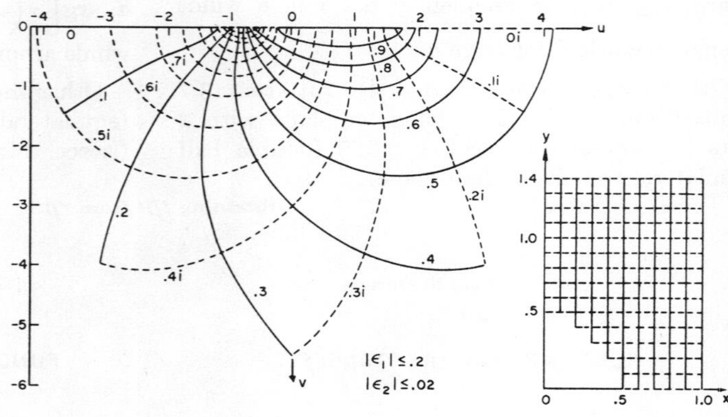

$\omega'=1.4i$

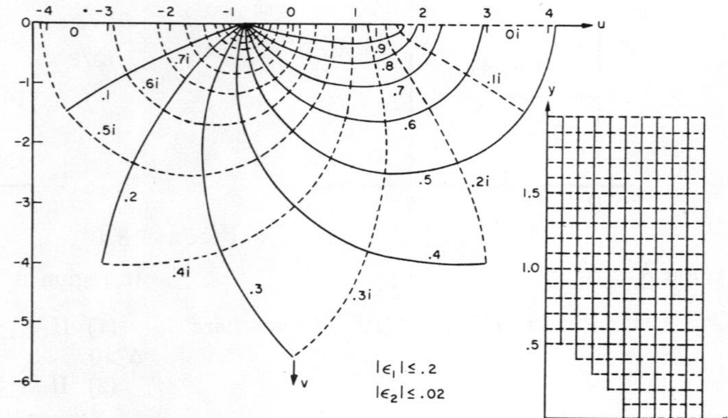

$\omega'=2.0i$

FIGURE 18.5

$$\Delta < 0 \qquad \omega_2 = 1$$

Map: $\wp(z) = u + iv$

Near zero: $\wp(z) = \frac{1}{z^2} + \epsilon_1$

$$\wp(z) = \frac{1}{z^2} + c_2 z^2 + \epsilon_2$$

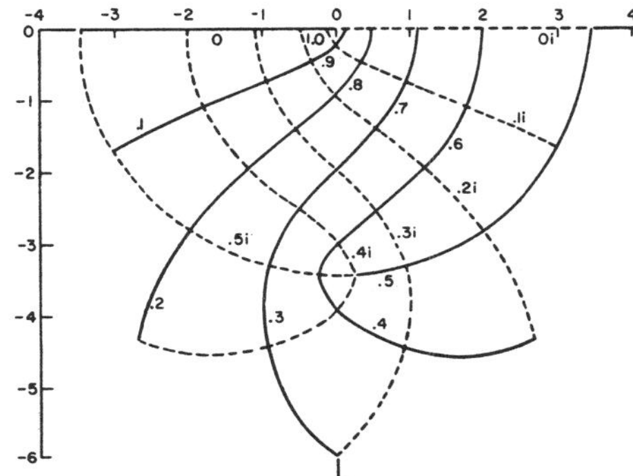

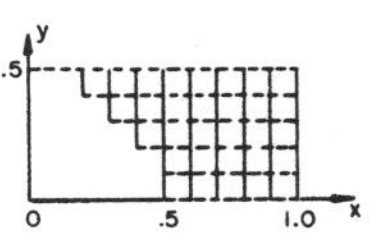

$|\epsilon_1| \leq .7$

$|\epsilon_2| \leq .05$

$\omega_2' = i$

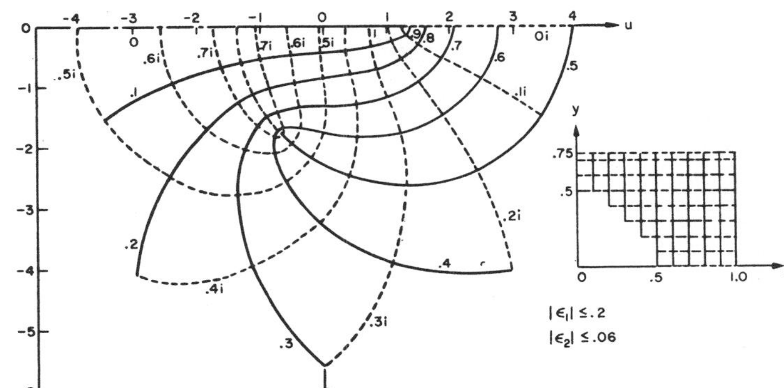

$|\epsilon_1| \leq .2$

$|\epsilon_2| \leq .06$

$\omega_2' = 1.5i$

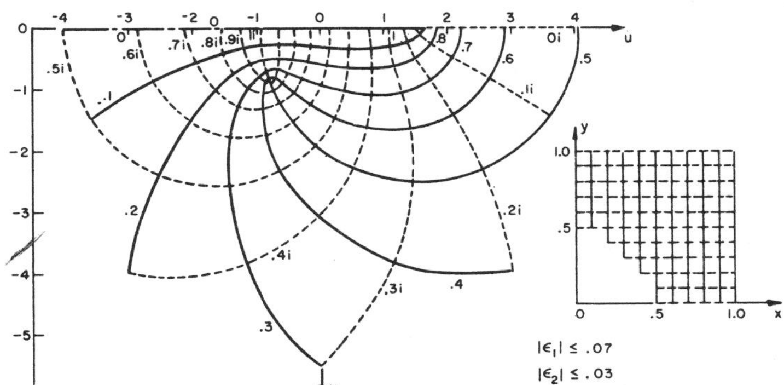

$|\epsilon_1| \leq .07$

$|\epsilon_2| \leq .03$

$\omega_2' = 2.0i$

FIGURE 18.6

$\Delta>0 \qquad \omega=1$

Map: $\zeta(z)=u+iv$

Near zero: $\zeta(z)=\frac{1}{z}+\epsilon_1$

$$\zeta(z)=\frac{1}{z}-\frac{c_2z^3}{3}+\epsilon_2$$

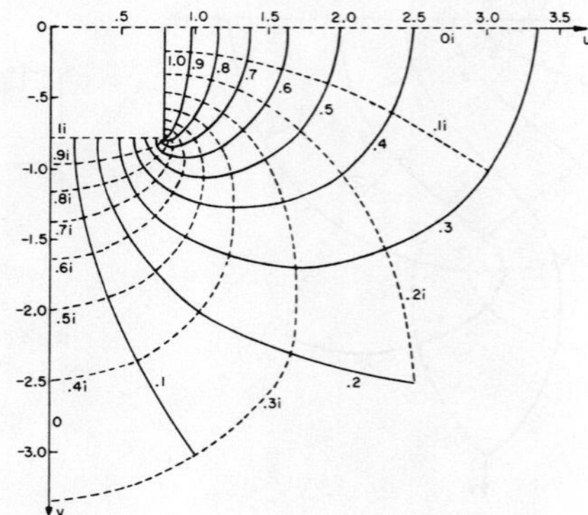

$\omega'=i$

$|\epsilon_1| \leq .01$
$|\epsilon_2| \leq 2\times10^{-5}$

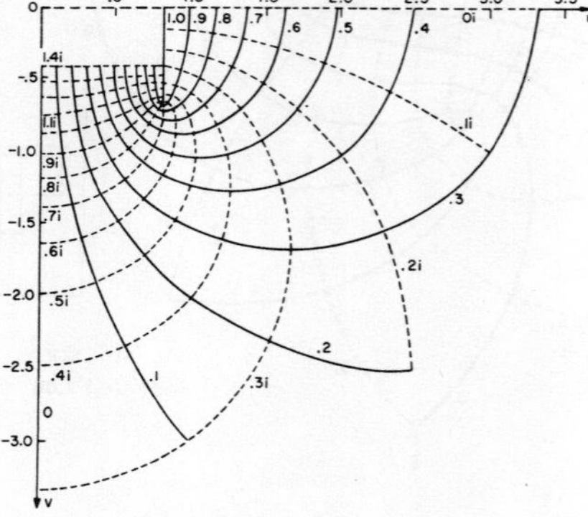

$\omega'=1.4i$

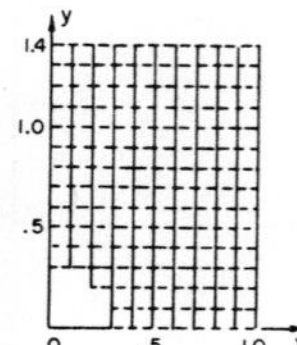

$|\epsilon_1| \leq .007$
$|\epsilon_2| \leq .0002$

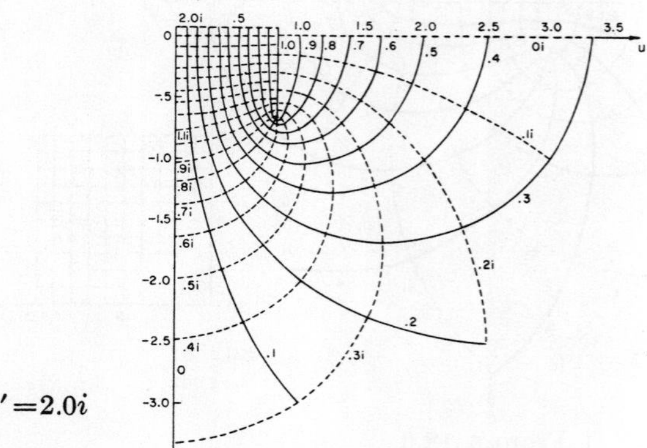

$\omega'=2.0i$

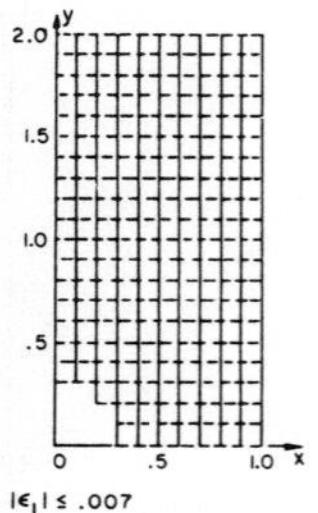

$|\epsilon_1| \leq .007$
$|\epsilon_2| \leq .0002$

FIGURE 18.7

$$\Delta<0 \qquad \omega_2=1$$

Map: $\zeta(z)=u+iv$

Near zero: $\zeta(z)=\frac{1}{z}+\epsilon_1$

$$\zeta(z)=\frac{1}{z}-\frac{c_2z^3}{3}+\epsilon_2$$

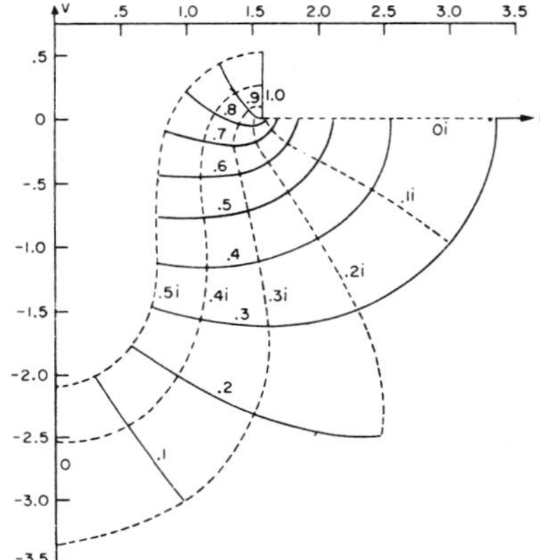

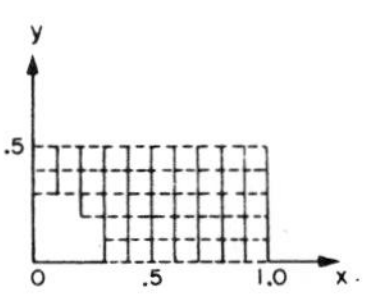

$|\epsilon_1|\le .04$
$|\epsilon_2|\le .0002$

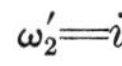

$\omega_2'=i$

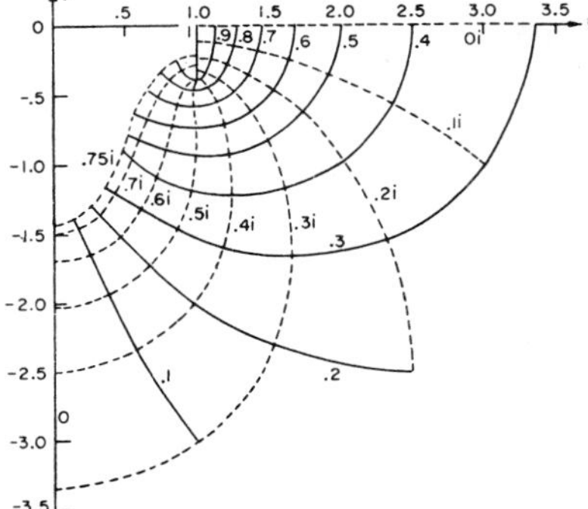

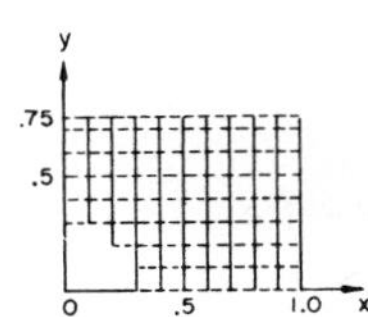

$|\epsilon_1|\le .007$
$|\epsilon_2|\le .0009$

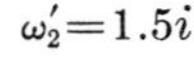

$\omega_2'=1.5i$

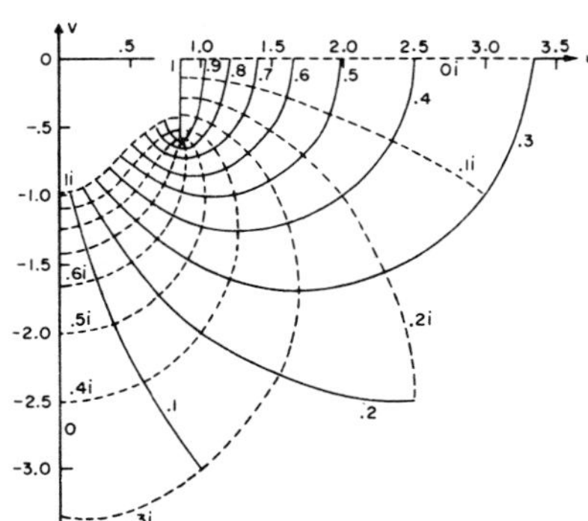

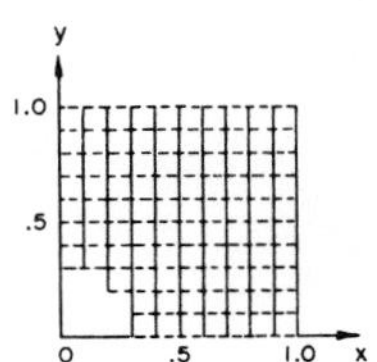

$|\epsilon_1|\le .004$
$|\epsilon_2|\le .0004$

$\omega_2'=2.0i$

FIGURE 18.8

$\Delta > 0 \qquad \omega = 1$

Map: $\sigma(z) = u + iv$

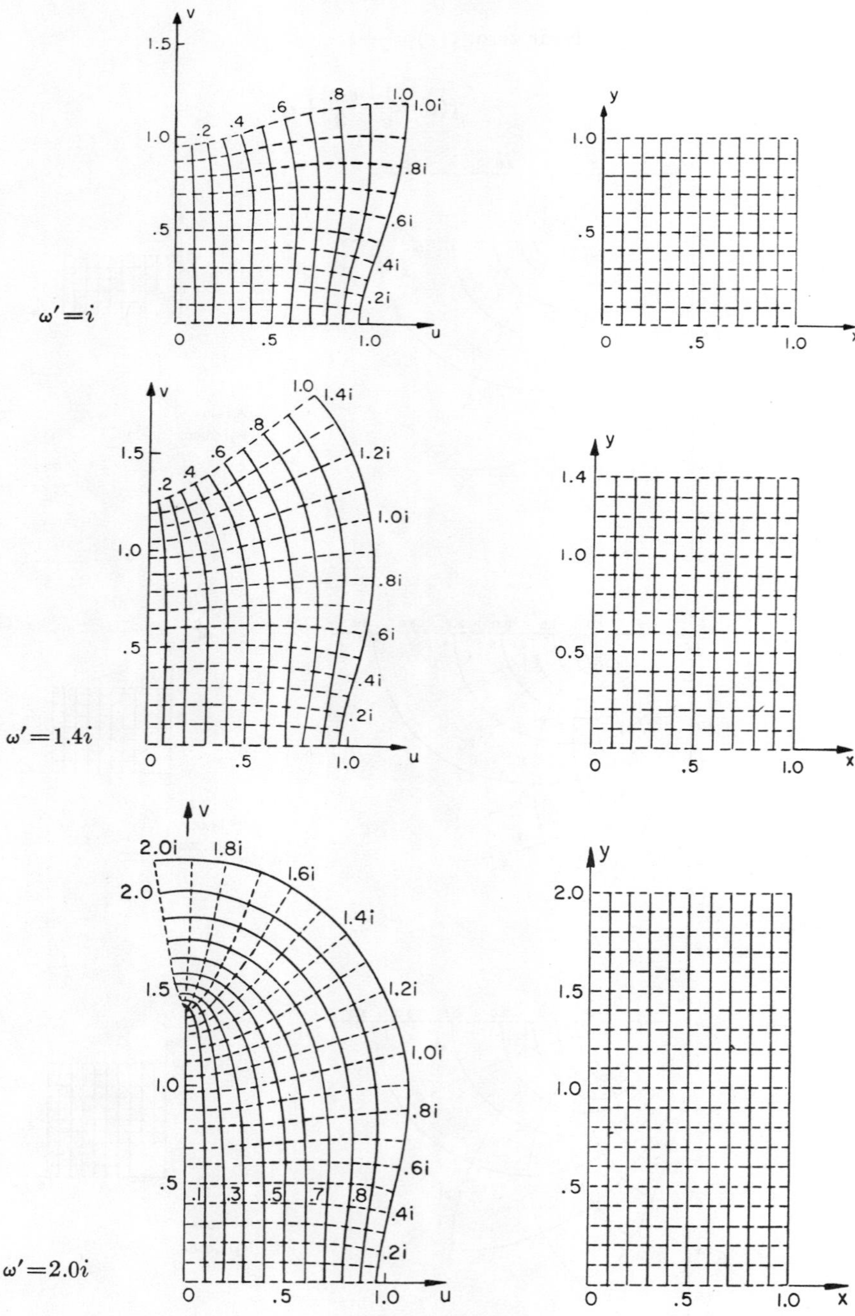

FIGURE 18.9

Map: $\sigma(z)=u+iv$

$\omega_2'=i$

$\omega_2'=1.5i$

$\omega_2'=2.0i$

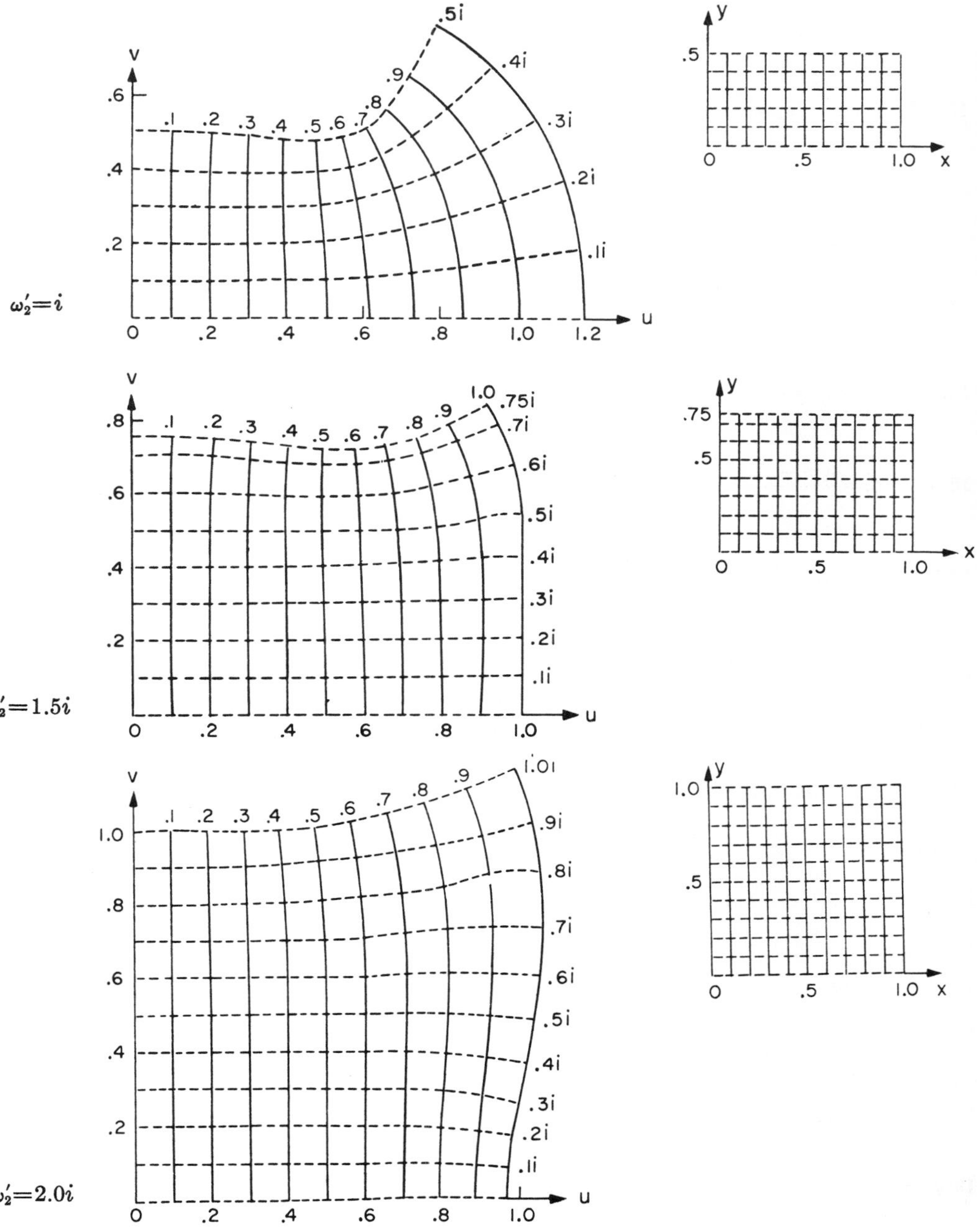

FIGURE 18.10

18.9. Relations with Complete Elliptic Integrals K and K' and Their Parameter m and with Jacobi's Elliptic Functions (see chapter 16)

(Here $K(m)$ and $K'(m)=K(1-m)$ are complete elliptic integrals of the 1st kind; see chapter **17**.)

	$\Delta>0$	$\Delta<0$
18.9.1	$e_1=\dfrac{(2-m)K^2(m)}{3\omega^2}$	$e_1=\dfrac{(2m-1)+6i\sqrt{m-m^2}}{3\omega_2^2}\cdot K^2(m)$
18.9.2	$e_2=\dfrac{(2m-1)K^2(m)}{3\omega^2}$	$e_2=\dfrac{2(1-2m)K^2(m)}{3\omega_2^2}$
18.9.3	$e_3=\dfrac{-(m+1)K^2(m)}{3\omega^2}$	$e_3=\dfrac{(2m-1)-6i\sqrt{m-m^2}}{3\omega_2^2}\cdot K^2(m)$
18.9.4	$g_2=\dfrac{4(m^2-m+1)K^4(m)}{3\omega^4}$	$g_2=\dfrac{4(16m^2-16m+1)K^4(m)}{3\omega_2^4}$
18.9.5	$g_3=\dfrac{4(m-2)(2m-1)(m+1)K^6(m)}{27\omega^6}$	$g_3=\dfrac{8(2m-1)(32m^2-32m-1)K^6(m)}{27\omega_2^6}$
18.9.6	$\Delta=\dfrac{16m^2(m-1)^2K^{12}(m)}{\omega^{12}}$	$\Delta=\dfrac{-256(m-m^2)K^{12}(m)}{\omega_2^{12}}$
18.9.7	$\omega'=\dfrac{iK'(m)\omega}{K(m)}$	$\omega_2'=\dfrac{iK'(m)\omega_2}{K(m)}$
18.9.8	$\omega=K(m)/(e_1-e_3)^{1/2}$	$\omega_2=K(m)/H_2^{1/2}$
18.9.9	$m=(e_2-e_3)/(e_1-e_3)$	$m=\dfrac{1}{2}-\dfrac{3e_2}{4H_2}$
18.9.10		$[0<m\leq\frac{1}{2}$, since $g_3\geq 0]$
18.9.11	$\wp(z)=e_3+(e_1-e_3)/\mathrm{sn}^2(z^*\vert m)$	$\wp(z)=e_2+H_2\dfrac{1+\mathrm{cn}(z'\vert m)}{1-\mathrm{cn}(z'\vert m)}$
18.9.12	$\wp'(z)=-2(e_1-e_3)^{3/2}\cdot\mathrm{cn}(z^*\vert m)\mathrm{dn}(z^*\vert m)/\mathrm{sn}^3(z^*\vert m)$ where $z^*=(e_1-e_3)^{\frac{1}{2}}z$	$\wp'(z)=\dfrac{-4H_2^{3/2}\mathrm{sn}(z'\vert m)\mathrm{dn}(z'\vert m)}{[1-\mathrm{cn}(z'\vert m)]^2}$ where $z'=2zH_2^{1/2}$
18.9.13	$\eta=\zeta(\omega)=\dfrac{K(m)}{3\omega}[3E(m)+(m-2)K(m)]$	$\eta_2=\zeta(\omega_2)=\dfrac{K(m)}{3\omega_2}[6E(m)+(4m-5)K(m)]$
18.9.14	$\eta'=\zeta(\omega')=\dfrac{\eta\omega'-\frac{1}{2}\pi i}{\omega}$	$\eta_2'=\zeta(\omega_2')=\dfrac{\eta_2\omega_2'-\pi i}{\omega_2}$

[$E(m)$ is a complete elliptic integral of the 2d kind (see chapter **17**).]

18.10. Relations with Theta Functions (chapter 16)

The formal definitions of the four ϑ functions are given by the series **16.27.1–16.27.4** which converge for all complex z and all q defined below. (Some authors use πz, instead of z, as the independent variable.)

These functions depend on z and on a parameter q, which is usually suppressed. Note that

$$\vartheta_1'(0)=\vartheta_2(0)\vartheta_3(0)\vartheta_4(0), \text{ where } \vartheta_i(0)=\vartheta_i(0, q).$$

	$\Delta>0$	$\Delta<0$
18.10.1	$\tau=\omega'/\omega$	$\tau_2=\omega_2'/2\omega_2$
18.10.2	$q=e^{i\pi\tau}=e^{-\pi K'/K}$	$q=iq_2=ie^{i\pi\tau_2}=ie^{-\pi\lvert\omega_2'\rvert/2\omega_2}$
18.10.3	q is real and since $g_3\geq 0(\lvert\omega'\rvert\geq\omega)$, $0<q\leq e^{-\pi}$	q is pure imaginary and since $g_3\geq 0(\lvert\omega_2'\rvert\geq\omega_2)$, $0<\lvert q\rvert\leq e^{-\pi/2}$
18.10.4	$(v=\pi z/2\omega)$	$(v=\pi z/2\omega_2)$
18.10.5	$\wp(z)=e_j+\frac{\pi^2}{4\omega^2}\left[\frac{\vartheta_1'(0)\vartheta_{j+1}(v)}{\vartheta_{j+1}(0)\vartheta_1(v)}\right]^2$ $j=1, 2, 3$	$\wp(z)=e_2+\frac{\pi^2}{4\omega_2^2}\left[\frac{\vartheta_1'(0)\vartheta_2(v)}{\vartheta_2(0)\vartheta_1(v)}\right]^2$
18.10.6	$\wp'(z)=-\frac{\pi^3}{4\omega^3}\frac{\vartheta_2(v)\vartheta_3(v)\vartheta_4(v)\vartheta_1'^3(0)}{\vartheta_2(0)\vartheta_3(0)\vartheta_4(0)\vartheta_1^3(v)}$	$\wp'(z)=-\frac{\pi^3}{4\omega_2^3}\frac{\vartheta_2(v)\vartheta_3(v)\vartheta_4(v)\vartheta_1'^3(0)}{\vartheta_2(0)\vartheta_3(0)\vartheta_4(0)\vartheta_1^3(v)}$
18.10.7	$\zeta(z)=\frac{\eta z}{\omega}+\frac{\pi\vartheta_1'(v)}{2\omega\vartheta_1(v)}$	$\zeta(z)=\frac{\eta_2 z}{\omega_2}+\frac{\pi\vartheta_1'(v)}{2\omega_2\vartheta_1(v)}$
18.10.8	$\sigma(z)=\frac{2\omega}{\pi}\exp\left(\frac{\eta z^2}{2\omega}\right)\frac{\vartheta_1(v)}{\vartheta_1'(0)}$	$\sigma(z)=\frac{2\omega_2}{\pi}\exp\left(\frac{\eta_2 z^2}{2\omega_2}\right)\frac{\vartheta_1(v)}{\vartheta_1'(0)}$
18.10.9	$12\omega^2 e_1=\pi^2[\vartheta_3^4(0)+\vartheta_4^4(0)]$	$12\omega_2^2 e_1=\pi^2[\vartheta_2^4(0)-\vartheta_4^4(0)]$
18.10.10	$12\omega^2 e_2=\pi^2[\vartheta_2^4(0)-\vartheta_4^4(0)]$	$12\omega_2^2 e_2=\pi^2[\vartheta_3^4(0)+\vartheta_4^4(0)]$
18.10.11	$12\omega^2 e_3=-\pi^2[\vartheta_2^4(0)+\vartheta_3^4(0)]$	$12\omega_2^2 e_3=-\pi^2[\vartheta_2^4(0)+\vartheta_3^4(0)]$
18.10.12	$(e_2-e_3)^{\frac{1}{2}}=-i(e_3-e_2)^{\frac{1}{2}}=\frac{\pi}{2\omega}\vartheta_2^2(0)$	$(e_2-e_3)^{\frac{1}{2}}=i(e_3-e_2)^{\frac{1}{2}}=\frac{\pi}{2\omega_2}\vartheta_3^2(0)$
18.10.13	$(e_1-e_3)^{\frac{1}{2}}=-i(e_3-e_1)^{\frac{1}{2}}=\frac{\pi}{2\omega}\vartheta_3^2(0)$	$(e_1-e_3)^{\frac{1}{2}}=i(e_3-e_1)^{\frac{1}{2}}=\frac{\pi}{2\omega_2}\vartheta_2^2(0)$
18.10.14	$(e_1-e_2)^{\frac{1}{2}}=-i(e_2-e_1)^{\frac{1}{2}}=\frac{\pi}{2\omega}\vartheta_4^2(0)$	$(e_2-e_1)^{\frac{1}{2}}=-i(e_1-e_2)^{\frac{1}{2}}=\frac{\pi}{2\omega_2}\vartheta_4^2(0)$
18.10.15	$g_2=\frac{2}{3}\left(\frac{\pi}{2\omega}\right)^4[\vartheta_2^8(0)+\vartheta_3^8(0)+\vartheta_4^8(0)]$	$g_2=\frac{2}{3}\left(\frac{\pi}{2\omega_2}\right)^4[\vartheta_2^8(0)+\vartheta_3^8(0)+\vartheta_4^8(0)]$
18.10.16	$g_3=4e_1e_2e_3$	$g_3=4e_1e_2e_3$
18.10.17	$\Delta^{\frac{1}{4}}=\frac{\pi^3}{4\omega^3}\vartheta_1'^2(0)$	$(-\Delta)^{\frac{1}{4}}=\frac{\pi^3}{4\omega_2^3}\vartheta_1'^2(0)e^{-i\pi/4}$
18.10.18	$\eta\equiv\zeta(\omega)=-\frac{\pi^2\vartheta_1'''(0)}{12\omega\vartheta_1'(0)}$	$\eta_2\equiv\zeta(\omega_2)=-\frac{\pi^2\vartheta_1'''(0)}{12\omega_2\vartheta_1'(0)}$
18.10.19	$\eta'\equiv\zeta(\omega')=\frac{\eta\omega'-\frac{1}{2}\pi i}{\omega}$	$\eta_2'\equiv\zeta(\omega_2')=\frac{\eta_2\omega_2'-\pi i}{\omega_2}$

Series

18.10.20 $$\vartheta_1(0)=0$$

18.10.21 $$\vartheta_2(0)=2q^{\frac{1}{4}}[1+q^{1\cdot 2}+q^{2\cdot 3}+q^{3\cdot 4}+\ldots+q^{n(n+1)}+\ldots]$$

18.10.22 $$\vartheta_3(0)=1+2[q+q^4+q^9+\ldots+q^{n^2}+\ldots]$$

18.10.23 $$\vartheta_4(0)=1+2[-q+q^4-q^9+\ldots+(-1)^n q^{n^2}+\ldots]$$

Attainable Accuracy

	$\Delta>0$	$\Delta<0$
	Note: $\vartheta_j(0)>0$, $j=2, 3, 4$	Note: $\vartheta_2(0)=Ae^{i\pi/8}$, $A>0$; $\mathscr{R}\vartheta_3(0)>0$; $\vartheta_4(0)=\overline{\vartheta_3(0)}$
$\vartheta_j(0)$:	2 terms give at least 5S	2 terms give at least 3S
$j=2, 3, 4$	3 terms give at least 11S	3 terms give at least 5S
	4 terms give at least 21S	4 terms give at least 10S

18.11 Expressing any Elliptic Function in Terms of $\wp$ and $\wp'$

If $f(z)$ is any elliptic function and $\wp(z)$ has same periods, write

18.11.1 $$f(z)=\tfrac{1}{2}[f(z)+f(-z)]+\tfrac{1}{2}[\{f(z)-f(-z)\}\{\wp'(z)\}^{-1}]\wp'(z).$$

Since both brackets represent even elliptic functions, we ask how to express an even elliptic function $g(z)$ (of order $2k$) in terms of $\wp(z)$. Because of the evenness, an irreducible set of zeros can be denoted by a_i ($i=1, 2, \ldots, k$) and the set of points congruent to $-a_i$ ($i=1, 2, \ldots, k$); correspondingly in connection with the poles we consider the points $\pm b_i$, $i=1, 2, \ldots, k$. Then

18.11.2 $$g(z)=A\prod_{i=1}^{k}\left\{\frac{\wp(z)-\wp(a_i)}{\wp(z)-\wp(b_i)}\right\},$$ where A is

a constant. If any a_i or b_i is congruent to the origin, the corresponding factor is omitted from the product. Factors corresponding to multiple poles (zeros) are repeated according to the multiplicity.

18.12. Case $\Delta=0$ $(c>0)$

Subcase I

18.12.1 $g_2>0$, $g_3<0$: $(e_1=e_2=c,\ e_3=-2c)$

18.12.2 $$H_1=H_2=0,\ H_3=3c$$

18.12.3

$$\wp(z;\,12c^2,-8c^3)=c+3c\{\sinh[(3c)^{\frac{1}{2}}z]\}^{-2}$$

18.12.4

$$\zeta(z;\,12c^2,-8c^3)=-cz+(3c)^{\frac{1}{2}}\coth[(3c)^{\frac{1}{2}}z]$$

18.12.5

$$\sigma(z;\,12c^2,-8c^3)=(3c)^{-\frac{1}{2}}\sinh[(3c)^{\frac{1}{2}}z]e^{-cz^2/2}$$

18.12.6 $$\omega=\infty,\ \omega'=(12c)^{-\frac{1}{2}}\pi i$$

18.12.7 $$\eta=\zeta(\omega)=-\infty$$

18.12.8 $$\eta'=\zeta(\omega')=-c\omega'$$

18.12.9 $$q=1,\qquad m=1$$

18.12.10 $$\sigma(\omega)=0$$

18.12.11 $$\sigma(\omega')=\frac{2\omega' e^{\pi^2/24}}{\pi}$$

18.12.12 $$\sigma(\omega_2)=0$$

18.12.13 $$\wp(\omega/2)=c$$

18.12.14 $$\wp'(\omega/2)=0$$

18.12.15 $$\zeta(\omega/2)=-\infty$$

18.12.16 $$\sigma(\omega/2)=0$$

18.12.17 $$\wp(\omega'/2)=-5c$$

18.12.18 $$\wp'(\omega'/2)=\frac{-\pi^3}{2\omega'^3}$$

18.12.19 $$\zeta(\omega'/2)=\tfrac{1}{2}(-c\omega'+\pi/\omega')$$

18.12.20 $\sigma(\omega'/2)=\frac{\omega' e^{\pi^2/96}\sqrt{2}}{\pi}$

18.12.21 $\wp(\omega_2/2)=c$

18.12.22 $\wp'(\omega_2/2)=0$

18.12.23 $\zeta(\omega_2/2)=-\infty-\frac{c\omega'}{2}$

18.12.24 $\sigma(\omega_2/2)=0$

Subcase II

18.12.25

$$g_2>0,\ g_3>0:\ (e_1=2c,\ e_2=e_3=-c)$$

18.12.26 $H_1=3c,\ H_2=H_3=0$

18.12.27 $\wp(z;\ 12c^2,\ 8c^3)=-c+3c\{\sin[(3c)^{\frac{1}{2}}z]\}^{-2}$

18.12.28

$$\zeta(z;\ 12c^2,\ 8c^3)=cz+(3c)^{\frac{1}{2}}\cot[(3c)^{\frac{1}{2}}z]$$

18.12.29

$$\sigma(z;\ 12c^2,\ 8c^3)=(3c)^{-\frac{1}{2}}\sin[(3c)^{\frac{1}{2}}z]e^{cz^2/2}$$

18.12.30 $\omega=(12c)^{-\frac{1}{2}}\pi,\ \omega'=i\infty$

18.12.31 $\eta=\zeta(\omega)=c\omega$

18.12.32 $\eta'=\zeta(\omega')=i\infty$

18.12.33 $q=0,\qquad m=0$

18.12.34 $\sigma(\omega)=\frac{2\omega e^{\pi^2/24}}{\pi}$

18.12.35 $\sigma(\omega')=0$

18.12.36 $\sigma(\omega_2)=0$

18.12.37 $\wp(\omega/2)=5c$

18.12.38 $\wp'(\omega/2)=\frac{-\pi^3}{2\omega^3}$

18.12.39 $\zeta(\omega/2)=\frac{1}{2}(c\omega+\pi/\omega)$

18.12.40 $\sigma(\omega/2)=\frac{e^{\pi^2/96}\omega\sqrt{2}}{\pi}$

18.12.41 $\wp(\omega'/2)=-c$

18.12.42 $\wp'(\omega'/2)=0$

18.12.43 $\zeta(\omega'/2)=+i\infty$

18.12.44 $\sigma(\omega'/2)=0$

18.12.45 $\wp(\omega_2/2)=-c$

18.12.46 $\wp'(\omega_2/2)=0$

18.12.47 $\zeta(\omega_2/2)=\frac{c\omega}{2}+i\infty$

18.12.48 $\sigma(\omega_2/2)=0$

Subcase III

18.12.49 $g_2=0,\ g_3=0\,(e_1=e_2=e_3=0)$

18.12.50 $\wp(z;\ 0,\ 0)=z^{-2}$

18.12.51 $\zeta(z;\ 0,\ 0)=z^{-1}$

18.12.52 $\sigma(z;\ 0,\ 0)=z$

18.12.53 $\omega=-i\omega'=\infty$

18.13. Equianharmonic Case ($g_2=0,\ g_3=1$)

If $g_2=0$ and $g_3>0$, homogeneity relations allow us to reduce our considerations of $\wp$ to $\wp(z;0,1)$ ($\wp'$, ζ and σ are handled similarly). Thus $\wp(z;0,g_3)=g_3^{1/3}\wp(zg_3^{1/6};0,1)$. The case $g_2=0$, $g_3=1$ is called the EQUIANHARMONIC case.

$\frac{1}{4}$ FPP; *Reduction to Fundamental Triangle*

$\Delta_1\equiv\Delta 0\omega_2 z_0$ is the Fundamental Triangle

Let ϵ denote $e^{i\pi/3}$ throughout **18.13.**

$\omega_2\approx 1.5299\ 54037\ 05719\ 28749\ 13194\ 17231$[6]

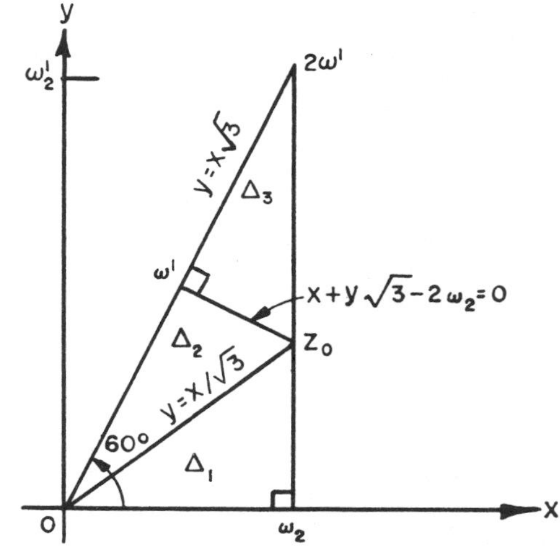

FIGURE 18.11

[6] This value was computed and checked by multiple precision on a desk calculator and is believed correct to 30S.

Reduction for z_2 in Δ_2: $z_1=\epsilon\bar{z}_2$ is in Δ_1.

18.13.1 $\wp(z_2)=\epsilon^{-2}\overline{\wp}(z_1)$

18.13.2 $\wp'(z_2)=-\overline{\wp}'(z_1)$

18.13.3 $\zeta(z_2)=\epsilon^{-1}\bar{\zeta}(z_1)$

18.13.4 $\sigma(z_2)=\epsilon\bar{\sigma}(z_1)$

Reduction for z_3 in Δ_3: $z_1=\epsilon^{-1}(2\omega'-z_3)$ is in Δ_1

18.13.5 $\wp(z_3)=\epsilon^{-2}\wp(z_1)$

18.13.6 $\wp'(z_3)=\wp'(z_1)$

18.13.7 $\zeta(z_3)=-\epsilon^{-1}\zeta(z_1)+2\eta', \qquad \eta'=\zeta(\omega')$

18.13.8 $\sigma(z_3)=\epsilon\sigma(z_1)\exp[(z_3-\omega')(2\eta')]$

Special Values and Formulas

18.13.9

$$\Delta=-27, \qquad H_1=\sqrt{3}(4^{-1/3})\bar{\epsilon},$$

$$H_2=\sqrt{3}(4^{-1/3}), \qquad H_3=\sqrt{3}(4^{-1/3})\epsilon$$

18.13.10 $m=\sin^2 15^\circ=\dfrac{2-\sqrt{3}}{4}, \qquad q=ie^{-\pi\sqrt{3}/2}$

18.13.11 $\vartheta_2(0)=Ae^{i\pi/8}$

18.13.12 $\vartheta_3(0)=Ae^{i\pi/24}$

18.13.13 $\vartheta_4(0)=Ae^{-i\pi/24}$

18.13.14

where $A=(\omega_2/\pi)^{1/2}2^{1/3}3^{1/8}\approx 1.0086\ 67$

18.13.15 $\omega_2=\dfrac{K(m)2^{1/3}}{3^{1/4}}=\dfrac{\Gamma^3(1/3)}{4\pi}$

Values at Half-periods

	$\wp$	$\wp'$	ζ	σ
18.13.16				
$\omega\equiv\omega_1$	$e_1=4^{-1/3}\epsilon^2$	0	$\eta=\epsilon\pi/2\omega_2\sqrt{3}$	$\epsilon^{-1}\sigma(\omega_2)$
18.13.17				
ω_2	$e_2=4^{-1/3}$	0	$\eta_2=\eta+\eta'=\pi/2\omega_2\sqrt{3}$	$\dfrac{e^{\pi/4\sqrt{3}}(2^{1/3})}{3^{1/4}}$
18.13.18				
$\omega'\equiv\omega_3$	$e_3=4^{-1/3}\epsilon^{-2}$	0	$\eta'=\epsilon^{-1}\pi/2\omega_2\sqrt{3}$	$\epsilon\sigma(w_2)$
18.13.19				
ω_2'	$e_2=4^{-1/3}$	0	$\eta_2'=-\pi i/2\omega_2=\eta'-\eta$	$\dfrac{ie^{3\pi/4\sqrt{3}}(2^{1/3})}{3^{1/4}}$

Values [7] along $(0, \omega_2)$

	$\wp$	$\wp'$	ζ	σ
18.13.20				
$2\omega_2/9$	$\dfrac{\sqrt[3]{\cos 80^\circ}}{\sqrt[3]{\cos 20^\circ}-\sqrt[3]{\cos 40^\circ}}$	$\dfrac{-\sqrt{3}[\sqrt[3]{\cos 20^\circ}+\sqrt[3]{\cos 40^\circ}]}{\sqrt[3]{\cos 20^\circ}-\sqrt[3]{\cos 40^\circ}}$		
18.13.21				
$\omega_2/3$	$1/(2^{1/3}-1)$	$-\sqrt{3}(2^{1/3}+1)/(2^{1/3}-1)$	$\dfrac{\eta_2}{3}+\dfrac{\sqrt{3}(2^{2/3}+2+2^{4/3})}{6}$	$\dfrac{e^{\pi/36\sqrt{3}}}{3^{1/6}}\sqrt[4]{\dfrac{2^{1/3}-1}{2^{1/3}+1}}$
18.13.22				
$4\omega_2/9$	$\dfrac{\sqrt[3]{\cos 40^\circ}}{\sqrt[3]{\cos 20^\circ}-\sqrt[3]{\cos 80^\circ}}$	$\dfrac{-\sqrt{3}[\sqrt[3]{\cos 20^\circ}+\sqrt[3]{\cos 80^\circ}]}{\sqrt[3]{\cos 20^\circ}-\sqrt[3]{\cos 80^\circ}}$		
18.13.23				
$\omega_2/2$	e_2+H_2	$-3^{3/4}\sqrt{2+\sqrt{3}}$	$(\pi/4\omega_2\sqrt{3})+(3^{1/4}\sqrt{2+\sqrt{3}}/2^{4/3})$	$\dfrac{e^{\pi/16\sqrt{3}}(2^{1/12})}{3^{1/4}\sqrt[8]{2+\sqrt{3}}}$
18.13.24				
$2\omega_2/3$	1	$-\sqrt{3}$	$\frac{2}{3}(\eta_2)+3^{-1/2}$	$e^{\pi/9\sqrt{3}}/3^{1/6}$
18.13.25				
$8\omega_2/9$	$\dfrac{\sqrt[3]{\cos 20^\circ}}{\sqrt[3]{\cos 40^\circ}+\sqrt[3]{\cos 80^\circ}}$	$\dfrac{-\sqrt{3}[\sqrt[3]{\cos 40^\circ}-\sqrt[3]{\cos 80^\circ}]}{\sqrt[3]{\cos 40^\circ}+\sqrt[3]{\cos 80^\circ}}$		

[7] Values at $2\omega_2/9$, $4\omega_2/9$ and $8\omega_2/9$ from [18.14].

Values along $(0, z_0)$

	$\wp$	$\wp'$	ζ	σ
18.13.26 $z_0/2$	$-2^{1/3}\epsilon^2$	$3i$	$\left[\frac{\eta_2}{\sqrt{3}}+2^{-1/3}\right]e^{-i\pi/6}$	$\frac{e^{\pi/12\sqrt{3}}e^{i\pi/6}}{3^{1/4}}$
18.13.27 $3z_0/4$	$\epsilon^2(e_2-H_2)$	$i(3^{3/4})\sqrt{2-\sqrt{3}}$	$\left[\frac{\pi}{4\omega_2}+\frac{3^{1/4}\sqrt{2-\sqrt{3}}}{2^{4/3}}\right]e^{-i\pi/6}$	$\frac{e^{3\pi/16\sqrt{3}}(2^{1/12})e^{i\pi/6}}{3^{1/4}\sqrt[8]{2-\sqrt{3}}}$
18.13.28 z_0	0	i	$\frac{2\eta_2}{\sqrt{3}}e^{-i\pi/6}$	$e^{\pi/3\sqrt{3}}\cdot e^{i\pi/6}$

Duplication Formulas

18.13.29 $$\wp(2z)=\frac{\wp(z)[\wp^3(z)+2]}{4\wp^3(z)-1}$$

18.13.30 $$\wp'(2z)=\frac{2\wp^6(z)-10\wp^3(z)-1}{[\wp'(z)]^3}$$

18.13.31 $$\zeta(2z)=2\zeta(z)+\frac{3\wp^2(z)}{\wp'(z)}$$

18.13.32 $$\sigma(2z)=-\wp'(z)\sigma^4(z)$$

Trisection Formulas (x real)

18.13.33 $$\wp\left(\frac{x}{3}\right)=\frac{\sqrt[3]{\cos\frac{\phi-\pi}{3}}}{\sqrt[3]{\cos\frac{\phi}{3}}-\sqrt[3]{\cos\frac{\phi+\pi}{3}}}$$

18.13.34 $$\wp'\left(\frac{x}{3}\right)=-\sqrt{3}\,\frac{\sqrt[3]{\cos\frac{\phi}{3}}+\sqrt[3]{\cos\frac{\phi+\pi}{3}}}{\sqrt[3]{\cos\frac{\phi}{3}}-\sqrt[3]{\cos\frac{\phi+\pi}{3}}}$$

where $\tan\phi=\wp'(x)$, $0<x<2\omega_2$ and we must choose ϕ in intervals

$$\left(-\frac{\pi}{2},\frac{\pi}{2}\right),\left(\frac{\pi}{2},\frac{3\pi}{2}\right),\left(\frac{3\pi}{2},\frac{5\pi}{2}\right)\text{ to get}$$

$$\wp\left(\frac{x}{3}\right),\wp\left(\frac{x}{3}+\frac{2\omega_2}{3}\right),\wp\left(\frac{x}{3}+\frac{4\omega_2}{3}\right),\text{ respectively.}$$

Complex Multiplication

18.13.35 $$\wp(\epsilon z)=\epsilon^{-2}\wp(z)$$

18.13.36 $$\wp'(\epsilon z)=-\wp'(z)$$

18.13.37 $$\zeta(\epsilon z)=\epsilon^{-1}\zeta(z)$$

18.13.38 $$\sigma(\epsilon z)=\epsilon\sigma(z)$$

In the above, ϵ denotes (as it does throughout section **18.13**), $e^{i\pi/3}$. The above equations are useful as follows, e.g.:

If z is real, ϵz is on $0\omega'$ **(Figure 18.11)**; if ϵz were purely imaginary, z would be on $0z_0$ **(Figure 18.11)**.

Conformal Maps

Equianharmonic Case

Map: $f(z)=u+iv$

$\wp(z)$

Near zero: $\wp(z)=\frac{1}{z^2}+\epsilon_1$

$$\wp(z)=\frac{1}{z^2}+\frac{z^4}{28}+\epsilon_2$$

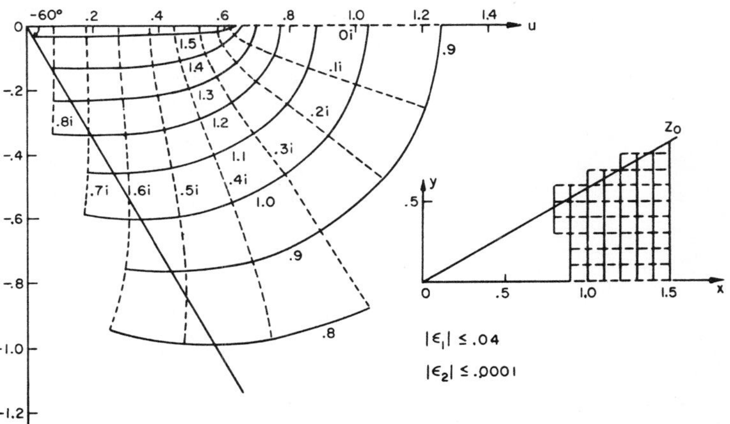

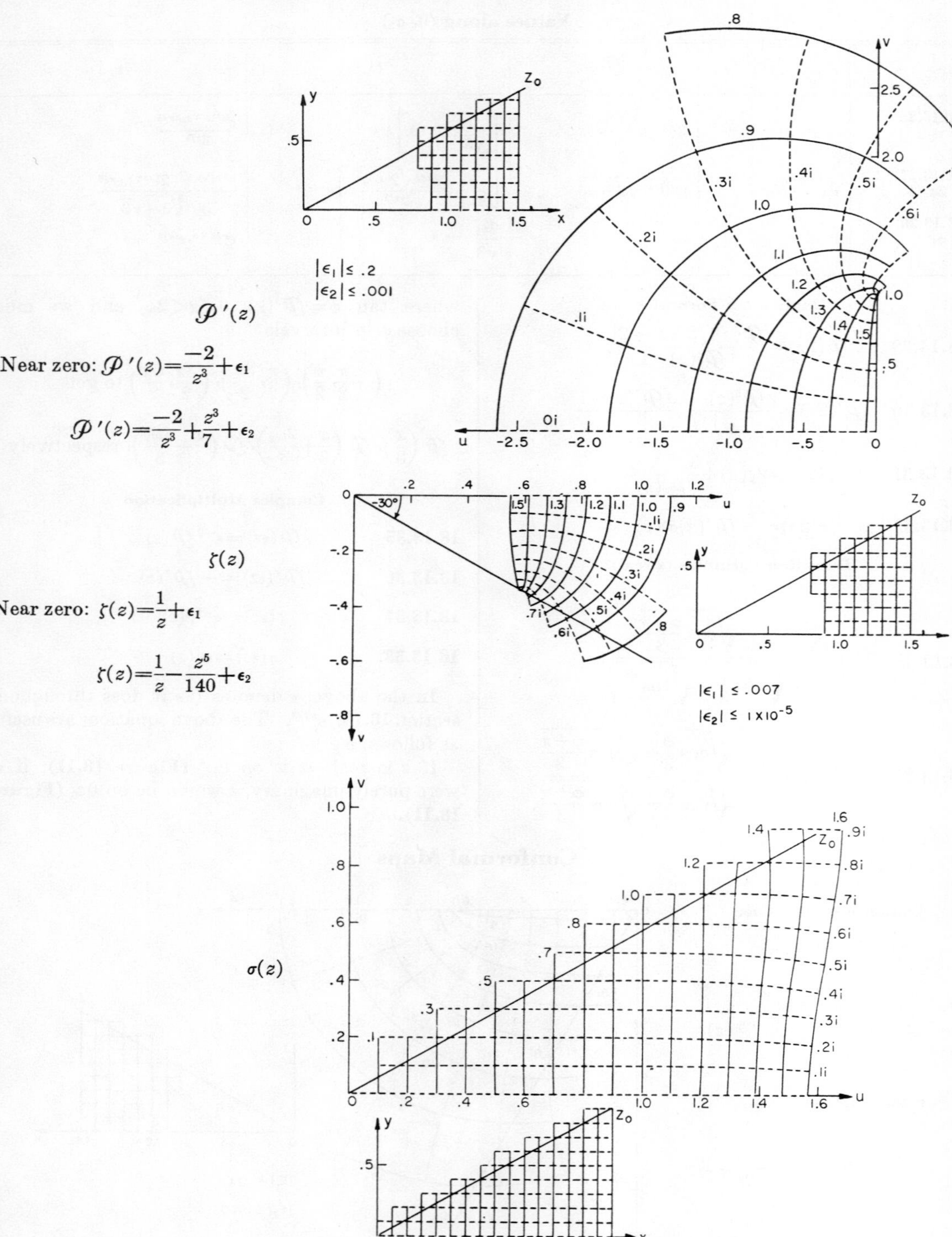
$\wp'(z)$
Near zero: $\wp'(z)=\frac{-2}{z^3}+\epsilon_1$
$\wp'(z)=\frac{-2}{z^3}+\frac{z^3}{7}+\epsilon_2$
$|\epsilon_1|\leq .2$
$|\epsilon_2|\leq .001$
$\zeta(z)$
Near zero: $\zeta(z)=\frac{1}{z}+\epsilon_1$
$\zeta(z)=\frac{1}{z}-\frac{z^5}{140}+\epsilon_2$
$|\epsilon_1|\leq .007$
$|\epsilon_2|\leq 1\times10^{-5}$
$\sigma(z)$
Z_0
-30°
u
v
x
y

FIGURE 18.12

Coefficients for Laurent Series for $\wp$, $\wp'$ and ζ

($c_m=0$ for $m\neq 3k$)

k	EXACT c_{3k}	APPROXIMATE c_{3k}
1	$1/28$	3. 5714 28571 42857 . . . $\times 10^{-2}$
2	$1/(13\cdot 28^2)=1/10192$	9. 8116 16954 47409 73312 40188$\times 10^{-5}$
3	$1/(13\cdot 19\cdot 28^3)=1/5422144$	1. 8442 88901 21693 55885 78983$\times 10^{-7}$
4	$3/(5\cdot 13^2\cdot 19\cdot 28^4)=234375/(7709611\times 10^8)$	3. 0400 36650 35758 61350 20301$\times 10^{-10}$
5	$4/(5\cdot 13^2\cdot 19\cdot 31\cdot 28^5)=78125/(16729\ 85587\times 10^8)$	4. 6697 95161 83961 00384 33643$\times 10^{-13}$
6	$(7\cdot 43)/(13^3\cdot 19^2\cdot 31\cdot 37\cdot 28^6)$	6. 8662 18676 79393 36788 98$\times 10^{-16}$
7	$(6\cdot 431)/(5\cdot 13^3\cdot 19^2\cdot 31\cdot 37\cdot 43\cdot 28^7)$	9. 7990 31742 57961 41839 66$\times 10^{-19}$
8	$(3\cdot 7\cdot 313)/(5^2\cdot 13^4\cdot 19^2\cdot 31\cdot 37\cdot 43\cdot 28^8)$	1. 3685 06574 79360 13026 87$\times 10^{-21}$
9	$(4\cdot 1201)/(5^2\cdot 13^4\cdot 19^3\cdot 31\cdot 37\cdot 43\cdot 28^9)$	1. 8800 72610 01329 79236 40$\times 10^{-24}$
10	$(2^2\cdot 3\cdot 41\cdot 1823)/(5\cdot 13^5\cdot 19^3\cdot 31^2\cdot 37\cdot 43\cdot 61\cdot 28^{10})$	2. 5497 66946 68202 63683$\times 10^{-27}$
11	$(3\cdot 79\cdot 733)/(5\cdot 13^4\cdot 19^3\cdot 31^2\cdot 37\cdot 43\cdot 61\cdot 67\cdot 28^{11})$	3. 4222 48599 51463 05316$\times 10^{-30}$
12	$\dfrac{3\cdot 1153\cdot 13963\cdot 29059}{5^3\cdot 13^6\cdot 19^4\cdot 31^2\cdot 37^2\cdot 43\cdot 61\cdot 67\cdot 73\cdot 28^{12}}$	4. 5541 38864 99184 30391$\times 10^{-33}$
13	$\dfrac{2^2\cdot 3^2\cdot 7\cdot 11\cdot 2647111}{5^3\cdot 13^5\cdot 19^4\cdot 31^2\cdot 37^2\cdot 61\cdot 67\cdot 73\cdot 79\cdot 28^{13}}$	6. 0171 15776 98241 99591$\times 10^{-36}$

First 5 approximate values determined from exact values of c_{3k}; subsequent values determined by using exact ratios c_{3k}/c_{3k-3}, using at least double precision arithmetic with a desk calculator. All approximate c's were checked with the use of the recursion relation; c_3-c_{27} are believed correct to at least 21S; $c_{30}-c_{39}$ are believed correct to 20S.

$$c_{3k}\leq\frac{c_3}{13^{k-1}\cdot 28^{k-1}},\quad k=2, 3, 4, \ldots$$

Other Series Involving $\wp$

Reversed Series for Large $|\wp|$

18.13.39

$$z=(\wp^{-1})^{1/2}\left[1+\frac{u}{7}+\frac{3u^2}{26}+\frac{5u^3}{38}+\frac{7u^4}{40}+\frac{63u^5}{248}+\frac{231u^6}{592}+\frac{429u^7}{688}+O(u^8)\right],$$

18.13.40 where $u=\wp^{-3}/8$ and z is in the Fundamental Triangle **(Figure 18.11)** if $\wp$ has an appropriate value.

Series near z_0

18.13.41

$$\wp=iu\left[1-\frac{u^6}{7}+\frac{3u^{12}}{364}\right]+u^4\left[-\tfrac{1}{2}+\frac{u^6}{28}\right]+O(u^{16})$$

18.13.42

$$u=-i\wp\left[1+\frac{\wp^3}{2}+\frac{6\wp^6}{7}+2\wp^9+\frac{70\wp^{12}}{13}+O(\wp^{15})\right],$$

18.13.43 where $u=(z-z_0)$

Series near ω_2

18.13.44

$$(\wp-e_2)=3e_2^2u\left[1+x+x^2+\frac{6}{7}x^3+\frac{5}{7}x^4+\frac{4}{7}x^5+\frac{285}{637}x^6+O(x^7)\right],$$

18.13.45 where $u=(z-\omega_2)^2,\ x=e_2u$

18.13.46

$$u=e_2^{-1}\left[w-w^2+w^3-\frac{6}{7}w^4+\frac{3}{7}w^5+\frac{3}{7}w^6-\frac{1143}{637}w^7+O(w^8)\right],$$

18.13.47 where $w=(\wp-e_2)/3e_2$

Other Series Involving $\wp'$

Reversed Series for Large $|\wp'|$

18.13.48

$$z=2^{1/3}(\wp'^{1/3})^{-1}e^{i\pi/3}\left[1-\frac{2}{21}(\wp')^{-2}+\frac{5}{117}(\wp')^{-4}+O(\wp'^{-6})\right],$$

z being in the Fundamental Triangle **(Figure 18.11)** if $\wp'$ has an appropriate value.

Series near z_0

18.13.49

$$(\wp'-i)=x\left[-2-ix+\frac{5}{14}x^2+\frac{3i}{28}x^3+O(x^4)\right]$$

18.13.50 where $x=(z-z_0)^3$

18.13.51 $$x=2\alpha\left[1-i\alpha-\frac{9}{7}\alpha^2+\frac{13i\alpha^3}{7}+O(\alpha^4)\right],$$

18.13.52 where $\alpha=(\wp'-i)/(-4)$

Series near ω_2

18.13.53

$$\wp'=6e_2^2(z-\omega_2)\left[1+2v+3v^2+\frac{24}{7}v^3+\frac{25}{7}v^4+\frac{24}{7}v^5+\frac{285}{91}v^6+O(v^7)\right],$$

18.13.54 where $v=e_2(z-\omega_2)^2$

18.13.55

$$(z-\omega_2)=(\wp'/6e_2^2)\left[1-2w+9w^2-\frac{360}{7}w^3+330w^4-2268w^5+\frac{212058}{13}w^6+O(w^7)\right],$$

18.13.56 where $w=\wp'^2/9$

Other Series Involving ζ

Reversed Series for Large $|\zeta|$

18.13.57

$$z=\zeta^{-1}\left[1-\frac{\gamma}{7}+\frac{17\gamma^2}{143}-\frac{496\gamma^3}{3553}+O(\gamma^4)\right],$$

18.13.58 $\gamma=\zeta^{-6}/20$

Series near z_0

18.13.59

$$(\zeta-\zeta_0)=i\left[-\frac{u^2}{2}+\frac{u^8}{56}-\frac{3u^{14}}{5096}\right]+\left[\frac{u^5}{8}-\frac{u^{11}}{308}\right]+O(u^{17}),$$

18.13.60 where $u=(z-z_0)$

Series near ω_2

18.13.61

$$(\zeta-\eta_2)=-e_2(z-\omega_2)\left[1+v+\frac{3}{5}v^2+\frac{3}{7}v^3+\frac{2}{7}v^4+\frac{15}{77}v^5+\frac{12}{91}v^6+\frac{57}{637}v^7+O(v^8)\right],$$

18.13.62 $v=e_2(z-\omega_2)^2$

18.13.63

$$(z-\omega_2)=\frac{(\zeta-\eta_2)}{-e_2}\left[1-w+\frac{12w^2}{5}-\frac{267w^3}{35}+\frac{139w^4}{5}-\frac{30192w^5}{275}+\frac{1634208}{3575}w^6+O(w^7)\right],$$

18.13.64 $w=(\zeta-\eta_2)^2/e_2$

Series Involving σ

18.13.65

$$\sigma=z-\frac{2\cdot3}{7!}z^7-\frac{2^3\cdot3^3}{13!}z^{13}+\frac{2^6\cdot3^4\cdot23}{19!}z^{19}+\frac{2^7\cdot3^5\cdot5^2\cdot31}{25!}z^{25}+\frac{2^8\cdot3^8\cdot5\cdot9103}{31!}z^{31}-\frac{2^{12}\cdot3^9\cdot5\cdot229\cdot2683}{37!}z^{37}-\frac{2^{14}\cdot3^{10}\cdot5\cdot23\cdot257\cdot18049}{43!}z^{43}-\frac{2^{15}\cdot3^{12}\cdot5\cdot59\cdot107895773}{49!}z^{49}+O(z^{55})$$

18.13.66

$$z=\sigma+\frac{\sigma^7}{2^3\cdot3\cdot5\cdot7}+\frac{41\sigma^{13}}{2^7\cdot3^2\cdot5^2\cdot11\cdot13}+\frac{13\cdot337\sigma^{19}}{2^{10}\cdot3^4\cdot5^3\cdot11\cdot17\cdot19}+\frac{31\cdot101\sigma^{25}}{2^{15}\cdot3^5\cdot5\cdot11^2\cdot17\cdot23}+O(\sigma^{31})$$

Economized Polynomials ($0\leq x\leq1.53$)

18.13.67 $x^2\wp(x)=\sum_0^6 a_nx^{6n}+\epsilon(x)$

$|\epsilon(x)|<2\times10^{-7}$

$a_0=(-1)9.99999\ 96$ $\quad a_4=-(-9)2.20892\ 47$

$a_1=(-2)3.57143\ 20$ $\quad a_5=(-10)1.74915\ 35$

$a_2=(-5)9.80689\ 93$ $\quad a_6=-(-12)4.46863\ 93$

$a_3=(-7)2.00835\ 02$

18.13.68 $x^3\wp'(x)=\sum_0^6 a_nx^{6n}+\epsilon(x)$

$|\epsilon(x)|<4\times10^{-7}$

$a_0=-2.00000\ 00$ $\quad a_4=-(-9)2.12719\ 66$

$a_1=(-1)1.42857\ 22$ $\quad a_5=(-10)6.53654\ 67$

$a_2=(-4)9.81018\ 03$ $\quad a_6=-(-11)1.70510\ 78$

$a_3=(-6)3.00511\ 93$

18.13.69 $x\zeta(x)=\sum_0^6 a_nx^{6n}+\epsilon(x)$

$|\epsilon(x)|<3\times10^{-8}$

$a_0=(-1)9.99999\ 98$ $\quad a_4=(-10)6.12486\ 14$

$a_1=-(-3)7.14285\ 86$ $\quad a_5=(-11)4.66919\ 85$

$a_2=-(-6)8.91165\ 65$ $\quad a_6=(-12)1.25014\ 65$

$a_3=-(-8)1.44381\ 84$

18.14. Lemniscatic Case

$(g_2=1,\ g_3=0)$

If $g_2>0$ and $g_3=0$, homogeneity relations allow us to reduce our consideration of $\wp$ to $\wp(z; 1, 0)$ ($\wp'$, ζ and σ are handled similarly). Thus $\wp(z; g_2, 0)=g_2^{\frac{1}{2}}\wp(zg_2^{\frac{1}{4}}; 1, 0)$. The case $g_2=1$, $g_3=0$ is called the LEMNISCATIC case.

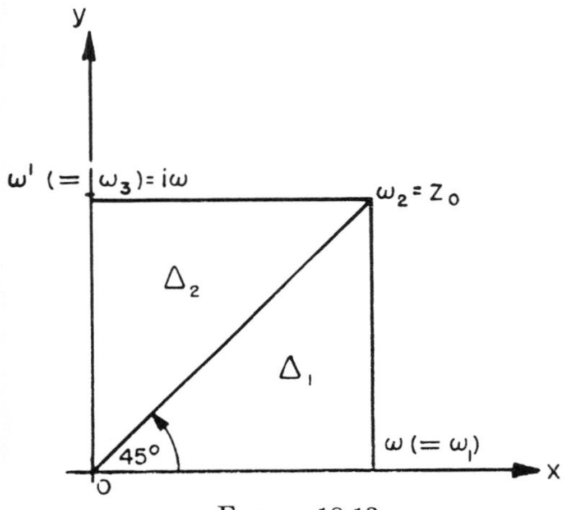

FIGURE 18.13

$\frac{1}{4}$FPP; *Reduction to Fundamental Triangle*

$\Delta_1\equiv\Delta 0\omega\omega_2$ is the Fundamental Triangle

$\omega\approx 1.8540\ 74677\ 30137\ 192$[8]

Reduction for z_2 in Δ_2: $z_1=i\bar{z}_2$ is in Δ_1

18.14.1 $$\wp(z_2)=-\overline{\wp}(z_1)$$

18.14.2 $$\wp'(z_2)=i\overline{\wp'}(z_1)$$

18.14.3 $$\zeta(z_2)=-i\bar{\zeta}(z_1)$$

18.14.4 $$\sigma(z_2)=i\bar{\sigma}(z_1)$$

Special Values and Formulas

18.14.5

$$\Delta=1,\ H_1=H_3=2^{-\frac{1}{2}},\ H_2=i/2,\qquad m=\sin^2 45°=\tfrac{1}{2},\ q=e^{-\pi}$$

18.14.6 $$\vartheta_2(0)=\vartheta_4(0)=(\omega\sqrt{2}/\pi)^{\frac{1}{2}};\ \vartheta_3(0)=(2\omega/\pi)^{\frac{1}{2}}$$

18.14.7 $$\omega=K(\sin^2 45°)=\frac{\Gamma^2(\frac{1}{4})}{4\sqrt{\pi}}=\frac{\tilde{\omega}}{\sqrt{2}}\text{ where}$$

$\tilde{\omega}\approx 2.62205\ 75542\ 92119\ 81046\ 48395\ 89891\ 11941\ 36827\ 54951\ 43162$ is the Lemniscate constant [18.9]

[8] This value was computed and checked by double precision methods on a desk calculator and is believed correct to 18S.

Values at Half-periods

	$\wp$	$\wp'$	ζ	σ
18.14.8 $\omega=\omega_1$	$e_1=\frac{1}{2}$	0	$\eta=\pi/4\omega$	$e^{\pi/8}(2^{1/4})$
18.14.9 $\omega_2=z_0$	$e_2=0$	0	$\eta+\eta'$	$e^{\pi/4}(\sqrt{2})e^{i\pi/4}$
18.14.10 $\omega'=\omega_3$	$e_3=-\frac{1}{2}$	0	$\eta'=-\pi i/4\omega$	$ie^{\pi/8}(2^{1/4})$

Values along $(0, \omega)$

	$\wp$	$\wp'$	ζ	σ
18.14.11 $\omega/4$	$\frac{\sqrt{\alpha}}{2}(\sqrt{\alpha}+2^{1/4})(1+2^{1/4})$			
18.14.12 $\omega/2$	$\alpha/2$	$-\alpha$	$\frac{\pi}{8\omega}+\frac{\alpha}{2\sqrt{2}}$	$\frac{e^{\pi/32}(2^{1/16})}{\alpha^{\frac{1}{4}}}$
18.14.13 $2\omega/3$	$\frac{1}{2}\sqrt{1+\sec 30°}$	$-\frac{\sqrt[4]{2\sqrt{3}+3}}{\sqrt{3}}$	$\frac{2\eta}{3}+\sqrt{\frac{\wp(2\omega/3)}{3}}$	$\frac{e^{\pi/18}(3^{1/8})}{(2+\sqrt{3})^{1/12}}$
18.14.14 $3\omega/4$	$\frac{\sqrt{\alpha}}{2}(\sqrt{\alpha}-2^{\frac{1}{4}})(1+2^{\frac{1}{4}})$			

$\alpha=1+\sqrt{2}$

Values along $(0, z_0)$

	$\wp$	$\wp'$	ζ	σ
18.14.15 $z_0/4$	$-\frac{i}{2}(\alpha+\sqrt{2\alpha})$	$\alpha(\sqrt{\alpha}+\sqrt{2})e^{i\pi/4}$		$\frac{e^{\pi/64}(2^{1/32})}{\alpha^{1/4}(\sqrt{\alpha}+\sqrt{2})^{1/4}}e^{i\pi/4}$
18.14.16 $z_0/2$	$-i/2$	$e^{i\pi/4}$	$\left[\frac{\pi}{4\omega\sqrt{2}}+\frac{1}{2}\right]e^{-i\pi/4}$	$e^{\pi/16}(2^{1/8})e^{i\pi/4}$
18.14.17 $2z_0/3$	$\frac{-i}{2}\sqrt{\sec 30^\circ-1}$	$\frac{e^{i\pi/4}\cdot\sqrt[4]{2\sqrt{3}-3}}{\sqrt{3}}$	$\frac{2\eta_2}{3}+\left[\frac{\wp(2z_0/3)}{3}\right]^{1/2}$	$\frac{e^{\pi/9}e^{i\pi/4}(3^{1/6})}{\sqrt[12]{2\sqrt{3}-3}}$
18.14.18 $3z_0/4$	$-\frac{i}{2}(\alpha-\sqrt{2\alpha})$	$\alpha(\sqrt{\alpha}-\sqrt{2})e^{i\pi/4}$		$\frac{e^{9\pi/64}(2^{1/32})}{\alpha^{1/4}(\sqrt{\alpha}-\sqrt{2})^{1/4}}e^{i\pi/4}$

$\alpha=1+\sqrt{2}$

Duplication Formulas

18.14.19 $$\wp(2z)=[\wp^2(z)+\tfrac{1}{4}]^2/\{\wp(z)[4\wp^2(z)-1]\}$$

18.14.20
$$\wp'(2z)=(\beta+1)(\beta^2-6\beta+1)/[32\wp'^3(z)],\quad \beta=4\wp^2(z)$$

18.14.21 $$\zeta(2z)=2\zeta(z)+\frac{6\wp^2(z)-\frac{1}{2}}{2\wp'(z)}$$

18.14.22 $$\sigma(2z)=-\wp'(z)\sigma^4(z)$$

Bisection Formulas $(0<x<2\omega)$

18.14.23
$$\wp\left(\frac{x}{2}\right)=[\wp^{\frac{1}{2}}(x)+\{\wp(x)+\tfrac{1}{2}\}^{\frac{1}{2}}][\wp^{\frac{1}{2}}(x)\pm\{\wp(x)-\tfrac{1}{2}\}^{\frac{1}{2}}]$$

[Use + on $0<x\leq\omega$, − on $\omega\leq x<2\omega$]

18.14.24
$$\tfrac{1}{2}\wp'\left(\frac{x}{2}\right)=\wp'(x)\mp[2\wp(x)+\tfrac{1}{2}]\sqrt{\wp(x)-\tfrac{1}{2}}-[2\wp(x)-\tfrac{1}{2}]\sqrt{\wp(x)+\tfrac{1}{2}}-2\wp^{3/2}(x)$$ (See [18.13].)

[Use − on $0<x\leq\omega$, + on $\omega\leq x<2\omega$]

Complex Multiplication

18.14.25 $$\wp(iz)=-\wp(z)$$

18.14.26 $$\wp'(iz)=i\wp'(z)$$

18.14.27 $$\zeta(iz)=-i\zeta(z)$$

18.14.28 $$\sigma(iz)=i\sigma(z)$$

The above equations could be used as follows, e.g.: If z were real, iz would be purely imaginary.

Conformal Maps

Lemniscatic Case

Map: $f(z)=u+iv$

$\wp(z)$

Near zero: $\wp(z)=\frac{1}{z^2}+\epsilon_1$

$$\wp(z)=\frac{1}{z^2}+\frac{z^2}{20}+\epsilon_2,\quad |z|<1$$

Near z_0: $\wp(z)=\frac{-(z-z_0)^2}{4}+\epsilon_3,\quad |z-z_0|<\sqrt{2}$

$$\wp(z)=\frac{-(z-z_0)^2}{4}+\frac{(z-z_0)^6}{80}+\epsilon_4$$

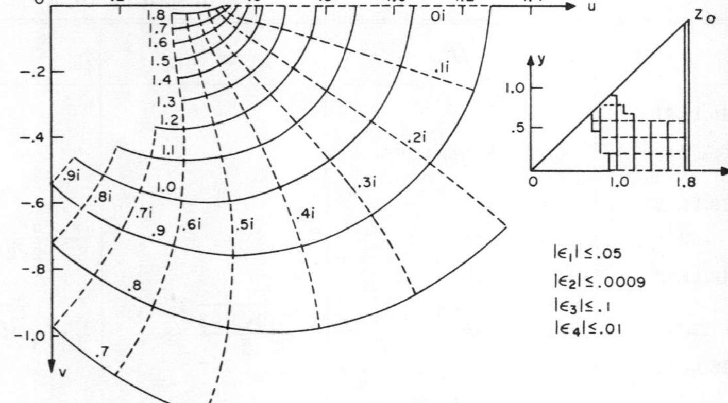

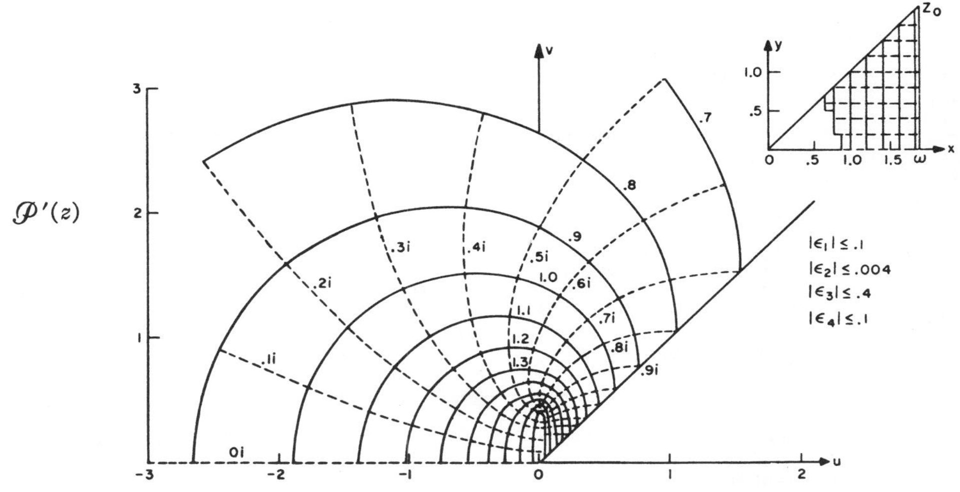

Near zero: $\wp'(z)=\dfrac{-2}{z^3}+\epsilon_1$

$$\wp'(z)=\frac{-2}{z^3}+\frac{z}{10}+\epsilon_2$$

Near z_0: $\wp'(z)=\dfrac{-(z-z_0)}{2}+\epsilon_3$

$$\wp'(z)=\frac{-(z-z_0)}{2}+\frac{3(z-z_0)^5}{40}+\epsilon_4$$

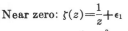

$\zeta(z)$

Near zero: $\zeta(z)=\dfrac{1}{z}+\epsilon_1$

$$\zeta(z)=\frac{1}{z}-\frac{z^3}{60}+\epsilon_2,\ |z|<1$$

Near z_0: $\zeta(z)=\zeta_0+\dfrac{(z-z_0)^3}{12}+\epsilon_3,$

$$|z-z_0|<\sqrt{2}$$

$$\zeta(z)=\zeta_0+\frac{(z-z_0)^3}{12}-\frac{(z-z_0)^7}{560}+\epsilon_4$$

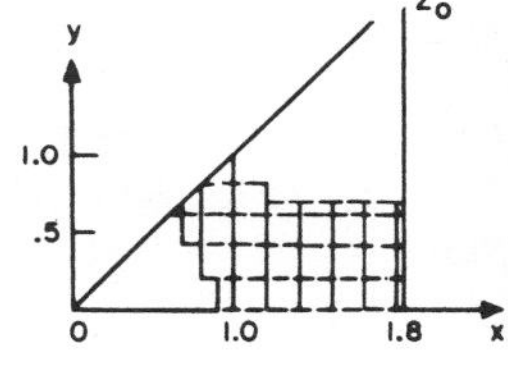

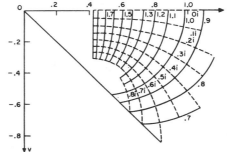

$|\epsilon_1|\leq .02$

$|\epsilon_2|\leq .0001$

$|\epsilon_3|\leq .02$

$|\epsilon_4|\leq .002$

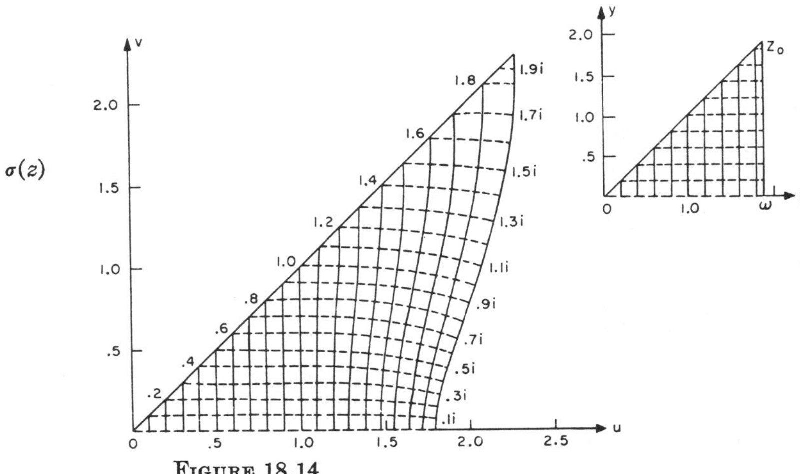

FIGURE 18.14

Coefficients for Laurent Series for $\wp$, $\wp'$, and ζ

($c_m=0$ for m odd)

k	EXACT c_{2k}	APPROXIMATE c_{2k}
1	$1/20$	$.05$
2	$1/(3\cdot 20^2)=1/1200$	$.8333\ \ldots \times 10^{-3}$
3	$2/(3\cdot 13\cdot 20^3)=1/156000$	$.641025\ 641025\ \ldots \times 10^{-5}$
4	$5/(3\cdot 13\cdot 17\cdot 20^4)=1/21216000$	$.47134\ 23831\ 07088\ 98944\times 10^{-7}$
5	$2/(3^2\cdot 13\cdot 17\cdot 20^5)=1/(31824\times 10^5)$	$.31422\ 82554\ 04725\ 99296\times 10^{-9}$
6	$10/(3^3\cdot 13^2\cdot 17\cdot 20^6)=1/(4964544\times 10^5)$	$.20142\ 83688\ 49183\ 32882\times 10^{-11}$
7	$4/(3\cdot 13^2\cdot 17\cdot 29\cdot 20^7)=1/(7998432\times 10^7)$	$.12502\ 45048\ 02941\ 37651\times 10^{-13}$
8	$2453/(3^4\cdot 11\cdot 13^2\cdot 17^2\cdot 29\cdot 20^8)=958203125/(1262002599\times 10^{16})$	$.75927\ 19109\ 76468\ 59917\times 10^{-16}$
9	$2\cdot 5\cdot 7\cdot 61/(3^3\cdot 13^3\cdot 17^2\cdot 29\cdot 37\cdot 20^9)=833984375/(18394643943\times 10^{17})$	$.45338\ 43533\ 93461\ 06092\times 10^{-18}$
	$c_{2k}\leq \frac{c_2^k}{3^{k-1}},\ k=1, 2, \ldots$	

Other Series Involving $\wp$

Reversed Series for Large $|\wp|$

18.14.29

$$z=(\wp^{-1})^{1/2}\left[1+\frac{w}{5}+\frac{w^2}{6}+\frac{5w^3}{26}+\frac{35w^4}{136}+\frac{3w^5}{8}+\frac{231w^6}{400}+\frac{429w^7}{464}+\frac{195w^8}{128}+\frac{12155w^9}{4736}+\frac{46189w^{10}}{10496}+O(w^{11})\right],$$

18.14.30 $w=\wp^{-2}/8$, and z is in the Fundamental Triangle **(Figure 18.13)** if $\wp$ has an appropriate value.

Series near z_0

18.14.31 $$2\wp=-x+\frac{x^3}{5}-\frac{2x^5}{75}+\frac{x^7}{325}+O(x^9),$$

18.14.32 $$x=(z-z_0)^2/2$$

18.14.33 $$x=-\left[w+\frac{w^3}{5}+\frac{7w^5}{75}+\frac{11w^7}{195}+O(w^9)\right]$$

$$w=2\wp$$

Series near ω

18.14.34

$$(\wp-e_1)=v+v^2+\frac{4v^3}{5}+\frac{3v^4}{5}+\frac{32v^5}{75}+\frac{22v^6}{75}+\frac{64v^7}{325}+O(v^8),$$

18.14.35 $$v=(z-\omega)^2/2$$

18.14.36

$$v=y\left[1-y+\frac{6y^2}{5}-\frac{8y^3}{5}+\frac{172y^4}{75}-\frac{52y^5}{15}+\frac{1064y^6}{195}+O(y^7)\right],$$

18.14.37 $$y=(\wp-e_1)$$

Other Series Involving $\wp'$

Reversed Series for Large $|\wp'|$

18.14.38

$$z=Au\left[1-\frac{v}{5}+\frac{5v^3}{39}-\frac{7v^4}{51}+O(v^5)\right],\quad u=(\wp'^{1/3})^{-1}e^{i\pi/3},$$

18.14.39 $A=2^{1/3}$, $v=Au^4/6$, and z is in the Fundamental Triangle **(Figure 18.13)** if $\wp'$ has an appropriate value.

Series near z_0

18.14.40

$$\wp'=\frac{1}{2}(z-z_0)\left[-1+3w-\frac{10w^2}{3}+\frac{35w^3}{13}+O(w^4)\right],$$

18.14.41 $$w=(z-z_0)^4/20$$

18.14.42

$$(z-z_0)=2\wp'\left[1+\frac{3u}{5}+\frac{5u^2}{3}+\frac{84u^3}{13}+O(u^4)\right],$$

18.14.43 $$u=4\wp'^4$$

Series near ω

18.14.44

$$\wp'=x\left[1+x^2+\frac{3}{5}x^4+\frac{3}{10}x^6+\frac{2}{15}x^8+\frac{11}{200}x^{10}+O(x^{12})\right],$$

18.14.45 $$x=(z-\omega)$$

18.14.46

$$x=\wp'-\wp'^3+\frac{12\wp'^5}{5}-\frac{15\wp'^7}{2}+\frac{80\wp'^9}{3}-\frac{819\wp'^{11}}{8}+O(\wp'^{13})$$

Other Series Involving ζ

Reversed Series for Large $|\zeta|$

18.14.47 $$z=\zeta^{-1}\left[1-\frac{v}{5}+\frac{v^2}{7}-\frac{136v^3}{1001}+\frac{1349v^4}{9163}+O(v^5)\right],$$

18.14.48 $$v=\zeta^{-4}/12$$

Series near z_0

18.14.49

$$(\zeta-\zeta_0)=\frac{1}{4}(z-z_0)^3\left[\frac{1}{3}-\frac{v}{7}+\frac{2v^2}{33}-\frac{v^3}{39}+O(v^4)\right],$$

18.14.50 $$v=(z-z_0)^4/20$$

Series near ω

18.14.51

$$(\zeta-\eta)=-\frac{x}{2}-\frac{x^3}{6}-\frac{x^5}{20}-\frac{x^7}{70}-\frac{x^9}{240}-\frac{x^{11}}{825}-\frac{11x^{13}}{31200}-\frac{x^{15}}{9750}+O(x^{17}),$$

18.14.52 $$x=(z-\omega)$$

18.14.53

$$x=w-\frac{w^3}{3}+\frac{7w^5}{30}-\frac{13w^7}{63}+\frac{929w^9}{4536}-\frac{194w^{11}}{891}+\frac{942883w^{13}}{3891888}+O(w^{15})$$

18.14.54 $$w=-2(\zeta-\eta)$$

Series Involving σ

18.14.55

$$\sigma=z-\frac{z^5}{2\cdot 5!}-\frac{3^2z^9}{2^2\cdot 9!}+\frac{3\cdot 23z^{13}}{2^3\cdot 13!}+\frac{3\cdot 107z^{17}}{2^4\cdot 17!}+\frac{3^3\cdot 7\cdot 23\cdot 37z^{21}}{2^5\cdot 21!}+\frac{3^2\cdot 313\cdot 503z^{25}}{2^6\cdot 25!}-\frac{3^4\cdot 7\cdot 685973z^{29}}{2^7\cdot 29!}+O(z^{33})$$

18.14.56

$$z=\sigma+\frac{\sigma^5}{2^4\cdot 3\cdot 5}+\frac{\sigma^9}{2^9\cdot 3\cdot 7}+\frac{17\cdot 113\sigma^{13}}{2^{13}\cdot 3^4\cdot 7\cdot 11\cdot 13}+\frac{122051\sigma^{17}}{2^{19}\cdot 3^5\cdot 7^2\cdot 11\cdot 17}+\frac{5\cdot 13\sigma^{21}}{2^{23}\cdot 3^2\cdot 11\cdot 19}+O(\sigma^{25})$$

Economized Polynomials ($0\le x\le 1.86$)

18.14.57 $$x^2\wp(x)=\sum_0^6 a_nx^{4n}+\epsilon(x)$$

$$|\epsilon(x)|<2\times 10^{-7}$$

$a_0=(-1)9.99999\ 98$	$a_4=(-8)4.81438\ 20$
$a_1=(-2)4.99999\ 62$	$a_5=(-10)2.29729\ 21$
$a_2=(-4)8.33352\ 77$	$a_6=(-12)4.94511\ 45$
$a_3=(-6)6.40412\ 86$	

18.14.58 $$x^3\wp'(x)=\sum_0^6 a_nx^{4n}+\epsilon(x)$$

$$|\epsilon(x)|<4\times 10^{-7}$$

$a_0=-2.00000\ 00$	$a_4=(-7)6.58947\ 52$
$a_1=(-1)1.00000\ 02$	$a_5=(-9)5.59262\ 49$
$a_2=(-3)4.99995\ 38$	$a_6=(-11)5.54177\ 69$
$a_3=(-5)6.41145\ 59$	

18.14.59 $$x\zeta(x)=\sum_0^6 a_nx^{4n}+\epsilon(x)$$

$$|\epsilon(x)|<3\times 10^{-8}$$

$a_0=(-1)9.99999\ 99$	$a_4=-(-9)2.57492\ 62$
$a_1=-(-2)1.66666\ 74$	$a_5=-(-11)5.67008\ 00$
$a_2=-(-4)1.19036\ 70$	$a_6=(-13)9.70015\ 80$
$a_3=-(-7)5.86451\ 63$	

18.15. Pseudo-Lemniscatic Case ($g_2=-1$, $g_3=0$)

If $g_2<0$ and $g_3=0$, homogeneity relations allow us to reduce our consideration of $\wp$ to $\wp(z;-1,0)$. Thus

18.15.1 $$\wp(z;g_2,0)=|g_2|^{1/2}\wp(z|g_2|^{1/4};-1,0)$$

[$\wp'$, ζ and σ are handled similarly]. Because of its similarity to the lemniscatic case, we refer to the case $g_2=-1$, $g_3=0$ as the pseudo-lemniscatic case. It plays the same role (period ratio unity) for $\Delta<0$ as does the lemniscatic case for $\Delta>0$.

$\omega_2=\sqrt{2}\times$(real half-period for lemniscatic case)
$=\tilde{\omega}$ (the Lemniscate Constant—see **18.14.7**)

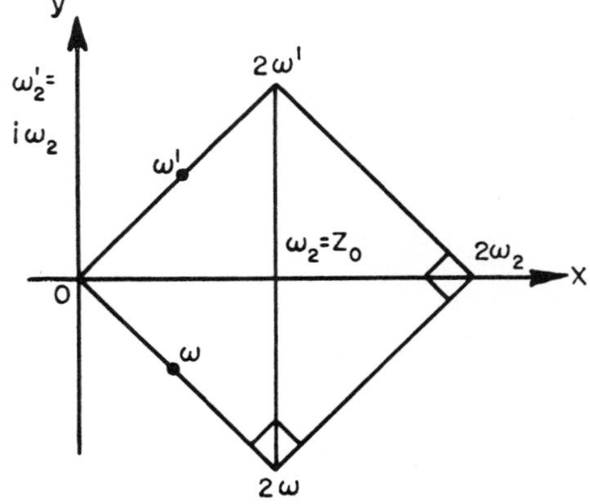

FIGURE 18.15

Special Values and Relations

18.15.2 $\Delta=-1,\ g_2=-1,\ g_3=0$

18.15.3

$H_1=-i/\sqrt{2},\ H_2=\tfrac{1}{2},\ H_3=i/\sqrt{2},\qquad m=\tfrac{1}{2},\ q=ie^{-\pi/2}$

18.15.4

$\vartheta_2(0)=R2^{1/4}e^{i\pi/8},\ \vartheta_3(0)=Re^{i\pi/8},\ \vartheta_4(0)=Re^{-i\pi/8},$

18.15.5 where $R=\sqrt{\omega_2\sqrt{2}/\pi}$

Values at Half-Periods

	$\wp$	$\wp'$	ζ	σ
18.15.6 $\omega\equiv\omega_1$	$i/2$	0	$\tfrac{1}{2}(\eta_2-\eta_2')$	$e^{-i\pi/4}e^{\pi/8}(2^{1/4})$
18.15.7 ω_2	0	0	$\eta_2=\pi/2\omega_2$	$e^{\pi/4}\sqrt{2}$
18.15.8 $\omega'=\omega_3$	$-i/2$	0	$\tfrac{1}{2}(\eta_2+\eta_2')$	$e^{i\pi/4}e^{\pi/8}(2^{1/4})$
18.15.9 ω_2'	0	0	$\eta_2'=-i\eta_2$	$i\sigma(\omega_2)$

Relations with Lemniscatic Values

18.15.10 $\wp(z;-1,0)=i\wp(ze^{i\pi/4};1,0)$

18.15.11 $\wp'(z;-1,0)=e^{3\pi i/4}\wp'(ze^{i\pi/4};1,0)$

18.15.12 $\zeta(z;-1,0)=e^{i\pi/4}\zeta(ze^{i\pi/4};1,0)$

18.15.13 $\sigma(z;-1,0)=e^{-i\pi/4}\sigma(ze^{i\pi/4};1,0)$

19.1. The Parabolic Cylinder Functions

Introductory

These are solutions of the differential equation

19.1.1 $$\frac{d^2y}{dx^2}+(ax^2+bx+c)y=0$$

with two real and distinct standard forms

19.1.2 $$\frac{d^2y}{dx^2}-(\tfrac{1}{4}x^2+a)y=0$$

19.1.3 $$\frac{d^2y}{dx^2}+(\tfrac{1}{4}x^2-a)y=0$$

The functions

19.1.4
$$y(a,x)\qquad y(a,-x)\qquad y(-a,ix)\qquad y(-a,-ix)$$

are all solutions either of **19.1.2** or of **19.1.3** if any one is such a solution.

Replacement of a by $-ia$ and x by $xe^{\frac{1}{4}i\pi}$ converts **19.1.2** into **19.1.3.** If $y(a, x)$ is a solution of **19.1.2,** then **19.1.3** has solutions:

19.1.5
$$y(-ia, xe^{\frac{1}{4}i\pi})\qquad y(-ia,-xe^{\frac{1}{4}i\pi})\qquad y(ia,-xe^{-\frac{1}{4}i\pi})\qquad y(ia, xe^{-\frac{1}{4}i\pi})$$

Both variable x and the parameter a may take on general complex values in this section and in many subsequent sections. Practical applications appear to be confined to real solutions of real equations; therefore attention is confined to such solutions, and, in general, formulas are given for the two equations **19.1.2** and **19.1.3** independently. The principal computational consequence of the remarks above is that reflection in the y-axis produces an independent solution in almost all cases (Hermite functions provide an exception), so that tables may be confined either to positive x or to a single solution of **19.1.2** or **19.1.3.**

The Equation $\frac{d^2y}{dx^2}-\left(\frac{1}{4}x^2+a\right)y=0$

19.2. Power Series in x

Even and odd solutions of **19.1.2** are given by

19.2.1
$$y_1=e^{-\frac{1}{4}x^2}M(\tfrac{1}{2}a+\tfrac{1}{4},\tfrac{1}{2},\tfrac{1}{2}x^2)$$
$$=e^{-\frac{1}{4}x^2}\left\{1+(a+\tfrac{1}{2})\frac{x^2}{2!}+(a+\tfrac{1}{2})(a+\tfrac{5}{2})\frac{x^4}{4!}+\dots\right\}$$
$$=e^{-\frac{1}{4}x^2}{}_1F_1(\tfrac{1}{2}a+\tfrac{1}{4};\tfrac{1}{2};\tfrac{1}{2}x^2)$$

19.2.2
$$=e^{\frac{1}{4}x^2}M(-\tfrac{1}{2}a+\tfrac{1}{4},\tfrac{1}{2},-\tfrac{1}{2}x^2)$$
$$=e^{\frac{1}{4}x^2}\left\{1+(a-\tfrac{1}{2})\frac{x^2}{2!}+(a-\tfrac{1}{2})(a-\tfrac{5}{2})\frac{x^4}{4!}+\dots\right\}$$

19.2.3
$$y_2=xe^{-\frac{1}{4}x^2}M(\tfrac{1}{2}a+\tfrac{3}{4},\tfrac{3}{2},\tfrac{1}{2}x^2)$$
$$=e^{-\frac{1}{4}x^2}\left\{x+(a+\tfrac{3}{2})\frac{x^3}{3!}+(a+\tfrac{3}{2})(a+\tfrac{7}{2})\frac{x^5}{5!}+\dots\right\}$$

19.2.4
$$=xe^{\frac{1}{4}x^2}M(-\tfrac{1}{2}a+\tfrac{3}{4},\tfrac{3}{2},-\tfrac{1}{2}x^2)$$
$$=e^{\frac{1}{4}x^2}\left\{x+(a-\tfrac{3}{2})\frac{x^3}{3!}+(a-\tfrac{3}{2})(a-\tfrac{7}{2})\frac{x^5}{5!}+\dots\right\}$$

these series being convergent for all values of x (see chapter **13** for $M(a, c, z)$).

Alternatively,

19.2.5
$$y_1=1+a\frac{x^2}{2!}+\left(a^2+\frac{1}{2}\right)\frac{x^4}{4!}+\left(a^3+\frac{7}{2}a\right)\frac{x^6}{6!}+\left(a^4+11a^2+\frac{15}{4}\right)\frac{x^8}{8!}+\left(a^5+25a^3+\frac{211}{4}a\right)\frac{x^{10}}{10!}+\dots$$

19.2.6
$$y_2=x+a\frac{x^3}{3!}+\left(a^2+\frac{3}{2}\right)\frac{x^5}{5!}+\left(a^3+\frac{13}{2}a\right)\frac{x^7}{7!}+\left(a^4+17a^2+\frac{63}{4}\right)\frac{x^9}{9!}+\left(a^5+35a^3+\frac{531}{4}a\right)\frac{x^{11}}{11!}+\dots$$

in which non-zero coefficients a_n of $x^n/n!$ are connected by

19.2.7 $$a_{n+2}=a\cdot a_n+\frac{1}{4}n(n-1)a_{n-2}$$

19.3. Standard Solutions

These have been chosen to have the asymptotic behavior exhibited in **19.8.** The first is Whittaker's function [19.8, 19.9] in a more symmetrical notation.

19.3.1

$$U(a,x)=D_{-a-\frac{1}{2}}(x)=\cos\pi(\tfrac{1}{4}+\tfrac{1}{2}a)\cdot Y_1 -\sin\pi(\tfrac{1}{4}+\tfrac{1}{2}a)\cdot Y_2$$

19.3.2

$$V(a,x)=\frac{1}{\Gamma(\frac{1}{2}-a)}\{\sin\pi(\tfrac{1}{4}+\tfrac{1}{2}a)\cdot Y_1 +\cos\pi(\tfrac{1}{4}+\tfrac{1}{2}a)\cdot Y_2\}$$

in which

19.3.3 $$Y_1=\frac{1}{\sqrt{\pi}}\frac{\Gamma(\frac{1}{4}-\frac{1}{2}a)}{2^{\frac{1}{2}a+\frac{1}{4}}}y_1=\sqrt{\pi}\frac{\sec\pi(\frac{1}{4}+\frac{1}{2}a)}{2^{\frac{1}{2}a+\frac{1}{4}}\Gamma(\frac{3}{4}+\frac{1}{2}a)}y_1$$

19.3.4 $$Y_2=\frac{1}{\sqrt{\pi}}\frac{\Gamma(\frac{3}{4}-\frac{1}{2}a)}{2^{\frac{1}{2}a-\frac{1}{4}}}y_2=\sqrt{\pi}\frac{\csc\pi(\frac{1}{4}+\frac{1}{2}a)}{2^{\frac{1}{2}a-\frac{1}{4}}\Gamma(\frac{1}{4}+\frac{1}{2}a)}y_2$$

19.3.5

$$U(a,0)=\frac{\sqrt{\pi}}{2^{\frac{1}{2}a+\frac{1}{4}}\Gamma(\frac{3}{4}+\frac{1}{2}a)}$$

$$U'(a,0)=-\frac{\sqrt{\pi}}{2^{\frac{1}{2}a-\frac{1}{4}}\Gamma(\frac{1}{4}+\frac{1}{2}a)}$$

19.3.6

$$V(a,0)=\frac{2^{\frac{1}{2}a+\frac{1}{4}}\sin\pi(\frac{3}{4}-\frac{1}{2}a)}{\Gamma(\frac{3}{4}-\frac{1}{2}a)}$$

$$V'(a,0)=\frac{2^{\frac{1}{2}a+\frac{3}{4}}\sin\pi(\frac{1}{4}-\frac{1}{2}a)}{\Gamma(\frac{1}{4}-\frac{1}{2}a)}$$

In terms of the more familiar $D_n(x)$ of Whittaker,

19.3.7 $$U(a,x)=D_{-a-\frac{1}{2}}(x)$$

19.3.8

$$V(a,x)=\frac{1}{\pi}\Gamma(\tfrac{1}{2}+a)\{\sin\pi a\cdot D_{-a-\frac{1}{2}}(x)+D_{-a-\frac{1}{2}}(-x)\}$$

19.4. Wronskian and Other Relations

19.4.1 $$W\{U,V\}=\sqrt{2/\pi}$$

19.4.2

$$\pi V(a,x)=\Gamma(\tfrac{1}{2}+a)\{\sin\pi a\cdot U(a,x)+U(a,-x)\}$$

19.4.3

$$\Gamma(\tfrac{1}{2}+a)U(a,x)=\pi\sec^2\pi a\{V(a,-x) -\sin\pi a\cdot V(a,x)\}$$

19.4.4

$$\frac{\Gamma(\frac{1}{4}-\frac{1}{2}a)\cos\pi(\frac{1}{4}+\frac{1}{2}a)}{\sqrt{\pi}2^{\frac{1}{2}a-\frac{3}{4}}}y_1=2\sin\pi(\tfrac{3}{4}+\tfrac{1}{2}a)\cdot Y_1 =U(a,x)+U(a,-x)$$

19.4.5

$$-\frac{\Gamma(\frac{3}{4}-\frac{1}{2}a)\sin\pi(\frac{1}{4}+\frac{1}{2}a)}{\sqrt{\pi}2^{\frac{1}{2}a-\frac{5}{4}}}y_2=2\cos\pi(\tfrac{3}{4}+\tfrac{1}{2}a)\cdot Y_2 =U(a,x)-U(a,-x)$$

19.4.6

$$\sqrt{2\pi}U(-a,\pm ix)= \Gamma(\tfrac{1}{2}+a)\{e^{-i\pi(\frac{1}{2}a-\frac{1}{4})}U(a,\pm x)+e^{i\pi(\frac{1}{2}a-\frac{1}{4})}U(a,\mp x)\}$$

19.4.7

$$\sqrt{2\pi}U(a,\pm x)= \Gamma(\tfrac{1}{2}-a)\{e^{-i\pi(\frac{1}{2}a+\frac{1}{4})}U(-a,\pm ix)+e^{i\pi(\frac{1}{2}a+\frac{1}{4})}U(-a,\mp ix)\}$$

19.5. Integral Representations

A full treatment is given in [19.11] section 4. Representations are given here for $U(a, z)$ only; others may be derived by use of the relations given in **19.4.**

19.5.1 $$U(a,z)=\frac{\Gamma(\frac{1}{2}-a)}{2\pi i}e^{-\frac{1}{4}z^2}\int_\alpha e^{zs-\frac{1}{2}s^2}s^{a-\frac{1}{2}}ds$$

19.5.2 $$=\frac{\Gamma(\frac{1}{2}-a)}{2\pi i}e^{\frac{1}{4}z^2}\int_\beta e^{-\frac{1}{2}t^2}(z+t)^{a-\frac{1}{2}}dt$$

where α and β are the contours shown in **Figures 19.1 and 19.2.**

When $a+\frac{1}{2}$ is a positive integer these integrals become indeterminate; in this case

19.5.3 $$U(a,z)=\frac{1}{\Gamma(\frac{1}{2}+a)}e^{-\frac{1}{4}z^2}\int_0^\infty e^{-zs-\frac{1}{2}s^2}s^{a-\frac{1}{2}}ds$$

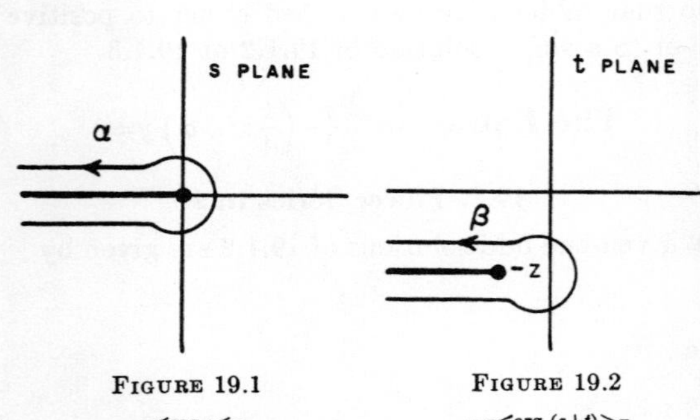

FIGURE 19.1 $-\pi<\arg s<\pi$

FIGURE 19.2 $-\pi<\arg (z+t)>\pi$

19.5.4 $$U(a,z)=\frac{1}{\sqrt{2\pi i}}\,e^{\frac{1}{4}z^2}\int_{\epsilon} e^{-zs+\frac{1}{2}s^2}s^{-a-\frac{1}{2}}ds$$

19.5.5 $$=\frac{e^{(a-\frac{1}{2})\pi i}}{\sqrt{2\pi i}}\,e^{\frac{1}{4}z^2}\int_{\epsilon_3} e^{zs+\frac{1}{2}s^2}s^{-a-\frac{1}{2}}ds$$

19.5.6 $$=\frac{e^{-(a-\frac{1}{2})\pi i}}{\sqrt{2\pi i}}\,e^{\frac{1}{4}z^2}\int_{\epsilon_4} e^{zs+\frac{1}{2}s^2}s^{-a-\frac{1}{2}}ds$$

where ϵ, ϵ_3 and ϵ_4 are shown in **Figures 19.3** and **19.4.**

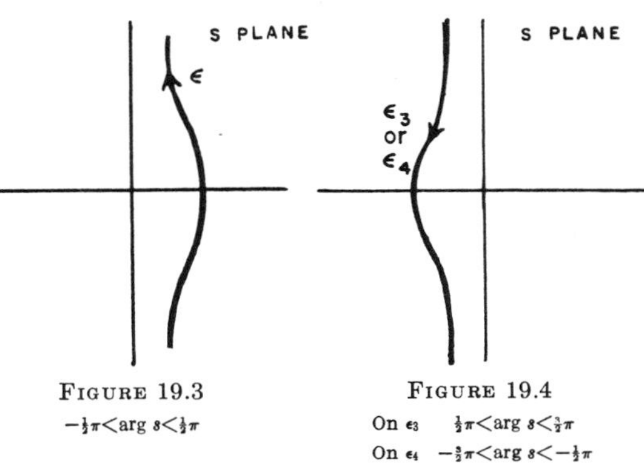

FIGURE 19.3
$-\frac{1}{2}\pi<\arg s<\frac{1}{2}\pi$

FIGURE 19.4
On ϵ_3 $\frac{1}{2}\pi<\arg s<\frac{3}{2}\pi$
On ϵ_4 $-\frac{3}{2}\pi<\arg s<-\frac{1}{2}\pi$

19.5.7
$$U(a,z)=\frac{\Gamma(\frac{3}{4}-\frac{1}{2}a)}{2^{\frac{1}{2}a+\frac{3}{4}}\pi i}\int_{(\zeta_1)} e^{\frac{1}{4}z^2t}(1+t)^{\frac{1}{2}a-\frac{3}{4}}(1-t)^{-\frac{1}{2}a-\frac{3}{4}}dt$$

19.5.8
$$=\frac{\Gamma(\frac{3}{4}-\frac{1}{2}a)}{2^{\frac{1}{2}a+\frac{3}{4}}\pi i}\int_{\zeta_1} \tfrac{1}{2}ze^{v}(\tfrac{1}{4}z^2+v)^{\frac{1}{2}a-\frac{3}{4}}(\tfrac{1}{4}z^2-v)^{-\frac{1}{2}a-\frac{3}{4}}dv$$

19.5.9
$$U(a,z)$$
$$=\frac{i\Gamma(\frac{1}{4}-\frac{1}{2}a)}{2^{\frac{1}{2}a+\frac{5}{4}}\pi}\int_{(\eta_1)} \tfrac{1}{2}ze^{-\frac{1}{4}z^2t}(1+t)^{-\frac{1}{2}a-\frac{1}{4}}(1-t)^{\frac{1}{2}a-\frac{1}{4}}dt$$

19.5.10
$$=\frac{i\Gamma(\frac{1}{4}-\frac{1}{2}a)}{2^{\frac{1}{2}a+\frac{5}{4}}\pi}\int_{\eta_1} e^{-v}(\tfrac{1}{4}z^2+v)^{-\frac{1}{2}a-\frac{1}{4}}(\tfrac{1}{4}z^2-v)^{\frac{1}{2}a-\frac{1}{4}}dv$$

The contour ζ_1 is such that $(\frac{1}{4}z^2+v)$ goes from $\infty e^{-i\pi}$ to $\infty e^{i\pi}$ while $v=\frac{1}{4}z^2$ is *not* encircled; $(\frac{1}{4}z^2-v)^{-\frac{1}{2}a-\frac{3}{4}}$ has its principal value except possibly in the immediate neighborhood of the branch-point when encirclement is being avoided. Likewise η_1 is such that $(\frac{1}{4}z^2-v)$ goes from $\infty e^{i\pi}$ to $\infty e^{-i\pi}$ while encirclement of $v=-\frac{1}{4}z^2$ is similarly avoided. The contours (ζ_1) and (η_1) may be obtained from ζ_1 and η_1 by use of the substitution $v=\frac{1}{4}z^2t$.

The expressions **19.5.7** and **19.5.8** become indeterminate when $a=\frac{3}{2},\frac{7}{2},\frac{11}{2},\ldots$; for these values

19.5.11
$$U(a,z)=\frac{1}{\Gamma(\frac{1}{4}+\frac{1}{2}a)}\,ze^{-\frac{1}{4}z^2}\int_0^\infty e^{-s}s^{\frac{1}{2}a-\frac{3}{4}}(z^2+2s)^{-\frac{1}{2}a-\frac{3}{4}}ds$$

Again **19.5.9** and **19.5.10** become indeterminate when $a=\frac{1}{2},\frac{5}{2},\frac{9}{2},\ldots$; for these values

19.5.12
$$U(a,z)=\frac{1}{\Gamma(\frac{3}{4}+\frac{1}{2}a)}\,e^{-\frac{1}{4}z^2}\int_0^\infty e^{-s}s^{\frac{1}{2}a-\frac{1}{4}}(z^2+2s)^{-\frac{1}{2}a-\frac{1}{4}}ds$$

Barnes-Type Integrals

19.5.13 $$U(a,z)=\frac{e^{-\frac{1}{4}z^2}}{2\pi i}\,z^{-a-\frac{1}{2}}\int_{-\infty i}^{+\infty i}\frac{\Gamma(s)\Gamma(\frac{1}{2}+a-2s)}{\Gamma(\frac{1}{2}+a)}(\sqrt{2}z)^{2s}ds \qquad (|\arg z|<\tfrac{3}{4}\pi)$$

where the contour separates the zeros of $\Gamma(s)$ from those of $\Gamma(a+\frac{1}{2}-2s)$. Similarly

19.5.14 $$V(a,z)=\sqrt{\frac{2}{\pi}}\,\frac{e^{\frac{1}{4}z^2}}{2\pi i}\,z^{a-\frac{1}{2}}\int_{-\infty i}^{+\infty i}\frac{\Gamma(s)\Gamma(\frac{1}{2}-a-2s)}{\Gamma(\frac{1}{2}-a)}(\sqrt{2}z)^{2s}\cos s\pi\,ds \qquad (|\arg z|<\tfrac{1}{4}\pi)$$

19.6. Recurrence Relations

19.6.1 $U'(a,x)+\frac{1}{2}xU(a,x)+(a+\frac{1}{2})U(a+1,x)=0$

19.6.2 $U'(a,x)-\frac{1}{2}xU(a,x)+U(a-1,x)=0$

19.6.3 $2U'(a,x)+U(a-1,x)+(a+\frac{1}{2})U(a+1,x)=0$

19.6.4 $xU(a,x)-U(a-1,x)+(a+\frac{1}{2})U(a+1,x)=0$

These are also satisfied by $\Gamma(\frac{1}{2}-a)V(a,x)$.

19.6.5 $V'(a,x)-\frac{1}{2}xV(a,x)-(a-\frac{1}{2})V(a-1,x)=0$

19.6.6 $V'(a,x)+\frac{1}{2}xV(a,x)-V(a+1,x)=0$

19.6.7
$$2V'(a,x)-V(a+1,x)-(a-\tfrac{1}{2})V(a-1,x)=0$$

19.6.8
$$xV(a,x)-V(a+1,x)+(a-\tfrac{1}{2})V(a-1,x)=0$$

These are also satisfied by $U(a,x)/\Gamma(\frac{1}{2}-a)$

19.6.9 $y_1'(a,x)+\frac{1}{2}xy_1(a,x)=(a+\frac{1}{2})y_2(a+1,x)$

19.6.10 $y_1'(a,x)-\frac{1}{2}xy_1(a,x)=(a-\frac{1}{2})y_2(a-1,x)$

19.6.11 $y_2'(a,x)+\frac{1}{2}xy_2(a,x)=y_1(a+1,x)$

19.6.12 $y_2'(a,x)-\frac{1}{2}xy_2(a,x)=y_1(a-1,x)$

Asymptotic Expansions

19.7. Expressions in Terms of Airy Functions

When a is large and negative, write, for $0\leq x<\infty$

$$x=2\sqrt{|a|}\xi \qquad t=(4|a|)^{\frac{2}{3}}\tau$$

19.7.1

$$\tau=-(\tfrac{3}{2}\vartheta_3)^{\frac{2}{3}}$$

$$\vartheta_3=\tfrac{1}{2}\int_\xi^1\sqrt{1-s^2}\,ds=\tfrac{1}{4}\arccos\xi-\tfrac{1}{4}\xi\sqrt{1-\xi^2}\qquad(\xi\leq 1)$$

19.7.2

$$\tau=+(\tfrac{3}{2}\vartheta_2)^{\frac{2}{3}}$$

$$\vartheta_2=\tfrac{1}{2}\int_1^\xi\sqrt{s^2-1}\,ds=\tfrac{1}{4}\xi\sqrt{\xi^2-1}-\tfrac{1}{4}\operatorname{arccosh}\xi\qquad(\xi\geq 1)$$

Then for $x\geq 0$, $a\rightarrow-\infty$

19.7.3

$$U(a,x)\sim 2^{-\frac{1}{4}-\frac{1}{2}a}\Gamma\left(\tfrac{1}{4}-\tfrac{1}{2}a\right)\left(\frac{t}{\xi^2-1}\right)^{\frac{1}{4}}\mathrm{Ai}(t)$$

19.7.4

$$\Gamma\left(\tfrac{1}{2}-a\right)V(a,x)\sim 2^{-\frac{1}{4}-\frac{1}{2}a}\Gamma\left(\tfrac{1}{4}-\tfrac{1}{2}a\right)\left(\frac{t}{\xi^2-1}\right)^{\frac{1}{4}}\mathrm{Bi}(t)$$

Table 19.3 gives τ as a function of ξ.
See [19.5] for further developments.

19.8. Expansions for x Large and a Moderate

When $x>>|a|$

19.8.1

$$U(a,x)\sim e^{-\frac{1}{4}x^2}x^{-a-\frac{1}{2}}\left\{1-\frac{(a+\frac{1}{2})(a+\frac{3}{2})}{2x^2}+\frac{(a+\frac{1}{2})(a+\frac{3}{2})(a+\frac{5}{2})(a+\frac{7}{2})}{2\cdot 4x^4}-\cdots\right\}$$

$$(x\rightarrow+\infty)$$

19.8.2

$$V(a,x)\sim\sqrt{\frac{2}{\pi}}e^{\frac{1}{4}x^2}x^{a-\frac{1}{2}}\left\{1+\frac{(a-\frac{1}{2})(a-\frac{3}{2})}{2x^2}+\frac{(a-\frac{1}{2})(a-\frac{3}{2})(a-\frac{5}{2})(a-\frac{7}{2})}{2\cdot 4x^4}+\cdots\right\}$$

$$(x\rightarrow+\infty)$$

These expansions form the basis for the choice of standard solutions in **19.3.** The former is valid for complex x, with $|\arg x|<\frac{3}{4}\pi$, in the complete sense of Watson [19.6], although valid for a wider range of $|\arg x|$ in Poincaré's sense; the second series is completely valid *only for x real and positive*.

19.9. Expansions for a Large With x Moderate

(i) a positive

When $a>>x^2$, with $p=\sqrt{a}$, then

19.9.1 $$U(a,x)=\frac{\sqrt{\pi}}{2^{\frac{1}{2}a+\frac{1}{4}}\Gamma(\frac{3}{4}+\frac{1}{2}a)}\exp\left(-px+v_1\right)$$

19.9.2 $$U(a,-x)=\frac{\sqrt{\pi}}{2^{\frac{1}{2}a+\frac{1}{4}}\Gamma(\frac{3}{4}+\frac{1}{2}a)}\exp\left(px+v_2\right)$$

where

19.9.3

$$v_1,\ v_2\sim\mp\frac{\frac{2}{3}(\frac{1}{2}x)^3}{2p}-\frac{(\frac{1}{2}x)^2}{(2p)^2}\mp\frac{\frac{1}{2}x-\frac{2}{5}(\frac{1}{2}x)^5}{(2p)^3}+\frac{2(\frac{1}{2}x)^4}{(2p)^4}\pm\frac{\frac{16}{3}(\frac{1}{2}x)^3-\frac{4}{7}(\frac{1}{2}x)^7}{(2p)^5}+\cdots$$

$$(a\rightarrow+\infty)$$

The upper sign gives the first function, and the lower sign the second function.

(ii) a negative

When $-a>>x^2$, with $p=\sqrt{-a}$, then

19.9.4

$$U(a,x)+i\Gamma\left(\tfrac{1}{2}-a\right)\cdot V(a,x)=\frac{e^{i\pi(\frac{1}{4}+\frac{1}{2}a)}\Gamma(\frac{1}{4}-\frac{1}{2}a)}{2^{\frac{1}{2}a+\frac{1}{4}}\sqrt{\pi}}e^{ipx}\exp\left(v_r+iv_i\right)$$

where

19.9.5

$$v_r\sim+\frac{(\frac{1}{2}x)^2}{(2p)^2}+\frac{2(\frac{1}{2}x)^4}{(2p)^4}-\frac{9(\frac{1}{2}x)^2-\frac{16}{3}(\frac{1}{2}x)^6}{(2p)^6}-\cdots$$

$$v_i\sim-\frac{\frac{2}{3}(\frac{1}{2}x)^3}{2p}+\frac{\frac{1}{2}x+\frac{2}{5}(\frac{1}{2}x)^5}{(2p)^3}+\frac{\frac{16}{3}(\frac{1}{2}x)^3-\frac{4}{7}(\frac{1}{2}x)^7}{(2p)^5}-\cdots$$

$$(a\rightarrow-\infty)$$

Further expansions of a similar type will be found in [19.11].

19.10. Darwin's Expansions

(i) a positive, x^2+4a large. Write

19.10.1 $$X=\sqrt{x^2+4a}$$

$$\theta=4a\vartheta_1(x/2\sqrt{a})=\tfrac{1}{2}\int_0^x X\,dx=\tfrac{1}{4}xX+a\ln\frac{x+X}{2\sqrt{a}}$$

$$=\frac{x}{4}\sqrt{x^2+4a}+a\operatorname{arcsinh}\frac{x}{2\sqrt{a}}$$

(see **Table 19.3** for ϑ_1), then

19.10.2 $$U(a,x)=\frac{(2\pi)^{1/4}}{\sqrt{\Gamma(\frac{1}{2}+a)}}\exp\{-\theta+v(a,x)\}$$

19.10.3 $$U(a,-x)=\frac{(2\pi)^{1/4}}{\sqrt{\Gamma(\frac{1}{2}+a)}}\exp\{\theta+v(a,-x)\}$$

where

19.10.4

$$v(a,x)\sim-\tfrac{1}{2}\ln X+\sum_{s=1}(-1)^s d_{3s}/X^{3s} \qquad (a>0,\ x^2+4a\to+\infty)$$

and d_{3s} is given by **19.10.13.**

(ii) a negative, x^2+4a large and positive. Write

19.10.5 $$X=\sqrt{x^2-4|a|}$$

$$\theta=4|a|\vartheta_2(x/2\sqrt{|a|})=\tfrac{1}{2}\int_{2\sqrt{|a|}}^{x}X\,dx=\tfrac{1}{4}xX+a\ln\frac{x+X}{2\sqrt{|a|}}$$
$$=\tfrac{1}{4}x\sqrt{x^2-4|a|}+a\ \text{arccosh}\ \frac{x}{2\sqrt{|a|}}$$

(see **Table 19.3** for ϑ_2), then

19.10.6 $$U(a,x)=\frac{\sqrt{\Gamma(\frac{1}{2}-a)}}{(2\pi)^{1/4}}\exp\{-\theta+v(a,x)\}$$

19.10.7

$$V(a,x)=\frac{2}{(2\pi)^{1/4}\sqrt{\Gamma(\frac{1}{2}-a)}}\exp\{\theta+v(a,-x)\}$$

where again

19.10.8

$$v(a,x)\sim-\tfrac{1}{2}\ln X+\sum_{s=1}(-1)^s d_{3s}/X^{3s} \qquad (a<0,\ x^2+4a\to+\infty)$$

and d_{3s} is given by **19.10.13.**

(iii) a large and negative and x moderate. Write

19.10.9 $$Y=\sqrt{4|a|-x^2}$$

$$\theta=4|a|\vartheta_4(x/2\sqrt{|a|})$$
$$=\tfrac{1}{2}\int_0^x Y\,dx=\tfrac{1}{4}xY+|a|\arcsin\frac{x}{2\sqrt{|a|}}$$

(see **Table 19.3** for $\vartheta_4=\frac{1}{8}\pi-\vartheta_3$), then

19.10.10

$$U(a,x)=\frac{2\sqrt{\Gamma(\frac{1}{2}-a)}}{(2\pi)^{1/4}}e^{v_r}\cos\left\{\tfrac{1}{4}\pi+\tfrac{1}{2}\pi a+\theta+v_i\right\}$$

19.10.11

$$V(a,x)=\frac{2}{(2\pi)^{\frac{1}{4}}\sqrt{\Gamma(\frac{1}{2}-a)}}e^{v_r}\sin\{\tfrac{1}{4}\pi+\tfrac{1}{2}\pi a+\theta+v_i\}$$

where

19.10.12 $$v_r\sim-\tfrac{1}{2}\ln Y-\frac{d_6}{Y^6}+\frac{d_{12}}{Y^{12}}-\ldots$$

$$v_i\sim\frac{d_3}{Y^3}-\frac{d_9}{Y^9}+\ldots \qquad (x^2+4a\to-\infty)$$

In each case the coefficients d_{3r} are given by

19.10.13

$$d_3=\frac{1}{a}\left(\frac{x^3}{48}+\tfrac{1}{2}ax\right)$$

$$d_6=\tfrac{3}{4}x^2-2a$$

$$d_9=\frac{1}{a^3}\left(-\frac{7}{5760}x^9-\frac{7}{320}ax^7-\frac{49}{320}a^2x^5+\frac{31}{12}a^3x^3-19a^4x\right)$$

$$d_{12}=\frac{153}{8}x^4-186ax^2+80a^2$$

See [19.11] for $d_{15}, \ldots, d_{24}$, and [19.5] for an alternative form.

19.11. Modulus and Phase

When a is negative and $|x|<2\sqrt{|a|}$, the functions U and V are oscillatory and it is sometimes convenient to write

19.11.1 $$U(a,x)+i\Gamma(\tfrac{1}{2}-a)V(a,x)=F(a,x)e^{i\chi(a,x)}$$

19.11.2 $$U'(a,x)+i\Gamma(\tfrac{1}{2}-a)V'(a,x)=-G(a,x)e^{i\psi(a,x)}$$

Then, when $a<0$ and $|a|>>x^2$,

19.11.3

$$F=\frac{\Gamma(\frac{1}{4}-\frac{1}{2}a)}{2^{\frac{1}{2}a+\frac{1}{4}}\sqrt{\pi}}e^{v_r}, \qquad \chi=(\tfrac{1}{2}a+\tfrac{1}{4})\pi+px+v_i$$

where v_r, v_i are given by **19.9.5** and $p=\sqrt{-a}$.

Alternatively, with $p=\sqrt{|a|}$, and again $-a>>x^2$,

19.11.4

$$F\sim\frac{\Gamma(\frac{1}{4}-\frac{1}{2}a)}{2^{\frac{1}{2}a+\frac{1}{4}}\sqrt{\pi}}\left\{1+\frac{x^2}{(4p)^2}+\frac{\frac{5}{2}x^4}{(4p)^4}+\frac{\frac{15}{2}x^6-144x^2}{(4p)^6}+\ldots\right\}$$

19.11.5 $$\chi\sim(\tfrac{1}{2}a+\tfrac{1}{4})\pi+px\left\{1-\frac{\frac{2}{3}x^2}{(4p)^2}-\frac{\frac{2}{5}x^4-16}{(4p)^4}-\frac{\frac{4}{7}x^6-\frac{256}{3}x^2}{(4p)^6}-\ldots\right\}$$

19.11.6 $$G\sim\frac{\Gamma(\frac{3}{4}-\frac{1}{2}a)}{2^{\frac{1}{2}a-\frac{1}{4}}\sqrt{\pi}}\left\{1-\frac{x^2}{(4p)^2}-\frac{\frac{3}{2}x^4}{(4p)^4}-\frac{\frac{7}{2}x^6-176x^2}{(4p)^6}-\ldots\right\}$$

19.11.7 $$\psi\sim(\tfrac{1}{2}a-\tfrac{1}{4})\pi+px\left\{1-\frac{\frac{2}{3}x^2}{(4p)^2}-\frac{\frac{2}{5}x^4+16}{(4p)^4}-\frac{\frac{4}{7}x^6+\frac{320}{3}x^2}{(4p)^6}-\ldots\right\}$$

Again, when x^2+4a is large and negative, with $Y=\sqrt{4|a|-x^2}$, then

19.11.8

$$F=\frac{2\sqrt{\Gamma(\frac{1}{2}-a)}}{(2\pi)^{\frac{1}{4}}}e^{v_r}\qquad \chi=\tfrac{1}{4}\pi+\tfrac{1}{2}\pi a+\theta+v_i$$

where θ, v_r and v_i are given by **19.10.9** and **19.10.12.**

Another form is

19.11.9

$$F\sim\frac{2\sqrt{\Gamma(\frac{1}{2}-a)}}{(2\pi)^{\frac{1}{4}}\sqrt{Y}}\left(1+\frac{3}{4Y^4}+\frac{5a}{Y^6}+\frac{621}{32Y^8}+\ldots\right)\qquad (x^2+4a\to-\infty)$$

19.11.10

$$G\sim\frac{\sqrt{Y}\sqrt{\Gamma(\frac{1}{2}-a)}}{(2\pi)^{\frac{1}{4}}}\left(1-\frac{5}{4Y^4}-\frac{7a}{Y^6}-\frac{835}{32Y^8}-\ldots\right)\qquad (x^2+4a\to-\infty)$$

while ψ and χ are connected by

19.11.11

$$\psi-\chi\sim-\tfrac{1}{2}\pi-\frac{x}{Y^3}\left(1+\frac{47}{6Y^4}+\frac{214a}{3Y^6}+\frac{14483}{40Y^8}+\ldots\right)\qquad (x^2+4a\to-\infty)$$

Connections With Other Functions

19.12. Connection With Confluent Hypergeometric Functions (see chapter 13)

19.12.1

$$U(a,\pm x)=\frac{\sqrt{\pi}2^{-\frac{1}{2}a}x^{-\frac{1}{2}}}{\Gamma(\frac{3}{4}+\frac{1}{2}a)}M_{-\frac{1}{2}a,-\frac{1}{4}}(\tfrac{1}{2}x^2)\mp\frac{\sqrt{\pi}2^{1-\frac{1}{2}a}x^{-\frac{1}{2}}}{\Gamma(\frac{1}{4}+\frac{1}{2}a)}M_{-\frac{1}{2}a,\frac{1}{4}}(\tfrac{1}{2}x^2)$$

19.12.2 $$U(a,x)=2^{-\frac{1}{2}a}x^{-\frac{1}{2}}W_{-\frac{1}{2}a,-\frac{1}{4}}(\tfrac{1}{2}x^2)$$

19.12.3

$$U(a,\pm x)=\frac{\sqrt{\pi}2^{-\frac{1}{4}-\frac{1}{2}a}e^{-\frac{1}{4}x^2}}{\Gamma(\frac{3}{4}+\frac{1}{2}a)}M(\tfrac{1}{2}a+\tfrac{1}{4},\tfrac{1}{2},\tfrac{1}{2}x^2)\mp\frac{\sqrt{\pi}2^{\frac{1}{4}-\frac{1}{2}a}xe^{-\frac{1}{4}x^2}}{\Gamma(\frac{1}{4}+\frac{1}{2}a)}M(\tfrac{1}{2}a+\tfrac{3}{4},\tfrac{3}{2},\tfrac{1}{2}x^2)$$

19.12.4

$$U(a,x)=2^{-\frac{1}{4}-\frac{1}{2}a}e^{-\frac{1}{4}x^2}U(\tfrac{1}{2}a+\tfrac{1}{4},\tfrac{1}{2},\tfrac{1}{2}x^2)=2^{-\frac{3}{4}-\frac{1}{2}a}xe^{-\frac{1}{4}x^2}U(\tfrac{1}{2}a+\tfrac{3}{4},\tfrac{3}{2},\tfrac{1}{2}x^2)$$

Expressions for $V(a,x)$ may be obtained from these by use of **19.4.2.**

19.13. Connection With Hermite Polynomials and Functions

When n is a non-negative integer

19.13.1

$$U(-n-\tfrac{1}{2},x)=e^{-\frac{1}{4}x^2}He_n(x)=2^{-\frac{1}{2}n}e^{-\frac{1}{4}x^2}H_n(x/\sqrt{2})$$

19.13.2

$$V(n+\tfrac{1}{2},x)=\sqrt{2/\pi}e^{\frac{1}{4}x^2}He_n^*(x)=2^{-\frac{1}{2}n}e^{\frac{1}{4}x^2}H_n^*(x/\sqrt{2})$$

in which $H_n(x)$ and $He_n(x)$ are Hermite polynomials (see chapter **22**) while

19.13.3 $$He_n^*(x)=e^{-\frac{1}{2}x^2}\frac{d^n}{dx^n}e^{\frac{1}{2}x^2}=(-i)^nHe_n(ix)$$

19.13.4 $$H_n^*(x)=e^{-x^2}\frac{d^n}{dx^n}e^{x^2}=(-i)^nH_n(ix)$$

This gives one elementary solution to **19.1.2** whenever $2a$ is an odd integer, positive or negative.

19.14. Connection With Probability Integrals and Dawson's Integral (see chapter 7)

If, as in [19.10]

19.14.1 $$Hh_{-1}(x)=e^{-\frac{1}{2}x^2}$$

19.14.2

$$Hh_n(x)=\int_x^\infty Hh_{n-1}(t)dt=(1/n!)\int_x^\infty(t-x)^ne^{-\frac{1}{2}t^2}dt\qquad (n\geq 0)$$

then

19.14.3 $$U(n+\tfrac{1}{2},x)=e^{\frac{1}{4}x^2}Hh_n(x)\qquad (n\geq -1)$$

Correspondingly

19.14.4 $$V(\tfrac{1}{2},x)=\sqrt{2/\pi}e^{\frac{1}{4}x^2}$$

and

19.14.5

$$V(-n-\tfrac{1}{2},x)=e^{-\frac{1}{4}x^2}\left\{\int_0^x e^{-\frac{1}{4}t^2}V(-n+\tfrac{1}{2},t)dt-\frac{\sin\frac{1}{2}n\pi}{2^{\frac{1}{2}n}\Gamma(\frac{1}{2}n+1)}\right\}\quad(n\geq 0)$$

Here $V(-\frac{1}{2},x)$ is closely related to Dawson's integral

$$\int_0^x e^{t^2}dt$$

These relations give a second solution of **19.1.2** whenever $2a$ is an odd integer, and a second solution is unobtainable from $U(a,x)$ by reflection in the y-axis.

19.15. Explicit Formula in Terms of Bessel Functions When 2a Is an Integer

Write

19.15.1 $$I_{-n}-I_n=(2/\pi)\sin n\pi\cdot K_n$$

19.15.2 $$I_{-n}+I_n=\cos n\pi\cdot\mathscr{I}_n$$

where the argument of all modified Bessel functions is $\frac{1}{4}x^2$. Then

19.15.3 $$U(1,x)=2\pi^{-\frac{1}{2}}(\tfrac{1}{2}x)^{\frac{3}{2}}(-K_{\frac{1}{4}}+K_{\frac{3}{4}})$$

19.15.4 $$U(2,x)=2\cdot\tfrac{2}{3}\pi^{-\frac{1}{2}}(\tfrac{1}{2}x)^{\frac{5}{2}}(2K_{\frac{1}{4}}-3K_{\frac{3}{4}}+K_{\frac{5}{4}})$$

19.15.5

$$U(3,x)=2\cdot\tfrac{2}{3}\cdot\tfrac{2}{5}\pi^{-\frac{1}{2}}(\tfrac{1}{2}x)^{\frac{7}{2}}(-5K_{\frac{1}{4}}+9K_{\frac{3}{4}}-5K_{\frac{5}{4}}+K_{\frac{7}{4}})$$

19.15.6 $$V(1,x)=\tfrac{1}{2}(\tfrac{1}{2}x)^{\frac{3}{2}}(\mathscr{I}_{\frac{1}{4}}-\mathscr{I}_{\frac{3}{4}})$$

19.15.7 $$V(2,x)=\tfrac{1}{2}(\tfrac{1}{2}x)^{\frac{5}{2}}(2\mathscr{I}_{\frac{1}{4}}-3\mathscr{I}_{\frac{3}{4}}+\mathscr{I}_{\frac{5}{4}})$$

19.15.8 $$V(3,x)=\tfrac{1}{2}(\tfrac{1}{2}x)^{\frac{7}{2}}(5\mathscr{I}_{\frac{1}{4}}-9\mathscr{I}_{\frac{3}{4}}+5\mathscr{I}_{\frac{5}{4}}-\mathscr{I}_{\frac{7}{4}})$$

19.15.9 $$U(0,x)=\pi^{-\frac{1}{2}}(\tfrac{1}{2}x)^{\frac{1}{2}}K_{\frac{1}{4}}$$

19.15.10 $$U(-1,x)=\pi^{-\frac{1}{2}}(\tfrac{1}{2}x)^{\frac{3}{2}}(K_{\frac{1}{4}}+K_{\frac{3}{4}})$$

19.15.11

$$U(-2,x)=\pi^{-\frac{1}{2}}(\tfrac{1}{2}x)^{\frac{5}{2}}(2K_{\frac{1}{4}}+3K_{\frac{3}{4}}-K_{\frac{5}{4}})$$

19.15.12

$$U(-3,x)=\pi^{-\frac{1}{2}}(\tfrac{1}{2}x)^{\frac{7}{2}}(5K_{\frac{1}{4}}+9K_{\frac{3}{4}}-5K_{\frac{5}{4}}-K_{\frac{7}{4}})$$

19.15.13 $$V(0,x)=\tfrac{1}{2}(\tfrac{1}{2}x)^{\frac{1}{2}}\mathscr{I}_{\frac{1}{4}}$$

19.15.14 $$V(-1,x)=(\tfrac{1}{2}x)^{\frac{3}{2}}(\mathscr{I}_{\frac{1}{4}}+\mathscr{I}_{\frac{3}{4}})$$

19.15.15 $$V(-2,x)=\tfrac{2}{3}(\tfrac{1}{2}x)^{\frac{5}{2}}(2\mathscr{I}_{\frac{1}{4}}+3\mathscr{I}_{\frac{3}{4}}-\mathscr{I}_{\frac{5}{4}})$$

19.15.16

$$V(-3,x)=\tfrac{2}{3}\cdot\tfrac{2}{5}(\tfrac{1}{2}x)^{\frac{7}{2}}(5\mathscr{I}_{\frac{1}{4}}+9\mathscr{I}_{\frac{3}{4}}-5\mathscr{I}_{\frac{5}{4}}-\mathscr{I}_{\frac{7}{4}})$$

19.15.17 $$U(-\tfrac{1}{2},x)=\sqrt{2/\pi}(\tfrac{1}{2}x)K_{\frac{1}{4}}$$

19.15.18 $$U(-\tfrac{3}{2},x)=\sqrt{2/\pi}(\tfrac{1}{2}x)^2 2K_{\frac{1}{4}}$$

19.15.19 $$U(-\tfrac{5}{2},x)=\sqrt{2/\pi}(\tfrac{1}{2}x)^3(5K_{\frac{1}{4}}-K_{\frac{3}{4}})$$

19.15.20 $$V(\tfrac{1}{2},x)=(\tfrac{1}{2}x)(I_{\frac{1}{4}}+I_{-\frac{1}{4}})$$

19.15.21 $$V(\tfrac{3}{2},x)=(\tfrac{1}{2}x)^2(2I_{\frac{1}{4}}+2I_{-\frac{1}{4}})$$

19.15.22 $$V(\tfrac{5}{2},x)=(\tfrac{1}{2}x)^3(5I_{\frac{1}{4}}+5I_{-\frac{1}{4}}-I_{\frac{3}{4}}-I_{-\frac{3}{4}})$$

The Equation $\frac{d^2y}{dx^2}+\left(\frac{1}{4}x^2-a\right)y=0$

19.16. Power Series in x

Even and odd solutions are given by **19.2.1** to **19.2.4** with $-ia$ written for a and $xe^{\frac{1}{4}i\pi}$ for x; the series involves complex quantities in which the imaginary part of the sum vanishes identically. Alternatively,

19.16.1

$$y_1=1+a\frac{x^2}{2!}+(a^2-\tfrac{1}{2})\frac{x^4}{4!}+(a^3-\tfrac{7}{2}a)\frac{x^6}{6!}+(a^4-11a^2+\tfrac{15}{4})\frac{x^8}{8!}+(a^5-25a^3+\tfrac{211}{4}a)\frac{x^{10}}{10!}+\ldots$$

19.16.2

$$y_2=x+a\frac{x^3}{3!}+(a^2-\tfrac{3}{2})\frac{x^5}{5!}+(a^3-\tfrac{13}{2}a)\frac{x^7}{7!}+(a^4-17a^2+\tfrac{63}{4})\frac{x^9}{9!}+(a^5-35a^3+\tfrac{531}{4}a)\frac{x^{11}}{11!}+\ldots$$

in which non-zero coefficients a_n of $x^n/n!$ are connected by

19.16.3 $$a_{n+2}=a\cdot a_n-\tfrac{1}{4}n(n-1)a_{n-2}$$

19.17. Standard Solutions (see [19.4])

19.17.1 $$W(a,\pm x)=\frac{(\cosh\pi a)^{\frac{1}{4}}}{2\sqrt{\pi}}(G_1y_1\mp\sqrt{2}G_3y_2)$$

19.17.2 $$=2^{-3/4}\left(\sqrt{\frac{G_1}{G_3}}\,y_1\mp\sqrt{\frac{2G_3}{G_1}}\,y_2\right)$$

where

19.17.3 $$G_1=|\Gamma(\tfrac{1}{4}+\tfrac{1}{2}ia)|\qquad G_3=|\Gamma(\tfrac{3}{4}+\tfrac{1}{2}ia)|$$

At $x=0$,

19.17.4 $$W(a,0)=\frac{1}{2^{\frac{3}{4}}}\left|\frac{\Gamma(\frac{1}{4}+\frac{1}{2}ia)}{\Gamma(\frac{3}{4}+\frac{1}{2}ia)}\right|^{\frac{1}{2}}=\frac{1}{2^{\frac{3}{4}}}\sqrt{\frac{G_1}{G_3}}$$

19.17.5

$$W'(a,0)=-\frac{1}{2^{\frac{1}{4}}}\left|\frac{\Gamma(\frac{3}{4}+\frac{1}{2}ia)}{\Gamma(\frac{1}{4}+\frac{1}{2}ia)}\right|^{\frac{1}{2}}=-\frac{1}{2^{\frac{1}{4}}}\sqrt{\frac{G_3}{G_1}}$$

Complex Solutions

19.17.6 $$E(a,x)=k^{-\frac{1}{2}}W(a,x)+ik^{\frac{1}{2}}W(a,-x)$$

19.17.7 $$E^*(a,x)=k^{-\frac{1}{2}}W(a,x)-ik^{\frac{1}{2}}W(a,-x)$$

where

19.17.8 $$k=\sqrt{1+e^{2\pi a}}-e^{\pi a}\qquad 1/k=\sqrt{1+e^{2\pi a}}+e^{\pi a}$$

In terms of $U(a,x)$ of **19.3**,

19.17.9 $$E(a,x)=\sqrt{2}e^{\frac{1}{4}\pi a+\frac{1}{8}i\pi+\frac{1}{2}i\phi_2}U(ia,xe^{-\frac{1}{4}i\pi})$$

with

19.17.10 $$\phi_2=\arg\Gamma(\tfrac{1}{2}+ia)$$

where the branch is defined by $\phi_2=0$ when $a=0$ and by continuity elsewhere.

Also

19.17.11

$$\sqrt{2\pi}U(ia,xe^{-\frac{1}{4}i\pi})=\Gamma(\tfrac{1}{2}-ia)\{e^{\frac{1}{2}\pi a-\frac{1}{4}i\pi}U(-ia,xe^{\frac{1}{4}i\pi})$$
$$+e^{-\frac{1}{2}\pi a+\frac{1}{4}i\pi}U(-ia,-xe^{\frac{1}{4}i\pi})\}$$

19.18. Wronskian and Other Relations

19.18.1 $$W\{W(a,x),W(a,-x)\}=1$$

19.18.2 $$W\{E(a,x),E^*(a,x)\}=-2i$$

19.18.3 $$\sqrt{1+e^{2\pi a}}E(a,x)=e^{\pi a}E^*(a,x)+iE^*(a,-x)$$

19.18.4 $$E^*(a,x)=e^{-i(\phi_2+\frac{1}{2}\pi)}E(-a,ix)$$

19.18.5

$$\sqrt{\Gamma(\tfrac{1}{2}+ia)}E^*(a,x)=e^{-\frac{1}{4}i\pi}\sqrt{\Gamma(\tfrac{1}{2}-ia)}E(-a,ix)$$

19.19. Integral Representations

These are covered for **19.1.3** as well as for **19.1.2** in **19.5** (general complex argument).

Asymptotic Expansions

19.20. Expressions in Terms of Airy Functions

When a is large and positive, write, for $0\leq x<\infty$

$$x=2\sqrt{a}\xi\qquad t=(4a)^{\frac{1}{3}}\tau$$

19.20.1

$$\tau=-(\tfrac{3}{2}\vartheta_3)^{\frac{2}{3}}$$

$$\vartheta_3=\frac{1}{2}\int_\xi^1\sqrt{1-s^2}\,ds=\tfrac{1}{4}\arccos\xi-\tfrac{1}{4}\xi\sqrt{1-\xi^2}\quad(\xi\leq 1)$$

19.20.2

$$\tau=+(\tfrac{3}{2}\vartheta_2)^{\frac{2}{3}}$$

$$\vartheta_2=\tfrac{1}{2}\int_1^\xi\sqrt{s^2-1}ds=\tfrac{1}{4}\xi\sqrt{\xi^2-1}-\tfrac{1}{4}\text{arccosh}\,\xi\qquad(\xi\geq 1)$$

Then for $x>0$, $a\to+\infty$

19.20.3

$$W(a,x)\sim\sqrt{\pi}(4a)^{-\frac{1}{4}}e^{-\frac{1}{2}\pi a}\left(\frac{t}{\xi^2-1}\right)^{\frac{1}{4}}\text{Bi}(-t)$$

19.20.4

$$W(a,-x)\sim 2\sqrt{\pi}(4a)^{-\frac{1}{4}}e^{\frac{1}{2}\pi a}\left(\frac{t}{\xi^2-1}\right)^{\frac{1}{4}}\text{Ai}(-t)$$

Table 19.3 gives τ as a function of ξ. See [19.5] for further developments.

19.21. Expansions for x Large and a Moderate

When $x>>|a|$,

19.21.1

$$E(a,x)=\sqrt{2/x}\exp\{i(\tfrac{1}{4}x^2-a\ln x+\tfrac{1}{2}\phi_2+\tfrac{1}{4}\pi)\}s(a,x)$$

19.21.2

$$W(a,x)=\sqrt{2k/x}\{s_1(a,x)\cos(\tfrac{1}{4}x^2-a\ln x+\tfrac{1}{4}\pi+\tfrac{1}{2}\phi_2)$$
$$-s_2(a,x)\sin(\tfrac{1}{4}x^2-a\ln x+\tfrac{1}{4}\pi+\tfrac{1}{2}\phi_2)\}$$

19.21.3

$$W(a,-x)=\sqrt{2/kx}\{s_1(a,x)\sin(\tfrac{1}{4}x^2-a\ln x+\tfrac{1}{4}\pi+\tfrac{1}{2}\phi_2)$$
$$+s_2(a,x)\cos(\tfrac{1}{4}x^2-a\ln x+\tfrac{1}{4}\pi+\tfrac{1}{2}\phi_2)\}$$

where ϕ_2 is defined by **19.17.10** and

19.21.4 $$s(a,x)=s_1(a,x)+is_2(a,x)$$

19.21.5

$$s_1(a,x)\sim 1+\frac{v_2}{1!2x^2}-\frac{u_4}{2!2^2x^4}-\frac{v_6}{3!2^3x^6}+\frac{u_8}{4!2^4x^8}+\dots$$

19.21.6

$$s_2(a,x)\sim-\frac{u_2}{1!2x^2}-\frac{v_4}{2!2^2x^4}+\frac{u_6}{3!2^3x^6}+\frac{v_8}{4!2^4x^8}-\dots$$

with

$(x\to+\infty)$

19.21.7 $u_r+iv_r=\Gamma(r+\frac{1}{2}+ia)/\Gamma(\frac{1}{2}+ia)$

or

19.21.8 $s(a,x)\sim\sum_{r=0}^{\infty}(-i)^r\frac{\Gamma(2r+\frac{1}{2}+ia)}{\Gamma(\frac{1}{2}+ia)}\frac{1}{2^r r! x^{2r}}$

19.22. Expansions for a Large With x Moderate

(i) a positive

When $a>>x^2$, with $p=\sqrt{a}$, then

19.22.1 $W(a,x)=W(a,0)\exp(-px+v_1)$

19.22.2 $W(a,-x)=W(a,0)\exp(px+v_2)$

where $W(a, 0)$ is given by **19.17.4**, and

19.22.3

$$v_1, v_2\sim\pm\frac{\frac{2}{3}(\frac{1}{2}x)^3}{2p}+\frac{(\frac{1}{2}x)^2}{(2p)^2}\pm\frac{\frac{1}{2}x+\frac{2}{5}(\frac{1}{2}x)^5}{(2p)^3}+\frac{2(\frac{1}{2}x)^4}{(2p)^4}\pm\frac{\frac{16}{3}(\frac{1}{2}x)^3+\frac{4}{7}(\frac{1}{2}x)^7}{(2p)^5}+\dots \qquad (a\to+\infty)$$

The upper sign gives the first function, and the lower sign the second function.

(ii) a negative

When $-a>>x^2$, with $p=\sqrt{-a}$, then

19.22.4

$$W(a,x)+iW(a,-x)=\sqrt{2}W(a,0)\exp\{v_r+i(px+\tfrac{1}{4}\pi+v_i)\}$$

where $W(a, 0)$ is given by **19.17.4**, and

19.22.5

$$v_r\sim-\frac{(\frac{1}{2}x)^2}{(2p)^2}+\frac{2(\frac{1}{2}x)^4}{(2p)^4}-\frac{9(\frac{1}{2}x)^2+\frac{16}{3}(\frac{1}{2}x)^6}{(2p)^6}+\dots$$

$$v_i\sim\frac{\frac{2}{3}(\frac{1}{2}x)^3}{2p}-\frac{\frac{1}{2}x+\frac{2}{5}(\frac{1}{2}x)^5}{(2p)^3}+\frac{\frac{16}{3}(\frac{1}{2}x)^3+\frac{4}{7}(\frac{1}{2}x)^7}{(2p)^5}-\dots \qquad (a\to-\infty)$$

Further expansions of a similar type will be found in [19.3].

19.23. Darwin's Expansions

(i) a positive, $x^2-4a>>0$

Write

19.23.1

$$X=\sqrt{x^2-4a} \qquad \theta=4a\vartheta_2(x/2\sqrt{a})=\tfrac{1}{2}\int_{2\sqrt{a}}^{x}X\,dx=\tfrac{1}{4}xX-a\ln\frac{x+X}{2\sqrt{a}}=\tfrac{1}{4}x\sqrt{x^2-4a}-a\,\mathrm{arccosh}\,\frac{x}{2\sqrt{a}}$$

(see **Table 19.3** for ϑ_2), then

19.23.2 $W(a,x)=\sqrt{2k}e^{v_r}\cos(\frac{1}{4}\pi+\theta+v_i)$

19.23.3 $W(a,-x)=\sqrt{2/k}e^{v_r}\sin(\frac{1}{4}\pi+\theta+v_i)$

where

19.23.4

$$v_r\sim-\tfrac{1}{2}\ln X-\frac{d_6}{X^6}+\frac{d_{12}}{X^{12}}-\dots$$

$$v_i\sim-\frac{d_3}{X^3}+\frac{d_9}{X^9}-\frac{d_{15}}{X^{15}}+\dots \qquad (x^2-4a\to\infty)$$

and d_{3r} is given by **19.23.12**.

(ii) a positive, $4a-x^2>>0$

Write

19.23.5

$$Y=\sqrt{4a-x^2} \qquad \theta=4a\vartheta_4(x/2\sqrt{a})=\tfrac{1}{2}\int_0^x Y\,dx=\tfrac{1}{4}xY+a\arcsin\frac{x}{2\sqrt{a}}$$

(see **Table 19.3** for $\vartheta_4=\frac{1}{8}\pi-\vartheta_3$), then

19.23.6 $W(a,x)=\exp\{-\theta+v(a,x)\}$

19.23.7 $W(a,-x)=\exp\{\theta+v(a,-x)\}$

where

19.23.8

$$v(a,x)\sim-\tfrac{1}{2}\ln Y+\frac{d_3}{Y^3}+\frac{d_6}{Y^6}+\frac{d_9}{Y^9}+\dots \qquad (x^2-4a\to-\infty)$$

and d_{3r} is again given by **19.23.12**.

(iii) a negative, $x^2-4a>>0$

Write

19.23.9

$$X=\sqrt{x^2+4|a|} \qquad \theta=4|a|\vartheta_1(x/2\sqrt{|a|})=\tfrac{1}{2}\int_0^x X\,dx=\tfrac{1}{4}xX-a\ln\frac{x+X}{2\sqrt{|a|}}=\tfrac{1}{4}x\sqrt{x^2+4|a|}-a\,\mathrm{arcsinh}\,\frac{x}{2\sqrt{|a|}}$$

(see **Table 19.3** for ϑ_1) then

19.23.10 $W(a,x)=\sqrt{2k}e^{v_r}\cos(\frac{1}{4}\pi+\theta+v_i)$

19.23.11 $W(a,-x)=\sqrt{2/k}e^{v_r}\sin(\frac{1}{4}\pi+\theta+v_i)$

where v_r and v_i are again given by **19.23.4**. In each case the coefficients d_{3r} are given by

19.23.12

$$d_3=-\frac{1}{a}\left(\frac{x^3}{48}-\tfrac{1}{2}ax\right)$$

$$d_6=\tfrac{3}{4}x^2+2a$$

$$d_9=\frac{1}{a^3}\left(\frac{7}{5760}x^9-\frac{7}{320}ax^7+\frac{49}{320}a^2x^5+\frac{31}{12}a^3x^3+19a^4x\right)$$

$$d_{12}=\frac{153}{8}x^4+186ax^2+80a^2$$

See [19.11] for $d_{15}, \ldots, d_{24}$, and [19.5] for an alternative form.

19.24. Modulus and Phase

When a is positive, the function $W(a, x)$ is oscillatory when $x<-2\sqrt{a}$ and when $x>2\sqrt{a}$; when a is negative, the function is oscillatory for all x. In such cases it is sometimes convenient to write

19.24.1

$$k^{-\frac{1}{2}}W(a, x)+ik^{\frac{1}{2}}W(a,-x)=E(a, x)=Fe^{i\chi} \qquad (x>0)$$

19.24.2

$$k^{-\frac{1}{2}}\frac{dW(a, x)}{dx}+ik^{\frac{1}{2}}\frac{dW(a,-x)}{dx}=E'(a, x)=-Ge^{i\psi} \qquad (x>0)$$

Then, when $x^2>>|a|$,

19.24.3

$$F\sim\sqrt{\frac{2}{x}}\left(1+\frac{a}{x^2}+\frac{10a^2-3}{4x^4}+\frac{30a^3-47a}{4x^6}+\ldots\right)$$

19.24.4

$$\chi\sim\tfrac{1}{4}x^2-a\ln x+\tfrac{1}{2}\phi_2+\tfrac{1}{4}\pi+\frac{4a^2-3}{8x^2}+\frac{4a^3-19a}{8x^4}+\ldots$$

19.24.5

$$G\sim\sqrt{\frac{x}{2}}\left(1-\frac{a}{x^2}-\frac{6a^2-5}{4x^4}-\frac{14a^3-63a}{4x^6}-\ldots\right)$$

19.24.6

$$\psi\sim\tfrac{1}{4}x^2-a\ln x+\tfrac{1}{2}\phi_2-\tfrac{1}{4}\pi+\frac{4a^2+5}{8x^2}+\frac{4a^3+29a}{8x^4}+\ldots$$

where ϕ_2 is defined by **19.17.10.**

When $a<0$, $|a|>>x^2$

19.24.7 $$F\sim\sqrt{2}W(a, 0)e^{v_r}$$

where v_r is given by **19.22.5** with $p=\sqrt{-a}$. Also

19.24.8

$$F\sim\frac{1}{\sqrt{p}}\left(1-\frac{x^2}{(4p)^2}+\frac{\frac{5}{2}x^4+8}{(4p)^4}-\frac{\frac{15}{2}x^6+152x^2}{(4p)^6}+\ldots\right)$$

19.24.9

$$\chi\sim\tfrac{1}{4}\pi+px\left(1+\frac{\frac{2}{3}x^2}{(4p)^2}-\frac{\frac{2}{5}x^4+16}{(4p)^4}+\frac{\frac{4}{7}x^6+\frac{256}{3}x^2}{(4p)^6}-\ldots\right)$$

19.24.10

$$G\sim\sqrt{p}\left(1+\frac{x^2}{(4p)^2}-\frac{\frac{3}{2}x^4+8}{(4p)^4}+\frac{\frac{7}{2}x^6+168x^2}{(4p)^6}-\ldots\right)$$

19.24.11

$$\psi\sim-\tfrac{1}{4}\pi+px\left(1+\frac{\frac{2}{3}x^2}{(4p)^2}-\frac{\frac{2}{5}x^4-16}{(4p)^4}+\frac{\frac{4}{7}x^6-\frac{320}{3}x^2}{(4p)^6}-\ldots\right)$$

Again, when $a<0$, $x^2-4a\gg0$, with $X=\sqrt{x^2+4|a|}$ then

19.24.12 $$F\sim\sqrt{2}e^{v_r} \qquad \chi=\tfrac{1}{4}\pi+\theta+v_i$$

where θ, v_r and v_i are given by **19.23.4** and **19.23.9.**

Another form also when $a>0$, $x^2-4a\to\infty$ is

19.24.13

$$F\sim\sqrt{\frac{2}{X}}\left(1-\frac{3}{4X^4}-\frac{5a}{X^6}+\frac{621}{32X^8}+\frac{1371a}{4X^{10}}-\ldots\right)$$

19.24.14

$$G\sim\sqrt{\frac{X}{2}}\left(1+\frac{5}{4X^4}+\frac{7a}{X^6}-\frac{835}{32X^8}-\frac{1729a}{4X^{10}}+\ldots\right)$$

while ψ and χ are connected by

19.24.15

$$\psi-\chi\sim-\frac{1}{2}\pi+\frac{x}{X^3}\left(1-\frac{47}{6X^4}-\frac{214a}{3X^6}+\frac{14483}{40X^8}+\ldots\right)$$

19.25. Connections With Other Functions

Connection With Confluent Hypergeometric and Bessel Functions

19.25.1

$$W(a, \pm x)=2^{-\frac{3}{4}}\left\{\sqrt{\frac{G_1}{G_3}}H(-\tfrac{3}{4}, \tfrac{1}{2}a, \tfrac{1}{4}x^2)\pm\sqrt{\frac{2G_3}{G_1}}xH(-\tfrac{1}{4}, \tfrac{1}{2}a, \tfrac{1}{4}x^2)\right\}$$

where

19.25.2

$$H(m, n, x)=e^{-ix}{}_1F_1(m+1-in; 2m+2; 2ix)$$

19.25.3 $$=e^{-ix}M(m+1-in, 2m+2, 2ix)$$

19.25.4

$$W(0, \pm x)=2^{-\frac{5}{4}}\sqrt{\pi x}\{J_{-\frac{1}{4}}(\tfrac{1}{4}x^2)\pm J_{\frac{1}{4}}(\tfrac{1}{4}x^2)\} \qquad (x\geq0)$$

19.25.5

$$\frac{d}{dx}W(0,\pm x)=-2^{-\frac{3}{4}}x\sqrt{\pi x}\{J_{\frac{3}{4}}(\tfrac{1}{4}x^2)\pm J_{-\frac{3}{4}}(\tfrac{1}{4}x^2)\}\qquad (x\geq 0)$$

19.26. Zeros

Zeros of solutions $U(a,x)$, $V(a,x)$ of **19.1.2** occur only for $|x|<2\sqrt{-a}$ when a is negative. A single exceptional zero is possible, for any a, in the general solution; neither $U(a,x)$ nor $V(a,x)$ has such a zero for $x>0$.

Approximations may be obtained by reverting the series for ψ (or χ for zeros of derivatives) in **19.11**, giving ψ (or χ) values that are multiples of $\frac{1}{2}\pi$, odd multiples for $U(a,x)$, even multiples for $V(a,x)$. Writing

$$\alpha=(\tfrac{1}{2}r-\tfrac{1}{2}a-\tfrac{1}{4})\pi$$

as an approximation to a zero of the function, or

$$\beta=(\tfrac{1}{2}r-\tfrac{1}{2}a+\tfrac{1}{4})\pi$$

as an approximation to a zero of the derivative, we obtain for the corresponding zero c or c', with $-a=p^2$ the expressions

19.26.1 $$c\approx\frac{\alpha}{p}+\frac{2\alpha^3-3\alpha}{48p^5}+\frac{52\alpha^5-240\alpha^3+315\alpha}{7680p^9}+\ldots$$

19.26.2 $$c'\approx\frac{\beta}{p}+\frac{2\beta^3+3\beta}{48p^5}+\frac{52\beta^5+280\beta^3-285\beta}{7680p^9}+\ldots$$

These expansions, however, are of little value in the neighborhood of the turning point $x=2\sqrt{-a}$. Here first approximations may be obtained by use of the formulas of **19.7.** If a_n (negative) is a zero of $\mathrm{Ai}(t)$, the corresponding zero c of $U(a,x)$ is obtained approximately by solving

19.26.3

$$\vartheta_3=\tfrac{1}{4}\{\arccos\xi-\xi\sqrt{1-\xi^2}\}=\frac{(-a_n)^{\frac{3}{2}}}{6|a|}$$

$$c=2\sqrt{|a|}\xi\qquad (a<<0)$$

This may be done by inverse use of **Table 19.3.** For a zero of $V(a,x)$, a_n must be replaced by b_n, a zero of $\mathrm{Bi}(t)$. For further developments see [19.5].

Zeros of solutions $W(a,x)$, $W(a,-x)$ of **19.1.3** occur for $|x|>2\sqrt{a}$ when a is positive; the general solution may, however, have a single zero between $-2\sqrt{a}$ and $+2\sqrt{a}$. If a is negative, zeros are unrestricted in range.

Approximations may be obtained by reverting the series for ψ (or χ) in **19.24.** With $-a=p^2$, $\alpha=(\frac{1}{2}r-\frac{1}{4})\pi$, $\beta=(\frac{1}{2}r+\frac{1}{4})\pi$, $r\geq 0$ being an odd integer for $W(a,x)$ or its derivative, or an even integer for $W(a,-x)$ or its derivative, the zeros $\pm c$, $\pm c'$ have expansions

19.26.4 $$c\approx\frac{\alpha}{p}-\frac{2\alpha^3-3\alpha}{48p^5}+\frac{52\alpha^5-240\alpha^3+315\alpha}{7680p^9}+\ldots$$

19.26.5 $$c'\approx\frac{\beta}{p}-\frac{2\beta^3+3\beta}{48p^5}+\frac{52\beta^5+280\beta^3-285\beta}{7680p^9}+\ldots$$

When x is large and a moderate, we may solve inversely the series **19.24.4** or **19.24.6** with $\alpha=\frac{1}{2}(r\pi-\frac{1}{2}\pi-\phi_2)$, $\beta=\frac{1}{2}(r\pi+\frac{1}{2}\pi-\phi_2)$, r odd or even as above; the presence of the logarithm makes it inconvenient to revert formally.

The expansions **19.26.4** and **19.26.5** fail when x is in the neighborhood of $2\sqrt{|a|}$. When a is positive, a zero c of $W(a,-x)$ is obtained approximately by solving

19.26.6

$$\vartheta_2=\tfrac{1}{4}\{\xi\sqrt{\xi^2-1}-\operatorname{arccosh}\xi\}=\frac{(-a_n)^{\frac{3}{2}}}{6a}$$

$$c=2\sqrt{a}\xi\qquad (a>>0)$$

with the aid of **Table 19.3.** For a zero of $W(a,x)$ we replace a_n by b_n. When a is negative we solve, again with the aid of **Table 19.3,**

19.26.7

$$\vartheta_1=\tfrac{1}{4}\{\xi\sqrt{\xi^2+1}+\operatorname{arcsinh}\xi\}=\frac{(n-\frac{1}{4})\pi}{4|a|}$$

$$c=2\sqrt{|a|}\xi\qquad (-a>>0)$$

where $n=1, 2, 3, \ldots$ for an approximate zero of $W(a,-x)$, and $n=\frac{1}{2}, \frac{3}{2}, \frac{5}{2}, \ldots$ for an approximate zero of $W(a,x)$. Further developments are given in [19.5].

Any of the approximations to zeros obtained above may readily be improved as follows:

Let c be a zero of y, and c' a zero of y', where y is a solution of

19.26.8 $$y''-Iy=0$$

Here $I=a\pm\frac{1}{4}x^2$, $I'=\pm\frac{1}{2}x$, $I''=\pm\frac{1}{2}$; the method is general and the following formulae may be used whenever $I'''=0$. Then if γ, γ' are approximations to the zeros c, c' and

19.26.9 $$u=y(\gamma)/y'(\gamma)\qquad v=y'(\gamma')/I^2y(\gamma')$$

with $I\equiv I(\gamma)$ or $I\equiv I(\gamma')$ respectively, then

19.26.10

$$c\sim\gamma-u-\tfrac{1}{3}Iu^3+\tfrac{1}{12}I'u^4-(\tfrac{1}{60}I''+\tfrac{1}{5}I^2)u^5+\tfrac{11}{90}II'u^6+\ldots$$

19.26.11

$$y'(c)\sim y'(\gamma)\{1-\tfrac{1}{2}Iu^2+\tfrac{1}{6}I'u^3-(\tfrac{1}{24}I''+\tfrac{1}{8}I^2)u^4+\tfrac{7}{60}II'u^5+\ldots\}$$

19.26.12

$$c'\sim\gamma'-Iv-\tfrac{1}{2}II'v^2+(\tfrac{1}{6}I^2I''-\tfrac{1}{2}II'^2-\tfrac{1}{3}I^4)v^3+(\tfrac{5}{12}I^2I'I''-\tfrac{5}{8}II'^3-\tfrac{5}{12}I^4I')v^4+\ldots$$

19.26.13

$$y(c')\sim y(\gamma')\{1-\tfrac{1}{2}I^3v^2-\tfrac{1}{6}I^3I'v^3-(\tfrac{1}{8}I^3I'^2-\tfrac{1}{24}I^4I''+\tfrac{1}{8}I^6)v^4+\ldots\}$$

The process can be repeated, if necessary, using as many terms at any stage as seems convenient.

Note the relations, holding at zeros,

19.26.14 $$U'(a,c)=-\sqrt{2/\pi}/V(a,c)$$

19.26.15 $$V'(a,c')=\sqrt{2/\pi}/U(a,c')$$

19.26.16 $$W'(a,c)=-1/W(a,-c)$$

19.26.17

$$W(a,c')=1/\left\{\frac{d}{dx}W(a,-x)\right\}_{x=c'}=-1/W'(a,-c')$$

19.27. Bessel Functions of Order $\pm\frac{1}{4}$, $\pm\frac{3}{4}$ as Parabolic Cylinder Functions

Most applications of these functions refer to cases where parabolic cylinder functions would be more appropriate. We have

19.27.1 $$J_{\pm\frac{1}{4}}(\tfrac{1}{4}x^2)=\frac{2^{\frac{1}{4}}}{\sqrt{\pi x}}\{W(0,-x)\mp W(0,x)\}$$

19.27.2 $$J_{\pm\frac{3}{4}}(\tfrac{1}{4}x^2)=\frac{-2^{\frac{3}{4}}}{x\sqrt{\pi x}}\{W(0,x)\pm W(0,-x)\}$$

Functions of other orders may be obtained by use of the recurrence relation **10.1.22**, which here becomes

19.27.3 $$\tfrac{1}{4}x^2J_{\nu+1}(\tfrac{1}{4}x^2)-2\nu J_\nu(\tfrac{1}{4}x^2)+\tfrac{1}{4}x^2J_{\nu-1}(\tfrac{1}{4}x^2)=0$$

Again

19.27.4 $$I_{-\frac{1}{4}}(\tfrac{1}{4}x^2)+I_{\frac{1}{4}}(\tfrac{1}{4}x^2)=\frac{2}{\sqrt{x}}V(0,x)$$

19.27.5

$$\frac{\sqrt{2}}{\pi}K_{\frac{1}{4}}(\tfrac{1}{4}x^2)=I_{-\frac{1}{4}}(\tfrac{1}{4}x^2)-I_{\frac{1}{4}}(\tfrac{1}{4}x^2)=\frac{2}{\sqrt{\pi x}}U(0,x)$$

19.27.6 $$I_{-\frac{3}{4}}(\tfrac{1}{4}x^2)+I_{\frac{3}{4}}(\tfrac{1}{4}x^2)=-\frac{4}{x\sqrt{x}}\frac{d}{dx}V(0,x)$$

19.27.7

$$\frac{\sqrt{2}}{\pi}K_{\frac{3}{4}}(\tfrac{1}{4}x^2)=I_{-\frac{3}{4}}(\tfrac{1}{4}x^2)-I_{\frac{3}{4}}(\tfrac{1}{4}x^2)=-\frac{4}{x\sqrt{\pi x}}\frac{d}{dx}U(0,x)$$

As before, Bessel functions of other orders may be obtained by use of the recurrence relation **10.2.23**, which here becomes

19.27.8 $$\tfrac{1}{4}x^2I_{\nu+1}(\tfrac{1}{4}x^2)+2\nu I_\nu(\tfrac{1}{4}x^2)-\tfrac{1}{4}x^2I_{\nu-1}(\tfrac{1}{4}x^2)=0$$

19.27.9 $$\tfrac{1}{4}x^2K_{\nu+1}(\tfrac{1}{4}x^2)-2\nu K_\nu(\tfrac{1}{4}x^2)-\tfrac{1}{4}x^2K_{\nu-1}(\tfrac{1}{4}x^2)=0$$

20.1. Mathieu's Equation

Canonical Form of the Differential Equation

20.1.1 $$\frac{d^2y}{dv^2}+(a-2q\cos 2v)y=0$$

Mathieu's Modified Differential Equation

20.1.2 $$\frac{d^2f}{du^2}-(a-2q\cosh 2u)f=0 \qquad (v=iu, y=f)$$

Relation Between Mathieu's Equation and the Wave Equation for the Elliptic Cylinder

The wave equation in Cartesian coordinates is

20.1.3 $$\frac{\partial^2W}{\partial x^2}+\frac{\partial^2W}{\partial y^2}+\frac{\partial^2W}{\partial z^2}+k^2W=0$$

A solution W is obtainable by separation of variables in elliptical coordinates. Thus, let

$$x=\rho\cosh u\cos v;\; y=\rho\sinh u\sin v;\; z=z;$$

ρ a positive constant; **20.1.3** becomes

20.1.4

$$\frac{\partial^2W}{\partial z^2}+\frac{2}{\rho^2(\cosh 2u-\cos 2v)}\left(\frac{\partial^2W}{\partial u^2}+\frac{\partial^2W}{\partial v^2}\right)+k^2W=0$$

Assuming a solution of the form

$$W=\varphi(z)f(u)g(v)$$

and substituting the above into **20.1.4** one obtains, after dividing through by W,

$$\frac{1}{\varphi}\frac{d^2\varphi}{dz^2}+G=0$$

where

$$G=\frac{2}{\rho^2(\cosh 2u-\cos 2v)}\left\{\frac{d^2f}{du^2}\frac{1}{f}+\frac{d^2g}{dv^2}\frac{1}{g}\right\}+k^2$$

Since z, u, v are independent variables, it follows that

20.1.5 $$\frac{d^2\varphi}{dz^2}+c\varphi=0$$

where c is a constant.

Again, from the fact that $G=c$ and that u, v are independent variables, one sets

20.1.6

$$a=\frac{d^2f}{du^2}\frac{1}{f}+\frac{(k^2-c)}{2}\rho^2\cosh 2u$$

$$a=-\frac{d^2g}{dv^2}\frac{1}{g}+\frac{(k^2-c)}{2}\rho^2\cos 2v$$

where a is a constant. The above are equivalent to **20.1.1** and **20.1.2.** The constants c and a are often referred to as *separation constants*, due to the role they play in **20.1.5** and **20.1.6.**

For some physically important solutions, the function g must be periodic, of period π or 2π. It can be shown that there exists a countably infinite set of *characteristic values* $a_r(q)$ which yield even periodic solutions of **20.1.1;** there is another countably infinite sequence of *characteristic values* $b_r(q)$ which yield odd periodic solutions of **20.1.1.**

It is known that there exist periodic solutions of period $k\pi$, where k is any positive integer. In what follows, however, the term *characteristic value* will be reserved for a value associated with solutions of period π or 2π only. These characteristic values are of basic importance to the general theory of the differential equation for arbitrary parameters a and q.

An Algebraic Form of Mathieu's Equation

20.1.7

$$(1-t^2)\frac{d^2y}{dt^2}-t\frac{dy}{dt}+(a+2q-4qt^2)y=0 \qquad (\cos v=t)$$

Relation to Spheroidal Wave Equation

20.1.8 $$(1-t^2)\frac{d^2y}{dt^2}-2(b+1)t\frac{dy}{dt}+(c-4qt^2)y=0$$

Thus, Mathieu's equation is a special case of **20.1.8,** with $b=-\frac{1}{2}$, $c=a+2q$.

20.2. Determination of Characteristic Values

A solution of **20.1.1** with v replaced by z, having period π or 2π is of the form

20.2.1 $$y=\sum_{m=0}^{\infty}(A_m\cos mz+B_m\sin mz)$$

where B_0 can be taken as zero. If the above is substituted into **20.1.1** one obtains

20.2.2

$$\sum_{m=-2}^{\infty}[(a-m^2)A_m-q(A_{m-2}+A_{m+2})]\cos mz$$

$$+\sum_{m=-1}^{\infty}[(a-m^2)B_m-q(B_{m-2}+B_{m+2})]\sin mz=0$$

$$A_{-m}, B_{-m}=0 \qquad m>0$$

Equation **20.2.2** can be reduced to one of four simpler types, given in **20.2.3** and **20.2.4** below

20.2.3 $y_0=\sum_{m=0}^{\infty} A_{2m+p}\cos(2m+p)z, \qquad p=0 \text{ or } 1$

20.2.4 $y_1=\sum_{m=0}^{\infty} B_{2m+p}\sin(2m+p)z, \qquad p=0 \text{ or } 1$

If $p=0$, the solution is of period π; if $p=1$, the solution is of period 2π.

Recurrence Relations Among the Coefficients

Even solutions of period π:

20.2.5 $aA_0-qA_2=0$

20.2.6 $(a-4)A_2-q(2A_0+A_4)=0$

20.2.7 $(a-m^2)A_m-q(A_{m-2}+A_{m+2})=0 \qquad (m\geq 3)$

Even solutions of period 2π:

20.2.8 $(a-1)A_1-q(A_1+A_3)=0,$

along with **20.2.7** for $m\geq 3$.

Odd solutions of period π:

20.2.9 $(a-4)B_2-qB_4=0$

20.2.10 $(a-m^2)B_m-q(B_{m-2}+B_{m+2})=0 \qquad (m\geq 3)$

Odd solutions of period 2π:

20.2.11 $(a-1)B_1+q(B_1-B_3)=0,$

along with **20.2.10** for $m\geq 3$.

Let

20.2.12 $Ge_m=A_m/A_{m-2},\ Go_m=B_m/B_{m-2};$

$G_m=Ge_m$ or Go_m when the same operations apply to both, and no ambiguity is likely to arise. Further let

20.2.13 $V_m=(a-m^2)/q.$

Equations **20.2.5–20.2.7** are equivalent to

20.2.14 $Ge_2=V_0;\ Ge_4=V_2-\dfrac{2}{Ge_2}$

20.2.15 $G_m=1/(V_m-G_{m+2}) \qquad (m\geq 3),$

for even solutions of period π.

Similarly

20.2.16 $V_1-1=Ge_3$; for even solutions of period 2π, along with **20.2.15**

20.2.17 $V_1+1=Go_3$, for odd solutions of period 2π, along with **20.2.15**

20.2.18 $V_2=Go_4$, for odd solutions of period π, along with **20.2.15**

These three-term recurrence relations among the coefficients indicate that every G_m can be developed into two types of continued fractions. Thus **20.2.15** is equivalent to

20.2.19

$$G_m=\frac{1}{V_m-G_{m+2}}=\frac{1}{V_m-}\,\frac{1}{V_{m+2}-}\,\frac{1}{V_{m+4}-}\cdots \quad (m\geq 3)$$

20.2.20

$$G_{m+2}=V_m-1/G_m$$

$$=V_m-\frac{1}{V_{m-2}-}\,\frac{1}{V_{m-4}-}\cdots\frac{\varphi_0}{V_{0+d}+\varphi_1} \qquad (m\geq 3)$$

where

$\varphi_1=d=0;\ \varphi_0=2$, if $G_{m+2}=A_{2s}/A_{2s-2}$

$\varphi_1=d=\varphi_0=0$, if $G_{m+2}=B_{2s}/B_{2s-2}$

$\varphi_1=-1;\ \varphi_0=d=1$, if $G_{m+2}=A_{2s+1}/A_{2s-1}$

$\varphi_1=d=\phi_0=1$, if $G_{m+2}=B_{2s+1}/B_{2s-1}$

The four choices of the parameters φ_1, φ_0, d correspond to the four types of solutions **20.2.3–20.2.4.** Hereafter, it will be convenient to separate the characteristic values a into two major subsets:

$a=a_r$, associated with even periodic solutions

$a=b_r$, associated with odd periodic solutions

If **20.2.19** is suitably combined with **20.2.13–20.2.18** there result four types of continued fractions, the roots of which yield the required characteristic values

20.2.21 $V_0-\dfrac{2}{V_2-}\,\dfrac{1}{V_4-}\,\dfrac{1}{V_6-}\cdots=0 \qquad \text{Roots: } a_{2r}$

20.2.22

$$V_1-1-\frac{1}{V_3-}\,\frac{1}{V_5-}\,\frac{1}{V_7-}\cdots=0 \qquad \text{Roots: } a_{2r+1}$$

20.2.23 $V_2-\dfrac{1}{V_4-}\,\dfrac{1}{V_6-}\,\dfrac{1}{V_8-}\cdots=0 \qquad \text{Roots: } b_{2r}$

20.2.24

$$V_1+1-\frac{1}{V_3-}\,\frac{1}{V_5-}\,\frac{1}{V_7-}\cdots=0 \qquad \text{Roots: } b_{2r+1}$$

If a is a root of **20.2.21–20.2.24,** then the corresponding solution exists and is an entire function of z, for general complex values of q.

If q is real, then the Sturmian theory of second order linear differential equations yields the following:

(a) For a fixed real q, characteristic values a_r and b_r are real and distinct, if $q\neq 0$; $a_0<b_1<a_1<b_2<a_2<\ldots$, $q>0$ and $a_r(q)$, $b_r(q)$ approach r^2 as q approaches zero.

(b) A solution of **20.1.1** associated with a_r or b_r has r zeros in the interval $0\leq z<\pi$, (q real).

(c) The form of **20.2.21** and **20.2.23** shows that if a_{2r} is a root of **20.2.21** and q is different from zero, then a_{2r} cannot be a root of **20.2.23;** similarly, no root of **20.2.22** can be a root of **20.2.24** if $q\neq 0$. It may be shown from other considerations that for a given point (a, q) there can be at most one periodic solution of period π or 2π if $q\neq 0$. This no longer holds for solutions of period $s\pi$, $s\geq 3$; for these all solutions are periodic, if one is.

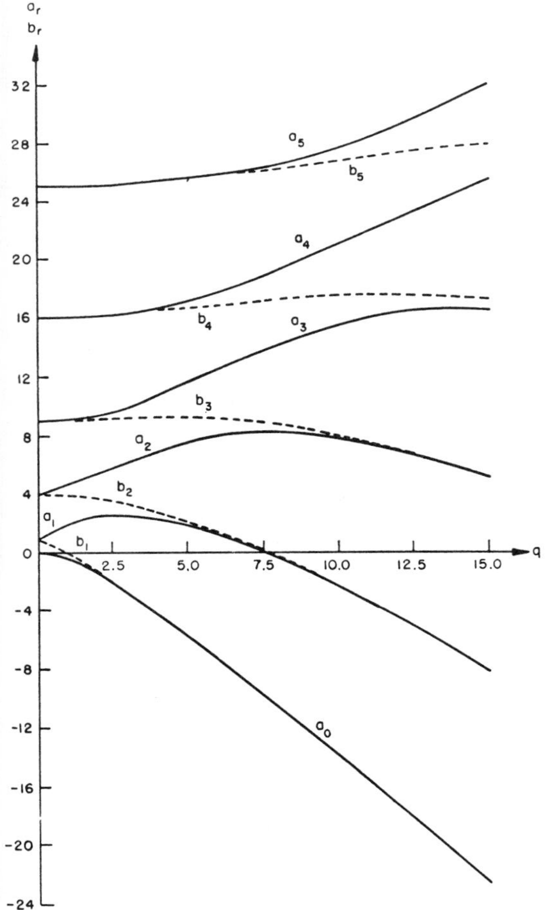

FIGURE 20.1. *Characteristic Values a_r, b_r* $r=0,1(1)5$

Power Series for Characteristic Values

20.2.25

$$a_0(q)=-\frac{q^2}{2}+\frac{7q^4}{128}-\frac{29q^6}{2304}+\frac{68687q^8}{18874368}+\ldots$$

$$\left.\begin{matrix}a_1(-q)\\ b_1(q)\end{matrix}\right\}=1-q-\frac{q^2}{8}+\frac{q^3}{64}-\frac{q^4}{1536}-\frac{11q^5}{36864}+\frac{49q^6}{589824}-\frac{55q^7}{9437184}-\frac{83q^8}{35389440}+\ldots$$

$$b_2(q)=4-\frac{q^2}{12}+\frac{5q^4}{13824}-\frac{289q^6}{79626240}+\frac{21391q^8}{458647142400}+\ldots$$

$$a_2(q)=4+\frac{5q^2}{12}-\frac{763q^4}{13824}+\frac{1002401q^6}{79626240}-\frac{1669068401q^8}{458647142400}+\ldots$$

$$\left.\begin{matrix}a_3(-q)\\ b_3(q)\end{matrix}\right\}=9+\frac{q^2}{16}-\frac{q^3}{64}+\frac{13q^4}{20480}+\frac{5q^5}{16384}-\frac{1961q^6}{23592960}+\frac{609q^7}{104857600}+\ldots$$

$$b_4(q)=16+\frac{q^2}{30}-\frac{317q^4}{864000}+\frac{10049q^6}{2721600000}+\ldots$$

$$a_4(q)=16+\frac{q^2}{30}+\frac{433q^4}{864000}-\frac{5701q^6}{2721600000}+\ldots$$

$$\left.\begin{matrix}a_5(-q)\\ b_5(q)\end{matrix}\right\}=25+\frac{q^2}{48}+\frac{11q^4}{774144}-\frac{q^5}{147456}+\frac{37q^6}{891813888}+\ldots$$

$$b_6(q)=36+\frac{q^2}{70}+\frac{187q^4}{43904000}-\frac{5861633q^6}{92935987200000}+\ldots$$

$$a_6(q)=36+\frac{q^2}{70}+\frac{187q^4}{43904000}+\frac{6743617q^6}{92935987200000}+\ldots$$

For $r\geq 7$, and $|q|$ not too large, a_r is approximately equal to b_r, and the following approximation may be used

20.2.26

$$\left.\begin{matrix}a_r\\ b_r\end{matrix}\right\}=r^2+\frac{q^2}{2(r^2-1)}+\frac{(5r^2+7)q^4}{32(r^2-1)^3(r^2-4)}+\frac{(9r^4+58r^2+29)q^6}{64(r^2-1)^5(r^2-4)(r^2-9)}+\ldots$$

The above expansion is not limited to integral values of r, and it is a very good approximation for r of the form $n+\frac{1}{2}$ where n is an integer. In case of integral values of $r=n$, the series holds only up to terms not involving r^2-n^2 in the denominator. Subsequent terms must be derived specially (as shown by Mathieu). Mulholland and Goldstein [20.38] have computed characteristic values for purely imaginary q and found that a_0 and a_2 have a common real value for $|q|$ in the neighborhood of 1.468; Bouwkamp [20.5] has computed this number as $q_0=\pm i\ 1.46876852$ to 8 decimals. For values of $-iq>-iq_0$, a_0 and a_2 are conjugate complex numbers. From equation **20.2.25** it follows that the radius of convergence for the series defining a_0 is no greater than $|q_0|$. It is shown in [20.36], section **2.25** that the radius of convergence for $a_{2n}(q)$, $n\geq 2$ is greater than 3. Furthermore

$$a_r-b_r=O(q^r/r^{r-1}),\ r\rightarrow\infty.$$

Power Series in q for the Periodic Functions (for sufficiently small $|q|$)

20.2.27

$$ce_0(z,q)=2^{-\frac{1}{2}}\left[1-\frac{q}{2}\cos 2z+q^2\left(\frac{\cos 4z}{32}-\frac{1}{16}\right)-q^3\left(\frac{\cos 6z}{1152}-\frac{11\cos 2z}{128}\right)+\cdots\right]$$

$$ce_1(z,q)=\cos z-\frac{q}{8}\cos 3z+q^2\left[\frac{\cos 5z}{192}-\frac{\cos 3z}{64}-\frac{\cos z}{128}\right]-q^3\left[\frac{\cos 7z}{9216}-\frac{\cos 5z}{1152}-\frac{\cos 3z}{3072}+\frac{\cos z}{512}\right]+\cdots$$

$$se_1(z,q)=\sin z-\frac{q}{8}\sin 3z+q^2\left[\frac{\sin 5z}{192}+\frac{\sin 3z}{64}-\frac{\sin z}{128}\right]-q^3\left[\frac{\sin 7z}{9216}+\frac{\sin 5z}{1152}-\frac{\sin 3z}{3072}-\frac{\sin z}{512}\right]+\cdots$$

$$ce_2(z,q)=\cos 2z-q\left(\frac{\cos 4z}{12}-\frac{1}{4}\right)+q^2\left(\frac{\cos 6z}{384}-\frac{19\cos 2z}{288}\right)+\cdots$$

$$se_2(z,q)=\sin 2z-q\frac{\sin 4z}{12}+q^2\left(\frac{\sin 6z}{384}-\frac{\sin 2z}{288}\right)+\cdots$$

20.2.28

$$\left.\begin{matrix}ce_r(z,q)\\ se_r(z,q)\end{matrix}\right\}=\cos(rz-p(\pi/2))-q\left\{\frac{\cos\left[(r+2)z-p\frac{\pi}{2}\right]}{4(r+1)}-\frac{\cos[(r-2)z-p(\pi/2)]}{4(r-1)}\right\}$$
$$+q^2\left\{\frac{\cos[(r+4)z-p(\pi/2)]}{32(r+1)(r+2)}+\frac{\cos[(r-4)z-p(\pi/2)]}{32(r-1)(r-2)}-\frac{\cos[rz-p(\pi/2)]}{32}\left[\frac{2(r^2+1)}{(r^2-1)^2}\right]\right\}+\cdots$$

with $p=0$ for $ce_r(z,q)$, $p=1$ for $se_r(z,q)$, $r\geq 3$.

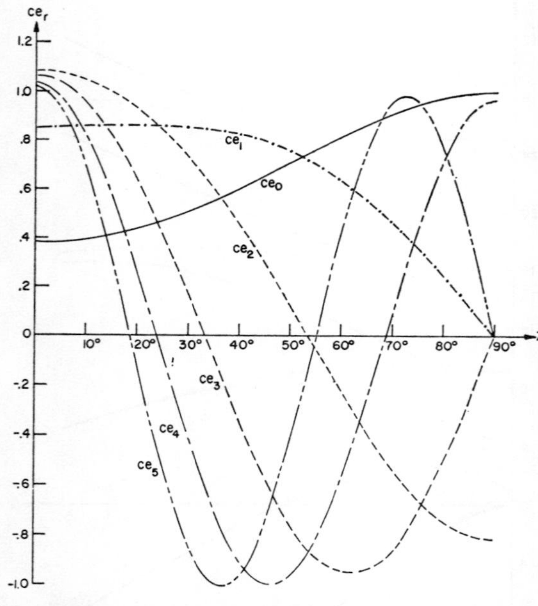

FIGURE 20.2. *Even Periodic Mathieu Functions, Orders 0–5* $q=1$.

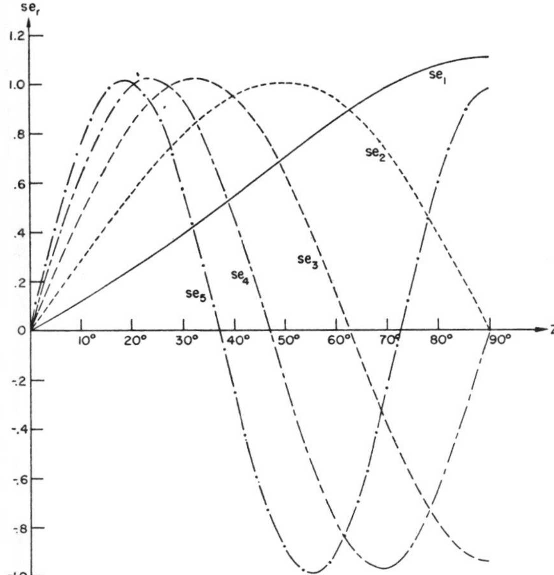

FIGURE 20.3. *Odd Periodic Mathieu Functions, Orders 1–5* $q=1$.

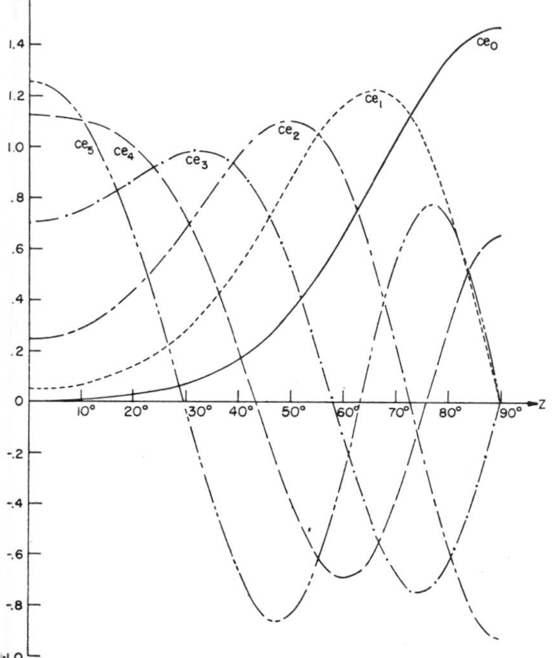

FIGURE 20.4. *Even Periodic Mathieu Functions, Orders 0–5* $q=10$.

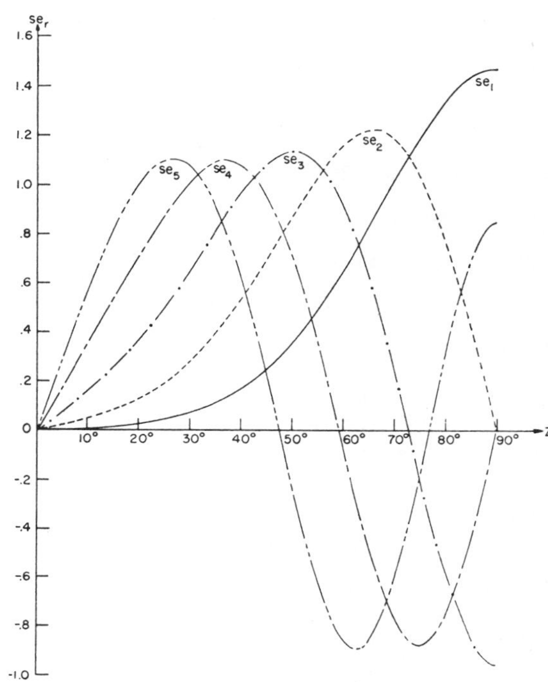

FIGURE 20.5. *Odd Periodic Mathieu Functions, Orders 1–5* $q=10$.

For coefficients associated with above functions

20.2.29

$$A_0^0(0)=2^{-\frac{1}{2}};\ A_r^r(0)=B_r^r(0)=1,\ r>0$$

$$A_{2s}^0=[(-1)^s q^s/s!\,s!\,2^{2s-1}]\,A_0^0+\ .\ .\ .,\ s>0$$

$$\begin{matrix}A_{r+2s}^r\\ B_{r+2s}^r\end{matrix}=[(-1)^s r!\ q^s/4^s(r+s)!\ s!]\ C_r^r+\ .\ .\ .$$

$$rs>0,\ C_r^r=A_r^r \text{ or } B_r^r$$

$$A_{r-2s}^r \text{ or } B_{r-2s}^r=\frac{(r-s-1)!}{s!(r-1)!}\frac{q^s}{4^s}C_r^r+\ .\ .\ .$$

Asymptotic Expansion for Characteristic Values, $q\gg 1$

Let $w=2r+1$, $q=w^4\varphi$, φ real. Then

20.2.30

$$a_r\sim b_{r+1}\sim -2q+2w\sqrt{q}-\frac{w^2+1}{8}-\frac{\left(w+\frac{3}{w}\right)}{2^7\sqrt{\varphi}}$$

$$-\frac{d_1}{2^{12}\varphi}-\frac{d_2}{2^{17}\varphi^{3/2}}-\frac{d_3}{2^{20}\varphi^2}-\frac{d_4}{2^{25}\varphi^{5/2}}-\ .\ .\ .$$

where

$$d_1=5+\frac{34}{w^2}+\frac{9}{w^4}$$

$$d_2=\frac{33}{w}+\frac{410}{w^3}+\frac{405}{w^5}$$

$$d_3=\frac{63}{w^2}+\frac{1260}{w^4}+\frac{2943}{w^6}+\frac{486}{w^8}$$

$$d_4=\frac{527}{w^3}+\frac{15617}{w^5}+\frac{69001}{w^7}+\frac{41607}{w^9}$$

20.2.31 $$b_{r+1}-a_r\sim 2^{4r+5}\sqrt{2/\pi}\,q^{\frac{1}{2}r+\frac{3}{4}}e^{-4\sqrt{q}}/r!, \qquad q\to\infty$$

(given in [20.36] without proof.)

20.3. Floquet's Theorem and Its Consequences

Since the coefficients of Mathieu's equation

20.3.1 $$y''+(a-2q\cos 2z)y=0$$

are periodic functions of z, it follows from the known theory relating to such equations that there exists a solution of the form

20.3.2 $$F_\nu(z)=e^{i\nu z}P(z),$$

where ν depends on a and q, and $P(z)$ is a periodic function, of the same period as that of the coefficients in **20.3.1,** namely π. (Floquet's theorem; see [20.16] or [20.22] for its more general form.) The constant ν is called the *characteristic exponent.* Similarly

20.3.3 $$F_\nu(-z)=e^{-i\nu z}P(-z)$$

satisfies **20.3.1** whenever **20.3.2** does. Both $F_\nu(z)$ and $F_\nu(-z)$ have the property

20.3.4

$$y(z+k\pi)=C^ky(z),\ y=F_\nu(z) \text{ or } F_\nu(-z),$$
$$C=e^{i\nu\pi} \text{ for } F_\nu(z),\ C=e^{-i\nu\pi} \text{ for } F_\nu(-z)$$

Solutions having the property **20.3.4** will hereafter be termed *Floquet* solutions. Whenever $F_\nu(z)$ and $F_\nu(-z)$ are linearly independent, the general solution of **20.3.1** can be put into the form

20.3.5 $$y=AF_\nu(z)+BF_\nu(-z)$$

If $AB\neq 0$, the above solution will *not be a Floquet solution.* It will be seen later, from the method for determining ν when a and q are given, that there is some ambiguity in the definition of ν; namely, ν can be replaced by $\nu+2k$, where k is an arbitrary integer. This is as it should be, since the addition of the factor $\exp(2ikz)$ in **20.3.2** still leaves a periodic function of period π for the coefficient of $\exp i\nu z$.

It turns out that when a belongs to the set of characteristic values a_r and b_r of **20.2,** then ν is zero or an integer. It is convenient to associate $\nu=r$ with $a_r(q)$, and $\nu=-r$ with $b_r(q)$; see [20.36]. In the special case when ν is an integer, $F_\nu(z)$ is proportional to $F_\nu(-z)$; the second, independent solution of **20.3.1** then has the form

20.3.6 $$y_2=zce_r(z,q)+\sum_{k=0}^{\infty} d_{2k+p}\sin(2k+p)z,$$ associated with $ce_r(z,q)$

20.3.7 $$y_2=zse_r(z,q)+\sum_{k=0}^{\infty} f_{2k+p}\cos(2k+p)z,$$ associated with $se_r(z,q)$

The coefficients d_{2k+p} and f_{2k+p} depend on the corresponding coefficients A_m and B_m, respectively, of **20.2,** as well as on a and q. See [20.30], section **(7.50)–(7.51)** and [20.58], section V, for details.

If ν is not an integer, then the Floquet solutions $F_\nu(z)$ and $F_\nu(-z)$ are linearly independent. It is clear that **20.3.2** can be written in the form

20.3.8 $$F_\nu(z)=\sum_{k=-\infty}^{\infty} c_{2k}e^{i(\nu+2k)z}.$$

From **20.3.8** it follows that if ν is a proper fraction m_1/m_2, then every solution of **20.3.1** is periodic, and of period at most $2\pi m_2$. This agrees with results already noted in **20.2;** i.e., both independent solutions are periodic, if one is, provided the period is different from π and 2π.

Method of Generating the Characteristic Exponent

Define two linearly independent solutions of **20.3.1,** for fixed a, q by

20.3.9
$$y_1(0)=1;\ y_1'(0)=0.$$
$$y_2(0)=0;\ y_2'(0)=1.$$

Then it can be shown that

20.3.10 $$\cos\pi\nu-y_1(\pi)=0$$

20.3.11 $$\cos\pi\nu-1-2y_1'\left(\frac{\pi}{2}\right)y_2\left(\frac{\pi}{2}\right)=0$$

Thus ν may be obtained from a knowledge of $y_1(\pi)$ or from a knowledge of both $y_1'\left(\frac{\pi}{2}\right)$ and $y_2\left(\frac{\pi}{2}\right)$.

For numerical purposes **20.3.11** may be more desirable because of the shorter range of integration, and hence the lesser accumulation of round-off errors. Either ν, $-\nu$, or $\pm\nu+2k$ (k an arbitrary integer) can be taken as the solution of **20.3.11.** Once ν has been fixed, the coefficients of **20.3.8** can be determined, except for an arbitrary multiplier which is independent of z.

The characteristic exponent can also be computed from a continued fraction, in a manner analogous to developments in **20.2,** if a sufficiently close first approximation to ν is available. For systematic tabulation, this method is considerably faster than the method of numerical integration. Thus, when **20.3.8** is substituted into **20.3.1,** there result the following recurrence relations:

20.3.12 $$V_{2n}c_{2n}=c_{2n-2}+c_{2n+2}$$

where

20.3.13 $$V_{2n}=[a-(2n+\nu)^2]/q, \quad -\infty<n<\infty.$$

When ν is complex, the coefficients V_{2n} may also be complex. As in **20.2,** it is possible to generate the ratios

$$G_m=c_m/c_{m-2} \text{ and } H_{-m}=c_{-m-2}/c_{-m}$$

from the continued fractions

20.3.14

$$G_m=\frac{1}{V_m-}\,\frac{1}{V_{m+2}-\ \ldots}, \qquad m\geq 0$$

$$H_{-m}=\frac{1}{V_{-m-2}-}\,\frac{1}{V_{-m-4}-\ \ldots}, \qquad m\geq 0.$$

From the form of **20.3.13** and the known properties of continued fractions it is assured that for sufficiently large values of $|m|$ both $|G_m|$ and $|H_{-m}|$ converge. Once values of G_m and H_{-m} are available for some sufficiently large value of m, then the finite number of ratios $G_{m-2}, G_{m-4}, \ldots, G_0$ can be computed in turn, if they exist. Similarly for $H_{-m+2}, \ldots, H_0$. It is easy to show that ν is the correct characteristic exponent, appropriate for the point (a, q), if and only if $H_0G_0=1$. An iteration technique can be used to improve the value of ν, by the method suggested in [20.3]. One coefficient c_j can be assigned arbitrarily; the rest are then completely determined. After all the c_j become available, a multiplier (depending on q but not on z) can be found to satisfy a prescribed normalization.

It is well known that continued fractions can be converted to determinantal form. Equation **20.3.14** can in fact be written as a determinant with an infinite number of rows—a special case of Hill's determinant. See [20.19], [20.36], [20.15], or [20.30] for details. Although the determinant has actually been used in computations where high-speed computers were available, the direct use of the continued fraction seems much less laborious.

Special Cases (*a*, *q* Real)

Corresponding to $q=0$, $y_1=\cos\sqrt{a}z$, $y_2=\sin\sqrt{a}z$; the Floquet solutions are $\exp(iaz)$ and $\exp(-iaz)$. As a, q vary continuously in the $q-a$ plane, ν describes curves; ν is real when (q, a), $q\geq 0$ lies in the region between $a_r(q)$ and $b_{r+1}(q)$ and

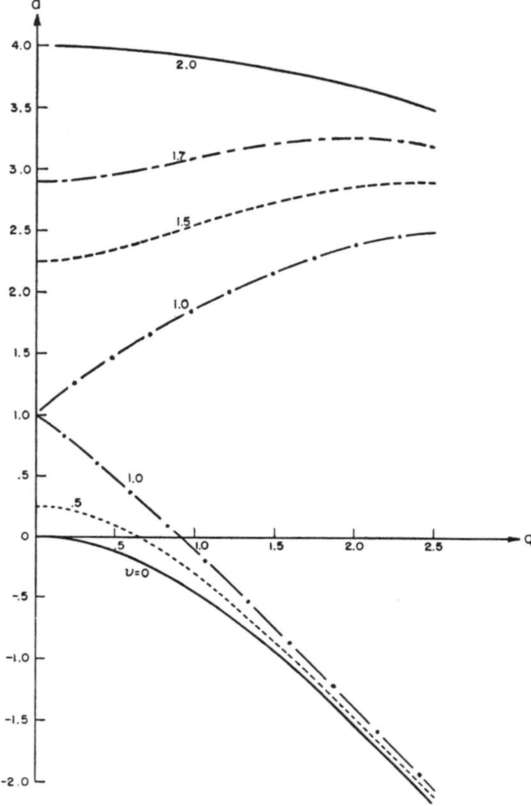

Figure 20.6. *Characteristic Exponent-First Two Stable Regions $y=e^{i\nu x}P(x)$ where $P(x)$ is a periodic function of period π.*

Definition of ν;
In first stable region, $0\leq\nu\leq 1$,
In second stable region, $1\leq\nu\leq 2$.

(Constructed from tabular values supplied by T. Tamir, Brooklyn Polytechnic Institute)

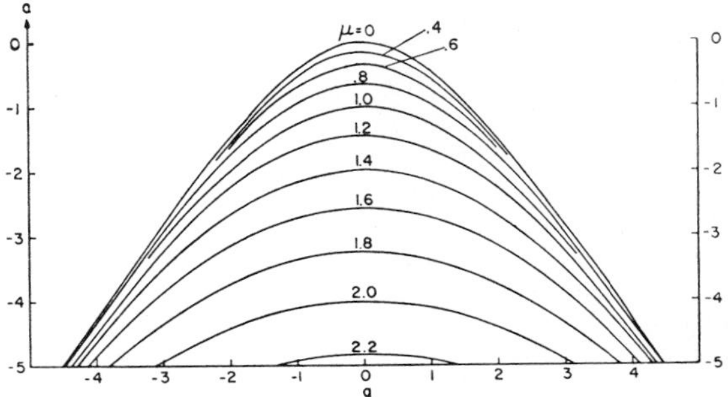

Figure 20.7. *Characteristic Exponent in First Unstable Region. Differential equation: $y''+(a-2q\cos 2x)y=0$. The Floquet solution $y=e^{i\nu x}P(x)$, where $P(x)$ is a periodic function of period π. In the first unstable region, $\nu=i\mu$; μ is given for $a\geq -5$.* (Constructed at NBS.)

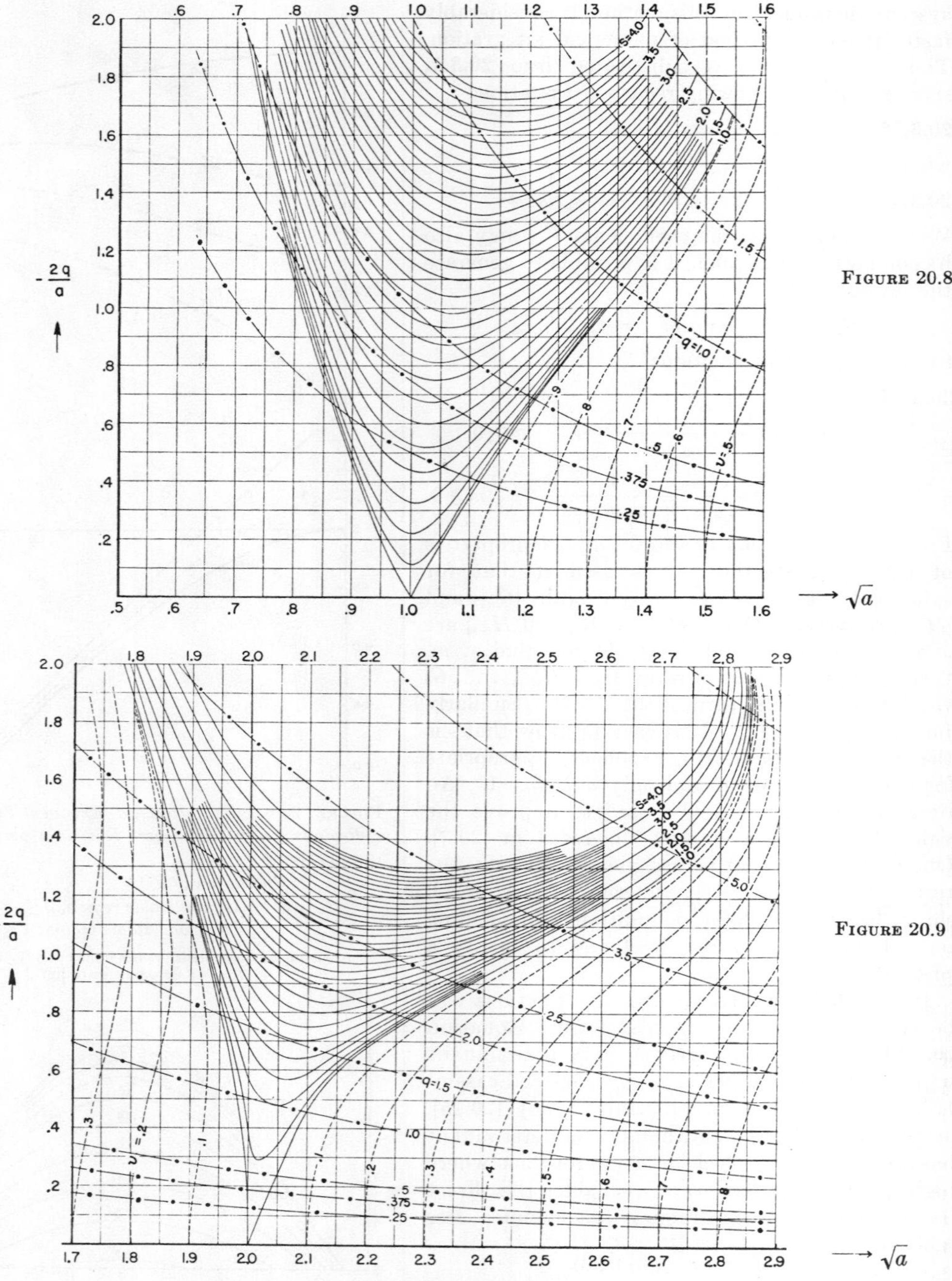

FIGURE 20.8

FIGURE 20.9

Charts of the Characteristic Exponent.

From S. J. Zaroodny, An elementary review of the Mathieu-Hill equation of real variable based on numerical solutions, Ballistic Research Laboratory Memo. Rept. 878, Aberdeen Proving Ground, Md., 1955.

——— $s=e^{i\nu\pi}$=*constant; in unstable regions*

– – – – ν=*constant; in stable regions*

–.–.– *Lines of constant values of* $-q$.

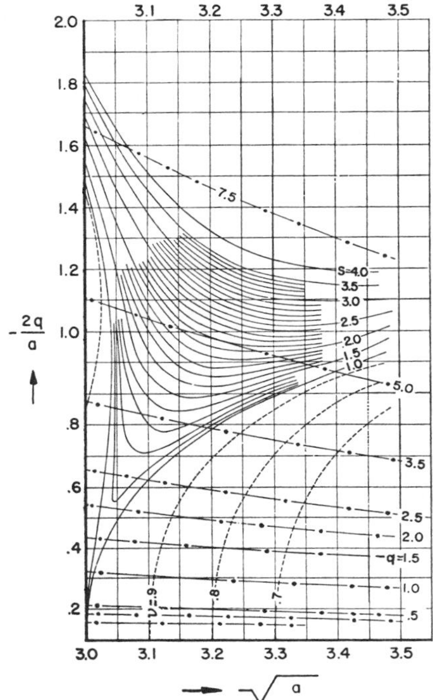

FIGURE 20.10. *Chart of the Characteristic Exponent.*

(From S. J. Zaroodny, An elementary review of the Mathieu-Hill equation of real variable based on numerical solutions, Ballistic Research Laboratory Memo. Rept. 878, Aberdeen Proving Ground, Md., 1955, with permission)

——— $s=e^{i\nu\pi}$=*constant; in unstable regions*

– – – – ν=*constant; in stable regions*

– . – . – *Lines of constant values of* $-q$.

all solutions of **20.1.1** for real z are therefore bounded (stable); ν is complex in regions between b_r and a_r; in these regions every solution becomes infinite at least once; hence these regions are termed "unstable regions". The characteristic curves a_r, b_r separate the regions of stability. For negative q, the stable regions are between b_{2r+1} and b_{2r+2}, a_{2r} and a_{2r+1}; the unstable regions are between a_{2r+1} and b_{2r+1}, a_{2r} and b_{2r}.

In some problems solutions are required for real values of z only. In such cases a knowledge of the characteristic exponent ν and the periodic function $P(z)$ is sufficient for the evaluation of the required functions. For complex values of z, however, the series defining $P(z)$ converges slowly. Other solutions will be determined in the next section; they all have the remarkable property that they depend on the same coefficients c_m developed in connection with Floquet's theorem (except for an arbitrary normalization factor).

Expansions for Small *q* ([20.36] chapter 2)

If ν, q are fixed:

20.3.15

$$a=\nu^2+\frac{q^2}{2(\nu^2-1)}+\frac{(5\nu^2+7)q^4}{32(\nu^2-1)^3(\nu^2-4)}+\frac{(9\nu^4+58\nu^2+29)q^6}{64(\nu^2-1)^5(\nu^2-4)(\nu^2-9)}+\ldots\quad(\nu\neq 1,2,3).$$

For the coefficients c_{2j} of **20.3.8**

20.3.16

$$c_2/c_0=\frac{-q}{4(\nu+1)}-\frac{(\nu^2+4\nu+7)q^3}{128(\nu+1)^3(\nu+2)(\nu-1)}+\ldots\quad(\nu\neq 1,2)$$

$$c_4/c_0=q^2/32(\nu+1)(\nu+2)+\ldots$$

$$c_{2s}/c_0=(-1)^s q^s\Gamma(\nu+1)/2^{2s}s!\Gamma(\nu+s+1)+\ldots$$

20.3.17

$$F_\nu(z)=c_0\left[e^{i\nu z}-q\left\{\frac{e^{i(\nu+2)z}}{4(\nu+1)}-\frac{e^{i(\nu-2)z}}{4(\nu-1)}\right\}\right]+\ldots\quad(\nu\text{ not an integer})$$

For small values of a

20.3.18

$$\cos\nu\pi=\left(1-\frac{a\pi^2}{2}+\frac{a^2\pi^4}{24}+\ldots\right)-\frac{q^2\pi^2}{4}\left[1+a\left(1-\frac{\pi^2}{6}\right)+\ldots\right]+q^4\left(\frac{\pi^4}{96}-\frac{25\pi^2}{256}+\ldots\right)+\ldots$$

20.4. Other Solutions of Mathieu's Equation

Following Erdélyi [20.14], [20.15], define

20.4.1 $$\varphi_k(z)=[e^{i\pi}\cos(z-b)/\cos(z+b)]^{\frac{1}{2}k}J_k(f)$$

where

20.4.2 $$f=2[q\cos(z-b)\cos(z+b)]^{\frac{1}{2}},$$

and $J_k(f)$ is the Bessel function of order k; b is a fixed, arbitrary complex number. By using the recurrence relations for Bessel functions the following may be verified:

20.4.3

$$\frac{d^2\varphi_k}{dz^2}-2q(\cos 2z)\varphi_k+q(\varphi_{k-2}+\varphi_{k+2})+k^2\varphi_k=0.$$

It follows that a formal solution of **20.1.1** is given by

20.4.4 $$y=\sum_{n=-\infty}^{\infty}c_{2n}\varphi_{2n+\nu}$$

where the coefficients c_{2n} are those associated with Floquet's solution. In the above, ν may be complex. Except for the special case when ν is an integer, the following holds:

$$\frac{\varphi_{2n+\nu-2}}{\varphi_{2n+\nu}} \sim \frac{\varphi_{-2n+\nu}}{\varphi_{-2n+\nu+2}} \sim \frac{-4n^2}{q[\cos(z-b)]^2} \qquad (n\to\infty)$$

If ν and n are integers, $J_{-2n+\nu}(f)=(-1)^\nu J_{2n-\nu}(f)$.

$$[\varphi_{2n+\nu}/\varphi_{2n+\nu-2}] \sim -[\cos(z-b)]^2 q/4n^2$$

$$[\varphi_{-2n+\nu}/\varphi_{-2n+\nu+2}] \sim -4n^2/q[\cos(z-b)]^2$$

On the other hand

$$\frac{c_{2n}}{c_{2n-2}} \sim \frac{c_{-2n}}{c_{-2n+2}} \sim \frac{-q}{4n^2} \qquad (n\to\infty)$$

It follows that **20.4.4** converges absolutely and uniformly in every closed region where

$|\cos(z-b)|>d_1>1$.

There are two such disjoint regions:

(I) $\mathscr{I}(z-b)>d_2>0$; $(|\cos(z-b)|>d_1>1)$
(II) $\mathscr{I}(z-b)<-d_2<0$; $(|\cos(z-b)|>d_1>1)$

If ν is an integer **20.4.4** converges for all values of z. Various representations are found by specializing b.

20.4.5

$$\text{If } b=0,\ y=e^{i\pi\nu/2}\sum_{n=-\infty}^{\infty} c_{2n}(-1)^n J_{2n+\nu}(2\sqrt{q}\cos z)$$
$$(|\cos z|>1,\ |\arg 2\sqrt{q}\cos z|\leq\pi)$$

20.4.6

$$\text{If } b=\frac{\pi}{2},\ y=\sum_{n=-\infty}^{\infty} c_{2n}J_{2n+\nu}(2i\sqrt{q}\sin z)$$
$$(|\sin z|>1,\ |\arg 2\sqrt{q}\sin z|\leq\pi)$$

If $b\to\infty i$, y reduces to a multiple of the solution **20.3.8.** The fact that **20.3.8, 20.4.5,** and **20.4.6** are special cases of **20.4.4** explains why it is that these apparently dissimilar expansions involve the same set of coefficients c_{2n}.

Since **20.4.4** results from the recurrence properties of Bessel functions, $J_k(f)$ can be replaced by $H_k^{(j)}(f)$, $j=1, 2$, where $H_k^{(j)}$ is the Hankel function, at least formally. Thus let

$$\psi_k^j=[e^{i\pi}\cos(z-b)/\cos(z+b)]^{\frac{1}{2}k}H_k^{(j)}(f)$$

where f satisfies **20.4.2.** An examination of the ratios $\psi_{2n+\nu}/\psi_{2n+\nu-2}$ shows that

$$y=\sum_{n=-\infty}^{\infty} c_{2n}\psi_{2n+\nu}^{(j)}$$

will be a solution provided

$$|\cos(z-b)|>1;\ |\cos(z+b)|>1.$$

The above two conditions are necessary even when ν is an integer. Once b is fixed, the regions in which the solutions converge can be readily established.

Following [20.36] let

20.4.7

$$J_p(x)=Z_p^{(1)}(x);\quad Y_p(x)=Z_p^{(2)}(x);$$
$$H_p^{(1)}(x)=Z_p^{(3)}(x);\quad H_p^{(2)}(x)=Z_p^{(4)}(x)$$

If z is replaced by $-iz$ in **20.4.5** and **20.4.6** solutions of **20.1.2** are obtained. Thus

20.4.8

$$y_1^{(j)}(z)=\sum_{n=-\infty}^{\infty} c_{2n}(-1)^n Z_{2n+\nu}^{(j)}(2\sqrt{q}\cosh z)$$
$$(|\cosh z|>1)$$

20.4.9

$$y_2^{(j)}(z)=\sum_{n=-\infty}^{\infty} c_{2n}Z_{2n+\nu}^{(j)}(2\sqrt{q}\sinh z)$$
$$(|\sinh z|>1,\ j=1, 2, 3, 4)$$

The relation between $y_1^{(j)}(z)$ and $y_2^{(j)}(z)$ can be determined from the asymptotic properties of the Bessel functions for large values of argument. It can be shown that

20.4.10

$$y_1^{(j)}(z)/y_2^{(j)}(z)=[F_\nu(0)/F_\nu\left(\frac{\pi}{2}\right)]e^{i\nu\pi/2} \qquad (\mathscr{R}z>0).$$

When ν is not an integer, the above solutions do not vanish identically. See **20.6** for integral values of ν.

Solutions Involving Products of Bessel Functions

20.4.11

$$y_3^{(j)}(z)=\frac{1}{c_{2s}}\sum_{n=-\infty}^{\infty} c_{2n}(-1)^n Z_{n+\nu+s}^{(j)}(\sqrt{q}e^{iz})J_{n-s}(\sqrt{q}e^{-iz})$$
$$(j=1, 2, 3, 4)$$

satisfies **20.1.1,** where $Z_n^{(j)}(u)$ is defined in **20.4.7,** the coefficients c_{2n} belong to the Floquet solution, and s is an arbitrary integer, $c_{2s}\neq 0$. The solution converges over the entire complex z-plane if $q\neq 0$. Written with z replaced by $-iz$, one obtains solutions of **20.1.2.**

20.4.12

$$M_\nu^j(z,q)=\frac{1}{c_{2s}^\nu}\sum_{n=-\infty}^{\infty} c_{2n}^\nu(-1)^n Z_{n+\nu+s}^{(j)}(\sqrt{q}e^z)J_{n-s}(\sqrt{q}e^{-z})$$

It can be verified from **20.4.8** and **20.4.12** that

20.4.13 $$\frac{y_1^{(j)}(z)}{M_j^j(z,q)}=F_\nu(0), \qquad (\mathscr{R}z>0)$$

provided $c_{2s}\neq 0$. If $c_{2s}=0$, the coefficient of $1/c_{2s}$ in **20.4.11** vanishes identically. For details see [20.43], [20.15], [20.36].

If s is chosen so that $|c_{2s}|$ is the largest coefficient of the set $|c_{2j}|$, then rapid convergence of **20.4.12** is obtained, when $\mathscr{R}z>0$. Even then one must be on guard against the possible loss of significant figures in the process of summing the series, especially so when q is large, and $|z|$ small. (If $j\neq 1$, then the phase of the logarithmic terms occurring in **20.4.12** must be defined, to make the functions single-valued.)

20.5. Properties of Orthogonality and Normalization

If $a(\nu+2p,\ q)$, $a(\nu+2s,\ q)$ are simple roots of **20.3.10** then

20.5.1 $$\int_0^\pi F_{\nu+2p}(z)F_{\nu+2s}(-z)dz=0, \text{ if } p\neq s.$$

Define

20.5.2 $$ce_\nu(z,q)=\frac{1}{2}[F_\nu(z)+F_\nu(-z)];$$

$$se_\nu(z,q)=-i\frac{1}{2}[F_\nu(z)-F_\nu(-z)]$$

$ce_\nu(z,q)$, $se_\nu(z,q)$ are thus even and odd functions of z, respectively, for all ν (when not identically zero).

If ν is an integer, then $ce_\nu(z,q)$, $se_\nu(z,q)$ are either Floquet solutions or identically zero. The solutions $ce_r(z,q)$ are associated with a_r; $se_r(z,q)$ are associated with b_r; r an integer.

Normalization for Integral Values of ν and Real q

20.5.3 $$\int_0^{2\pi}[ce_r(z,q)]^2dz=\int_0^{2\pi}[se_r(z,q)]^2dz=\pi$$

For integral values of ν the summation in **20.3.8** reduces to the simpler forms **20.2.3–20.2.4**; on account of **20.5.3**, the coefficients A_m and B_m (for all orders r) have the property

20.5.4

$$2A_0^2+A_2^2+\ldots=A_1^2+A_3^2+\ldots$$
$$=B_1^2+B_3^2+\ldots=B_2^2+B_4^2+\ldots=1.$$

20.5.5

$$A_0^{2s}=\frac{1}{2\pi}\int_0^{2\pi}ce_{2s}(z,q)dz;\ A_n^r=\frac{1}{\pi}\int_0^{2\pi}ce_r(z,q)\cos nz dz$$

$$B_n^r=\frac{1}{\pi}\int_0^{2\pi}se_r(z,q)\sin nz dz \qquad n\neq 0$$

For integral values of ν, the functions $ce_r(z,q)$ and $se_r(z,q)$ form a complete orthogonal set for the interval $0\leq z\leq 2\pi$. Each of the four systems $ce_{2r}(z)$, $ce_{2r+1}(z)$, $se_{2r}(z)$, $se_{2r+1}(z)$ is complete in the smaller interval $0\leq z\leq \frac{1}{2}\pi$, and each of the systems $ce_r(z)$, $se_r(z)$ is complete in $0\leq z\leq\pi$.

If q is not real, there exist multiple roots of **20.3.10**; for such special values of $a(q)$, the integrals in **20.5.3** vanish, and the normalization is therefore impossible. In applications, the particular normalization adopted is of little importance, except possibly for obtaining quantitative relations between solutions of various types. For this reason the normalization of $F_\nu(z)$, for arbitrary complex values of a, q, will not be specified here. It is worth noting, however, that solutions

$$\alpha ce_r(z,q), \qquad \beta se_r(z,q)$$

defined so that

$$\alpha ce_r(0,q)=1; \qquad \left[\frac{d}{dz}\beta se_r(z,q)\right]_{z=0}=1$$

are always possible. This normalization has in fact been used in [20.59], and also in [20.58], where the most extensive tabular material is available. The tabulated entries in [20.58] supply the conversion factors $A=1/\alpha$, $B=1/\beta$, along with the coefficients. Thus conversion from one normalization to another is rather easy.

In a similar vein, no general normalization will be imposed on the functions defined in **20.4.8.**

20.6. Solutions of Mathieu's Modified Equation 20.1.2 for Integral ν (Radial Solutions)

Solutions of the first kind

20.6.1

$$Ce_{2r+p}(z,q)=ce_{2r+p}(iz,q)$$
$$=\sum_{k=0}^{\infty}A_{2k+p}^{2r+p}(q)\cosh(2k+p)z$$

associated with a_r

20.6.2 $$Se_{2r+p}(z,q)=-ise_{2r+p}(iz,q)=\sum_{k=0}^{\infty}B_{2k+p}^{2r+p}(q)\sinh(2k+p)z, \text{ associated with } b_r$$

writing $A_{2k+p}^{2r+p}(q)=A_{2k+p}$ for brevity; similarly for B_{2k+p}; $p=0, 1$,

20.6.3 $$Ce_{2r}(z,q)=\frac{ce_{2r}\left(\frac{\pi}{2},q\right)}{A_0^{2r}}\sum_{k=0}^{\infty}(-1)^kA_{2k}J_{2k}(2\sqrt{q}\cosh z)=\frac{ce_{2r}(0,q)}{A_0^{2r}}\sum_{k=0}^{\infty}A_{2k}J_{2k}(2\sqrt{q}\sinh z)$$

20.6.4 $$Ce_{2r+1}(z,q)=\frac{ce'_{2r+1}\left(\frac{\pi}{2},q\right)}{\sqrt{q}A_1^{2r+1}}\sum_{k=0}^{\infty}(-1)^{k+1}A_{2k+1}J_{2k+1}(2\sqrt{q}\cosh z)$$

$$=\frac{ce_{2r+1}(0,q)}{\sqrt{q}A_1^{2r+1}}\coth z\sum_{k=0}^{\infty}(2k+1)A_{2k+1}J_{2k+1}(2\sqrt{q}\sinh z)$$

20.6.5 $$Se_{2r}(z,q)=\frac{se'_{2r}\left(\frac{\pi}{2},q\right)\tanh z}{qB_2^{2r}}\sum_{k=1}^{\infty}(-1)^k2kB_{2k}J_{2k}(2\sqrt{q}\cosh z)$$

$$=\frac{se'_{2r}(0,q)}{qB_2^{2r}}\coth z\sum_{k=1}^{\infty}2kB_{2k}J_{2k}(2\sqrt{q}\sinh z)$$

20.6.6 $$Se_{2r+1}(z,q)=\frac{se_{2r+1}\left(\frac{\pi}{2},q\right)}{\sqrt{q}B_1^{2r+1}}\tanh z\sum_{k=0}^{\infty}(-1)^k(2k+1)B_{2k+1}J_{2k+1}(2\sqrt{q}\cosh z)$$

$$=\frac{se'_{2r+1}(0,q)}{\sqrt{q}B_1^{2r+1}}\sum_{k=0}^{\infty}B_{2k+1}J_{2k+1}(2\sqrt{q}\sinh z)$$

See [20.30] for still other forms.

Solutions of the second kind, as well as solutions of the third and fourth kind (analogous to Hankel functions) are obtainable from **20.4.12**.

20.6.7 $$Mc_{2r}^{(j)}(z,q)=\sum_{k=0}^{\infty}(-1)^{r+k}A_{2k}^{2r}(q)[J_{k-s}(u_1)Z_{k+s}^{(j)}(u_2)+J_{k+s}(u_1)Z_{k-s}^{(j)}(u_2)]/\epsilon_sA_{2s}^{2r}$$

where $\epsilon_0=2$, $\epsilon_s=1$, for $s=1, 2, \ldots$; s arbitrary, associated with a_{2r}

20.6.8 $$Mc_{2r+1}^{(j)}(z,q)=\sum_{k=0}^{\infty}(-1)^{r+k}A_{2k+1}^{2r+1}(q)[J_{k-s}(u_1)Z_{k+s+1}^{(j)}(u_2)+J_{k+s+1}(u_1)Z_{k-s}^{(j)}(u_2)]/A_{2s+1}^{2r+1}$$

associated with a_{2r+1}

20.6.9 $$Ms_{2r}^{(j)}(z,q)=\sum_{k=1}^{\infty}(-1)^{k+r}B_{2k}^{2r}(q)[J_{k-s}(u_1)Z_{k+s}^{(j)}(u_2)-J_{k+s}(u_1)Z_{k-s}^{(j)}(u_2)]/B_{2s}^{2r}, \text{ associated with } b_{2r}$$

20.6.10 $$Ms_{2r+1}^{(j)}(z,q)=\sum_{k=0}^{\infty}(-1)^{k+r}B_{2k+1}^{2r+1}(q)[J_{k-s}(u_1)Z_{k+s+1}^{(j)}(u_2)-J_{k+s+1}(u_1)Z_{k-s}^{(j)}(u_2)]/B_{2s+1}^{2r+1}$$

associated with b_{2r+1}

where

$$u_1=\sqrt{q}e^{-z},\ u_2=\sqrt{q}e^{z},\ B_{2s+p}^{2r+p},\ A_{2s+p}^{2r+p}\neq0,\ p=0, 1.$$

See **20.4.7** for definition of $Z_m^{(j)}(x)$.

Solutions **20.6.7–20.6.10** converge for all values of z, when $q\neq0$. If $j=2, 3, 4$ the logarithmic terms entering into the Bessel functions $Y_m(u_2)$ must be defined, to make the functions single-valued. This can be accomplished as follows:

Define (as in [20.58])

20.6.11 $$\ln(\sqrt{q}e^z)=\ln(\sqrt{q})+z$$

See [20.15] and [20.36], section **2.75** for derivation.

Other Expressions for the Radial Functions (Valid Over More Limited Regions)

20.6.12 $$Mc_{2r}^{(j)}(z, q)=[ce_{2r}(0, q)]^{-1} \sum_{k=0}^{\infty} (-1)^{k+r}A_{2k}^{2r}(q)Z_{2k}^{(j)}(2\sqrt{q} \cosh z)$$

$$Mc_{2r+1}^{(j)}(z, q)=[ce_{2r+1}(0, q)]^{-1} \sum_{k=0}^{\infty} (-1)^{k+r}A_{2k+1}^{2r+1}(q)Z_{2k+1}^{(j)}(2\sqrt{q} \cosh z)$$

20.6.13 $$Ms_{2r}^{(j)}(z, q)=[se'_{2r}(0, q)]^{-1} \tanh z \sum_{k=1}^{\infty} (-1)^{k+r}2kB_{2k}^{2r}(q)Z_{2k}^{(j)}(2\sqrt{q} \cosh z)$$

$$Ms_{2r+1}^{(j)}(z, q)=[se'_{2r+1}(0, q)]^{-1} \tanh z \sum_{k=0}^{\infty} (-1)^{k+r}(2k+1)B_{2k+1}^{2r+1}(q)Z_{2k+1}^{(j)}(2\sqrt{q} \cosh z)$$

Valid for $\mathscr{R}z>0$, $|\cosh z|>1$; if $j=1$, valid for all z. They agree with **20.6.7–20.6.10** if the Bessel functions $Y_m(2q^{\frac{1}{2}} \cosh z)$ are made single-valued in a suitable way. For example, let

$$Y_m(u)=\frac{2}{\pi} (\ln u)J_m(u)+\phi(u)$$

where $\phi(u)$ is single-valued for all finite values of u. With $u=2q^{\frac{1}{2}} \cosh z$, define

20.6.14 $$\ln (2q^{\frac{1}{2}} \cosh z)=\ln 2q^{\frac{1}{2}}+z+\ln \tfrac{1}{2}(1+e^{-2z}) \qquad -\frac{\pi}{2} \leq \arg \tfrac{1}{2}(1+e^{-2z}) \leq \frac{\pi}{2}.$$

(If q is not positive, the phase of $\ln 2q^{\frac{1}{2}}$ must also be specified, although this specification will not affect continuity with respect to z. If $Y_m(u)$ is defined from some other expression, the definition must be compatible with **20.6.14**.)

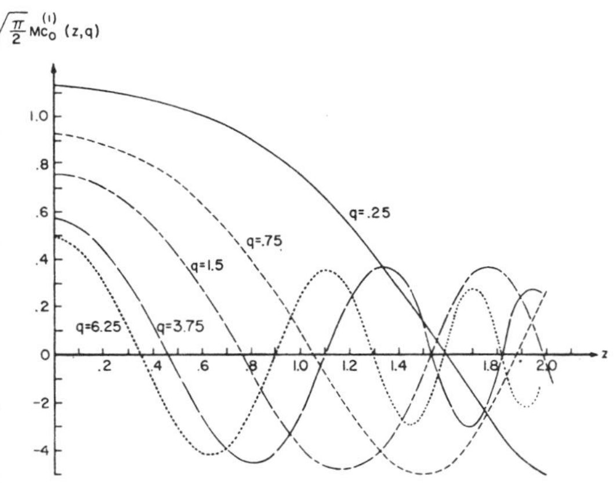

FIGURE 20.11. *Radial Mathieu Function of the First Kind.*

From J. C. Wiltse and M. J. King, Values of the Mathieu functions, The Johns Hopkins Univ. Radiation Laboratory Tech. Rept. AF-53, 1958

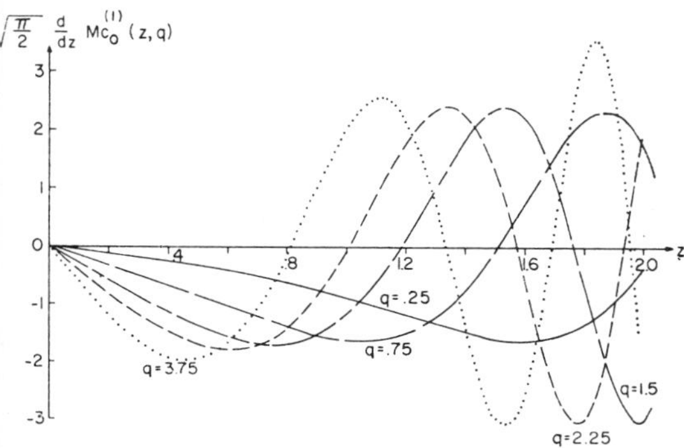

FIGURE 20.12. *Derivative of the Radial Mathieu Function of the First Kind.*

From J. C. Wiltse and M. J. King, Derivatives, zeros, and other data pertaining to Mathieu functions, The Johns Hopkins Univ. Radiation Laboratory Tech. Rept. AF-57, 1958

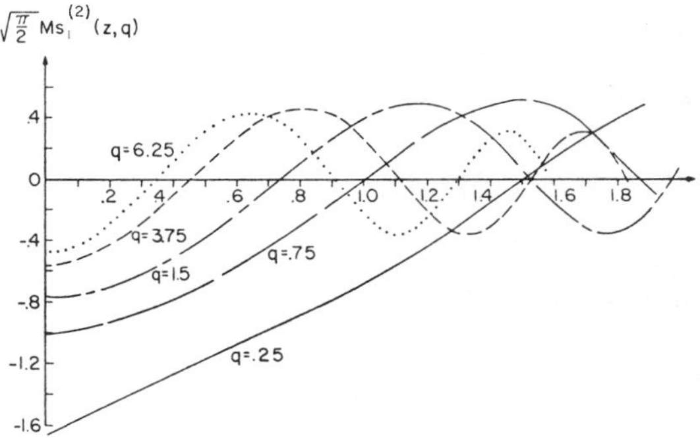

FIGURE 20.13. *Radial Mathieu Function of the Second Kind.*

From J. C. Wiltse and M. J. King, Values of the Mathieu functions, The Johns Hopkins Univ. Radiation Laboratory Tech. Rept. AF-53, 1958

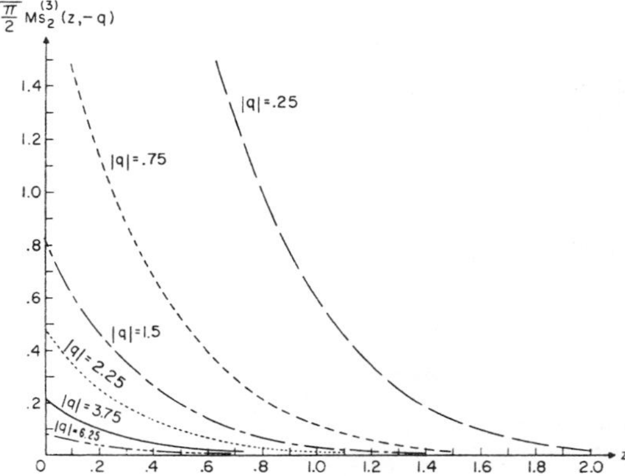

FIGURE 20.14. *Radial Mathieu Function of the Third Kind.*

From J. C. Wiltse and M. J. King, Values of the Mathieu functions, The Johns Hopkins Univ. Radiation Laboratory Tech. Rept. AF-53, 1958

If $j=1$, $Mc^{(1)}_{2r+p}$ and $Ms^{(1)}_{2r+p}$, $p=0, 1$ are solutions of the first kind, proportional to Ce_{2r+p} and Se_{2r+p}, respectively.

Thus

20.6.15

$$Ce_{2r}(z,q)=\frac{ce_{2r}\left(\frac{\pi}{2},q\right)ce_{2r}(0,q)}{(-1)^r A_0^{2r}}\,Mc^{(1)}_{2r}(z,q)$$

$$Ce_{2r+1}(z,q)=\frac{ce'_{2r+1}\left(\frac{\pi}{2},q\right)ce_{2r+1}(0,q)}{(-1)^{r+1}\sqrt{q}A_1^{2r+1}}\,Mc^{(1)}_{2r+1}(z,q)$$

$$Se_{2r}(z,q)=\frac{se'_{2r}(0,q)se'_{2r}\left(\frac{\pi}{2},q\right)}{(-1)^r qB_2^{2r}}\,Ms^{(1)}_{2r}(z,q)$$

$$Se_{2r+1}(z,q)=\frac{se'_{2r+1}(0,q)\,se_{2r+1}\left(\frac{\pi}{2},q\right)}{(-1)^r\sqrt{q}B_1^{2r+1}}\,Ms^{(1)}_{2r+1}(z,q)$$

The Mathieu-Hankel functions are

20.6.16

$$M^{(3)}_r(z,q)=M^{(1)}_r(z,q)+iM^{(2)}_r(z,q)$$

$$M^{(4)}_r(z,q)=M^{(1)}_r(z,q)-iM^{(2)}_r(z,q)$$

$$M^{(j)}_r=Mc^{(j)}_r \text{ or } Ms^{(j)}_r.$$

From **20.6.7–20.6.11** and the known properties of Bessel functions one obtains

20.6.17

$$M^{(2)}_{2r+p}(z+in\pi,q)=(-1)^{np}[M^{(2)}_{2r+p}(z,q)+2niM^{(1)}_{2r+p}(z,q)]$$

$$M^{(3)}_{2r+p}(z+in\pi,q)=(-1)^{np}[M^{(3)}_{2r+p}(z,q)-2nM^{(1)}_{2r+p}(z,q)]$$

$$M^{(4)}_{2r+p}(z+in\pi,q)=(-1)^{np}[M^{(4)}_{2r+p}(z,q)+2nM^{(1)}_{2r+p}(z,q)]$$

where $M=Mc$ or Ms throughout any of the above equations.

Other Properties of Characteristic Functions, q Real (Associated With a_r and b_r)

Consider

20.6.18

$$X_1=Mc^{(2)}_r(z,q)+Mc^{(2)}_r(-z,q);$$
$$X_2=Ms^{(2)}_r(z,q)-Ms^{(2)}_r(-z,q)$$

Since X_1 is an even solution it must be proportional to $Mc^{(1)}_r(z,q)$; for **20.1.2** admits of only one even solution (aside from an arbitrary constant factor). Similarly, X_2 is proportional to $Ms^{(1)}_r(z,q)$. The proportionality factors can be found by considering values of the functions at $z=0$. Define, therefore,

20.6.19

$$Mc^{(2)}_r(-z,q)=-Mc^{(2)}_r(z,q)-2f_{e,r}Mc^{(1)}_r(z,q)$$

20.6.20

$$Ms^{(2)}_r(-z,q)=Ms^{(2)}_r(z,q)-2f_{o,r}Ms^{(1)}_r(z,a)$$

where

20.6.21

$$f_{e,r}=-Mc^{(2)}_r(0,q)/Mc^{(1)}_r(0,q)$$

$$f_{o,r}=\left[\frac{d}{dz}Ms^{(2)}_r(z,q)/\frac{d}{dz}Ms^{(1)}_r(z,q)\right]_{z=0}$$

See [20.58].

In particular the above equations can be used to extend solutions of **20.6.12–20.6.13** when $\mathscr{R}z<0$. For although the latter converge for $\mathscr{R}z<0$, provided only $|\cosh z|>1$, they do not represent the same functions as **20.6.9–20.6.10.**

20.7. Representations by Integrals and Some Integral Equations

Let

20.7.1 $$G(u)=\oint_C K(u,t)V(t)dt$$

be defined for u in a domain U and let the contour C belong to the region T of the complex t-plane, with $t=\gamma_0$ as the starting point of the contour and $t=\gamma_1$ as its end-point. The kernel $K(u,t)$ and the function $V(t)$ satisfy **20.7.3** and the hypotheses in **20.7.2.**

20.7.2 $K(u,t)$ and its first two partial derivatives with respect to u and t are continuous for t on C and u in U; V and $\frac{dV}{dt}$ are continuous in t.

20.7.3

$$\left[\frac{\partial K}{\partial t}V-\frac{dV}{dt}K\right]_{\gamma_0}^{\gamma_1}=0;\quad \frac{d^2V}{dt^2}+(a-2q\cos 2t)V=0.$$

If K satisfies

20.7.4 $$\frac{\partial^2K}{\partial u^2}+\frac{\partial^2K}{\partial t^2}+2q(\cosh 2u-\cos 2t)K=0$$

then $G(u)$ is a solution of Mathieu's modified equation **20.1.2.**

If $K(u,t)$ satisfies

20.7.5 $$\frac{\partial^2K}{\partial u^2}+\frac{\partial^2K}{\partial t^2}+2q(\cos 2u-\cos 2t)K=0$$

then $G(u)$ is a solution of Mathieu's equation **20.1.1,** with u replacing v.

Kernels $K_1(z, t)$ and $K_2(z, t)$

20.7.6 $K_1(z, t)=Z_\nu^{(j)}(u)[M(z, t)]^{-\nu/2}, \qquad (\mathscr{R}z>0)$

where

20.7.7 $u=\sqrt{2q(\cosh 2z+\cos 2t)}$

20.7.8 $M(z, t)=\cosh (z+it)/\cosh (z-it)$

To make $M^{-\frac{1}{2}\nu}$ single-valued, define

20.7.9

$$\cosh (z+i\pi)=e^{i\pi}\cosh z$$
$$\cosh (z-i\pi)=e^{-i\pi}\cosh z$$
$$M(z, 0)=1$$
$$[M(z, \pi)]^{-\frac{1}{2}\nu}=e^{-i\nu\pi}M(z, 0)$$

Let

20.7.10 $G(z, q)=\frac{1}{\pi}\int_0^\pi K_1(u, t)F_\nu(t)dt, \qquad (\mathscr{R}z>0)$

where $F_\nu(t)$ is defined in **20.3.8.** It may be verified that K_1F_ν satisfies **20.7.3,** K satisfies **20.7.2** and **20.7.4.** Hence G is a solution of **20.1.2** (with z replacing u). It can be shown that K_1 may be replaced by the more general function

20.7.11

$K_2(z, t)=Z^{(j)}_{\nu+2s}(u)[M(z, t)]^{-\frac{1}{2}\nu+s}$, s any integer.

See **20.4.7** for definition of $Z^{(j)}_{\nu+2s}(u)$.

From the known expansions for $Z^{(j)}_{\nu+2s}(u)$ when $\mathscr{R}z$ is large and positive it may be verified that

20.7.12

$$M_\nu^{(j)}(z, q)=$$

$$\frac{(-1)^s}{\pi c_{2s}}\int_0^\pi Z^{(j)}_{\nu+2s}(u)\left[\frac{\cosh z+it}{\cosh z-it}\right]^{-\frac{1}{2}\nu-s}F_\nu(t)dt$$
$$(\mathscr{R}z>0, \mathscr{R}(\nu+\tfrac{1}{2})>0)$$

where $M_\nu^{(j)}(z, q)$ is given by **20.4.12,** $s=0, 1, \ldots$, $c_{2s}\neq 0$, and $F_\nu(t)$ is the Floquet solution, **20.3.8.**

Kernel $K_3(z, t, a)$

20.7.13 $K_3(z, t, a)=e^{2i\sqrt{q}\,w}$

where

20.7.14 $w=\cosh z\cos a\cos t+\sinh z\sin a\sin t$

20.7.15 $G(z, q, a)=\frac{1}{\pi}\oint_C e^{2i\sqrt{q}\,w}F_\nu(t)dt$

where $F_\nu(t)$ is the Floquet solution **20.3.8.** The path C is chosen so that $G(z, t, a)$ exists, and **20.7.2, 20.7.3** are satisfied. Then it may be verified that $K_3(z, t, a)$, considered as a function of z and t, satisfies **20.7.4;** also, considered as a function of a and t, K_3 satisfies **20.7.5.** Consequently $G(z, q, a)=Y(z, q)y(a, q)$, where Y and y satisfy **20.1.2** and **20.1.1,** respectively.

Choice of Path C. Three paths will be defined:

20.7.16

Path C_3: from $-d_1+i\infty$ to $d_2-i\infty$, d_1, d_2 real

$$-d_1<\arg[\sqrt{q}\{\cosh(z+ia)\pm 1\}]<\pi-d_1$$
$$-d_2<\arg[\sqrt{q}\{\cosh(z-ia)\pm 1\}]<\pi-d_2$$

20.7.17

Path C_4: from $d_2-i\infty$ to $2\pi+i\infty-d_1$

(same d_1, d_2 as in **20.7.16**)

20.7.18

$$F_\nu(a)M_\nu^j(z, q)=\frac{e^{-i\nu\frac{\pi}{2}}}{\pi}\oint_{C_j}e^{2i\sqrt{q}\,w}F_\nu(t)dt \qquad j=3, 4$$

where $M_\nu^j(z, q)$ is also given by **20.4.12.**

20.7.19 Path C_1: from $-d_1+i\infty$ to $2\pi-d_1+i\infty$

$$F_\nu(a)M_\nu^{(1)}(z, q)=\frac{e^{-i\nu\frac{\pi}{2}}}{2\pi}\oint_{C_1}e^{2i\sqrt{q}\,w}F_\nu(t)dt$$

See [20.36], section **2.68.**

If ν is an integer the paths can be simplified; for in that case $F_\nu(t)$ is periodic and the integrals exist when the path is taken from 0 to 2π. Still further simplifications are possible, if z is also real.

The following are among the more important integral representations for the periodic functions $ce_r(z, q)$, $se_r(z, q)$ and for the associated radial solutions.

Let $r=2s+p$, $p=0$ or 1

20.7.20

$$ce_r(z, q)=\rho_r\int_0^{\pi/2}\cos\left(2\sqrt{q}\cos z\cos t-p\frac{\pi}{2}\right)ce_r(t, q)dt$$

20.7.21 $$ce_r(z,q)=\sigma_r\int_0^{\pi/2}\cosh\,(2\sqrt{q}\sin z\sin t)[(1-p)+p\cos z\cos t]ce_r(t,q)dt$$

20.7.22 $$se_r(z,q)=\rho_r\int_0^{\pi/2}\sin\left(2\sqrt{q}\cos z\cos t+p\frac{\pi}{2}\right)\sin z\sin t\; se_r(t,q)dt$$

20.7.23 $$se_r(z,q)=\sigma_r\int_0^{\pi/2}\sinh\,(2\sqrt{q}\sin z\sin t)[(1-p)\cos z\cos t+p]se_r(t,q)dt$$

where

20.7.24 $$\rho_r=\frac{2}{\pi}ce_{2s}\left(\frac{\pi}{2},q\right)/A_0^{2s}(q);\;p=0\;\rho_r=\frac{-2}{\pi}ce'_{2s+1}\left(\frac{\pi}{2},q\right)/\sqrt{q}A_1^{2s+1}(q)\text{ if }p=1,\text{ for functions }ce_r(z,q)$$

$$\rho_r=\frac{-4}{\pi}se'_{2s}\left(\frac{\pi}{2},q\right)/\sqrt{q}B_2^{2s}(q);\;\rho_r=\frac{4}{\pi}se_{2s+1}\left(\frac{\pi}{2},q\right)/B_1^{2s+1}(q),\text{ for functions }se_r(z,q)$$

$$\sigma_r=\frac{2}{\pi}ce_{2s}(0,q)/A_0^{2s}(q)\text{ if }p=0;\qquad\sigma_r=\frac{4}{\pi}ce_{2s+1}(0,q)/A_1^{2s+1}(q),\text{ if }p=1;\text{ associated with functions }ce_r(z,q)$$

$$\sigma_r=\frac{4}{\pi}se'_{2s}(0,q)/\sqrt{q}B_2^{2s}(q),\text{ if }p=0;\qquad\sigma_r=\frac{2}{\pi}se'_{2s+1}(0,q)/\sqrt{q}B_1^{2s+1}(q),\text{ if }p=1;\text{ associated with }se_r(z,q)$$

Integrals Involving Bessel Function Kernels

Let

20.7.25 $$u=\sqrt{2q(\cosh 2z+\cos 2t)},\;(\mathscr{R}\cosh 2z>1;\text{ if }j=1,\text{ valid also when }z=0)$$

20.7.26

$$Mc_{2r}^{(j)}(z,q)=\frac{(-1)^r 2}{\pi A_0^{2r}}\int_0^{\frac{\pi}{2}}Z_0^{(j)}(u)ce_{2r}(t,q)dt;\;Mc_{2r+1}^{(j)}(z,q)=\frac{(-1)^r 8\sqrt{q}\cosh z}{\pi A_1^{2r+1}}\int_0^{\frac{\pi}{2}}\frac{Z_1^{(j)}(u)\cos t}{u}ce_{2r+1}(t,q)dt$$

20.7.27 $$Ms_{2r}^{(j)}(z,q)=\frac{(-1)^{r+1}8q\sinh 2z}{\pi B_2^{2r}}\int_0^{\frac{\pi}{2}}\frac{Z_2^{(j)}(u)\sin 2t\; se_{2r}(t,q)dt}{u^2}$$

$$Ms_{2r+1}^{(j)}(z,q)=\frac{(-1)^r 8\sqrt{q}\sinh z}{\pi B_1^{2r+1}}\int_0^{\frac{\pi}{2}}\frac{Z_1^{(j)}(u)\sin t\; se_{2r+1}(t,q)dt}{u}$$

In the above the j-convention of **20.4.7** applies and the functions Mc, Ms are defined in **20.5.1–20.5.4.** (These solutions are normalized so that they approach the corresponding Bessel-Hankel functions as $\mathscr{R}z\rightarrow\infty$.)

Other Integrals for $Mc_r^{(1)}(z,q)$ and $Ms_r^{(1)}(z,q)$

20.7.28 $$Mc_r^{(1)}(z,q)=\frac{(-1)^s 2}{\pi ce_r(0,q)}\int_0^{\frac{\pi}{2}}\cos\left(2\sqrt{q}\cosh z\cos t-p\frac{\pi}{2}\right)ce_r(t,q)dt$$

20.7.29 $$Mc_r^{(1)}(z,q)=\tau_r\int_0^{\frac{\pi}{2}}[(1-p)+p\cosh z\cos t]\cos\,(2\sqrt{q}\sinh z\sin t)ce_r(t,q)dt$$

$$r=2s+p,\;p=0,1;\;\tau_r=\frac{2}{\pi}(-1)^s/ce_{2s}\left(\frac{\pi}{2},q\right),\text{ if }p=0;\;\tau_r=\frac{2}{\pi}(-1)^{s+1}2\sqrt{q}/ce'_{2s+1}\left(\frac{\pi}{2},q\right)$$

20.7.30 $$Ms_{2r+1}^{(1)}(z,q)=\frac{2}{\pi}\frac{(-1)^r}{se_{2r+1}\left(\frac{\pi}{2},q\right)}\int_0^{\frac{\pi}{2}}\sin\,(2\sqrt{q}\sinh z\sin t)se_{2r+1}(t,q)dt$$

20.7.31 $$Ms_{2r+1}^{(1)}(z,q)=\frac{4}{\pi}\frac{\sqrt{q}(-1)^r}{se'_{2r+1}(0,q)}\int_0^{\frac{\pi}{2}}\sinh z\sin t\cos\,(2\sqrt{q}\cosh z\cos t)se_{2r+1}(t,q)dt$$

20.7.32 $$Ms_{2r}^{(1)}(z,q)=\frac{4}{\pi}\sqrt{q}\frac{(-1)^{r+1}}{se'_{2r}(0,q)}\int_0^{\frac{\pi}{2}}\sin\,(2\sqrt{q}\cosh z\cos t)\,[\sinh z\sin t\; se_{2r}(t,q)]dt$$

20.7.33 $$Ms_{2r}^{(1)}(z,q)=\frac{4}{\pi}\frac{(-1)^r\sqrt{q}}{se'_{2r}\left(\frac{\pi}{2},q\right)}\int_0^{\frac{\pi}{2}}\sin\,(2\sqrt{q}\sinh z\sin t)[\cosh z\cos t\; se_{2r}(t,q)]dt$$

Further with $w=\cosh z \cos \alpha \cos t+\sinh z \sin \alpha \sin t$

20.7.34 $$ce_r(\alpha, q)Mc_r^{(1)}(z, q)=\frac{(-1)^s(i)^{-p}}{2\pi}\int_0^{2\pi} e^{2i\sqrt{q}\,w}ce_r(t, q)dt$$

20.7.35 $$se_r(\alpha, q)Ms_r^{(1)}(z, q)=\frac{(-1)^s(-i)^p}{2\pi}\int_0^{2\pi} e^{2i\sqrt{q}\,w}se_r(t, q)dt.$$

The above can be differentiated with respect to α, and we obtain

20.7.36 $$ce_r'(\alpha, q)Mc_r^{(1)}(z, q)=\frac{(-1)^s(i)^{-p+1}\sqrt{q}}{\pi}\int_0^{2\pi} e^{2i\sqrt{q}\,w}\frac{\partial w}{\partial\alpha}ce_r(t, q)dt$$

20.7.37 $$se_r'(\alpha, q)Ms_r^{(1)}(z, q)=\frac{(-1)^{s+p}(i)^{-p+1}\sqrt{q}}{\pi}\int_0^{2\pi} e^{2i\sqrt{q}\,w}\frac{\partial w}{\partial\alpha}se_r(t, q)dt$$

Integrals With Infinite Limits

$$r=2s+p$$

In **20.7.38–20.7.41** below, z and q are positive.

20.7.38 $$Mc_r^{(1)}(z, q)=\gamma_r\int_0^\infty \sin\left(2\sqrt{q}\cosh z\cosh t+p\frac{\pi}{2}\right)Mc_r^{(1)}(t, q)dt$$

$$\gamma_r=2ce_{2s}\left(\frac{\pi}{2}, q\right)/\pi A_0^{2s}, \text{ if } p=0 \qquad \gamma_r=2ce_{2s+1}'\left(\frac{\pi}{2}, q\right)/\sqrt{q}\,\pi A_1^{2s+1}, \text{ if } p=1$$

20.7.39 $$Ms_r^{(1)}(z, q)=\gamma_r\int_0^\infty \sinh z\sinh t\left[\cos\left(2\sqrt{q}\cosh z\cosh t-p\frac{\pi}{2}\right)\right]Ms_r^{(1)}(t, q)dt$$

$$\gamma_r=-4se_{2s}'\left(\frac{\pi}{2}, q\right)/\sqrt{q}\pi B_2^{2s}, \text{ if } p=0 \qquad \gamma_r=-4se_{2s+1}\left(\frac{\pi}{2}, q\right)/\pi B_1^{2s+1}, \text{ if } p=1$$

20.7.40 $$Mc_r^{(2)}(z, q)=\gamma_r\int_0^\infty \cos\left(2\sqrt{q}\cosh z\cosh t-p\frac{\pi}{2}\right)Mc_r^{(1)}(t, q)dt$$

$$\gamma_r=-2ce_{2s}(\tfrac{1}{2}\pi, q)/\pi A_0^{2s}, \text{ if } p=0 \qquad \gamma_r=2ce_{2s+1}'(\tfrac{1}{2}\pi, q)/\pi\sqrt{q}A_1^{2s+1}, \text{ if } p=1$$

20.7.41 $$Ms_r^{(2)}(z, q)=\gamma_r\int_0^\infty \sin\left(2\sqrt{q}\cosh z\cosh t+p\frac{\pi}{2}\right)\sinh z\sinh t\, Ms_r^{(1)}(t, q)dt$$

$$\gamma_r=-4se_{2s}'(\tfrac{1}{2}\pi, q)/\sqrt{q}\,\pi B_2{}^{2s}, \text{ if } p=0 \qquad \gamma_r=4se_{2s+1}(\tfrac{1}{2}\pi, q)/\pi B_1{}^{2s+1}, \text{ if } p=1$$

Additional forms in [20.30], [20.36], [20.15].

20.8. Other Properties

Relations Between Solutions for Parameters q and $-q$

Replacing z by $\frac{1}{2}\pi-z$ in **20.1.1** one obtains

20.8.1 $$y''+(a+2q\cos 2z)y=0$$

Hence if $u(z)$ is a solution of **20.1.1** then $u(\frac{1}{2}\pi-z)$ satisfies **20.8.1**. It can be shown that

20.8.2

$$a(-\nu, q)=a(\nu, -q)=a(\nu, q), \nu \text{ not an integer}$$

$$c_{2m}^\nu(-q)=\rho(-1)^m c_{2m}^\nu(q), \nu \text{ not an integer}$$

(c_{2m} defined in **20.3.8**) and ρ depending on the normalization;

$$F_\nu(z, -q)=\rho e^{-i\nu\pi/2}F_\nu\left(z+\frac{\pi}{2}, q\right)=\rho e^{i\nu\pi/2}F_\nu\left(z-\frac{\pi}{2}, q\right)$$

20.8.3

$$a_{2r}(-q)=a_{2r}(q)\,;\ b_{2r}(-q)=b_{2r}(q),\ \text{for integral } \nu$$

$$a_{2r+1}(-q)=b_{2r+1}(q),\ b_{2r+1}(-q)=a_{2r+1}(q)$$

20.8.4

$$ce_{2r}(z,\ -q)=(-1)^r ce_{2r}(\tfrac{1}{2}\pi-z,\ q)$$

$$ce_{2r+1}(z,\ -q)=(-1)^r se_{2r+1}(\tfrac{1}{2}\pi-z,\ q)$$

$$se_{2r+1}(z,\ -q)=(-1)^r ce_{2r+1}(\tfrac{1}{2}\pi-z,\ q)$$

$$se_{2r}(z,\ -q)=(-1)^{r-1} se_{2r}(\tfrac{1}{2}\pi-z,\ q)$$

For the coefficients associated with the above solutions for integral ν:

20.8.5

$$A_{2m}^{2r}(-q)=(-1)^{m-r}A_{2m}^{2r}(q)\,;\quad B_{2m}^{2r}(-q)=(-1)^{m-r}B_{2m}^{2r}(q)$$

$$A_{2m+1}^{2r+1}(-q)=(-1)^{m-r}B_{2m+1}^{2r+1}(q)\,;\quad B_{2m+1}^{2r+1}(-q)=(-1)^{m-r}A_{2m+1}^{2r+1}(q).$$

For the corresponding modified equation

20.8.6 $$y''-(a+2q\cosh 2z)y=0$$

20.8.7

$$M_\nu^{(j)}(z,\ -q)=M_\nu^{(j)}\left(z+i\frac{\pi}{2},\ q\right),$$

$M_\nu^{(j)}(z,\ q)$ defined in **20.4.12.**

For integral values of ν let

20.8.8

$$Ie_{2r}(z,\ q)=\sum_{k=0}^{\infty}(-1)^{k+s}A_{2k}[I_{k-s}(u_1)I_{k+s}(u_2)+I_{k+s}(u_1)I_{k-s}(u_2)]/A_{2s}\epsilon_s$$

$$Io_{2r}(z,\ q)=\sum_{k=1}^{\infty}(-1)^{k+s}B_{2k}[I_{k-s}(u_1)I_{k+s}(u_2)-I_{k+s}(u_1)I_{k-s}(u_2)]/B_{2s}$$

$$Ie_{2r+1}(z,\ q)=\sum_{k=0}^{\infty}(-1)^{k+s}B_{2k+1}[I_{k-s}(u_1)I_{k+s+1}(u_2)+I_{k+s+1}(u_1)I_{k-s}(u_2)]/B_{2s+1}$$

$$Io_{2r+1}(z,\ q)=\sum_{k=0}^{\infty}(-1)^{k+s}A_{2k+1}[I_{k-s}(u_1)I_{k+s+1}(u_2)-I_{k+s+1}(u_1)I_{k-s}(u_2)]/A_{2s+1}$$

20.8.9

$$Ke_{2r}(z,\ q)=\sum_{k=0}^{\infty}A_{2k}[I_{k-s}(u_1)K_{k+s}(u_2)+I_{k+s}(u_1)K_{k-s}(u_2)]/A_{2s}\epsilon_s$$

$$Ko_{2r}(z,\ q)=\sum_{k=0}^{\infty}B_{2k}[I_{k-s}(u_1)K_{k+s}(u_2)-I_{k+s}(u_1)K_{k-s}(u_2)]/B_{2s}$$

$$Ke_{2r+1}(z,\ q)=\sum_{k=0}^{\infty}B_{2k+1}[I_{k-s}(u_1)K_{k+s+1}(u_2)-I_{k+s+1}(u_1)K_{k-s}(u_2)]/B_{2s+1}$$

$$Ko_{2r+1}(z,\ q)=\sum_{k=0}^{\infty}A_{2k+1}[I_{k-s}(u_1)K_{k+s+1}(u_2)+I_{k+s+1}(u_1)K_{k-s}(u_2)]/A_{2s+1}$$

where $I_m(x)$, $K_m(x)$ are the modified Bessel functions, u_1, u_2 are defined below **20.6.10.** Superscripts are omitted, $\epsilon_s=2$, if $s=0$, $\epsilon_s=1$ if $s\neq 0$.

Then for functions of first kind:

20.8.10

$$Mc_{2r}^{(1)}(z,\ -q)=(-1)^r Ie_{2r}(z,\ q)$$

$$Ms_{2r}^{(1)}(z,\ -q)=(-1)^r Io_{2r}(z,\ q)$$

$$Mc_{2r+1}^{(1)}(z,\ -q)=(-1)^r iIe_{2r+1}(z,\ q)$$

$$Ms_{2r+1}^{(1)}(z,\ -q)=(-1)^r iIo_{2r+1}(z,\ q)$$

For the Mathieu-Hankel function of first kind:

20.8.11

$$Mc_{2r}^{(3)}(z,\ -q)=(-1)^{r+1}i\frac{2}{\pi}Ke_{2r}(z,\ q)$$

$$Ms_{2r}^{(3)}(z,\ -q)=(-1)^{r+1}i\frac{2}{\pi}Ko_{2r}(z,\ q)$$

$$Mc_{2r+1}^{(3)}(z,\ -q)=(-1)^{r+1}\frac{2}{\pi}Ke_{2r+1}(z,\ q)$$

$$Ms_{2r+1}^{(3)}(z,\ -q)=(-1)^{r+1}\frac{2}{\pi}Ko_{2r+1}(z,\ q)$$

For $M_r^{(j)}(z,\ -q)$, $j=2,\ 4$, one may use the definitions

$$M_r^{(2)}=-i(M_r^{(3)}-M_r^{(1)})\,;\ M_r=Mc_r \text{ or } Ms_r$$

also

$$M_r^{(4)}(z,\ -q)=2M_r^{(1)}(z,\ -q)-M_r^{(3)}(z,\ -q)$$

$M=Mc$ or Ms; for real z, q, $M_r^{(j)}(z,\ -q)$ are in general complex if $j=2,4$.

Zeros of the Functions for Real Values of q.

See [20.36], section **2.8** for further results.

Zeros of $ce_r(z,\ q)$ and $se_r(z,\ q)$, $Mc_r^{(1)}(z,\ q)$, $Ms_r^{(1)}(z,\ q)$.

In $0\leq z<\pi$, $ce_r(z,\ q)$ and $se_r(z,\ q)$ have r real zeros.

There are complex zeros if $q>0$.

If $z_0=x_0+iy_0$ is any zero of $ce_r(z,\ q)$, $se_r(z,\ q)$ in

$$-\frac{\pi}{2}<x_0<\frac{\pi}{2},\ \text{then } k\pi\pm z_0,\ k\pi\pm\bar{z}_0$$

are also zeros, k an integer.

In the strip $-\frac{\pi}{2}<x_0<\frac{\pi}{2}$, the imaginary zeros of $ce_r(z, q)$, $se_r(z, q)$ are the real zeros of $Ce_r(z, q)$, $Se_r(z, q)$, hence also the real zeros of $Mc_r^{(1)}(z, q)$ and $Ms_r^{(1)}(z, q)$, respectively.

For small q, the large zeros of $Ce_r(z, q)$, $Se_r(z, q)$ approach the zeros of $J_r(2\sqrt{q}\cosh z)$.

Tabulation of Zeros

Ince [20.56] tabulates the first "non-trivial" zero $\left(\text{i.e. different from } 0, \frac{\pi}{2}, \pi\right)$ for $ce_r(z)$, $se_r(z)$, $r=2(1)5$ and for $se_6(z)$ to within $°10^{-4}$, for $q=0(1)10(2)40$. He also gives the "turning" points (zeros of the derivative) and also expansions for them for small q. Wiltse and King [20.61,2] tabulate the first two (non-trivial) zeros of $Mc_r^{(1)}(z, q)$ and $Ms_r^{(1)}(z, q)$ and of their derivatives $r=0, 1, 2$ for 6 or 7 values of q between .25 and 10. The graphs reproduced here indicate their location.

Between two real zeros of $Mc_r^{(1)}(z, q)$, $Ms_r^{(1)}(z, q)$ there is a zero of $Mc_r^{(2)}(z, q)$, $Ms_r^{(2)}(z, q)$, respectively. No tabulation of such zeros exists yet.

Available tables are described in the References.

The most comprehensive tabulation of the characteristic values a_r, b_r (in a somewhat different notation) and of the coefficients proportional to A_m and B_m as defined in **20.5.4** and **20.5.5** can be found in [20.58]. In addition, the table contains certain important "joining factors", with the aid of which it is possible to obtain values of $Mc_r^{(j)}(z, q)$ and $Ms_r^{(j)}(z, q)$ as well as their derivatives, at $x=0$. Values of the functions $ce_r(x, q)$ and $se_r(x, q)$ for orders up to five or six can be found in [20.56]. Tabulations of less extensive character, but important in some aspects, are outlined in the other references cited. In this chapter only representative values of the various functions are given, along with several graphs.

Special Values for Arguments 0 and $\frac{\pi}{2}$

20.8.12

$$ce_{2r}\left(\frac{\pi}{2}, q\right)=(-1)^r g_{e,2r}(q)A_0^{2r}(q)\sqrt{\frac{\pi}{2}}$$

$$ce'_{2r+1}\left(\frac{\pi}{2}, q\right)=(-1)^{r+1} g_{e,2r+1}(q)A_1^{2r+1}(q)\sqrt{\frac{\pi}{2}q}$$

$$se'_{2r}\left(\frac{\pi}{2}, q\right)=(-1)^r g_{o,2r}(q)B_2^{2r}(q)\cdot q\sqrt{\frac{\pi}{2}}$$

$$se_{2r+1}\left(\frac{\pi}{2}, q\right)=(-1)^r g_{o,2r+1}(q)B_1^{2r+1}(q)\sqrt{\frac{\pi}{2}q}$$

$$Mc_r^{(1)}(0, q)=\sqrt{\frac{2}{\pi}}\frac{1}{g_{e,r}(q)}$$

$$Mc_r^{(2)}(0, q)=-\sqrt{\frac{2}{\pi}}f_{e,r}(q)/g_{e,r}(q)$$

$$\frac{d}{dz}[Mc_r^{(2)}(z, q)]_{z=0}=\sqrt{\frac{2}{\pi}}g_{e,r}(q)$$

$$\frac{d}{dz}[Ms_r^{(1)}(z, q)]_{z=0}=\sqrt{\frac{2}{\pi}}\frac{1}{g_{o,r}(q)}$$

$$\frac{d}{dz}\left[Ms_r^{(2)}(z, q)\right]_{z=0}=\sqrt{\frac{2}{\pi}}f_{o,r}(q)/g_{o,r}(q)$$

$$Ms_r^{(2)}(z, q)=-g_{o,r}(q)\sqrt{\frac{2}{\pi}}$$

The functions $f_{o,r}$, $g_{o,r}$, $f_{e,r}$, $g_{e,r}$ are tabulated in [20.58] for $q\leq 25$.

20.9. Asymptotic Representations

The representations given below are applicable to the *characteristic solutions*, for real values of q, unless otherwise noted. The Floquet exponent ν is defined below, as in [20.36] to be as follows:

In solutions associated with a_r: $\nu=r$
In solutions associated with b_r: $\nu=-r$.

For the functions defined in **20.6.7–20.6.10:**

20.9.1

$$\begin{matrix} Mc_r^{(3)}(z, q) \\ (-1)^r Ms_r^{(3)}(z, q) \end{matrix} \sim \frac{e^{i\left(2\sqrt{q}\cosh z-\frac{\nu\pi}{2}-\frac{\pi}{4}\right)}}{\pi^{\frac{1}{2}}q^{1/4}(\cosh z-\sigma)^{\frac{1}{2}}}\sum_{m=0}^{\infty}\frac{D_m}{[-4i\sqrt{q}(\cosh z-\sigma)]^m}$$

where $D_{-1}=D_{-2}=0$; $D_0=1$, and the coefficients D_m are obtainable from the following recurrence formula:

20.9.2

$$(m+1)D_{m+1}+\left[\left(m+\frac{1}{2}\right)^2-\left(m+\frac{1}{4}\right)8i\sqrt{q}\,\sigma+2q-a\right]D_m+\left(m-\frac{1}{2}\right)[16q(1-\sigma^2)-8i\sqrt{q}\,\sigma m]D_{m-1}+4q(2m-3)(2m-1)(1-\sigma^2)D_{m-2}=0$$

20.9.3

$$\begin{matrix} Mc_r^{(4)}(z, q) \\ (-1)^r Ms_r^{(4)}(z, q) \end{matrix} \sim \frac{e^{-i\left[2\sqrt{q}\cosh z-\frac{1}{2}\nu\pi-\frac{1}{4}\pi\right]}}{\pi^{\frac{1}{2}}q^{1/4}(\cosh z-\sigma)^{\frac{1}{2}}}\sum_{m=0}^{\infty}\frac{d_m}{[4i\sqrt{q}(\cosh z-\sigma)]^m}$$

$d_{-1}=d_{-2}=0$; $d_0=1$, and

20.9.4

$$(m+1)d_{m+1}+\left[\left(m+\frac{1}{2}\right)^2+\left(m+\frac{1}{4}\right)8i\sqrt{q}\,\sigma+2q-a\right]d_m+\left(m-\frac{1}{2}\right)[16q(1-\sigma^2)+8i\sqrt{q}\,\sigma m]d_{m-1}+4q(2m-3)(2m-1)(1-\sigma^2)d_{m-2}=0.$$

In the above

$$-2\pi<\arg\sqrt{q}\cosh z<\pi$$

$$|\cosh z-\sigma|>|\sigma\pm 1|,\ \mathscr{R}z>0,$$

but σ is otherwise arbitrary. If $\sigma^2=1$, **20.9.2** and **20.9.4** become three-term recurrence relations.

Formulas **20.9.1** and **20.9.3** are valid for arbitrary a, q, provided ν is also known; they give multiples of **20.4.12,** normalized so as to approach the corresponding Hankel functions $H_\nu^{(1)}(\sqrt{q}e^z)$, $H_\nu^{(2)}(\sqrt{q}e^z)$, as $z\to\infty$. See [20.36], section **2.63.** The formula is especially useful if $|\cosh z|$is large and q is not too large; thus if $\sigma=-1$, the absolute ratio of two successive terms in the expansion is essentially

$$\left|\left(\frac{\sqrt{q}}{m}+\frac{m}{4\sqrt{q}}+2\right)/(\cosh z+1)\right|.$$

If a, q, z, ν are real, the real and imaginary components of $Mc_r^{(3)}(z,q)$ are $Mc_r^{(1)}(z,q)$ and $Mc_r^{(2)}(z,q)$, respectively; similarly for the components of $Ms_r^{(3)}(z,q)$. If the parameters are complex

20.9.5 $$Mc_r^{(1)}(z,q)=\tfrac{1}{2}\,[Mc_r^{(3)}(z,q)+Mc_r^{(4)}(z,q)]$$

20.9.6 $$Mc_r^{(2)}(z,q)=-\frac{i}{2}\,[Mc_r^{(3)}(z,q)-Mc_r^{(4)}(z,q)]$$

Replacing c by s in the above will yield corresponding relations among $Ms_r^{(j)}(z,q)$.

Formulas in which the parameter a does not enter explicitly:

Goldstein's Expansions

20.9.7

$$Mc_r^{(3)}(z,q)\sim iMs_{r+1}^{(3)}(z,q)\approx[F_0(z)-iF_1(z)]e^{i\phi}/\pi^{\frac{1}{2}}q^{\frac{1}{4}}(\cosh z)^{\frac{1}{2}}$$

where

20.9.8

$$\phi=2\sqrt{q}\sinh z-\frac{1}{2}(2r+1)\arctan\sinh z,$$

$$\mathscr{R}z>0,\ q>>1,\ w=2r+1$$

20.9.9

$$F_0(z)\sim 1+\frac{w}{8\sqrt{q}\cosh^2 z}+\frac{1}{2048q}\left[\frac{w^4+86w^2+105}{\cosh^4 z}-\frac{w^4+22w^2+57}{\cosh^2 z}\right]+\frac{1}{16384q^{3/2}}\left[\frac{-(w^5+14w^3+33w)}{\cosh^2 z}-\frac{(2w^5+124w^3+1122w)}{\cosh^4 z}+\frac{3w^5+290w^3+1627w}{\cosh^6 z}\right]+\ldots$$

20.9.10

$$F_1(z)\sim\frac{\sinh z}{\cosh^2 z}\left[\frac{w^2+3}{32\sqrt{q}}+\frac{1}{512q}\left(w^3+3w+\frac{4w^3+44w}{\cosh^2 z}\right)+\frac{1}{16384q^{3/2}}\left\{5w^4+34w^2+9-\frac{(w^6-47w^4+667w^2+2835)}{12\cosh^2 z}+\frac{(w^6+505w^4+12139w^2+10395)}{12\cosh^4 z}\right\}\right]+\ldots$$

See [20.18] for details and an added term in $q^{-5/2}$; a correction to the latter is noted in [20.58].

The expansions **20.9.7** are especially useful when q is large and z is bounded away from zero. The order of magnitude of $Mc_r^2(0,q)$ cannot be obtained from the expansion. The expansion can also be used, with some success, for $z=ix$, when q is large, if $|\cos x|>>0$; they fail at $x=\frac{1}{2}\pi$. Thus, if q, x are real, one obtains

20.9.11

$$ce_r(x,q)\sim\frac{ce_r(0,q)2^{r-\frac{1}{2}}}{F_0(0)}\{W_1[P_0(x)-P_1(x)]+W_2[P_0(x)+P_1(x)]\}$$

20.9.12

$$se_{r+1}(x,q)\sim se'_{r+1}(0,q)\tau_{r+1}\{W_1[P_0(x)-P_1(x)]-W_2[P_0(x)+P_1(x)]\}$$

In the above, $P_0(x)$ and $P_1(x)$ are obtainable from $F_0(z)$, $F_1(x)$ in **20.9.9–20.9.10** by replacing $\cosh z$ with $\cos x$ and $\sinh z$ with $\sin x$. Thus $P_0(x)=F_0(ix)$; $P_1(x)=-iF_1(ix)$:

20.9.13

$$W_1=e^{2\sqrt{q}\sin x}\,[\cos(\tfrac{1}{2}x+\tfrac{1}{4}\pi)]^{2r+1}/(\cos x)^{r+1}$$

$$W_2=e^{-2\sqrt{q}\sin x}\,[\sin(\tfrac{1}{2}x+\tfrac{1}{4}\pi)]^{2r+1}/(\cos x)^{r+1}$$

20.9.14

$$\tau_{r+1}\sim 2^{r-\frac{1}{2}}\bigg/\left[2\sqrt{q}-\tfrac{1}{4}w-\frac{(2w^2+3)}{64\sqrt{q}}-\frac{(7w^3+47w)}{1024q}-\ldots\right]$$

See **20.9.23–20.9.24** for expressions relating to $ce_r(0,q)$ and $se_r'(0,q)$. When $|\cos x|>\sqrt{4r+2}/q^{\frac{1}{4}}$, **20.9.11–20.9.12** are useful. The approximations become poorer as r increases.

Expansions in Terms of Parabolic Cylinder Functions

(Good for angles close to $\frac{1}{2}\pi$, for large values of q, especially when $|\cos x|<2^{\frac{1}{2}}/q^{\frac{1}{4}}$.) Due to Sips [20.44–20.46].

20.9.15 $$ce_r(x,q)\sim C_r[Z_0(\alpha)+Z_1(\alpha)]$$

20.9.16

$$se_{r+1}(x,q)\sim S_r[Z_0(\alpha)-Z_1(\alpha)]\sin x,\qquad \alpha=2q^{\frac{1}{4}}\cos x.$$

Let $D_k=D_k(\alpha)=(-1)^k e^{\frac{1}{4}\alpha^2}\dfrac{d^k}{d\alpha^k}e^{-\frac{1}{2}\alpha^2}$.

20.9.17

$$Z_0(\alpha)\sim D_r+\frac{1}{4q^{\frac{1}{2}}}\left[-\frac{D_{r+4}}{16}+\frac{3}{2}\binom{r}{4}D_{r-4}\right]$$
$$+\frac{1}{16q}\left[\frac{D_{r+8}}{512}-\frac{(r+2)D_{r+4}}{16}+\frac{3}{2}(r-1)\binom{r}{4}D_{r-4}\right.$$
$$\left.+\frac{315}{4}\binom{r}{8}D_{r-8}\right]+\ldots$$

20.9.18

$$Z_1(\alpha)\sim\frac{1}{4q^{\frac{1}{2}}}\left[-\frac{1}{4}D_{r+2}-\frac{r(r-1)}{4}D_{r-2}\right]$$
$$+\frac{1}{16q}\left[\frac{D_{r+6}}{64}+\frac{(r^2-25r-36)}{64}D_{r+2}\right.$$
$$\left.+\frac{r(r-1)(-r^2-27r+10)}{64}D_{r-2}-\frac{45}{4}\binom{r}{6}D_{r-6}+\ldots\right]$$

20.9.19

$$C_r\sim\left(\frac{\pi}{2}\right)^{\frac{1}{4}}q^{\frac{1}{8}}/(r!)^{\frac{1}{2}}\left[1+\frac{2r+1}{8q^{\frac{1}{2}}}\right.$$
$$\left.+\frac{r^4+2r^3+263r^2+262r+108}{2048q}+\frac{f_1}{16384q^{\frac{3}{2}}}+\ldots\right]^{-\frac{1}{2}}$$
$$f_1=6r^5+15r^4+1280r^3+1905r^2+1778r+572$$

20.9.20

$$S_r\sim\left(\frac{\pi}{2}\right)^{\frac{1}{4}}q^{\frac{1}{8}}/(r!)^{\frac{1}{2}}\left[1-\frac{2r+1}{8q^{\frac{1}{2}}}\right.$$
$$\left.+\frac{r^4+2r^3-121r^2-122r-84}{2048q}+\frac{f_2}{16384q^{\frac{3}{2}}}+\ldots\right]^{-\frac{1}{2}}$$
$$f_2=2r^5+5r^4-416r^3-629r^2-1162r-476$$

It should be noted that **20.9.15** is also valid as an approximation for $se_{r+1}(x,q)$, but **20.9.16** may give slightly better results. See [20.4.]

Explicit Expansions for Orders 0, 1, to Terms in $q^{-3/2}$ (q Large)

20.9.21 For $r=0$:

$$Z_0\sim D_0-\frac{D_4}{64\sqrt{q}}+\frac{1}{16q}\left(-\frac{D_4}{8}+\frac{D_8}{512}\right)$$
$$+\frac{1}{64q^{3/2}}\left(-\frac{99D_4}{256}+\frac{3D_8}{256}-\frac{D_{12}}{24576}\right)+\ldots$$

$$Z_1\sim\frac{-D_2}{16\sqrt{q}}+\frac{1}{16q}\left(-\frac{9D_2}{16}+\frac{D_6}{64}\right)$$
$$+\frac{1}{64q^{3/2}}\left(-\frac{61D_2}{32}+\frac{25D_6}{256}-\frac{5D_{10}}{10240}\right)+\ldots$$

20.9.22 For $r=1$:

$$Z_0\sim D_1-\frac{D_5}{64\sqrt{q}}+\frac{1}{16q}\left(-\frac{3D_5}{16}+\frac{D_9}{512}\right)$$
$$+\frac{1}{64q^{3/2}}\left(-\frac{207D_5}{256}+\frac{D_9}{64}-\frac{D_{13}}{24576}\right)+\ldots$$

$$Z_1\sim\frac{-D_3}{16\sqrt{q}}+\frac{1}{16q}\left(-\frac{15D_3}{16}+\frac{D_7}{64}\right)$$
$$+\frac{1}{64q^{3/2}}\left(-\frac{153D_3}{32}+\frac{35D_7}{256}-\frac{D_{11}}{2048}\right)+\ldots$$

Formulas Involving $ce_r(0,q)$ and $se_r(0,q)$

20.9.23

$$\frac{ce_0(0,q)}{ce_0(\frac{1}{2}\pi,q)}\sim 2\sqrt{2}\,e^{-2\sqrt{q}}\left(1+\frac{1}{16\sqrt{q}}+\frac{9}{256q}+\ldots\right)$$

$$\frac{ce_2(0,q)}{ce_2(\frac{1}{2}\pi,q)}\sim -32q\sqrt{2}\,e^{-2\sqrt{q}}\left(1-\frac{1}{16\sqrt{q}}+\frac{29}{128q}+\ldots\right)$$

$$\frac{ce_1(0,q)}{ce_1'(\frac{1}{2}\pi,q)}\sim -4\sqrt{2}e^{-2\sqrt{q}}\left(1+\frac{3}{16\sqrt{q}}+\frac{45}{256q}+\ldots\right)$$

$$\frac{ce_3(0,q)}{ce_3'(\frac{1}{2}\pi,q)}\sim \frac{64}{3}\,q\sqrt{2}\,e^{-2\sqrt{q}}\left(1-\frac{3}{16\sqrt{q}}+\frac{47}{128q}+\ldots\right)$$

20.9.24

$$\frac{se_1'(0,q)}{se_1(\frac{1}{2}\pi,q)}\sim 4\,q\sqrt{2}\,e^{-2\sqrt{q}}\left(1-\frac{3}{16\sqrt{q}}-\frac{11}{256q}+\ldots\right)$$

$$\frac{se_3'(0,q)}{se_3(\frac{1}{2}\pi,q)}\sim -64\,q\sqrt{2}\,e^{-2\sqrt{q}}\left(1-\frac{21}{16\sqrt{q}}-\frac{17}{128q}+\ldots\right)$$

$$\frac{se_2'(0,q)}{se_2'(\frac{1}{2}\pi,q)}\sim -8\,q\sqrt{2}\,e^{-2\sqrt{q}}\left(1-\frac{9}{16\sqrt{q}}-\frac{39}{256q}+\ldots\right)$$

$$\frac{se_4'(0,q)}{se_4'(\frac{1}{2}\pi,q)}\sim \frac{128}{3}\,q\sqrt{2}e^{-2\sqrt{q}}\left(1-\frac{31}{16\sqrt{q}}-\frac{15}{128q}+\ldots\right)$$

For higher orders, these ratios are increasingly more difficult to obtain. One method of estimating values at the origin is to evaluate both **20.9.11** and **20.9.15** for some x where both expansions are satisfactory, and so to use **20.9.11** as a means to solve for $ce_r(0,q)$; similarly for $se_r'(0,q)$.

Other asymptotic expansions, valid over various regions of the complex z-plane, for real values of a, q, have been given by Langer [20.25]. It is not always easy, however, to determine the linear combinations of Langer's solutions which coincide with those defined here.

20.10. Comparative Notations

	This Volume	[20.58] NBS	[20.59] Stratton-Morse, etc.	[20.36] Meixner and Schäfke	[20.30] McLachlan	[20.15] Bateman Manuscript	Comments
Parameters in **20.1.1**	a	$b=a+2q$	b	λ	a	h	
	q	$s=4q$	$c=2\sqrt{q}$	h^2	q	θ	
	a_r	$be_r=a_r+2q$	$b_r=a_r+2q$	a_r	a_r	a_r	
	b_r	$bo_r=b_r+2q$	$b'_r=b_r+2q$	b_r	b_r	b_r	
Periodic Solutions, of **20.1.1**:							
Even	$ce_r(z,q)$	$A^r\, Se_r(s,x)$	$A^r\, Se_r^{(1)}(c, \cos x)$	$ce_r(z,h^2)$	$ce_r(z,q)$	$ce_r(z,\theta)$	See Note 1.
Odd	$se_r(z,q)$	$B^r\, So_r(s,x)$	$A^r\, So_r^{(1)}(c, \cos x)$	$se_r(z,h^2)$	$se_r(z,q)$	$se_r(z,\theta)$	
Coefficients in Periodic Solutions:							
Even	$A_m^r(q)$	$A^r\, De_m^r(s)$	$A^r\, D_m^r$	A_m^r	A_m^r	A_m^r	
Odd	$B_m^r(q)$	$B^r\, Do_m^r(s)$	$B^r F_m^r$	B_m^r	B_m^r	B_m^r	
$\frac{1}{\pi}\int_0^{2\pi} y^2\,dx$, y is the Standard Solution of **20.1.1.**	1	$(A^r)^{-2}$ or $(B^r)^{-2}$	$(A^r)^{-2}$ or $(B^r)^{-2}$	1	1	1	See Note 1.
Floquet's Solutions **20.3.8**	$F_\nu(z)$			$me_\nu(z,h^2)$	$\phi(z)$		
Characteristic Exponent	ν	$\mu=i\nu$		ν	$\mu=i\nu$	$\mu=i\nu$	
Normalizations of Floquet's Solutions.	Unspecified			$\frac{1}{\pi}\int_0^\pi (me_\nu(z,h^2)me_{-\nu}(z,h^2))=1$			
Solutions of Modified Equation **20.1.2.**	$Ce_r(z,q)$	$Ag_{e,r}(s)Je_r(s,q)$	$Ag_{e,r}(s)Je_r(c, \cosh z)$	$Ce_r(z,q)$	$Ce_r(z,q)$	$Ce_r(z,\theta)$	
	$Se_r(z,q)$	$Bg_{o,r}(s)Jo_r(s,q)$	$Bg_{o,r}(s)Jo_r(c, \cosh z)$	$Se_r(z,q)$	$Se_r(z,q)$	$Se_r(z,\theta)$	
	$Mc_r^{(1)}(z,q)$	$\sqrt{\frac{2}{\pi}}\, Je_r(s,z)$	$\sqrt{\frac{2}{\pi}}\, Je_r(c, \cosh z)$	$Mc_r^{(1)}(z,h)$	$\sqrt{\frac{2}{\pi}}\, Ce_r(z,q)/Ag_{e,r}(q)$	$\sqrt{\frac{2}{\pi}}\, Ce_r(z,\theta)/Ag_{e,r}(q)$	
	$Ms_r^{(1)}(z,q)$	$\sqrt{\frac{2}{\pi}}\, Jo_r(s,z)$	$\sqrt{\frac{2}{\pi}}\, Jo_r(c, \cosh z)$	$Ms_r^{(1)}(z,h)$	$\sqrt{\frac{2}{\pi}}\, Se_r(z,q)/Bg_{o,r}(q)$	$\sqrt{\frac{2}{\pi}}\, Se_r(z,\theta)/Bg_{o,r}(q)$	
	$Mc_r^{(2)}(z,q)$	$\sqrt{\frac{2}{\pi}}\, Ne_r(s,z)$	$\sqrt{\frac{2}{\pi}}\, Ne_r(c, \cosh z)$	$Mc_r^{(2)}(z,h)$	$\sqrt{\frac{2}{\pi}}\, Fey_r(z,q)/Ag_{e,r}(q)$	$\sqrt{\frac{2}{\pi}}\, Fey_r(z,\theta)/Ag_{e,r}(q)$	
	$Ms_r^{(2)}(z,q)$	$\sqrt{\frac{2}{\pi}}\, No_r(s,z)$	$\sqrt{\frac{2}{\pi}}\, No_r(c, \cosh z)$	$Ms_r^{(2)}(z,h)$	$\sqrt{\frac{2}{\pi}}\, Gey_r(z,q)/Bg_{o,r}(q)$	$\sqrt{\frac{2}{\pi}}\, Gey_r(z,\theta)/Bg_{o,r}(q)$	
Joining Factors	$\sqrt{2/\pi}/Mc_r^{(1)}(0,q)$	$g_{e,r}(s)$	$\sqrt{2\pi}\,\lambda_r^{(e)}$	$\sqrt{2/\pi}/Mc_r^{(1)}(0,h)$	$(-1)^r p_r \sqrt{\frac{2}{\pi}}/A$	Same as [20.30]	See Note 2.
	$\sqrt{2/\pi}/\frac{d}{dz}[Ms_r^{(1)}(z,q)]_{z=0}$	$g_{o,r}(s)$	$\sqrt{2\pi}\,\lambda_r^{(0)}$	$\sqrt{2/\pi}/\frac{d}{dz}[Ms_r^{(1)}(z,h)]_{z=0}$	$(-1)^r s_r \sqrt{\frac{2}{\pi}}/B$		
	$-Mc_r^{(2)}(0,q)/Mc_r^{(1)}(0,q)$	$f_{e,r}(s)$	$-\frac{2}{\pi}\frac{K'_1}{K_1}$	$-Mc_r^{(2)}(0,h)/Mc_r^{(1)}(0,h)$	$\frac{-Fey_r(0,q)}{Ce_r(0,q)}$	Same as [20.30]	See Note 3.
	$\left[\frac{\frac{d}{dz}Ms_r^{(2)}(z,q)}{\frac{d}{dz}Ms_r^{(1)}(z,q)}\right]_{z=0}$	$f_{o,r}(s)$	$\frac{2}{\pi}\frac{K'_3}{K_3}$	Same as this volume	$\left[\frac{\frac{d}{dz}Gey_r(z,q)}{\frac{d}{dz}Se_r(z,q)}\right]_{z=0}$	Same as [20.30]	

NOTE: 1. The conversion factors A^r and B^r are tabulated in [20.58] along with the coefficients.

2. The multipliers p_r and s_r are defined in [20.30], Appendix **1**, section **3**, equations **3, 4, 5, 6.**

3. See [20.59], sections **(5.3)** and **(5.5).** In eq. **(316)** of **(5.5),** the first term should have a minus sign.

Table 20.1 CHARACTERISTIC VALUES, JOINING FACTORS, SOME CRITICAL VALUES

EVEN SOLUTIONS

r	q	a_r	$ce_r(0, q)$	$ce_r(\frac{1}{2}\pi, q)$	$(4q)^{\frac{1}{2}r} g_{e,r}(q)$	$(4q)^r f_{e,r}(q)$
0	0	0.00000 000	(-1)7.07106 781	(-1) 7.07106 78	(-1)7.97884 56	∞
	5	- 5.80004 602	(-2)4.48001 817	1.33484 87	1.97009 00	(- 3)1.86132 97
	10	- 13.93697 996	(-3)7.62651 757	1.46866 05	2.40237 95	(- 5)5.54257 96
	15	- 22.51303 776	(-3)1.93250 832	1.55010 82	2.68433 53	(- 6)3.59660 89
	20	- 31.31339 007	(-4)6.03743 829	1.60989 09	2.90011 25	(- 7)3.53093 01
	25	- 40.25677 955	(-4)2.15863 018	1.65751 03	3.07743 91	(- 8)4.53098 68
2	0	4.00000 000	1.00000 000	-1.00000 00	(1)1.27661 53	(1)8.14873 31
	5	7.44910 974	(-1)7.35294 308	(-1)-7.24488 15	(1)2.63509 89	(2)1.68665 79
	10	7.71736 985	(-1)2.45888 349	(-1)-9.26759 26	(1)7.22275 58	(1)6.89192 56
	15	5.07798 320	(-2)7.87928 278	-1.01996 62	(2)1.32067 71	(1)1.73770 48
	20	+ 1.15428 288	(-2)2.86489 431	-1.07529 32	(2)1.98201 14	4.29953 32
	25	- 3.52216 473	(-2)1.15128 663	-1.11627 90	(2)2.69191 26	1.11858 69
10	0	100.00000 000	1.00000 000	-1.00000 00	(12)1.51800 43	(23)2.30433 72
	5	100.12636 922	1.02599 503	(-1)-9.75347 49	(12)1.48332 54	(23)2.31909 77
	10	100.50677 002	1.05381 599	(-1)-9.51645 32	(12)1.45530 39	(23)2.36418 54
	15	101.14520 345	1.08410 631	(-1)-9.28548 06	(12)1.43299 34	(23)2.44213 04
	20	102.04891 602	1.11778 863	(-1)-9.05710 78	(12)1.41537 24	(23)2.55760 55
	25	103.23020 480	1.15623 992	(-1)-8.82691 92	(12)1.40118 52	(23)2.71854 15

r	q	a_r	$ce_r(0, q)$	$ce_r'(\frac{1}{2}\pi, q)$	$(4q)^{\frac{1}{2}r} g_{e,r}(q)$	$(4q)^r f_{e,r}(q)$
1	0	1.00000 000	1.00000 000	-1.00000 00	1.59576 91	2.54647 91
	5	+ 1.85818 754	(-1)2.56542 879	-3.46904 21	7.26039 84	1.02263 46
	10	- 2.39914 240	(-2)5.35987 478	-4.85043 83	(1)1.35943 49	(- 2)9.72660 12
	15	- 8.10110 513	(-2)1.50400 665	-5.76420 64	(1)1.91348 51	(- 2)1.19739 95
	20	- 14.49130 142	(-3)5.05181 376	-6.49056 58	(1)2.42144 01	(- 3)1.84066 20
	25	- 21.31489 969	(-3)1.91105 151	-7.10674 15	(1)2.89856 94	(- 4)3.33747 55
5	0	25.00000 000	1.00000 000	-5.00000 00	(4)4.90220 27	(8)4.80631 83
	5	25.54997 175	1.12480 725	-5.39248 61	(4)4.43075 22	(8)5.11270 71
	10	27.70376 873	1.25801 994	-5.32127 65	(4)4.19827 66	(8)6.83327 77
	15	31.95782 125	1.19343 223	-5.11914 99	(4)5.25017 04	(9)1.18373 72
	20	36.64498 973	(-1)9.36575 531	-5.77867 52	(4)8.96243 97	(9)1.85341 57
	25	40.05019 099	(-1)6.10694 310	-7.05988 45	(5)1.71582 55	(9)2.09679 12
15	0	225.00000 000	1.00000 000	(1) 1.50000 00	(20)5.60156 72	(40)2.09183 70
	5	225.05581 248	1.01129 373	(1) 1.51636 57	(20)5.54349 84	(40)2.09575 00
	10	225.22335 698	1.02287 828	(1) 1.53198 84	(20)5.49405 67	(40)2.10754 45
	15	225.50295 624	1.03479 365	(1) 1.54687 43	(20)5.45287 72	(40)2.12738 84
	20	225.89515 341	1.04708 434	(1) 1.56102 79	(20)5.41964 26	(40)2.15556 69
	25	226.40072 004	1.05980 044	(1) 1.57444 72	(20)5.39407 68	(40)2.19249 18

Compiled from National Bureau of Standards, Tables relating to Mathieu functions, Columbia Univ. Press, New York, N.Y., 1951

$$a_r + 2q - (4r+2)\sqrt{q}$$

$q^{-\frac{1}{2}} \backslash r$	0	1	2	5	10	15	$\langle q \rangle$
0.16	-0.25532 994	-1.30027 212	-3.45639 483	-17.84809 551	-76.04295 314	- 80.93485 048	39
0.12	-0.25393 098	-1.28658 972	-3.39777 782	-16.92019 225	-76.84607 855	-141.64507 841	69
0.08	-0.25257 851	-1.27371 191	-3.34441 938	-16.25305 645	-63.58155 264	-162.30500 052	156
0.04	-0.25126 918	-1.26154 161	-3.29538 745	-15.70968 373	-58.63500 546	-132.08298 271	625
0.00	-0.25000 000	-1.25000 000	-3.25000 000	-15.25000 000	-55.25000 000	-120.25000 000	∞

For $g_{e,r}$ and $f_{e,r}$ see **20.8.12.**

$\langle q \rangle$ = nearest integer to q.

Compiled from G. Blanch and I. Rhodes, Table of characteristic values of Mathieu's equation for large values of the parameter, Jour. Wash. Acad. Sci., **45**, 6, 1955

ODD SOLUTIONS

r	q	b_r	$se'_r(0,q)$	$se'_r(\frac{1}{2}\pi,q)$	$(4q)^{\frac{1}{2}r}g_{o,r}(q)$	$(4q)^r f_{o,r}(q)$
2	0	4.00000 000	2.00000 00	-2.00000 00	6.38307 65	(1)8.14873 31
	5	+ 2.09946 045	(-1)7.33166 22	-3.64051 79	(1)1.24474 88	(1)2.24948 08
	10	- 2.38215 824	(-1)2.48822 84	-4.86342 21	(1)1.86133 36	3.91049 85
	15	- 8.09934 680	(-2)9.18197 14	-5.76557 38	(1)2.42888 57	(- 1)7.18762 28
	20	- 14.49106 325	(-2)3.70277 78	-6.49075 22	(1)2.95502 89	(- 1)1.47260 95
	25	- 21.31486 062	(-2)1.60562 17	-7.10677 19	(1)3.44997 83	(- 2)3.33750 27
10	0	100.00000 000	(1)1.00000 00	(1)-1.00000 00	(11)1.51800 43	(23)2.30433 72
	5	100.12636 922	9.73417 32	(1)-1.02396 46	(11)1.56344 50	(23)2.31909 77
	10	100.50676 946	9.44040 54	(1)-1.04539 48	(11)1.62453 03	(23)2.36418 52
	15	101.14517 229	9.11575 13	(1)-1.06429 00	(11)1.70421 18	(23)2.44211 78
	20	102.04839 286	8.75554 51	(1)-1.08057 24	(11)1.80695 19	(23)2.55740 30
	25	103.22568 004	8.35267 84	(1)-1.09413 54	(11)1.93959 86	(23)2.71681 11

r	q	b_r	$se'_r(0,q)$	$se_r(\frac{1}{2}\pi,q)$	$(4q)^{\frac{1}{2}r}g_{o,r}(q)$	$(4q)^r f_{o,r}(q)$
1	0	+ 1.00000 000	1.00000 00	1.00000 00	1.59576 91	2.54647 91
	5	- 5.79008 060	(-1)1.74675 40	1.33743 39	2.27041 76	(- 2)3.74062 82
	10	- 13.93655 248	(-2)4.40225 66	1.46875 57	2.63262 99	(- 3)2.21737 88
	15	- 22.51300 350	(-2)1.39251 35	1.55011 51	2.88561 87	(- 4)2.15798 83
	20	- 31.31338 617	(-3)5.07788 49	1.60989 16	3.08411 21	(- 4)2.82474 71
	25	- 40.25677 898	(-3)2.04435 94	1.65751 04	3.24945 50	(- 6)4.53098 74
5	0	25.00000 000	5.00000 00	1.00000 00	(3)9.80440 55	(8)4.80631 83
	5	25.51081 605	4.33957 00	(-1) 9.06077 93	(4)1.14793 21	(8)5.05257 20
	10	26.76642 636	3.40722 68	(-1) 8.46038 43	(4)1.52179 77	(8)5.46799 57
	15	27.96788 060	2.41166 65	(-1) 8.37949 34	(4)2.20680 20	(8)5.27524 17
	20	28.46822 133	1.56889 69	(-1) 8.63543 12	(4)3.27551 12	(8)4.26215 66
	25	28.06276 590	(-1)9.64071 62	(-1) 8.99268 33	(4)4.76476 62	(8)2.94147 89
15	0	225.00000 000	(1)1.50000 00	-1.00000 00	(19)3.73437 81	(40)2.09183 70
	5	225.05581 248	(1)1.48287 89	(-1)-9.88960 70	(19)3.78055 49	(40)2.09575 00
	10	225.22335 698	(1)1.46498 60	(-1)-9.78142 35	(19)3.83604 43	(40)2.10754 45
	15	225.50295 624	(1)1.44630 01	(-1)-9.67513 70	(19)3.90140 52	(40)2.12738 84
	20	225.89515 341	(1)1.42679 46	(-1)-9.57045 25	(19)3.97732 29	(40)2.15556 69
	25	226.40072 004	(1)1.40643 73	(-1)-9.46708 70	(19)4.06462 83	(40)2.19249 18

$$b_r+2q-(4r-2)\sqrt{q}$$

$q^{-\frac{1}{2}}\backslash r$	1	2	5	10	15	<q>
0.16	-0.25532 994	-1.30027 164	-11.53046 855	-51.32546 875	- 55.93485 112	39
0.12	-0.25393 098	-1.28658 971	-11.12574 983	-56.10964 961	-108.31442 060	69
0.08	-0.25257 851	-1.27371 191	-10.78895 146	-51.15347 975	-132.59692 424	156
0.04	-0.25126 918	-1.26154 161	-10.50135 748	-47.72149 533	-114.76358 461	625
0.00	-0.25000 000	-1.25000 000	-10.25000 000	-45.25000 000	-105.25000 000	∞

For $g_{o,r}$ and $f_{o,r}$ see **20.8.12.**

<q> = nearest integer to q.

Table 20.2 COEFFICIENTS A_m AND B_m

A_m

$q=5$

$m\backslash r$	0	2	10
0	+0.54061 2446	+0.43873 7166	+0.00000 1679
2	-0.62711 5414	+0.65364 0260	+0.00003 3619
4	+0.14792 7090	-0.42657 8935	+0.00064 2987
6	-0.01784 8061	+0.07588 5673	+0.01078 4807
8	+0.00128 2863	-0.00674 1769	+0.13767 5121
10	-0.00006 0723	+0.00036 4942	+0.98395 5640
12	+0.00000 2028	-0.00001 3376	-0.11280 6780
14	-0.00000 0050	+0.00000 0355	+0.00589 2962
16	+0.00000 0001	-0.00000 0007	-0.00018 9166
18			+0.00000 4226
20			-0.00000 0071
22			+0.00000 0001

$m\backslash r$	1	5	15
1	+0.76246 3686	+0.07768 5798	0.00000 0000
3	-0.63159 6319	+0.30375 1030	+0.00000 0002
5	+0.13968 4806	+0.92772 8396	+0.00000 0106
7	-0.01491 5596	-0.20170 6148	+0.00000 4227
9	+0.00094 4842	+0.01827 4579	+0.00014 8749
11	-0.00003 9702	-0.00095 9038	+0.00428 1393
13	+0.00000 1189	+0.00003 3457	+0.08895 2014
15	-0.00000 0027	-0.00000 0839	+0.99297 4092
17	+0.00000 0001	+0.00000 0016	-0.07786 7946
19			+0.00286 6409
21			-0.00006 6394
23			+0.00000 1092
25			-0.00000 0014

$q=25$

$m\backslash r$	0	2	10
0	+0.42974 1038	+0.33086 5777	+0.00502 6361
2	-0.69199 9610	-0.04661 4551	+0.02075 4891
4	+0.36554 4890	-0.64770 5862	+0.07232 7761
6	-0.13057 5523	+0.55239 9372	+0.23161 1726
8	+0.03274 5863	-0.22557 4897	+0.55052 4391
10	-0.00598 3606	+0.05685 2843	+0.63227 5658
12	+0.00082 3792	-0.00984 6277	-0.46882 9197
14	-0.00008 7961	+0.00124 8919	+0.13228 7155
16	+0.00000 7466	-0.00012 1205	-0.02206 0893
18	-0.00000 0514	+0.00000 9296	+0.00252 2374
20	+0.00000 0029	-0.00000 0578	-0.00021 3672
22	-0.00000 0001	+0.00000 0030	+0.00001 4078
24		-0.00000 0001	-0.00000 0746
26			+0.00000 0032
28			-0.00000 0001

$m\backslash r$	1	5	15
1	+0.39125 2265	+0.65659 0398	+0.00000 4658
3	-0.74048 2467	+0.36900 8820	+0.00003 7337
5	+0.50665 3803	-0.19827 8625	+0.00032 0026
7	-0.19814 2336	-0.48837 4067	+0.00254 0806
9	+0.05064 0536	+0.37311 2810	+0.01770 9603
11	-0.00910 8920	-0.12278 1866	+0.10045 8755
13	+0.00121 2864	+0.02445 3933	+0.40582 7402
15	-0.00012 4121	-0.00335 1335	+0.83133 2650
17	+0.00001 0053	+0.00033 9214	-0.35924 8831
19	-0.00000 0660	-0.00002 6552	+0.06821 6074
21	+0.00000 0036	+0.00000 1661	-0.00802 4550
23	-0.00000 0002	-0.00000 0085	+0.00066 6432
25		+0.00000 0004	-0.00004 1930
27			+0.00000 2090
29			-0.00000 0085
31			+0.00000 0003

B_m

$q=5$

$m\backslash r$	2	10
2	+0.93342 9442	+0.00003 3444
4	-0.35480 3915	+0.00064 2976
6	+0.05296 3730	+0.01078 4807
8	-0.00429 5885	+0.13767 5120
10	+0.00021 9797	+0.98395 5640
12	-0.00000 7752	-0.11280 6780
14	+0.00000 0200	+0.00589 2962
16	-0.00000 0004	-0.00018 9166
18		+0.00000 4227
20		-0.00000 0070
22		+0.00000 0001

$m\backslash r$	1	5	15
1	+0.94001 9024	+0.05038 2462	0.00000 0000
3	-0.33654 1963	+0.29736 5513	+0.00000 0002
5	+0.05547 7529	+0.93156 6997	+0.00000 0106
7	-0.00508 9553	-0.20219 3638	+0.00000 4227
9	+0.00029 3879	+0.01830 5721	+0.00014 8749
11	-0.00001 1602	-0.00096 0277	+0.00428 1392
13	+0.00000 0332	+0.00003 3493	+0.08895 2014
15	-0.00000 0007	-0.00000 0842	+0.99297 4092
17		+0.00000 0017	-0.07786 7946
19			+0.00286 6409
21			-0.00006 6394
23			+0.00000 1093
25			-0.00000 0013

$q=25$

$m\backslash r$	2	10
2	+0.65743 9912	+0.01800 3596
4	-0.66571 9990	+0.07145 6762
6	+0.33621 0033	+0.23131 0990
8	-0.10507 3258	+0.55054 4783
10	+0.02236 2380	+0.63250 8750
12	-0.00344 2304	-0.46893 3949
14	+0.00040 0182	+0.13230 9765
16	-0.00003 6315	-0.02206 3990
18	+0.00000 2640	+0.00252 2676
20	-0.00000 0157	-0.00021 3694
22	+0.00000 0008	+0.00001 4079
24		-0.00000 0746
26		+0.00000 0033

$m\backslash r$	1	5	15
1	+0.81398 3846	+0.30117 4196	+0.00000 3717
3	-0.52931 0219	+0.62719 8468	+0.00003 7227
5	+0.22890 0813	+0.17707 1306	+0.00032 0013
7	-0.06818 2972	-0.60550 5349	+0.00254 0804
9	+0.01453 0886	+0.33003 2984	+0.01770 9603
11	-0.00229 5765	-0.09333 5984	+0.10045 8755
13	+0.00027 7422	+0.01694 2545	+0.40582 7403
15	-0.00002 6336	-0.00217 7430	+0.83133 2650
17	+0.00000 2009	+0.00021 0135	-0.35924 8830
19	-0.00000 0126	-0.00001 5851	+0.06821 6074
21	+0.00000 0007	+0.00000 0962	-0.00802 4551
23		-0.00000 0048	+0.00066 6432
25		+0.00000 0002	-0.00004 1930
27			+0.00000 2090
29			-0.00000 0086
31			+0.00000 0003

For A_m and B_m see **20.2.3–20.2.11**

Compiled from National Bureau of Standards, Tables relating to Mathieu functions, Columbia Univ. Press, New York, N.Y., 1951

21.1. Definition of Elliptical Coordinates

21.1.1 $$\xi=\frac{r_1+r_2}{2f};\quad \eta=\frac{r_1-r_2}{2f}$$

r_1 and r_2 are the distances to the foci of a family of confocal ellipses and hyperbolas; $2f$ is the distance between foci.

21.1.2 $$a=f\xi,\ b=f\sqrt{\xi^2-1},\qquad e=\frac{f}{a}$$

a=semi-major axis; b=semi-minor axis; e=eccentricity.

Equation of Family of Confocal Ellipses

21.1.3 $$\frac{x^2}{\xi^2}+\frac{y^2}{\xi^2-1}=f^2 \qquad (1<\xi<\infty)$$

Equation of Family of Confocal Hyperbolas

21.1.4 $$\frac{x^2}{\eta^2}-\frac{y^2}{1-\eta^2}=f^2 \qquad (-1<\eta<1)$$

Relations Between Cartesian and Elliptical Coordinates

21.1.5 $$x=f\xi\eta;\ y=f\sqrt{(\xi^2-1)(1-\eta^2)}$$

21.2. Definition of Prolate Spheroidal Coordinates

If the system of confocal ellipses and hyberbolas referred to in **21.1.3** and **21.1.4** revolves around the major axis, then

21.2.1 $$\frac{x^2}{\xi^2}+\frac{r^2}{\xi^2-1}=f^2;\qquad \frac{x^2}{\eta^2}-\frac{r^2}{1-\eta^2}=f^2$$

$$y=r\cos\phi;\quad z=r\sin\phi;\quad 0\leq\phi\leq 2\pi$$

where ξ, η and ϕ are prolate spheroidal coordinates.

Relations Between Cartesian and Prolate Spheroidal Coordinates

21.2.2

$$x=f\xi\eta;\ y=f\sqrt{(\xi^2-1)(1-\eta^2)}\cos\phi;$$
$$z=f\sqrt{(\xi^2-1)(1-\eta^2)}\sin\phi$$

21.3. Definition of Oblate Spheroidal Coordinates

If the system of confocal ellipses and hyperbolas referred to in **21.1.3** and **21.1.4** revolves around the minor axis, then

21.3.1 $$\frac{r^2}{\xi^2}+\frac{y^2}{\xi^2-1}=f^2;\qquad \frac{r^2}{\eta^2}-\frac{y^2}{1-\eta^2}=f^2$$

$$z=r\cos\phi;\ x=r\sin\phi;\ 0\leq\phi\leq 2\pi$$

where ξ, η and ϕ are oblate spheroidal coordinates.

Relations Between Cartesian and Oblate Spheroidal Coordinates

21.3.2

$$x=f\xi\eta\sin\phi;\ y=f\sqrt{(\xi^2-1)(1-\eta^2)};\ z=f\xi\eta\cos\varphi$$

21.4. Laplacian in Spheroidal Coordinates

21.4.1

$$\nabla^2=\frac{1}{h_\xi h_\eta h_\phi}\left[\frac{\partial}{\partial\xi}\left(\frac{h_\eta h_\phi}{h_\xi}\frac{\partial}{\partial\xi}\right)+\frac{\partial}{\partial\eta}\left(\frac{h_\xi h_\phi}{h_\eta}\frac{\partial}{\partial\eta}\right)+\frac{\partial}{\partial\phi}\left(\frac{h_\xi h_\eta}{h_\phi}\frac{\partial}{\partial\phi}\right)\right]$$

$$h_\xi^2=\left(\frac{\partial x}{\partial\xi}\right)^2+\left(\frac{\partial y}{\partial\xi}\right)^2+\left(\frac{\partial z}{\partial\xi}\right)^2$$

$$h_\eta^2=\left(\frac{\partial x}{\partial\eta}\right)^2+\left(\frac{\partial y}{\partial\eta}\right)^2+\left(\frac{\partial z}{\partial\eta}\right)^2$$

$$h_\phi^2=\left(\frac{\partial x}{\partial\phi}\right)^2+\left(\frac{\partial y}{\partial\phi}\right)^2+\left(\frac{\partial z}{\partial\phi}\right)^2$$

Metric Coefficients for Prolate Spheroidal Coordinates

21.4.2

$$h_\xi=f\sqrt{\frac{\xi^2-\eta^2}{\xi^2-1}};\ h_\eta=f\sqrt{\frac{\xi^2-\eta^2}{1-\eta^2}};\ h_\phi=f\sqrt{(\xi^2-1)(1-\eta^2)}$$

Metric Coefficients for Oblate Spheroidal Coordinates

21.4.3

$$h_\xi=f\sqrt{\frac{\xi^2-\eta^2}{\xi^2-1}};\ h_\eta=f\sqrt{\frac{\xi^2-\eta^2}{1-\eta^2}};\ h_\phi=f\xi\eta$$

21.5. Wave Equation in Prolate and Oblate Spheroidal Coordinates

Wave Equation in Prolate Spheroidal Coordinates

21.5.1

$$\nabla^2\Phi+k^2\Phi=\frac{\partial}{\partial\xi}\left[(\xi^2-1)\frac{\partial\Phi}{\partial\xi}\right]+\frac{\partial}{\partial\eta}\left[(1-\eta^2)\frac{\partial\Phi}{\partial\eta}\right]$$
$$+\frac{\xi^2-\eta^2}{(\xi^2-1)(1-\eta^2)}\frac{\partial^2\Phi}{\partial\phi^2}+c^2(\xi^2-\eta^2)\Phi=0$$

$$\left(c=\frac{1}{2}fk\right)$$

Wave Equation in Oblate Spheroidal Coordinates

21.5.2

$$\nabla^2\Phi+k^2\Phi=\frac{\partial}{\partial\xi}\left[(\xi^2+1)\frac{\partial\Phi}{\partial\xi}\right]+\frac{\partial}{\partial\eta}\left[(1-\eta^2)\frac{\partial\Phi}{\partial\eta}\right]$$
$$+\frac{\xi^2+\eta^2}{(\xi^2+1)(1-\eta^2)}\frac{\partial^2\Phi}{\partial\phi^2}+c^2(\xi^2+\eta^2)\Phi=0$$
$$\left(c=\frac{1}{2}fk\right)$$

21.5.2 may be obtained from **21.5.1** by the transformations

$$\xi\rightarrow\pm i\xi,\ c\rightarrow\mp ic.$$

21.6. Differential Equations for Radial and Angular Prolate Spheroidal Wave Functions

If in **21.5.1** we put

$$\Phi=R_{mn}(c,\xi)S_{mn}(c,\eta)\begin{matrix}\cos\\ \sin\end{matrix}\ m\phi$$

then the "radial solution" $R_{mn}(c,\ \xi)$ and the "angular solution" $S_{mn}(c,\ \eta)$ satisfy the differential equations

21.6.1

$$\frac{d}{d\xi}\left[(\xi^2-1)\frac{d}{d\xi}R_{mn}(c,\xi)\right]-\left(\lambda_{mn}-c^2\xi^2+\frac{m^2}{\xi^2-1}\right)R_{mn}(c,\xi)=0$$

21.6.2

$$\frac{d}{d\eta}\left[(1-\eta^2)\frac{d}{d\eta}S_{mn}(c,\eta)\right]+\left(\lambda_{mn}-c^2\eta^2-\frac{m^2}{1-\eta^2}\right)S_{mn}(c,\eta)=0$$

where the separation constants (or eigenvalues) λ_{mn} are to be determined so that $R_{mn}(c,\ \xi)$ and $S_{mn}(c,\ \eta)$ are finite at $\xi=\pm1$ and $\eta=\pm1$ respectively.

(**21.6.1** and **21.6.2** are identical. Radial and angular prolate spheroidal functions satisfy the same differential equation over different ranges of the variable.)

Differential Equations for Radial and Angular Oblate Spheroidal Functions

21.6.3

$$\frac{d}{d\xi}\left[(\xi^2+1)\frac{d}{d\xi}R_{mn}(c,\xi)\right]-\left(\lambda_{mn}-c^2\xi^2-\frac{m^2}{\xi^2+1}\right)R_{mn}(c,\xi)=0$$

21.6.4

$$\frac{d}{d\eta}\left[(1-\eta^2)\frac{d}{d\eta}S_{mn}(c,\eta)\right]+\left(\lambda_{mn}+c^2\eta^2-\frac{m^2}{1-\eta^2}\right)S_{mn}(c,\eta)=0$$

(**21.6.3** may be obtained from **21.6.1** by the transformations $\xi\rightarrow\pm i\xi,\ c\rightarrow\mp ic$; **21.6.4** may be obtained from **21.6.2** by the transformation $c\rightarrow\mp ic$.)

21.7. Prolate Angular Functions

21.7.1

$$S_{mn}^{(1)}(c,\eta)=\sum_{r=0,1}^{\infty}{}' d_r^{mn}(c)P_{m+r}^m(\eta)$$

=Prolate angular function of the first kind

21.7.2

$$S_{mn}^{(2)}(c,\eta)=\sum_{r=-\infty}^{\infty}{}' d_r^{mn}(c)Q_{m+r}^m(\eta)$$

=Prolate angular function of the second kind

($P_n^m(\eta)$ and $Q_n^m(\eta)$ are associated Legendre functions of the first and second kinds respectively. However, for $-1\leq z\leq1$, $P_n^m(z)=(1-z^2)^{m/2}d^mP_n(z)/dz^m$ (see **8.6.6**). The summation is extended over even values or odd values of r.)

Recurrence Relations Between the Coefficients

21.7.3

$$\alpha_kd_{k+2}+(\beta_k-\lambda_{mn})d_k+\gamma_kd_{k-2}=0$$

$$\alpha_k=\frac{(2m+k+2)(2m+k+1)c^2}{(2m+2k+3)(2m+2k+5)}$$

$$\beta_k=(m+k)(m+k+1)+\frac{2(m+k)(m+k+1)-2m^2-1}{(2m+2k-1)(2m+2k+3)}c^2$$

$$\gamma_k=\frac{k(k-1)c^2}{(2m+2k-3)(2m+2k-1)}$$

Transcendental Equation for λ_{mn}

21.7.4

$$U(\lambda_{mn})=U_1(\lambda_{mn})+U_2(\lambda_{mn})=0$$

$$U_1(\lambda_{mn})=\gamma_r^m-\lambda_{mn}-\frac{\beta_r^m}{\gamma_{r-2}^m-\lambda_{mn}-}\ \frac{\beta_{r-2}^m}{\gamma_{r-4}^m-\lambda_{mn}-}\ \cdots$$

$$U_2(\lambda_{mn})=-\frac{\beta_{r+2}^m}{\gamma_{r+2}^m-\lambda_{mn}-}\ \frac{\beta_{r+4}^m}{\gamma_{r+4}^m-\lambda_{mn}-}\ \cdots$$

$$\beta_k^m=\frac{k(k-1)(2m+k)(2m+k-1)c^4}{(2m+2k-1)^2(2m+2k+1)(2m+2k-3)}\qquad(k\geq2)$$

$$\gamma_k^m=(m+k)(m+k+1)+\tfrac{1}{2}c^2\left[1-\frac{4m^2-1}{(2m+2k-1)(2m+2k+3)}\right]\qquad(k\geq0)$$

(The choice of r in **21.7.4** is arbitrary.)

Power Series Expansion for λ_{mn}

21.7.5

$$\lambda_{mn}=\sum_{k=0}^{\infty} l_{2k}c^{2k}$$

$$l_0=n(n+1)$$

$$l_2=\frac{1}{2}\left[1-\frac{(2m-1)(2m+1)}{(2n-1)(2n+3)}\right]$$

$$l_4=\frac{-(n-m+1)(n-m+2)(n+m+1)(n+m+2)}{2(2n+1)(2n+3)^3(2n+5)}+\frac{(n-m-1)(n-m)(n+m-1)(n+m)}{2(2n-3)(2n-1)^3(2n+1)}$$

$$l_6=(4m^2-1)\left[\frac{(n-m+1)(n-m+2)(n+m+1)(n+m+2)}{(2n-1)(2n+1)(2n+3)^5(2n+5)(2n+7)}-\frac{(n-m-1)(n-m)(n+m-1)(n+m)}{(2n-5)(2n-3)(2n-1)^5(2n+1)(2n+3)}\right]$$

$$l_8=2(4m^2-1)^2A+\frac{1}{16}B+\frac{1}{8}C+\frac{1}{2}D$$

$$A=\frac{(n-m-1)(n-m)(n+m-1)(n+m)}{(2n-5)^2(2n-3)(2n-1)^7(2n+1)(2n+3)^2}-\frac{(n-m+1)(n-m+2)(n+m+1)(n+m+2)}{(2n-1)^2(2n+1)(2n+3)^7(2n+5)(2n+7)^2}$$

$$B=\frac{(n-m-3)(n-m-2)(n-m-1)(n-m)(n+m-3)(n+m-2)(n+m-1)(n+m)}{(2n-7)(2n-5)^2(2n-3)^3(2n-1)^4(2n+1)}$$
$$-\frac{(n-m+1)(n-m+2)(n-m+3)(n-m+4)(n+m+1)(n+m+2)(n+m+3)(n+m+4)}{(2n+1)(2n+3)^4(2n+5)^3(2n+7)^2(2n+9)}$$

$$C=\frac{(n-m+1)^2(n-m+2)^2(n+m+1)^2(n+m+2)^2}{(2n+1)^2(2n+3)^7(2n+5)^2}-\frac{(n-m-1)^2(n-m)^2(n+m-1)^2(n+m)^2}{(2n-3)^2(2n-1)^7(2n+1)^2}$$

$$D=\frac{(n-m-1)(n-m)(n-m+1)(n-m+2)(n+m-1)(n+m)(n+m+1)(n+m+2)}{(2n-3)(2n-1)^4(2n+1)^2(2n+3)^4(2n+5)}$$

Asymptotic Expansion for λ_{mn}

21.7.6

$$\lambda_{mn}(c)=cq+m^2-\frac{1}{8}(q^2+5)-\frac{q}{64c}(q^2+11-32m^2)$$
$$-\frac{1}{1024c^2}[5(q^4+26q^2+21)-384m^2(q^2+1)]$$
$$-\frac{1}{c^3}\left[\frac{1}{128^2}(33q^5+1594q^3+5621q)-\frac{m^2}{128}(37q^3+167q)+\frac{m^4}{8}q\right]$$
$$-\frac{1}{c^4}\left[\frac{1}{256^2}(63q^6+4940q^4+43327q^2+22470)-\frac{m^2}{512}(115q^4+1310q^2+735)+\frac{3m^4}{8}(q^2+1)\right]$$
$$-\frac{1}{c^5}\left[\frac{1}{1024^2}(527q^7+61529q^5+1043961q^3+2241599q)-\frac{m^2}{32\cdot 1024}(5739q^5+127550q^3+298951q)+\frac{m^4}{512}(355q^3+1505q)-\frac{m^6q}{16}\right]+O(c^{-6})$$
$$q=2(n-m)+1$$

Refinement of Approximate Values of λ_{mn}

If $\lambda_{mn}^{(1)}$ is an approximation to λ_{mn} obtained either from **21.7.5** or **21.7.6** then

21.7.7

$$\lambda_{mn}=\lambda_{mn}^{(1)}+\delta\lambda_{mn}$$

$$\delta\lambda_{mn}=\frac{U_1(\lambda_{mn}^{(1)})+U_2(\lambda_{mn}^{(1)})}{\Delta_1+\Delta_2}$$

$$\Delta_1=1+\frac{\beta_r^m}{(N_r^m)^2}+\frac{\beta_r^m\beta_{r-2}^m}{(N_r^mN_{r-2}^m)^2}+\frac{\beta_r^m\beta_{r-2}^m\beta_{r-4}^m}{(N_r^mN_{r-2}^mN_{r-4}^m)^2}+\dots$$

$$\Delta_2=\frac{(N_{r+2}^m)^2}{\beta_{r+2}^m}+\frac{(N_{r+2}^mN_{r+4}^m)^2}{\beta_{r+2}^m\beta_{r+4}^m}+\frac{(N_{r+2}^mN_{r+4}^mN_{r+6}^m)^2}{\beta_{r+2}^m\beta_{r+4}^m\beta_{r+6}^m}+\dots$$

$$N_r^m=\frac{(2m+r)(2m+r-1)c^2}{(2m+2r-1)(2m+2r+1)}\frac{d_r}{d_{r-2}}\qquad (r\geq 2)$$

$$\beta_r^m=\frac{r(r-1)(2m+r)(2m+r-1)c^4}{(2m+2r-1)^2(2m+2r+1)(2m+2r-3)}\qquad (r\geq 2)$$

Evaluation of Coefficients

Step 1. Calculate N_r^m's from

21.7.8

$$N_{r+2}^m=\gamma_r^m-\lambda_{mn}-\frac{\beta_r^m}{N_r^m} \qquad (r\geq 2)$$

$$N_2^m=\gamma_0^m-\lambda_{mn};\; N_3^m=\gamma_1^m-\lambda_{mn}$$

$$\gamma_r^m=(m+r)(m+r+1)$$
$$+\frac{1}{2}c^2\left[1-\frac{4m^2-1}{(2m+2r-1)(2m+2r+3)}\right] (r\geq 0)$$

Step 2. Calculate ratios $\frac{d_0}{d_{2r}}$ and $\frac{d_1}{d_{2p+1}}$ from

21.7.9 $$\frac{d_0}{d_{2r}}=\left(\frac{d_0}{d_2}\right)\left(\frac{d_2}{d_4}\right)\cdots\left(\frac{d_{2r-2}}{d_{2r}}\right)$$

21.7.10 $$\frac{d_1}{d_{2p+1}}=\left(\frac{d_1}{d_3}\right)\left(\frac{d_3}{d_5}\right)\cdots\left(\frac{d_{2p-1}}{d_{2p+1}}\right)$$

and the formula for N_r^m in **21.7.7.**

The coefficients d_r^{mn} are determined to within the arbitrary factor d_0 for r even and d_1 for r odd. The choice of these factors depends on the normalization scheme adopted.

Normalization of Angular Functions

Meixner-Schäfke Scheme

21.7.11 $$\int_{-1}^{1}[S_{mn}(c,\eta)]^2d\eta=\frac{2}{2n+1}\frac{(n+m)!}{(n-m)!}$$

Stratton-Morse-Chu-Little-Corbató Scheme

21.7.12 $$\sum_{r=0,1}^{\infty}{}' \frac{(r+2m)!}{r!}d_r=\frac{(n+m)!}{(n-m)!}$$

(This normalization has the effect that $S_{mn}(c,\eta)\to P_n^m(\eta)$ as $\eta\to 1$.)

Flammer Scheme [21.4]

21.7.13

$$S_{mn}(c,0)=P_n^m(0)=\frac{(-1)^{\frac{n-m}{2}}(n+m)!}{2^n\left(\frac{n-m}{2}\right)!\left(\frac{n+m}{2}\right)!} \qquad (n-m) \text{ even}$$

21.7.14

$$S'_{mn}(c,0)=P_n^{m\prime}(0)=\frac{(-1)^{\frac{n-m-1}{2}}(n+m+1)!}{2^n\left(\frac{n-m-1}{2}\right)!\left(\frac{n+m+1}{2}\right)!} \qquad (n-m) \text{ odd}$$

The above lead to the following conditions for d_r^{mn}

21.7.15

$$\sum_{r=0}^{\infty}{}' \frac{(-1)^{r/2}(r+2m)!}{2^r\left(\frac{r}{2}\right)!\left(\frac{r+2m}{2}\right)!}d_r^{mn}=\frac{(-1)^{\frac{n-m}{2}}(n+m)!}{2^{n-m}\left(\frac{n-m}{2}\right)!\left(\frac{n+m}{2}\right)!} \qquad (n-m) \text{ even}$$

21.7.16

$$\sum_{r=1}^{\infty}{}' \frac{(-1)^{\frac{r-1}{2}}(r+2m+1)!}{2^r\left(\frac{r-1}{2}\right)!\left(\frac{r+2m+1}{2}\right)!}d_r^{mn}$$
$$=\frac{(-1)^{\frac{n-m-1}{2}}(n+m+1)!}{2^{n-m}\left(\frac{n-m-1}{2}\right)!\left(\frac{n+m+1}{2}\right)!} \qquad (n-m) \text{ odd}$$

(The normalization scheme **21.7.13** and **21.7.14** is also used in [21.10].)

Asymptotic Expansions for $S_{mn}(c,\eta)$

21.7.17

$$S_{mn}(c,\eta)=(1-\eta^2)^{\frac{1}{2}}U_{mn}(c,\eta) \qquad (c\to\infty)$$

$$U_{mn}(x)=\sum_{r=-\infty}^{\infty}h_r^l D_{l+r}(x) \qquad l=n-m$$

where the $D_r(x)$'s are the parabolic cylinder functions (see chapter **19**).

$$D_r(x)=(-1)^r e^{x^2/4}\frac{d^2}{dx^2}e^{-x^2/2}=2^{-r/2}e^{-x^2/4}H_r\left(\frac{x}{\sqrt{2}}\right)$$

and the $H_r(x)$ are the Hermite polynomials (see chapter **22**). (For tables of $h_{\pm r}^l/h_0^l$ see [21.4].)

Expansion of $S_{mn}(c,\eta)$ in Powers of η

21.7.18

$$S_{mn}(c,\eta)=(1-\eta^2)^{m/2}\sum_{r=0,1}^{\infty}{}' p_r^{mn}(c)\eta^r$$

$$(r+1)(r+2)p_{r+2}^{mn}(c)-[r(r+2m+1)+m(m+1)$$
$$-\lambda_{mn}(c)]p_r^{mn}(c)-c^2p_{r-2}^{mn}(c)=0$$

(The derivation of the transcendental equation for λ_{mn} is similar to the derivation of **21.7.4** from **21.7.3.**)

Expansion of $S_{mn}(c,\eta)$ in Powers of $(1-\eta^2)$

21.7.19

$$S_{mn}(c,\eta)=(1-\eta^2)^{m/2}\sum_{k=0}^{\infty}c_{2k}^{mn}(1-\eta^2)^k \qquad (n-m) \text{ even}$$

21.7.20

$$S_{mn}(c,\eta)=\eta(1-\eta^2)^{m/2}\sum_{k=0}^{\infty} c_{2k}^{mn}(1-\eta^2)^k \qquad (n-m) \text{ odd}$$

$$c_{2k}^{mn}=\frac{1}{2^m k!(m+k)!}\sum_{r=k}^{\infty}\frac{(2m+2r)!}{(2r)!}(-r)_k\left(m+r+\frac{1}{2}\right)_k d_{2r}^{mn} \qquad (n-m) \text{ even}$$

$$c_{2k}^{mn}=\frac{1}{2^m k!(m+k)!}\sum_{r=k}^{\infty}\frac{(2m+2r+1)!}{(2r+1)!}(-r)_k\left(m+r+\frac{3}{2}\right)_k d_{2r+1}^{mn} \qquad (n-m) \text{ odd}$$

$$(\alpha)_k=\alpha(\alpha+1)(\alpha+2)\ \ldots\ (\alpha+k+1)$$

(The d_r^{mn}'s are the coefficients in **21.7.1.**)

Prolate Angular Functions—Second Kind

Expansion **21.7.2** ultimately leads to

21.7.21

$$S_{mn}^{(2)}(c,\eta)=\sum_{r=-2m,\,-2m+1}^{\infty}{}' d_r^{mn}Q_{m+r}^m(\eta)+\sum_{r=2m+2,\,2m+1}^{\infty}{}' d_{\rho|r}^{mn}P_{r-m-1}^m(\eta)$$

(The coefficients d_r^{mn} are the same as in **21.7.1**; the coefficients $d_{\rho|r}^{mn}$ are tabulated in [21.4].)

21.8. Oblate Angular Functions

Power Series Expansion for Eigenvalues

21.8.1 $$\lambda_{mn}=\sum_{k=0}^{\infty}(-1)^k l_{2k}c^{2k}$$

where the l_k's are the same as in **21.7.5.**

Asymptotic Expansion for Eigenvalues [21.4]

21.8.2

$$\lambda_{mn}=-c^2+2c(2\nu+m+1)-2\nu(\nu+m+1)-(m+1)+\Lambda_{mn}$$

$$\nu=\frac{1}{2}(n-m) \text{ for } (n-m) \text{ even};$$

$$\nu=\frac{1}{2}(n-m-1) \text{ for } (n-m) \text{ odd}$$

$$\Lambda_{mn}=\sum_{k=1}^{\infty}\beta_k^{mn}c^{-k}$$

$$\beta_1^{mn}=-2^{-3}q(q^2+1-m^2)$$

$$\beta_2^{mn}=-2^{-6}[5q^4+10q^2+1-2m^2(3q^2+1)+m^4]$$

$$\beta_3^{mn}=-2^{-9}q[33q^4+114q^2+37-2m^2(23q^2+25)+13m^4]$$

$$\beta_4^{mn}=-2^{-10}[63q^6+340q^4+239q^2+14-10m^2(10q^4+23q^2+3)+m^4(39q^2-18)-2m^6]$$

$$\beta_k^{mn}=\nu(\nu+m)a_k^{-1}+(\nu+1)(\nu+m+1)a_k^{+1}$$

$q=n+1$ for $(n-m)$ even; $q=n$ for $(n-m)$ odd

(For the definition of $a_k^{\pm r}$ see **21.8.3.**)

Asymptotic Expansion for Oblate Angular Functions

21.8.3

$$S_{mn}(-ic,\eta)\sim(1-\eta^2)^{m/2}\sum_{s=-\nu}^{\infty}A_s^{mn}\{e^{-c(1-\eta)}L_{\nu+s}^{(m)}[2c(1-\eta)]+(-1)^{n-m}e^{-c(1+\eta)}L_{\nu+s}^{(m)}[2c(1+\eta)]\}$$

where the $L_\nu^{(m)}(x)$ are Laguerre polynomials (see chapter **22**) and

$$\frac{A_{\pm r}^{mn}}{A_0^{mn}}=\sum_{k=r}^{\infty}a_k^{\pm r}(m,n)c^{-k}$$

(Expressions of $a_k{}^{\pm r}$ are given in [21.4].)

21.9. Radial Spheroidal Wave Functions

21.9.1

$$R_{mn}^{(p)}(c,\xi)=\left\{\sum_{r=0,\,1}^{\infty}{}'\frac{(2m+r)!}{r!}d_r^{mn}\right\}^{-1}\left(\frac{\xi^2-1}{\xi^2}\right)^{m/2}\cdot\sum_{r=0,\,1}^{\infty}{}' i^{r+m-n}\frac{(2m+r)!}{r!}d_r^{mn}Z_{m+r}^{(p)}(c\xi)$$

$$Z_n^{(p)}(z)=\sqrt{\frac{\pi}{2z}}J_{n+\frac{1}{2}}(z) \qquad (p=1)$$

$$=\sqrt{\frac{\pi}{2z}}Y_{n+\frac{1}{2}}(z) \qquad (p=2)$$

($J_{n+\frac{1}{2}}(z)$ and $Y_{n+\frac{1}{2}}(z)$ are Bessel functions, order $n+\frac{1}{2}$, of the first and second kind respectively (see chapter **10**).)

21.9.2 $$R_{mn}^{(3)}(c,\xi)=R_{mn}^{(1)}(c,\xi)+iR_{mn}^{(2)}(c,\xi)$$

21.9.3 $$R_{mn}^{(4)}(c,\xi)=R_{mn}^{(1)}(c,\xi)-iR_{mn}^{(2)}(c,\xi)$$

Asymptotic Behavior of $R_{mn}^{(1)}(c,\xi)$ and $R_{mn}^{(2)}(c,\xi)$

21.9.4 $$R_{mn}^{(1)}(c,\xi)\underset{c\xi\to\infty}{\longrightarrow}\frac{1}{c\xi}\cos\,[c\xi-\tfrac{1}{2}(n+1)\pi]$$

21.9.5 $$R_{mn}^{(2)}(c,\xi)\underset{c\xi\to\infty}{\longrightarrow}\frac{1}{c\xi}\sin\,[c\xi-\tfrac{1}{2}(n+1)\pi]$$

21.10. Joining Factors for Prolate Spheroidal Wave Functions

21.10.1

$$S_{mn}^{(1)}(c,\xi)=\kappa_{mn}^{(1)}(c)R_{mn}^{(1)}(c,\xi)$$

$$\kappa_{mn}^{(1)}(c)=\frac{(2m+1)(n+m)!\sum_{r=0}^{\infty}{}' d_r^{mn}(2m+r)!/r!}{2^{n+m}d_0^{mn}(c)c^m m!\left(\frac{n-m}{2}\right)!\left(\frac{n+m}{2}\right)!}\qquad (n-m) \text{ even}$$

$$=\frac{(2m+3)(n+m+1)!\sum_{r=1}^{\infty}{}' d_r^{mn}(2m+r)!/r!}{2^{n+m}d_1^{mn}(c)c^{m+1}m!\left(\frac{n-m-1}{2}\right)!\left(\frac{n+m+1}{2}\right)!}\qquad (n-m) \text{ odd}$$

21.10.2

$$S_{mn}^{(2)}(c,\xi)=\kappa_{mn}^{(2)}(c)R_{mn}^{(2)}(c,\xi)$$

$$\kappa_{mn}^{(2)}(c)=\frac{2^{n-m}(2m)!\left(\frac{n-m}{2}\right)!\left(\frac{n+m}{2}\right)!\,d_{-2m}^{mn}(c)}{(2m-1)m!(n+m)!c^{m-1}}\sum_{r=0}^{\infty}{}'\frac{(2m+r)!}{r!}d_r^{mn}(c)\qquad (n-m) \text{ even}$$

$$=-\frac{2^{n-m}(2m)!\left(\frac{n-m-1}{2}\right)!\left(\frac{n+m+1}{2}\right)!\,d_{-2m+1}^{mn}(c)}{(2m-3)(2m-1)m!(n+m+1)!\,c^{m-2}}\sum_{r=1}^{\infty}{}'\frac{(2m+r)!}{r!}d_r^{mn}(c)\qquad (n-m) \text{ odd}$$

(The expression for joining factors appropriate to the oblate case may be obtained from the above formulas by the transformation $c\rightarrow -ic$.)

Notation for Prolate Spheroidal Wave Functions

	Ang. coord.	Rad. coord.	Independent variable	Ang. wave function	Rad. wave function	Eigenvalue	Normalization of angular functions	Remarks
Stratton, Morse, Chu, Little and Corbató	η	ξ	h	$S_{ml}(h, \eta)$	$je_{ml}(h, \xi)$ $ne_{ml}(h, \xi)$ $he_{ml}(h, \xi)$	$A_{ml}(h)$	$S_{ml}(h, 1)=P_l^m(1)$	$l=$Flammer's n $A_{ml}=\lambda_{mn}$
Flammer and this chapter	η	ξ	c	$S_{mn}(c, \eta)$	$R_{mn}^{(i)}(c, \xi)$	$\lambda_{mn}(c)$	$S_{mn}(c, 0)=P_n^m(0)$ $(n-m)$ even $S'_{mn}(c, 0)=P_n^{m\prime}(0)$ $(n-m)$ odd	
Chu and Stratton	η	ξ	c	$S_{ml}^{(1)}(c, \eta)$	$R_{ml}^{(i)}(c, \xi)$	A_{ml}	$S_{ml}^{(1)}(c, 0)=P_{m+l}^m(0)$ $(l$ even$)$ $S_{ml}^{(1)\prime}(c, 0)=P_{m+l}^{m\prime}(0)$ $(l$ odd$)$	$l=$Flammer's $n-m$ $A_{ml}=-\lambda_{m,\,n-m}$
Meixner and Schäfke	η	ξ	γ	$PS_n^m(\eta, \gamma^2)$	$S_n^{m(i)}(\xi, \gamma^2)$	$\lambda_n^m(\gamma^2)$	$\int_{-1}^{1}[PS_n^m(\eta, \gamma^2)]^2 d\eta$ $=\frac{2}{2n+1}\frac{(n+m)!}{(n-m)!}$	$\lambda_n^m(\gamma^2)=\lambda_{mn}(c)-c^2$
Morse and Feshbach	$\eta=\cos\vartheta$	$\xi=\cosh\mu$	h	$S_{ml}(h, \eta)$	$je_{ml}(h, \xi)$ $ne_{ml}(h, \xi)$ $he_{ml}(h, \xi)$	A_{ml}	$[(1-\eta^2)^{-m/2}S_{ml}(h, \eta)]_{\eta=1}$ $=[(1-\eta^2)^{-m/2}P_l^m(\eta)]_{\eta=1}$	$l=$Flammer's n $A_{ml}=\lambda_{mn}$
Page	ξ	η	ϵ	$U_{lm}(\xi)$	$v_{lm}(\eta)$ $p_{lm}(\eta)$ $q_{lm}(\eta)$	α_{lm}	$[(1-\xi^2)^{-m/2}U_{lm}(\xi)]=1$ $\xi=1$	$l=$Flammer's n $\alpha_{lm}=\lambda_{mn}-c^2$

Notation for Oblate Spheroidal Wave Functions

	Ang. coord.	Rad. coord.	Independent variable	Ang. wave function	Rad. wave function	Eigenvalue	Normalization of angular functions	Remarks
Stratton, Morse, Chu, Little and Corbató	η	ξ	g	$S_{ml}(ig, \eta)$	$je_{ml}(ig, -i\xi)$	A_{ml}	$S_{ml}(ig, 1)=P_l^m(1)$	$l=$Flammer's n $A_{ml}=\lambda_{mn}$
Flammer and this chapter	η	ξ	c	$S_{mn}(-ic, \eta)$	$R_{mn}^{(i)}(-ic, i\xi)$	$\lambda_{mn}(-ic)$	$S_{mn}(-ic,0)=P_n^m(0)$ $(n-m)$ even $S'_{mn}(-ic, 0)=P_n^{m\prime}(0)$ $(n-m)$odd	
Chu and Stratton	η	ξ	c	$S_{ml}^{(1)}(-ic, \eta)$	$R_{ml}^{(1)}(-ic, i\xi)$	B_{ml}	$S_{ml}^{(1)}(-ic, 0)=P_{m+l}^m(0)$ $(l$ even$)$ $S_{ml}^{(1)\prime}(-ic, 0)=P_{m+l}^{m\prime}(0)$ $(l$ odd$)$	$l=$Flammer's $n-m$ $B_{lm}=-\lambda_{m,\,n-m}$
Meixner and Schäfke	η	ξ	γ	$ps_n^m(\eta,-\gamma^2)$	$S_n^{m(i)}(-i\xi, i\gamma^2)$	$\lambda_n^m(-\gamma^2)$	$\int_{-1}^{1}[ps_n^m(\eta, -\gamma^2)]^2 d\eta$ $=\frac{2}{2n+1}\frac{(n+m)!}{(n-m)!}$	$\lambda_n^m(-\gamma^2)=\lambda_{mn}(-ic)+c^2$
Morse and Feshbach	$\eta=\cos\vartheta$	$\xi=\sinh\mu$	g	$S_{ml}(ig, \eta)$	$je_{ml}(ig, -i\xi)$ $ne_{ml}(ig, -i\xi)$ $he_{ml}(ig, -i\xi)$	A_{ml}	$[(1-\eta^2)^{-m/2}S_{ml}(ig, \eta)]_{\eta=1}$ $=[(1-\eta^2)^{-m/2}P_l^m(\eta)]_{\eta=1}$	$l=$Flammer's n $A_{ml}=\lambda_{mn}$
Leitner and Spence	η	ξ	ϵ	$U_{lm}(\eta)$	(i) $v_{lm}(\xi)$	α_{lm}	$[(1-\eta^2)^{-m/2}U_{lm}(\eta)]_{\eta=1}=1$	$l=$Flammer's n $\alpha_{lm}=\lambda_{mn}+c^2$

The notation in this chapter closely follows the notation in [21.4].

Table 21.1 **EIGENVALUES—PROLATE AND OBLATE**

PROLATE

$\lambda_{mn}(c)-m(m+1)$

$\lambda_{0n}(c)$

$c^2\backslash n$	0	1	2	3	4
0	0.000000	2.000000	6.000000	12.000000	20.000000
1	0.319000	2.593084	6.533471	12.514462	20.508274
2	0.611314	3.172127	7.084258	13.035830	21.020137
3	0.879933	3.736869	7.649317	13.564354	21.535636
4	1.127734	4.287128	8.225713	14.100203	22.054829
5	1.357356	4.822809	8.810735	14.643458	22.577779
6	1.571155	5.343903	9.401958	15.194110	23.104553
7	1.771183	5.850492	9.997251	15.752059	23.635223
8	1.959206	6.342739	10.594773	16.317122	24.169860
9	2.136732	6.820888	11.192938	16.889030	24.708534
10	2.305040	7.285254	11.790394	17.467444	25.251312
11	2.465217	7.736212	12.385986	18.051962	25.798254
12	2.618185	8.174189	12.978730	18.642128	26.349411
13	2.764731	8.599648	13.567791	19.237446	26.904827
14	2.905523	9.013085	14.152458	19.837389	27.464530
15	3.041137	9.415010	14.732130	20.441413	28.028539
16	3.172067	9.805943	15.306299	21.048960	28.596854

$c^{-1}[\lambda_{0n}(c)]$

$c^{-1}\backslash n$	0	1	2	3	4
0.25	0.793016	2.451485	3.826574	5.26224	7.14921
0.24	0.802442	2.477117	3.858771	5.25133	7.05054
0.23	0.811763	2.503218	3.895890	5.25040	6.96237
0.22	0.820971	2.529593	3.937869	5.26046	6.88638
0.21	0.830059	2.556036	3.984499	5.28251	6.82460
0.20	0.839025	2.582340	4.035382	5.31747	6.77941
0.19	0.847869	2.608310	4.089903	5.36610	6.75360
0.18	0.856592	2.633778	4.147207	5.42883	6.75030
0.17	0.865200	2.658616	4.206229	5.50551	6.77286
0.16	0.873698	2.682743	4.265772	5.59516	6.82451
0.15	0.882095	2.706127	4.324653	5.69566	6.90779
0.14	0.890399	2.728784	4.381878	5.80359	7.02356
0.13	0.898617	2.750762	4.436798	5.91452	7.16962
0.12	0.906758	2.772133	4.489168	6.02383	7.33916
0.11	0.914827	2.792971	4.539096	6.12806	7.52035
0.10	0.922830	2.813346	4.586895	6.22577	7.69932
0.09	0.930772	2.833316	4.632927	6.31730	7.86638
0.08	0.938657	2.852927	4.677506	6.40385	8.01951
0.07	0.946487	2.872213	4.720863	6.48655	8.16148
0.06	0.954267	2.891203	4.763160	6.56618	8.29538
0.05	0.961998	2.909920	4.804519	6.64326	8.42315
0.04	0.969683	2.928382	4.845033	6.71812	8.54594
0.03	0.977324	2.946608	4.884779	6.79104	8.66452
0.02	0.984923	2.964611	4.923820	6.86221	8.77945
0.01	0.992481	2.982404	4.962212	6.93182	8.89116
0.00	1.000000	3.000000	5.000000	7.00000	9.00000

EIGENVALUES—PROLATE AND OBLATE

Table 21.1

OBLATE

$\lambda_{mn}(-ic)-m(m+1)$

$\lambda_{0n}(-ic)$

$c^2\backslash n$	0	1	2	3	4
0	0.000000	2.000000	6.000000	12.000000	20.000000
1	-0.348602	1.393206	5.486800	11.492120	19.495276
2	-0.729391	0.773097	4.996484	10.990438	18.994079
3	-1.144328	+0.140119	4.531027	10.494512	18.496395
4	-1.594493	-0.505243	4.091509	10.003863	18.002228
5	-2.079934	-1.162477	3.677958	9.517982	17.511597
6	-2.599668	-1.831050	3.289357	9.036338	17.024540
7	-3.151841	-2.510421	2.923796	8.558395	16.541110
8	-3.733981	-3.200049	2.578730	8.083615	16.061382
9	-4.343292	-3.899400	2.251269	7.611465	15.585448
10	-4.976895	-4.607952	1.938419	7.141427	15.113424
11	-5.632021	-5.325200	1.637277	6.673001	14.645441
12	-6.306116	-6.050659	1.345136	6.205705	14.181652
13	-6.996903	-6.783867	1.059541	5.739084	13.722230
14	-7.702385	-7.524384	0.778305	5.272706	13.267364
15	-8.420841	-8.271795	0.499495	4.806165	12.817261
16	-9.150793	-9.025710	0.221407	4.339082	12.372144

$c^{-2}[\lambda_{0n}(-ic)]$

$c^{-1}\backslash n$	0	1	2	3	4
0.25	-0.571924	-0.564106	+0.013837	0.271192	0.77325
0.24	-0.585248	-0.579552	-0.009136	0.213225	0.67822
0.23	-0.599067	-0.595037	-0.031481	0.157464	0.58772
0.22	-0.613349	-0.610591	-0.053477	0.103825	0.50191
0.21	-0.628058	-0.626242	-0.075480	0.052196	0.42099
0.20	-0.643161	-0.642016	-0.097943	+0.002437	0.34521
0.19	-0.658625	-0.657938	-0.121428	-0.045635	0.27490
0.18	-0.674418	-0.674031	-0.146603	-0.092251	0.21043
0.17	-0.690515	-0.690310	-0.174201	-0.137692	0.15215
0.16	-0.706891	-0.706792	-0.204894	-0.182301	0.10020
0.15	-0.723530	-0.723486	-0.239109	-0.226469	0.05428
0.14	-0.740416	-0.740399	-0.276886	-0.270627	+0.01332
0.13	-0.757541	-0.757535	-0.317881	-0.315206	-0.02476
0.12	-0.774896	-0.774894	-0.361548	-0.360594	-0.06337
0.11	-0.792476	-0.792476	-0.407352	-0.407081	-0.10723
0.10	-0.810279	-0.810279	-0.454896	-0.454839	-0.16065
0.09	-0.828301	-0.828301	-0.503937	-0.503928	-0.22419
0.08	-0.846539	-0.846539	-0.554337	-0.554337	-0.29513
0.07	-0.864992	-0.864992	-0.606021	-0.606021	-0.37117
0.06	-0.883657	-0.883657	-0.658931	-0.658931	-0.45125
0.05	-0.902532	-0.902532	-0.713025	-0.713025	-0.53495
0.04	-0.921616	-0.921616	-0.768262	-0.768262	-0.62200
0.03	-0.940906	-0.940906	-0.824608	-0.824608	-0.71218
0.02	-0.960402	-0.960402	-0.882031	-0.882031	-0.80533
0.01	-0.980100	-0.980100	-0.940503	-0.940503	-0.90131
0.00	-1.000000	-1.000000	-1.000000	-1.000000	-1.00000

Table 21.1 **EIGENVALUES—PROLATE AND OBLATE**

PROLATE

$\lambda_{mn}(c)-m(m+1)$

$\lambda_{1n}(c)-2$

$c^2\backslash n$	1	2	3	4	5
0	0.000000	4.000000	10.000000	18.000000	28.000000
1	0.195548	4.424699	10.467915	18.481696	28.488065
2	0.382655	4.841718	10.937881	18.965685	28.977891
3	0.561975	5.251162	11.409266	19.451871	29.469456
4	0.734111	5.653149	11.881493	19.940143	29.962738
5	0.899615	6.047807	12.354034	20.430382	30.457716
6	1.058995	6.435272	12.826413	20.922458	30.954363
7	1.212711	6.815691	13.298196	21.416235	31.452653
8	1.361183	7.189213	13.768997	21.911569	31.952557
9	1.504795	7.555998	14.238466	22.408312	32.454044
10	1.643895	7.916206	14.706292	22.906311	32.957080
11	1.778798	8.270004	15.172199	23.405410	33.461629
12	1.909792	8.617558	15.635940	23.905451	33.967652
13	2.037141	8.959038	16.097297	24.406277	34.475109
14	2.161081	9.294612	16.556078	24.907729	34.983956
15	2.281832	9.624450	17.012115	25.409649	35.494147
16	2.399593	9.948719	17.465260	25.911881	36.005634

$c^{-1}[\lambda_{1n}(c)-2]$

$c^{-1}\backslash n$	1	2	3	4	5
0.25	0.599898	2.487179	4.366315	6.47797	9.00140
0.24	0.613295	2.491544	4.338520	6.38296	8.80891
0.23	0.627023	2.497852	4.315609	6.29522	8.62445
0.22	0.641073	2.506130	4.297923	6.21556	8.44916
0.21	0.655431	2.516383	4.285792	6.14494	8.28436
0.20	0.670084	2.528591	4.279522	6.08438	8.13163
0.19	0.685014	2.542705	4.279366	6.03498	7.99282
0.18	0.700204	2.558644	4.285495	5.99788	7.87010
0.17	0.715632	2.576296	4.297965	5.97420	7.76598
0.16	0.731281	2.595516	4.316672	5.96496	7.68328
0.15	0.747129	2.616135	4.341320	5.97090	7.62508
0.14	0.763159	2.637968	4.371397	5.99230	7.59446
0.13	0.779353	2.660829	4.406191	6.02874	7.59407
0.12	0.795696	2.684536	4.444844	6.07889	7.62539
0.11	0.812174	2.708934	4.486445	6.14051	7.68773
0.10	0.828776	2.733891	4.530151	6.21063	7.77728
0.09	0.845493	2.759305	4.575277	6.28624	7.88714
0.08	0.862316	2.785099	4.621329	6.36482	8.00897
0.07	0.879237	2.811212	4.667984	6.44473	8.13579
0.06	0.896251	2.837600	4.715031	6.52505	8.26355
0.05	0.913352	2.864224	4.762333	6.60532	8.39048
0.04	0.930535	2.891056	4.809790	6.68528	8.51592
0.03	0.947796	2.918069	4.857332	6.76480	8.63963
0.02	0.965129	2.945243	4.904906	6.84378	8.76153
0.01	0.982531	2.972558	4.952472	6.92219	8.88164
0.00	1.000000	3.000000	5.000000	7.00000	9.00000

EIGENVALUES—PROLATE AND OBLATE Table 21.1

OBLATE

$\lambda_{mn}(-ic)-m(m+1)$

$\lambda_{1n}(-ic)-2$

$c^2\backslash n$	1	2	3	4	5
0	0.000000	4.000000	10.000000	18.000000	28.000000
1	-0.204695	3.567527	9.534818	17.520683	27.513713
2	-0.419293	3.127202	9.073104	17.043817	27.029223
3	-0.644596	2.678958	8.615640	16.569461	26.546548
4	-0.881446	2.222747	8.163245	16.097655	26.065706
5	-1.130712	1.758534	7.716768	15.628426	25.586715
6	-1.393280	1.286300	7.277072	15.161786	25.109592
7	-1.670028	0.806045	6.845015	14.697727	24.634357
8	-1.961809	+0.317782	6.421425	14.236229	24.161031
9	-2.269420	-0.178458	6.007074	13.777252	23.689634
10	-2.593577	-0.682630	5.602649	13.320743	23.220190
11	-2.934882	-1.194673	5.208724	12.866634	22.752726
12	-3.293803	-1.714511	4.825732	12.414840	22.287271
13	-3.670646	-2.242055	4.453947	11.965266	21.823856
14	-4.065548	-2.777205	4.093464	11.517803	21.362516
15	-4.478470	-3.319848	3.744202	11.072331	20.903290
16	-4.909200	-3.869861	3.405903	10.628718	20.446222

$c^{-2}[\lambda_{1n}(-ic)-2]$

$c^{-1}\backslash n$	1	2	3	4	5
0.25	-0.306825	-0.241866	0.21286	0.66429	1.2778
0.24	-0.318148	-0.266693	0.17062	0.57759	1.1420
0.23	-0.330984	-0.291340	0.13125	0.49460	1.0120
0.22	-0.345469	-0.315894	0.09476	0.41533	0.8879
0.21	-0.361702	-0.340450	0.06107	0.33974	0.7697
0.20	-0.379735	-0.365113	0.03001	0.26779	0.6575
0.19	-0.399564	-0.389998	+0.00127	0.19942	0.5515
0.18	-0.421125	-0.415222	-0.02563	0.13449	0.4520
0.17	-0.444308	-0.440907	-0.05142	0.07282	0.3591
0.16	-0.468974	-0.467166	-0.07710	+0.01411	0.2735
0.15	-0.494976	-0.494104	-0.10406	-0.04205	0.1958
0.14	-0.522180	-0.521805	-0.13412	-0.09625	0.1271
0.13	-0.550474	-0.550335	-0.16924	-0.14929	0.0680
0.12	-0.579775	-0.579732	-0.21076	-0.20210	+0.0183
0.11	-0.610027	-0.610016	-0.25868	-0.25572	-0.0250
0.10	-0.641193	-0.641191	-0.31185	-0.31111	-0.0685
0.09	-0.673251	-0.673251	-0.36901	-0.36888	-0.1219
0.08	-0.706186	-0.706186	-0.42934	-0.42932	-0.1907
0.07	-0.739985	-0.739985	-0.49242	-0.49242	-0.2714
0.06	-0.774638	-0.774638	-0.55807	-0.55807	-0.3598
0.05	-0.810135	-0.810135	-0.62616	-0.62616	-0.4542
0.04	-0.846468	-0.846468	-0.69657	-0.69657	-0.5540
0.03	-0.883628	-0.883628	-0.76923	-0.76923	-0.6588
0.02	-0.921608	-0.921608	-0.84406	-0.84406	-0.7682
0.01	-0.960401	-0.960401	-0.92100	-0.92100	-0.8820
0.00	-1.000000	-1.000000	-1.00000	-1.00000	-1.0000

Table 21.1

EIGENVALUES—PROLATE AND OBLATE

PROLATE

$\lambda_{mn}(c)-m(m+1)$

$\lambda_{2n}(c)-6$

$c^2\backslash n$	2	3	4	5	6
0	0.000000	6.000000	14.000000	24.000000	36.000000
1	0.140948	6.331101	14.402353	24.436145	36.454889
2	0.278219	6.657791	14.804100	24.872744	36.910449
3	0.412006	6.980147	15.205077	25.309731	37.366657
4	0.542495	7.298250	15.605133	25.747043	37.823486
5	0.669857	7.612179	16.004126	26.184612	38.280913
6	0.794252	7.922016	16.401931	26.622373	38.738910
7	0.915832	8.227840	16.798429	27.060261	39.197451
8	1.034738	8.529734	17.193516	27.498208	39.656510
9	1.151100	8.827778	17.587093	27.936151	40.116059
10	1.265042	9.122052	17.979073	28.374023	40.576070
11	1.376681	9.412636	18.369377	28.811761	41.036514
12	1.486122	9.699610	18.757932	29.249302	41.497364
13	1.593469	9.983052	19.144675	29.686584	41.958589
14	1.698816	10.263039	19.529549	30.123544	42.420160
15	1.802252	10.539650	19.912501	30.560125	42.882048
16	1.903860	10.812958	20.293486	30.996267	43.344222

$c^{-1}[\lambda_{2n}(c)-6]$

$c^{-1}\backslash n$	2	3	4	5	6
0.25	0.475965	2.703239	5.073371	7.74906	10.8360
0.24	0.489447	2.683149	4.994116	7.58138	10.5536
0.23	0.503526	2.665356	4.919290	7.41971	10.2781
0.22	0.518220	2.650003	4.849313	7.26479	10.0103
0.21	0.533551	2.637236	4.784640	7.11743	9.7512
0.20	0.549534	2.627196	4.725757	6.97858	9.5023
0.19	0.566185	2.620017	4.673177	6.84931	9.2649
0.18	0.583513	2.615819	4.627427	6.73081	9.0409
0.17	0.601526	2.614701	4.589031	6.62442	8.8323
0.16	0.620224	2.616735	4.558480	6.53155	8.6417
0.15	0.639604	2.621954	4.536196	6.45371	8.4718
0.14	0.659659	2.630349	4.522485	6.39236	8.3260
0.13	0.680376	2.641862	4.517479	6.34878	8.2078
0.12	0.701737	2.656384	4.521086	6.32389	8.1208
0.11	0.723722	2.673764	4.532956	6.31794	8.0678
0.10	0.746308	2.693817	4.552484	6.33030	8.0507
0.09	0.769471	2.716339	4.578871	6.35935	8.0688
0.08	0.793186	2.741120	4.611219	6.40263	8.1184
0.07	0.817429	2.767960	4.648642	6.45738	8.1932
0.06	0.842175	2.796673	4.690346	6.52096	8.2864
0.05	0.867402	2.827089	4.735658	6.59127	8.3919
0.04	0.893087	2.859059	4.784022	6.66670	8.5057
0.03	0.919209	2.892449	4.834980	6.74607	8.6249
0.02	0.945747	2.927138	4.888160	6.82849	8.7477
0.01	0.972684	2.963019	4.943252	6.91330	8.8730
0.00	1.000000	3.000000	5.000000	7.00000	9.0000

EIGENVALUES—PROLATE AND OBLATE Table 21.1

OBLATE

$\lambda_{mn}(-ic)-m(m+1)$

$\lambda_{2n}(-ic)-6$

$c^2\backslash n$	2	3	4	5	6
0	0.000000	6.000000	14.000000	24.000000	36.000000
1	-0.144837	5.664409	13.597220	23.564371	35.545806
2	-0.293786	5.324253	13.194206	23.129322	35.092330
3	-0.447086	4.979458	12.791168	22.694912	34.639597
4	-0.604989	4.629951	12.388328	22.261201	34.187627
5	-0.767764	4.275662	11.985928	21.828245	33.736444
6	-0.935698	3.916525	11.584224	21.396098	33.286069
7	-1.109090	3.552475	11.183489	20.964812	32.836522
8	-1.288259	3.183450	10.784014	20.534436	32.387826
9	-1.473539	2.809393	10.386106	20.105013	31.940000
10	-1.665278	2.430250	9.990084	19.676587	31.493066
11	-1.863838	2.045970	9.596286	19.249195	31.047043
12	-2.069595	1.656508	9.205059	18.822869	30.601952
13	-2.282933	1.261822	8.816762	18.397640	30.157814
14	-2.504245	0.861875	8.431761	17.973532	29.714648
15	-2.733927	0.456635	8.050424	17.550565	29.272476
16	-2.972375	0.046076	7.673121	17.128753	28.831317

$c^{-2}[\lambda_{2n}(-ic)-6]$

$c^{-1}\backslash n$	2	3	4	5	6
0.25	-0.185773	+0.002879	0.47957	1.07054	1.8019
0.24	-0.190754	-0.030028	0.41280	0.95365	1.6261
0.23	-0.196680	-0.062228	0.34933	0.84167	1.4577
0.22	-0.203790	-0.093813	0.28933	0.73461	1.2965
0.21	-0.212386	-0.124893	0.23297	0.63251	1.1428
0.20	-0.222841	-0.155607	0.18049	0.53537	0.9964
0.19	-0.235596	-0.186120	0.13215	0.44322	0.8574
0.18	-0.251126	-0.216631	0.08816	0.35607	0.7260
0.17	-0.269873	-0.247375	0.04864	0.27389	0.6022
0.16	-0.292149	-0.278624	+0.01342	0.19662	0.4863
0.15	-0.318047	-0.310677	-0.01813	0.12409	0.3785
0.14	-0.347414	-0.343847	-0.04727	+0.05600	0.2795
0.13	-0.379928	-0.378432	-0.07609	-0.00822	0.1901
0.12	-0.415213	-0.414688	-0.10778	-0.06954	0.1120
0.11	-0.452947	-0.452800	-0.14643	-0.12937	+0.0470
0.10	-0.492902	-0.492871	-0.19508	-0.18959	-0.0051
0.09	-0.534942	-0.534937	-0.25333	-0.25217	-0.0517
0.08	-0.578991	-0.578991	-0.31876	-0.31861	-0.1076
0.07	-0.625006	-0.625006	-0.38955	-0.38955	-0.1844
0.06	-0.672956	-0.672956	-0.46494	-0.46494	-0.2768
0.05	-0.722813	-0.722813	-0.54456	-0.54456	-0.3791
0.04	-0.774556	-0.774556	-0.62821	-0.62821	-0.4895
0.03	-0.828164	-0.828164	-0.71571	-0.71571	-0.6073
0.02	-0.883618	-0.883618	-0.80691	-0.80691	-0.7319
0.01	-0.940902	-0.940902	-0.90171	-0.90171	-0.8629
0.00	-1.000000	-1.000000	-1.00000	-1.00000	-1.0000

22. Orthogonal Polynomials

22.1. Definition of Orthogonal Polynomials

A system of polynomials $f_n(x)$, degree $[f_n(x)]=n$, is called orthogonal on the interval $a \leq x \leq b$, with respect to the weight function $w(x)$, if

22.1.1

$$\int_a^b w(x) f_n(x) f_m(x) dx = 0 \qquad (n \neq m; n, m=0, 1, 2, \ldots)$$

The weight function $w(x)[w(x) \geq 0]$ determines the system $f_n(x)$ up to a constant factor in each polynomial. The specification of these factors is referred to as standardization. For suitably standardized orthogonal polynomials we set

22.1.2

$$\int_a^b w(x) f_n^2(x) dx = h_n, f_n(x) = k_n x^n + k_n' x^{n-1} + \ldots \qquad (n=0, 1, 2, \ldots)$$

These polynomials satisfy a number of relationships of the same general form. The most important ones are:

Differential Equation

22.1.3 $\qquad g_2(x) f_n'' + g_1(x) f_n' + a_n f_n = 0$

where $g_2(x)$, $g_1(x)$ are independent of n and a_n a constant depending only on n.

Recurrence Relation

22.1.4 $\qquad f_{n+1} = (a_n + x b_n) f_n - c_n f_{n-1}$

where

22.1.5

$$b_n = \frac{k_{n+1}}{k_n}, \quad a_n = b_n \left(\frac{k_{n+1}'}{k_{n+1}} - \frac{k_n'}{k_n} \right), \quad c_n = \frac{k_{n+1} k_{n-1} h_n}{k_n^2 h_{n-1}}$$

Rodrigues' Formula

22.1.6 $\qquad f_n = \frac{1}{e_n w(x)} \frac{d^n}{dx_n} \{ w(x) [g(x)]^n \}$

where $g(x)$ is a polynomial in x independent of n. The system $\left\{ \frac{df_n}{dx} \right\}$ consists again of orthogonal polynomials.

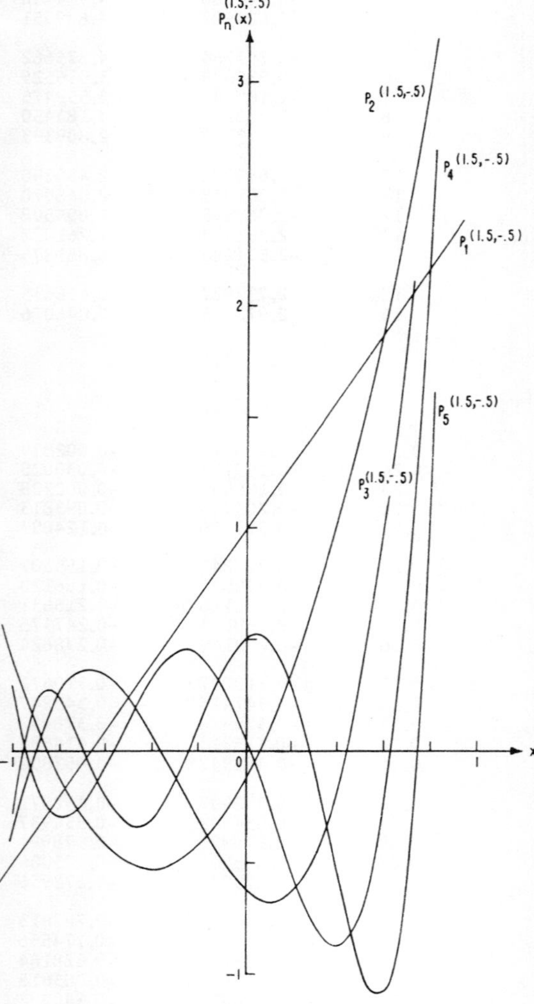

FIGURE 22.1. *Jacobi Polynomials* $P_n^{(\alpha,\beta)}(x)$, $\alpha=1.5$, $\beta=-.5$, $n=1(1)5$.

22.2. Orthogonality Relations

	$f_n(x)$	Name of Polynomial	a	b	$w(x)$	Standardization	h_n	Remarks
22.2.1	$P_n^{(\alpha,\beta)}(x)$	Jacobi	-1	1	$(1-x)^{\alpha}(1+x)^{\beta}$	$P_n^{(\alpha,\beta)}(1)=\binom{n+\alpha}{n}$	$\frac{2^{\alpha+\beta+1}}{2n+\alpha+\beta+1}\frac{\Gamma(n+\alpha+1)\Gamma(n+\beta+1)}{n!\Gamma(n+\alpha+\beta+1)}$	$\alpha>-1,\ \beta>-1$
22.2.2	$G_n(p,q,x)$	Jacobi	0	1	$(1-x)^{p-q}x^{q-1}$	$k_n=1$	$\frac{n!\Gamma(n+q)\Gamma(n+p)\Gamma(n+p-q+1)}{(2n+p)\Gamma^2(2n+p)}$	$p-q>-1,\ q>0$
22.2.3	$C_n^{(\alpha)}(x)$	Ultraspherical (Gegenbauer)	-1	1	$(1-x^2)^{\alpha-\frac{1}{2}}$	$C_n^{(\alpha)}(1)=\binom{n+2\alpha-1}{n}$ $(\alpha\neq 0)$	$\frac{\pi 2^{1-2\alpha}\Gamma(n+2\alpha)}{n!(n+\alpha)[\Gamma(\alpha)]^2}$ $\alpha\neq 0$	$\alpha>-\frac{1}{2}$
						$C_n^{(0)}(1)=\frac{2}{n}$, $C_0^{(0)}(1)=1$	$\frac{2\pi}{n^2}$ $\alpha=0$	
22.2.4	$T_n(x)$	Chebyshev of the first kind	-1	1	$(1-x^2)^{-\frac{1}{2}}$	$T_n(1)=1$	$\begin{cases}\frac{\pi}{2} & n\neq 0\\ \pi & n=0\end{cases}$	
22.2.5	$U_n(x)$	Chebyshev of the second kind	-1	1	$(1-x^2)^{\frac{1}{2}}$	$U_n(1)=n+1$	$\frac{\pi}{2}$	∞
22.2.6	$C_n(x)$	Chebyshev of the first kind	-2	2	$\left(1-\frac{x^2}{4}\right)^{-\frac{1}{2}}$	$C_n(2)=2$	$\begin{cases}4\pi & n\neq 0\\ 8\pi & n=0\end{cases}$	
22.2.7	$S_n(x)$	Chebyshev of the second kind	-2	2	$\left(1-\frac{x^2}{4}\right)^{\frac{1}{2}}$	$S_n(2)=n+1$	π	
22.2.8	$T_n^*(x)$	Shifted Chebyshev of the first kind	0	1	$(x-x^2)^{-\frac{1}{2}}$	$T_n^*(1)=1$	$\begin{cases}\frac{\pi}{2} & n\neq 0\\ \pi & n=0\end{cases}$	
22.2.9	$U_n^*(x)$	Shifted Chebyshev of the second kind	0	1	$(x-x^2)^{\frac{1}{2}}$	$U_n^*(1)=n+1$	$\frac{\pi}{8}$	
22.2.10	$P_n(x)$	Legendre (Spherical)	-1	1	1	$P_n(1)=1$	$\frac{2}{2n+1}$	
22.2.11	$P_n^*(x)$	Shifted Legendre	0	1	1		$\frac{1}{2n+1}$	

22.2. Orthogonality Relations—Continued

22.2.12	$L_n^{(\alpha)}(x)$	Generalized Laguerre	0	∞	$e^{-x}x^{\alpha}$	$k_n=\frac{(-1)^n}{n!}$	$\frac{\Gamma(\alpha+n+1)}{n!}$	$\alpha>-1$
22.2.13	$L_n(x)$	Laguerre	0	∞	e^{-x}	$k_n=\frac{(-1)^n}{n!}$	1	
22.2.14	$H_n(x)$	Hermite	$-\infty$	∞	e^{-x^2}	$e_n=(-1)^n$	$\sqrt{\pi}2^n n!$	
22.2.15	$He_n(x)$	Hermite	$-\infty$	∞	$e^{-\frac{x^2}{2}}$	$e_n=(-1)^n$	$\sqrt{2\pi}n!$	

22.3. Explicit Expressions

$$f_n(x)=d_n\sum_{m=0}^{N}c_m g_m(x)$$

	$f_n(x)$	N	d_n	c_m	$g_m(x)$	k_n	Remarks
22.3.1	$P_n^{(\alpha,\beta)}(x)$	n	$\frac{1}{2^n}$	$\binom{n+\alpha}{m}\binom{n+\beta}{n-m}$	$(x-1)^{n-m}(x+1)^m$	$\frac{1}{2^n}\binom{2n+\alpha+\beta}{n}$	$\alpha>-1,\ \beta>-1$
22.3.2	$P_n^{(\alpha,\beta)}(x)$	n	$\frac{\Gamma(\alpha+n+1)}{n!\Gamma(\alpha+\beta+n+1)}$	$\binom{n}{m}\frac{\Gamma(\alpha+\beta+n+m+1)}{2^m\Gamma(\alpha+m+1)}$	$(x-1)^m$	$\frac{1}{2^n}\binom{2n+\alpha+\beta}{n}$	$\alpha>-1,\ \beta>-1$
22.3.3	$G_n(p,q,x)$	n	$\frac{\Gamma(q+n)}{\Gamma(p+2n)}$	$(-1)^m\binom{n}{m}\frac{\Gamma(p+2n-m)}{\Gamma(q+n-m)}$	x^{n-m}	1	$p-q>-1,\ q>0$
22.3.4	$C_n^{(\alpha)}(x)$	$\left[\frac{n}{2}\right]$	$\frac{1}{\Gamma(\alpha)}$	$(-1)^m\frac{\Gamma(\alpha+n-m)}{m!(n-2m)!}$	$(2x)^{n-2m}$	$\frac{2^n}{n!}\frac{\Gamma(\alpha+n)}{\Gamma(\alpha)}$	$\alpha>-\frac{1}{2},\ \alpha\neq0$
22.3.5	$C_n^{(0)}(x)$	$\left[\frac{n}{2}\right]$	1	$(-1)^m\frac{(n-m-1)!}{m!(n-2m)!}$	$(2x)^{n-2m}$	$\frac{2^n}{n}$ $n\neq0$	$n\neq0,\ C_0^{(0)}(1)=1$
22.3.6	$T_n(x)$	$\left[\frac{n}{2}\right]$	$\frac{n}{2}$	$(-1)^m\frac{(n-m-1)!}{m!(n-2m)!}$	$(2x)^{n-2m}$	2^{n-1}	
22.3.7	$U_n(x)$	$\left[\frac{n}{2}\right]$	1	$(-1)^m\frac{(n-m)!}{m!(n-2m)!}$	$(2x)^{n-2m}$	2^n	
22.3.8	$P_n(x)$	$\left[\frac{n}{2}\right]$	$\frac{1}{2^n}$	$(-1)^m\binom{n}{m}\binom{2n-2m}{n}$	x^{n-2m}	$\frac{(2n)!}{2^n(n!)^2}$	
22.3.9	$L_n^{(\alpha)}(x)$	n	1	$(-1)^m\binom{n+\alpha}{n-m}\frac{1}{m!}$	x^m	$\frac{(-1)^n}{n!}$	$\alpha>-1$
22.3.10	$H_n(x)$	$\left[\frac{n}{2}\right]$	$n!$	$(-1)^m\frac{1}{m!(n-2m)!}$	$(2x)^{n-2m}$	2^n	see **22.11**
22.3.11	$He_n(x)$	$\left[\frac{n}{2}\right]$	$n!$	$(-1)^m\frac{1}{m!2^m(n-2m)!}$	x^{n-2m}	1	

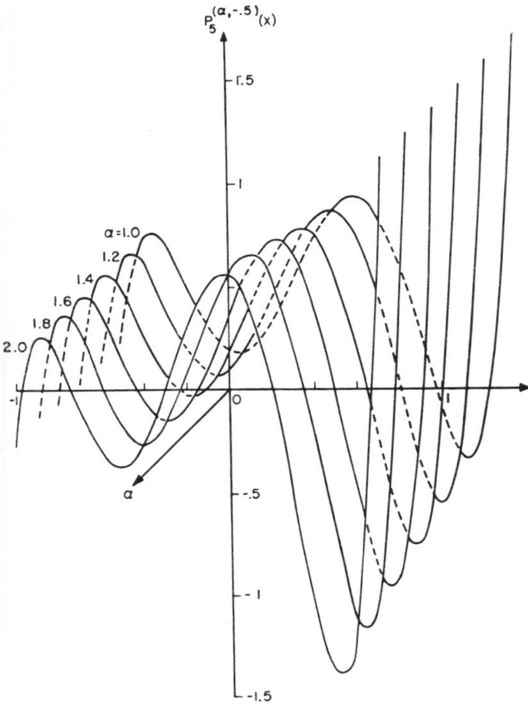

FIGURE 22.2. *Jacobi Polynomials* $P_n^{(\alpha,\beta)}(x)$, $\alpha=1(.2)2$, $\beta=-.5$, $n=5$.

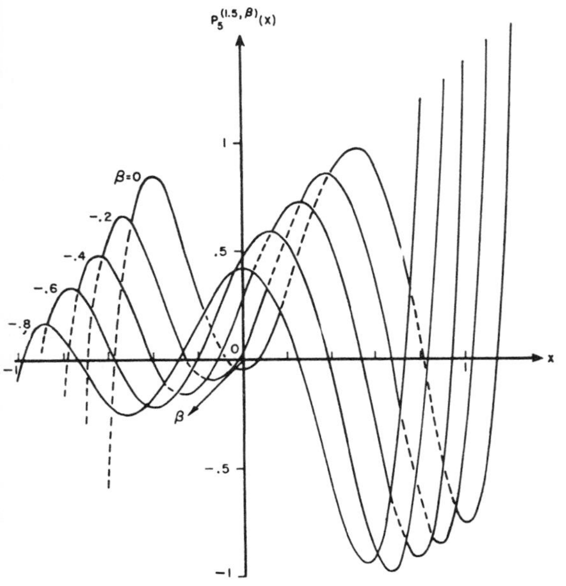

FIGURE 22.3. *Jacobi Polynomials* $P_n^{(\alpha,\beta)}(x)$, $\alpha=1.5$, $\beta=-.8(.2)0$, $n=5$.

Explicit Expressions Involving Trigonometric Functions

$$f_n(\cos\theta)=\sum_{m=0}^{n} a_m \cos(n-2m)\theta$$

	$f_n(\cos\theta)$	a_m	Remarks
22.3.12	$C_n^{(\alpha)}(\cos\theta)$	$\frac{\Gamma(\alpha+m)\Gamma(\alpha+n-m)}{m!(n-m)![\Gamma(\alpha)]^2}$	$\alpha\neq 0$
22.3.13	$P_n(\cos\theta)$	$\frac{1}{4^n}\binom{2m}{m}\binom{2n-2m}{n-m}$	

22.3.14 $$C_n^{(0)}(\cos\theta)=\frac{2}{n}\cos n\theta$$

22.3.15 $$T_n(\cos\theta)=\cos n\theta$$

22.3.16 $$U_n(\cos\theta)=\frac{\sin(n+1)\theta}{\sin\theta}$$

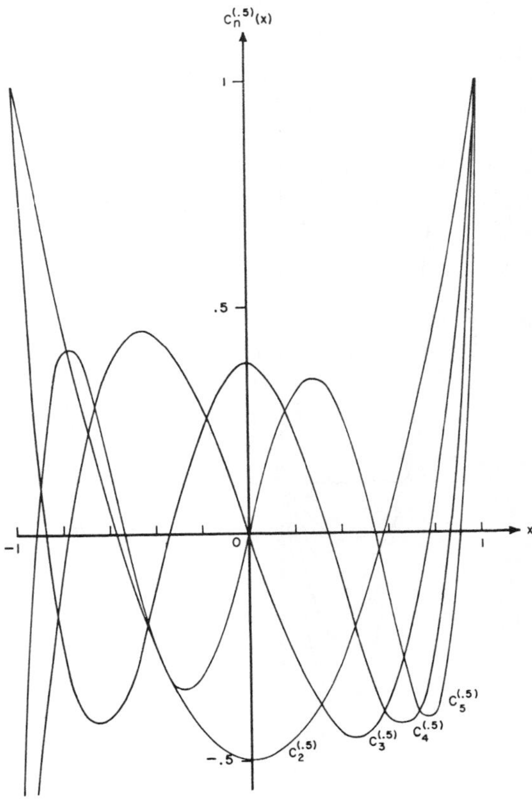

FIGURE 22.4. *Gegenbauer (Ultraspherical) Polynomials* $C_n^{(\alpha)}(x)$, $\alpha=.5$, $n=2(1)5$.

22.4. Special Values

	$f_n(x)$	$f_n(-x)$	$f_n(1)$	$f_n(0)$	$f_0(x)$	$f_1(x)$
22.4.1	$P_n^{(\alpha,\beta)}(x)$	$(-1)^n P_n^{(\beta,\alpha)}(x)$	$\binom{n+\alpha}{n}$		1	$\frac{1}{2}[\alpha-\beta+(\alpha+\beta+2)x]$
22.4.2	$C_n^{(\alpha)}(x)$ $\alpha\neq 0$	$(-1)^n C_n^{(\alpha)}(x)$	$\binom{n+2\alpha-1}{n}$	$\begin{cases}0, & n=2m+1\\ (-1)^{n/2}\dfrac{\Gamma(\alpha+n/2)}{\Gamma(\alpha)(n/2)!}, & n=2m\end{cases}$	1	$2\alpha x$
22.4.3	$C_n^{(0)}(x)$	$(-1)^n C_n^{(0)}(x)$	$\frac{2}{n},\ n\neq 0$	$\begin{cases}\dfrac{(-1)^m}{m}, & n=2m\neq 0\\ 0, & n=2m+1\end{cases}$	1	$2x$
22.4.4	$T_n(x)$	$(-1)^n T_n(x)$	1	$\begin{cases}(-1)^m, & n=2m\\ 0, & n=2m+1\end{cases}$	1	x
22.4.5	$U_n(x)$	$(-1)^n U_n(x)$	$n+1$	$\begin{cases}(-1)^m, & n=2m\\ 0, & n=2m+1\end{cases}$	1	$2x$
22.4.6	$P_n(x)$	$(-1)^n P_n(x)$	1	$\begin{cases}\dfrac{(-1)^m}{4^m}\dbinom{2m}{m}, & n=2m\\ 0, & n=2m+1\end{cases}$	1	x
22.4.7	$L_n^{(\alpha)}(x)$			$\binom{n+\alpha}{n}$	1	$-x+\alpha+1$
22.4.8	$H_n(x)$	$(-1)^n H_n(x)$		$\begin{cases}(-1)^m\dfrac{(2m)!}{m!}, & n=2m\\ 0, & n=2m+1\end{cases}$	1	$2x$

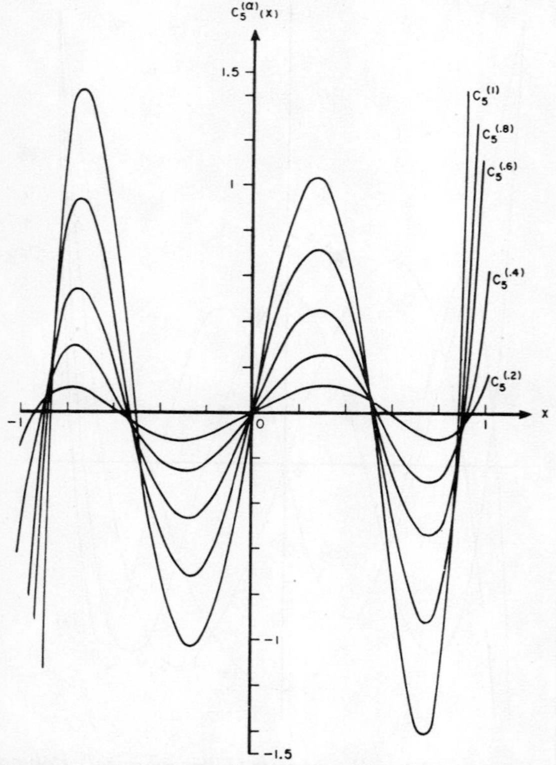

FIGURE 22.5. *Gegenbauer (Ultraspherical) Polynomials* $C_n^{(\alpha)}(x)$, $\alpha=.2(.2)1$, $n=5$.

22.5. Interrelations

Interrelations Between Orthogonal Polynomials of the Same Family

Jacobi Polynomials

22.5.1

$$P_n^{(\alpha,\beta)}(x)=\frac{\Gamma(2n+\alpha+\beta+1)}{n!\Gamma(n+\alpha+\beta+1)}G_n\left(\alpha+\beta+1,\beta+1,\frac{x+1}{2}\right)$$

22.5.2

$$G_n(p,q,x)=\frac{n!\Gamma(n+p)}{\Gamma(2n+p)}P_n^{(p-q,q-1)}(2x-1)$$

(see [22.21]).

22.5.3

$$F_n(p,q,x)=(-1)^n n!\frac{\Gamma(q)}{\Gamma(q+n)}P_n^{(p-q,q-1)}(2x-1)$$

(see [22.13]).

Ultraspherical Polynomials

22.5.4 $$C_n^{(0)}(x)=\lim_{\alpha\to 0}\frac{1}{\alpha}C_n^{(\alpha)}(x)$$

Chebyshev Polynomials

22.5.5 $$T_n(x)=\tfrac{1}{2}C_n(2x)=T_n^*\left(\frac{1+x}{2}\right)$$

22.5.6 $$T_n(x)=U_n(x)-xU_{n-1}(x)$$

22.5.7 $$T_n(x)=xU_{n-1}(x)-U_{n-2}(x)$$

22.5.8 $$T_n(x)=\tfrac{1}{2}[U_n(x)-U_{n-2}(x)]$$

22.5.9 $$U_n(x)=S_n(2x)=U_n^*\left(\frac{1+x}{2}\right)$$

22.5.10 $$U_{n-1}(x)=\frac{1}{1-x^2}[xT_n(x)-T_{n+1}(x)]$$

22.5.11 $$C_n(x)=2T_n\left(\frac{x}{2}\right)=2T_n^*\left(\frac{x+2}{4}\right)$$

22.5.12 $$C_n(x)=S_n(x)-S_{n-2}(x)$$

22.5.13 $$S_n(x)=U_n\left(\frac{x}{2}\right)=U_n^*\left(\frac{x+2}{4}\right)$$

22.5.14 $$T_n^*(x)=T_n(2x-1)=\tfrac{1}{2}C_n(4x-2)$$

(see [22.22]).

22.5.15 $$U_n^*(x)=S_n(4x-2)=U_n(2x-1)$$

(see [22.22]).

Generalized Laguerre Polynomials

22.5.16 $$L_n^{(0)}(x)=L_n(x)$$

22.5.17 $$L_n^{(m)}(x)=(-1)^m\frac{d^m}{dx^m}[L_{n+m}(x)]$$

Hermite Polynomials

22.5.18 $$He_n(x)=2^{-n/2}H_n\left(\frac{x}{\sqrt{2}}\right)$$

(see [22.20]).

22.5.19 $$H_n(x)=2^{n/2}He_n(x\sqrt{2})$$

(see [22.13], [22.20]).

Interrelations Between Orthogonal Polynomials of Different Families

Jacobi Polynomials

22.5.20

$$P_n^{(\alpha-\frac{1}{2},\alpha-\frac{1}{2})}(x)=\frac{\Gamma(2\alpha)\Gamma(\alpha+n+\frac{1}{2})}{\Gamma(2\alpha+n)\Gamma(\alpha+\frac{1}{2})}C_n^{(\alpha)}(x)$$

22.5.21

$$P_n^{(\alpha,\frac{1}{2})}(x)=\frac{(\frac{1}{2})_{n+1}}{\sqrt{\frac{x+1}{2}}\,(\alpha+\frac{1}{2})_{n+1}}C_{2n+1}^{(\alpha+\frac{1}{2})}\left(\sqrt{\frac{x+1}{2}}\right)$$

22.5.22 $$P_n^{(\alpha,-\frac{1}{2})}(x)=\frac{(\frac{1}{2})_n}{(\alpha+\frac{1}{2})_n}C_{2n}^{(\alpha+\frac{1}{2})}\left(\sqrt{\frac{x+1}{2}}\right)$$

22.5.23 $$P_n^{(-\frac{1}{2},-\frac{1}{2})}(x)=\frac{1}{4^n}\binom{2n}{n}T_n(x)$$

22.5.24 $$P_n^{(0,0)}(x)=P_n(x)$$

Ultraspherical Polynomials

22.5.25

$$C_{2n}^{(\alpha)}(x)=\frac{\Gamma(\alpha+n)n!2^{2n}}{\Gamma(\alpha)(2n)!}P_n^{(\alpha-\frac{1}{2},-\frac{1}{2})}(2x^2-1)$$

$(\alpha\neq0)$

22.5.26

$$C_{2n+1}^{(\alpha)}(x)=\frac{\Gamma(\alpha+n+1)n!2^{2n+1}}{\Gamma(\alpha)(2n+1)!}xP_n^{(\alpha-\frac{1}{2},\frac{1}{2})}(2x^2-1)$$

$(\alpha\neq0)$

22.5.27

$$C_n^{(\alpha)}(x)=\frac{\Gamma(\alpha+\frac{1}{2})\Gamma(2\alpha+n)}{\Gamma(2\alpha)\Gamma(\alpha+n+\frac{1}{2})}P_n^{(\alpha-\frac{1}{2},\alpha-\frac{1}{2})}(x)$$

$(\alpha\neq0)$

22.5.28

$$C_n^{(0)}(x)=\frac{2}{n}T_n(x)=2\frac{(n-1)!}{\Gamma(n+\frac{1}{2})}\sqrt{\pi}P_n^{(-\frac{1}{2},-\frac{1}{2})}(x)$$

Chebyshev Polynomials

22.5.29 $$T_{2n+1}(x)=\frac{n!\sqrt{\pi}}{\Gamma(n+\frac{1}{2})}xP_n^{(-\frac{1}{2},\frac{1}{2})}(2x^2-1)$$

22.5.30 $$U_{2n}(x)=\frac{n!\sqrt{\pi}}{\Gamma(n+\frac{1}{2})}P_n^{(\frac{1}{2},-\frac{1}{2})}(2x^2-1)$$

22.5.31 $$T_n(x)=\frac{n!\sqrt{\pi}}{\Gamma(n+\frac{1}{2})}P_n^{(-\frac{1}{2},-\frac{1}{2})}(x)$$

22.5.32 $$U_n(x)=\frac{(n+1)!\sqrt{\pi}}{2\Gamma(n+\frac{3}{2})}P_n^{(\frac{1}{2},\frac{1}{2})}(x)$$

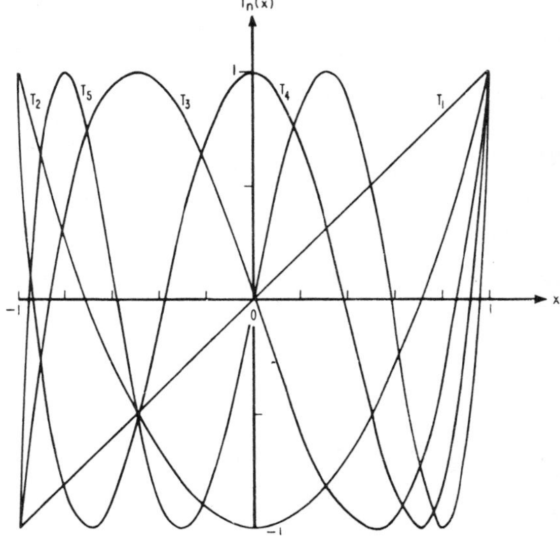

FIGURE 22.6. *Chebyshev Polynomials* $T_n(x)$, $n=1(1)5$.

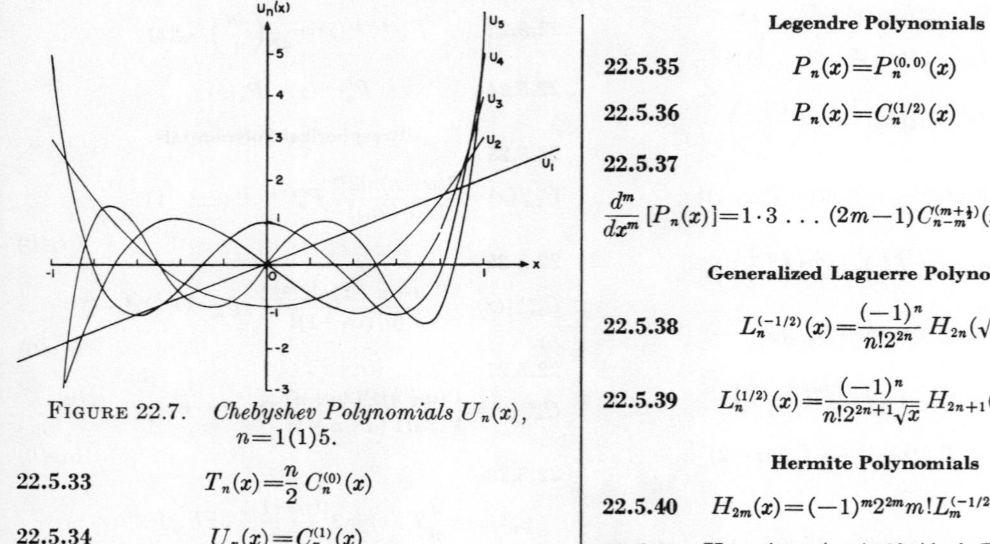

FIGURE 22.7. *Chebyshev Polynomials* $U_n(x)$, $n=1(1)5$.

22.5.33 $$T_n(x)=\frac{n}{2}C_n^{(0)}(x)$$

22.5.34 $$U_n(x)=C_n^{(1)}(x)$$

Legendre Polynomials

22.5.35 $$P_n(x)=P_n^{(0,0)}(x)$$

22.5.36 $$P_n(x)=C_n^{(1/2)}(x)$$

22.5.37

$$\frac{d^m}{dx^m}[P_n(x)]=1\cdot 3\ldots(2m-1)C_{n-m}^{(m+\frac{1}{2})}(x)\qquad(m\leq n)$$

Generalized Laguerre Polynomials

22.5.38 $$L_n^{(-1/2)}(x)=\frac{(-1)^n}{n!2^{2n}}H_{2n}(\sqrt{x})$$

22.5.39 $$L_n^{(1/2)}(x)=\frac{(-1)^n}{n!2^{2n+1}\sqrt{x}}H_{2n+1}(\sqrt{x})$$

Hermite Polynomials

22.5.40 $$H_{2m}(x)=(-1)^m 2^{2m}m!L_m^{(-1/2)}(x^2)$$

22.5.41 $$H_{2m+1}(x)=(-1)^m 2^{2m+1}m!xL_m^{(1/2)}(x^2)$$

Orthogonal Polynomials as Hypergeometric Functions (see chapter 15)

$$f_n(x)=dF(a,\ b;\ c;\ g(x))$$

For each of the listed polynomials there are numerous other representations in terms of hypergeometric functions.

	$f_n(x)$	d	a	b	c	$g(x)$
22.5.42	$P_n^{(\alpha,\beta)}(x)$	$\binom{n+\alpha}{n}$	$-n$	$n+\alpha+\beta+1$	$\alpha+1$	$\frac{1-x}{2}$
22.5.43	$P_n^{(\alpha,\beta)}(x)$	$\binom{2n+\alpha+\beta}{n}\left(\frac{x-1}{2}\right)^n$	$-n$	$-n-\alpha$	$-2n-\alpha-\beta$	$\frac{2}{1-x}$
22.5.44	$P_n^{(\alpha,\beta)}(x)$	$\binom{n+\alpha}{n}\left(\frac{1+x}{2}\right)^n$	$-n$	$-n-\beta$	$\alpha+1$	$\frac{x-1}{x+1}$
22.5.45	$P_n^{(\alpha,\beta)}(x)$	$\binom{n+\beta}{n}\left(\frac{x-1}{2}\right)^n$	$-n$	$-n-\alpha$	$\beta+1$	$\frac{x+1}{x-1}$
22.5.46	$C_n^{(\alpha)}(x)$	$\frac{\Gamma(n+2\alpha)}{n!\Gamma(2\alpha)}$	$-n$	$n+2\alpha$	$\alpha+\frac{1}{2}$	$\frac{1-x}{2}$
22.5.47	$T_n(x)$	1	$-n$	n	$\frac{1}{2}$	$\frac{1-x}{2}$
22.5.48	$U_n(x)$	$n+1$	$-n$	$n+2$	$\frac{3}{2}$	$\frac{1-x}{2}$
22.5.49	$P_n(x)$	1	$-n$	$n+1$	1	$\frac{1-x}{2}$
22.5.50	$P_n(x)$	$\binom{2n}{n}\left(\frac{x-1}{2}\right)^n$	$-n$	$-n$	$-2n$	$\frac{2}{1-x}$
22.5.51	$P_n(x)$	$\binom{2n}{n}\left(\frac{x}{2}\right)^n$	$-\frac{n}{2}$	$\frac{1-n}{2}$	$\frac{1}{2}-n$	$\frac{1}{x^2}$
22.5.52	$P_{2n}(x)$	$(-1)^n\frac{(2n)!}{2^{2n}(n!)^2}$	$-n$	$n+\frac{1}{2}$	$\frac{1}{2}$	x^2
22.5.53	$P_{2n+1}(x)$	$(-1)^n\frac{(2n+1)!}{2^{2n}(n!)^2}x$	$-n$	$n+\frac{3}{2}$	$\frac{3}{2}$	x^2

Orthogonal Polynomials as Confluent Hypergeometric Functions (see chapter **13**)

22.5.54 $L_n^{(\alpha)}(x)=\binom{n+\alpha}{n}M(-n,\alpha+1,x)$

Orthogonal Polynomials as Parabolic Cylinder Functions (see chapter **19**)

22.5.55 $H_n(x)=2^nU\left(\frac{1}{2}-\frac{1}{2}n,\frac{3}{2},x^2\right)$

22.5.56 $H_{2m}(x)=(-1)^m\frac{(2m)!}{m!}M\left(-m,\frac{1}{2},x^2\right)$

22.5.57

$$H_{2m+1}(x)=(-1)^m\frac{(2m+1)!}{m!}2xM\left(-m,\frac{3}{2},x^2\right)$$

22.5.58

$$H_n(x)=2^{n/2}e^{x^2/2}D_n(\sqrt{2}x)=2^{n/2}e^{x^2/2}U\left(-n-\frac{1}{2},\sqrt{2}x\right)$$

22.5.59 $He_n(x)=e^{x^2/4}D_n(x)=e^{x^2/4}U\left(-n-\frac{1}{2},x\right)$

Orthogonal Polynomials as Legendre Functions (see chapter **8**)

22.5.60

$C_n^{(\alpha)}(x)=$

$$\frac{\Gamma(\alpha+\frac{1}{2})\Gamma(2\alpha+n)}{n!\Gamma(2\alpha)}\left[\frac{1}{4}(x^2-1)\right]^{\frac{1}{4}-\frac{\alpha}{2}}P_{n+\alpha-\frac{1}{2}}^{(\frac{1}{2}-\alpha)}(x)$$

$(\alpha\neq 0)$

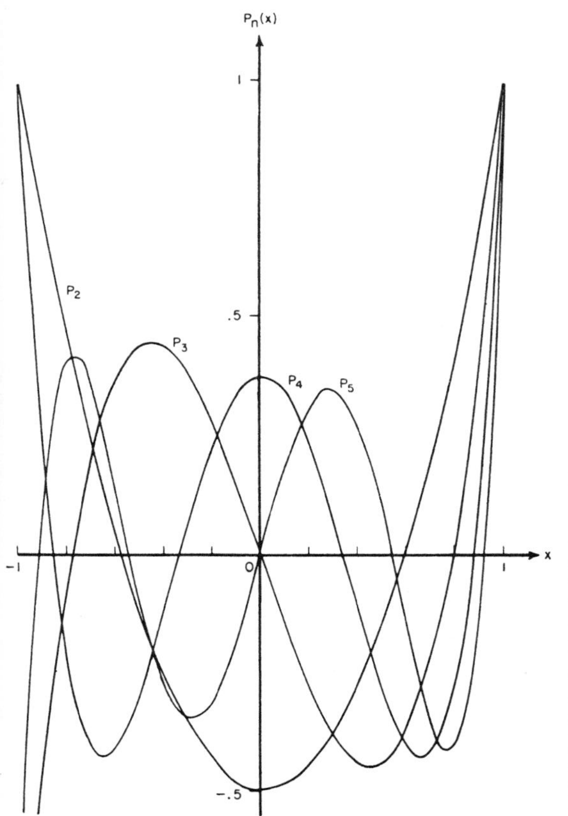

FIGURE 22.8. *Legendre Polynomials* $P_n(x)$, $n=2(1)5$.

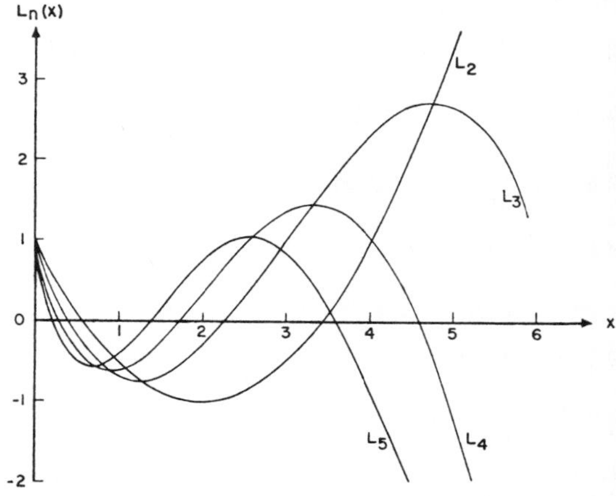

FIGURE 22.9. *Laguerre Polynomials* $L_n(x)$, $n=2(1)5$.

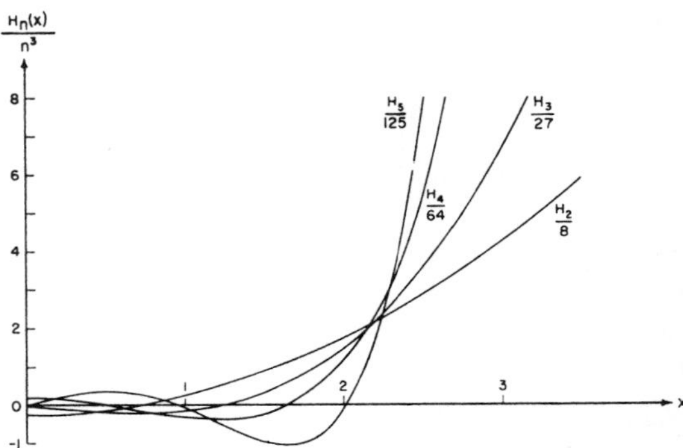

FIGURE 22.10. *Hermite Polynomials* $\frac{H_n(x)}{n^3}$, $n=2(1)5$.

22.6. Differential Equations

$$g_2(x)y''+g_1(x)y'+g_0(x)y=0$$

	y	$g_2(x)$	$g_1(x)$	$g_0(x)$
22.6.1	$P_n^{(\alpha,\beta)}(x)$	$1-x^2$	$\beta-\alpha-(\alpha+\beta+2)x$	$n(n+\alpha+\beta+1)$
22.6.2	$(1-x)^\alpha(1+x)^\beta P_n^{(\alpha,\beta)}(x)$	$1-x^2$	$\alpha-\beta+(\alpha+\beta-2)x$	$(n+1)(n+\alpha+\beta)$
22.6.3	$(1-x)^{\frac{\alpha+1}{2}}(1+x)^{\frac{\beta+1}{2}}P_n^{(\alpha,\beta)}(x)$	1	0	$\frac{1}{4}\frac{1-\alpha^2}{(1-x)^2}+\frac{1}{4}\frac{1-\beta^2}{(1+x)^2}+\frac{2n(n+\alpha+\beta+1)+(\alpha+1)(\beta+1)}{2(1-x^2)}$
22.6.4	$\left(\sin\frac{x}{2}\right)^{\alpha+\frac{1}{2}}\left(\cos\frac{x}{2}\right)^{\beta+\frac{1}{2}}P_n^{(\alpha,\beta)}(\cos x)$	1	0	$\frac{1-4\alpha^2}{16\sin^2\frac{x}{2}}+\frac{1-4\beta^2}{16\cos^2\frac{x}{2}}+\left(n+\frac{\alpha+\beta+1}{2}\right)^2$
22.6.5	$C_n^{(\alpha)}(x)$	$1-x^2$	$-(2\alpha+1)x$	$n(n+2\alpha)$
22.6.6	$(1-x^2)^{\alpha-\frac{1}{2}}C_n^{(\alpha)}(x)$	$1-x^2$	$(2\alpha-3)x$	$(n+1)(n+2\alpha-1)$
22.6.7	$(1-x^2)^{\frac{\alpha}{2}+\frac{1}{4}}C_n^{(\alpha)}(x)$	1	0	$\frac{(n+\alpha)^2}{1-x^2}+\frac{2+4\alpha-4\alpha^2+x^2}{4(1-x^2)^2}$
22.6.8	$(\sin x)^\alpha C_n^{(\alpha)}(\cos x)$	1	0	$(n+\alpha)^2+\frac{\alpha(1-\alpha)}{\sin^2 x}$
22.6.9	$T_n(x)$	$1-x^2$	$-x$	n^2
22.6.10	$T_n(\cos x)$	1	0	n^2
22.6.11	$\frac{1}{\sqrt{1-x^2}}T_n(x)$; $U_{n-1}(x)$	$1-x^2$	$-3x$	n^2-1
22.6.12	$U_n(x)$	$1-x^2$	$-3x$	$n(n+2)$
22.6.13	$P_n(x)$	$1-x^2$	$-2x$	$n(n+1)$
22.6.14	$\sqrt{1-x^2}P_n(x)$	1	0	$\frac{n(n+1)}{1-x^2}+\frac{1}{(1-x^2)^2}$
22.6.15	$L_n^{(\alpha)}(x)$	x	$\alpha+1-x$	n
22.6.16	$e^{-x}x^{\alpha/2}L_n^{(\alpha)}(x)$	x	$x+1$	$n+\frac{\alpha}{2}+1-\frac{\alpha^2}{4x}$
22.6.17	$e^{-x/2}x^{(\alpha+1)/2}L_n^{(\alpha)}(x)$	1	0	$\frac{2n+\alpha+1}{2x}+\frac{1-\alpha^2}{4x^2}-\frac{1}{4}$
22.6.18	$e^{-x^2/2}x^{\alpha+\frac{1}{2}}L_n^{(\alpha)}(x^2)$	1	0	$4n+2\alpha+2-x^2+\frac{1-4\alpha^2}{4x^2}$
22.6.19	$H_n(x)$	1	$-2x$	$2n$
22.6.20	$e^{-\frac{x^2}{2}}H_n(x)$	1	0	$2n+1-x^2$
22.6.21	$He_n(x)$	1	$-x$	n

22.7. Recurrence Relations

Recurrence Relations With Respect to the Degree n

$$a_{1n}f_{n+1}(x)=(a_{2n}+a_{3n}x)f_n(x)-a_{4n}f_{n-1}(x)$$

	f_n	a_{1n}	a_{2n}	a_{3n}	a_{4n}
22.7.1	$P_n^{(\alpha,\beta)}(x)$	$2(n+1)(n+\alpha+\beta+1)(2n+\alpha+\beta)$	$(2n+\alpha+\beta+1)(\alpha^2-\beta^2)$	$(2n+\alpha+\beta)_3$	$2(n+\alpha)(n+\beta)(2n+\alpha+\beta+2)$
22.7.2	$G_n(p,q,x)$	$(2n+p-2)_4(2n+p-1)$	$-[2n(n+p)+q(p-1)](2n+p-2)_3$	$(2n+p-2)_4(2n+p-1)$	$n(n+q-1)(n+p-1)(n+p-q)(2n+p+1)$
22.7.3	$C_n^{(\alpha)}(x)$	$n+1$	0	$2(n+\alpha)$	$n+2\alpha-1$
22.7.4	$T_n(x)$	1	0	2	1
22.7.5	$U_n(x)$	1	0	2	1
22.7.6	$S_n(x)$	1	0	1	1
22.7.7	$C_n(x)$	1	0	1	1
22.7.8	$T_n^*(x)$	1	-2	4	1
22.7.9	$U_n^*(x)$	1	-2	4	1
22.7.10	$P_n(x)$	$n+1$	0	$2n+1$	n
22.7.11	$P_n^*(x)$	$n+1$	$-2n-1$	$4n+2$	n
22.7.12	$L_n^{(\alpha)}(x)$	$n+1$	$2n+\alpha+1$	-1	$n+\alpha$
22.7.13	$H_n(x)$	1	0	2	$2n$
22.7.14	$He_n(x)$	1	0	1	n

Miscellaneous Recurrence Relations

Jacobi Polynomials

22.7.15

$$\left(n+\frac{\alpha}{2}+\frac{\beta}{2}+1\right)(1-x)P_n^{(\alpha+1,\beta)}(x)=(n+\alpha+1)P_n^{(\alpha,\beta)}(x)-(n+1)P_{n+1}^{(\alpha,\beta)}(x)$$

22.7.16

$$\left(n+\frac{\alpha}{2}+\frac{\beta}{2}+1\right)(1+x)P_n^{(\alpha,\beta+1)}(x)=(n+\beta+1)P_n^{(\alpha,\beta)}(x)+(n+1)P_{n+1}^{(\alpha,\beta)}(x)$$

22.7.17

$$(1-x)P_n^{(\alpha+1,\beta)}(x)+(1+x)P_n^{(\alpha,\beta+1)}(x)=2P_n^{(\alpha,\beta)}(x)$$

22.7.18

$$(2n+\alpha+\beta)P_n^{(\alpha-1,\beta)}(x)=(n+\alpha+\beta)P_n^{(\alpha,\beta)}(x)-(n+\beta)P_{n-1}^{(\alpha,\beta)}(x)$$

22.7.19

$$(2n+\alpha+\beta)P_n^{(\alpha,\beta-1)}(x)=(n+\alpha+\beta)P_n^{(\alpha,\beta)}(x)+(n+\alpha)P_{n-1}^{(\alpha,\beta)}(x)$$

22.7.20 $P_n^{(\alpha,\beta-1)}(x)-P_n^{(\alpha-1,\beta)}(x)=P_{n-1}^{(\alpha,\beta)}(x)$

Ultraspherical Polynomials

22.7.21

$$2\alpha(1-x^2)C_{n-1}^{(\alpha+1)}(x)=(2\alpha+n-1)C_{n-1}^{(\alpha)}(x)-nxC_n^{(\alpha)}(x)$$

22.7.22

$$=(n+2\alpha)xC_n^{(\alpha)}(x)-(n+1)C_{n+1}^{(\alpha)}(x)$$

22.7.23 $(n+\alpha)C_{n+1}^{(\alpha-1)}(x)=(\alpha-1)[C_{n+1}^{(\alpha)}(x)-C_{n-1}^{(\alpha)}(x)]$

Chebyshev Polynomials

22.7.24

$$2T_m(x)T_n(x)=T_{n+m}(x)+T_{n-m}(x)\qquad(n\geq m)$$

22.7.25

$$2(x^2-1)U_{m-1}(x)U_{n-1}(x)=T_{n+m}(x)-T_{n-m}(x)\qquad(n\geq m)$$

22.7.26

$$2T_m(x)U_{n-1}(x)=U_{n+m-1}(x)+U_{n-m-1}(x)\qquad(n>m)$$

22.7.27

$$2T_n(x)U_{m-1}(x)=U_{n+m-1}(x)-U_{n-m-1}(x)\qquad(n>m)$$

22.7.28 $2T_n(x)U_{n-1}(x)=U_{2n-1}(x)$

Generalized Laguerre Polynomials

22.7.29

$$L_n^{(\alpha+1)}(x)=\frac{1}{x}\left[(x-n)L_n^{(\alpha)}(x)+(\alpha+n)L_{n-1}^{(\alpha)}(x)\right]$$

22.7.30 $L_n^{(\alpha-1)}(x)=L_n^{(\alpha)}(x)-L_{n-1}^{(\alpha)}(x)$

22.7.31

$$L_n^{(\alpha+1)}(x)=\frac{1}{x}\left[(n+\alpha+1)L_n^{(\alpha)}(x)-(n+1)L_{n+1}^{(\alpha)}(x)\right]$$

22.7.32

$$L_n^{(\alpha-1)}(x)=\frac{1}{n+\alpha}\left[(n+1)L_{n+1}^{(\alpha)}(x)-(n+1-x)L_n^{(\alpha)}(x)\right]$$

22.8. Differential Relations

$$g_2(x)\frac{d}{dx}f_n(x)=g_1(x)f_n(x)+g_0(x)f_{n-1}(x)$$

	f_n	g_2	g_1	g_0
22.8.1	$P_n^{(\alpha,\beta)}(x)$	$(2n+\alpha+\beta)(1-x^2)$	$n[\alpha-\beta-(2n+\alpha+\beta)x]$	$2(n+\alpha)(n+\beta)$
22.8.2	$C_n^{(\alpha)}(x)$	$1-x^2$	$-nx$	$n+2\alpha-1$
22.8.3	$T_n(x)$	$1-x^2$	$-nx$	n
22.8.4	$U_n(x)$	$1-x^2$	$-nx$	$n+1$
22.8.5	$P_n(x)$	$1-x^2$	$-nx$	n
22.8.6	$L_n^{(\alpha)}(x)$	x	n	$-(n+\alpha)$
22.8.7	$H_n(x)$	1	0	$2n$
22.8.8	$He_n(x)$	1	0	n

22.9. Generating Functions

$$g(x,z)=\sum_{n=0}^{\infty}a_nf_n(x)z^n \qquad R=\sqrt{1-2xz+z^2}$$

	$f_n(x)$	a_n	$g(x,z)$	Remarks
22.9.1	$P_n^{(\alpha,\beta)}(x)$	$2^{-\alpha-\beta}$	$R^{-1}(1-z+R)^{-\alpha}(1+z+R)^{-\beta}$	$\|z\|<1$
22.9.2	$C_n^{(\alpha)}(x)$	$\frac{2^{\frac{1}{2}-\alpha}\Gamma(\alpha+\frac{1}{2}+n)\Gamma(2\alpha)}{\Gamma(\alpha+\frac{1}{2})\Gamma(2\alpha+n)}$	$R^{-1}(1-xz+R)^{\frac{1}{2}-\alpha}$	$\|z\|<1, \alpha\neq 0$
22.9.3	$C_n^{(\alpha)}(x)$	1	$R^{-2\alpha}$	$\|z\|<1, \alpha\neq 0$
22.9.4	$C_n^{(0)}(x)$	1	$-\ln R^2$	$\|z\|<1$
22.9.5	$C_n^{(\alpha)}(x)$	$\frac{\Gamma(2\alpha)}{\Gamma(\alpha+\frac{1}{2})\Gamma(2\alpha+n)}$	$e^{z\cos\theta}\left(\frac{z}{2}\sin\theta\right)^{\frac{1}{2}-\alpha}J_{\alpha-\frac{1}{2}}(z\sin\theta)$	$x=\cos\theta$
22.9.6	$T_n(x)$	2	$\left(\frac{1-z^2}{R^2}+1\right)$	$-1<x<1$ $\|z\|<1$
22.9.7	$T_n(x)$	$\frac{\sqrt{2}}{4^n}\binom{2n}{n}$	$R^{-1}(1-xz+R)^{1/2}$	$-1<x<1$ $\|z\|<1$
22.9.8	$T_n(x)$	$\frac{1}{n}$	$1-\frac{1}{2}\ln R^2$	$a_0=1$ $-1<x<1$ $\|z\|<1$
22.9.9	$T_n(x)$	1	$\frac{1-xz}{R^2}$	$-1<x<1$ $\|z\|<1$
22.9.10	$U_n(x)$	1	R^{-2}	$-1<x<1$ $\|z\|<1$
22.9.11	$U_n(x)$	$\frac{\sqrt{2}}{4^{n+1}}\binom{2n+2}{n+1}$	$\frac{1}{R}(1-xz+R)^{-1/2}$	$-1<x<1$ $\|z\|<1$

22.9. Generating Functions—Continued

$$g(x,z)=\sum_{n=0}^{\infty} a_n f_n(x) z^n \qquad R=\sqrt{1-2xz+z^2}$$

	$f_n(x)$	a_n	$g(x,z)$	Remarks
22.9.12	$P_n(x)$	1	R^{-1}	$-1<x<1$ $\lvert z\rvert<1$
22.9.13	$P_n(x)$	$\frac{1}{n!}$	$e^{z\cos\theta}J_0(z\sin\theta)$	$x=\cos\theta$
22.9.14	$S_n(x)$	1	$(1-xz+z^2)^{-1}$	$-2<x<2$ $\lvert z\rvert<1$
22.9.15	$L_n^{(\alpha)}(x)$	1	$(1-z)^{-\alpha-1}\exp\left(\frac{xz}{z-1}\right)$	$\lvert z\rvert<1$
22.9.16	$L_n^{(\alpha)}(x)$	$\frac{1}{\Gamma(n+\alpha+1)}$	$(xz)^{-\frac{1}{2}\alpha}e^zJ_\alpha[2(xz)^{1/2}]$	
22.9.17	$H_n(x)$	$\frac{1}{n!}$	e^{2xz-z^2}	
22.9.18	$H_{2n}(x)$	$\frac{(-1)^n}{(2n)!}$	$e^z\cos(2x\sqrt{z})$	
22.9.19	$H_{2n+1}(x)$	$\frac{(-1)^n}{(2n+1)!}$	$z^{-1/2}e^z\sin(2x\sqrt{z})$	

22.10. Integral Representations

Contour Integral Representations

$f_n(x)=\frac{g_0(x)}{2\pi i}\int_C [g_1(z,x)]^n g_2(z,x)dz$ where C is a closed contour taken around $z=a$ in the positive sense

	$f_n(x)$	$g_0(x)$	$g_1(z,x)$	$g_2(z,x)$	a	Remarks
22.10.1	$P_n^{(\alpha,\beta)}(x)$	$\frac{1}{(1-x)^\alpha(1+x)^\beta}$	$\frac{z^2-1}{2(z-x)}$	$\frac{(1-z)^\alpha(1+z)^\beta}{z-x}$	x	± 1 outside C
22.10.2	$C_n^{(\alpha)}(x)$	1	$1/z$	$(1-2xz+z^2)^{-\alpha}z^{-1}$	0	Both zeros of $1-2xz+z^2$ outside C, $\alpha>0$
22.10.3	$T_n(x)$	$1/2$	$1/z$	$\frac{1-z^2}{z(1-2xz+z^2)}$	0	Both zeros of $1-2xz+z^2$ outside C
22.10.4	$U_n(x)$	1	$1/z$	$\frac{1}{z(1-2xz+z^2)}$	0	Both zeros of $1-2xz+z^2$ outside C
22.10.5	$P_n(x)$	1	$1/z$	$\frac{1}{z}(1-2xz+z^2)^{-1/2}$	0	Both zeros of $1-2xz+z^2$ outside C
22.10.6	$P_n(x)$	$\frac{1}{2^n}$	$\frac{z^2-1}{z-x}$	$\frac{1}{z-x}$	x	
22.10.7	$L_n^{(\alpha)}(x)$	$e^x x^{-\alpha}$	$\frac{z}{z-x}$	$\frac{z^\alpha}{z-x}e^{-z}$	x	Zero outside C
22.10.8	$L_n^{(\alpha)}(x)$	1	$1+\frac{x}{z}$	$e^{-z}\left(1+\frac{z}{x}\right)^\alpha 1/z$	0	$z=-x$ outside C
22.10.9	$H_n(x)$	$n!$	$1/z$	$\frac{e^{2xz-z^2}}{z}$	0	

Miscellaneous Integral Representations

22.10.10 $$C_n^{(\alpha)}(x)=\frac{2^{(1-2\alpha)}\Gamma(n+2\alpha)}{n![\Gamma(\alpha)]^2}\int_0^\pi [x+\sqrt{x^2-1}\cos\phi]^n(\sin\phi)^{2\alpha-1}d\phi \qquad (\alpha>0)$$

22.10.11 $$C_n^{(\alpha)}(\cos\theta)=\frac{2^{1-\alpha}\Gamma(n+2\alpha)}{n![\Gamma(\alpha)]^2}(\sin\theta)^{1-2\alpha}\int_0^\theta \frac{\cos(n+\alpha)\phi}{(\cos\phi-\cos\theta)^{1-\alpha}}d\phi \qquad (\alpha>0)$$

22.10.12 $P_n(\cos\theta)=\frac{1}{\pi}\int_0^{\pi}(\cos\theta+i\sin\theta\cos\phi)^n d\phi$

22.10.13 $P_n(\cos\theta)=\frac{\sqrt{2}}{\pi}\int_{\theta}^{\pi}\frac{\sin(n+\frac{1}{2})\phi d\phi}{(\cos\theta-\cos\phi)^{\frac{1}{2}}}$

22.10.14 $L_n^{(\alpha)}(x)=\frac{e^x x^{-\frac{\alpha}{2}}}{n!}\int_0^{\infty}e^{-t}t^{n+\frac{\alpha}{2}}J_{\alpha}(2\sqrt{tx})dt$

22.10.15

$$H_n(x)=e^{x^2}\frac{2^{n+1}}{\sqrt{\pi}}\int_0^{\infty}e^{-t^2}t^n\cos\left(2xt-\frac{n}{2}\pi\right)dt$$

22.11. Rodrigues' Formula

$$f_n(x)=\frac{1}{a_n\rho(x)}\frac{d^n}{dx^n}\{\rho(x)(g(x))^n\}$$

The polynomials given in the following table are the only orthogonal polynomials which satisfy this formula.

	$f_n(x)$	a_n	$\rho(x)$	$g(x)$
22.11.1	$P_n^{(\alpha,\beta)}(x)$	$(-1)^n 2^n n!$	$(1-x)^{\alpha}(1+x)^{\beta}$	$1-x^2$
22.11.2	$C_n^{(\alpha)}(x)$	$(-1)^n 2^n n!\frac{\Gamma(2\alpha)\Gamma(\alpha+n+\frac{1}{2})}{\Gamma(\alpha+\frac{1}{2})\Gamma(n+2\alpha)}$	$(1-x^2)^{\alpha-\frac{1}{2}}$	$1-x^2$
22.11.3	$T_n(x)$	$(-1)^n 2^n\frac{\Gamma(n+\frac{1}{2})}{\sqrt{\pi}}$	$(1-x^2)^{-\frac{1}{2}}$	$1-x^2$
22.11.4	$U_n(x)$	$(-1)^n 2^{n+1}\frac{\Gamma(n+\frac{3}{2})}{(n+1)\sqrt{\pi}}$	$(1-x^2)^{\frac{1}{2}}$	$1-x^2$
22.11.5	$P_n(x)$	$(-1)^n 2^n n!$	1	$1-x^2$
22.11.6	$L_n^{(\alpha)}(x)$	$n!$	$e^{-x}x^{\alpha}$	x
22.11.7	$H_n(x)$	$(-1)^n$	e^{-x^2}	1
22.11.8	$He_n(x)$	$(-1)^n$	$e^{-x^2/2}$	1

22.12. Sum Formulas

Christoffel-Darboux Formula

22.12.1

$$\sum_{m=0}^{n}\frac{1}{h_m}f_m(x)f_m(y)=\frac{k_n}{k_{n+1}h_n}\frac{f_{n+1}(x)f_n(y)-f_n(x)f_{n+1}(y)}{x-y}$$

Miscellaneous Sum Formulas (Only a Limited Selection Is Given Here.)

22.12.2 $\sum_{m=0}^{n}T_{2m}(x)=\frac{1}{2}[1+U_{2n}(x)]$

22.12.3 $\sum_{m=0}^{n-1}T_{2m+1}(x)=\frac{1}{2}U_{2n-1}(x)$

22.12.4 $\sum_{m=0}^{n}U_{2m}(x)=\frac{1-T_{2n+2}(x)}{2(1-x^2)}$

22.12.5 $\sum_{m=0}^{n-1}U_{2m+1}(x)=\frac{x-T_{2n+1}(x)}{2(1-x^2)}$

22.12.6 $\sum_{m=0}^{n}L_m^{(\alpha)}(x)L_{n-m}^{(\beta)}(y)=L_n^{(\alpha+\beta+1)}(x+y)$

22.12.7 $\sum_{m=0}^{n}\binom{n+\alpha}{m}\mu^{n-m}(1-\mu)^m L_{n-m}^{(\alpha)}(x)=L_n^{(\alpha)}(\mu x)$

22.12.8

$$H_n(x+y)=\frac{1}{2^{n/2}}\sum_{k=0}^{n}\binom{n}{k}H_k(\sqrt{2}x)H_{n-k}(\sqrt{2}y)$$

22.13. Integrals Involving Orthogonal Polynomials

22.13.1

$$2n\int_0^x(1-y)^{\alpha}(1+y)^{\beta}P_n^{(\alpha,\beta)}(y)dy$$
$$=P_{n-1}^{(\alpha+1,\beta+1)}(0)-(1-x)^{\alpha+1}(1+x)^{\beta+1}P_{n-1}^{(\alpha+1,\beta+1)}(x)$$

22.13.2

$$\frac{n(2\alpha+n)}{2\alpha}\int_0^x(1-y^2)^{\alpha-\frac{1}{2}}C_n^{(\alpha)}(y)dy$$
$$=C_{n-1}^{(\alpha+1)}(0)-(1-x^2)^{\alpha+\frac{1}{2}}C_{n-1}^{(\alpha+1)}(x)$$

22.13.3 $\int_{-1}^{1}\frac{T_n(y)dy}{(y-x)\sqrt{1-y^2}}=\pi U_{n-1}(x)$

22.13.4 $\int_{-1}^{1}\frac{\sqrt{1-y^2}U_{n-1}(y)dy}{(y-x)}=-\pi T_n(x)$

22.13.5 $\int_{-1}^{1}(1-x)^{-1/2}P_n(x)dx=\frac{2^{3/2}}{2n+1}$

22.13.6 $\int_0^{\pi}P_{2n}(\cos\theta)d\theta=\frac{\pi}{16^n}\binom{2n}{n}^2$

22.13.7 $\int_0^{\pi}P_{2n+1}(\cos\theta)\cos\theta d\theta=\frac{\pi}{4^{2n+1}}\binom{2n}{n}\binom{2n+2}{n+1}$

22.13.8

$$\int_0^1 x^\lambda P_{2n}(x)dx=\frac{(-1)^n\Gamma\left(n-\frac{\lambda}{2}\right)\Gamma\left(\frac{1}{2}+\frac{\lambda}{2}\right)}{2\Gamma\left(-\frac{\lambda}{2}\right)\Gamma\left(n+\frac{3}{2}+\frac{\lambda}{2}\right)}\quad(\lambda>-1)$$

22.13.9

$$\int_0^1 x^\lambda P_{2n+1}(x)dx=\frac{(-1)^n\Gamma\left(n+\frac{1}{2}-\frac{\lambda}{2}\right)\Gamma\left(1+\frac{\lambda}{2}\right)}{2\Gamma\left(n+2+\frac{\lambda}{2}\right)\Gamma\left(\frac{1}{2}-\frac{\lambda}{2}\right)}\quad(\lambda>-2)$$

22.13.10

$$\int_{-1}^x \frac{P_n(t)dt}{\sqrt{x-t}}=\frac{1}{(n+\frac{1}{2})\sqrt{1+x}}\left[T_n(x)+T_{n+1}(x)\right]$$

22.13.11

$$\int_x^1 \frac{P_n(t)dt}{\sqrt{t-x}}=\frac{1}{(n+\frac{1}{2})\sqrt{1-x}}\left[T_n(x)-T_{n+1}(x)\right]$$

22.13.12 $\displaystyle\int_x^\infty e^{-t}L_n^{(\alpha)}(t)dt=e^{-x}[L_n^{(\alpha)}(x)-L_{n-1}^{(\alpha)}(x)]$

22.13.13

$$\Gamma(\alpha+\beta+n+1)\int_0^x (x-t)^{\beta-1}t^\alpha L_n^{(\alpha)}(t)dt=\Gamma(\alpha+n+1)\Gamma(\beta)x^{\alpha+\beta}L_n^{(\alpha+\beta)}(x)\quad(\mathscr{R}\alpha>-1,\ \mathscr{R}\beta>0)$$

22.13.14

$$\int_0^x L_m(t)L_n(x-t)dt=\int_0^x L_{m+n}(t)dt=L_{m+n}(x)-L_{m+n+1}(x)$$

22.13.15 $\displaystyle\int_0^x e^{-t^2}H_n(t)dt=H_{n-1}(0)-e^{-x^2}H_{n-1}(x)$

22.13.16 $\displaystyle\int_0^x H_n(t)dt=\frac{1}{2(n+1)}\left[H_{n+1}(x)-H_{n+1}(0)\right]$

22.13.17 $\displaystyle\int_{-\infty}^\infty e^{-t^2}H_{2m}(tx)dt=\sqrt{\pi}\,\frac{(2m)!}{m!}\,(x^2-1)^m$

22.13.18

$$\int_{-\infty}^\infty e^{-t^2}tH_{2m+1}(tx)dt=\sqrt{\pi}\,\frac{(2m+1)!}{m!}\,x(x^2-1)^m$$

22.13.19 $\displaystyle\int_{-\infty}^\infty e^{-t^2}t^nH_n(xt)dt=\sqrt{\pi}n!P_n(x)$

22.13.20

$$\int_0^\infty e^{-t^2}[H_n(t)]^2\cos(xt)dt=\sqrt{\pi}2^{n-1}n!e^{-\frac{1}{4}x^2}L_n\left(\frac{x^2}{2}\right)$$

22.14. Inequalities

22.14.1

$$|P_n^{(\alpha,\beta)}(x)|\leqq\begin{cases}\binom{n+q}{n}\approx n^q, \text{ if } q=\max(\alpha,\beta)\geq-1/2\\ \qquad\qquad(\alpha>-1,\beta>-1)\\ |P_n^{(\alpha,\beta)}(x')|\approx\sqrt{\frac{1}{n}}, \text{ if } q<-\frac{1}{2}\end{cases}$$

x' maximum point nearest to $\dfrac{\beta-\alpha}{\alpha+\beta+1}$

22.14.2

$$|C_n^{(\alpha)}(x)|\leq\begin{cases}\binom{n+2\alpha-1}{n} & (\alpha>0)\\ |C_n^{(\alpha)}(x')| & \left(-\frac{1}{2}<\alpha<0\right)\end{cases}$$

$x'=0$ if $n=2m$; $x'=$maximum point nearest zero if $n=2m+1$

22.14.3

$$|C_n^{(\alpha)}(\cos\theta)|<2^{1-\alpha}\frac{n^{\alpha-1}}{(\sin\theta)^\alpha\Gamma(\alpha)}\quad(0<\alpha<1,0<\theta<\pi)$$

22.14.4 $|T_n(x)|\leq1\qquad(-1\leq x\leq1)$

22.14.5 $\left|\dfrac{dT_n(x)}{dx}\right|\leq n^2\qquad(-1\leq x\leq1)$

22.14.6 $|U_n(x)|\leq n+1\qquad(-1\leq x\leq1)$

22.14.7 $|P_n(x)|\leq1\qquad(-1\leq x\leq1)$

22.14.8 $\left|\dfrac{dP_n(x)}{dx}\right|\leq\dfrac{1}{2}n(n+1)\qquad(-1\leq x\leq1)$

22.14.9 $|P_n(x)|\leq\sqrt{\dfrac{2}{\pi n}}\,\dfrac{1}{\sqrt[4]{1-x^2}}\qquad(-1<x\leq1)$

22.14.10

$$P_n^2(x)-P_{n-1}(x)P_{n+1}(x)<\frac{2n+1}{3n(n+1)}\qquad(-1\leq x\leq1)$$

22.14.11

$$P_n^2(x)-P_{n-1}(x)P_{n+1}(x)\geq\frac{1-P_n^2(x)}{(2n-1)(n+1)}\qquad(-1\leq x\leq1)$$

22.14.12 $|L_n(x)|\leq e^{x/2}\qquad(x\geq0)$

22.14.13 $|L_n^{(\alpha)}(x)|\leq\dfrac{\Gamma(\alpha+n+1)}{n!\Gamma(\alpha+1)}e^{x/2}\qquad(\alpha\geq0,\ x\geq0)$

22.14.14

$$|L_n^{(\alpha)}(x)|\leq\left[2-\frac{\Gamma(\alpha+n+1)}{n!\Gamma(\alpha+1)}\right]e^{x/2}\qquad(-1<\alpha<0,\ x\geq0)$$

22.14.15 $|H_{2m}(x)|\leq e^{x^2/2}2^{2m}m!\left[2-\frac{1}{2^{2m}}\binom{2m}{m}\right]$

22.14.16 $|H_{2m+1}(x)|\leq xe^{x^2/2}\frac{(2m+2)!}{(m+1)!}\qquad(x\geq 0)$

22.14.17 $|H_n(x)|<e^{x^2/2}k2^{n/2}\sqrt{n!}\qquad k\approx 1.086435$

22.15. Limit Relations

22.15.1

$$\lim_{n\to\infty}\left[\frac{1}{n^\alpha}P_n^{(\alpha,\beta)}\left(\cos\frac{x}{n}\right)\right]$$

$$=\lim_{n\to\infty}\frac{1}{n^\alpha}P_n^{(\alpha,\beta)}\left(1-\frac{x^2}{2n^2}\right)=\left(\frac{2}{x}\right)^\alpha J_\alpha(x)$$

22.15.2 $\lim_{n\to\infty}\left[\frac{1}{n^\alpha}L_n^{(\alpha)}\left(\frac{x}{n}\right)\right]=x^{-\alpha/2}J_\alpha(2\sqrt{x})$

22.15.3 $\lim_{n\to\infty}\left[\frac{(-1)^n\sqrt{n}}{4^n n!}H_{2n}\left(\frac{x}{2\sqrt{n}}\right)\right]=\frac{1}{\sqrt{\pi}}\cos x$

22.15.4 $\lim_{n\to\infty}\left[\frac{(-1)^n}{4^n n!}H_{2n+1}\left(\frac{x}{2\sqrt{n}}\right)\right]=\frac{2}{\sqrt{\pi}}\sin x$

22.15.5 $\lim_{\beta\to\infty}P_n^{(\alpha,\beta)}\left(1-\frac{2x}{\beta}\right)=L_n^{(\alpha)}(x)$

22.15.6 $\lim_{\alpha\to\infty}\frac{1}{\alpha^{n/2}}C_n^{(\alpha)}\left(\frac{x}{\sqrt{\alpha}}\right)=\frac{1}{n!}H_n(x)$

For asymptotic expansions, see [22.5] and [22.17].

22.16. Zeros

For tables of the zeros and associated weight factors necessary for the Gaussian-type quadrature formulas see chapter **25.** All the zeros of the orthogonal polynomials are real, simple and located in the interior of the interval of orthogonality.

Explicit and Asymptotic Formulas and Inequalities

Notations:

$x_m^{(n)}$ mth zero of $f_n(x)$ $(x_1^{(n)}<x_2^{(n)}<\ldots<x_n^{(n)})$

$\theta_m^{(n)}=\arccos x_{n-m+1}^{(n)}$ $(0<\theta_1^{(n)}<\theta_2^{(n)}<\ldots<\theta_n^{(n)}<\pi)$

$j_{\alpha,m}$, mth positive zero of the Bessel function $J_\alpha(x)$

$0<j_{\alpha,1}<j_{\alpha,2}<\ldots$

	$f_n(x)$	Relation
22.16.1	$P_n^{(\alpha,\beta)}(\cos\theta)$	$\lim_{n\to\infty}n\theta_m^{(n)}=j_{\alpha,m}\qquad(\alpha>-1,\ \beta>-1)$
22.16.2	$C_n^{(\alpha)}(x)$	$x_m^{(n)}=1-\frac{j^2_{\alpha-\frac{1}{2},m}}{2n^2}\left[1-\frac{2\alpha}{n}+O\left(\frac{1}{n^2}\right)\right]$
22.16.3	$C_n^{(\alpha)}(\cos\theta)$	$\frac{(m+\alpha-1)\pi}{n+\alpha}\leq\theta_m^{(n)}\leq\frac{m\pi}{n+\alpha}\qquad(0\leq\alpha\leq 1)$
22.16.4	$T_n(x)$	$x_m^{(n)}=\cos\frac{2m-1}{2n}\pi$
22.16.5	$U_n(x)$	$x_m^{(n)}=\cos\frac{m}{n+1}\pi$
22.16.6	$P_n(\cos\theta)$	$\frac{2m-1}{2n+1}\pi\leq\theta_m^{(n)}\leq\frac{2m}{2n+1}\pi$ $\theta_m^{(n)}=\frac{4m-1}{4n+2}\pi+\frac{1}{8n^2}\cot\frac{4m-1}{4n+2}\pi+O(n^{-3})$
22.16.7	$P_n(x)$	$x_m^{(n)}=1-\frac{j^2_{0,m}}{2n^2}\left[1-\frac{1}{n}+O(n^{-2})\right]$ $x_m^{(n)}=1-\frac{4\xi_m^{(n)}}{2n+1+\xi_m^{(n)}};\ \xi_m^{(n)}=\frac{j^2_{0,m}}{4n+2}\left[1+\frac{j^2_{0,m-2}}{12(2n+1)^2}\right]+O\left(\frac{1}{n^5}\right)$
22.16.8	$L_n^{(\alpha)}(x)$	$x_m^{(n)}>\frac{j^2_{\alpha,m}}{4k_n}$ $x_m^{(n)}<\frac{k_m}{k_n}(2k_m+\sqrt{4k_m^2+\frac{1}{4}-\alpha^2})$ $x_m^{(n)}=\frac{j^2_{\alpha,m}}{4k_n}\left(1+\frac{2(\alpha^2-1)+j^2_{\alpha,m}}{48k_n^2}\right)+O(n^{-5})$ $k_\tau=\tau+\frac{\alpha+1}{2}$

For error estimates see [22.6].

22.17. Orthogonal Polynomials of a Discrete Variable

In this section some polynomials $f_n(x)$ are listed which are orthogonal with respect to the scalar product

22.17.1 $$(f_n, f_m)=\sum_i w^*(x_i)f_n(x_i)f_m(x_i).$$

The x_i are the integers in the interval $a\leq x_i\leq b$ and $w^*(x_i)$ is a positive function such that $\sum_i w^*(x_i)$ is finite. The constant factor which is still free in each polynomial when only the orthogonality condition is given is defined here by the explicit representation (which corresponds to the Rodrigues' formula)

22.17.2 $$f_n(x)=\frac{1}{r_n w^*(x)}\Delta^n[w^*(x)g(x, n)]$$

where $g(x, n)=g(x)g(x-1) \ldots g(x-n+1)$ and $g(x)$ is a polynomial in x independent of n.

Name	a	b	$w^*(x)$	r_n	$g(x, n)$	Remarks
Chebyshev	0	$N-1$	1	$1/n!$	$\binom{x}{n}\binom{x-N}{n}$	
Krawtchouk	0	N	$p^x q^{N-x}\binom{N}{x}$	$(-1)^n n!$	$\frac{q^n x!}{(x-n)!}$	$p, q>0;$ $p+q=1$
Charlier	0	∞	$\frac{e^{-a}a^x}{x!}$	$(-1)^n\sqrt{a^n}n!$	$\frac{x!}{(x-n)!}$	$a>0$
Meixner	0	∞	$\frac{c^x\Gamma(b+x)}{\Gamma(b)x!}$	c^n	$\frac{x!}{(x-n)!}$	$b>0,\ 0<c<1$
Hahn	0	∞	$\frac{\Gamma(b)\Gamma(c+x)\Gamma(d+x)}{x!\Gamma(b+x)\Gamma(c)\Gamma(d)}$	$n!$	$\frac{x!\Gamma(b+x)}{(x-n)!\Gamma(b+x-n)}$	

For a more complete list of the properties of these polynomials see [22.5] and [22.17].

22.18. Use and Extension of the Tables

Evaluation of an orthogonal polynomial using the explicit representation when the coefficients are not given numerically.

If an isolated value of the orthogonal polynomial $f_n(x)$ is to be computed, use the proper explicit expression rewritten in the form

$$f_n(x)=d_n(x)a_0(x)$$

and generate $a_0(x)$ recursively, where

$$a_{m-1}(x)=1-\frac{b_m}{c_m}f(x)a_m(x) \qquad (m=n,\ n-1,\ .\ .\ .,\ 2,\ 1,\ a_n(x)=1).$$

The $d_n(x)$, b_m, c_m, $f(x)$ for the polynomials of this chapter are listed in the following table:

$f_n(x)$	$d_n(x)$	b_m	c_m	$f(x)$
$P_n^{(\alpha,\beta)}$	$\binom{n+\alpha}{n}$	$(n-m+1)(\alpha+\beta+n+m)$	$2m(\alpha+m)$	$1-x$
$C_{2n}^{(\alpha)}$	$(-1)^n\frac{(\alpha)_n}{n!}$	$2(n-m+1)(\alpha+n+m-1)$	$m(2m-1)$	x^2
$C_{2n+1}^{(\alpha)}$	$(-1)^n\frac{(\alpha)_{n+1}}{n!}2x$	$2(n-m+1)(\alpha+n+m)$	$m(2m+1)$	x^2
T_{2n}	$(-1)^n$	$2(n-m+1)(n+m-1)$	$m(2m-1)$	x^2
T_{2n+1}	$(-1)^n(2n+1)x$	$2(n-m+1)(n+m)$	$m(2m+1)$	x^2
U_{2n}	$(-1)^n$	$2(n-m+1)(n+m)$	$m(2m-1)$	x^2
U_{2n+1}	$(-1)^n2(n+1)x$	$2(n-m+1)(n+m+1)$	$m(2m+1)$	x^2
P_{2n}	$\frac{(-1)^n}{4^n}\binom{2n}{n}$	$(n-m+1)(2n+2m-1)$	$m(2m-1)$	x^2
P_{2n+1}	$\frac{(-1)^n}{4^n}\binom{2n+1}{n}(n+1)x$	$(n-m+1)(2n+2m+1)$	$m(2m+1)$	x^2
$L_n^{(\alpha)}$	$\binom{n+\alpha}{n}$	$n-m+1$	$m(\alpha+m)$	x
H_{2n}	$(-1)^n\frac{(2n)!}{n!}$	$2(n-m+1)$	$m(2m-1)$	x^2
H_{2n+1}	$(-1)^n\frac{(2n+1)!}{n!}2x$	$2(n-m+1)$	$m(2m+1)$	x^2

Change of Interval of Orthogonality

In some applications it is more convenient to use polynomials orthogonal on the interval [0, 1]. One can obtain the new polynomials from the ones given in this chapter by the substitution $x=2\bar{x}-1$. The coefficients of the new polynomial can be computed from the old by the following recursive scheme, provided the standardization is not changed. If

$$f_n(x)=\sum_{m=0}^{n} a_m x^m, \quad f_n^*(x)=f_n(2x-1)=\sum_{m=0}^{n} a_m^* x^m$$

then the a_m^* are given recursively by the a_m through the relations

$a_m^{(j)}=2a_m^{(j-1)}-a_{m+1}^{(j)}$; $m=n-1, n-2, \ldots, j$; $j=0, 1, 2, \ldots, n$

$a_m^{(-1)}=a_m/2$, $m=0, 1, 2, \ldots, n$

$a_n^{(j)}=2^j a_n$, $j=0, 1, 2, \ldots, n$ and $a_m^{(m)}=a_m^*$; $m=0, 1, 2, \ldots, n$.

Example 4. Given $T_5(x)=5x-20x^3+16x^5$, find $T_5^*(x)$.

j \ m	5	4	3	2	1	0
−1	$8=a_5^{(-1)}$	0	$-10=a_3^{(-1)}$	0	$2.5=a_1^{(-1)}$	0
0	16	−16	−4	4	1	$-1=a_0^*$
1	32	−64	56	−48	$50=a_1^*$	
2	64	−192	304	$-400=a_2^*$		
3	128	−512	$1120=a_3^*$			
4	256	$-1280=a_4^*$				
5	$512=a_5^*$					

Hence, $T_5^*(x)=512x^5-1280x^4+1120x^3-400x^2+50x-1$.

22.19. Least Square Approximations

Problem: Given a function $f(x)$ (analytically or in form of a table) in a domain D (which may be a continuous interval or a set of discrete points).[2] Approximate $f(x)$ by a polynomial $F_n(x)$ of given degree n such that a weighted sum of the squares of the errors in D is least.

Solution: Let $w(x)\geq 0$ be the weight function chosen according to the relative importance of the errors in different parts of D. Let $f_m(x)$ be orthogonal polynomials in D relative to $w(x)$, i.e. $(f_m, f_n)=0$ for $m\neq n$, where

$$(f,g)=\begin{cases} \int_D w(x)f(x)g(x)dx & \text{if } D \text{ is a continuous interval} \\ \sum_{m=1}^{N} w(x_m)f(x_m)g(x_m) & \text{if } D \text{ is a set of } N \text{ discrete points } x_m. \end{cases}$$

Then

$$F_n(x)=\sum_{m=0}^{n} a_m f_m(x)$$

where

$$a_m=(f, f_m)/(f_m, f_m).$$

[2] $f(x)$ has to be square integrable, see e.g. [22.17].

D a Continuous Interval

Example 5. Find a least square polynomial of degree 5 for $f(x)=\frac{1}{1+x}$, in the interval $2\leq x\leq 5$, using the weight function

$$w(x)=\frac{1}{\sqrt{(x-2)(5-x)}}$$

which stresses the importance of the errors at the ends of the interval.

Reduction to interval $[-1,1]$, $t=\frac{2x-7}{3}$

$$w(x(t))=\frac{2}{3}\frac{1}{\sqrt{1-t^2}}$$

From **22.2**, $f_m(t)=T_m(t)$ and

$$a_m=\frac{4}{3\pi}\int_{-1}^{1}\frac{1}{\sqrt{1-t^2}}\frac{1}{t+3}T_m(t)dt \qquad (m\neq 0)$$

$$a_0=\frac{2}{3\pi}\int_{-1}^{1}\frac{1}{\sqrt{1-t^2}}\frac{dt}{t+3}$$

Evaluating the integrals numerically we get

$$\frac{1}{1+x}\sim .235703-.080880T_1\left(\frac{2x-7}{3}\right)+.013876T_2\left(\frac{2x-7}{3}\right)-.002380T_3\left(\frac{2x-7}{3}\right)$$
$$+.000408T_4\left(\frac{2x-7}{3}\right)-.000070T_5\left(\frac{2x-7}{3}\right)$$

D a Set of Discrete Points

If $x_m=m(m=0, 1, 2, \ldots, N)$ and $w(x)=1$, use the Chebyshev polynomials in the discrete range **22.17**. It is convenient to introduce here a slightly different standardization such that

$$f_n(x)=\sum_{m=0}^{n}(-1)^m\binom{n}{m}\binom{n+m}{m}\frac{x!(N-m)!}{(x-m)!N!}$$

$$(f_n, f_n)=\frac{(N+n+1)!(N-n)!}{(2n+1)(N!)^2}$$

Recurrence relation: $f_0(x)=1, f_1(x)=1-\frac{2x}{N}$

$$(n+1)(N-n)f_{n+1}(x)=(2n+1)(N-2x)f_n(x)-n(N+n+1)f_{n-1}(x)$$

Example 6. Approximate in the least square sense the function $f(x)$ given in the following table by a third degree polynomial.

x	$f(x)$	$\bar{x}=\frac{x-10}{2}$	$f_0(\bar{x})$	$f_1(\bar{x})$	$f_2(\bar{x})$	$f_3(\bar{x})$
10	.3162	0	1	1	1	1
12	.2887	1	1	1/2	−1/2	−2
14	.2673	2	1	0	−1	0
16	.2500	3	1	−1/2	−1/2	2
18	.2357	4	1	−1	1	−1

	$f_0(\bar{x})$	$f_1(\bar{x})$	$f_2(\bar{x})$	$f_3(\bar{x})$
$(f_n, f_n)=\sum_{\bar{x}=0}^{4} f_n^2(\bar{x})$	5	2.5	3.5	10
$(f, f_n)=\sum_{\bar{x}=0}^{4} f_n(\bar{x})f(2\bar{x}+10)$	1.3579	.09985	.01525	.0031
$a_n=\frac{(f, f_n)}{(f_n, f_n)}$	.271580	.039940	.0043571	.000310

$$f(x)\sim .27158+.03994(3.5-.25x)+.0043571(23.5-3.5x+.125x^2)+.00031(266-59.8333x+4.375x^2-.10417x^3)$$

$$f(x)\sim .59447-.043658x+.0019009x^2-.000032292x^3$$

22.20. Economization of Series

Problem: Given $f(x)=\sum_{m=0}^{n} a_m x^m$ in the interval $-1\leq x\leq 1$ and $R>0$. Find $\bar{f}(x)=\sum_{m=0}^{N} b_m x^m$ with N as small as possible, such that $|\bar{f}(x)-f(x)|<R$.

Solution: Express $f(x)$ in terms of Chebyshev polynomials using **Table 22.3**,

$$f(x)=\sum_{m=0}^{n} b_m T_m(x)$$

Then, since $|T_m(x)|\leq 1 (-1\leq x\leq 1)$

$$\bar{f}(x)=\sum_{m=0}^{N} b_m T_m(x)$$

within the desired accuracy if

$$\sum_{m=N+1}^{n}|b_m|<R$$

$\bar{f}(x)$ is evaluated most conveniently by using the recurrence relation (see **22.7**).

Example 7. Economize $f(x)=1+x/2+x^2/3+x^3/4+x^4/5+x^5/6$ with $R=.05$. From **Table 22.3**

$$f(x)=\frac{1}{120}[149T_0(x)+32T_2(x)+3T_4(x)]+\frac{1}{96}[76T_1(x)+11T_3(x)+T_5(x)]$$

$$\text{so } \bar{f}(x)=\frac{1}{120}[149T_0(x)+32T_2(x)]+\frac{1}{96}[76T_1(x)+11T_3(x)]$$

$$\text{since } |\bar{f}(x)-f(x)|\leq\frac{1}{40}+\frac{1}{96}<.05$$

Coefficients for the Jacobi Polynomials $P_n^{(\alpha,\beta)}(x)=a_n^{-1}\sum_{m=0}^{n} c_m(x-1)^m$ **Table 22.1**

	a_n	$(x-1)^0$	$(x-1)^1$	$(x-1)^2$	$(x-1)^3$	$(x-1)^4$	$(x-1)^5$	$(x-1)^6$
$P_0^{(\alpha,\beta)}$	1	1						
$P_1^{(\alpha,\beta)}$	2	$2(\alpha+1)$	$\alpha+\beta+2$					
$P_2^{(\alpha,\beta)}$	8	$4(\alpha+1)_2$	$4(\alpha+\beta+3)(\alpha+2)$	$(\alpha+\beta+3)_2$				
$P_3^{(\alpha,\beta)}$	48	$8(\alpha+1)_3$	$12(\alpha+\beta+4)(\alpha+2)_2$	$6(\alpha+\beta+4)_2(\alpha+3)$	$(\alpha+\beta+4)_3$			
$P_4^{(\alpha,\beta)}$	384	$16(\alpha+1)_4$	$32(\alpha+\beta+5)(\alpha+2)_3$	$24(\alpha+\beta+5)_2(\alpha+3)_2$	$8(\alpha+\beta+5)_3(\alpha+4)$	$(\alpha+\beta+5)_4$		
$P_5^{(\alpha,\beta)}$	3840	$32(\alpha+1)_5$	$80(\alpha+\beta+6)(\alpha+2)_4$	$80(\alpha+\beta+6)_2(\alpha+3)_3$	$40(\alpha+\beta+6)_3(\alpha+4)_2$	$10(\alpha+\beta+6)_4(\alpha+5)$	$(\alpha+\beta+6)_5$	
$P_6^{(\alpha,\beta)}$	46080	$64(\alpha+1)_6$	$192(\alpha+\beta+7)(\alpha+2)_5$	$240(\alpha+\beta+7)_2(\alpha+3)_4$	$160(\alpha+\beta+7)_3(\alpha+4)_3$	$60(\alpha+\beta+7)_4(\alpha+5)_2$	$12(\alpha+\beta+7)_5(\alpha+6)$	$(\alpha+\beta+7)_6$

$$(m)_n=m(m+1)(m+2)\ .\ .\ .\ (m+n-1)$$

$$P_5^{(1,1)}(x)=\frac{1}{3840}[(8)_5(x-1)^5+10(8)_4(6)(x-1)^4+40(8)_3(5)_2(x-1)^3+80(8)_2(4)_3(x-1)^2+80(8)(3)_4(x-1)+32(2)_5]$$

$$P_5^{(1,1)}(x)=\frac{1}{3840}[95040(x-1)^5+475200(x-1)^4+864000(x-1)^3+691200(x-1)^2+230400(x-1)+23040]$$

Table 22.2 **Coefficients for the Ultraspherical Polynomials $C_n^{(\alpha)}(x)$ and for x^n in terms of $C_m^{(\alpha)}(x)$**

$$C_n^{(\alpha)}(x)=a_n^{-1}\sum_{m=0}^{n} c_m x^m \text{ and } x^n=b_n^{-1}\sum_{m=0}^{n} d_m C_m^{(\alpha)}(x) \qquad (\alpha\neq 0)$$

		x^0	x^1	x^2	x^3	x^4	x^5	x^6	
	b_n	1	2α	$2(\alpha)_2$	$4(\alpha)_3$	$4(\alpha)_4$	$8(\alpha)_5$	$8(\alpha)_6$	
	a_n								
$C_0^{(\alpha)}$	1	$1 \quad 1$		α		$3\alpha(\alpha+3)$		$15\alpha(\alpha+4)(\alpha+5)$	$C_0^{(\alpha)}$
$C_1^{(\alpha)}$	1		$2\alpha \quad 1$		$3(\alpha+1)$		$15(\alpha+1)(\alpha+4)$		$C_1^{(\alpha)}$
$C_2^{(\alpha)}$	1	$-\alpha$		$2(\alpha)_2 \quad 1$		$6(\alpha+2)$		$45(\alpha+2)(\alpha+5)$	$C_2^{(\alpha)}$
$C_3^{(\alpha)}$	3		$-6(\alpha)_2$		$4(\alpha)_3 \quad 3$		$30(\alpha+3)$		$C_3^{(\alpha)}$
$C_4^{(\alpha)}$	6	$3(\alpha)_2$		$-12(\alpha)_3$		$4(\alpha)_4 \quad 6$		$90(\alpha+4)$	$C_4^{(\alpha)}$
$C_5^{(\alpha)}$	15		$15(\alpha)_3$		$-20(\alpha)_4$		$4(\alpha)_5 \quad 30$		$C_5^{(\alpha)}$
$C_6^{(\alpha)}$	90	$-15(\alpha)_3$		$90(\alpha)_4$		$-60(\alpha)_5$		$8(\alpha)_6 \quad 90$	$C_6^{(\alpha)}$
		x^0	x^1	x^2	x^3	x^4	x^5	x^6	

$$(\alpha)_n=\alpha(\alpha+1)(\alpha+2)\ .\ .\ .\ (\alpha+n-1)$$

$$C_3^{(2)}(x)=\frac{1}{3}\,[4(2)_3x^3-6(2)_2x] \qquad x^3=\frac{1}{4(2)_3}\,[3(3)\,C_1^{(2)}(x)+3C_3^{(2)}(x)]$$

$$C_3^{(2)}(x)=\frac{1}{3}\,[96x^3-36x] \qquad x^3=\frac{1}{96}\,[9C_1^{(2)}(x)+3C_3^{(2)}(x)]$$

Table 22.3

Coefficients for the Chebyshev Polynomials $T_n(x)$ and for x^n in terms of $T_m(x)$

$$T_n(x)=\sum_{m=0}^{n} c_m x^m \qquad x^n=b_n^{-1}\sum_{m=0}^{n} d_m T_m(x)$$

	x^0	x^1	x^2	x^3	x^4	x^5	x^6	x^7	x^8	x^9	x^{10}	x^{11}	x^{12}	
b_n	1	1	2	4	8	16	32	64	128	256	512	1024	2048	
T_0	1 1		1		3		10		35		126		462	T_0
T_1		1 1		3		10		35		126		462		T_1
T_2	−1		2 1		4		15		56		210		792	T_2
T_3		−3		4 1		5		21		84		330		T_3
T_4	1		−8		8 1		6		28		120		495	T_4
T_5		5		−20		16 1		7		36		165		T_5
T_6	−1		18		−48		32 1		8		45		220	T_6
T_7		−7		56		−112		64 1		9		55		T_7
T_8	1		−32		160		−256		128 1		10		66	T_8
T_9		9		−120		432		−576		256 1		11		T_9
T_{10}	−1		50		−400		1120		−1280		512 1		12	T_{10}
T_{11}		−11		220		−1232		2816		−2816		1024 1		T_{11}
T_{12}	1		−72		840		−3584		6912		−6144		2048 1	T_{12}
	x^0	x^1	x^2	x^3	x^4	x^5	x^6	x^7	x^8	x^9	x^{10}	x^{11}	x^{12}	

$$T_6(x)=32x^6-48x^4+18x^2-1 \qquad x^6=\frac{1}{32}\,[10T_0+15T_2+6T_4+T_6]$$

Table 22.5

Coefficients for the Chebyshev Polynomials $U_n(x)$ and for x^n in terms of $U_m(x)$

$$U_n(x)=\sum_{m=0}^{n} c_m x^m \qquad x^n=b_n^{-1}\sum_{m=0}^{n} d_m U_m(x)$$

	x^0	x^1	x^2	x^3	x^4	x^5	x^6	x^7	x^8	x^9	x^{10}	x^{11}	x^{12}	
b_n	1	2	4	8	16	32	64	128	256	512	1024	2048	4096	
U_0	1 1		1		2		5		14		42		132	U_0
U_1		2 1		2		5		14		42		132		U_1
U_2	−1		4 1		3		9		28		90		297	U_2
U_3		−4		8 1		4		14		48		165		U_3
U_4	1		−12		16 1		5		20		75		275	U_4
U_5		6		−32		32 1		6		27		110		U_5
U_6	−1		24		−80		64 1		7		35		154	U_6
U_7		−8		80		−192		128 1		8		44		U_7
U_8	1		−40		240		−448		256 1		9		54	U_8
U_9		10		−160		672		−1024		512 1		10		U_9
U_{10}	−1		60		−560		1792		−2304		1024 1		11	U_{10}
U_{11}		−12		280		−1792		4608		−5120		2048 1		U_{11}
U_{12}	1		−84		1120		−5376		11520		−11264		4096 1	U_{12}
	x^0	x^1	x^2	x^3	x^4	x^5	x^6	x^7	x^8	x^9	x^{10}	x^{11}	x^{12}	

$$U_6(x)=64x^6-80x^4+24x^2-1 \qquad x^6=\frac{1}{64}\,[5U_0+9U_2+5U_4+U_6]$$

Table 22.7

Coefficients for the Chebyshev Polynomials $C_n(x)$ and for x^n in terms of $C_m(x)$

$$C_n(x)=\sum_{m=0}^{n} c_m x^m \qquad x^n=b_n^{-1}\sum_{m=0}^{n} d_m C_m(x)$$

	x^0	x^1	x^2	x^3	x^4	x^5	x^6	x^7	x^8	x^9	x^{10}	x^{11}	x^{12}	
b_n	2	1	1	1	1	1	1	1	1	1	1	1	1	
C_0	2 1		1		3		10		35		126		462	C_0
C_1		1 1		3		10		35		126		462		C_1
C_2	−2		1 1		4		15		56		210		792	C_2
C_3		−3		1 1		5		21		84		330		C_3
C_4	2		−4		1 1		6		28		120		495	C_4
C_5*		5		−5		1 1		7		36		165		C_5
C_6	−2		9		−6		1 1		8		45		220	C_6
C_7		−7		14		−7		1 1		9		55		C_7
C_8	2		−16		20		−8		1 1		10		66	C_8
C_9		9		−30		27		−9		1 1		11		C_9
C_{10}	−2		25		−50		35		−10		1 1		12	C_{10}
C_{11}		−11		55		−77		44		−11		1 1		C_{11}
C_{12}	2		−36		105		−112		54		−12		1 1	C_{12}
	x^0	x^1	x^2	x^3	x^4	x^5	x^6	x^7	x^8	x^9	x^{10}	x^{11}	x^{12}	

$C_6(x)=x^6-6x^4+9x^2-2 \qquad x^6=10C_0+15C_2+6C_4+C_6$

Table 22.8

Coefficients for the Chebyshev Polynomials $S_n(x)$ and for x^n in terms of $S_m(x)$

$$S_n(x)=\sum_{m=0}^{n} c_m x^m \qquad x^n=\sum_{m=0}^{n} d_m S_m(x)$$

	x^0	x^1	x^2	x^3	x^4	x^5	x^6	x^7	x^8	x^9	x^{10}	x^{11}	x^{12}	
S_0	1 1		1		2		5		14		42		132	S_0
S_1		1 1		2		5		14		42		132		S_1
S_2	−1		1 1		3		9		28		90		297	S_2
S_3		−2		1 1		4		14		48		165		S_3
S_4	1		−3		1 1		5		20		75		275	S_4
S_5		3		−4		1 1		6		27		110		S_5
S_6	−1		6		−5		1 1		7		35		154	S_6
S_7		−4		10		−6		1 1		8		44		S_7
S_8	1		−10		15		−7		1 1		9		54	S_8
S_9		5		−20		21		−8		1 1		10		S_9
S_{10}	−1		15		−35		28		−9		1 1		11	S_{10}
S_{11}		−6		35		−56		36		−10		1 1		S_{11}
S_{12}	1		−21		70		−84		45		−11		1 1	S_{12}
	x^0	x^1	x^2	x^3	x^4	x^5	x^6	x^7	x^8	x^9	x^{10}	x^{11}	x^{12}	

$S_6(x)=x^6-5x^4+6x^2-1 \qquad x^6=5S_0+9S_2+5S_4+S_6$

Table 22.9 **Coefficients for the Legendre Polynomials $P_n(x)$ and for x^n in terms of $P_m(x)$**

$$P_n(x)=a_n^{-1}\sum_{m=0}^{n} c_m x^m \qquad x^n=b_n^{-1}\sum_{m=0}^{n} d_m P_m(x)$$

		x^0	x^1	x^2	x^3	x^4	x^5	x^6	x^7	x^8	x^9	x^{10}	x^{11}	x^{12}	
	a_n b_n	1	1	3	5	35	63	231	429	6435	12155	46189	88179	676039	b_n
P_0	1	1 1		1		7		33		715		4199		52003	P_0
P_1	1		1 1		3		27		143		3315		20349		P_1
P_2	2	−1		3 2		20		110		2600		16150		208012	P_2
P_3	2		−3		5 2		28		182		4760		31654		P_3
P_4	8	3		−30		35 8		72		2160		15504		220248	P_4
P_5	8		15		−70		63 8		88		2992		23408		P_5
P_6	16	−5		105		−315		231 16		832		7904		133952	P_6
P_7	16		−35		315		−693		429 16		960		10080		P_7
P_8	128	35		−1260		6930		−12012		6435 128		2176		50048	P_8
P_9	128		315		−4620		18018		−25740		12155 128		2432		P_9
P_{10}	256	−63		3465		−30030		90090		−109395		46189 256		10752	P_{10}
P_{11}	256		−693		15015		−90090		218790		−230945		88179 256		P_{11}
P_{12}	1024	231		−18018		225225		−1021020		2078505		−1939938		676039 1024	P_{12}
		x^0	x^1	x^2	x^3	x^4	x^5	x^6	x^7	x^8	x^9	x^{10}	x^{11}	x^{12}	

$$P_6(x)=\frac{1}{16}[231x^6-315x^4+105x^2-5] \qquad x^6=\frac{1}{231}[33P_0+110P_2+72P_4+16P_6]$$

For values of $P_n(x)$, see chapter 8.

Coefficients for the Laguerre Polynomials $L_n(x)$ and for x^n in terms of $L_m(x)$ — Table 22.10

$$L_n(x)=a_n^{-1}\sum_{m=0}^{n} c_m x^m \qquad x^n=\sum_{m=0}^{n} d_m L_m(x)$$

	a_n	x^0	x^1	x^2	x^3	x^4	x^5	x^6	x^7	x^8	x^9	x^{10}	x^{11}	x^{12}	
L_0	1	1 1	1	2	6	24	120	720	5040	40320	362880	3628800	39916800	479001600	L_0
L_1	1	1	−1 −1	−4	−18	−96	−600	−4320	−35280	−322560	−3265920	−36288000	−439084800	−5748019200	L_1
L_2	2	2	−4	1 2	18	144	1200	10800	105840	1128960	13063680	163296000	2195424000	31614105600	L_2
L_3	6	6	−18	9	−1 −6	−96	−1200	−14400	−176400	−2257920	−30481920	−435456000	−6586272000	−105380352000	L_3
L_4	24	24	−96	72	−16	1 24	600	10800	176400	2822400	45722880	762048000	13172544000	237105792000	L_4
L_5	120	120	−600	600	−200	25	−1 −120	−4320	−105840	−2257920	−45722880	−914457600	−18441561600	−379369267200	L_5
L_6	720	720	−4320	5400	−2400	450	−36	1 720	35280	1128960	30481920	762048000	18441561600	442597478400	L_6
L_7	5040	5040	−35280	52920	−29400	7350	−882	49	−1 −5040	−322560	−13063680	−435456000	−13172544000	−379369267200	L_7
L_8	40320	40320	−322560	564480	−376320	117600	−18816	1568	−64	1 40320	* 3265920	163296000	6586272000	237105792000	L_8
L_9	362880	362880	−3265920	6531840	−5080320	1905120	−381024	42336	−2592	81	−1 −362880	−36288000	−2195424000	−105380352000	L_9
L_{10}	3628800	3628800	−36288000	81648000	−72576000	31752000	−7620480	1058400	−86400	4050	−100	1 3628800	439084800	31614105600	L_{10}
L_{11}	39916800	39916800	−439084800	1097712000	−1097712000	548856000	−153679680	25613280	−2613600	163350	−6050	121	−1 −39916800	−5748019200	L_{11}
L_{12}	479001600	479001600	−5748019200	15807052800	−17563392000	9879408000	−3161410560	614718720	−75271680	5880600	−290400	8712	−144	1 479001600	L_{12}
	a_n	x^0	x^1	x^2	x^3	x^4	x^5	x^6	x^7	x^8	x^9	x^{10}	x^{11}	x^{12}	

*See page II.

$$L_6(x)=\frac{1}{720}[x^6-36x^5+450x^4-2400x^3+5400x^2-4320x+720] \qquad x^6=720L_0-4320L_1+10800L_2-14400L_3+10800L_4-4320L_5+720L_6$$

Coefficients for the Hermite Polynomials $H_n(x)$ and for x^n in terms of $H_m(x)$

Table 22.12

$$H_n(x)=\sum_{m=0}^{n} c_m x^m \qquad x^n=b_n^{-1}\sum_{m=0}^{n} d_m H_m(x)$$

	x^0	x^1	x^2	x^3	x^4	x^5	x^6	x^7	x^8	x^9	x^{10}	x^{11}	x^{12}	
b_n	1	2	4	8	16	32	64	128	256	512	1024	2048	4096	b_n
H_0	1 1		2		12		120		1680		30240		665280	H_0
H_1		2 1		6		60		840		15120		332640		H_1
H_2	−2		4 1		12		180		3360		75600		1995840	H_2
H_3		−12		8 1		20		420		10080		277200		H_3
H_4	12		−48		16 1		30		840		25200		831600	H_4
H_5		120		−160		32 1		42		1512		55440		H_5
H_6	−120		720		−480		64 1		56		2520		110880	H_6
H_7		−1680		3360		−1344		128 1		72		3960		H_7
H_8	1680		−13440		13440		−3584		256 1		90		5940	H_8
H_9		30240		−80640		48384		−9216		512 1		110		H_9
H_{10}	−30240		302400		−403200		161280		−23040		1024 1		132	H_{10}
H_{11}		−665280		2217600		−1774080		506880		−56320		2048 1		H_{11}
H_{12}	665280		−7983360		13305600		−7096320		1520640		−135168		4096 1	H_{12}
	x^0	x^1	x^2	x^3	x^4	x^5	x^6	x^7	x^8	x^9	x^{10}	x^{11}	x^{12}	

$$H_6(x)=64x^6-480x^4+720x^2-120 \qquad x^6=\frac{1}{64}\,[120H_0+180H_2+30H_4+H_6]$$

23. Bernoulli and Euler Polynomials—Riemann Zeta Function

23.1. Bernoulli and Euler Polynomials and the Euler-Maclaurin Formula

Generating Functions

23.1.1 $\frac{te^{xt}}{e^t-1}=\sum_{n=0}^{\infty} B_n(x)\frac{t^n}{n!}$ $\quad |t|<2\pi$ $\qquad$ $\frac{2e^{xt}}{e^t+1}=\sum_{n=0}^{\infty} E_n(x)\frac{t^n}{n!}$ $\quad |t|<\pi$

Bernoulli and Euler Numbers

23.1.2 $B_n=B_n(0)$ $\quad n=0, 1, \ldots$ $\qquad$ $E_n=2^nE_n\left(\frac{1}{2}\right)=$ integer $\quad n=0, 1, \ldots$

23.1.3 $B_0=1,\ B_1=-\frac{1}{2},\ B_2=\frac{1}{6},\ B_4=-\frac{1}{30}$ $\qquad$ $E_0=1,\ E_2=-1,\ E_4=5$

(For occurrence of B_n and E_n in series expansions of circular functions, see chapter 4.)

Sums of Powers

23.1.4 $\sum_{k=1}^{m} k^n=\frac{B_{n+1}(m+1)-B_{n+1}}{n+1}$ $\quad m, n=1, 2, \ldots$ $\qquad$ $\sum_{k=1}^{m} (-1)^{m-k}k^n=\frac{E_n(m+1)+(-1)^mE_n(0)}{2}$ $\quad m, n=1, 2, \ldots$

Derivatives and Differences

23.1.5 $B_n'(x)=nB_{n-1}(x)$ $\quad n=1, 2, \ldots$ $\qquad$ $E_n'(x)=nE_{n-1}(x)$ $\quad n=1, 2, \ldots$

23.1.6 $B_n(x+1)-B_n(x)=nx^{n-1}$ $\quad n=0, 1, \ldots$ $\qquad$ $E_n(x+1)+E_n(x)=2x^n$ $\quad n=0, 1, \ldots$

Expansions

23.1.7

$B_n(x+h)=\sum_{k=0}^{n}\binom{n}{k} B_k(x)h^{n-k}$ $\quad n=0, 1, \ldots$

$E_n(x+h)=\sum_{k=0}^{n}\binom{n}{k} E_k(x)h^{n-k}$ $\quad n=0, 1, \ldots$

$E_n(x)=\sum_{k=0}^{n}\binom{n}{k}\frac{E_k}{2^k}\left(x-\frac{1}{2}\right)^{n-k}$ $\quad n=0, 1, \ldots$

Symmetry

23.1.8 $B_n(1-x)=(-1)^nB_n(x)$ $\quad n=0, 1, \ldots$ $\qquad$ $E_n(1-x)=(-1)^nE_n(x)$ $\quad n=0, 1, \ldots$

23.1.9 $(-1)^nB_n(-x)=B_n(x)+nx^{n-1}$ $\quad n=0, 1, \ldots$ $\qquad$ $(-1)^{n+1}E_n(-x)=E_n(x)-2x^n$ $\quad n=0, 1, \ldots$

Multiplication Theorem

23.1.10

$B_n(mx)=m^{n-1}\sum_{k=0}^{m-1} B_n\left(x+\frac{k}{m}\right)$ $\quad n=0, 1, \ldots;\ m=1, 2, \ldots$

$E_n(mx)=m^n\sum_{k=0}^{m-1} (-1)^kE_n\left(x+\frac{k}{m}\right)$ $\quad n=0, 1, \ldots;\ m=1, 3, \ldots$

$E_n(mx)=-\frac{2}{n+1}m^n\sum_{k=0}^{m-1} (-1)^kB_{n+1}\left(x+\frac{k}{m}\right)$ $\quad n=0, 1, \ldots;\ m=2, 4, \ldots$

Integrals

23.1.11 $\int_a^x B_n(t)dt=\frac{B_{n+1}(x)-B_{n+1}(a)}{n+1}$

$\int_a^x E_n(t)dt=\frac{E_{n+1}(x)-E_{n+1}(a)}{n+1}$

23.1.12 $\int_0^1 B_n(t)B_m(t)dt=(-1)^{n-1}\frac{m!n!}{(m+n)!}B_{m+n}$ $\quad m,n=1,2,\ldots$

$\int_0^1 E_n(t)E_m(t)dt$

$=(-1)^n 4(2^{m+n+2}-1)\frac{m!n!}{(m+n+2)!}B_{m+n+2}$ $\quad m,n=0,1,\ldots$

(The polynomials are orthogonal for $m+n$ odd.)

Inequalities

23.1.13 $|B_{2n}|>|B_{2n}(x)|\qquad n=1,2,\ldots,\quad 1>x>0$

$4^{-n}|E_{2n}|>(-1)^n E_{2n}(x)>0\qquad n=1,2,\ldots,\quad \frac{1}{2}>x>0$

23.1.14

$\frac{2(2n+1)!}{(2\pi)^{2n+1}}\left(\frac{1}{1-2^{-2n}}\right)>(-1)^{n+1}B_{2n+1}(x)>0$ $\quad n=1,2,\ldots,\quad \frac{1}{2}>x>0$

$\frac{4(2n-1)!}{\pi^{2n}}\left(1+\frac{1}{2^{2n}-2}\right)>(-1)^n E_{2n-1}(x)>0$ $\quad n=1,2,\ldots,\quad \frac{1}{2}>x>0$

23.1.15

$\frac{2(2n)!}{(2\pi)^{2n}}\left(\frac{1}{1-2^{1-2n}}\right)>(-1)^{n+1}B_{2n}>\frac{2(2n)!}{(2\pi)^{2n}}$ $\quad n=1,2,\ldots$

$\frac{4^{n+1}(2n)!}{\pi^{2n+1}}>(-1)^n E_{2n}>\frac{4^{n+1}(2n)!}{\pi^{2n+1}}\left(\frac{1}{1+3^{-1-2n}}\right)$ $\quad n=0,1,\ldots$

Fourier Expansions

23.1.16

$B_n(x)=-2\frac{n!}{(2\pi)^n}\sum_{k=1}^{\infty}\frac{\cos(2\pi kx-\frac{1}{2}\pi n)}{k^n}$

$n>1,\ 1\geq x\geq 0$

$n=1,\ 1>x>0$

$E_n(x)=4\frac{n!}{\pi^{n+1}}\sum_{k=0}^{\infty}\frac{\sin((2k+1)\pi x-\frac{1}{2}\pi n)}{(2k+1)^{n+1}}$

$n>0,\ 1\geq x\geq 0$

$n=0,\ 1>x>0$

23.1.17

$B_{2n-1}(x)=\frac{(-1)^n 2(2n-1)!}{(2\pi)^{2n-1}}\sum_{k=1}^{\infty}\frac{\sin 2k\pi x}{k^{2n-1}}$

$n>1,\ 1\geq x\geq 0$

$n=1,\ 1>x>0$

$E_{2n-1}(x)=\frac{(-1)^n 4(2n-1)!}{\pi^{2n}}\sum_{k=0}^{\infty}\frac{\cos(2k+1)\pi x}{(2k+1)^{2n}}$

$n=1,2,\ldots,\quad 1\geq x\geq 0$

23.1.18

$B_{2n}(x)=\frac{(-1)^{n-1}2(2n)!}{(2\pi)^{2n}}\sum_{k=1}^{\infty}\frac{\cos 2k\pi x}{k^{2n}}$

$n=1,2,\ldots,\quad 1\geq x\geq 0$

$E_{2n}(x)=\frac{(-1)^n 4(2n)!}{\pi^{2n+1}}\sum_{k=0}^{\infty}\frac{\sin(2k+1)\pi x}{(2k+1)^{2n+1}}$

$n>0,\ 1\geq x\geq 0$

$n=0,\ 1>x>0$

Special Values

23.1.19 $B_{2n+1}=0\qquad n=1,2,\ldots$

$E_{2n+1}=0\qquad n=0,1,\ldots$

23.1.20 $B_n(0)=(-1)^n B_n(1)$

$=B_n\qquad n=0,1,\ldots$

$E_n(0)=-E_n(1)$

$=-2(n+1)^{-1}(2^{n+1}-1)B_{n+1}\qquad n=1,2,\ldots$

23.1.21 $B_n(\frac{1}{2})=-(1-2^{1-n})B_n\qquad n=0,1,\ldots$

$E_n(\frac{1}{2})=2^{-n}E_n\qquad n=0,1,\ldots$

23.1.22 $B_n(\tfrac{1}{4})=(-1)^n B_n(\tfrac{3}{4})$
$$=-2^{-n}(1-2^{1-n})B_n-n4^{-n}E_{n-1} \qquad n=1,2,\ldots$$

23.1.23 $B_{2n}(\tfrac{1}{3})=B_{2n}(\tfrac{2}{3})$
$$=-2^{-1}(1-3^{1-2n})B_{2n} \qquad n=0,1,\ldots$$

23.1.24 $B_{2n}(\tfrac{1}{6})=B_{2n}(\tfrac{5}{6})$
$$=2^{-1}(1-2^{1-2n})(1-3^{1-2n})B_{2n} \qquad n=0,1,\ldots$$

$E_{2n-1}(\tfrac{1}{3})=-E_{2n-1}(\tfrac{2}{3})$
$$=-(2n)^{-1}(1-3^{1-2n})(2^{2n}-1)B_{2n} \qquad n=1,2,\ldots$$

Symbolic Operations

23.1.25 $p(B(x)+1)-p(B(x))=p'(x)$ | $p(E(x)+1)+p(E(x))=2p(x)$

23.1.26 $B_n(x+h)=(B(x)+h)^n \qquad n=0,1,\ldots$ | $E_n(x+h)=(E(x)+h)^n \qquad n=0,1,\ldots$

Here $p(x)$ denotes a polynomial in x and after expanding we set $\{B(x)\}^n=B_n(x)$ and $\{E(x)\}^n=E_n(x)$.

Relations Between the Polynomials

23.1.27
$$E_{n-1}(x)=\frac{2^n}{n}\left\{B_n\left(\frac{x+1}{2}\right)-B_n\left(\frac{x}{2}\right)\right\}$$
$$=\frac{2}{n}\left\{B_n(x)-2^nB_n\left(\frac{x}{2}\right)\right\} \qquad n=1,2,\ldots$$

23.1.28
$$E_{n-2}(x)=2\binom{n}{2}^{-1}\sum_{k=0}^{n-2}\binom{n}{k}(2^{n-k}-1)B_{n-k}B_k(x) \qquad n=2,3,\ldots$$

23.1.29
$$B_n(x)=2^{-n}\sum_{k=0}^{n}\binom{n}{k}B_{n-k}E_k(2x) \qquad n=0,1,\ldots$$

Euler-Maclaurin Formulas

Let $F(x)$ have its first $2n$ derivatives continuous on an interval (a, b). Divide the interval into m equal parts and let $h=(b-a)/m$. Then for some θ, $1>\theta>0$, depending on $F^{(2n)}(x)$ on (a, b), we have

23.1.30
$$\sum_{k=0}^{m} F(a+kh)=\frac{1}{h}\int_a^b F(t)dt+\frac{1}{2}\{F(b)+F(a)\}$$
$$+\sum_{k=1}^{n-1}\frac{h^{2k-1}}{(2k)!}B_{2k}\{F^{(2k-1)}(b)-F^{(2k-1)}(a)\}$$
$$+\frac{h^{2n}}{(2n)!}B_{2n}\sum_{k=0}^{m-1}F^{(2n)}(a+kh+\theta h)$$

Equivalent to this is

23.1.31
$$\frac{1}{h}\int_x^{x+h}F(t)dt=\frac{1}{2}\{F(x+h)+F(x)\}$$
$$-\sum_{k=1}^{n-1}\frac{h^{2k-1}}{(2k)!}B_{2k}\{F^{(2k-1)}(x+h)-F^{(2k-1)}(x)\}$$
$$-\frac{h^{2n}}{(2n)!}B_{2n}F^{(2n)}(x+\theta h) \qquad b-h\geq x\geq a$$

Let $\hat{B}_n(x)=B_n(x-[x])$. The Euler Summation Formula is

23.1.32
$$\sum_{k=0}^{m-1}F(a+kh+\omega h)=\frac{1}{h}\int_a^b F(t)dt$$
$$+\sum_{k=1}^{p}\frac{h^{k-1}}{k!}B_k(\omega)\{F^{(k-1)}(b)-F^{(k-1)}(a)\}$$
$$-\frac{h^p}{p!}\int_0^1\hat{B}_p(\omega-t)\left\{\sum_{k=0}^{m-1}F^{(p)}(a+kh+th)\right\}dt$$
$$p\leq 2n,\ 1\geq\omega\geq 0$$

23.2. Riemann Zeta Function and Other Sums of Reciprocal Powers

23.2.1 $$\zeta(s)=\sum_{k=1}^{\infty} k^{-s} \qquad \mathscr{R}s>1$$

23.2.2 $$=\prod_{p} (1-p^{-s})^{-1} \qquad \mathscr{R}s>1$$

(product over all primes p).

23.2.3 $$=\frac{1}{s-1}+\frac{1}{2}+\sum_{k=1}^{n} \frac{B_{2k}}{2k}\binom{s+2k-2}{2k-1} -\binom{s+2n}{2n+1}\int_1^{\infty} \frac{B_{2n+1}(x-[x])}{x^{s+2n+1}}\,dx$$
$$s\neq 1,\ n=1, 2, \ldots, \quad \mathscr{R}s>-2n$$

23.2.4 $$=-\frac{\Gamma(1-s)}{2\pi i}\int_C \frac{(-z)^{s-1}}{e^z-1}\,dz$$

23.2.5 $$=\frac{1}{s-1}+\sum_{n=0}^{\infty} \frac{(-1)^n}{n!}\gamma_n(s-1)^n$$

where

$$\gamma_n=\lim_{m\to\infty}\left\{\sum_{k=1}^{m} \frac{(\ln k)^n}{k}-\frac{(\ln m)^{n+1}}{n+1}\right\}$$
$$\mathscr{R}s>0$$

23.2.6 $$=2^s\pi^{s-1}\sin\left(\tfrac{1}{2}\pi s\right)\Gamma(1-s)\zeta(1-s)$$

23.2.7 $$=\frac{1}{\Gamma(s)}\int_0^{\infty}\frac{x^{s-1}}{e^x-1}\,dx \qquad \mathscr{R}s>1$$

23.2.8 $$=\frac{1}{(1-2^{1-s})\Gamma(s)}\int_0^{\infty}\frac{x^{s-1}}{e^x+1}\,dx$$

23.2.9 $$=\sum_{k=1}^{n} k^{-s}+(s-1)^{-1}n^{1-s}-s\int_n^{\infty}\frac{x-[x]}{x^{s+1}}\,dx$$
$$n=1, 2, \ldots, \quad \mathscr{R}s>0$$

23.2.10 $$=\frac{\exp\left(\ln 2\pi-1-\frac{1}{2}\gamma\right)s}{2(s-1)\Gamma\left(\frac{1}{2}s+1\right)}\prod_{\rho}\left(1-\frac{s}{\rho}\right)e^{\frac{s}{\rho}}$$

product over all zeros ρ of $\zeta(s)$ with $\mathscr{R}\rho>0$.

The contour C in the fourth formula starts at infinity on the positive real axis, circles the origin once in the positive direction excluding the points $\pm 2ni\pi$ for $n=1, 2, \ldots$, and returns to the starting point. Therefore $\zeta(s)$ is regular for all values of s except for a simple pole at $s=1$ with residue 1.

Special Values

23.2.11 $$\zeta(0)=-\tfrac{1}{2}$$

23.2.12 $$\zeta(1)=\infty$$

23.2.13 $$\zeta'(0)=-\tfrac{1}{2}\ln 2\pi$$

23.2.14 $$\zeta(-2n)=0 \qquad n=1, 2, \ldots$$

23.2.15 $$\zeta(1-2n)=-\frac{B_{2n}}{2n} \qquad n=1,2,\ldots$$

23.2.16 $$\zeta(2n)=\frac{(2\pi)^{2n}}{2(2n)!}|B_{2n}| \qquad n=1,2,\ldots$$

23.2.17

$$\zeta(2n+1)=\frac{(-1)^{n+1}(2\pi)^{2n+1}}{2(2n+1)!}\int_0^1 B_{2n+1}(x)\cot(\pi x)\,dx$$
$$n=1,2,\ldots$$

Sums of Reciprocal Powers

The sums referred to are

23.2.18 $$\zeta(n)=\sum_{k=1}^{\infty} k^{-n} \qquad n=2,3,\ldots$$

23.2.19

$$\eta(n)=\sum_{k=1}^{\infty}(-1)^{k-1}k^{-n}=(1-2^{1-n})\zeta(n) \qquad n=1,2,\ldots$$

23.2.20

$$\lambda(n)=\sum_{k=0}^{\infty}(2k+1)^{-n}=(1-2^{-n})\zeta(n) \qquad n=2,3,\ldots$$

23.2.21

$$\beta(n)=\sum_{k=0}^{\infty}(-1)^k(2k+1)^{-n} \qquad n=1,2,\ldots$$

These sums can be calculated from the Bernoulli and Euler polynomials by means of the last two formulas for special values of the zeta function (note that $\eta(1)=\ln 2$), and

23.2.22 $$\beta(2n+1)=\frac{(\pi/2)^{2n+1}}{2(2n)!}|E_{2n}| \qquad n=0, 1, \ldots$$

23.2.23

$$\beta(2n)=\frac{(-1)^n\pi^{2n}}{4(2n-1)!}\int_0^1 E_{2n-1}(x)\sec(\pi x)\,dx$$
$$n=1, 2, \ldots$$

$\beta(2)$ is known as Catalan's constant. Some other special values are

23.2.24 $$\zeta(2)=1+\frac{1}{2^2}+\frac{1}{3^2}+\ldots=\frac{\pi^2}{6}$$

23.2.25 $$\zeta(4)=1+\frac{1}{2^4}+\frac{1}{3^4}+\ldots=\frac{\pi^4}{90}$$

23.2.26 $\eta(2)=1-\frac{1}{2^2}+\frac{1}{3^2}-\ldots=\frac{\pi^2}{12}$

23.2.27 $\eta(4)=1-\frac{1}{2^4}+\frac{1}{3^4}-\ldots=\frac{7\pi^4}{720}$

23.2.28 $\lambda(2)=1+\frac{1}{3^2}+\frac{1}{5^2}+\ldots=\frac{\pi^2}{8}$

23.2.29 $\lambda(4)=1+\frac{1}{3^4}+\frac{1}{5^4}+\ldots=\frac{\pi^4}{96}$

23.2.30 $\beta(1)=1-\frac{1}{3}+\frac{1}{5}-\ldots=\frac{\pi}{4}$

23.2.31 $\beta(3)=1-\frac{1}{3^3}+\frac{1}{5^3}-\ldots=\frac{\pi^3}{32}$

n	$\lambda(n)=\sum_{k=0}^{\infty}(2k+1)^{-n}$	$\beta(n)=\sum_{k=0}^{\infty}(-1)^k(2k+1)^{-n}$
1	∞	0.78539 81633 97448 310
2	1.23370 05501 36169 82735	0.91596 55941 77219 015
3	1.05179 97902 64644 99972	0.96894 61462 59369 380
4	1.01467 80316 04192 05455	0.98894 45517 41105 336
5	1.00452 37627 95139 61613	0.99615 78280 77088 064
6	1.00144 70766 40942 12191	0.99868 52222 18438 135
7	1.00047 15486 52376 55476	0.99955 45078 90539 909
8	1.00015 51790 25296 11930	0.99984 99902 46829 657
9	1.00005 13451 83843 77259	0.99994 96841 87220 090
10	1.00001 70413 63044 82549	0.99998 31640 26196 877
11	1.00000 56660 51090 10935	0.99999 43749 73823 699
12	1.00000 18858 48583 11958	0.99999 81223 50587 882

n	$\zeta(n)=\sum_{k=1}^{\infty}k^{-n}$	$\eta(n)=\sum_{k=1}^{\infty}(-1)^{k-1}k^{-n}$
1	∞	0.69314 71805 59945 30942
2	1.64493 40668 48226 43647	0.82246 70334 24113 21824
3	1.20205 69031 59594 28540	0.90154 26773 69695 71405
4	1.08232 32337 11138 19152	0.94703 28294 97245 91758
5	1.03692 77551 43369 92633	0.97211 97704 46909 30594
6	1.01734 30619 84449 13971	0.98555 10912 97435 10410
7	1.00834 92773 81922 82684	0.99259 38199 22830 28267
8	1.00407 73561 97944 33938	0.99623 30018 52647 89923
9	1.00200 83928 26082 21442	0.99809 42975 41605 33077
10	1.00099 45751 27818 08534	0.99903 95075 98271 56564
11	1.00049 41886 04119 46456	0.99951 71434 98060 75414
12	1.00024 60865 53308 04830	0.99975 76851 43858 19085

COEFFICIENTS b_k OF THE BERNOULLI POLYNOMIALS $B_n(x)=\sum_{k=0}^{n} b_k x^k$ Table 23.1

$n\backslash k$	0	1	2	3	4	5	6	7	8	9	10	11	12	13	14	15
0	1															
1	$-\frac{1}{2}$	1														
2	$\frac{1}{6}$	-1	1													
3	0	$\frac{1}{2}$	$-\frac{3}{2}$	1												
4	$-\frac{1}{30}$	0	1	-2	1											
5	0	$-\frac{1}{6}$	0	$\frac{5}{3}$	$-\frac{5}{2}$	1										
6	$\frac{1}{42}$	0	$-\frac{1}{2}$	0	$\frac{5}{2}$	-3	1									
7	0	$\frac{1}{6}$	0	$-\frac{7}{6}$	0	$\frac{7}{2}$	$-\frac{7}{2}$	1								
8	$-\frac{1}{30}$	0	$\frac{2}{3}$	0	$-\frac{7}{3}$	0	$\frac{14}{3}$	-4	1							
9	0	$-\frac{3}{10}$	0	2	0	$-\frac{21}{5}$	0	6	$-\frac{9}{2}$	1						
10	$\frac{5}{66}$	0	$-\frac{3}{2}$	0	5	0	-7	0	$\frac{15}{2}$	-5	1					
11	0	$\frac{5}{6}$	0	$-\frac{11}{2}$	0	11	0	-11	0	$\frac{55}{6}$	$-\frac{11}{2}$	1				
12	$-\frac{691}{2730}$	0	5	0	$-\frac{33}{2}$	0	22	0	$-\frac{33}{2}$	0	11	-6	1			
13	0	$-\frac{691}{210}$	0	$\frac{65}{3}$	0	$-\frac{429}{10}$	0	$\frac{286}{7}$	0	$-\frac{143}{6}$	0	13	$-\frac{13}{2}$	1		
14	$\frac{7}{6}$	0	$-\frac{691}{30}$	0	$\frac{455}{6}$	0	$-\frac{1001}{10}$	0	$\frac{143}{2}$	0	$-\frac{1001}{30}$	0	$\frac{91}{6}$	-7	1	
15	0	$\frac{35}{2}$	0	$-\frac{691}{6}$	0	$\frac{455}{2}$	0	$-\frac{429}{2}$	0	$\frac{715}{6}$	0	$-\frac{91}{2}$	0	$\frac{35}{2}$	$-\frac{15}{2}$	1

COEFFICIENTS e_k OF THE EULER POLYNOMIALS $E_n(x)=\sum_{k=0}^{n} e_k x^k$

$n\backslash k$	0	1	2	3	4	5	6	7	8	9	10	11	12	13	14	15
0	1															
1	$-\frac{1}{2}$	1														
2	0	-1	1													
3	$\frac{1}{4}$	0	$-\frac{3}{2}$	1												
4	0	1	0	-2	1											
5	$-\frac{1}{2}$	0	$\frac{5}{2}$	0	$-\frac{5}{2}$	1										
6	0	-3	0	5	0	-3	1									
7	$\frac{17}{8}$	0	$-\frac{21}{2}$	0	$\frac{35}{4}$	0	$-\frac{7}{2}$	1								
8	0	17	0	-28	0	14	0	-4	1							
9	$-\frac{31}{2}$	0	$\frac{153}{2}$	0	-63	0	21	0	$-\frac{9}{2}$	1						
10	0	-155	0	255	0	-126	0	30	0	-5	1					
11	$\frac{691}{4}$	0	$-\frac{1705}{2}$	0	$\frac{2805}{4}$	0	-231	0	$\frac{165}{4}$	0	$-\frac{11}{2}$	1				
12	0	2073	0	-3410	0	1683	0	-396	0	55	0	-6	1			
13	$-\frac{5461}{2}$	0	$\frac{26949}{2}$	0	$-\frac{22165}{2}$	0	$\frac{7293}{2}$	0	$-\frac{1287}{2}$	0	$\frac{143}{2}$	0	$-\frac{13}{2}$	1		
14	0	-38227	0	62881	0	-31031	0	7293	0	-1001	0	91	0	-7	1	
15	$\frac{929569}{16}$	0	$-\frac{573405}{2}$	0	$\frac{943215}{4}$	0	$-\frac{155155}{2}$	0	$\frac{109395}{8}$	0	$-\frac{3003}{2}$	0	$\frac{455}{4}$	0	$-\frac{15}{2}$	1

Table 23.2 **BERNOULLI AND EULER NUMBERS**

$B_n = N/D$

n	N	D	B_n
0	1	1	(0) 1.0000 00000
1	−1	2	(− 1)−5.0000 00000
2	1	6	(− 1) 1.6666 66667
4	−1	30	(− 2)−3.3333 33333
6	1	42	(− 2) 2.3809 52381
8	−1	30	(− 2)−3.3333 33333
10	5	66	(− 2) 7.5757 57576
12	−691	2730	(− 1)−2.5311 35531
14	7	6	(0) 1.1666 66667
16	−3617	510	(0)−7.0921 56863
18	43867	798	(1) 5.4971 17794
20	−1 74611	330	(2)−5.2912 42424
22	8 54513	138	(3) 6.1921 23188
24	−2363 64091	2730	(4)−8.6580 25311
26	85 53103	6	(6) 1.4255 17167
28	−2 37494 61029	870	(7)−2.7298 23107
30	861 58412 76005	14322	(8) 6.0158 08739
32	−770 93210 41217	510	(10)−1.5116 31577
34	257 76878 58367	6	(11) 4.2961 46431
36	−26315 27155 30534 77373	19 19190	(13)−1.3711 65521
38	2 92999 39138 41559	6	(14) 4.8833 23190
40	−2 61082 71849 64491 22051	13530	(16)−1.9296 57934
42	15 20097 64391 80708 02691	1806	(17) 8.4169 30476
44	−278 33269 57930 10242 35023	690	(19)−4.0338 07185
46	5964 51111 59391 21632 77961	282	(21) 2.1150 74864
48	−560 94033 68997 81768 62491 27547	46410	(23)−1.2086 62652
50	49 50572 05241 07964 82124 77525	66	(24) 7.5008 66746
52	−80116 57181 35489 95734 79249 91853	1590	(26)−5.0387 78101
54	29 14996 36348 84862 42141 81238 12691	798	(28) 3.6528 77648
56	−2479 39292 93132 26753 68541 57396 63229	870	(30)−2.8498 76930
58	84483 61334 88800 41862 04677 59940 36021	354	(32) 2.3865 42750
60	−121 52331 40483 75557 20403 04994 07982 02460 41491	567 86730	(34)−2.1399 94926

n	E_n
0	1
2	−1
4	5
6	−61
8	1385
10	−50521
12	27 02765
14	−1993 60981
16	1 93915 12145
18	−240 48796 75441
20	37037 11882 37525
22	−69 34887 43931 37901
24	15514 53416 35570 86905
26	−40 87072 50929 31238 92361
28	12522 59641 40362 98654 68285
30	−44 15438 93249 02310 45536 82821
32	17751 93915 79539 28943 66647 89665
34	−80 72329 92358 87898 06216 82474 53281
36	41222 06033 95177 02122 34707 96712 59045
38	−234 89580 52704 31082 52017 82857 61989 47741
40	1 48511 50718 11498 00178 77156 78140 58266 84425
42	−1036 46227 33519 61211 93979 57304 74518 59763 10201
44	7 94757 94225 97592 70360 80405 10088 07061 95192 73805
46	−6667 53751 66855 44977 43502 84747 73748 19752 41076 84661
48	60 96278 64556 85421 58691 68574 28768 43153 97653 90444 35185
50	−60532 85248 18862 18963 14383 78511 16490 88103 49822 51468 15121
52	650 61624 86684 60884 77158 70634 08082 29834 83644 23676 53855 76565
54	−7 54665 99390 08739 09806 14325 65889 73674 42122 40024 71169 98586 45581
56	9420 32189 64202 41204 20228 62376 90583 22720 93888 52599 64600 93949 05945
58	−126 22019 25180 62187 19903 40923 72874 89255 48234 10611 91825 59406 99649 20041
60	181089 11496 57923 04965 45807 74165 21586 88733 48734 92363 14106 00809 54542 31325

From H. T. Davis, Tables of the higher mathematical functions, vol. II. Principia Press, Bloomington, Ind., 1935 (with permission).

In each sub-section of this chapter we use a fixed format which emphasizes the use and methods of extending the accompanying tables. The format follows this form:

I. **Definitions**

A. Combinatorial

B. Generating functions

C. Closed form

II. **Relations**

A. Recurrences

B. Checks in computing

C. Basic use in numerical analysis

III. **Asymptotic and Special Values**

In general the notations used are standard. This includes the difference operator Δ defined on functions of x by $\Delta f(x)=f(x+1)-f(x)$, $\Delta^{n+1}f(x)=\Delta(\Delta^n f(x))$, the Kronecker delta δ_{ij}, the Riemann zeta function $\zeta(s)$ and the greatest common divisor symbol (m, n). The range of the summands for a summation sign without limits is explained to the right of the formula.

The notations which are not standard are those for the multinomials which are arbitrary shorthand for use in this chapter, and those for the Stirling numbers which have never been standardized. A short table of various notations for these numbers follows:

Notations for the Stirling Numbers

Reference	First Kind	Second Kind
This chapter	$S_n^{(m)}$	$\mathfrak{S}_n^{(m)}$
[24.2] Fort	$S_n^{(m)}$	$\mathscr{S}_n^{(m)}$
[24.7] Jordan	S_n^m	$\mathfrak{S}_n^m$
[24.10] Moser and Wyman	S_n^m	σ_n^m
[24.9] Milne-Thomson	$\binom{n-1}{m-1}B_{n-m}^{(n)}$	$\binom{n}{m}B_{n-m}^{(-m)}$
[24.15] Riordan	$s(n, m)$	$S(n, m)$
[24.1] Carlitz, [24.3] Gould	$(-1)^{n-m}S_1(n-1, n-m)$	$S_2(m, n-m)$
Miksa (Unpublished tables)	$S(n-m+1, n)$	${}_mS_n$
[24.17] Gupta		$u(n, m)$

We feel that a capital S is natural for Stirling numbers of the first kind; it is infrequently used for other notation in this context. But once it is used we have difficulty finding a suitable symbol for Stirling numbers of the second kind. The numbers are sufficiently important to warrant a special and easily recognizable symbol, and yet that symbol must be easy to write. We have settled on a script capital $\mathfrak{S}$ without any certainty that we have settled this question permanently.

We feel that the subscript-superscript notation emphasizes the generating functions (which are powers of mutually inverse functions) from which most of the important relations flow.

24.1. Basic Numbers

24.1.1 Binomial Coefficients

I. Definitions

A. $\binom{n}{m}$ is the number of ways of choosing m objects from a collection of n distinct objects without regard to order.

B. Generating functions

$$(1+x)^n=\sum_{m=0}^{n}\binom{n}{m}x^m \qquad n=0, 1, \ldots$$

$$(1-x)^{-m-1}=\sum_{n=m}^{\infty}\binom{n}{m}x^{n-m} \qquad |x|<1$$

C. Closed form

$$\binom{n}{m}=\frac{n!}{m!(n-m)!}=\binom{n}{n-m} \qquad n\geq m$$

$$=\frac{n(n-1)\ldots(n-m+1)}{m!}$$

II. Relations

A. Recurrences

$$\binom{n+1}{m}=\binom{n}{m}+\binom{n}{m-1} \qquad n\geq m\geq 1$$

$$=\binom{n}{m}+\binom{n-1}{m-1}+\ldots+\binom{n-m}{0} \qquad n\geq m$$

B. Checks

$$\sum_{m=0}^{n}\binom{r}{m}\binom{s}{n-m}=\binom{r+s}{n} \qquad r+s\geq n$$

$$\sum_{m=0}^{n}(-1)^{n-m}\binom{r}{m}=\binom{r-1}{n} \qquad r\geq n+1$$

$$\binom{n}{m}\equiv\binom{n_0}{m_0}\binom{n_1}{m_1}\ldots(\text{mod}\, p) \qquad p \text{ a prime}$$

where

$$n=\sum_{k=0}^{\infty} n_k p^k, \qquad m=\sum_{k=0}^{\infty} m_k p^k \qquad p>m_k,\ n_k\geq 0$$

C. Numerical analysis

$$\Delta^n f(x)=\sum_{m=0}^{n}(-1)^{n-m}\binom{n}{m}f(x+m)$$

$$=\sum_{k=0}^{r}\binom{r}{k}\Delta^{n+k}f(x-r)$$

$$\sum_{m=0}^{s}(-1)^m\binom{n}{m}f(x-m)$$

$$=\sum_{k=0}^{s}(-1)^{s-k}\binom{n-k-1}{s-k}\Delta^k f(x-s) \qquad s<n$$

III. Special Values

$$\binom{n}{0}=\binom{n}{n}=1$$

$$\binom{2n}{n}=\frac{2^n(2n-1)(2n-3)\ldots 3\cdot 1}{n!}$$

24.1.2 Multinomial Coefficients

I. Definitions

A. $(n; n_1, n_2, \ldots, n_m)$ is the number of ways of putting $n=n_1+n_2+\ldots+n_m$ different objects into m different boxes with n_k in the k-th box, $k=1, 2, \ldots, m$.

$(n; a_1, a_2, \ldots, a_n)^*$ is the number of permutations of $n=a_1+2a_2+\ldots+na_n$ symbols composed of a_k cycles of length k for $k=1, 2, \ldots, n$.

$(n; a_1, a_2, \ldots, a_n)'$ is the number of ways of partitioning a set of $n=a_1+2a_2+\ldots+na_n$ different objects into a_k subsets containing k objects for $k=1, 2, \ldots, n$.

B. Generating functions

$$(x_1+x_2+\ldots+x_m)^n=\Sigma(n; n_1, n_2, \ldots, n_m)x_1^{n_1}x_2^{n_2}\ldots x_m^{n_m} \qquad \text{summed over } n_1+n_2+\ldots+n_m=n$$

$$\left(\sum_{k=1}^{\infty}\frac{x_k}{k}t^k\right)^m=m!\sum_{n=m}^{\infty}\frac{t^n}{n!}\Sigma(n; a_1, a_2, \ldots, a_n)^* x_1^{a_1}x_2^{a_2}\ldots x_n^{a_n}$$

summed over $a_1+2a_2+\ldots+na_n=n$ and $a_1+a_2+\ldots+a_n=m$

$$\left(\sum_{k=1}^{\infty}\frac{x_k}{k!}t^k\right)^m=m!\sum_{n=m}^{\infty}\frac{t^n}{n!}\Sigma(n; a_1, a_2, \ldots, a_n)' x_1^{a_1}x_2^{a_2}\ldots x_n^{a_n}$$

C. Closed forms

$$(n; n_1, n_2, \ldots, n_m)=n!/n_1!n_2!\ldots n_m! \qquad n_1+n_2+\ldots+n_m=n$$

$$(n; a_1, a_2, \ldots, a_n)^*=n!/1^{a_1}a_1!2^{a_2}a_2!\ldots n^{a_n}a_n! \qquad a_1+2a_2+\ldots+na_n=n$$

$$(n; a_1, a_2, \ldots, a_n)'=n!/(1!)^{a_1}a_1!(2!)^{a_2}a_2!\ldots(n!)^{a_n}a_n! \qquad a_1+2a_2+\ldots+na_n=n$$

II. Relations

A. Recurrence

$$(n+m; n_1+1, n_2+1, \ldots, n_m+1)=\sum_{k=1}^{m}(n+m-1; n_1+1, \ldots, n_{k-1}+1, n_k, n_{k+1}+1, \ldots, n_m+1)$$

B. Checks

$$\Sigma(n; n_1, n_2, \ldots, n_m)=\begin{cases} m^n & \text{all } n_i\geq 1 \\ m!\ \mathfrak{S}_n^{(m)} & \end{cases} \qquad \text{summed over } n_1+n_2+\ldots+n_m=n$$

$$\Sigma(n; a_1, a_2, \ldots, a_n)^*=(-1)^{n-m}S_n^{(m)}$$

$$\Sigma(n; a_1, a_2, \ldots, a_n)'=\mathfrak{S}_n^{(m)}$$

summed over $a_1+2a_2+\ldots+na_n=n$ and $a_1+a_2+\ldots+a_n=m$

C. Numerical analysis (Faà di Bruno's formula)

$$\frac{d^n}{dx^n}f(g(x))=\sum_{m=0}^{n}f^{(m)}(g(x))\Sigma(n; a_1, a_2, \ldots, a_n)'\{g'(x)\}^{a_1}\{g''(x)\}^{a_2}\ldots\{g^{(n)}(x)\}^{a_n}$$

summed over $a_1+2a_2+\ldots+na_n=n$ and $a_1+a_2+\ldots+a_n=m$.

$$\begin{vmatrix} P_1 & 1 & 0 & \ldots & 0 \\ P_2 & P_1 & 2 & \ldots & . \\ P_3 & P_2 & P_1 & \ldots & . \\ . & . & . & \ldots & . \\ . & . & . & \ldots & 0 \\ . & . & . & \ldots & n-1 \\ P_n & P_{n-1} & P_{n-2} & \ldots & P_1 \end{vmatrix} = \Sigma(-1)^{n-\Sigma a_i}(n; a_1, a_2, \ldots, a_n)^* P_1^{a_1} P_2^{a_2} \ldots P_n^{a_n}$$

summed over $a_1+2a_2+\ldots+na_n=n$; e.g. if $P_k=\Sigma_{j=1}^{r} x_j^k$ for $k=1, 2, \ldots, n$ then the determinant and sum equal $n!\Sigma x_1x_2 \ldots x_n$, the latter sum denoting the n-th elementary symmetric function of $x_1, x_2, \ldots, x_r$.

24.1.3 Stirling Numbers of the First Kind

I. Definitions

A. $(-1)^{n-m}S_n^{(m)}$ is the number of permutations of n symbols which have exactly m cycles.

B. Generating functions

$$x(x-1)\ldots(x-n+1)=\sum_{m=0}^{n} S_n^{(m)}x^m$$

$$\{\ln(1+x)\}^m=m!\sum_{n=m}^{\infty} S_n^{(m)}\frac{x^n}{n!} \qquad |x|<1$$

C. Closed form (see closed form for $\mathfrak{S}_n^{(m)}$)

$$S_n^{(m)}=\sum_{k=0}^{n-m}(-1)^k\binom{n-1+k}{n-m+k}\binom{2n-m}{n-m-k}\mathfrak{S}_{n-m+k}^{(k)}$$

II. Relations

A. Recurrences

$$S_{n+1}^{(m)}=S_n^{(m-1)}-nS_n^{(m)} \qquad n\geq m\geq 1$$

$$\binom{m}{r}S_n^{(m)}=\sum_{k=m-r}^{n-r}\binom{n}{k}S_{n-k}^{(r)}S_k^{(m-r)} \qquad n\geq m\geq r$$

B. Checks

$$\sum_{m=1}^{n}S_n^{(m)}=0 \qquad n>1$$

$$\sum_{m=0}^{n}(-1)^{n-m}S_n^{(m)}=n!$$

$$\sum_{k=m}^{n}S_{n+1}^{(k+1)}n^{k-m}=S_n^{(m)}$$

C. Numerical analysis

$$\frac{d^m}{dx^m}f(x)=m!\sum_{n=m}^{\infty}\frac{S_n^{(m)}}{n!}\Delta^n f(x)$$

if convergent.

III. Asymptotics and Special Values

$$|S_n^{(m)}|\sim(n-1)!(\gamma+\ln n)^{m-1}/(m-1)! \qquad \text{for } m=o(\ln n)$$

$$\lim_{m\to\infty}\frac{S_{n+m}^{(m)}}{m^{2n}}=\frac{(-1)^n}{2^n n!}$$

$$\lim_{n\to\infty}\frac{S_{n+1}^{(m)}}{nS_n^{(m)}}=-1$$

$$S_n^{(0)}=\delta_{0n}$$

$$S_n^{(1)}=(-1)^{n-1}(n-1)!$$

$$S_n^{(n-1)}=-\binom{n}{2}$$

$$S_n^{(n)}=1$$

24.1.4 Stirling Numbers of the Second Kind

I. Definitions

A. $\mathfrak{S}_n^{(m)}$ is the number of ways of partitioning a set of n elements into m non-empty subsets.

B. Generating functions

$$x^n=\sum_{m=0}^{n}\mathfrak{S}_n^{(m)}x(x-1)\ldots(x-m+1)$$

$$(e^x-1)^m=m!\sum_{n=m}^{\infty}\mathfrak{S}_n^{(m)}\frac{x^n}{n!}$$

$$(1-x)^{-1}(1-2x)^{-1}\ldots(1-mx)^{-1}=\sum_{n=m}^{\infty}\mathfrak{S}_n^{(m)}x^{n-m} \qquad |x|<m^{-1}$$

C. Closed form

$$\mathfrak{S}_n^{(m)}=\frac{1}{m!}\sum_{k=0}^{m}(-1)^{m-k}\binom{m}{k}k^n$$

II. Relations

A. Recurrences

$$\mathfrak{S}_{n+1}^{(m)}=m\,\mathfrak{S}_n^{(m)}+\mathfrak{S}_n^{(m-1)} \qquad n\geq m\geq 1$$

$$\binom{m}{r}\mathfrak{S}_n^{(m)}=\sum_{k=m-r}^{n-r}\binom{n}{k}\mathfrak{S}_{n-k}^{(r)}\mathfrak{S}_k^{(m-r)} \qquad n\geq m\geq r$$

B. Checks

$$\sum_{m=0}^{n}(-1)^{n-m}m!\,\mathfrak{S}_n^{(m)}=1$$

$$\sum_{k=m}^{n}\mathfrak{S}_{k-1}^{(m-1)}m^{n-k}=\mathfrak{S}_n^{(m)}$$

$$\mathfrak{S}_n^{(m)}=\sum_{k=0}^{n-m}(-1)^k\binom{n-1+k}{n-m+k}\binom{2n-m}{n-m-k}S_{n-m+k}^{(k)}$$

$$\sum_{k=m}^{n}S_k^{(m)}\mathfrak{S}_n^{(k)}=\sum_{k=m}^{n}S_n^{(k)}\mathfrak{S}_k^{(m)}=\delta_{mn}$$

C. Numerical analysis

$$\Delta^m f(x)=m!\sum_{n=m}^{\infty}\frac{\mathfrak{S}_n^{(m)}}{n!}f^{(n)}(x) \qquad \text{if convergent}$$

$$\sum_{k=0}^{n}k^m=\sum_{k=0}^{m}k!\,\mathfrak{S}_m^{(k)}\binom{n+1}{k+1}$$

$$\sum_{k=0}^{n}k^m x^k=\sum_{j=0}^{m}\mathfrak{S}_m^{(j)}x^j\frac{d^j}{dx^j}\left\{\frac{1-x^{n+1}}{1-x}\right\}$$

III. Asymptotics and Special Values

$$\lim_{n\to\infty}m^{-n}\mathfrak{S}_n^{(m)}=(m!)^{-1}$$

$$\mathfrak{S}_{n+m}^{(m)}\sim\frac{m^{2n}}{2^n n!} \qquad \text{for } n=o(m^{\frac{1}{2}})$$

$$\lim_{n\to\infty}\frac{\mathfrak{S}_{n+1}^{(m)}}{\mathfrak{S}_n^{(m)}}=m$$

$$\mathfrak{S}_n^{(0)}=\delta_{0n}$$

$$\mathfrak{S}_n^{(1)}=\mathfrak{S}_n^{(n)}=1$$

$$\mathfrak{S}_n^{(n-1)}=\binom{n}{2}$$

24.2. Partitions

24.2.1 Unrestricted Partitions

I. Definitions

A. $p(n)$ is the number of decompositions of n into integer summands without regard to order. E.g., $5=1+4=2+3=1+1+3=1+2+2=1+1+1+2=1+1+1+1+1$ so that $p(5)=7$.

B. Generating function

$$\sum_{n=0}^{\infty}p(n)x^n=\prod_{n=1}^{\infty}(1-x^n)^{-1}=\left\{\sum_{n=-\infty}^{\infty}(-1)^n x^{\frac{3n^2+n}{2}}\right\}^{-1} \qquad |x|<1$$

C. Closed form

$$p(n)=\frac{1}{\pi\sqrt{2}}\sum_{k=1}^{\infty}\sqrt{k}A_k(n)\frac{d}{dn}\frac{\sinh\left\{\frac{\pi}{k}\sqrt{\frac{2}{3}}\sqrt{n-\frac{1}{24}}\right\}}{\sqrt{n-\frac{1}{24}}}$$

where

$$A_k(n)=\sum_{\substack{0<h\leq k\\(h,k)=1}}e^{\pi i s(h,k)}e^{-\frac{2\pi i h n}{k}}$$

$$s(h,k)=\sum_{j=1}^{k-1}\frac{j}{k}\left(\left(\frac{hj}{k}\right)\right)$$

$$((x))=x-[x]-\tfrac{1}{2} \text{ if } x \text{ is not an integer}$$
$$=0 \qquad \text{if } x \text{ is an integer}$$

II. Relations

A. Recurrence

$$p(n)=\sum_{1\leq\frac{3k^2\pm k}{2}\leq n}(-1)^{k-1}p\left(n-\frac{3k^2\pm k}{2}\right) \qquad p(0)=1$$

$$=\frac{1}{n}\sum_{k=1}^{n}\sigma_1(k)p(n-k)$$

B. Check

$$p(n)+\sum_{1\leq\frac{3k^2\pm k}{2}\leq n}(-1)^k\frac{3k^2\pm k}{2}p\left(n-\frac{3k^2\pm k}{2}\right)=\sigma_1(n)$$

III. Asymptotics

$$p(n)\sim\frac{1}{4n\sqrt{3}}e^{\pi\sqrt{2/3}\sqrt{n}}$$

24.2.2 Partitions Into Distinct Parts

I. Definitions

A. $q(n)$ is the number of decompositions of n into distinct integer summands without regard to order. E.g., $5=1+4=2+3$ so that $q(5)=3$.

B. Generating function

$$\sum_{n=0}^{\infty}q(n)x^n=\prod_{n=1}^{\infty}(1+x^n)=\prod_{n=1}^{\infty}(1-x^{2n-1})^{-1} \qquad |x|<1$$

C. Closed form

$$q(n)=\frac{1}{\sqrt{2}}\sum_{k=1}^{\infty}A_{2k-1}(n)\frac{d}{dn}J_0\left(\frac{\pi i}{2k-1}\sqrt{\frac{1}{3}}\sqrt{n+\frac{1}{24}}\right)$$

where $J_0(x)$ is the Bessel function of order 0 and $A_{2k-1}(n)$ was defined in part I.C. of the previous subsection.

II. Relations

A. Recurrences

$$\sum_{0\le\frac{3k^2\pm k}{2}\le n}(-1)^k q\left(n-\frac{3k^2\pm k}{2}\right)=(-1)^r \text{ if } n=3r^2\pm r$$
$$q(0)=1$$
$$=0 \text{ otherwise}$$

$$q(n)=\frac{1}{n}\sum_{k=1}^{n}\left\{\sigma_1(k)-2\sigma_1\left(\frac{k}{2}\right)\right\}q(n-k)$$

B. Check

$$\sum_{0\le 3k^2\pm k\le n}(-1)^k q(n-(3k^2\pm k))=1 \text{ if } n=\frac{r^2-r}{2}$$
$$=0 \text{ otherwise.}$$

III. Asymptotics

$$q(n)\sim\frac{1}{4\cdot 3^{1/4}\cdot n^{3/4}}e^{\pi\sqrt{1/3}\sqrt{n}}$$

24.3. Number Theoretic Functions

24.3.1 The Möbius Function

I. Definitions

A. $\mu(n)=1$ if $n=1$
$=(-1)^k$ if n is the product of k distinct primes
$=0$ if n is divisible by a square >1.

B. Generating functions

$$\sum_{n=1}^{\infty}\mu(n)n^{-s}=1/\zeta(s) \qquad \mathscr{R}s>1$$

$$\sum_{n=1}^{\infty}\frac{\mu(n)x^n}{1-x^n}=x \qquad |x|<1$$

II. Relations

A. Recurrence

$$\mu(mn)=\mu(m)\mu(n) \text{ if } (m,n)=1$$
$$=0 \qquad \text{if } (m,n)>1$$

B. Check

$$\sum_{d|n}\mu(d)=\delta_{n1}$$

C. Numerical analysis

$g(n)=\sum_{d|n}f(d)$ for all n if and only if

$$f(n)=\sum_{d|n}\mu(d)g(n/d) \text{ for all } n$$

$g(n)=\prod_{d|n}f(d)$ for all n if and only if

$$f(n)=\prod_{d|n}g(n/d)^{\mu(d)} \text{ for all } n$$

$g(x)=\sum_{n=1}^{[x]}f(x/n)$ for all $x>0$ if and only if

$$f(x)=\sum_{n=1}^{[x]}\mu(n)g(x/n) \text{ for all } x>0$$

$g(x)=\sum_{n=1}^{\infty}f(nx)$ for all $x>0$ if and only if

$$f(x)=\sum_{n=1}^{\infty}\mu(n)g(nx) \text{ for all } x>0$$

and if $\sum_{m=1}^{\infty}\sum_{n=1}^{\infty}|f(mnx)|=\sum_{n=1}^{\infty}\sigma_0(n)|f(nx)|$ converges.

The cyclotomic polynomial of order n is $\prod_{d|n}(x^d-1)^{\mu(n/d)}$

III. Asymptotics

$$\sum_{n=1}^{\infty}\frac{\mu(n)}{n}=0$$

$$\sum_{n=1}^{\infty}\frac{\mu(n)}{n}\ln n=-1$$

$$\sum_{n\le x}\mu(n)=0(xe^{-c\sqrt{\ln x}})$$

24.3.2 The Euler Totient Function

I. Definitions

A. $\varphi(n)$ is the number of integers not exceeding and relatively prime to n.

B. Generating functions

$$\sum_{n=1}^{\infty}\varphi(n)n^{-s}=\frac{\zeta(s-1)}{\zeta(s)} \qquad \mathscr{R}s>2$$

$$\sum_{n=1}^{\infty}\frac{\varphi(n)x^n}{1-x^n}=\frac{x}{(1-x)^2} \qquad |x|<1$$

C. Closed form

$$\varphi(n)=n\prod_{p|n}\left(1-\frac{1}{p}\right)$$

over distinct primes p dividing n.

II. Relations

A. Recurrence

$$\varphi(mn)=\varphi(m)\varphi(n) \qquad (m,n)=1$$

B. Checks

$$\sum_{d|n}\varphi(d)=n$$

$$\varphi(n)=\sum_{d|n}\mu\left(\frac{n}{d}\right)d$$

$$a^{\varphi(n)}\equiv 1 \pmod n \qquad (a,n)=1$$

III. Asymptotics

$$\frac{1}{n^2}\sum_{k=1}^{n}\varphi(k)=\frac{3}{\pi^2}+O\left(\frac{\ln n}{n}\right)$$

24.3.3 Divisor Functions

I. Definitions

A. $\sigma_k(n)$ is the sum of the k-th powers of the divisors of n. Often $\sigma_0(n)$ is denoted by $d(n)$, and $\sigma_1(n)$ by $\sigma(n)$.

B. Generating functions

$$\sum_{n=1}^{\infty} \sigma_k(n) n^{-s} = \zeta(s)\zeta(s-k) \qquad \mathscr{R}s > k+1$$

$$\sum_{n=1}^{\infty} \sigma_k(n) x^n = \sum_{n=1}^{\infty} \frac{n^k x^n}{1-x^n} \qquad |x|<1$$

C. Closed form

$$\sigma_k(n) = \sum_{d|n} d^k = \prod_{i=1}^{s} \frac{p_i^{k(a_i+1)}-1}{p_i^k-1} \qquad n = p_1^{a_1} p_2^{a_2} \ldots p_s^{a_s}$$

II. Relations

A. Recurrences

$$\sigma_k(mn) = \sigma_k(m)\sigma_k(n) \qquad (m, n)=1$$

$$\sigma_k(np) = \sigma_k(n)\sigma_k(p) - p^k \sigma_k(n/p) \qquad p \text{ prime}$$

III. Asymptotics

$$\frac{1}{n}\sum_{m=1}^{n} \sigma_0(m) = \ln n + 2\gamma - 1 + O(n^{-\frac{1}{2}})$$

(γ=Euler's constant)

$$\frac{1}{n^2}\sum_{m=1}^{n} \sigma_1(m) = \frac{\pi^2}{12} + O\left(\frac{\ln n}{n}\right)$$

24.3.4 Primitive Roots

I. Definitions

The integers not exceeding and relatively prime to a fixed integer n form a group; the group is cyclic if and only if $n=2$, 4 or n is of the form p^k or $2p^k$ where p is an odd prime. Then g is a primitive root of n if it generates that group; i.e., if $g, g^2, \ldots, g^{\varphi(n)}$ are distinct modulo n. There are $\varphi(\varphi(n))$ primitive roots of n.

II. Relations

A. Recurrences. If g is a primitive root of a prime p and $g^{p-1} \not\equiv 1 \pmod{p^2}$ then g is a primitive root of p^k for all k. If $g^{p-1} \equiv 1 \pmod{p^2}$ then $g+p$ is a primitive root of p^k for all k.

If g is a primitive root of p^k then either g or $g+p^k$, whichever is odd, is a primitive root of $2p^k$.

B. Checks. If g is a primitive root of n then g^k is a primitive root of n if and only if $(k, \varphi(n))=1$, and each primitive root of n is of this form.

25. Numerical Interpolation, Differentiation, and Integration

Numerical analysts have a tendency to accumulate a multiplicity of tools each designed for highly specialized operations and each requiring special knowledge to use properly. From the vast stock of formulas available we have culled the present selection. We hope that it will be useful. As with all such compendia, the reader may miss his favorites and find others whose utility he thinks is marginal.

We would have liked to give examples to illuminate the formulas, but this has not been feasible. Numerical analysis is partially a science and partially an art, and short of writing a textbook on the subject it has been impossible to indicate where and under what circumstances the various formulas are useful or accurate, or to elucidate the numerical difficulties to which one might be led by uncritical use. The formulas are therefore issued together with a caveat against their blind application.

Formulas

Notation: Abscissas: $x_0<x_1<\ldots$; functions: $f, g, \ldots$; values: $f(x_i)=f_i$, $f'(x_i)=f'_i$. $f', f^{(2)}, \ldots$ indicate 1st, 2d, ... derivatives. If abscissas are equally spaced, $x_{i+1}-x_i=h$ and $f_p=f(x_0+ph)$ (p not necessarily integral). R, R_n indicate remainders.

25.1. Differences

Forward Differences

25.1.1

$$\Delta(f_n)=\Delta_n=\Delta_n^1=f_{n+1}-f_n$$

$$\Delta_n^2=\Delta_{n+1}^1-\Delta_n^1=f_{n+2}-2f_{n+1}+f_n$$

$$\Delta_n^3=\Delta_{n+1}^2-\Delta_n^2=f_{n+3}-3f_{n+2}+3f_{n+1}-f_n$$

$$\Delta_n^k=\Delta_{n+1}^{k-1}-\Delta_n^{k-1}=\sum_{j=0}^{k}(-1)^j\binom{k}{j}f_{n+k-j}$$

Central Differences

25.1.2

$$\delta(f_{n+\frac{1}{2}})=\delta_{n+\frac{1}{2}}=\delta_{n+\frac{1}{2}}^1=f_{n+1}-f_n$$

$$\delta_n^2=\delta_{n+\frac{1}{2}}^1-\delta_{n-\frac{1}{2}}^1=f_{n+1}-2f_n+f_{n-1}$$

$$\delta_{n+\frac{1}{2}}^3=\delta_{n+1}^2-\delta_n^2=f_{n+2}-3f_{n+1}+3f_n-f_{n-1}$$

$$\delta_n^{2k}=\sum_{j=0}^{2k}(-1)^j\binom{2k}{j}f_{n+k-j}$$

$$\delta_{n+\frac{1}{2}}^{2k+1}=\sum_{j=0}^{2k+1}(-1)^j\binom{2k+1}{j}f_{n+k+1-j}$$

$\delta_{\frac{1}{2}n}^k=\Delta_{\frac{1}{2}(n-k)}^k$ if n and k are of same parity.

Forward Differences

x_0	f_0			
		Δ_0		
x_1	f_1		Δ_0^2	
		Δ_1		Δ_0^3
x_2	f_2		Δ_1^2	
		Δ_2		
x_3	f_3			

Central Differences

x_{-1}	f_{-1}			
		$\delta_{-\frac{1}{2}}$		
x_0	f_0		δ_0^2	
		$\delta_{\frac{1}{2}}$		$\delta_{\frac{1}{2}}^3$
x_1	f_1		δ_1^2	
		$\delta_{3/2}$		
x_2	f_2			

Mean Differences

25.1.3 $$\mu(f_n)=\frac{1}{2}(f_{n+\frac{1}{2}}+f_{n-\frac{1}{2}})$$

Divided Differences

25.1.4 $$[x_0,x_1]=\frac{f_0-f_1}{x_0-x_1}=[x_1,x_0]$$

$$[x_0,x_1,x_2]=\frac{[x_0,x_1]-[x_1,x_2]}{x_0-x_2}$$

$$[x_0,x_1,\ldots,x_k]=\frac{[x_0,\ldots,x_{k-1}]-[x_1,\ldots,x_k]}{x_0-x_k}$$

Divided Differences in Terms of Functional Values

25.1.5 $$[x_0,x_1,\ldots,x_n]=\sum_{k=0}^{n}\frac{f_k}{\pi_n'(x_k)}$$

25.1.6 where $\pi_n(x)=(x-x_0)\ (x-x_1)\ .\ .\ .\ (x-x_n)$ and $\pi_n'(x)$ is its derivative:

25.1.7

$$\pi_n'(x_k)=(x_k-x_0)\ .\ .\ .\ (x_k-x_{k-1})(x_k-x_{k+1})\ .\ .\ .\ (x_k-x_n)$$

Let D be a simply connected domain with a piecewise smooth boundary C and contain the points $z_0, \ldots, z_n$ in its interior. Let $f(z)$ be analytic in D and continuous in $D+C$. Then,

25.1.8 $$[z_0,z_1,\ldots,z_n]=\frac{1}{2\pi i}\int_C \frac{f(z)}{\prod_{k=0}^{n}(z-z_k)}\,dz$$

25.1.9 $$\Delta_0^n=h^n f^{(n)}(\xi) \qquad (x_0<\xi<x_n)$$

25.1.10

$$[x_0,x_1,\ldots,x_n]=\frac{\Delta_0^n}{n!h^n}=\frac{f^{(n)}(\xi)}{n!} \qquad (x_0<\xi<x_n)$$

25.1.11

$$[x_{-n},x_{-n+1},\ldots,x_0,\ldots,x_n]=\frac{\delta_0^{2n}}{h^{2n}(2n)!}$$

Reciprocal Differences

25.1.12

$$\rho(x_0,x_1)=\frac{x_0-x_1}{f_0-f_1}$$

$$\rho_2(x_0,x_1,x_2)=\frac{x_0-x_2}{\rho(x_0,x_1)-\rho(x_1,x_2)}+f_1$$

$$\rho_3(x_0,x_1,x_2,x_3)=\frac{x_0-x_3}{\rho_2(x_0,x_1,x_2)-\rho_2(x_1,x_2,x_3)}+\rho(x_1,x_2)$$

$$\vdots$$

$$\rho_n(x_0,x_1,\ldots,x_n)=\frac{x_0-x_n}{\rho_{n-1}(x_0,\ldots,x_{n-1})-\rho_{n-1}(x_1,\ldots,x_n)}+\rho_{n-2}(x_1,\ldots,x_{n-1})$$

25.2. Interpolation

Lagrange Interpolation Formulas

25.2.1 $$f(x)=\sum_{i=0}^{n} l_i(x)f_i+R_n(x)$$

25.2.2

$$l_i(x)=\frac{\pi_n(x)}{(x-x_i)\pi_n'(x_i)}=\frac{(x-x_0)\ldots(x-x_{i-1})(x-x_{i+1})\ldots(x-x_n)}{(x_i-x_0)\ldots(x_i-x_{i-1})(x_i-x_{i+1})\ldots(x_i-x_n)}$$

Remainder in Lagrange Interpolation Formula

25.2.3

$$R_n(x)=\pi_n(x)\cdot[x_0,x_1,\ldots,x_n,x]=\pi_n(x)\cdot\frac{f^{n+1}(\xi)}{(n+1)!} \qquad (x_0<\xi<x_n)$$

25.2.4

$$|R_n(x)|\leq\frac{(x_n-x_0)^{n+1}}{(n+1)!}\max_{x_0\leq x\leq x_n}|f^{(n+1)}(x)|$$

25.2.5

$$R_n(z)=\frac{\pi_n(z)}{2\pi i}\int_C\frac{f(t)}{(t-z)(t-z_0)\ldots(t-z_n)}\,dt$$

The conditions of **25.1.8** are assumed here.

Lagrange Interpolation, Equally Spaced Abscissas

***n* Point Formula**

25.2.6 $$f(x_0+ph)=\sum_k A_k^n(p)f_k+R_{n-1}$$

For n even, $\left(-\frac{1}{2}(n-2)\leq k\leq\frac{1}{2}n\right)$.

For n odd, $\left(-\frac{1}{2}(n-1)\leq k\leq\frac{1}{2}(n-1)\right)$.

25.2.7

$$A_k^n(p)=\frac{(-1)^{\frac{1}{2}n+k}}{\left(\frac{n-2}{2}+k\right)!(\frac{1}{2}n-k)!(p-k)}\prod_{t=1}^{n}(p+\tfrac{1}{2}n-t) \qquad n \text{ even.}$$

$$A_k^n(p)=\frac{(-1)^{\frac{1}{2}(n-1)+k}}{\left(\frac{n-1}{2}+k\right)!\left(\frac{n-1}{2}-k\right)!(p-k)}\prod_{t=0}^{n-1}\left(p+\frac{n-1}{2}-t\right), \qquad n \text{ odd.}$$

25.2.8

$$R_{n-1}=\frac{1}{n!}\prod_k(p-k)h^nf^{(n)}(\xi)\approx\frac{1}{n!}\prod_k(p-k)\Delta_0^n \qquad (x_0<\xi<x_n)$$

k has the same range as in **25.2.6.**

Lagrange Two Point Interpolation Formula (Linear Interpolation)

25.2.9 $$f(x_0+ph)=(1-p)f_0+pf_1+R_1$$

25.2.10 $$R_1(p)\approx.125h^2f^{(2)}(\xi)\approx.125\Delta^2$$

Lagrange Three Point Interpolation Formula

25.2.11

$$f(x_0+ph)=A_{-1}f_{-1}+A_0f_0+A_1f_1+R_2 \approx\frac{p(p-1)}{2}f_{-1}+(1-p^2)f_0+\frac{p(p+1)}{2}f_1$$

25.2.12

$$R_2(p)\approx .065h^3f^{(3)}(\xi)\approx .065\Delta^3 \qquad (|p|\leq 1)$$

Lagrange Four Point Interpolation Formula

25.2.13

$$f(x_0+ph)=A_{-1}f_{-1}+A_0f_0+A_1f_1+A_2f_2+R_3$$
$$\approx\frac{-p(p-1)(p-2)}{6}f_{-1}+\frac{(p^2-1)(p-2)}{2}f_0 -\frac{p(p+1)(p-2)}{2}f_1+\frac{p(p^2-1)}{6}f_2$$

25.2.14 $R_3(p)\approx$

$.024h^4f^{(4)}(\xi)\approx .024\Delta^4 \qquad (0<p<1)$

$.042h^4f^{(4)}(\xi)\approx .042\Delta^4 \qquad (-1<p<0,\ 1<p<2)$

$(x_{-1}<\xi<x_2)$

Lagrange Five Point Interpolation Formula

25.2.15

$$f(x_0+ph)=\sum_{i=-2}^{2}A_if_i+R_4$$
$$\approx\frac{(p^2-1)p(p-2)}{24}f_{-2}-\frac{(p-1)p(p^2-4)}{6}f_{-1} +\frac{(p^2-1)(p^2-4)}{4}f_0-\frac{(p+1)p(p^2-4)}{6}f_1 +\frac{(p^2-1)p(p+2)}{24}f_2$$

25.2.16 $R_4(p)\approx$

$.012h^5f^{(5)}(\xi)\approx .012\Delta^5 \qquad (|p|<1)$

$.031h^5f^{(5)}(\xi)\approx .031\Delta^5 \qquad (1<|p|<2) \qquad (x_{-2}<\xi<x_2)$

Lagrange Six Point Interpolation Formula

25.2.17

$$f(x_0+ph)=\sum_{i=-2}^{3}A_if_i+R_5$$
$$\approx\frac{-p(p^2-1)(p-2)(p-3)}{120}f_{-2} +\frac{p(p-1)(p^2-4)(p-3)}{24}f_{-1} -\frac{(p^2-1)(p^2-4)(p-3)}{12}f_0 +\frac{p(p+1)(p^2-4)(p-3)}{12}f_1-\frac{p(p^2-1)(p+2)(p-3)}{24}f_2 +\frac{p(p^2-1)(p^2-4)}{120}f_3$$

25.2.18 $R_5(p)\approx$

$.0049h^6f^{(6)}(\xi)\approx .0049\Delta^6 \qquad (0<p<1)$

$.0071h^6f^{(6)}(\xi)\approx .0071\Delta^6 \qquad (-1<p<0,\ 1<p<2)$

$.024h^6f^{(6)}(\xi)\approx .024\Delta^6 \qquad (-2<p<-1,\ 2<p<3)$

$(x_{-2}<\xi<x_3)$

Lagrange Seven Point Interpolation Formula

25.2.19

$$f(x_0+ph)=\sum_{i=-3}^{3}A_if_i+R_6$$

25.2.20

$$R_6(p)\approx\begin{cases} .0025h^7f^{(7)}(\xi)\doteq .0025\Delta^7 & (|p|<1)\\ .0046h^7f^{(7)}(\xi)\approx .0046\Delta^7 & (1<|p|<2)\\ .019h^7f^{(7)}(\xi)\approx .019\Delta^7 & (2<|p|<3)\end{cases}$$

$(x_{-3}<\xi<x_3)$

Lagrange Eight Point Interpolation Formula

25.2.21

$$f(x_0+ph)=\sum_{i=-3}^{4}A_if_i+R_7$$

25.2.22

$$R_7(p)\approx\begin{cases} .0011h^8f^{(8)}(\xi)\approx .0011\Delta^8 & (0<p<1)\\ .0014h^8f^{(8)}(\xi)\approx .0014\Delta^8 & (-1<p<0)\ (1<p<2)\\ .0033h^8f^{(8)}(\xi)\approx .0033\Delta^8 & (-2<p<-1)\ (2<p<3)\\ .016h^8f^{(8)}(\xi)\approx .016\Delta^8 & (-3<p<-2)\ (3<p<4)\end{cases}$$

$(x_{-3}<\xi<x_4)$

Aitken's Iteration Method

Let $f(x|x_0, x_1, \ldots, x_k)$ denote the unique polynomial of kth degree which coincides in value with $f(x)$ at $x_0, \ldots, x_k$.

25.2.23

$$f(x|x_0,x_1)=\frac{1}{x_1-x_0}\begin{vmatrix} f_0 & x_0-x\\ f_1 & x_1-x\end{vmatrix}$$

$$f(x|x_0,x_2)=\frac{1}{x_2-x_0}\begin{vmatrix} f_0 & x_0-x\\ f_2 & x_2-x\end{vmatrix}$$

$$f(x|x_0,x_1,x_2)=\frac{1}{x_2-x_1}\begin{vmatrix} f(x|x_0,x_1) & x_1-x\\ f(x|x_0,x_2) & x_2-x\end{vmatrix}$$

$$f(x|x_0,x_1,x_2,x_3)=\frac{1}{x_3-x_2}\begin{vmatrix} f(x|x_0,x_1,x_2) & x_2-x\\ f(x|x_0,x_1,x_3) & x_3-x\end{vmatrix}$$

Taylor Expansion

25.2.24

$$f(x)=f_0+(x-x_0)f_0'+\frac{(x-x_0)^2}{2!}f_0^{(2)}+\ldots+\frac{(x-x_0)^n}{n!}f_0^{(n)}+R_n$$

25.2.25

$$R_n=\int_{x_0}^{x}f^{(n+1)}(t)\,\frac{(x-t)^n}{n!}\,dt=\frac{(x-x_0)^{n+1}}{(n+1)!}f^{(n+1)}(\xi)\qquad(x_0<\xi<x)$$

Newton's Divided Difference Interpolation Formula

25.2.26

$$f(x)=f_0+\sum_{k=1}^{n}\pi_{k-1}(x)\,[x_0,x_1,\ldots,x_k]+R_n$$

$$\begin{array}{llllll} x_0 & f_0 & & & & \\ & & [x_0,x_1] & & & \\ x_1 & f_1 & & [x_0,x_1,x_2] & & \\ & & [x_1,x_2] & & [x_0,x_1,x_2,x_3] & \\ x_2 & f_2 & & [x_1,x_2,x_3] & & \\ & & [x_2,x_3] & & & \\ x_3 & f_3 & & & & \end{array}$$

25.2.27

$$R_n(x)=\pi_n(x)\,[x_0,\ldots,x_n,x]=\pi_n(x)\,\frac{f^{(n+1)}(\xi)}{(n+1)!}\qquad(x_0<\xi<x_n)$$

(For π_n see **25.1.6.**)

Newton's Forward Difference Formula

25.2.28

$$f(x_0+ph)=f_0+p\Delta_0+\binom{p}{2}\Delta_0^2+\ldots+\binom{p}{n}\Delta_0^n+R_n$$

$$\begin{array}{lllll} x_0 & f_0 & & & \\ & & \Delta_0 & & \\ x_1 & f_1 & & \Delta_0^2 & \\ & & \Delta_1 & & \Delta_0^3 \\ x_2 & f_2 & & \Delta_1^2 & \\ & & \Delta_2 & & \\ x_3 & f_3 & & & \end{array}$$

25.2.29

$$R_n=h^{n+1}\binom{p}{n+1}f^{(n+1)}(\xi)\approx\binom{p}{n+1}\Delta_0^{n+1}\qquad(x_0<\xi<x_n)$$

Relation Between Newton and Lagrange Coefficients

25.2.30

$$\binom{p}{2}=A_{-1}^3(p)\qquad\binom{p}{3}=-A_{-1}^4(p)\qquad\binom{p}{4}=A_2^5(1-p)\qquad\binom{p}{5}=A_3^6(2-p)$$

Everett's Formula

25.2.31

$$\begin{aligned}f(x_0+ph)&=(1-p)f_0+pf_1-\frac{p(p-1)(p-2)}{3!}\delta_0^2+\frac{(p+1)p(p-1)}{3!}\delta_1^2+\ldots-\binom{p+n-1}{2n+1}\delta_0^{2n}+\binom{p+n}{2n+1}\delta_1^{2n}+R_{2n}\\&=(1-p)f_0+pf_1+E_2\delta_0^2+F_2\delta_1^2+E_4\delta_0^4+F_4\delta_1^4+\ldots+R_{2n}\end{aligned}$$

$$\begin{array}{lllll} x_0 & f_0 & \delta_0^2 & & \delta_0^4 \\ & & \delta_{\frac12} & \delta_{\frac12}^3 & \\ x_1 & f_1 & \delta_1^2 & & \delta_1^4 \end{array}$$

25.2.32

$$R_{2n}=h^{2n+2}\binom{p+n}{2n+2}f^{(2n+2)}(\xi)\approx\binom{p+n}{2n+2}\left[\frac{\Delta_{-n-1}^{2n+2}+\Delta_{-n}^{2n+2}}{2}\right]\qquad(x_{-n}<\xi<x_{n+1})$$

Relation Between Everett and Lagrange Coefficients

25.2.33

$$E_2=A_{-1}^4\qquad E_4=A_{-2}^6\qquad E_6=A_{-3}^8$$

$$F_2=A_2^4\qquad F_4=A_3^6\qquad F_6=A_4^8$$

Everett's Formula With Throwback (Modified Central Difference)

25.2.34

$$f(x_0+ph)=(1-p)f_0+pf_1+E_2\delta_{m,0}^2+F_2\delta_{m,1}^2+R$$

25.2.35 $$\delta_m^2=\delta^2-.184\delta^4$$

25.2.36 $$R\approx.00045|\mu\delta_{\frac12}^4|+.00061|\delta_{\frac12}^5|$$

25.2.37

$$f(x_0+ph)=(1-p)f_0+pf_1+E_2\delta_0^2+F_2\delta_1^2+E_4\delta_{m,0}^4+F_4\delta_{m,1}^4+R$$

25.2.38 $$\delta_m^4=\delta^4-.207\delta^6+\ldots$$

25.2.39 $$R\approx.000032|\mu\delta_{\frac12}^6|+.000052|\delta_{\frac12}^7|$$

25.2.40

$$f(x_0+ph)=(1-p)f_0+pf_1+E_2\delta_0^2+F_2\delta_1^2+E_4\delta_0^4+F_4\delta_1^4+E_6\delta_{m,0}^6+F_6\delta_{m,1}^6+R$$

25.2.41 $$\delta_m^6=\delta^6-.218\delta^8+.049\delta^{10}+\ldots$$

25.2.42 $$R\approx.0000037|\mu\delta_{\frac12}^8|+\ldots$$

Simultaneous Throwback

25.2.43

$$f(x_0+ph)=(1-p)f_0+pf_1+E_2\delta^2_{m,0}+F_2\delta^2_{m,1}+E_4\delta^4_{m,0}+F_4\delta^4_{m,1}+R$$

25.2.44 $\delta^2_m=\delta^2-.01312\delta^6+.0043\delta^8-.001\delta^{10}$

25.2.45 $\delta^4_m=\delta^4-.27827\delta^6+.0685\delta^8-.016\delta^{10}$

25.2.46 $R\approx.00000083|\mu\delta^6_{\frac{1}{2}}|+.0000094\delta^7$

Bessel's Formula With Throwback

25.2.47

$$f(x_0+ph)=(1-p)f_0+pf_1+B_2(\delta^2_{m,0}+\delta^2_{m,1})+B_3\delta^3_{\frac{1}{2}}+R,\ B_2=\frac{p(p-1)}{4},\ B_3=\frac{p(p-1)\,(p-\frac{1}{2})}{6}$$

25.2.48 $\delta^2_m=\delta^2-.184\delta^4$

25.2.49 $R\approx.00045|\mu\delta^4_{\frac{1}{2}}|+.00087|\delta^5_{\frac{1}{2}}|$

Thiele's Interpolation Formula

25.2.50

$$f(x)=f(x_1)+\cfrac{x-x_1}{\rho(x_1,x_2)+\cfrac{x-x_2}{\rho_2(x_1,x_2,x_3)-f(x_1)+\cfrac{x-x_3}{\left(\begin{array}{l}\rho_3(x_1,x_2,x_3,x_4)\\ \quad-\rho(x_1,x_2)+\ldots\end{array}\right)}}}$$

(For reciprocal differences, ρ, see **25.1.12.**)

Trigonometric Interpolation

Gauss' Formula

25.2.51 $f(x)\approx\sum_{k=0}^{2n}f_k\zeta_k(x)=t_n(x)$

25.2.52

$$\zeta_k(x)=\frac{\sin\frac{1}{2}(x-x_0)\ldots\sin\frac{1}{2}(x-x_{k-1})}{\sin\frac{1}{2}(x_k-x_0)\ldots\sin\frac{1}{2}(x_k-x_{k-1})}\cdot\frac{\sin\frac{1}{2}(x-x_{k+1})\ldots\sin\frac{1}{2}(x-x_{2n})}{\sin\frac{1}{2}(x_k-x_{k+1})\ldots\sin\frac{1}{2}(x_k-x_{2n})}$$

$t_n(x)$ is a trigonometric polynomial of degree n such that $t_n(x_k)=f_k$ $(k=0,1,\ldots,2n)$

Harmonic Analysis

Equally spaced abscissas

$$x_0=0,\qquad x_1,\ldots,x_{m-1},x_m=2\pi$$

25.2.53

$$f(x)\approx\frac{1}{2}a_0+\sum_{k=1}^{n}(a_k\cos kx+b_k\sin kx)$$

25.2.54 $m=2n+1$

$$a_k=\frac{2}{2n+1}\sum_{r=0}^{2n}f_r\cos kx_r;\qquad b_k=\frac{2}{2n+1}\sum_{r=0}^{2n}f_r\sin kx_r$$

$$(k=0,1,\ldots,n)$$

25.2.55 $m=2n$

$$a_k=\frac{1}{n}\sum_{r=0}^{2n-1}f_r\cos kx_r;\qquad b_k=\frac{1}{n}\sum_{r=0}^{2n-1}f_r\sin kx_r$$

$(k=0,1,\ldots,n)$ $\qquad(k=0,1,\ldots,n-1)$

b_n is arbitrary.

Subtabulation

Let $f(x)$ be tabulated initially in intervals of width h. It is desired to subtabulate $f(x)$ in intervals of width h/m. Let Δ and $\overline{\Delta}$ designate differences with respect to the original and the final intervals respectively. Thus $\overline{\Delta}_0=f\left(x_0+\frac{h}{m}\right)-f(x_0)$. Assuming that the original 5th order differences are zero,

25.2.56

$$\overline{\Delta}_0=\frac{1}{m}\Delta_0+\frac{1-m}{2m^2}\Delta^2_0+\frac{(1-m)(1-2m)}{6m^3}\Delta^3_0+\frac{(1-m)(1-2m)(1-3m)}{24m^4}\Delta^4_0$$

$$\overline{\Delta}^2_0=\frac{1}{m^2}\Delta^2_0+\frac{1-m}{m^3}\Delta^3_0+\frac{(1-m)(7-11m)}{12m^4}\Delta^4_0$$

$$\overline{\Delta}^3_0=\frac{1}{m^3}\Delta^3_0+\frac{3(1-m)}{2m^4}\Delta^4_0$$

$$\overline{\Delta}^4_0=\frac{1}{m^4}\Delta^4_0$$

From this information we may construct the final tabulation by addition. For $m=10$,

25.2.57

$$\overline{\Delta}_0=.1\Delta_0-.045\Delta^2_0+.0285\Delta^3_0-.02066\Delta^4_0$$
$$\overline{\Delta}^2_0=.01\Delta^2_0-.009\Delta^3_0+.007725\Delta^4_0$$
$$\overline{\Delta}^3_0=.001\Delta^3_0-.00135\Delta^4_0$$
$$\overline{\Delta}^4_0=.0001\Delta^4_0$$

Linear Inverse Interpolation

Find p, given $f_p(=f(x_0+ph))$.

Linear

25.2.58 $p\approx\frac{f_p-f_0}{f_1-f_0}$

Quadratic Inverse Interpolation

25.2.59

$$(f_1-2f_0+f_{-1})p^2+(f_1-f_{-1})p+2(f_0-f_p)\approx 0$$

Inverse Interpolation by Reversion of Series

25.2.60 Given $f(x_0+ph)=f_p=\sum_{k=0}^{\infty} a_k p^k$

25.2.61

$$p=\lambda+c_2\lambda^2+c_3\lambda^3+\ldots,\ \lambda=(f_p-a_0)/a_1$$

25.2.62

$$c_2=-a_2/a_1$$

$$c_3=\frac{-a_3}{a_1}+2\left(\frac{a_2}{a_1}\right)^2$$

$$c_4=\frac{-a_4}{a_1}+\frac{5a_2a_3}{a_1^2}-\frac{5a_2^3}{a_1^3}$$

$$c_5=\frac{-a_5}{a_1}+\frac{6a_2a_4}{a_1^2}+\frac{3a_3^2}{a_1^2}-\frac{21a_2^2a_3}{a_1^3}+\frac{14a_2^4}{a_1^4}$$

Inversion of Newton's Forward Difference Formula

25.2.63

$$a_0=f_0$$

$$a_1=\Delta_0-\frac{\Delta_0^2}{2}+\frac{\Delta_0^3}{3}-\frac{\Delta_0^4}{4}+\ldots$$

$$a_2=\frac{\Delta_0^2}{2}-\frac{\Delta_0^3}{2}+\frac{11\Delta_0^4}{24}+\ldots$$

$$a_3=\frac{\Delta_0^3}{6}-\frac{\Delta_0^4}{4}+\ldots$$

$$a_4=\frac{\Delta_0^4}{24}+\ldots$$

(Used in conjunction with **25.2.62.**)

Inversion of Everett's Formula

25.2.64

$$a_0=f_0$$

$$a_1=\delta_{\frac{1}{2}}-\frac{\delta_0^2}{3}-\frac{\delta_1^2}{6}+\frac{\delta_0^4}{20}+\frac{\delta_1^4}{30}+\ldots$$

$$a_2=\frac{\delta_0^2}{2}-\frac{\delta_0^4}{24}+\ldots$$

$$a_3=\frac{-\delta_0^2+\delta_1^2}{6}-\frac{\delta_0^4+\delta_1^4}{24}+\ldots$$

$$a_4=\frac{\delta_0^4}{24}+\ldots$$

$$a_5=\frac{-\delta_0^4+\delta_1^4}{120}+\ldots$$

(Used in conjunction with **25.2.62.**)

Bivariate Interpolation

Three Point Formula (Linear)

25.2.65

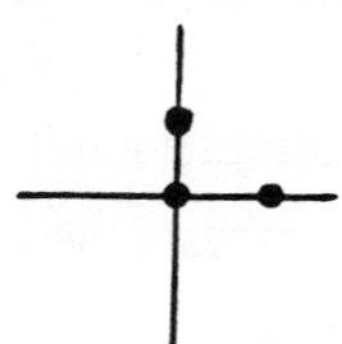

$$f(x_0+ph,y_0+qk)=(1-p-q)f_{0,0}+pf_{1,0}+qf_{0,1}+O(h^2)$$

Four Point Formula

25.2.66

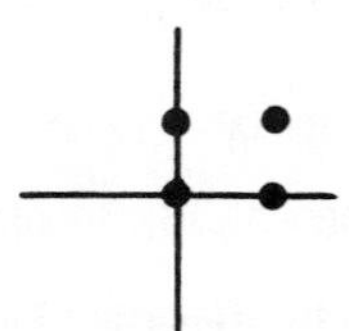

$$f(x_0+ph,y_0+qk)=(1-p)(1-q)f_{0,0}+p(1-q)f_{1,0}+q(1-p)f_{0,1}+pqf_{1,1}+O(h^2)$$

Six Point Formula

25.2.67

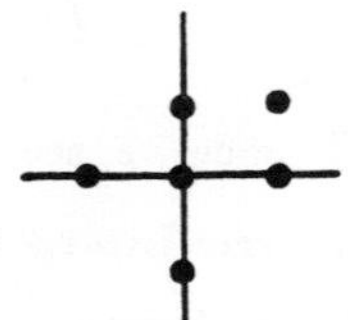

$$f(x_0+ph,y_0+qk)=\frac{q(q-1)}{2}f_{0,-1}+\frac{p(p-1)}{2}f_{-1,0}+(1+pq-p^2-q^2)f_{0,0}+\frac{p(p-2q+1)}{2}f_{1,0}+\frac{q(q-2p+1)}{2}f_{0,1}+pqf_{1,1}+O(h^3)$$

25.3. Differentiation

Lagrange's Formula

25.3.1 $$f'(x)=\sum_{k=0}^{n} l_k'(x)f_k+R_n'(x)$$

(See **25.2.1.**)

25.3.2 $$l_k'(x)=\sum_{\substack{j=0\\ j\neq k}}^{n}\frac{\pi_n(x)}{(x-x_k)(x-x_j)\pi_n'(x_k)}$$

25.3.3

$$R'_n(x)=\frac{f^{(n+1)}}{(n+1)!}(\xi)\pi'_n(x)+\frac{\pi_n(x)}{(n+1)!}\frac{d}{dx}f^{(n+1)}(\xi)$$

$$\xi=\xi(x)\ (x_0<\xi<x_n)$$

Equally Spaced Abscissas

Three Points

25.3.4

$$f'_p=f'(x_0+ph)$$

$$=\frac{1}{h}\{(p-\tfrac{1}{2})f_{-1}-2pf_0+(p+\tfrac{1}{2})f_1\}+R'_2$$

Four Points

25.3.5

$$f'_p=f'(x_0+ph)=\frac{1}{h}\left\{-\frac{3p^2-6p+2}{6}f_{-1}+\frac{3p^2-4p-1}{2}f_0-\frac{3p^2-2p-2}{2}f_1+\frac{3p^2-1}{6}f_2\right\}+R'_3$$

Five Points

25.3.6

$$f'_p=f'(x_0+ph)=\frac{1}{h}\left\{\frac{2p^3-3p^2-p+1}{12}f_{-2}-\frac{4p^3-3p^2-8p+4}{6}f_{-1}+\frac{2p^3-5p}{2}f_0-\frac{4p^3+3p^2-8p-4}{6}f_1+\frac{2p^3+3p^2-p-1}{12}f_2\right\}+R'_4$$

For numerical values of differentiation coefficients see **Table 25.2.**

Markoff's Formulas

(Newton's Forward Difference Formula Differentiated)

25.3.7

$$f'(a_0+ph)=\frac{1}{h}\left[\Delta_0+\frac{2p-1}{2}\Delta_0^2+\frac{3p^2-6p+2}{6}\Delta_0^3+\ldots+\frac{d}{dp}\binom{p}{n}\Delta_0^n\right]+R'_n$$

25.3.8

$$R'_n=h^nf^{(n+1)}(\xi)\frac{d}{dp}\binom{p}{n+1}+h^{n+1}\binom{p}{n+1}\frac{d}{dx}f^{(n+1)}(\xi)$$

$$(a_0<\xi<a_n)$$

25.3.9 $$hf'_0=\Delta_0-\frac{1}{2}\Delta_0^2+\frac{1}{3}\Delta_0^3-\frac{1}{4}\Delta_0^4+\ldots$$

25.3.10 $$h^2f_0^{(2)}=\Delta_0^2-\Delta_0^3+\frac{11}{12}\Delta_0^4-\frac{5}{6}\Delta_0^5+\ldots$$

25.3.11

$$h^3f_0^{(3)}=\Delta_0^3-\frac{3}{2}\Delta_0^4+\frac{7}{4}\Delta_0^5-\frac{15}{8}\Delta_0^6+\ldots$$

25.3.12

$$h^4f_0^{(4)}=\Delta_0^4-2\Delta_0^5+\frac{17}{6}\Delta_0^6-\frac{7}{2}\Delta_0^7+\ldots$$

25.3.13

$$h^5f_0^{(5)}=\Delta_0^5-\frac{5}{2}\Delta_0^6+\frac{25}{6}\Delta_0^7-\frac{35}{6}\Delta_0^8+\ldots$$

Everett's Formula

25.3.14

$$hf'(x_0+ph)\approx-f_0+f_1-\frac{3p^2-6p+2}{6}\delta_0^2+\frac{3p^2-1}{6}\delta_1^2-\frac{5p^4-20p^3+15p^2+10p-6}{120}\delta_0^4+\frac{5p^4-15p^2+4}{120}\delta_1^4+\ldots-\left[\binom{p+n-1}{2n+1}\right]'\delta_0^{2n}+\left[\binom{p+n}{2n+1}\right]'\delta_1^{2n}$$

25.3.15

$$hf'_0\approx-f_0+f_1-\frac{1}{3}\delta_0^2-\frac{1}{6}\delta_1^2+\frac{1}{20}\delta_0^4+\frac{1}{30}\delta_1^4$$

Differences in Terms of Derivatives

25.3.16

$$\Delta_0\approx hf'_0+\frac{h^2}{2!}f_0^{(2)}+\frac{h^3}{3!}f_0^{(3)}+\frac{h^4}{4!}f_0^{(4)}+\frac{h^5}{5!}f_0^{(5)}$$

25.3.17

$$\Delta_0^2\approx h^2f_0^{(2)}+h^3f_0^{(3)}+\frac{7}{12}h^4f_0^{(4)}+\frac{1}{4}h^5f_0^{(5)}$$

25.3.18 $$\Delta_0^3\approx h^3f_0^{(3)}+\frac{3}{2}h^4f_0^{(4)}+\frac{5}{4}f_0^{(5)}$$

25.3.19 $$\Delta_0^4\approx h^4f_0^{(4)}+2h^5f_0^{(5)}$$

25.3.20 $$\Delta_0^5\approx h^5f_0^{(5)}$$

Partial Derivatives

25.3.21

$$\frac{\partial f_{0,0}}{\partial x}=\frac{1}{2h}(f_{1,0}-f_{-1,0})+O(h^2)$$

25.3.22

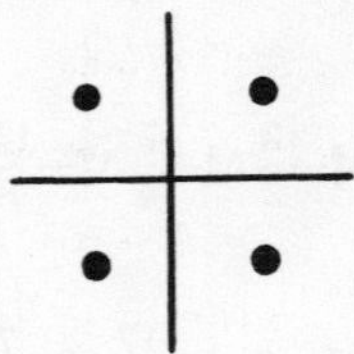

$$\frac{\partial f_{0,0}}{\partial x}=\frac{1}{4h}(f_{1,1}-f_{-1,1}+f_{1,-1}-f_{-1,-1})+O(h^2)$$

25.3.23

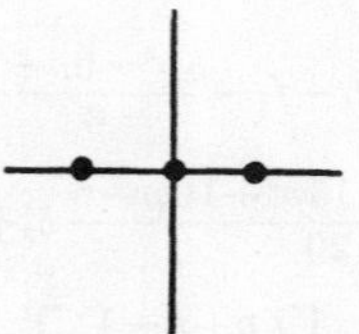

$$\frac{\partial^2 f_{0,0}}{\partial x^2}=\frac{1}{h^2}(f_{1,0}-2f_{0,0}+f_{-1,0})+O(h^2)$$

25.3.24

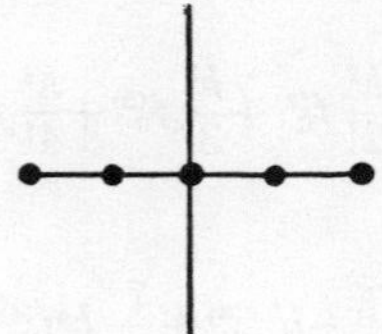

$$\frac{\partial^2 f_{0,0}}{\partial x^2}=\frac{1}{12h^2}(-f_{2,0}+16f_{1,0}-30f_{0,0}+16f_{-1,0}-f_{-2,0})+O(h^4)$$

25.3.25

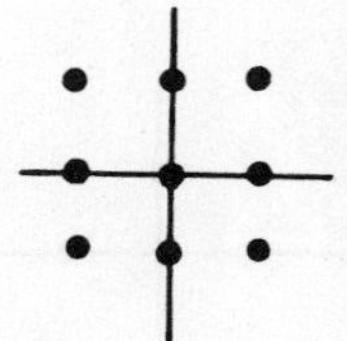

$$\frac{\partial^2 f_{0,0}}{\partial x^2}=\frac{1}{3h^2}(f_{1,1}-2f_{0,1}+f_{-1,1}+f_{1,0}-2f_{0,0}+f_{-1,0}+f_{1,-1}-2f_{0,-1}+f_{-1,-1})+O(h^2)$$

25.3.26

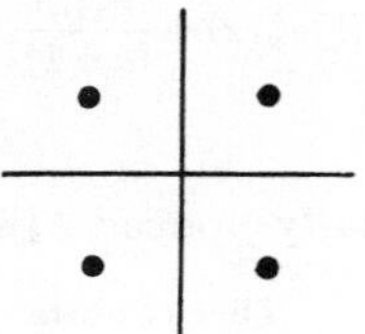

$$\frac{\partial^2 f_{0,0}}{\partial x\partial y}=\frac{1}{4h^2}(f_{1,1}-f_{1,-1}-f_{-1,1}+f_{-1,-1})+O(h^2)$$

25.3.27

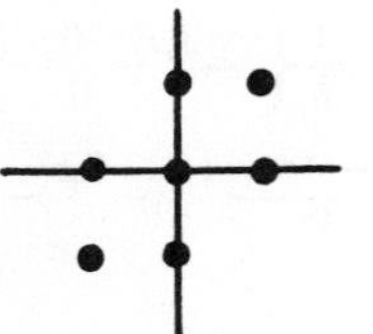

$$\frac{\partial^2 f_{0,0}}{\partial x\partial y}=\frac{-1}{2h^2}(f_{1,0}+f_{-1,0}+f_{0,1}+f_{0,-1}-2f_{0,0}-f_{1,1}-f_{-1,-1})+O(h^2)$$

25.3.28

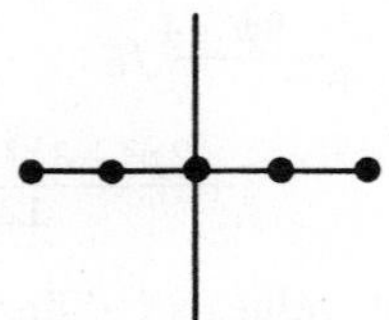

$$\frac{\partial^4 f_{0,0}}{\partial x^4}=\frac{1}{h^4}(f_{2,0}-4f_{1,0}+6f_{0,0}-4f_{-1,0}+f_{-2,0})+O(h^2)$$

25.3.29

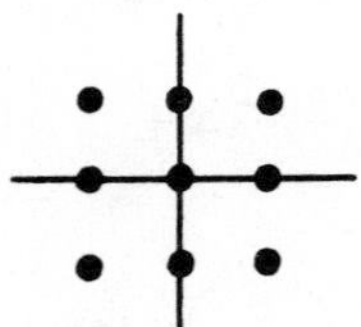

$$\frac{\partial^4 f_{0,0}}{\partial x^2\partial y^2}=\frac{1}{h^4}(f_{1,1}+f_{-1,1}+f_{1,-1}+f_{-1,-1}-2f_{1,0}-2f_{-1,0}-2f_{0,1}-2f_{0,-1}+4f_{0,0})+O(h^2)$$

Laplacian

25.3.30

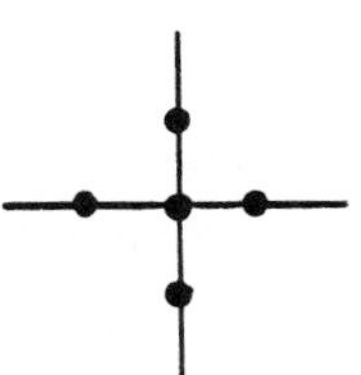

$$\nabla^2 u_{0,0}=\left(\frac{\partial^2 u}{\partial x^2}+\frac{\partial^2 u}{\partial y^2}\right)_{0,0}$$

$$=\frac{1}{h^2}(u_{1,0}+u_{0,1}+u_{-1,0}+u_{0,-1}-4u_{0,0})+O(h^2)$$

25.3.31

$$\nabla^2 u_{0,0}=\frac{1}{12h^2}[-60u_{0,0}+16(u_{1,0}+u_{0,1}+u_{-1,0}+u_{0,-1})$$

$$-(u_{2,0}+u_{0,2}+u_{-2,0}+u_{0,-2})]+O(h^4)$$

Biharmonic Operator

25.3.32

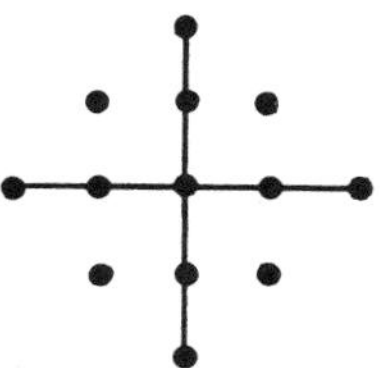

$$\nabla^4 u_{0,0}=\left(\frac{\partial^4 u}{\partial x^4}+2\frac{\partial^4 u}{\partial x^2\partial y^2}+\frac{\partial^4 u}{\partial y^4}\right)_{0,0}$$

$$=\frac{1}{h^4}[20u_{0,0}-8(u_{1,0}+u_{0,1}+u_{-1,0}+u_{0,-1})$$

$$+2(u_{1,1}+u_{1,-1}+u_{-1,1}+u_{-1,-1})$$

$$+(u_{0,2}+u_{2,0}+u_{-2,0}+u_{0,-2})]+O(h^2)$$

25.3.33

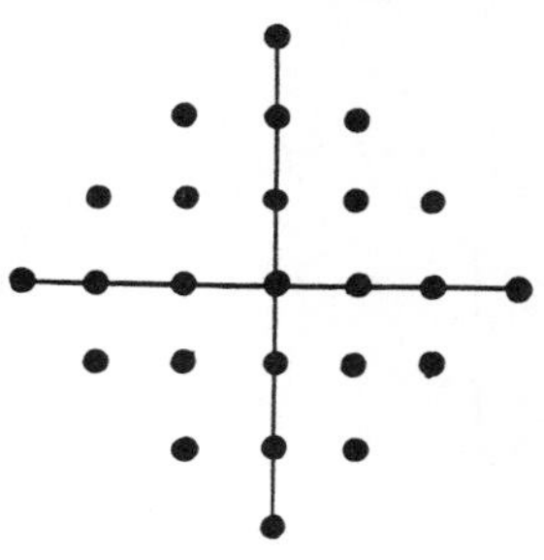

$$\nabla^4 u_{0,0}=\frac{1}{6h^4}[-(u_{0,3}+u_{0,-3}+u_{3,0}+u_{-3,0})$$

$$+14(u_{0,2}+u_{0,-2}+u_{2,0}+u_{-2,0})$$

$$-77(u_{0,1}+u_{0,-1}+u_{1,0}+u_{-1,0})$$

$$+184u_{0,0}+20(u_{1,1}+u_{1,-1}+u_{-1,1}+u_{-1,-1})$$

$$-(u_{1,2}+u_{2,1}+u_{1,-2}+u_{2,-1}+u_{-1,2}+u_{-2,1}$$

$$+u_{-1,-2}+u_{-2,-1})]+O(h^4)$$

25.4. Integration

Trapezoidal Rule

25.4.1

$$\int_{x_0}^{x_1} f(x)dx=\frac{h}{2}(f_0+f_1)-\frac{1}{2}\int_{x_0}^{x_1}(t-x_0)(x_1-t)f''(t)\,dt$$

$$=\frac{h}{2}(f_0+f_1)-\frac{h^3}{12}f''(\xi)\qquad (x_0<\xi<x_1)$$

Extended Trapezoidal Rule

25.4.2

$$\int_{x_0}^{x_m} f(x)dx=h\left[\frac{f_0}{2}+f_1+\ldots+f_{m-1}+\frac{f_m}{2}\right]-\frac{mh^3}{12}f''(\xi)$$

Error Term in Trapezoidal Formula for Periodic Functions

If $f(x)$ is periodic and has a continuous k^{th} derivative, and if the integral is taken over a period, then

25.4.3 $$|\text{Error}|\leq\frac{\text{constant}}{m^k}$$

Modified Trapezoidal Rule

25.4.4

$$\int_{x_0}^{x_m} f(x)dx=h\left[\frac{f_0}{2}+f_1+\ldots+f_{m-1}+\frac{f_m}{2}\right]$$

$$+\frac{h}{24}[-f_{-1}+f_1+f_{m-1}-f_{m+1}]+\frac{11m}{720}h^5f^{(4)}(\xi)$$

Simpson's Rule

25.4.5

$$\int_{x_0}^{x_2} f(x)dx=\frac{h}{3}[f_0+4f_1+f_2]+\frac{1}{6}\int_{x_0}^{x_1}(x_0-t)^2(x_1-t)f^{(3)}(t)dt+\frac{1}{6}\int_{x_1}^{x_2}(x_2-t)^2(x_1-t)f^{(3)}(t)dt=\frac{h}{3}[f_0+4f_1+f_2]-\frac{h^5}{90}f^{(4)}(\xi)$$

Extended Simpson's Rule

25.4.6

$$\int_{x_0}^{x_{2n}} f(x)dx=\frac{h}{3}[f_0+4(f_1+f_3+\ldots+f_{2n-1})+2(f_2+f_4+\ldots+f_{2n-2})+f_{2n}]-\frac{nh^5}{90}f^{(4)}(\xi)$$

Euler-Maclaurin Summation Formula

25.4.7

$$\int_{x_0}^{x_n} f(x)dx=h\left[\frac{f_0}{2}+f_1+f_2+\ldots+f_{n-1}+\frac{f_n}{2}\right]-\frac{B_2}{2!}h^2(f'_n-f'_0)-\ldots-\frac{B_{2k}h^{2k}}{(2k)!}[f_n^{(2k-1)}-f_0^{(2k-1)}]+R_{2k}$$

$$R_{2k}=\frac{\theta nB_{2k+2}h^{2k+3}}{(2k+2)!}\max_{x_0\le x\le x_n}|f^{(2k+2)}(x)|,\qquad(-1\le\theta\le1)$$

(For B_{2k}, Bernoulli numbers, see chapter **23.**)

If $f^{(2k+2)}(x)$ and $f^{(2k+4)}(x)$ do not change sign for $x_0<x<x_n$ then $|R_{2k}|$ is less than the first neglected term. If $f^{(2k+2)}(x)$ does not change sign for $x_0<x<x_n$, $|R_{2k}|$ is less than twice the first neglected term.

Lagrange Formula

25.4.8

$$\int_a^b f(x)dx=\sum_{i=0}^{n}(L_i^{(n)}(b)-L_i^{(n)}(a))f_i+R_n$$

(See **25.2.1.**)

25.4.9

$$L_i^{(n)}(x)=\frac{1}{\pi'_n(x_i)}\int_{x_0}^{x}\frac{\pi_n(t)}{t-x_i}dt=\int_{x_0}^{x}l_i(t)dt$$

25.4.10 $R_n=\frac{1}{(n+1)!}\int_a^b\pi_n(x)f^{(n+1)}(\xi(x))dx$

Equally Spaced Abscissas

25.4.11

$$\int_{x_0}^{x_k} f(x)dx=\frac{1}{h^n}\sum_{i=0}^{n}f_i\frac{(-1)^{n-i}}{i!(n-i)!}\int_{x_0}^{x_k}\frac{\pi_n(x)}{x-x_i}dx+R_n$$

25.4.12 $\int_{x_m}^{x_{m+1}} f(x)dx=h\sum_{i=-\left[\frac{n-1}{2}\right]}^{\left[\frac{n}{2}\right]}A_i(m)f_i+R_n$

(See **Table 25.3** for $A_i(m)$.)

Newton-Cotes Formulas (Closed Type)

(For Trapezoidal and Simpson's Rules see **25.4.1–25.4.6.**)

25.4.13 **(Simpson's $\frac{3}{8}$ rule)**

$$\int_{x_0}^{x_3} f(x)dx=\frac{3h}{8}(f_0+3f_1+3f_2+f_3)-\frac{3f^{(4)}(\xi)h^5}{80}$$

25.4.14 **(Bode's rule)**

$$\int_{x_0}^{x_4} f(x)dx=\frac{2h}{45}(7f_0+32f_1+12f_2+32f_3+7f_4)-\frac{8f^{(6)}(\xi)h^7}{945}$$

25.4.15

$$\int_{x_0}^{x_5} f(x)dx=\frac{5h}{288}(19f_0+75f_1+50f_2+50f_3+75f_4+19f_5)-\frac{275f^{(6)}(\xi)h^7}{12096}$$

25.4.16

$$\int_{x_0}^{x_6} f(x)dx=\frac{h}{140}(41f_0+216f_1+27f_2+272f_3+27f_4+216f_5+41f_6)-\frac{9f^{(8)}(\xi)h^9}{1400}$$

25.4.17

$$\int_{x_0}^{x_7} f(x)dx=\frac{7h}{17280}(751f_0+3577f_1+1323f_2+2989f_3+2989f_4+1323f_5+3577f_6+751f_7)-\frac{8183f^{(8)}(\xi)h^9}{518400}$$

25.4.18

$$\int_{x_0}^{x_8} f(x)dx=\frac{4h}{14175}(989f_0+5888f_1-928f_2+10496f_3-4540f_4+10496f_5-928f_6+5888f_7+989f_8)-\frac{2368}{467775}f^{(10)}(\xi)h^{11}$$

25.4.19

$$\int_{x_0}^{x_9} f(x)dx=\frac{9h}{89600}\{2857(f_0+f_9)+15741(f_1+f_8)+1080(f_2+f_7)+19344(f_3+f_6)+5778(f_4+f_5)\}-\frac{173}{14620}f^{(10)}(\xi)h^{11}$$

25.4.20

$$\int_{x_0}^{x_{10}} f(x)dx=\frac{5h}{299376}\{16067(f_0+f_{10})$$
$$+106300(f_1+f_9)-48525(f_2+f_8)+272400(f_3+f_7)$$
$$-260550(f_4+f_6)+427368f_5\}$$
$$-\frac{1346350}{326918592}f^{(12)}(\xi)h^{13}$$

Newton-Cotes Formulas (Open Type)

25.4.21

$$\int_{x_0}^{x_3} f(x)dx=\frac{3h}{2}(f_1+f_2)+\frac{f^{(2)}(\xi)h^3}{4}$$

25.4.22

$$\int_{x_0}^{x_4} f(x)dx=\frac{4h}{3}(2f_1-f_2+2f_3)+\frac{28f^{(4)}(\xi)h^5}{90}$$

25.4.23

$$\int_{x_0}^{x_5} f(x)dx=\frac{5h}{24}(11f_1+f_2+f_3+11f_4)+\frac{95f^{(4)}(\xi)h^5}{144}$$

25.4.24

$$\int_{x_0}^{x_6} f(x)dx=\frac{6h}{20}(11f_1-14f_2+26f_3-14f_4+11f_5)$$
$$+\frac{41f^{(6)}(\xi)h^7}{140}$$

25.4.25

$$\int_{x_0}^{x_7} f(x)dx=\frac{7h}{1440}(611f_1-453f_2+562f_3+562f_4$$
$$-453f_5+611f_6)+\frac{5257}{8640}f^{(6)}(\xi)h^7$$

25.4.26

$$\int_{x_0}^{x_8} f(x)dx=\frac{8h}{945}(460f_1-954f_2+2196f_3-2459f_4$$
$$+2196f_5-954f_6+460f_7)+\frac{3956}{14175}f^{(8)}(\xi)h^9$$

Five Point Rule for Analytic Functions

25.4.27

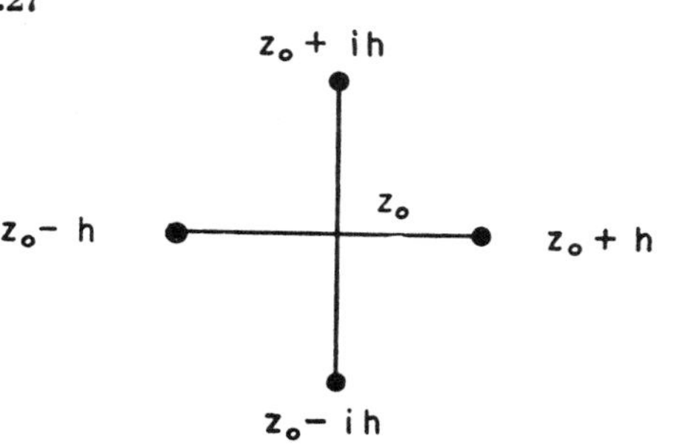

$$\int_{z_0-h}^{z_0+h} f(z)dz=\frac{h}{15}\{24f(z_0)+4[f(z_0+h)+f(z_0-h)]$$
$$-[f(z_0+ih)+f(z_0-ih)]\}+R$$

$|R|\leq\frac{|h|^7}{1890}\max_{z\in S}|f^{(6)}(z)|$, S designates the square with vertices $z_0+i^kh(k=0,1,2,3)$; h can be complex.

Chebyshev's Equal Weight Integration Formula

25.4.28 $$\int_{-1}^{1} f(x)dx=\frac{2}{n}\sum_{i=1}^{n} f(x_i)+R_n$$

Abscissas: x_i is the ith zero of the polynomial part of

$$x^n \exp\left[\frac{-n}{2\cdot 3x^2}-\frac{n}{4\cdot 5x^3}-\frac{n}{6\cdot 7x^4}-\ldots\right]$$

(See **Table 25.5** for x_i.)

For $n=8$ and $n\geq 10$ some of the zeros are complex.

Remainder:

$$R_n=\int_{-1}^{+1}\frac{x^{n+1}}{(n+1)!}f^{(n+1)}(\xi)dx$$
$$-\frac{2}{n(n+1)!}\sum_{i=1}^{n} x_i^{n+1}f^{(n+1)}(\xi_i)$$

where $\xi=\xi(x)$ satisfies $0\leq\xi\leq x$ and $0\leq\xi_i\leq x_i$

$$(i=1,\ldots,n)$$

Integration Formulas of Gaussian Type

(For Orthogonal Polynomials see chapter **22**)

Gauss' Formula

25.4.29 $$\int_{-1}^{1} f(x)dx=\sum_{i=1}^{n} w_i f(x_i)+R_n$$

Related orthogonal polynomials: Legendre polynomials $P_n(x)$, $P_n(1)=1$

Abscissas: x_i is the ith zero of $P_n(x)$

Weights: $w_i=2/(1-x_i^2)[P_n'(x_i)]^2$

(See **Table 25.4** for x_i and w_i.)

$$R_n=\frac{2^{2n+1}(n!)^4}{(2n+1)[(2n)!]^3}f^{(2n)}(\xi)\qquad(-1<\xi<1)$$

Gauss' Formula, Arbitrary Interval

25.4.30 $$\int_a^b f(y)dy=\frac{b-a}{2}\sum_{i=1}^{n} w_i f(y_i)+R_n$$

$$y_i=\left(\frac{b-a}{2}\right)x_i+\left(\frac{b+a}{2}\right)$$

Related orthogonal polynomials: $P_n(x)$, $P_n(1)=1$
Abscissas: x_i is the ith zero of $P_n(x)$
Weights: $w_i=2/(1-x_i^2)\,[P'_n(x_i)]^2$

$$R_n=\frac{(b-a)^{2n+1}(n!)^4}{(2n+1)[(2n)!]^3}f^{(2n)}(\xi)$$

Radau's Integration Formula

25.4.31

$$\int_{-1}^{1} f(x)dx=\frac{2}{n^2}f_{-1}+\sum_{i=1}^{n-1} w_i f(x_i)+R_n$$

Related polynomials:

$$\frac{P_{n-1}(x)+P_n(x)}{x+1}$$

Abscissas: x_i is the ith zero of

$$\frac{P_{n-1}(x)+P_n(x)}{x+1}$$

Weights:

$$w_i=\frac{1}{n^2}\frac{1-x_i}{[P_{n-1}(x_i)]^2}=\frac{1}{1-x_i}\frac{1}{[P'_{n-1}(x_i)]^2}$$

Remainder:

$$R_n=\frac{2^{2n-1}\cdot n}{[(2n-1)!]^3}[(n-1)!]^4 f^{(2n-1)}(\xi) \qquad (-1<\xi<1)$$

Lobatto's Integration Formula

25.4.32

$$\int_{-1}^{1} f(x)dx=\frac{2}{n(n-1)}[f(1)+f(-1)]+\sum_{i=2}^{n-1} w_i f(x_i)+R_n$$

Related polynomials: $P'_{n-1}(x)$

Abscissas: x_i is the $(i-1)^{\text{st}}$ zero of $P'_{n-1}(x)$

Weights:

$$w_i=\frac{2}{n(n-1)[P_{n-1}(x_i)]^2} \qquad (x_i\neq\pm1)$$

(See **Table 25.6** for x_i and w_i.)

Remainder:

$$R_n=\frac{-n(n-1)^3 2^{2n-1}[(n-2)!]^4}{(2n-1)[(2n-2)!]^3}f^{(2n-2)}(\xi) \qquad (-1<\xi<1)$$

25.4.33 $$\int_0^1 x^k f(x)dx=\sum_{i=1}^{n} w_i f(x_i)+R_n$$

Related orthogonal polynomials:

$$q_n(x)=\sqrt{k+2n+1}P_n^{(k,0)}(1-2x)$$

(For the Jacobi polynomials $P_n^{(k,0)}$ see chapter **22.**)

Abscissas:

x_i is the ith zero of $q_n(x)$

Weights:

$$w_i=\left\{\sum_{j=0}^{n-1}[q_j(x_i)]^2\right\}^{-1}$$

(See **Table 25.8** for x_i and w_i.)

Remainder:

$$R_n=\frac{f^{(2n)}(\xi)}{(k+2n+1)(2n)!}\left[\frac{n!(k+n)!}{(k+2n)!}\right]^2 \qquad (0<\xi<1)$$

25.4.34

$$\int_0^1 f(x)\sqrt{1-x}\,dx=\sum_{i=1}^{n} w_i f(x_i)+R_n$$

Related orthogonal polynomials:

$$\frac{1}{\sqrt{1-x}}P_{2n+1}(\sqrt{1-x}),\ P_{2n+1}(1)=1$$

Abscissas: $x_i=1-\xi_i^2$ where ξ_i is the ith positive zero of $P_{2n+1}(x)$.
Weights: $w_i=2\xi_i^2 w_i^{(2n+1)}$ where $w_i^{(2n+1)}$ are the Gaussian weights of order $2n+1$.
Remainder:

$$R_n=\frac{2^{4n+3}[(2n+1)!]^4}{(2n)!(4n+3)[(4n+2)!]^2}f^{(2n)}(\xi) \qquad (0<\xi<1)$$

25.4.35

$$\int_a^b f(y)\sqrt{b-y}\,dy=(b-a)^{3/2}\sum_{i=1}^{n} w_i f(y_i)$$

$$y_i=a+(b-a)x_i$$

Related orthogonal polynomials:

$$\frac{1}{\sqrt{1-x}}P_{2n+1}(\sqrt{1-x}),\ P_{2n+1}(1)=1$$

Abscissas: $x_i=1-\xi_i^2$ where ξ_i is the ith positive zero of $P_{2n+1}(x)$.
Weights: $w_i=2\xi_i^2 w_i^{(2n+1)}$ where $w_i^{(2n+1)}$ are the Gaussian weights of order $2n+1$.

25.4.36 $$\int_0^1 \frac{f(x)}{\sqrt{1-x}}\,dx=\sum_{i=1}^n w_i f(x_i)+R_n$$

Related orthogonal polynomials:

$$P_{2n}(\sqrt{1-x}),\ P_{2n}(1)=1$$

Abscissas: $x_i=1-\xi_i^2$ where ξ_i is the ith positive zero of $P_{2n}(x)$.
Weights: $w_i=2w_i^{(2n)}$, $w_i^{(2n)}$ are the Gaussian weights of order $2n$.
Remainder:

$$R_n=\frac{2^{4n+1}}{4n+1}\frac{[(2n)!]^3}{[(4n)!]^2}f^{(2n)}(\xi)\qquad(0<\xi<1)$$

25.4.37 $$\int_a^b \frac{f(y)}{\sqrt{b-y}}\,dy=\sqrt{b-a}\sum_{i=1}^n w_i f(y_i)+R_n$$

$$y_i=a+(b-a)x_i$$

Related orthogonal polynomials:

$$P_{2n}(\sqrt{1-x}),P_{2n}(1)=1$$

Abscissas:
$x_i=1-\xi_i^2$ where ξ_i is the ith positive zero of $P_{2n}(x)$.

Weights: $w_i=2w_i^{(2n)}$, $w_i^{(2n)}$ are the Gaussian weights of order $2n$.

25.4.38 $$\int_{-1}^{+1} \frac{f(x)}{\sqrt{1-x^2}}\,dx=\sum_{i=1}^n w_i f(x_i)+R_n$$

Related orthogonal polynomials: Chebyshev Polynomials of First Kind

$$T_n(x),T_n(1)=\frac{1}{2^{n-1}}$$

Abscissas:

$$x_i=\cos\frac{(2i-1)\pi}{2n}$$

Weights:

$$w_i=\frac{\pi}{n}$$

Remainder:

$$R_n=\frac{\pi}{(2n)!2^{2n-1}}f^{(2n)}(\xi)\quad(-1<\xi<1)$$

25.4.39

$$\int_a^b \frac{f(y)dy}{\sqrt{(y-a)(b-y)}}=\sum_{i=1}^n w_i f(y_i)+R_n$$

$$y_i=\frac{b+a}{2}+\frac{b-a}{2}x_i$$

Related orthogonal polynomials:

$$T_n(x),T_n(1)=\frac{1}{2^{n-1}}$$

Abscissas:

$$x_i=\cos\frac{(2i-1)\pi}{2n}$$

Weights:

$$w_i=\frac{\pi}{n}$$

25.4.40

$$\int_{-1}^{+1} f(x)\sqrt{1-x^2}dx=\sum_{i=1}^n w_i f(x_i)+R_n$$

Related orthogonal polynomials: Chebyshev Polynomials of Second Kind

$$U_n(x)=\frac{\sin[(n+1)\arccos x]}{\sin(\arccos x)}$$

Abscissas:

$$x_i=\cos\frac{i}{n+1}\pi$$

Weights:

$$w_i=\frac{\pi}{n+1}\sin^2\frac{i}{n+1}\pi$$

Remainder:

$$R_n=\frac{\pi}{(2n)!2^{2n+1}}f^{(2n)}(\xi)\qquad(-1<\xi<1)$$

25.4.41

$$\int_a^b \sqrt{(y-a)(b-y)}f(y)dy=\left(\frac{b-a}{2}\right)^2\sum_{i=1}^n w_i f(y_i)+R_n$$

$$y_i=\frac{b+a}{2}+\frac{b-a}{2}x_i$$

Related orthogonal polynomials:

$$U_n(x)=\frac{\sin[(n+1)\arccos x]}{\sin(\arccos x)}$$

Abscissas:

$$x_i=\cos\frac{i}{n+1}\pi$$

Weights:

$$w_i=\frac{\pi}{n+1}\sin^2\frac{i}{n+1}\pi$$

25.4.42 $$\int_0^1 f(x)\sqrt{\frac{x}{1-x}}\,dx=\sum_{i=1}^n w_i f(x_i)+R_n$$

Related orthogonal polynomials:

$$\frac{1}{\sqrt{x}}T_{2n+1}(\sqrt{x})$$

Abscissas:

$$x_i=\cos^2\frac{2i-1}{2n+1}\cdot\frac{\pi}{2}$$

Weights:

$$w_i=\frac{2\pi}{2n+1}x_i$$

Remainder:

$$R_n=\frac{\pi}{(2n)!2^{4n+1}}f^{(2n)}(\xi) \qquad (0<\xi<1)$$

25.4.43

$$\int_a^b f(x)\sqrt{\frac{x-a}{b-x}}\,dx=(b-a)\sum_{i=1}^n w_i f(y_i)+R_n$$

$$y_i=a+(b-a)x_i$$

Related orthogonal polynomials:

$$\frac{1}{\sqrt{x}}\,T_{2n+1}(\sqrt{x})$$

Abscissas:

$$x_i=\cos^2\frac{2i-1}{2n+1}\cdot\frac{\pi}{2}$$

Weights:

$$w_i=\frac{2\pi}{2n+1}\,x_i$$

25.4.44 $$\int_0^1 \ln x\, f(x)dx=\sum_{i=1}^n w_i f(x_i)+R_n$$

Related orthogonal polynomials: polynomials orthogonal with respect to the weight function $-\ln x$
Abscissas: See **Table 25.7**
Weights: See **Table 25.7**

25.4.45

$$\int_0^\infty e^{-x}f(x)dx=\sum_{i=1}^n w_i f(x_i)+R_n$$

Related orthogonal polynomials: Laguerre polynomials $L_n(x)$.
Abscissas: x_i is the ith zero of $L_n(x)$
Weights:

$$w_i=\frac{x_i}{(n+1)^2[L_{n+1}(x_i)]^2}$$

(See **Table 25.9** for x_i and w_i.)
Remainder:

$$R_n=\frac{(n!)^2}{(2n)!}f^{(2n)}(\xi) \qquad (0<\xi<\infty)$$

25.4.46

$$\int_{-\infty}^\infty e^{-x^2}f(x)dx=\sum_{i=1}^n w_i f(x_i)+R_n$$

Related orthogonal polynomials: Hermite polynomials $H_n(x)$.
Abscissas: x_i is the ith zero of $H_n(x)$
Weights:

$$\frac{2^{n-1}n!\sqrt{\pi}}{n^2[H_{n-1}(x_i)]^2}$$

(See **Table 25.10** for x_i and w_i.)

Remainder:

$$R_n=\frac{n!\sqrt{\pi}}{2^n(2n)!}f^{(2n)}(\xi) \qquad (-\infty<\xi<\infty)$$

Filon's Integration Formula [3]

25.4.47

$$\int_{x_0}^{x_{2n}} f(x)\cos tx\,dx=h\Big[\alpha(th)(f_{2n}\sin tx_{2n}-f_0\sin tx_0)+\beta(th)\cdot C_{2n}+\gamma(th)\cdot C_{2n-1}+\frac{2}{45}\,th^4S'_{2n-1}\Big]-R_n$$

25.4.48

$$C_{2n}=\sum_{i=0}^n f_{2i}\cos(tx_{2i})-\tfrac{1}{2}[f_{2n}\cos tx_{2n}+f_0\cos tx_0]$$

25.4.49

$$C_{2n-1}=\sum_{i=1}^n f_{2i-1}\cos tx_{2i-1}$$

25.4.50

$$S'_{2n-1}=\sum_{i=1}^n f^{(3)}_{2i-1}\sin tx_{2i-1}$$

25.4.51

$$R_n=\frac{1}{90}nh^5f^{(4)}(\xi)+O(th^7)$$

25.4.52

$$\alpha(\theta)=\frac{1}{\theta}+\frac{\sin 2\theta}{2\theta^2}-\frac{2\sin^2\theta}{\theta^3}$$

$$\beta(\theta)=2\left(\frac{1+\cos^2\theta}{\theta^2}-\frac{\sin 2\theta}{\theta^3}\right)$$

$$\gamma(\theta)=4\left(\frac{\sin\theta}{\theta^3}-\frac{\cos\theta}{\theta^2}\right)$$

For small θ we have

25.4.53

$$\alpha=\frac{2\theta^3}{45}-\frac{2\theta^5}{315}+\frac{2\theta^7}{4725}-\dots$$

$$\beta=\frac{2}{3}+\frac{2\theta^2}{15}-\frac{4\theta^4}{105}+\frac{2\theta^6}{567}-\dots$$

$$\gamma=\frac{4}{3}-\frac{2\theta^2}{15}+\frac{\theta^4}{210}-\frac{\theta^6}{11340}+\dots$$

25.4.54

$$\int_{x_0}^{x_{2n}} f(x)\sin tx\,dx=h\Big[\alpha(th)(f_0\cos tx_0-f_{2n}\cos tx_{2n})+\beta S_{2n}+\gamma S_{2n-1}+\frac{2}{45}\,th^4C'_{2n-1}\Big]-R_n$$

25.4.55

$$S_{2n}=\sum_{i=0}^n f_{2i}\sin(tx_{2i})-\frac{1}{2}\,[f_{2n}\sin(tx_{2n})+f_0\sin(tx_0)]$$

[3] For certain difficulties associated with this formula, see the article by J. W. Tukey, p. 400, "On Numerical Approximation," Ed. R. E. Langer, Madison, 1959.

25.4.56 $$S_{2n-1}=\sum_{i=1}^{n} f_{2i-1} \sin (tx_{2i-1})$$

25.4.57 $$C'_{2n-1}=\sum_{i=1}^{n} f_{2i-1}^{(3)} \cos (tx_{2i-1})$$

(See **Table 25.11** for α, β, γ.)

Iterated Integrals

25.4.58

$$\int_0^x dt_n \int_0^{t_n} dt_{n-1} \ldots \int_0^{t_3} dt_2 \int_0^{t_2} f(t_1)dt_1 = \frac{1}{(n-1)!} \int_0^x (x-t)^{n-1} f(t)dt$$

25.4.59

$$\int_a^x dt_n \int_a^{t_n} dt_{n-1} \ldots \int_a^{t_3} dt_2 \int_a^{t_2} f(t_1)dt_1 = \frac{(x-a)^n}{(n-1)!} \int_0^1 t^{n-1} f(x-(x-a)t)dt$$

Multidimensional Integration

Circumference of Circle Γ: $x^2+y^2=h^2$.

25.4.60

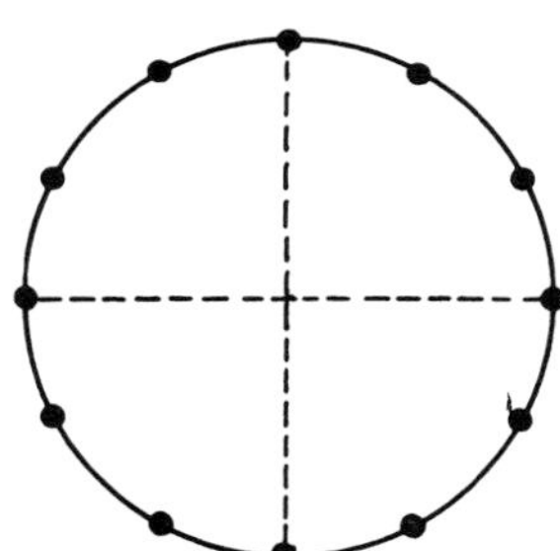

$$\frac{1}{2\pi h} \int_\Gamma f(x,y)ds = \frac{1}{2m} \sum_{n=1}^{2m} f\left(h \cos \frac{\pi n}{m}, h \sin \frac{\pi n}{m}\right) + O(h^{2m-2})$$

Circle C: $x^2+y^2 \leq h^2$.

25.4.61

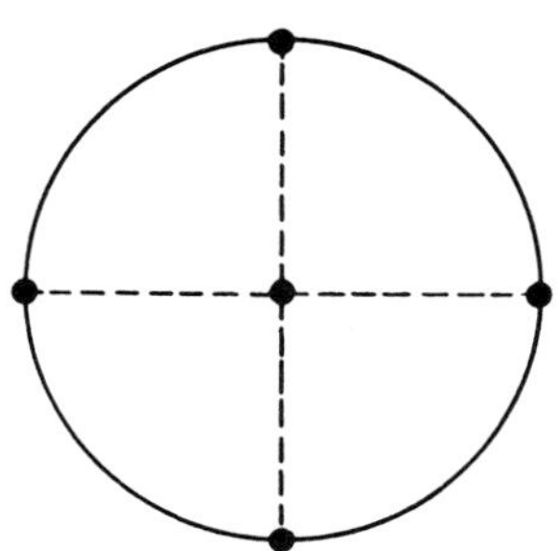

$$\frac{1}{\pi h^2} \iint_C f(x,y)dxdy = \sum_{i=1}^{n} w_i f(x_i,y_i) + R$$

(x_i, y_i)	w_i	
$(0,0)$	1/2	$R=O(h^4)$
$(\pm h, 0)$, $(0, \pm h)$	1/8	

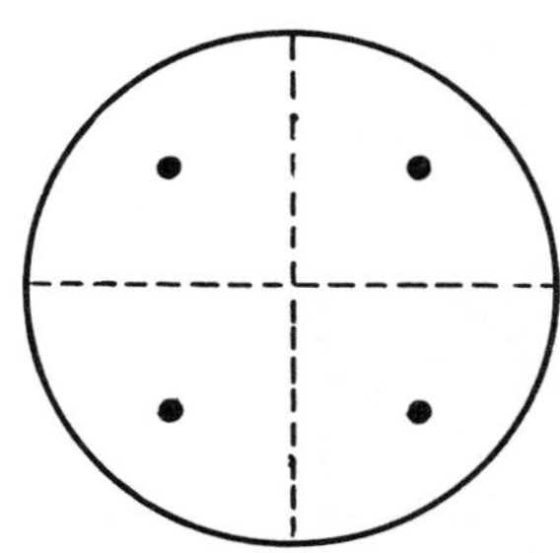

(x_i, y_i)	w_i	
$\left(\pm\frac{h}{2}, \pm\frac{h}{2}\right)$	1/4	$R=O(h^4)$

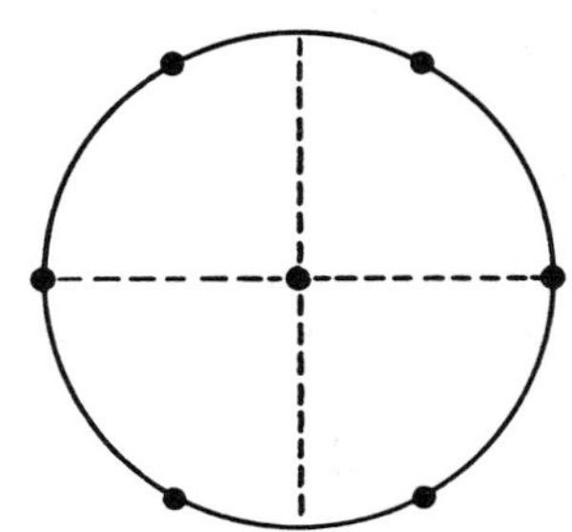

(x_i, y_i)	w_i	
$(0,0)$	1/2	
$(\pm h, 0)$	1/12	$R=O(h^4)$
$\left(\pm\frac{h}{2}, \pm\frac{h}{2}\sqrt{3}\right)$	1/12	

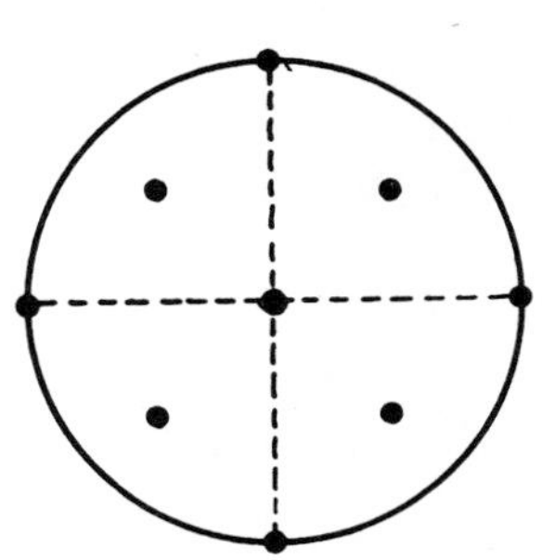

(x_i, y_i)	w_i	
$(0,0)$	$1/6$	
$(\pm h, 0)$	$1/24$	$R=O(h^6)$
$(0, \pm h)$	$1/24$	
$\left(\pm\frac{h}{2}, \pm\frac{h}{2}\right)$	$1/6$	

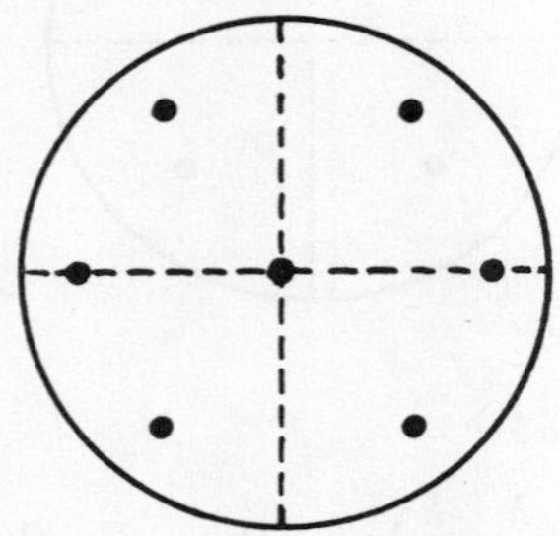

(x_i, y_i)	w_i	
$(0,0)$	$1/4$	
$\left(\pm\sqrt{\frac{2}{3}}\,h, 0\right)$	$1/8$	$R=O(h^6)$
$\left(\pm\sqrt{\frac{1}{6}}\,h, \pm\frac{h}{2}\sqrt{2}\right)$	$1/8$	

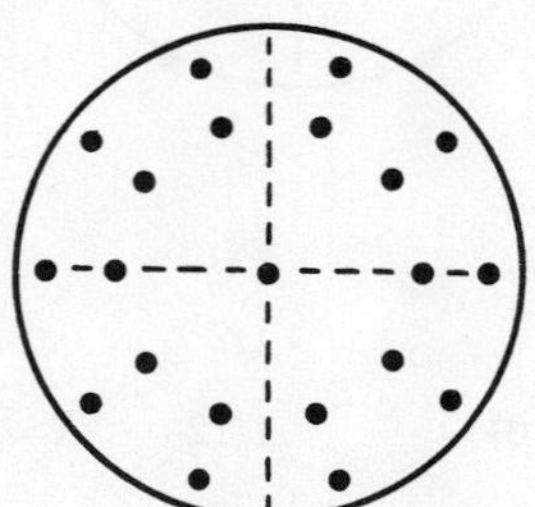

(x_i, y_i)	w_i
$(0,0)$	$1/9$
$\left(\sqrt{\frac{6-\sqrt{6}}{10}}\,h\cos\frac{2\pi k}{10}, \sqrt{\frac{6-\sqrt{6}}{10}}\,h\sin\frac{2\pi k}{10}\right)$	$\frac{16+\sqrt{6}}{360}$
	$(k=1, \ldots, 10)$
$\left(\sqrt{\frac{6+\sqrt{6}}{10}}\,h\cos\frac{2\pi k}{10}, \sqrt{\frac{6+\sqrt{6}}{10}}\,h\sin\frac{2\pi k}{10}\right)$	$\frac{16-\sqrt{6}}{360}$

$R=O(h^{10})$

Square[4] S: $|x|\leq h, |y|\leq h$

25.4.62

$$\frac{1}{4h^2}\iint_S f(x,y)\,dx\,dy=\sum_{i=1}^{n} w_i f(x_i, y_i)+R$$

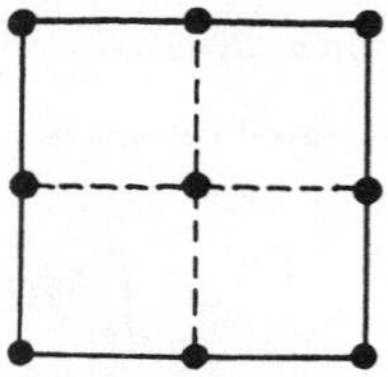

(x_i, y_i)	w_i	
$(0,0)$	$4/9$	
$(\pm h, \pm h)$	$1/36$	$R=O(h^4)$
$(\pm h, 0)$	$1/9$	
$(0, \pm h)$	$1/9$	

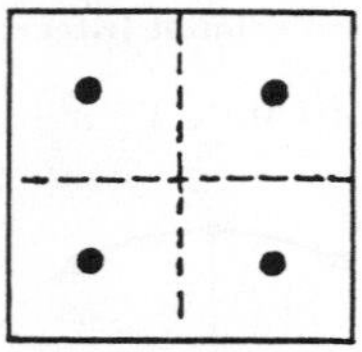

(x_i, y_i)	w_i	
$\left(\pm h\sqrt{\frac{1}{3}}, \pm h\sqrt{\frac{1}{3}}\right)$	$1/4$	$R=O(h^4)$

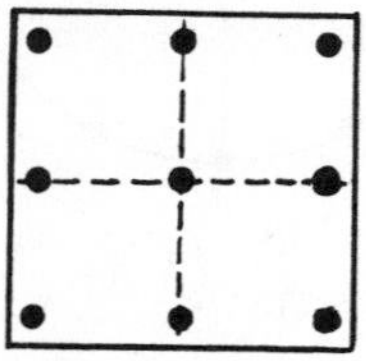

(x_i, y_i)	w_i
$(0,0)$	$16/81$

[4] For regions, such as the square, cube, cylinder, etc., which are the Cartesian products of lower dimensional regions, one may always develop integration rules by "multiplying together" the lower dimensional rules. Thus if

$$\int_0^1 f(x)\,dx\approx\sum_{i=1}^{n} w_i f(x_i)$$

is a one dimensional rule, then

$$\int_0^1\int_0^1 f(x,y)\,dx\,dy\approx\sum_{i,j=1}^{n} w_i w_j f(x_i, x_j)$$

becomes a two dimensional rule. Such rules are not necessarily the most "economical".

(x_i,y_i)	w_i	
$\left(\pm\sqrt{\frac{3}{5}}h,\pm\sqrt{\frac{3}{5}}h\right)$	25/324	$R=O(h^6)$
$\left(0,\pm\sqrt{\frac{3}{5}}h\right)$	10/81	
$\left(\pm\sqrt{\frac{3}{5}}h,0\right)$	10/81	

Equilateral Triangle T

Radius of Circumscribed Circle$=h$

25.4.63

$$\frac{1}{\frac{3}{4}\sqrt{3}h^2}\iint_T f(x,y)dxdy=\sum_{i=1}^{n} w_i f(x_i,y_i)+R$$

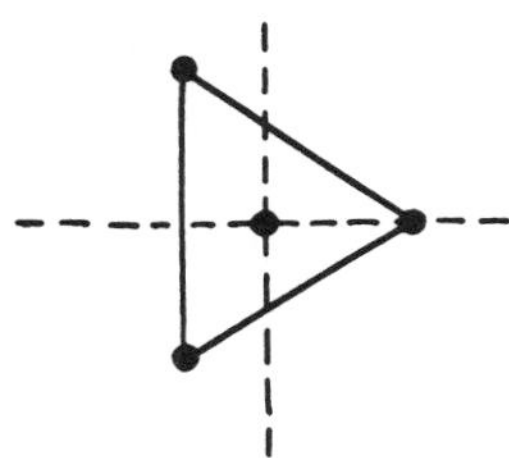

(x_i,y_i)	w_i	
$(0,0)$	3/4	
$(h,0)$	1/12	$R=O(h^3)$
$\left(-\frac{h}{2},\pm\frac{h}{2}\sqrt{3}\right)$	1/12	

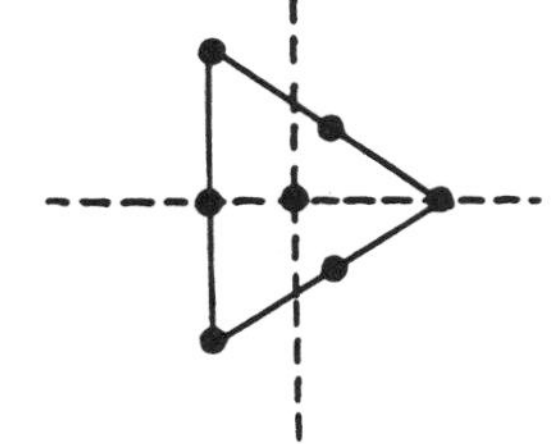

(x_i,y_i)	w_i	
$(0,0)$	27/60	
$(h,0)$	3/60	
$\left(-\frac{h}{2},\pm\frac{h}{2}\sqrt{3}\right)$	3/60	$R=O(h^4)$
$\left(-\frac{h}{2},0\right)$	8/60	
$\left(\frac{h}{4},\pm\frac{h}{4}\sqrt{3}\right)$	8/60	

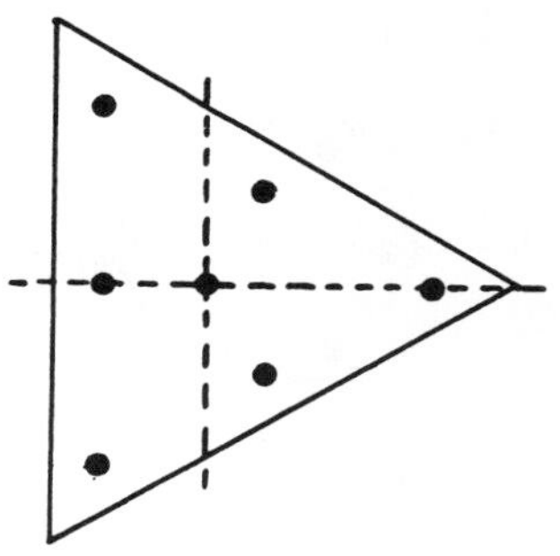

(x_i,y_i)	w_i	
$(0,0)$	270/1200	
$\left(\left(\frac{\sqrt{15}+1}{7}\right)h,0\right)$	$\frac{155-\sqrt{15}}{1200}$	
$\left(\left(\frac{-\sqrt{15}+1}{14}\right)h,\pm\left(\frac{\sqrt{15}+1}{14}\right)\sqrt{3}h\right)$		$R=O(h^6)$
$\left(\left(-\frac{\sqrt{15}-1}{7}\right)h,0\right)$	$\frac{155+\sqrt{15}}{1200}$	
$\left(\left(\frac{\sqrt{15}-1}{14}\right)h,\pm\left(\frac{\sqrt{15}-1}{14}\right)\sqrt{3}h\right)$		

Regular Hexagon H

Radius of Circumscribed Circle$=h$

25.4.64

$$\frac{1}{\frac{3}{2}\sqrt{3}h^2}\iint_H f(x,y)dxdy=\sum_{i=1}^{n} w_i f(x_i,y_i)+R$$

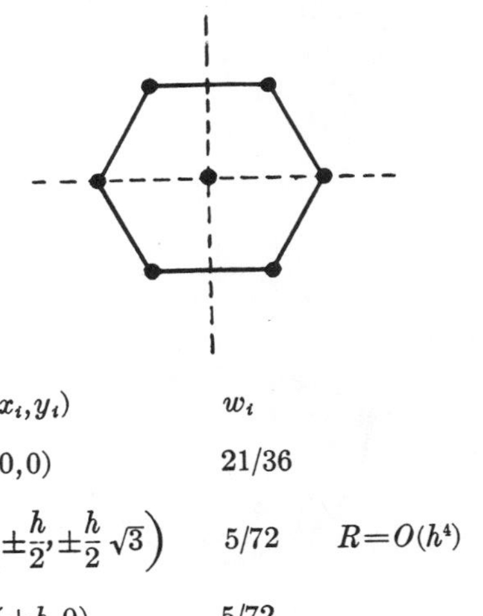

(x_i,y_i)	w_i	
$(0,0)$	21/36	
$\left(\pm\frac{h}{2},\pm\frac{h}{2}\sqrt{3}\right)$	5/72	$R=O(h^4)$
$(\pm h,0)$	5/72	

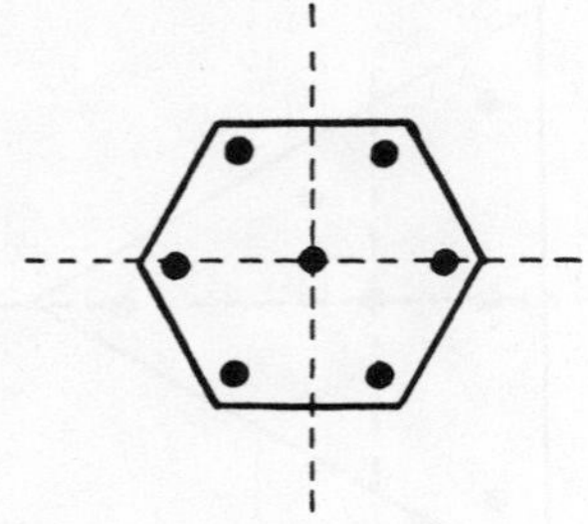

(x_i,y_i)	w_i	
$(0,0)$	258/1008	
$\left(\pm\frac{h}{10}\sqrt{14},\pm\frac{h}{10}\sqrt{42}\right)$	125/1008	$R=O(h^6)$
$\left(\pm h\frac{\sqrt{14}}{5},0\right)$	125/1008	

Surface of Sphere Σ: $x^2+y^2+z^2=h^2$

25.4.65

$$\frac{1}{4\pi h^2}\iint_\Sigma f(x,y,z)d\sigma=\sum_{i=1}^n w_if(x_i,y_i,z_i)+R$$

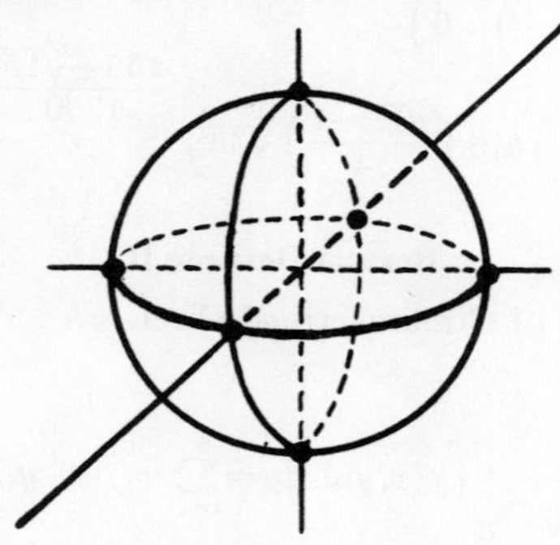

(x_i,y_i,z_i)	w_i	
$(\pm h,0,0)$	1/6	
$(0,\pm h,0)$	1/6	$R=O(h^4)$
$(0,0,\pm h)$	1/6	

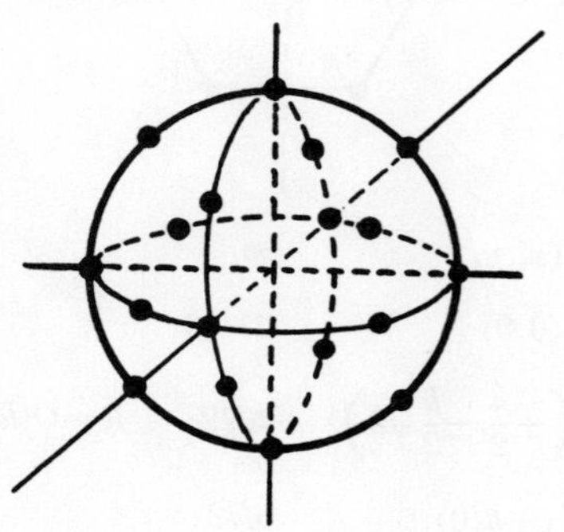

(x_i,y_i,z_i)	w_i	
$\left(\pm\sqrt{\frac{1}{2}}h,\pm\sqrt{\frac{1}{2}}h,0\right)$		
$\left(\pm\sqrt{\frac{1}{2}}h,0,\pm\sqrt{\frac{1}{2}}h\right)$	1/15	
$\left(0,\pm\sqrt{\frac{1}{2}}h,\pm\sqrt{\frac{1}{2}}h\right)$		$R=O(h^6)$
$(\pm h,0,0)$		
$(0,\pm h,0)$	1/30	
$(0,0,\pm h)$		

(x_i,y_i,z_i)	w_i	
$\left(\pm\sqrt{\frac{1}{3}}h,\pm\sqrt{\frac{1}{3}}h,\pm\sqrt{\frac{1}{3}}h\right)$	27/840	
$\left(\pm\sqrt{\frac{1}{2}}h,\pm\sqrt{\frac{1}{2}}h,0\right)$		
$\left(\pm\sqrt{\frac{1}{2}}h,0,\pm\sqrt{\frac{1}{2}}h\right)$	32/840	$R=O(h^8)$
$\left(0,\pm\sqrt{\frac{1}{2}}h,\pm\sqrt{\frac{1}{2}}h\right)$		
$(\pm h,0,0)$		
$(0,\pm h,0)$	40/840	
$(0,0,\pm h)$		

Sphere S: $x^2+y^2+z^2\leq h^2$

25.4.66

$$\frac{1}{\frac{4}{3}\pi h^3}\iiint_S f(x,y,z)dxdydz=\sum_{i=1}^n w_if(x_i,y_i,z_i)+R$$

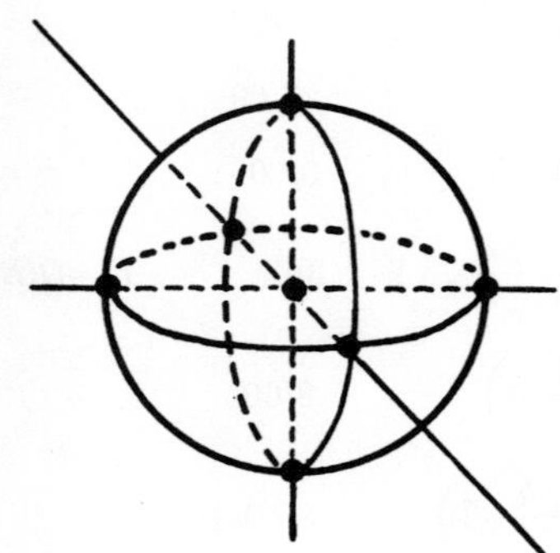

(x_i, y_i, z_i)	w_i
$(0,0,0)$	2/5
$(\pm h,0,0)$	1/10
$(0,\pm h,0)$	1/10
$(0,0,\pm h)$	1/10

$R=O(h^4)$

Cube[5] C: $|x|\leq h$

$|y|\leq h$

$|z|\leq h$

25.4.67

$$\frac{1}{8h^3}\iiint_C f(x,y,z)dxdydz=\sum_{i=1}^{n} w_i f(x_i,y_i,z_i)+R$$

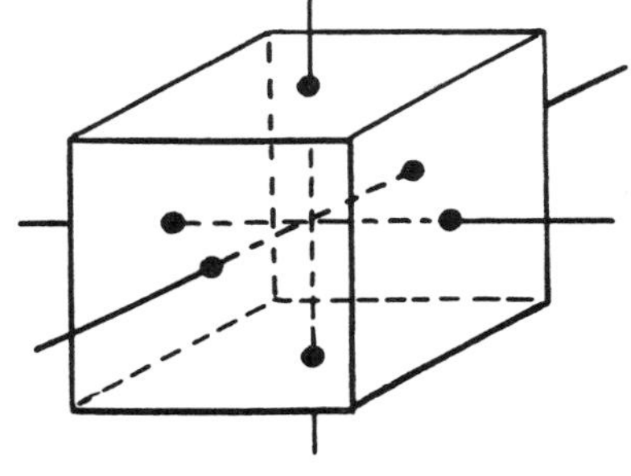

(x_i, y_i, z_i)	w_i
$(\pm h,0,0)$	1/6
$(0,\pm h,0)$	1/6
$(0,0,\pm h)$	1/6

$R=O(h^4)$

25.4.68

$$\frac{1}{8h^3}\iiint_C f(x,y,z)dxdydz$$

$$=\frac{1}{360}[-496f_m+128\sum f_r+8\sum f_f+5\sum f_v]+O(h^6)$$

25.4.69

$$=\frac{1}{450}[91\sum f_f-40\sum f_e+16\sum f_d]+O(h^6)$$

where $f_m=f(0,0,0)$.

$\sum f_r$=sum of values of f at the 6 points midway from the center of C to the 6 faces.

$\sum f_f$=sum of values of f at the 6 centers of the faces of C.

$\sum f_v$=sum of values of f at the 8 vertices of C.

$\sum f_e$=sum of values of f at the 12 midpoints of edges of C.

$\sum f_d$=sum of values of f at the 4 points on the diagonals of each face at a distance of $\frac{1}{2}\sqrt{5}h$ from the center of the face.

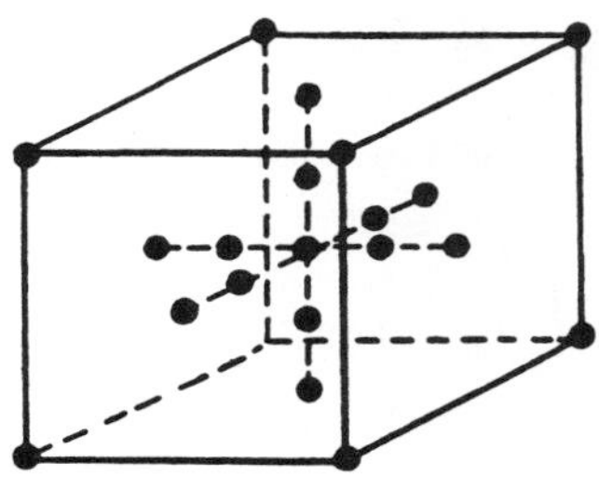

Tetrahedron: $\mathscr{T}$

25.4.70

$$\frac{1}{V}\iiint_{\mathscr{T}} f(x,y,z)dxdydz=\frac{1}{40}\sum f_v+\frac{9}{40}\sum f_f$$

+terms of 4th order

$$=\frac{32}{60}f_m+\frac{1}{60}\sum f_v+\frac{4}{60}\sum f_e$$

+terms of 4th order

where

V: Volume of $\mathscr{T}$

$\sum f_v$: Sum of values of the function at the vertices of $\mathscr{T}$.

$\sum f_e$: Sum of values of the function at midpoints of the edges of $\mathscr{T}$.

$\sum f_f$: Sum of values of the function at the center of gravity of the faces of $\mathscr{T}$.

f_m: Value of function at center of gravity of $\mathscr{T}$.

[5] See footnote to **25.4.62**.

25.5. Ordinary Differential Equations[6]

First Order: $y'=f(x, y)$

Point Slope Formula

25.5.1 $$y_{n+1}=y_n+hy'_n+O(h^2)$$

25.5.2 $$y_{n+1}=y_{n-1}+2hy'_n+O(h^3)$$

Trapezoidal Formula

25.5.3 $$y_{n+1}=y_n+\frac{h}{2}(y'_{n+1}+y'_n)+O(h^3)$$

Adams' Extrapolation Formula

25.5.4

$$y_{n+1}=y_n+\frac{h}{24}(55y'_n-59y'_{n-1}+37y'_{n-2}-9y'_{n-3})+O(h^5)$$

Adams' Interpolation Formula

25.5.5

$$y_{n+1}=y_n+\frac{h}{24}(9y'_{n+1}+19y'_n-5y'_{n-1}+y'_{n-2})+O(h^5)$$

Runge-Kutta Methods

Second Order

25.5.6

$$y_{n+1}=y_n+\frac{1}{2}(k_1+k_2)+O(h^3)$$

$$k_1=hf(x_n,y_n),k_2=hf(x_n+h,y_n+k_1)$$

25.5.7

$$y_{n+1}=y_n+k_2+O(h^3)$$

$$k_1=hf(x_n,y_n),k_2=hf\left(x_n+\frac{1}{2}h,y_n+\frac{1}{2}k_1\right)$$

Third Order

25.5.8

$$y_{n+1}=y_n+\frac{1}{6}k_1+\frac{2}{3}k_2+\frac{1}{6}k_3+O(h^4)$$

$$k_1=hf(x_n,y_n),k_2=hf\left(x_n+\frac{1}{2}h,y_n+\frac{1}{2}k_1\right)$$

$$k_3=hf(x_n+h,y_n-k_1+2k_2)$$

[6] The reader is cautioned against possible instabilities especially in formulas **25.5.2** and **25.5.13**. See, e.g. [25.11], [25.12].

25.5.9

$$y_{n+1}=y_n+\frac{1}{4}k_1+\frac{3}{4}k_3+O(h^4)$$

$$k_1=hf(x_n,y_n),k_2=hf\left(x_n+\frac{1}{3}h,y_n+\frac{1}{3}k_1\right)$$

$$k_3=hf\left(x_n+\frac{2}{3}h,y_n+\frac{2}{3}k_2\right)$$

Fourth Order

25.5.10

$$y_{n+1}=y_n+\frac{1}{6}k_1+\frac{1}{3}k_2+\frac{1}{3}k_3+\frac{1}{6}k_4+O(h^5)$$

$$k_1=hf(x_n,y_n),k_2=hf\left(x_n+\frac{1}{2}h,y_n+\frac{1}{2}k_1\right)$$

$$k_3=hf\left(x_n+\frac{1}{2}h,y_n+\frac{1}{2}k_2\right), k_4=hf(x_n+h,y_n+k_3)$$

25.5.11

$$y_{n+1}=y_n+\frac{1}{8}k_1+\frac{3}{8}k_2+\frac{3}{8}k_3+\frac{1}{8}k_4+O(h^5)$$

$$k_1=hf(x_n,y_n),k_2=hf\left(x_n+\frac{1}{3}h,y_n+\frac{1}{3}k_1\right)$$

$$k_3=hf\left(x_n+\frac{2}{3}h,y_n-\frac{1}{3}k_1+k_2\right),$$

$$k_4=hf(x_n+h,y_n+k_1-k_2+k_3)$$

Gill's Method

25.5.12

$$y_{n+1}=y_n+\frac{1}{6}\left(k_1+2\left(1-\sqrt{\frac{1}{2}}\right)k_2\right.$$

$$\left.+2\left(1+\sqrt{\frac{1}{2}}\right)k_3+k_4\right)+O(h^5)$$

$$k_1=hf(x_n,y_n)$$

$$k_2=hf\left(x_n+\frac{1}{2}h, y_n+\frac{1}{2}k_1\right)$$

$$k_3=hf\left(x_n+\frac{1}{2}h, y_n+\left(-\frac{1}{2}+\sqrt{\frac{1}{2}}\right)k_1\right.$$

$$\left.+\left(1-\sqrt{\frac{1}{2}}\right)k_2\right)$$

$$k_4=hf\left(x_n+h,y_n-\sqrt{\frac{1}{2}}k_2+\left(1+\sqrt{\frac{1}{2}}\right)k_3\right)$$

Predictor-Corrector Methods

Milne's Methods

25.5.13

$$\text{P:}\quad y_{n+1}=y_{n-3}+\frac{4h}{3}(2y'_n-y'_{n-1}+2y'_{n-2})+O(h^5)$$

$$\text{C:}\quad y_{n+1}=y_{n-1}+\frac{h}{3}(y'_{n-1}+4y'_n+y'_{n+1})+O(h^5)$$

25.5.14

$$\text{P:}\quad y_{n+1}=y_{n-5}+\frac{3h}{10}(11y'_n-14y'_{n-1}+26y'_{n-2}-14y'_{n-3}+11y'_{n-4})+O(h^7)$$

$$\text{C:}\quad y_{n+1}=y_{n-3}+\frac{2h}{45}(7y'_{n+1}+32y'_n+12y'_{n-1}+32y'_{n-2}+7y'_{n-3})+O(h^7)$$

Formulas Using Higher Derivatives

25.5.15

$$\text{P:}\quad y_{n+1}=y_{n-2}+3(y_n-y_{n-1})+h^2(y''_n-y''_{n-1})+O(h^5)$$

$$\text{C:}\quad y_{n+1}=y_n+\frac{h}{2}(y'_{n+1}+y'_n)-\frac{h^2}{12}(y''_{n+1}-y''_n)+O(h^5)$$

25.5.16

$$\text{P:}\quad y_{n+1}=y_{n-2}+3(y_n-y_{n-1})+\frac{h^3}{2}(y'''_n+y'''_{n-1})+O(h^7)$$

$$\text{C:}\quad y_{n+1}=y_n+\frac{h}{2}(y'_{n+1}+y'_n)-\frac{h^2}{10}(y''_{n+1}-y''_n)+\frac{h^3}{120}(y'''_{n+1}+y'''_n)+O(h^7)$$

Systems of Differential Equations

First Order: $y'=f(x,y,z),\ z'=g(x,y,z).$

Second Order Runge-Kutta

25.5.17

$$y_{n+1}=y_n+\frac{1}{2}(k_1+k_2)+O(h^3),\qquad z_{n+1}=z_n+\frac{1}{2}(l_1+l_2)+O(h^3)$$

$$k_1=hf(x_n,y_n,z_n),\qquad l_1=hg(x_n,y_n,z_n)$$

$$k_2=hf(x_n+h,y_n+k_1,z_n+l_1),\qquad l_2=hg(x_n+h,y_n+k_1,z_n+l_1)$$

Fourth Order Runge-Kutta

25.5.18

$$y_{n+1}=y_n+\frac{1}{6}(k_1+2k_2+2k_3+k_4)+O(h^5),\qquad z_{n+1}=z_n+\frac{1}{6}(l_1+2l_2+2l_3+l_4)+O(h^5)$$

$$k_1=hf(x_n,y_n,z_n)\qquad l_1=hg(x_n,y_n,z_n)$$

$$k_2=hf\left(x_n+\frac{1}{2}h,y_n+\frac{1}{2}k_1,z_n+\frac{1}{2}l_1\right)\qquad l_2=hg\left(x_n+\frac{h}{2},y_n+\frac{k_1}{2},z_n+\frac{l_1}{2}\right)$$

$$k_3=hf\left(x_n+\frac{1}{2}h,y_n+\frac{1}{2}k_2,z_n+\frac{1}{2}l_2\right)\qquad l_3=hg\left(x_n+\frac{h}{2},y_n+\frac{k_2}{2},z_n+\frac{l_2}{2}\right)$$

$$k_4=hf(x_n+h,y_n+k_3,z_n+l_3)\qquad l_4=hg(x_n+h,y_n+k_3,z_n+l_3)$$

Second Order: $y''=f(x,y,y')$

Milne's Method

25.5.19

$$\text{P:}\quad y'_{n+1}=y'_{n-3}+\frac{4h}{3}(2y''_{n-2}-y''_{n-1}+2y''_n)+O(h^5)$$

$$\text{C:}\quad y'_{n+1}=y'_{n-1}+\frac{h}{3}(y''_{n-1}+4y''_n+y''_{n+1})+O(h^5)$$

Runge-Kutta Method

25.5.20

$$y_{n+1}=y_n+h\left[y'_n+\frac{1}{6}(k_1+k_2+k_3)\right]+O(h^5)$$

$$y'_{n+1}=y'_n+\frac{1}{6}(k_1+2k_2+2k_3+k_4)$$

$$k_1=hf(x_n,y_n,y'_n)$$

$$k_2=hf\left(x_n+\frac{1}{2}h,y_n+\frac{h}{2}y'_n+\frac{h}{8}k_1,y'_n+\frac{k_1}{2}\right)$$

$$k_3=hf\left(x_n+\frac{1}{2}h,y_n+\frac{h}{2}y'_n+\frac{h}{8}k_1,y'_n+\frac{k_2}{2}\right)$$

$$k_4=hf\left(x_n+h,y_n+hy'_n+\frac{h}{2}k_3,y'_n+k_3\right)$$

Second Order: $y''=f(x,y)$

Milne's Method

25.5.21

$$\text{P:}\quad y_{n+1}=y_n+y_{n-2}-y_{n-3}+\frac{h^2}{4}(5y''_n+2y''_{n-1}+5y''_{n-2})+O(h^6)$$

$$\text{C:}\quad y_n=2y_{n-1}-y_{n-2}+\frac{h^2}{12}(y''_n+10y''_{n-1}+y''_{n-2})+O(h^6)$$

Runge-Kutta Method

25.5.22 $$y_{n+1}=y_n+h\left(y'_n+\frac{1}{6}(k_1+2k_2)\right)+O(h^4)$$

$$y'_{n+1}=y'_n+\frac{1}{6}k_1+\frac{2}{3}k_2+\frac{1}{6}k_3$$

$$k_1=hf(x_n,y_n)$$

$$k_2=hf\left(x_n+\frac{h}{2},y_n+\frac{h}{2}y'_n+\frac{h}{8}k_1\right)$$

$$k_3=hf\left(x_n+h,y_n+hy'_n+\frac{h}{2}k_2\right).$$

Table 25.2

COEFFICIENTS FOR DIFFERENTIATION

Differentiation Formula: $\left.\frac{d^kf(x)}{dx^k}\right|_{x=x_j}\approx\frac{k!}{m!h^k}\sum_{i=0}^{m}A_if(x_i)$

FIRST DERIVATIVE (k=1)

Three Point (m=2)

j	A_0	A_1	A_2	A_3	A_4	A_5	$\frac{h^k}{k!}$ Error
0	−3	4	−1				1/3
1	−1	0	1				−1/6 $h^3f^{(3)}$
2	1	−4	3				1/3

Four Point (m=3)

j	A_0	A_1	A_2	A_3	A_4	A_5	$\frac{h^k}{k!}$ Error
0	−11	18	−9	2			−1/4
1	−2	−3	6	−1			1/12 $h^4f^{(4)}$
2	1	−6	3	2			−1/12
3	−2	9	−18	11			1/4

Five Point (m=4)

j	A_0	A_1	A_2	A_3	A_4	A_5	$\frac{h^k}{k!}$ Error
0	−50	96	−72	32	−6		1/5
1	−6	−20	36	−12	2		−1/20
2	2	−16	0	16	−2		1/30 $h^5f^{(5)}$
3	−2	12	−36	20	6		−1/20
4	6	−32	72	−96	50		1/5

Six Point (m=5)

j	A_0	A_1	A_2	A_3	A_4	A_5	$\frac{h^k}{k!}$ Error
0	−274	600	−600	400	−150	24	−1/6
1	−24	−130	240	−120	40	−6	1/30
2	6	−60	−40	120	−30	4	−1/60 $h^6f^{(6)}$
3	−4	30	−120	40	60	−6	1/60
4	6	−40	120	−240	130	24	−1/30
5	−24	150	−400	600	−600	274	1/6

SECOND DERIVATIVE (k=2)

Three Point (m=2)

j	A_0	A_1	A_2	A_3	A_4	A_5	$\frac{h^k}{k!}$ Error
0	1	−2	1				−1/2 $h^3f^{(3)}$
1	1	−2	1				−1/24 $h^4f^{(4)}$
2	1	−2	1				1/2 $h^3f^{(3)}$

Four Point (m=3)

j	A_0	A_1	A_2	A_3	A_4	A_5	$\frac{h^k}{k!}$ Error
0	6	−15	12	−3			11/24
1	3	−6	3	0			−1/24
2	0	3	−6	3			−1/24 $h^4f^{(4)}$
3	−3	12	−15	6			11/24

Five Point (m=4)

j	A_0	A_1	A_2	A_3	A_4	A_5	$\frac{h^k}{k!}$ Error
0	35	−104	114	−56	11		−5/12 $h^5f^{(5)}$
1	11	−20	6	4	−1		1/24
2	−1	16	−30	16	−1		1/180 $h^6f^{(6)}$
3	−1	4	6	−20	11		−1/24 $h^5f^{(5)}$
4	11	−56	114	−104	35		5/12

Six Point (m=5)

j	A_0	A_1	A_2	A_3	A_4	A_5	$\frac{h^k}{k!}$ Error
0	225	−770	1070	−780	305	−50	137/360
1	50	−75	−20	70	−30	5	−13/360
2	−5	80	−150	80	−5	0	1/180 $h^6f^{(6)}$
3	0	−5	80	−150	80	−5	1/180
4	5	−30	70	−20	−75	50	−13/360
5	−50	305	−780	1070	−770	225	137/360

THIRD DERIVATIVE (k=3)

Four Point (m=3)

j	A_0	A_1	A_2	A_3	A_4	A_5	$\frac{h^k}{k!}$ Error
0	−1	3	−3	1			−1/4
1	−1	3	−3	1			−1/12 $h^4f^{(4)}$
2	−1	3	−3	1			1/12
3	−1	3	−3	1			1/4

Five Point (m=4)

j	A_0	A_1	A_2	A_3	A_4	A_5	$\frac{h^k}{k!}$ Error
0	−10	36	−48	28	−6		7/24
1	−6	20	−24	12	−2		1/24
2	−2	4	0	−4	2		−1/24 $h^5f^{(5)}$
3	2	−12	24	−20	6		1/24
4	6	−28	48	−36	10		7/24

Six Point (m=5)

j	A_0	A_1	A_2	A_3	A_4	A_5	$\frac{h^k}{k!}$ Error
0	−85	355	−590	490	−205	35	−5/16
1	−35	125	−170	110	−35	5	−1/48
2	−5	−5	50	−70	35	−5	1/48 $h^6f^{(6)}$
3	5	−35	70	−50	5	5	−1/48
4	−5	35	−110	170	−125	35	1/48
5	−35	205	−490	590	−355	85	5/16

FOURTH DERIVATIVE (k=4)

Five Point (m=4)

j	A_0	A_1	A_2	A_3	A_4	A_5	$\frac{h^k}{k!}$ Error
0	1	−4	6	−4	1		−1/12 $h^5f^{(5)}$
1	1	−4	6	−4	1		−1/24
2	1	−4	6	−4	1		−1/144 $h^6f^{(6)}$
3	1	−4	6	−4	1		1/24 $h^5f^{(5)}$
4	1	−4	6	−4	1		1/12

Six Point (m=5)

j	A_0	A_1	A_2	A_3	A_4	A_5	$\frac{h^k}{k!}$ Error
0	15	−70	130	−120	55	−10	17/144
1	10	−45	80	−70	30	−5	5/144
2	5	−20	30	−20	5	0	−1/144 $h^6f^{(6)}$
3	0	5	−20	30	−20	5	−1/144
4	−5	30	−70	80	−45	10	5/144
5	−10	55	−120	130	−70	15	17/144

FIFTH DERIVATIVE (k=5)

Six Point (m=5)

j	A_0	A_1	A_2	A_3	A_4	A_5	$\frac{h^k}{k!}$ Error
0	−1	5	−10	10	−5	1	−1/48
1	−1	5	−10	10	−5	1	−1/80
2	−1	5	−10	10	−5	1	−1/240 $h^6f^{(6)}$
3	−1	5	−10	10	−5	1	1/240
4	−1	5	−10	10	−5	1	1/80
5	−1	5	−10	10	−5	1	1/48

LAGRANGIAN INTEGRATION COEFFICIENTS

Table 25.3

$$\int_{x_m}^{x_{m+1}} f(x)dx \approx h \sum_k A_k(m) f(x_k)$$

$$DA_k^n(m)$$

$n=$ odd

n	$m\backslash k$	-4	-3	-2	-1	0	1	2	3	4		D
3	−1				5	8	−1				0	12
5	−2			251	646	−264	106	−19			1	720
	−1			−19	346	456	−74	11			0	
7	−3		19087	65112	−46461	37504	−20211	6312	−863		2	60480
	−2		−863	25128	46989	−16256	7299	−2088	271		1	
	−1		271	−2760	30819	37504	−6771	1608	−191		0	
9	−4	1070017	4467094	−4604594	5595358	−5033120	3146338	−1291214	312874	−33953	3	3628800
	−3	−33953	1375594	3244786	−1752542	1317280	−755042	294286	−68906	7297	2	
	−2	7297	−99626	1638286	2631838	−833120	397858	−142094	31594	−3233	1	
	−1	−3233	36394	−216014	1909858	2224480	−425762	126286	−25706	2497	0	
		4	3	2	1	0	-1	-2	-3	-4	$k\backslash m$	

$n=$ even

n	$m\backslash k$	-4	-3	-2	-1	0	1	2	3	4	5		D
4	−1				9	19	−5	1				1	24
	0				−1	13	13	−1				0	
6	−2			475	1427	−798	482	−173	27			2	1440
	−1			−27	637	1022	−258	77	−11			1	
	0			11	−93	802	802	−93	11			0	
8	−3		36799	139849	−121797	123133	−88547	41499	−11351	1375		3	120960
	−2		−1375	47799	101349	−44797	26883	−11547	2999	−351		2	
	−1		351	−4183	57627	81693	−20227	7227	−1719	191		1	
	0		−191	1879	−9531	68323	68323	−9531	1879	−191		0	
10	−4	2082753	9449717	−11271304	16002320	−17283646	13510082	−7394032	2687864	−583435	57281	4	7257600
	−3	−57281	2655563	6872072	−4397584	3973310	−2848834	1481072	−520312	110219	−10625	3	
	−2	10625	−163531	3133688	5597072	−2166334	1295810	−617584	206072	−42187	3969	2	
	−1	−3969	50315	−342136	3609968	4763582	−1166146	462320	−141304	27467	−2497	1	
	0	2497	−28939	162680	−641776	4134338	4134338	−641776	162680	−28939	2497	0	
		5	4	3	2	1	0	-1	-2	-3	-4	$k\backslash m$	

Table 25.4 ABSCISSAS AND WEIGHT FACTORS FOR GAUSSIAN INTEGRATION

$$\int_{-1}^{+1} f(x)dx \approx \sum_{i=1}^{n} w_i f(x_i)$$

Abscissas $=\pm x_i$ (Zeros of Legendre Polynomials) Weight Factors $=w_i$

$\pm x_i$	w_i
$n=2$	
0.57735 02691 89626	1.00000 00000 00000
$n=3$	
0.00000 00000 00000	0.88888 88888 88889
0.77459 66692 41483	0.55555 55555 55556
$n=4$	
0.33998 10435 84856	0.65214 51548 62546
0.86113 63115 94053	0.34785 48451 37454
$n=5$	
0.00000 00000 00000	0.56888 88888 88889
0.53846 93101 05683	0.47862 86704 99366
0.90617 98459 38664	0.23692 68850 56189
$n=6$	
0.23861 91860 83197	0.46791 39345 72691
0.66120 93864 66265	0.36076 15730 48139
0.93246 95142 03152	0.17132 44923 79170
$n=7$	
0.00000 00000 00000	0.41795 91836 73469
0.40584 51513 77397	0.38183 00505 05119
0.74153 11855 99394	0.27970 53914 89277
0.94910 79123 42759	0.12948 49661 68870

$\pm x_i$	w_i
$n=8$	
0.18343 46424 95650	0.36268 37833 78362
0.52553 24099 16329	0.31370 66458 77887
0.79666 64774 13627	0.22238 10344 53374
0.96028 98564 97536	0.10122 85362 90376
$n=9$	
0.00000 00000 00000	0.33023 93550 01260
0.32425 34234 03809	0.31234 70770 40003
0.61337 14327 00590	0.26061 06964 02935
0.83603 11073 26636	0.18064 81606 94857
0.96816 02395 07626	0.08127 43883 61574
$n=10$	
0.14887 43389 81631	0.29552 42247 14753
0.43339 53941 29247	0.26926 67193 09996
0.67940 95682 99024	0.21908 63625 15982
0.86506 33666 88985	0.14945 13491 50581
0.97390 65285 17172	0.06667 13443 08688
$n=12$	
0.12523 34085 11469	0.24914 70458 13403
0.36783 14989 98180	0.23349 25365 38355
0.58731 79542 86617	0.20316 74267 23066
0.76990 26741 94305	0.16007 83285 43346
0.90411 72563 70475	0.10693 93259 95318
0.98156 06342 46719	0.04717 53363 86512

$\pm x_i$	w_i
$n=16$	
0.09501 25098 37637 440185	0.18945 06104 55068 496285
0.28160 35507 79258 913230	0.18260 34150 44923 588867
0.45801 67776 57227 386342	0.16915 65193 95002 538189
0.61787 62444 02643 748447	0.14959 59888 16576 732081
0.75540 44083 55003 033895	0.12462 89712 55533 872052
0.86563 12023 87831 743880	0.09515 85116 82492 784810
0.94457 50230 73232 576078	0.06225 35239 38647 892863
0.98940 09349 91649 932596	0.02715 24594 11754 094852
$n=20$	
0.07652 65211 33497 333755	0.15275 33871 30725 850698
0.22778 58511 41645 078080	0.14917 29864 72603 746788
0.37370 60887 15419 560673	0.14209 61093 18382 051329
0.51086 70019 50827 098004	0.13168 86384 49176 626898
0.63605 36807 26515 025453	0.11819 45319 61518 417312
0.74633 19064 60150 792614	0.10193 01198 17240 435037
0.83911 69718 22218 823395	0.08327 67415 76704 748725
0.91223 44282 51325 905868	0.06267 20483 34109 063570
0.96397 19272 77913 791268	0.04060 14298 00386 941331
0.99312 85991 85094 924786	0.01761 40071 39152 118312
$n=24$	
0.06405 68928 62605 626085	0.12793 81953 46752 156974
0.19111 88674 73616 309159	0.12583 74563 46828 296121
0.31504 26796 96163 374387	0.12167 04729 27803 391204
0.43379 35076 26045 138487	0.11550 56680 53725 601353
0.54542 14713 88839 535658	0.10744 42701 15965 634783
0.64809 36519 36975 569252	0.09761 86521 04113 888270
0.74012 41915 78554 364244	0.08619 01615 31953 275917
0.82000 19859 73902 921954	0.07334 64814 11080 305734
0.88641 55270 04401 034213	0.05929 85849 15436 780746
0.93827 45520 02732 758524	0.04427 74388 17419 806169
0.97472 85559 71309 498198	0.02853 13886 28933 663181
0.99518 72199 97021 360180	0.01234 12297 99987 199547

Table 25.4

ABSCISSAS AND WEIGHT FACTORS FOR GAUSSIAN INTEGRATION

$$\int_{-1}^{+1} f(x)dx \approx \sum_{i=1}^{n} w_i f(x_i)$$

Abscissas$=\pm x_i$ (Zeros of Legendre Polynomials) Weight Factors$=w_i$

$\pm x_i$		w_i
	$n=32$	
0.04830 76656 87738 316235		0.09654 00885 14727 800567
0.14447 19615 82796 493485		0.09563 87200 79274 859419
0.23928 73622 52137 074545		0.09384 43990 80804 565639
0.33186 86022 82127 649780		0.09117 38786 95763 884713
0.42135 12761 30635 345364		0.08765 20930 04403 811143
0.50689 99089 32229 390024		0.08331 19242 26946 755222
0.58771 57572 40762 329041		0.07819 38957 87070 306472
0.66304 42669 30215 200975		0.07234 57941 08848 506225
0.73218 21187 40289 680387		0.06582 22227 76361 846838
0.79448 37959 67942 406963		0.05868 40934 78535 547145
0.84936 76137 32569 970134		0.05099 80592 62376 176196
0.89632 11557 66052 123965		0.04283 58980 22226 680657
0.93490 60759 37739 689171		0.03427 38629 13021 433103
0.96476 22555 87506 430774		0.02539 20653 09262 059456
0.98561 15115 45268 335400		0.01627 43947 30905 670605
0.99726 38618 49481 563545		0.00701 86100 09470 096600
	$n=40$	
0.03877 24175 06050 821933		0.07750 59479 78424 811264
0.11608 40706 75255 208483		0.07703 98181 64247 965588
0.19269 75807 01371 099716		0.07611 03619 00626 242372
0.26815 21850 07253 681141		0.07472 31690 57968 264200
0.34199 40908 25758 473007		0.07288 65823 95804 059061
0.41377 92043 71605 001525		0.07061 16473 91286 779695
0.48307 58016 86178 712909		0.06791 20458 15233 903826
0.54946 71250 95128 202076		0.06480 40134 56601 038075
0.61255 38896 67980 237953		0.06130 62424 92928 939167
0.67195 66846 14179 548379		0.05743 97690 99391 551367
0.72731 82551 89927 103281		0.05322 78469 83936 824355
0.77830 56514 26519 387695		0.04869 58076 35072 232061
0.82461 22308 33311 663196		0.04387 09081 85673 271992
0.86595 95032 12259 503821		0.03878 21679 74472 017640
0.90209 88069 68874 296728		0.03346 01952 82547 847393
0.93281 28082 78676 533361		0.02793 70069 80023 401098
0.95791 68192 13791 655805		0.02224 58491 94166 957262
0.97725 99499 83774 262663		0.01642 10583 81907 888713
0.99072 62386 99457 006453		0.01049 82845 31152 813615
0.99823 77097 10559 200350		0.00452 12770 98533 191258
	$n=48$	
0.03238 01709 62869 362033		0.06473 76968 12683 922503
0.09700 46992 09462 698930		0.06446 61644 35950 082207
0.16122 23560 68891 718056		0.06392 42385 84648 186624
0.22476 37903 94689 061225		0.06311 41922 86254 025657
0.28736 24873 55455 576736		0.06203 94231 59892 663904
0.34875 58862 92160 738160		0.06070 44391 65893 880053
0.40868 64819 90716 729916		0.05911 48396 98395 635746
0.46690 29047 50958 404545		0.05727 72921 00403 215705
0.52316 09747 22233 033678		0.05519 95036 99984 162868
0.57722 47260 83972 703818		0.05289 01894 85193 667096
0.62886 73967 76513 623995		0.05035 90355 53854 474958
0.67787 23796 32663 905212		0.04761 66584 92490 474826
0.72403 41309 23814 654674		0.04467 45608 56694 280419
0.76715 90325 15740 339254		0.04154 50829 43464 749214
0.80706 62040 29442 627083		0.03824 13510 65830 706317
0.84358 82616 24393 530711		0.03477 72225 64770 438893
0.87657 20202 74247 885906		0.03116 72278 32798 088902
0.90587 91367 15569 672822		0.02742 65097 08356 948200
0.93138 66907 06554 333114		0.02357 07608 39324 379141
0.95298 77031 60430 860723		0.01961 61604 57355 527814
0.97059 15925 46247 250461		0.01557 93157 22943 848728
0.98412 45837 22826 857745		0.01147 72345 79234 539490
0.99353 01722 66350 757548		0.00732 75539 01276 262102
0.99877 10072 52426 118601		0.00315 33460 52305 838633

Table 25.4

ABSCISSAS AND WEIGHT FACTORS FOR GAUSSIAN INTEGRATION

$$\int_{-1}^{+1} f(x)dx \approx \sum_{i=1}^{n} w_i f(x_i)$$

Abscissas $=\pm x_i$ (Zeros of Legendre Polynomials) $\pm x_i$	Weight Factors $=w_i$ w_i
$n=64$	
0.02435 02926 63424 432509	0.04869 09570 09139 720383
0.07299 31217 87799 039450	0.04857 54674 41503 426935
0.12146 28192 96120 554470	0.04834 47622 34802 957170
0.16964 44204 23992 818037	0.04799 93885 96458 307728
0.21742 36437 40007 084150	0.04754 01657 14830 308662
0.26468 71622 08767 416374	0.04696 81828 16210 017325
0.31132 28719 90210 956158	0.04628 47965 81314 417296
0.35722 01583 37668 115950	0.04549 16279 27418 144480
0.40227 01579 63991 603696	0.04459 05581 63756 563060
0.44636 60172 53464 087985	0.04358 37245 29323 453377
0.48940 31457 07052 957479	0.04247 35151 23653 589007
0.53127 94640 19894 545658	0.04126 25632 42623 528610
0.57189 56462 02634 034284	0.03995 37411 32720 341387
0.61115 53551 72393 250249	0.03855 01531 78615 629129
0.64896 54712 54657 339858	0.03705 51285 40240 046040
0.68523 63130 54233 242564	0.03547 22132 56882 383811
0.71988 18501 71610 826849	0.03380 51618 37141 609392
0.75281 99072 60531 896612	0.03205 79283 54851 553585
0.78397 23589 43341 407610	0.03023 46570 72402 478868
0.81326 53151 22797 559742	0.02833 96726 14259 483228
0.84062 92962 52580 362752	0.02637 74697 15054 658672
0.86599 93981 54092 819761	0.02435 27025 68710 873338
0.88931 54459 95114 105853	0.02227 01738 08383 254159
0.91052 21370 78502 805756	0.02013 48231 53530 209372
0.92956 91721 31939 575821	0.01795 17157 75697 343085
0.94641 13748 58402 816062	0.01572 60304 76024 719322
0.96100 87996 52053 718919	0.01346 30478 96718 642598
0.97332 68277 89910 963742	0.01116 81394 60131 128819
0.98333 62538 84625 956931	0.00884 67598 26363 947723
0.99101 33714 76744 320739	0.00650 44579 68978 362856
0.99634 01167 71955 279347	0.00414 70332 60562 467635
0.99930 50417 35772 139457	0.00178 32807 21696 432947
$n=80$	
0.01951 13832 56793 997654	0.03901 78136 56306 654811
0.05850 44371 52420 668629	0.03895 83959 62769 531199
0.09740 83984 41584 599063	0.03883 96510 59051 968932
0.13616 40228 09143 886559	0.03866 17597 74076 463327
0.17471 22918 32646 812559	0.03842 49930 06959 423185
0.21299 45028 57666 132572	0.03812 97113 14477 638344
0.25095 23583 92272 120493	0.03777 63643 62001 397490
0.28852 80548 84511 853109	0.03736 54902 38730 490027
0.32566 43707 47701 914619	0.03689 77146 38276 008839
0.36230 47534 99487 315619	0.03637 37499 05835 978044
0.39839 34058 81969 227024	0.03579 43939 53416 054603
0.43387 53708 31756 093062	0.03516 05290 44747 593496
0.46869 66151 70544 477036	0.03447 31204 51753 928794
0.50280 41118 88784 987594	0.03373 32149 84611 522817
0.53614 59208 97131 932020	0.03294 19393 97645 401383
0.56867 12681 22709 784725	0.03210 04986 73487 773148
0.60033 06228 29751 743155	0.03121 01741 88114 701642
0.63107 57730 46871 966248	0.03027 23217 59557 980661
0.66085 98989 86119 801736	0.02928 83695 83267 847693
0.68963 76443 42027 600771	0.02825 98160 57276 862397
0.71736 51853 62099 880254	0.02718 82275 00486 380674
0.74400 02975 83597 272317	0.02607 52357 67565 117903
0.76950 24201 35041 373866	0.02492 25357 64115 491105
0.79383 27175 04605 449949	0.02373 18828 65930 101293
0.81695 41386 81463 470371	0.02250 50902 46332 461926
0.83883 14735 80255 275617	0.02124 40261 15782 006389
0.85943 14066 63111 096977	0.01995 06108 78141 998929
0.87872 25676 78213 828704	0.01862 68142 08299 031429
0.89667 55794 38770 683194	0.01727 46520 56269 306359
0.91326 31025 71757 654165	0.01589 61835 83725 688045
0.92845 98771 72445 795953	0.01449 35080 40509 076117
0.94224 27613 09872 674752	0.01306 87615 92401 339294
0.95459 07663 43634 905493	0.01162 41141 20797 826916
0.96548 50890 43799 251452	0.01016 17660 41103 064521
0.97490 91405 85727 793386	0.00868 39452 69260 858426
0.98284 85727 38629 070418	0.00719 29047 68117 312753
0.98929 13024 99755 531027	0.00569 09224 51403 198649
0.99422 75409 65688 277892	0.00418 03131 24694 895237
0.99764 98643 98237 688900	0.00266 35335 89512 681669
0.99955 38226 51630 629880	0.00114 49500 03186 941534

Table 25.4

ABSCISSAS AND WEIGHT FACTORS FOR GAUSSIAN INTEGRATION

$$\int_{-1}^{+1} f(x)dx \approx \sum_{i=1}^{n} w_i f(x_i)$$

Abscissas $= \pm x_i$ (Zeros of Legendre Polynomials) Weight Factors $= w_i$

$n=96$

$\pm x_i$	w_i
0.01627 67448 49602 969579	0.03255 06144 92363 166242
0.04881 29851 36049 731112	0.03251 61187 13868 835987
0.08129 74954 64425 558994	0.03244 71637 14064 269364
0.11369 58501 10665 920911	0.03234 38225 68575 928429
0.14597 37146 54896 941989	0.03220 62047 94030 250669
0.17809 68823 67618 602759	0.03203 44562 31992 663218
0.21003 13104 60567 203603	0.03182 87588 94411 006535
0.24174 31561 63840 012328	0.03158 93307 70727 168558
0.27319 88125 91049 141487	0.03131 64255 96861 355813
0.30436 49443 54496 353024	0.03101 03325 86313 837423
0.33520 85228 92625 422616	0.03067 13761 23669 149014
0.36569 68614 72313 635031	0.03029 99154 20827 593794
0.39579 76498 28908 603285	0.02989 63441 36328 385984
0.42547 89884 07300 545365	0.02946 10899 58167 905970
0.45470 94221 67743 008636	0.02899 46141 50555 236543
0.48345 79739 20596 359768	0.02849 74110 65085 385646
0.51169 41771 54667 673586	0.02797 00076 16848 334440
0.53938 81083 24357 436227	0.02741 29627 26029 242823
0.56651 04185 61397 168404	0.02682 68667 25591 762198
0.59303 23647 77572 080684	0.02621 23407 35672 413913
0.61892 58401 25468 570386	0.02557 00360 05349 361499
0.64416 34037 84967 106798	0.02490 06332 22483 610288
0.66871 83100 43916 153953	0.02420 48417 92364 691282
0.69256 45366 42171 561344	0.02348 33990 85926 219842
0.71567 68123 48967 626225	0.02273 70696 58329 374001
0.73803 06437 44400 132851	0.02196 66444 38744 349195
0.75960 23411 76647 498703	0.02117 29398 92191 298988
0.78036 90438 67433 217604	0.02035 67971 54333 324595
0.80030 87441 39140 817229	0.01951 90811 40145 022410
0.81940 03107 37931 675539	0.01866 06796 27411 467385
0.83762 35112 28187 121494	0.01778 25023 16045 260838
0.85495 90334 34601 455463	0.01688 54798 64245 172450
0.87138 85059 09296 502874	0.01597 05629 02562 291381
0.88689 45174 02420 416057	0.01503 87210 26994 938006
0.90146 06353 15852 341319	0.01409 09417 72314 860916
0.91507 14231 20898 074206	0.01312 82295 66961 572637
0.92771 24567 22308 690965	0.01215 16046 71088 319635
0.93937 03397 52755 216932	0.01116 21020 99838 498591
0.95003 27177 84437 635756	0.01016 07705 35008 415758
0.95968 82914 48742 539300	0.00914 86712 30783 386633
0.96832 68284 63264 212174	0.00812 68769 25698 759217
0.97593 91745 85136 466453	0.00709 64707 91153 865269
0.98251 72635 63014 677447	0.00605 85455 04235 961683
0.98805 41263 29623 799481	0.00501 42027 42927 517693
0.99254 39003 23762 624572	0.00396 45543 38444 686674
0.99598 18429 87209 290650	0.00291 07318 17934 946408
0.99836 43758 63181 677724	0.00185 39607 88946 921732
0.99968 95038 83230 766828	0.00079 67920 65552 012429

Table 25.5 ABSCISSAS FOR EQUAL WEIGHT CHEBYSHEV INTEGRATION

$$\int_{-1}^{+1} f(x)dx \approx \frac{2}{n} \sum_{i=1}^{n} f(x_i)$$

Abscissas $= \pm x_i$

n	$\pm x_i$
2	0.57735 02692
3	0.70710 67812
	0.00000 00000
4	0.79465 44723
	0.18759 24741
5	0.83249 74870
	0.37454 14096
	0.00000 00000
6	0.86624 68181
	0.42251 86538
	0.26663 54015
7	0.88386 17008
	0.52965 67753
	0.32391 18105
	0.00000 00000
9	0.91158 93077
	0.60101 86554
	0.52876 17831
	0.16790 61842
	0.00000 00000

Table 25.6 ABSCISSAS AND WEIGHT FACTORS FOR LOBATTO INTEGRATION

$$\int_{-1}^{+1} f(x)dx \approx w_1 f(-1) + \sum_{i=2}^{n-1} w_i f(x_i) + w_n f(1)$$

Abscissas $= \pm x_i$ Weight Factors $= w_i$

n	$\pm x_i$	w_i
3	1.00000 000	0.33333 333
	0.00000 000	1.33333 333
4	1.00000 000	0.16666 667
	0.44721 360	0.83333 333
5	1.00000 000	0.10000 000
	0.65465 367	0.54444 444
	0.00000 000	0.71111 111
6	1.00000 000	0.06666 667
	0.76505 532	0.37847 496
	0.28523 152	0.55485 838
7	1.00000 000	0.04761 904
	0.83022 390	0.27682 604
	0.46884 879	0.43174 538
	0.00000 000	0.48761 904
8	1.00000 000	0.03571 428
	0.87174 015	0.21070 422
	0.59170 018	0.34112 270
	0.20929 922	0.41245 880
9	1.00000 00000	0.02777 77778
	0.89975 79954	0.16549 53616
	0.67718 62795	0.27453 87126
	0.36311 74638	0.34642 85110
	0.00000 00000	0.37151 92744
10	1.00000 00000	0.02222 22222
	0.91953 39082	0.13330 59908
	0.73877 38651	0.22488 93420
	0.47792 49498	0.29204 26836
	0.16527 89577	0.32753 97612

Table 25.7 ABSCISSAS AND WEIGHT FACTORS FOR GAUSSIAN INTEGRATION FOR INTEGRANDS WITH A LOGARITHMIC SINGULARITY

$$\int_0^1 f(x) \ln x \, dx = \sum_{i=1}^{n} w_i f(x_i) + \frac{f^{(2n)}(\xi)}{(2n)!} K_n$$

Abscissas $= x_i$ Weight Factors $= w_i$

n	x_i	$-w_i$	K_n
2	0.112009	0.718539	0.00285
	0.602277	0.281461	
3	0.063891	0.513405	0.00017
	0.368997	0.391980	
	0.766880	0.094615	
4	0.041448	0.383464	0.00001
	0.245275	0.386875	
	0.556165	0.190435	
	0.848982	0.039225	

ABSCISSAS AND WEIGHT FACTORS FOR GAUSSIAN INTEGRATION OF MOMENTS Table 25.8

$$\int_0^1 x^k f(x)dx \approx \sum_{i=1}^{n} w_i f(x_i)$$

Abscissas $=x_i$ Weight Factors $=w_i$

n	$k=0$ x_i	$k=0$ w_i	$k=1$ x_i	$k=1$ w_i	$k=2$ x_i	$k=2$ w_i
1	0.50000 00000	1.00000 00000	0.66666 66667	0.50000 00000	0.75000 00000	0.33333 33333
2	0.21132 48654	0.50000 00000	0.35505 10257	0.18195 86183	0.45584 81560	0.10078 58821
	0.78867 51346	0.50000 00000	0.84494 89743	0.31804 13817	0.87748 51773	0.23254 74513
3	0.11270 16654	0.27777 77778	0.21234 05382	0.06982 69799	0.29499 77901	0.02995 07030
	0.50000 00000	0.44444 44444	0.59053 31356	0.22924 11064	0.65299 62340	0.14624 62693
	0.88729 83346	0.27777 77778	0.91141 20405	0.20093 19137	0.92700 59759	0.15713 63611
4	0.06943 18442	0.17392 74226	0.13975 98643	0.03118 09710	0.20414 85821	0.01035 22408
	0.33000 94782	0.32607 25774	0.41640 95676	0.12984 75476	0.48295 27049	0.06863 38872
	0.66999 05218	0.32607 25774	0.72315 69864	0.20346 45680	0.76139 92624	0.14345 87898
	0.93056 81558	0.17392 74226	0.94289 58039	0.13550 69134	0.95149 94506	0.11088 84156
5	0.04691 00770	0.11846 34425	0.09853 50858	0.01574 79145	0.14894 57871	0.00411 38252
	0.23076 53449	0.23931 43352	0.30453 57266	0.07390 88701	0.36566 65274	0.03205 56007
	0.50000 00000	0.28444 44444	0.56202 51898	0.14638 69871	0.61011 36129	0.08920 01612
	0.76923 46551	0.23931 43352	0.80198 65821	0.16717 46381	0.82651 96792	0.12619 89619
	0.95308 99230	0.11846 34425	0.96019 01429	0.09678 15902	0.96542 10601	0.08176 47843
6	0.03376 52429	0.08566 22462	0.07305 43287	0.00873 83018	0.11319 43838	0.00183 10758
	0.16939 53068	0.18038 07865	0.23076 61380	0.04395 51656	0.28431 88727	0.01572 02972
	0.38069 04070	0.23395 69673	0.44132 84812	0.09866 11509	0.49096 35868	0.05128 95711
	0.61930 95930	0.23395 69673	0.66301 53097	0.14079 25538	0.69756 30820	0.09457 71867
	0.83060 46932	0.18038 07865	0.85192 14003	0.13554 24972	0.86843 60583	0.10737 64997
	0.96623 47571	0.08566 22462	0.97068 35728	0.07231 03307	0.97409 54449	0.06253 87027
7	0.02544 60438	0.06474 24831	0.05626 25605	0.00521 43622	0.08881 68334	0.00089 26880
	0.12923 44072	0.13985 26957	0.18024 06917	0.02740 83567	0.22648 27534	0.00816 29256
	0.29707 74243	0.19091 50253	0.35262 47171	0.06638 46965	0.39997 84867	0.02942 22113
	0.50000 00000	0.20897 95918	0.54715 36263	0.10712 50657	0.58599 78554	0.06314 63787
	0.70292 25757	0.19091 50253	0.73421 01772	0.12739 08973	0.75944 58740	0.09173 38033
	0.87076 55928	0.13985 26957	0.88532 09468	0.11050 92582	0.89691 09709	0.09069 88246
	0.97455 39562	0.06474 24831	0.97752 06136	0.05596 73634	0.97986 72262	0.04927 65018
8	0.01985 50718	0.05061 42681	0.04463 39553	0.00329 51914	0.07149 10350	0.00046 85178
	0.10166 67613	0.11119 05172	0.14436 62570	0.01784 29027	0.18422 82964	0.00447 45217
	0.23723 37950	0.15685 33229	0.28682 47571	0.04543 93195	0.33044 77282	0.01724 68638
	0.40828 26788	0.18134 18917	0.45481 33152	0.07919 95995	0.49440 29218	0.04081 44264
	0.59171 73212	0.18134 18917	0.62806 78354	0.10604 73594	0.65834 80085	0.06844 71834
	0.76276 62050	0.15685 33229	0.78569 15206	0.11250 57995	0.80452 48315	0.08528 47692
	0.89833 32387	0.11119 05172	0.90867 63921	0.09111 90236	0.91709 93825	0.07681 80933
	0.98014 49282	0.05061 42681	0.98222 00849	0.04455 08044	0.98390 22404	0.03977 89578

Table 25.8 ABSCISSAS AND WEIGHT FACTORS FOR GAUSSIAN INTEGRATION OF MOMENTS

$$\int_0^1 x^k f(x)dx \approx \sum_{i=1}^{n} w_i f(x_i)$$

Abscissas $=x_i$ Weight Factors $=w_i$

	$k=3$		$k=4$		$k=5$	
n	x_i	w_i	x_i	w_i	x_i	w_i
1	0.80000 00000	0.25000 00000	0.83333 33333	0.20000 00000	0.85714 28571	0.16666 66667
2	0.52985 79359	0.06690 52498	0.58633 65823	0.04908 24923	0.63079 15938	0.03833 75627
	0.89871 34927	0.18309 47502	0.91366 34177	0.15091 75077	0.92476 39617	0.12832 91039
3	0.36326 46302	0.01647 90593	0.42011 30593	0.01046 90422	0.46798 32355	0.00729 70036
	0.69881 12692	0.10459 98976	0.73388 93552	0.08027 66735	0.76162 39697	0.06459 66123
	0.93792 41006	0.12892 10432	0.94599 75855	0.10925 42844	0.95221 09767	0.09477 30507
4	0.26147 77888	0.00465 83671	0.31213 54928	0.00251 63516	0.35689 37290	0.00153 44797
	0.53584 64461	0.04254 17241	0.57891 56596	0.02916 93822	0.61466 93899	0.02142 84046
	0.79028 32300	0.10900 43689	0.81289 15166	0.08706 77121	0.83107 90039	0.07205 63642
	0.95784 70806	0.09379 55399	0.96272 39976	0.08124 65541	0.96658 86465	0.07164 74181
5	0.19621 20074	0.00152 06894	0.23979 20448	0.00069 69771	0.27969 31248	0.00036 97155
	0.41710 02118	0.01695 73249	0.46093 36745	0.01021 05417	0.49870 98270	0.00672 96904
	0.64857 00042	0.06044 49532	0.68005 92327	0.04402 44695	0.70633 38189	0.03376 77450
	0.84560 51500	0.10031 65045	0.86088 63437	0.08271 27131	0.87340 27279	0.07007 13397
	0.96943 57035	0.07076 05281	0.97261 44185	0.06235 52986	0.97519 38347	0.05572 81761
6	0.15227 31618	0.00056 17109	0.18946 95839	0.00021 94140	0.22446 89954	0.00010 13258
	0.33130 04570	0.00708 53159	0.37275 11560	0.00372 67844	0.40953 33505	0.00218 79257
	0.53241 15667	0.03052 61922	0.56757 23729	0.01995 62647	0.59778 90484	0.01396 96531
	0.72560 27783	0.06844 32818	0.74883 64975	0.05223 99543	0.76841 36046	0.04148 63470
	0.88161 66844	0.08830 09912	0.89238 51584	0.07464 91503	0.90135 07338	0.06445 88592
	0.97679 53517	0.05508 25080	0.97898 52313	0.04920 84323	0.98079 72084	0.04446 25560
7	0.12142 71288	0.00022 99041	0.15324 14389	0.00007 70737	0.18382 87683	0.00003 11046
	0.26836 34403	0.00314 75964	0.30632 65225	0.00144 70088	0.34080 75951	0.00075 53838
	0.44086 64606	0.01531 21671	0.47654 00930	0.00892 69676	0.50794 05240	0.00566 04137
	0.61860 40284	0.04099 51686	0.64638 93025	0.02854 78428	0.67036 34101	0.02095 92982
	0.78025 35520	0.06975 00981	0.79771 66898	0.05522 48742	0.81258 84660	0.04510 49816
	0.90636 25341	0.07655 65614	0.91421 99006	0.06602 18459	0.92085 64173	0.05790 76135
	0.98176 99145	0.04400 85043	0.98334 38305	0.03975 43870	0.98466 74508	0.03624 78712
8	0.09900 17577	0.00010 24601	0.12637 29744	0.00002 97092	0.15315 06616	0.00001 05316
	0.22124 35074	0.00148 56841	0.25552 90521	0.00059 89500	0.28726 44039	0.00027 83586
	0.36912 39000	0.00785 50738	0.40364 12989	0.00407 79241	0.43462 74067	0.00233 53415
	0.52854 54312	0.02363 15807	0.55831 66758	0.01490 99334	0.58451 85666	0.01004 46144
	0.68399 32484	0.04745 43798	0.70600 95429	0.03471 99507	0.72512 64097	0.02648 53011
	0.82028 39497	0.06736 18394	0.83367 15420	0.05491 00973	0.84518 94879	0.04588 56532
	0.92409 37129	0.06618 20353	0.92999 57161	0.05800 05653	0.93504 35075	0.05153 42238
	0.98529 34401	0.03592 69468	0.98646 31979	0.03275 28699	0.98746 05085	0.03009 26424

ABSCISSAS AND WEIGHT FACTORS FOR LAGUERRE INTEGRATION

Table 25.9

$$\int_0^\infty e^{-x} f(x)dx \approx \sum_{i=1}^{n} w_i f(x_i) \qquad \int_0^\infty g(x)dx \approx \sum_{i=1}^{n} w_i e^{x_i} g(x_i)$$

Abscissas $=x_i$ (Zeros of Laguerre Polynomials) Weight Factors $=w_i$

$n=2$

x_i	w_i	$w_i e^{x_i}$
0.58578 64376 27	(-1)8.53553 390593	1.53332 603312
3.41421 35623 73	(-1)1.46446 609407	4.45095 733505

$n=3$

x_i	w_i	$w_i e^{x_i}$
0.41577 45567 83	(-1)7.11093 009929	1.07769 285927
2.29428 03602 79	(-1)2.78517 733569	2.76214 296190
6.28994 50829 37	(-2)1.03892 565016	5.60109 462543

$n=4$

x_i	w_i	$w_i e^{x_i}$
0.32254 76896 19	(-1)6.03154 104342	0.83273 91238 38
1.74576 11011 58	(-1)3.57418 692438	2.04810 243845
4.53662 02969 21	(-2)3.88879 085150	3.63114 630582
9.39507 09123 01	(-4)5.39294 705561	6.48714 508441

$n=5$

x_i	w_i	$w_i e^{x_i}$
0.26356 03197 18	(-1)5.21755 610583	0.67909 40422 08
1.41340 30591 07	(-1)3.98666 811083	1.63848 787360
3.59642 57710 41	(-2)7.59424 496817	2.76944 324237
7.08581 00058 59	(-3)3.61175 867992	4.31565 690092
12.64080 08442 76	(-5)2.33699 723858	7.21918 635435

$n=6$

x_i	w_i	$w_i e^{x_i}$
0.22284 66041 79	(-1)4.58964 673950	0.57353 55074 23
1.18893 21016 73	(-1)4.17000 830772	1.36925 259071
2.99273 63260 59	(-1)1.13373 382074	2.26068 459338
5.77514 35691 05	(-2)1.03991 974531	3.35052 458236
9.83746 74183 83	(-4)2.61017 202815	4.88682 680021
15.98287 39806 02	(-7)8.98547 906430	7.84901 594560

$n=7$

x_i	w_i	$w_i e^{x_i}$
0.19304 36765 60	(-1)4.09318 951701	0.49647 75975 40
1.02666 48953 39	(-1)4.21831 277862	1.17764 306086
2.56787 67449 51	(-1)1.47126 348658	1.91824 978166
4.90035 30845 26	(-2)2.06335 144687	2.77184 863623
8.18215 34445 63	(-3)1.07401 014328	3.84124 912249
12.73418 02917 98	(-5)1.58654 643486	5.38067 820792
19.39572 78622 63	(-8)3.17031 547900	8.40543 248683

$n=8$

x_i	w_i	$w_i e^{x_i}$
0.17027 96323 05	(-1)3.69188 589342	0.43772 34104 93
0.90370 17767 99	(-1)4.18786 780814	1.03386 934767
2.25108 66298 66	(-1)1.75794 986637	1.66970 976566
4.26670 01702 88	(-2)3.33434 922612	2.37692 470176
7.04590 54023 93	(-3)2.79453 623523	3.20854 091335
10.75851 60101 81	(-5)9.07650 877336	4.26857 551083
15.74067 86412 78	(-7)8.48574 671627	5.81808 336867
22.86313 17368 89	(-9)1.04800 117487	8.90622 621529

$n=9$

x_i	w_i	$w_i e^{x_i}$
0.15232 22277 32	(- 1)3.36126 421798	0.39143 11243 16
0.80722 00227 42	(- 1)4.11213 980424	0.92180 50285 29
2.00513 51556 19	(- 1)1.99287 525371	1.48012 790994
3.78347 39733 31	(- 2)4.74605 627657	2.08677 080755
6.20495 67778 77	(- 3)5.59962 661079	2.77292 138971
9.37298 52516 88	(- 4)3.05249 767093	3.59162 606809
13.46623 69110 92	(- 6)6.59212 302608	4.64876 600214
18.83359 77889 92	(- 8)4.11076 933035	6.21227 541975
26.37407 18909 27	(-11)3.29087 403035	9.36321 823771

$n=10$

x_i	w_i	$w_i e^{x_i}$
0.13779 34705 40	(- 1)3.08441 115765	0.35400 97386 07
0.72945 45495 03	(- 1)4.01119 929155	0.83190 23010 44
1.80834 29017 40	(- 1)2.18068 287612	1.33028 856175
3.40143 36978 55	(- 2)6.20874 560987	1.86306 390311
5.55249 61400 64	(- 3)9.50151 697518	2.45025 555808
8.33015 27467 64	(- 4)7.53008 388588	3.12276 415514
11.84378 58379 00	(- 5)2.82592 334960	3.93415 269556
16.27925 78313 78	(- 7)4.24931 398496	4.99241 487219
21.99658 58119 81	(- 9)1.83956 482398	6.57220 248513
29.92069 70122 74	(-13)9.91182 721961	9.78469 584037

$n=12$

x_i	w_i	$w_i e^{x_i}$
0.11572 21173 58	(- 1)2.64731 371055	0.29720 96360 44
0.61175 74845 15	(- 1)3.77759 275873	0.69646 29804 31
1.51261 02697 76	(- 1)2.44082 011320	1.10778 139462
2.83375 13377 44	(- 2)9.04492 222117	1.53846 423904
4.59922 76394 18	(- 2)2.01023 811546	1.99832 760627
6.84452 54531 15	(- 3)2.66397 354187	2.50074 576910
9.62131 68424 57	(- 4)2.03231 592663	3.06532 151828
13.00605 49933 06	(- 6)8.36505 585682	3.72328 911078
17.11685 51874 62	(- 7)1.66849 387654	4.52981 402998
22.15109 03793 97	(- 9)1.34239 103052	5.59725 846184
28.48796 72509 84	(-12)3.06160 163504	7.21299 546093
37.09912 10444 67	(-16)8.14807 746743	10.54383 74619

$n=15$

x_i	w_i	$w_i e^{x_i}$
0.09330 78120 17	(- 1)2.18234 885940	0.23957 81703 11
0.49269 17403 02	(- 1)3.42210 177923	0.56010 08427 93
1.21559 54120 71	(- 1)2.63027 577942	0.88700 82629 19
2.26994 95262 04	(- 1)1.26425 818106	1.22366 440215
3.66762 27217 51	(- 2)4.02068 649210	1.57444 872163
5.42533 66274 14	(- 3)8.56387 780361	1.94475 197653
7.56591 62266 13	(- 3)1.21243 614721	2.34150 205664
10.12022 85680 19	(- 4)1.11674 392344	2.77404 192683
13.13028 24821 76	(- 6)6.45992 676202	3.25564 334640
16.65440 77083 30	(- 7)2.22631 690710	3.80631 171423
20.77647 88994 49	(- 9)4.22743 038498	4.45847 775384
25.62389 42267 29	(-11)3.92189 726704	5.27001 778443
31.40751 91697 54	(-13)1.45651 526407	6.35956 346973
38.53068 33064 86	(-16)1.48302 705111	8.03178 763212
48.02608 55726 86	(-20)1.60059 490621	11.52777 21009

Table 25.10 ABSCISSAS AND WEIGHT FACTORS FOR HERMITE INTEGRATION

$$\int_{-\infty}^{\infty} e^{-x^2} f(x)dx \approx \sum_{i=1}^{n} w_i f(x_i) \qquad \int_{-\infty}^{\infty} g(x)dx \approx \sum_{i=1}^{n} w_i e^{x_i^2} g(x_i)$$

Abscissas $= \pm x_i$ (Zeros of Hermite Polynomials) Weight Factors $= w_i$

$\pm x_i$	w_i	$w_i e^{x_i^2}$
	$n=2$	
0.70710 67811 86548	(-1)8.86226 92545 28	1.46114 11826 611
	$n=3$	
0.00000 00000 00000	(0)1.18163 59006 04	1.18163 59006 037
1.22474 48713 91589	(-1)2.95408 97515 09	1.32393 11752 136
	$n=4$	
0.52464 76232 75290	(-1)8.04914 09000 55	1.05996 44828 950
1.65068 01238 85785	(-2)8.13128 35447 25	1.24022 58176 958
	$n=5$	
0.00000 00000 00000	(-1)9.45308 72048 29	0.94530 87204 829
0.95857 24646 13819	(-1)3.93619 32315 22	0.98658 09967 514
2.02018 28704 56086	(-2)1.99532 42059 05	1.18148 86255 360
	$n=6$	
0.43607 74119 27617	(-1)7.24629 59522 44	0.87640 13344 362
1.33584 90740 13697	(-1)1.57067 32032 29	0.93558 05576 312
2.35060 49736 74492	(-3)4.53000 99055 09	1.13690 83326 745
	$n=7$	
0.00000 00000 00000	(-1)8.10264 61755 68	0.81026 46175 568
0.81628 78828 58965	(-1)4.25607 25261 01	0.82868 73032 836
1.67355 16287 67471	(-2)5.45155 82819 13	0.89718 46002 252
2.65196 13568 35233	(-4)9.71781 24509 95	1.10133 07296 103
	$n=8$	
0.38118 69902 07322	(-1)6.61147 01255 82	0.76454 41286 517
1.15719 37124 46780	(-1)2.07802 32581 49	0.79289 00483 864
1.98165 67566 95843	(-2)1.70779 83007 41	0.86675 26065 634
2.93063 74202 57244	(-4)1.99604 07221 14	1.07193 01442 480
	$n=9$	
0.00000 00000 00000	(-1)7.20235 21560 61	0.72023 52156 061
0.72355 10187 52838	(-1)4.32651 55900 26	0.73030 24527 451
1.46855 32892 16668	(-2)8.84745 27394 38	0.76460 81250 946
2.26658 05845 31843	(-3)4.94362 42755 37	0.84175 27014 787
3.19099 32017 81528	(-5)3.96069 77263 26	1.04700 35809 767
	$n=10$	
0.34290 13272 23705	(- 1)6.10862 63373 53	0.68708 18539 513
1.03661 08297 89514	(- 1)2.40138 61108 23	0.70329 63231 049
1.75668 36492 99882	(- 2)3.38743 94455 48	0.74144 19319 436
2.53273 16742 32790	(- 3)1.34364 57467 81	0.82066 61264 048
3.43615 91188 37738	(- 6)7.64043 28552 33	1.02545 16913 657
	$n=12$	
0.31424 03762 54359	(- 1)5.70135 23626 25	0.62930 78743 695
0.94778 83912 40164	(- 1)2.60492 31026 42	0.63962 12320 203
1.59768 26351 52605	(- 2)5.16079 85615 88	0.66266 27732 669
2.27950 70805 01060	(- 3)3.90539 05846 29	0.70522 03661 122
3.02063 70251 20890	(- 5)8.57368 70435 88	0.78664 39394 633
3.88972 48978 69782	(- 7)2.65855 16843 56	0.98969 90470 923
	$n=16$	
0.27348 10461 3815	(- 1)5.07929 47901 66	0.54737 52050 378
0.82295 14491 4466	(- 1)2.80647 45852 85	0.55244 19573 675
1.38025 85391 9888	(- 2)8.38100 41398 99	0.56321 78290 882
1.95178 79909 1625	(- 2)1.28803 11535 51	0.58124 72754 009
2.54620 21578 4748	(- 4)9.32284 00862 42	0.60973 69582 560
3.17699 91619 7996	(- 5)2.71186 00925 38	0.65575 56728 761
3.86944 79048 6012	(- 7)2.32098 08448 65	0.73824 56222 777
4.68873 89393 0582	(-10)2.65480 74740 11	0.93687 44928 841
	$n=20$	
0.24534 07083 009	(- 1)4.62243 66960 06	0.49092 15006 667
0.73747 37285 454	(- 1)2.86675 50536 28	0.49384 33852 721
1.23407 62153 953	(- 1)1.09017 20602 00	0.49992 08713 363
1.73853 77121 166	(- 2)2.48105 20887 46	0.50967 90271 175
2.25497 40020 893	(- 3)3.24377 33422 38	0.52408 03509 486
2.78880 60584 281	(- 4)2.28338 63601 63	0.54485 17423 644
3.34785 45673 832	(- 6)7.80255 64785 32	0.57526 24428 525
3.94476 40401 156	(- 7)1.08606 93707 69	0.62227 86961 914
4.60368 24495 507	(-10)4.39934 09922 73	0.70433 29611 769
5.38748 08900 112	(-13)2.22939 36455 34	0.89859 19614 532

Table 25.11 COEFFICIENTS FOR FILON'S QUADRATURE FORMULA

θ	α	β	γ
0.00	0.00000 000	0.66666 667	1.33333 333
0.01	0.00000 004	0.66668 000	1.33332 000
0.02	0.00000 036	0.66671 999	1.33328 000
0.03	0.00000 120	0.66678 664	1.33321 334
0.04	0.00000 284	0.66687 990	1.33312 001
0.05	0.00000 555	0.66699 976	1.33300 003
0.06	0.00000 961	0.66714 617	1.33285 340
0.07	0.00001 524	0.66731 909	1.33268 012
0.08	0.00002 274	0.66751 844	1.33248 020
0.09	0.00003 237	0.66774 417	1.33225 365
0.1	0.00004 438	0.66799 619	1.33200 048
0.2	0.00035 354	0.67193 927	1.32800 761
0.3	0.00118 467	0.67836 065	1.32137 184
0.4	0.00278 012	0.68703 909	1.31212 154
0.5	0.00536 042	0.69767 347	1.30029 624
0.6	0.00911 797	0.70989 111	1.28594 638
0.7	0.01421 151	0.72325 813	1.26913 302
0.8	0.02076 156	0.73729 136	1.24992 752
0.9	0.02884 683	0.75147 168	1.22841 118
1.0	0.03850 188	0.76525 831	1.20467 472

See **25.4.47**.

26.1. Probability Functions: Definitions and Properties

Univariate Cumulative Distribution Functions

A real-valued function $F(x)$ is termed a (univariate) cumulative distribution function (c.d.f.) or simply distribution function if

i) $F(x)$ is non-decreasing, i.e., $F(x_1)\leq F(x_2)$ for $x_1\leq x_2$

ii) $F(x)$ is everywhere continuous from the right, i.e., $F(x)=\lim_{\epsilon\to 0+} F(x+\epsilon)$

iii) $F(-\infty)=0$, $F(\infty)=1$.

The function $F(x)$ signifies the probability of the event "$X\leq x$" where X is a random variable, i.e., $Pr\{X\leq x\}=F(x)$, and thus describes the c.d.f. of X. The two principal types of distribution functions are termed *discrete* and *continuous*.

Discrete Distributions: Discrete distributions are characterized by the random variable X taking on an enumerable number of values $\ldots, x_{-1}, x_0, x_1, \ldots$ with point probabilities

$$p_n=Pr\{X=x_n\}\geq 0$$

which need only be subject to the restriction

$$\sum_n p_n=1.$$

The corresponding distribution function can then be written

26.1.1 $$F(x)=Pr\{X\leq x\}=\sum_{x_n\leq x} p_n$$

where the summation is over all values of x for which $x_n\leq x$. The set $\{x_n\}$ of values for which $p_n>0$ is termed the domain of the random variable X. A discrete distribution of a random variable is called a *lattice distribution* if there exist numbers a and $b\neq 0$ such that every possible value of X can be represented in the form $a+bn$ where n takes on only integral values. A summary of some properties of certain discrete distributions is presented in **26.1.19–26.1.24.**

Continuous Distributions. Continuous distributions are characterized by $F(x)$ being absolutely continuous. Hence $F(x)$ possesses a derivative $F'(x)=f(x)$ and the c.d.f. can be written

26.1.2 $$F(x)=Pr\{X\leq x\}=\int_{-\infty}^{x} f(t)dt.$$

The derivative $f(x)$ is termed the *probability density function* (p.d.f.) or *frequency function*, and the values of x for which $f(x)>0$ make up the domain of the random variable X. A summary of some properties of certain selected continuous distributions is presented in **26.1.25–26.1.34.**

Multivariate Probability Functions

The real-valued function $F(x_1, x_2, \ldots x_n)$ defines an n-variate cumulative distribution function if

i) $F(x_1, x_2, \ldots x_n)$ is a non-decreasing function for each x_i

ii) $F(x_1, x_2, \ldots x_n)$ is continuous from the right in each x_i; i.e., $F(x_1, x_2, \ldots x_n) =\lim_{\epsilon\to 0+} F(x_1, \ldots, x_i+\epsilon, \ldots, x_n)$

iii) $F(x_1, x_2, \ldots x_n)=0$ when any $x_i=-\infty$; $F(\infty, \infty, \ldots, \infty)=1$.

iv) $F(x_1, x_2, \ldots, x_n)$ assigns nonnegative probability to the event $x_1<X_1\leq x_1+h_1$, $x_2<X_2\leq x_2+h_2, \ldots, x_n<X_n\leq x_n+h_n$ for all $x_1, x_2, \ldots, x_n$ and all nonnegative $h_1, h_2, \ldots, h_n$, e.g., for $n=2$, $F(x_1+h_1, x_2+h_2)-F(x_1, x_2+h_2)-F(x_1+h_1, x_2)+F(x_1, x_2)\geq 0$ and in general for $x_i<X_i\leq x_i+h_i$ $(i=1, 2, \ldots, n)$, the kth order difference $\Delta_k F(x_1, x_2, \ldots, x_n)>0$ for $k=1, 2, \ldots, n$.

Comment on notation and conventions.

a. We follow the customary convention of denoting a random variable by a capital letter, i.e., X, and using the corresponding lower case letter, i.e., x, for a particular value that the random variable assumes.

b. For statistical applications it is often convenient to have tabulated the "upper tail area," $1-F(x)$, or the c.d.f. for $|X|$, $F(x)-F(-x)$, instead of simply the c.d.f. $F(x)$. We use the notation P to indicate the c.d.f. of X, $Q=1-P$ to indicate the "upper tail area" and $A=P-Q$ to denote the c.d.f. of $|X|$. In particular we use $P(x)$, $Q(x)$, and $A(x)$ to denote the corresponding functions for the normal or Gaussian probability function, see **26.2.2–26.2.4.** When these distributions depend on other parameters, say θ_1 and θ_2, we indicate this by writing $P(x|\theta_1, \theta_2)$, $Q(x|\theta_1, \theta_2)$, or $A(x|\theta_1, \theta_2)$. For example the chi-square distribution **26.4** depends on the parameter ν and the tabulated function is written $Q(\chi^2|\nu)$.

The joint probability of the event $X_1 \leq x_1$, $X_2 \leq x_2, \ldots, X_n \leq x_n$ is $F(x_1, x_2, \ldots x_n)$. Analogous to the one-dimensional case, *discrete* distributions assign all probability to an enumerable set of vectors $(x_1, x_2, \ldots, x_n)$ and *continuous* distributions are characterized by absolute continuity of $F(x_1, x_2, \ldots, x_n)$.

Characteristics of distribution functions: Moments, characteristic functions, cumulants

		Continuous distributions	Discrete distributions
26.1.3	n^{th} moment about origin	$\mu_n' = \int_{-\infty}^{\infty} x^n f(x) dx$	$\mu_n' = \sum_s x_s^n p_s$
26.1.4	mean	$m = \mu_1' = \int_{-\infty}^{\infty} x f(x) dx$	$m = \mu_1' = \sum_s x_s p_s$
26.1.5	variance	$\sigma^2 = \mu_2' - m^2 = \int_{-\infty}^{\infty} (x-m)^2 f(x) dx$	$\sigma^2 = \mu_2' - m^2 = \sum_s (x_s - m)^2 p_s$
26.1.6	n^{th} central moment	$\mu_n = \int_{-\infty}^{\infty} (x-m)^n f(x) dx$	$\mu_n = \sum_s (x_s - m)^n p_s$
26.1.7	expected value operator for the function $g(x)$	$E[g(X)] = \int_{-\infty}^{\infty} g(x) f(x) dx$	$E[g(X)] = \sum_s g(x_s) p_s$
26.1.8	characteristic function of X	$\phi(t) = E(e^{itX}) = \int_{-\infty}^{\infty} e^{itx} f(x) dx$	$\phi(t) = E(e^{itX}) = \sum_s e^{itx_s} p_s$
26.1.9	characteristic function of $g(X)$	$\phi_g(t) = E(e^{itg(X)}) = \int_{-\infty}^{\infty} e^{itg(x)} f(x) dx$	$\phi_g(t) = E(e^{itg(X)}) = \sum_s e^{itg(x_s)} p_s$
26.1.10	inversion formula	$f(x) = \frac{1}{2\pi} \int_{-\infty}^{\infty} e^{-itx} \phi(t) dt$	$p_n = \frac{b}{2\pi} \int_{-\pi/b}^{\pi/b} e^{-itx_n} \phi(t) dt$ (lattice distributions only)

Relation of the Characteristic Function to Moments About the Origin

26.1.11 $$\phi^{(n)}(0) = \left[\frac{d^n}{dt^n} \phi(t)\right]_{t=0} = i^n \mu_n'$$

Cumulant Function

26.1.12 $$\ln \phi(t) = \sum_{n=0}^{\infty} \kappa_n \frac{(it)^n}{n!}$$

κ_n is called the nth cumulant.

26.1.13 $$\kappa_1 = m, \quad \kappa_2 = \sigma^2, \quad \kappa_3 = \mu_3, \quad \kappa_4 = \mu_4 - 3\mu_2^2$$

Relation of Central Moments to Moments About the Origin

26.1.14 $$\mu_n = \sum_{j=0}^{n} \binom{n}{j} (-1)^{n-j} \mu_j' m^{n-j}$$

Coefficients of Skewness and Excess

26.1.15 $$\gamma_1 = \frac{\kappa_3}{\kappa_2^{3/2}} = \frac{\mu_3}{\sigma^3} \qquad \text{(skewness)}$$

26.1.16 $$\gamma_2 = \frac{\kappa_4}{\kappa_2^2} = \frac{\mu_4}{\sigma^4} - 3 \qquad \text{(excess)}$$

Occasionally coefficients of skewness and excess (or kurtosis) are given by

26.1.17 $$\beta_1 = \gamma_1^2 = \left(\frac{\mu_3}{\sigma^3}\right)^2 \qquad \text{(skewness)}$$

26.1.18 $$\beta_2 = \gamma_2 + 3 = \frac{\mu_4}{\sigma^4} \qquad \text{(excess or kurtosis)}$$

Some one-dimensional discrete distribution functions

Name	Domain	Point Probabilities	Restrictions on Parameters	Mean	Variance	Skewness γ_1	Excess γ_2	Characteristic function	Cumulants
26.1.19 Single point or degenerate	$x=c$ (c a constant)	$p=1$	$-\infty<c<+\infty$	c	0	----------	----------	$e^{i\lambda t}$	$\kappa_1=\lambda$, $\kappa_r=0$ for $r>1$
26.1.20 Binomial	$x_s=s$, for $s=0, 1, 2, \ldots, n$	$\binom{n}{s} p^s(1-p)^{n-s}$	$0<p<1$ $(q=1-p)$	np	npq	$\frac{q-p}{\sqrt{npq}}$	$\frac{1-6pq}{npq}$	$(q+pe^{it})^n$	$\kappa_1=np$ $\kappa_{r+1}=pq\frac{d\kappa_r}{dp}$ for $r\geq 1$
26.1.21 Hypergeometric	$x_s=s$, for $s=0, 1, \ldots \min(n, N_1)$	$\frac{\binom{N_1}{s}\binom{N_2}{n-s}}{\binom{N_1+N_2}{n}}$	N_1 and N_2 integers, and $n\leq N_1+N_2$ $(N=N_1+N_2,$ $p=N_1/N$ and $q=1-p=N_2/N)$	np	$npq\left(\frac{N-n}{N-1}\right)$	$\frac{q-p}{\sqrt{npq}}\left(\frac{N-1}{N-n}\right)^{\frac{1}{2}}\left(\frac{N-2n}{N-2}\right)$	Complicated	$\frac{\binom{N_2}{n}}{\binom{N}{n}} F(-n, -N_1; N_2-n+1; e^{it})$	Complicated
26.1.22 Poisson	$x_s=s$, for $s=0, 1, 2, \ldots, \infty$	$\frac{e^{-m}m^s}{s!}$	$0<m<\infty$	m	m	$m^{-\frac{1}{2}}$	m^{-1}	$e^{m(e^{it}-1)}$	$\kappa_r=m$ for $r=1, 2, \ldots$
26.1.23 Negative binomial	$x_s=s$, for $s=0, 1, 2, \ldots, \infty$	$\binom{n+s-1}{s} p^n(1-p)^s$	$n\geq 0$ and $0<p<1$ $(p=1/Q$, and $1-p=P/Q)$	nP	nPQ	$\frac{Q+P}{\sqrt{nPQ}}$	$\frac{1+6PQ}{nPQ}$	$(Q-Pe^{it})^{-n}$	$\kappa_1=nP$ $\kappa_{r+1}=PQ\frac{d\kappa_r}{dQ}$ for $r\geq 1$
26.1.24 Geometric	$x_s=s$, for $s=0, 1, 2, \ldots, \infty$	$p(1-p)^s$	$0<p<1$	$\frac{1-p}{p}$	$\frac{1-p}{p^2}$	$\frac{2-p}{\sqrt{1-p}}$	$6+\frac{p^2}{1-p}$	$p[1-(1-p)e^{it}]^{-1}$	$\kappa_1=\frac{1-p}{p}$, $\kappa_{r+1}=-(1-p)\frac{d\kappa_r}{dp}$, $r\geq 1$

Some one-dimensional continuous distribution functions

	Name	Domain	Probability Density Function $f(x)$	Restrictions on Parameters	Mean	Variance	Skewness γ_1	Excess γ_2	Characteristic function	Cumulants
26.1.25	Error function	$-\infty<x<\infty$	$\frac{h}{\sqrt{\pi}}e^{-h^2x^2}$	$0<h<\infty$	0	$\frac{1}{2h^2}$	0	0	$e^{\frac{-t^2}{4h^2}}$	$\kappa_1=0,\ \kappa_2=\frac{1}{2h^2}$ $\kappa_n=0$ for $n>2$
26.1.26	Normal	$-\infty<x<\infty$	$\frac{1}{\sigma\sqrt{2\pi}}e^{-\frac{1}{2}\left(\frac{x-m}{\sigma}\right)^2}$	$-\infty<m<\infty$ $0<\sigma<\infty$	m	σ^2	0	0	$e^{imt-\frac{\sigma^2t^2}{2}}$	$\kappa_1=m,\ \kappa_2=\sigma^2,\ \kappa_n=0$ for $n>2$
26.1.27	Cauchy	$-\infty<x<\infty$	$\frac{1}{\pi\beta}\frac{1}{1+\left(\frac{x-\alpha}{\beta}\right)^2}$	$-\infty<\alpha<\infty$ $0<\beta<\infty$	not defined	not defined	not defined	not defined	$e^{i\alpha t-\beta\|t\|}$	not defined
26.1.28	Exponential	$\alpha\leq x<\infty$	$\frac{1}{\beta}e^{-\left(\frac{x-\alpha}{\beta}\right)}$	$-\infty<\alpha<\infty$ $0<\beta<\infty$	$\alpha+\beta$	β^2	2	6	$e^{i\alpha t}(1-i\beta t)^{-1}$	$\kappa_1=\alpha+\beta,\ \kappa_n=\beta^n\Gamma(n)$ for $n>1$
26.1.29	Laplace, or double exponential	$-\infty<x<\infty$	$\frac{1}{2\beta}e^{-\left\|\frac{x-\alpha}{\beta}\right\|}$	$-\infty<\alpha<\infty$ $0<\beta<\infty$	α	$2\beta^2$	0	3	$e^{i\alpha t}(1+\beta^2t^2)^{-1}$	$\kappa_1=\alpha,\ \kappa_2=2\beta^2$ $\kappa_{2n+1}=0,\ \kappa_{2n}=\frac{(2n)!}{n}\beta^{2n}$ for $n=1, 2, \ldots$
26.1.30	Extreme-Value,[4] (Fisher-Tippett Type I or doubly exponential)	$-\infty<x<\infty$	$\frac{1}{\beta}\exp\left(-y-e^{-y}\right)$ with $y=\frac{x-\alpha}{\beta}$	$-\infty<\alpha<\infty$ $0<\beta<\infty$	$\alpha+\gamma\beta$	$\frac{(\pi\beta)^2}{6}$	1.3	2.4	$\Gamma(1-i\beta t)e^{i\alpha t}$	$\kappa_1=\gamma,\ \kappa_2=\frac{(\pi\beta)^2}{6}$ $\kappa_n=\beta^n\Gamma(n)\sum_{r=1}^{\infty}\frac{1}{r^n}$ for $n>2$
26.1.31	Pearson Type III	$\alpha\leq x<\infty$	$\frac{1}{\beta\Gamma(p)}y^{p-1}e^{-y}$ with $y=\frac{x-\alpha}{\beta}$	$-\infty<\alpha<\infty$ $0<\beta<\infty$ $0<p<\infty$	$\alpha+p\beta$	$p\beta^2$	$\frac{2}{\sqrt{p}}$	$6/p$	$e^{i\alpha t}(1-i\beta t)^{-p}$	$\kappa_1=\alpha+\beta p,\ \kappa_n=\beta^n p\Gamma(n)$ for $n>1$
26.1.32	Gamma distribution	$0\leq x<\infty$	$\frac{1}{\Gamma(p)}x^{p-1}e^{-x}$	$0<p<\infty$	p	p	$\frac{2}{\sqrt{p}}$	$6/p$	$(1-it)^{-p}$	$\kappa_1=p,\ \kappa_n=p\Gamma(n)$ for $n>1$
26.1.33	Beta distribution	$0\leq x\leq 1$	$\frac{1}{B(a,b)}x^{a-1}(1-x)^{b-1}$	$1\leq a<\infty$ $1\leq b<\infty$	$\frac{a}{a+b}$	$\frac{ab}{(a+b)^2(a+b+1)}$	$\frac{2(a-b)}{(a+b+2)}$	See footnote 5.	$M(a, a+b, it)$	
26.1.34	Rectangular, or uniform	$m-\frac{h}{2}\leq x\leq m+\frac{h}{2}$	$\frac{1}{h}$	$-\infty<m<\infty$ $0<h<\infty$	m	$\frac{h^2}{12}$	0	-1.2	$\frac{2}{ht}\sin\left(\frac{ht}{2}\right)e^{imt}$	$\kappa_1=m,\ \kappa_{2n+1}=0$ $\kappa_{2n}=\frac{h^{2n}B_{2n}}{2n}$ B_{2n} (Bernoulli numbers), $B_2=\frac{1}{6},\ B_4=-\frac{1}{30},\ \ldots$

[4] γ (Euler's constant) $=.57721\ 56649\ \ldots$

[5] $\gamma_2=\sqrt{\frac{a+b+1}{ab}}\left\{\frac{3(a+b+1)[2(a+b)^2+ab(a+b-6)]}{ab(a+b+2)(a+b+3)}-3\right\}.$

Inequalities for distribution functions

($F(x)$ denotes the c.d.f. of the random variable X and t denotes a positive constant; further m is always assumed to be finite and all expectations are assumed to exist.)

Inequality	Conditions
26.1.35 $Pr\{g(X)\geq t\}\leq E[g(X)]/t$	(i) $g(X)\geq 0$
26.1.36 $Pr\{X\geq t\}\leq m/t$ $F(t)\geq 1-\frac{m}{t}$	(i) $Pr\{X<0\}=0$ (ii) $E(X)=m$
26.1.37 $Pr\{\lvert X-m\rvert\geq t\sigma\}\leq 1/t^2$ $F(m+t\sigma)-F(m-t\sigma)\geq 1-\frac{1}{t^2}$	(i) $E(X)=m$ (ii) $E(X-m)^2=\sigma^2$
26.1.38 $Pr\{\lvert\overline{X}-\overline{m}\rvert\geq t\overline{\sigma}\}\leq\frac{1}{nt^2}$	(i) $E(X_i)=m_i$ (ii) $E(X_i-m_i)^2=\sigma_i^2$ (iii) $E([X_i-m_i][X_j-m_j])=0\,(i\neq j)$ (iv) $\overline{X}=\sum_{i=1}^{n}\frac{X_i}{n}$, $\overline{m}=\sum_{i=1}^{n}\frac{m_i}{n},\ \overline{\sigma}=\left[\sum_{i=1}^{n}\frac{\sigma_i^2}{n}\right]^{\frac{1}{2}}$
26.1.39 $Pr\{\lvert X-m\rvert\geq t\sigma\}\leq\frac{4}{9}\left\{\frac{1+\left(\frac{m-x_0}{\sigma}\right)^2}{\left(t-\left\lvert\frac{m-x_0}{\sigma}\right\rvert\right)^2}\right\}$ $F(m+t\sigma)-F(m-t\sigma)\geq 1-\frac{4}{9}\left\{\frac{1+\left(\frac{m-x_0}{\sigma}\right)^2}{\left(t-\left\lvert\frac{m-x_0}{\sigma}\right\rvert\right)^2}\right\}$	(i) $E(X-m)^2=\sigma^2$ (ii) $F(x)$ is a continuous c.d.f. (iii) $F(x)$ is unimodal at x_0[6]
26.1.40 $Pr\{\lvert X-m\rvert\geq t\sigma\}\leq 4/9t^2$ $F(m+t\sigma)-F(m-t\sigma)\geq 1-\frac{4}{9t^2}$	(i) $E(X-m)^2=\sigma^2$ (ii) $F(x)$ is a continuous c.d.f. (iii) $F(x)$ is unimodal at x_0[6] (iv) $m=x_0$
26.1.41 $Pr\{\lvert X-m\rvert\geq t\sigma\}\leq\frac{\mu_4-\sigma^4}{\mu_4+t^4\sigma^4-2t^2\sigma^4}$ $F(m+t\sigma)-F(m-t\sigma)\geq 1-\frac{\mu_4-\sigma^4}{\mu_4+t^4\sigma^4-2t^2\sigma^4}$	(i) $E(X-m)^2=\sigma^2$ (ii) $E(X-m)^4=\mu_4$

[6] x_0 is such that $F'(x_0)>F'(x)$ for $x\neq x_0$.

26.2. Normal or Gaussian Probability Function

26.2.1 $$Z(x)=\frac{1}{\sqrt{2\pi}}e^{-x^2/2}$$

26.2.2 $$P(x)=\frac{1}{\sqrt{2\pi}}\int_{-\infty}^{x}e^{-t^2/2}dt=\int_{-\infty}^{x}Z(t)dt$$

26.2.3 $$Q(x)=\frac{1}{\sqrt{2\pi}}\int_{x}^{\infty}e^{-t^2/2}dt=\int_{x}^{\infty}Z(t)dt$$

26.2.4 $$A(x)=\frac{1}{\sqrt{2\pi}}\int_{-x}^{x}e^{-t^2/2}dt=\int_{-x}^{x}Z(t)dt$$

26.2.5 $$P(x)+Q(x)=1$$

26.2.6 $$P(-x)=Q(x)$$

26.2.7 $$A(x)=2P(x)-1$$

Probability Integral with Mean m and Variance σ^2

A random variable X is said to be normally distributed with mean m and variance σ^2 if the probability that X is less than or equal to x is given by

26.2.8
$$Pr\{X\leq x\}=\frac{1}{\sigma\sqrt{2\pi}}\int_{-\infty}^{x}e^{-\frac{(t-m)^2}{2\sigma^2}}dt$$
$$=\frac{1}{\sqrt{2\pi}}\int_{-\infty}^{(x-m)/\sigma}e^{-t^2/2}dt=P\left(\frac{x-m}{\sigma}\right).$$

The corresponding probability density function is

26.2.9
$$\frac{\partial}{\partial x}P\left(\frac{x-m}{\sigma}\right)=\frac{1}{\sigma}Z\left(\frac{x-m}{\sigma}\right)=\frac{1}{\sigma\sqrt{2\pi}}e^{-\frac{(x-m)^2}{2\sigma^2}}$$

and is symmetric around m, i.e.

$$Z\left(\frac{m+x}{\sigma}\right)=Z\left(\frac{m-x}{\sigma}\right).$$

The inflexion points of the probability density function are at $m\pm\sigma$.

Power Series ($x\geq 0$)

26.2.10 $$P(x)=\frac{1}{2}+\frac{1}{\sqrt{2\pi}}\sum_{n=0}^{\infty}\frac{(-1)^n x^{2n+1}}{n!2^n(2n+1)}$$

26.2.11 $$P(x)=\frac{1}{2}+Z(x)\sum_{n=0}^{\infty}\frac{x^{2n+1}}{1\cdot 3\cdot 5\ldots(2n+1)}$$

Asymptotic Expansions ($x>0$)

26.2.12

$$Q(x)=\frac{Z(x)}{x}\left\{1-\frac{1}{x^2}+\frac{1\cdot 3}{x^4}+\ldots+\frac{(-1)^n 1\cdot 3\ldots(2n-1)}{x^{2n}}\right\}+R_n$$

where

$$R_n=(-1)^{n+1}1\cdot 3\ldots(2n+1)\int_x^{\infty}\frac{Z(t)}{t^{2n+2}}\,dt$$

which is less in absolute value than the first neglected term.

26.2.13

$$Q(x)\sim\frac{Z(x)}{x}\left\{1-\frac{a_1}{x^2+2}+\frac{a_2}{(x^2+2)(x^2+4)}-\frac{a_3}{(x^2+2)(x^2+4)(x^2+6)}+\ldots\right\}$$

where $a_1=1$, $a_2=1$, $a_3=5$, $a_4=9$, $a_5=129$ and the general term is

$$a_n=c_0 1\cdot 3\ldots(2n-1)+2c_1 1\cdot 3\ldots(2n-3)+2^2c_2 1\cdot 3\ldots(2n-5)+\ldots+2^{n-1}c_{n-1}$$

and c_s is the coefficient of t^{n-s} in the expansion of $t(t-1)\ldots(t-n+1)$.

Continued Fraction Expansions

26.2.14

$$Q(x)=Z(x)\left\{\frac{1}{x+}\,\frac{1}{x+}\,\frac{2}{x+}\,\frac{3}{x+}\,\frac{4}{x+}\cdots\right\}\qquad(x>0)$$

26.2.15

$$Q(x)=\frac{1}{2}-Z(x)\left\{\frac{x}{1-}\,\frac{x^2}{3+}\,\frac{2x^2}{5-}\,\frac{3x^2}{7+}\,\frac{4x^2}{9-}\cdots\right\}\qquad(x\geq 0)$$

Polynomial and Rational Approximations[7] for $P(x)$ and $Z(x)$

$$0\leq x<\infty$$

26.2.16

$$P(x)=1-Z(x)(a_1t+a_2t^2+a_3t^3)+\epsilon(x),\qquad t=\frac{1}{1+px}$$

$$|\epsilon(x)|<1\times 10^{-5}$$

$p=.33267$ $\quad a_1=.43618\ 36$

$a_2=-.12016\ 76$

$a_3=.93729\ 80$

26.2.17

$$P(x)=1-Z(x)(b_1t+b_2t^2+b_3t^3+b_4t^4+b_5t^5)+\epsilon(x),\qquad t=\frac{1}{1+px}$$

$$|\epsilon(x)|<7.5\times 10^{-8}$$

$p=.23164\ 19$

$b_1=\ .31938\ 1530$ $\quad b_4=-1.82125\ 5978$

$b_2=-.35656\ 3782$ $\quad b_5=\ 1.33027\ 4429$

$b_3=\ 1.78147\ 7937$

26.2.18

$$P(x)=1-\frac{1}{2}(1+c_1x+c_2x^2+c_3x^3+c_4x^4)^{-4}+\epsilon(x)$$

$$|\epsilon(x)|<2.5\times 10^{-4}$$

$c_1=.196854$ $\quad c_3=.000344$

$c_2=.115194$ $\quad c_4=.019527$

26.2.19

$$P(x)=1-\frac{1}{2}(1+d_1x+d_2x^2+d_3x^3+d_4x^4+d_5x^5+d_6x^6)^{-16}+\epsilon(x)$$

$$|\epsilon(x)|<1.5\times 10^{-7}$$

$d_1=.04986\ 73470$ $\quad d_4=.00003\ 80036$

$d_2=.02114\ 10061$ $\quad d_5=.00004\ 88906$

$d_3=.00327\ 76263$ $\quad d_6=.00000\ 53830$

26.2.20 $$Z(x)=(a_0+a_2x^2+a_4x^4+a_6x^6)^{-1}+\epsilon(x)$$

$$|\epsilon(x)|<2.7\times 10^{-3}$$

$a_0=2.490895$ $\quad a_4=-.024393$

$a_2=1.466003$ $\quad a_6=\ .178257$

---

[7] Based on approximations in C. Hastings, Jr., Approximations for digital computers. Princeton Univ. Press, Princeton, N.J., 1955

26.2.21

$$Z(x)=(b_0+b_2x^2+b_4x^4+b_6x^6+b_8x^8+b_{10}x^{10})^{-1}+\epsilon(x)$$

$$|\epsilon(x)|<2.3\times10^{-4}$$

$b_0=2.50523\ 67$ $\qquad b_6=\ .13064\ 69$

$b_2=1.28312\ 04$ $\qquad b_8=-.02024\ 90$

$b_4=\ .22647\ 18$ $\qquad b_{10}=\ .00391\ 32$

Rational Approximations[7] for x_p where $Q(x_p)=p$

$$0<p\leq .5$$

26.2.22

$$x_p=t-\frac{a_0+a_1t}{1+b_1t+b_2t^2}+\epsilon(p),\qquad t=\sqrt{\ln\frac{1}{p^2}}$$

$$|\epsilon(p)|<3\times10^{-3}$$

$a_0=2.30753$ $\qquad b_1=.99229$

$a_1=\ .27061$ $\qquad b_2=.04481$

26.2.23

$$x_p=t-\frac{c_0+c_1t+c_2t^2}{1+d_1t+d_2t^2+d_3t^3}+\epsilon(p),\qquad t=\sqrt{\ln\frac{1}{p^2}}$$

$$|\epsilon(p)|<4.5\times10^{-4}$$

$c_0=2.515517$ $\qquad d_1=1.432788$

$c_1=\ .802853$ $\qquad d_2=\ .189269$

$c_2=\ .010328$ $\qquad d_3=\ .001308$

Bounds Useful as Approximations to the Normal Distribution Function

26.2.24

$$P(x)\leq\begin{cases}P_1(x)=\frac{1}{2}+\frac{1}{2}\,(1-e^{-2x^2/\pi})^{\frac{1}{2}} & (x>0)\\[2ex] P_2(x)=1-\frac{(4+x^2)^{\frac{1}{2}}-x}{2}\,(2\pi)^{-\frac{1}{2}}e^{-x^2/2} & (x>1.4)\end{cases}$$

26.2.25

$$P(x)\geq\begin{cases}P_3(x)=\frac{1}{2}+\frac{1}{2}\left(1-e^{-2x^2/\pi}-\frac{2(\pi-3)}{3\pi^2}\,x^4e^{-x^2/2}\right)^{\frac{1}{2}} & (x>0)\\[2ex] P_4(x)=1-\frac{1}{x}\,(2\pi)^{-\frac{1}{2}}e^{-x^2/2} & (x>2.2)\end{cases}$$

See **Figure 26.1** for error curves.

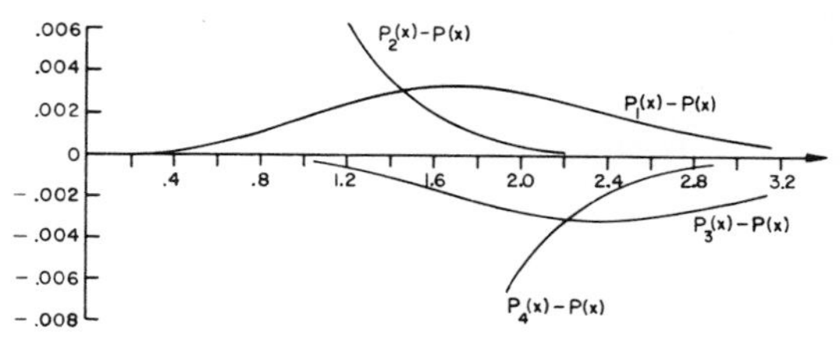

FIGURE 26.1. *Error curves for bounds on normal distribution.*

Derivatives of the Normal Probability Density Function

26.2.26 $$Z^{(m)}(x)=\frac{d^m}{dx^m}Z(x)$$

Differential Equation

26.2.27 $$Z^{(m+2)}(x)+xZ^{(m+1)}(x)+(m+1)Z^{(m)}(x)=0$$

Value at $x=0$

26.2.28

$$Z^{(m)}(0)=\begin{cases}\dfrac{(-1)^{m/2}m!}{\sqrt{2\pi}2^{m/2}\left(\frac{m}{2}\right)!} & \text{for } m=2r,\ r=0,1,\ldots\\[2ex] 0 & \text{for odd } m>0\end{cases}$$

Relation of $P(x)$ and $Z^{(m)}(x)$ to Other Functions

	Function	*Relation*	
26.2.29	Error function	$\mathrm{erf}\, x=2P(x\sqrt{2})-1$	$(x\geq 0)$
26.2.30	Incomplete gamma function (special case)	$\frac{\gamma\left(\frac{1}{2}, x\right)}{\Gamma\left(\frac{1}{2}\right)}=[2P(\sqrt{2x})-1]$	$(x\geq 0)$
26.2.31	Hermite polynomial	$He_n(x)=(-1)^n\frac{Z^{(n)}(x)}{Z(x)}$	
26.2.32	"	$H_n(x)=(-1)^n 2^{n/2}\frac{Z^{(n)}(x\sqrt{2})}{Z(x\sqrt{2})}$	
26.2.33	*Hh* function	$Hh_{-n}(x)=(-1)^{n-1}\sqrt{2\pi}Z^{(n-1)}(x)$	$(n>0)$
26.2.34	"	$Hh_n(x)=\frac{(-1)^n}{n!}Hh_{-1}(x)\frac{d^n}{dx^n}\left(\frac{Q(x)}{Z(x)}\right)$	$(n>0)$
26.2.35	Tetrachoric function	$\tau_n(x)=\frac{(-1)^{n-1}}{\sqrt{n!}}Z^{(n-1)}(x)$	
26.2.36	Confluent hypergeometric function (special case)	$M\left(\frac{1}{2}, \frac{3}{2}, -\frac{x^2}{2}\right)=\frac{\sqrt{2\pi}}{x}\left\{P(x)-\frac{1}{2}\right\}$	$(x>0)$
26.2.37	"	$M\left(1, \frac{3}{2}, \frac{x^2}{2}\right)=\frac{1}{xZ(x)}\left\{P(x)-\frac{1}{2}\right\}$	$(x>0)$
26.2.38	"	$M\left(\frac{2m+1}{2}, \frac{1}{2}, -\frac{x^2}{2}\right)=\frac{Z^{(2m)}(x)}{Z^{(2m)}(0)}$	$(x\geq 0)$
26.2.39	"	$M\left(\frac{2m+2}{2}, \frac{3}{2}, -\frac{x^2}{2}\right)=\frac{Z^{(2m-1)}(x)}{xZ^{(2m)}(0)}$	$(x\geq 0)$
26.2.40	Parabolic cylinder function	$U\left(-n-\frac{1}{2}, x\right)=e^{-\frac{1}{4}x^2}(-1)^n\frac{Z^{(n)}(x)}{Z(x)}$	$(n>0)$

Repeated Integrals of the Normal Probability Integral

26.2.41 $$I_n(x)=\int_x^\infty I_{n-1}(t)dt \qquad (n\geq 0)$$

where $I_{-1}(x)=Z(x)$

26.2.42

$$I_{-n}(x)=\left(-\frac{d}{dx}\right)^{n-1}Z(x)=(-1)^{n-1}Z^{(n-1)}(x) \qquad (n\geq -1)$$

26.2.43 $$\left(\frac{d^2}{dx^2}+x\frac{dx}{dn}-n\right)I_n(x)=0$$

26.2.44

$$(n+1)I_{n+1}(x)+xI_n(x)-I_{n-1}(x)=0 \qquad (n>-1)$$

26.2.45

$$I_n(x)=\int_x^\infty \frac{(t-x)^n}{n!} Z(t)dt=e^{-x^2/2}\int_0^\infty \frac{t^n}{n!} Z(t)dt \qquad (n>-1)$$

26.2.46 $$I_n(0)=I_{-n}(0)=\frac{1}{\left(\frac{n}{2}\right)!2^{\frac{n+2}{2}}} \qquad (n \text{ even})$$

Asymptotic Expansions of an Arbitrary Probability Density Function and Distribution Function

Let Y_i $(i=1, 2, \ldots, n)$ be n independent random variables with mean m_i, variance σ_i^2, and higher cumulants $\kappa_{r,i}$. Then asymptotic expansions with respect to n for the probability density and cumulative distribution function of

$$X=\frac{\sum_{i=1}^{m}(Y_i-m_i)}{\left(\sum_{i=1}^{m}\sigma_i^2\right)^{\frac{1}{2}}} \text{ are}$$

26.2.47

$$f(x)\sim Z(x)-\left[\frac{\gamma_1}{6}Z^{(3)}(x)\right]+\left[\frac{\gamma_2}{24}Z^{(4)}(x)+\frac{\gamma_1^2}{72}Z^{(6)}(x)\right]$$
$$-\left[\frac{\gamma_3}{120}Z^{(5)}(x)+\frac{\gamma_1\gamma_2}{144}Z^{(7)}(x)+\frac{\gamma_1^3}{1296}Z^{(9)}(x)\right]$$
$$+\left[\frac{\gamma_4}{720}Z^{(6)}(x)+\frac{\gamma_2^2}{1152}Z^{(8)}(x)+\frac{\gamma_1\gamma_3}{720}Z^{(8)}(x)\right.$$
$$\left.+\frac{\gamma_1^2\gamma_2}{1728}Z^{(10)}(x)+\frac{\gamma_1^4}{31104}Z^{(12)}(x)\right]+\ldots$$

26.2.48

$$F(x)\sim P(x)-\left[\frac{\gamma_1}{6}Z^{(2)}(x)\right]+\left[\frac{\gamma_2}{24}Z^{(3)}(x)+\frac{\gamma_1^2}{72}Z^{(5)}(x)\right]$$
$$-\left[\frac{\gamma_3}{120}Z^{(4)}(x)+\frac{\gamma_1\gamma_2}{144}Z^{(6)}(x)+\frac{\gamma_1^3}{1296}Z^{(8)}(x)\right]$$
$$+\left[\frac{\gamma_4}{720}Z^{(5)}(x)+\frac{\gamma_2^2}{1152}Z^{(7)}(x)+\frac{\gamma_1\gamma_3}{720}Z^{(7)}(x)\right.$$
$$\left.+\frac{\gamma_1^2\gamma_2}{1728}Z^{(9)}(x)+\frac{\gamma_1^4}{31104}Z^{(11)}(x)\right]+\ldots$$

where

$$\gamma_{r-2}=\frac{1}{n^{\frac{r}{2}-1}}\frac{\left(\frac{1}{n}\sum_{i=1}^{n}\kappa_{r,i}\right)}{\left(\frac{1}{n}\sum_{i=1}^{n}\sigma_i^2\right)^{r/2}}$$

Terms in brackets are terms of the same order with respect to n. When the Y_i have the same distribution, then $m_i=m$, $\sigma_i^2=\sigma^2$, $\kappa_{r,i}=\kappa_r$ and

$$\gamma_{r-2}=\frac{1}{n^{\frac{1}{2}r-1}}\left(\frac{\kappa_r}{\sigma^r}\right)$$

Asymptotic Expansion for the Inverse Function of an Arbitrary Distribution Function

Let the cumulative distribution function of $Y=\sum_{i=1}^{n}Y_i$ be denoted by $F(y)$. Then the (Cornish-Fisher) asymptotic expansion with respect to n for the value of y_p such that $F(y_p)=1-p$ is

26.2.49 $$y_p\sim m+\sigma w$$

where

$$w=x+[\gamma_1 h_1(x)]$$
$$+[\gamma_2 h_2(x)+\gamma_1^2 h_{11}(x)]$$
$$+[\gamma_3 h_3(x)+\gamma_1\gamma_2 h_{12}(x)+\gamma_1^3 h_{111}(x)]$$
$$+[\gamma_4 h_4(x)+\gamma_2^2 h_{22}(x)+\gamma_1\gamma_3 h_{13}(x)+\gamma_1^2\gamma_2 h_{112}(x)$$
$$+\gamma_1^4 h_{1111}(x)]+\ldots$$

and

$$Q(x)=p, \qquad \gamma_{r-2}=\frac{\kappa_r}{\kappa_2^{r/2}}, \qquad r=3, 4, \ldots$$

26.2.50

$$h_1(x)=\frac{1}{6}He_2(x)$$

$$h_2(x)=\frac{1}{24}He_3(x)$$

$$h_{11}(x)=-\frac{1}{36}[2He_3(x)+He_1(x)]$$

$$h_3(x)=\frac{1}{120}[He_4(x)]$$

$$h_{12}(x)=-\frac{1}{24}[He_4(x)+He_2(x)]$$

$$h_{111}(x)=\frac{1}{324}[12He_4(x)+19He_2(x)]$$

$$h_4(x)=\frac{1}{720}He_5(x)$$

$$h_{22}(x)=-\frac{1}{384}[3He_5(x)+6He_3(x)+2He_1(x)]$$

$$h_{13}(x)=-\frac{1}{180}[2He_5(x)+3He_3(x)]$$

$$h_{112}(x)=\frac{1}{288}[14He_5(x)+37He_3(x)+8He_1(x)]$$

$$h_{1111}(x)=-\frac{1}{7776}[252He_5(x)+832He_3(x)+227He_1(x)]$$

Terms in brackets in **26.2.49** are terms of the same order with respect to n. The $He_n(x)$ are the Hermite polynomials. (See chapter 22.)

26.2.51 $$He_n(x)=(-1)^n \frac{Z^{(n)}(x)}{Z(x)}=n! \sum_{m=0}^{\left[\frac{n}{2}\right]} \frac{(-1)^m}{2^m m!(n-2m)!} x^{n-2m}$$

In the following auxiliary table, the polynomial functions $h_1(x)$, $h_2(x)$ . . . $h_{1111}(x)$ are tabulated for

$p=.25$, .1, .05, .025, .01, .005, .0025, .001, .0005.

Auxiliary coefficients[8] *for use with Cornish-Fisher asymptotic expansion.* **26.2.49**

	p								
	.25	.10	.05	.025	.01	.005	.0025	.001	.0005
x	.67449	1.28155	1.64485	1.95996	2.32635	2.57583	2.80703	3.09022	3.29053
$h_1(x)$	−.09084	.10706	.28426	.47358	.73532	.93915	1.14657	1.42491	1.63793
$h_2(x)$	−.07153	−.07249	−.02018	.06872	.23379	.39012	.57070	.84331	1.07320
$h_{11}(x)$	.07663	.06106	−.01878	−.14607	−.37634	−.59171	−.83890	−1.21025	−1.52234
$h_3(x)$	.00398	−.03464	−.04928	−.04410	−.00152	.06010	.14841	.30746	.46059
$h_{12}(x)$	.00282	.14644	.17532	.10210	−.17621	−.53531	−1.02868	−1.89355	−2.71243
$h_{111}(x)$	−.01428	−.11629	−.11900	−.02937	.25195	.59757	1.06301	1.86787	2.62337
$h_4(x)$	.00998	.00227	−.01082	−.02357	−.03176	−.02621	−.00666	.04591	.10950
$h_{22}(x)$	−.03285	.00776	.05985	.09659	.07888	−.01226	−.19116	−.59060	−1.03555
$h_{13}(x)$	−.05126	.01086	.09462	.16106	.16058	.05366	−.17498	−.70464	−1.30531
$h_{112}(x)$	.14764	−.10858	−.39517	−.55856	−.32621	.35696	1.60445	4.29304	7.23307
$h_{1111}(x)$	−.06898	.09585	.25623	.31624	.07286	−.46534	−1.39199	−3.32708	−5.40702

[8] From R. A. Fisher, Contributions to mathematical statistics, Paper 30 (with E. A. Cornish) Extrait de la Revue de l'Institute International de Statistique 4, 1–14 (1937) (with permission).

26.3. Bivariate Normal Probability Function

26.3.1

$$g(x,y,\rho)=[2\pi\sqrt{1-\rho^2}]^{-1}\exp-\frac{1}{2}\left(\frac{x^2-2\rho xy+y^2}{1-\rho^2}\right)$$

26.3.2 $$g(x,y,\rho)=(1-\rho^2)^{-\frac{1}{2}}Z(x)Z\left(\frac{y-\rho x}{\sqrt{1-\rho^2}}\right)$$

26.3.3

$$L(h,k,\rho)=\int_h^\infty dx\int_k^\infty g(x,y,\rho)dy$$

$$=\int_h^\infty Z(x)dx\int_w^\infty Z(w)\,dw,\qquad w=\left(\frac{k-\rho x}{\sqrt{1-\rho^2}}\right)$$

26.3.4 $$L(-h,-k,\rho)=\int_{-\infty}^h dx\int_{-\infty}^k g(x,y,\rho)dy$$

26.3.5 $$L(-h,k,-\rho)=\int_{-\infty}^h dx\int_k^\infty g(x,y,\rho)dy$$

26.3.6 $$L(h,-k,-\rho)=\int_h^\infty dx\int_{-\infty}^k g(x,y,\rho)dy$$

26.3.7 $$L(h,k,\rho)=L(k,h,\rho)$$

26.3.8 $$L(-h,k,\rho)+L(h,k,-\rho)=Q(k)$$

26.3.9 $$L(-h,-k,\rho)-L(h,k,\rho)=P(k)-Q(h)$$

26.3.10

$$2[L(h,k,\rho)+L(h,k,-\rho)+P(h)-Q(k)]-1$$

$$=\int_{-h}^h dx\int_{-k}^k g(x,y,\rho)dy$$

Probability Function With Means m_x, m_y, Variances σ_x^2, σ_y^2, and Correlation ρ

The random variables X, Y are said to be distributed as a bivariate Normal distribution with means and variances (m_x, m_y) and (σ_x^2, σ_y^2) and correlation ρ if the joint probability that X is less than or equal to h and Y less than or equal to k is given by

26.3.11

$$Pr\{X\leq h, Y\leq k\}=\frac{1}{\sigma_x\sigma_y}\int_{-\infty}^{\frac{h-m_x}{\sigma_x}}\int_{-\infty}^{\frac{k-m_y}{\sigma_y}} g(s,t,\rho)ds\,dt$$

$$=L\left(-\left(\frac{h-m_x}{\sigma_x}\right), -\left(\frac{k-m_y}{\sigma_y}\right), \rho\right)$$

The probability density function is

26.3.12

$$\frac{1}{2\pi\sigma_x\sigma_y\sqrt{1-\rho^2}}\exp\frac{-Q}{2(1-\rho^2)}=\frac{1}{\sigma_x\sigma_y}g\left(\frac{x-m_x}{\sigma_x},\frac{y-m_y}{\sigma_y},\rho\right)$$

where

$$Q=\frac{(x-m_x)^2}{\sigma_x^2}-\frac{2\rho(x-m_x)(y-m_y)}{\sigma_x\sigma_y}+\frac{(y-m_y)^2}{\sigma_y^2}$$

Circular Normal Probability Density Function

26.3.13

$$\frac{1}{\sigma^2}g\left(\frac{x-m_x}{\sigma},\frac{y-m_y}{\sigma},0\right)=$$

$$\frac{1}{2\pi\sigma^2}\exp-\frac{(x-m_x)^2+(y-m_y)^2}{2\sigma^2}$$

Special Values of $L(h, k, \rho)$

26.3.14 $$L(h,k,0)=Q(h)Q(k)$$

26.3.15 $$L(h,k,-1)=0 \qquad (h+k\geq 0)$$

26.3.16 $$L(h,k,-1)=P(h)-Q(k) \qquad (h+k\leq 0)$$

26.3.17 $$L(h,k,1)=Q(h) \qquad (k\leq h)$$

26.3.18 $$L(h,k,1)=Q(k) \qquad (k\geq h)$$

26.3.19 $$L(0,0,\rho)=\frac{1}{4}+\frac{\arcsin \rho}{2\pi}$$

$L(h, k, \rho)$ as a Function of $L(h, 0, \rho)$

26.3.20
$$L(h,k,\rho)=L\left(h,0,\frac{(\rho h-k)(\operatorname{sgn} h)}{\sqrt{h^2-2\rho hk+k^2}}\right)+L\left(k,0,\frac{(\rho k-h)(\operatorname{sgn} k)}{\sqrt{h^2-2\rho hk+k^2}}\right)-\begin{cases}0 & \text{if } hk>0 \text{ or } hk=0 \text{ and } h+k\geq 0\\ \frac{1}{2} & \text{otherwise}\end{cases}$$

where sgn $h=1$ if $h\geq 0$ and sgn $h=-1$ if $h<0$.

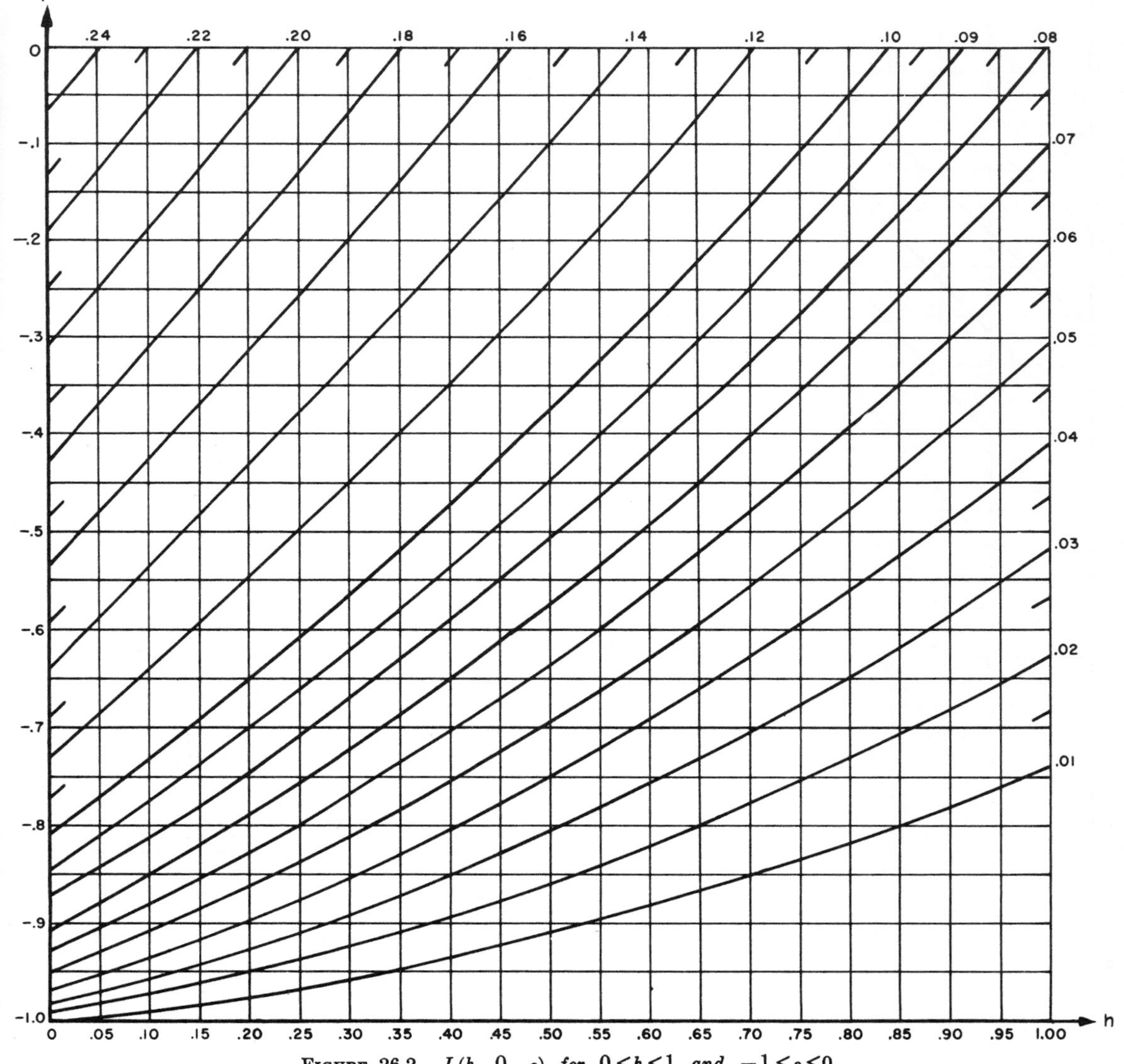

FIGURE 26.2. $L(h,\ 0,\ \rho)$ *for* $0\leq h\leq 1$ *and* $-1\leq\rho\leq 0$.

Values for $h<0$ can be obtained using $L(h,0,-\rho)=\frac{1}{2}-L(-h,0,\rho)$.

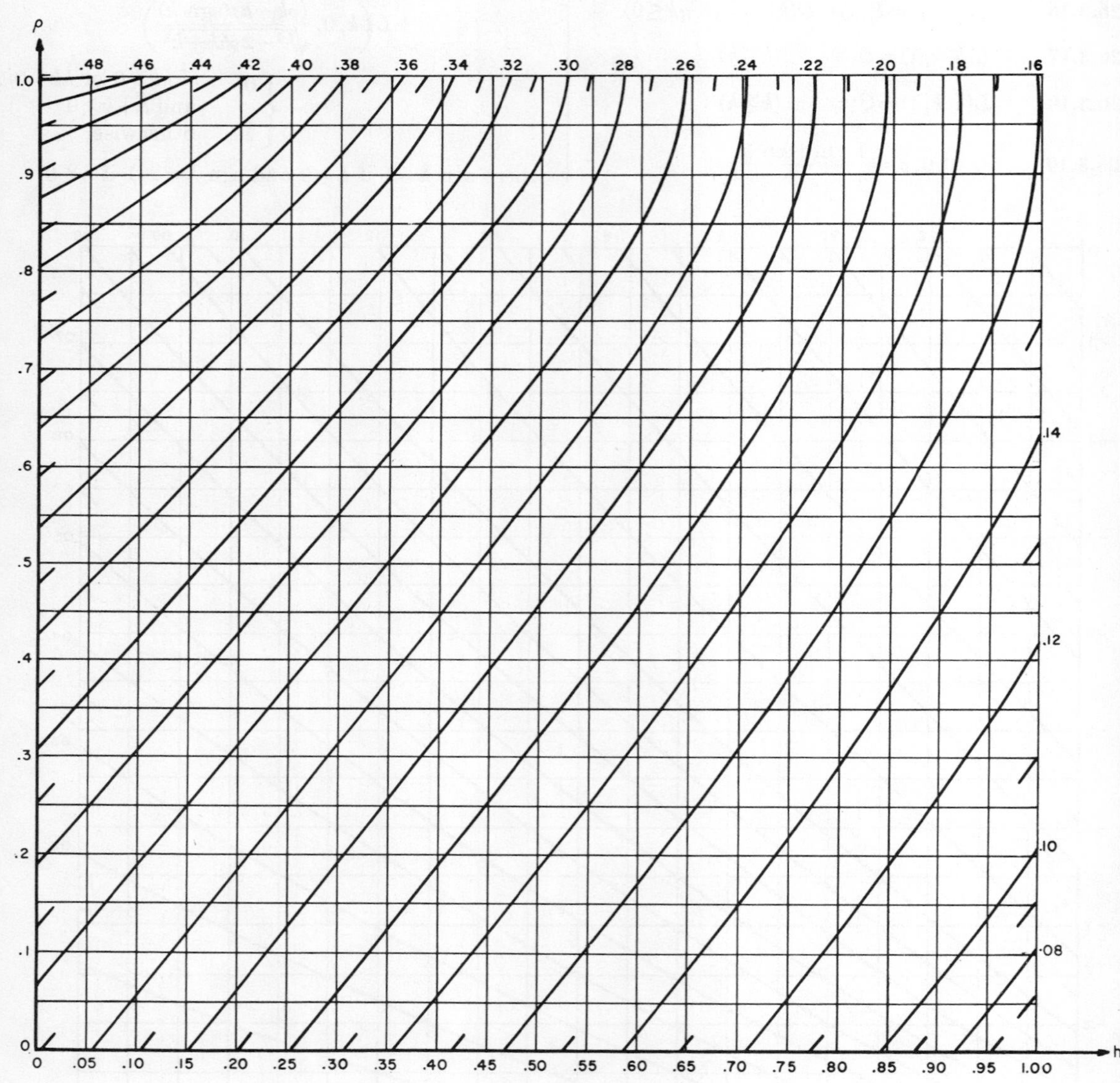

FIGURE 26.3. $L(h,\ 0,\ \rho)$ *for* $0 \leq h \leq 1$ *and* $0 \leq \rho \leq 1$.

Values for $h<0$ can be obtained using $L(h, 0, -\rho)=\frac{1}{2}-L(-h, 0, \rho)$.

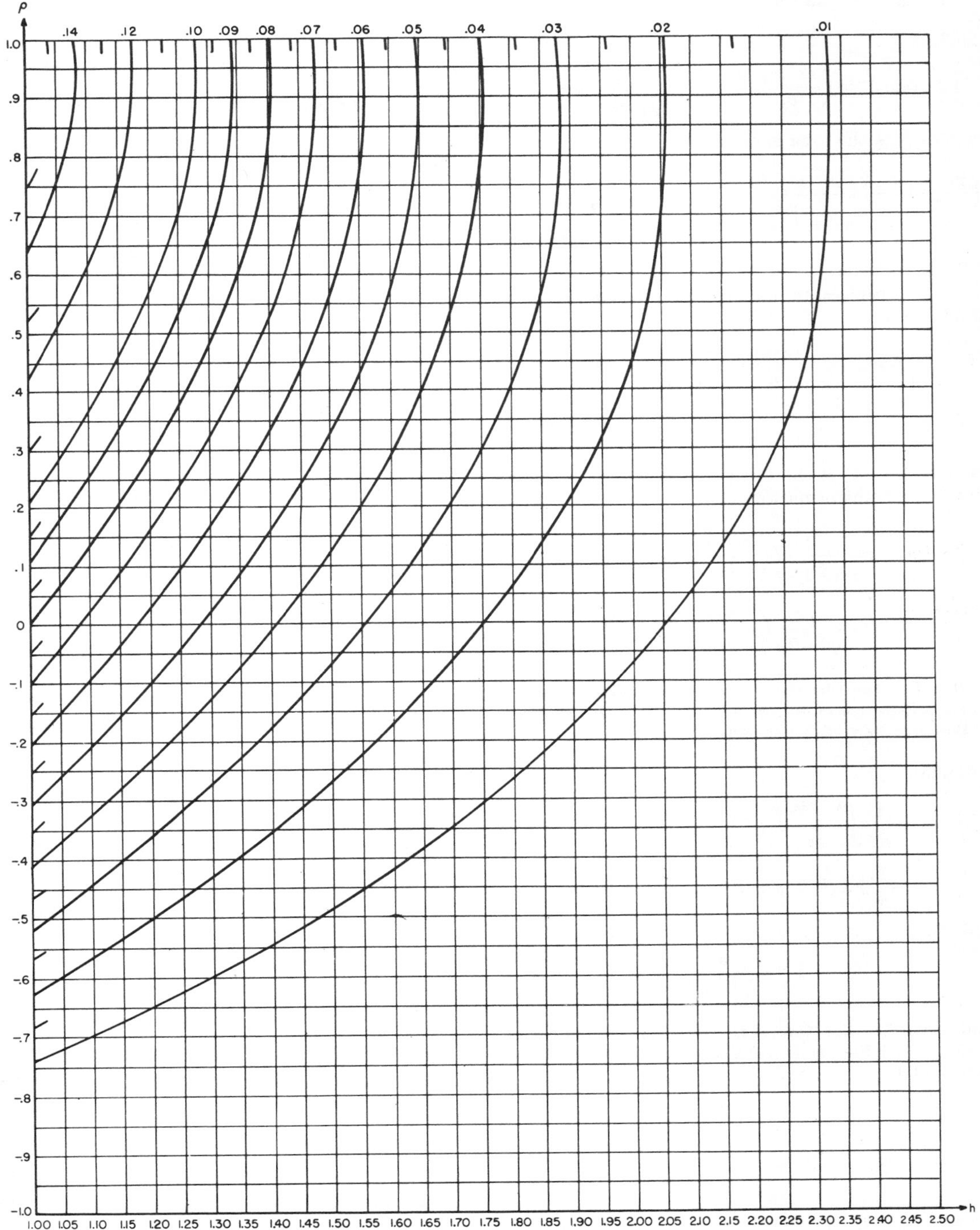

FIGURE 26.4. $L(h, 0, \rho)$ *for* $h \geq 1$ *and* $-1 \leq \rho \leq 1$.

Values for $h<0$ can be obtained using $L(h, 0, -\rho) = \frac{1}{2} - L(-h, 0, \rho)$.

Integral Over an Ellipse With Center at (m_x, m_y)

26.3.21

$$\iint_A (\sigma_x\sigma_y)^{-1} g\left(\frac{x-m_x}{\sigma_x}, \frac{y-m_y}{\sigma_y}, \rho\right) dxdy = 1-e^{-a^2/2}$$

where A is the area enclosed by the ellipse

$$\left(\frac{x-m_x}{\sigma_x}\right)^2 - \frac{2\rho(x-m_x)(y-m_y)}{\sigma_x\sigma_y} + \left(\frac{y-m_y}{\sigma_y}\right)^2 = a^2(1-\rho^2)$$

Integral Over an Arbitrary Region

26.3.22

$$\iint_{A(x,y)} (\sigma_x\sigma_y)^{-1} g\left(\frac{x-m_x}{\sigma_x}, \frac{y-m_y}{\sigma_y}, \rho\right) dxdy = \iint_{A^*(s,t)} g(s, t, o) dsdt$$

where $A^*(s, t)$ is the transformed region obtained from the transformation

$$s = \frac{1}{\sqrt{2+2\rho}}\left(\frac{x-m_x}{\sigma_x} + \frac{y-m_y}{\sigma_y}\right)$$

$$t = \frac{-1}{\sqrt{2-2\rho}}\left(\frac{x-m_x}{\sigma_x} - \frac{y-m_y}{\sigma_y}\right)$$

Integral of the Circular Normal Probability Function With Parameters $m_x=m_y=0$, $\sigma=1$ Over the Triangle Bounded by $y=0$, $y=ax$, $x=h$

26.3.23

$$V(h, ah) = \frac{1}{2\pi}\int_0^h \int_0^{ax} e^{-\frac{1}{2}(x^2+y^2)} dxdy$$

$$= \frac{1}{4} + L(h, 0, \rho) - L(0, 0, \rho) - \frac{1}{2} Q(h)$$

where

$$\rho = -\frac{a}{\sqrt{1+a^2}}$$

Integral of Circular Normal Distribution Over an Offset Circle With Radius $R\sigma$ and Center a Distance $r\sigma$ From (m_x, m_y)

26.3.24

$$\int_A\int \sigma^{-2} g\left(\frac{x-m_x}{\sigma}, \frac{y-m_y}{\sigma}, 0\right) dxdy = P(R^2|2, r^2)$$

where $P(R^2|2, r^2)$ is the c.d.f. of the non-central χ^2 distribution (see **26.4.25**) with $\nu=2$ degrees of freedom and noncentrality parameter r^2.

Approximation to $P(R^2|2, r^2)$

26.3.25

	Approximation	*Condition*
26.3.25	$\frac{2R^2}{4+R^2} \exp -\frac{2r^2}{4+R^2}$	$R<1$
26.3.26	$P(x_1)$	$R>1$
26.3.27	$P(x_2)$	$R>5$

$$x_1 = \frac{[R^2/(2+r^2)]^{1/3} - \left[1-\frac{2}{9}\frac{2+2r^2}{(2+r^2)^2}\right]}{\left[\frac{2}{9}\frac{2+2r^2}{(2+r^2)^2}\right]^{\frac{1}{2}}}$$

$$x_2 = R - \sqrt{r^2-1} \qquad R, r \text{ both large}$$

Inequality

26.3.28

$$Q(h) - \frac{1-\rho^2}{\rho h-k} Z(k)\left[Q\left(\frac{h-\rho k}{\sqrt{1-\rho^2}}\right)\right] < L(h, k, \rho) < Q(h)$$

where

$$\rho h - k > 0, \qquad 0<\rho<1.$$

Series Expansion

26.3.29

$$L(h, k, \rho) = Q(h)Q(k) + \sum_{n=0}^{\infty} \frac{Z^{(n)}(h)Z^{(n)}(k)}{(n+1)!} \rho^{n+1}$$

26.4. Chi-Square Probability Function

26.4.1

$$P(\chi^2|\nu) = \left[2^{\nu/2}\Gamma\left(\frac{\nu}{2}\right)\right]^{-1} \int_0^{\chi^2} (t)^{\frac{\nu}{2}-1} e^{-\frac{t}{2}} dt \qquad (0\leq\chi^2<\infty)$$

26.4.2

$$Q(\chi^2|\nu) = 1-P(\chi^2|\nu) \qquad (0\leq\chi^2<\infty)$$

$$= \left[2^{\nu/2}\Gamma\left(\frac{\nu}{2}\right)\right]^{-1} \int_{\chi^2}^{\infty} (t)^{\frac{\nu}{2}-1} e^{-\frac{t}{2}} dt$$

Relation to Normal Distribution

Let $X_1, X_2, \ldots, X_\nu$ be independent and identically distributed random variables each following a normal distribution with mean zero and unit variance. Then $X^2 = \sum_{i=1}^{\nu} X_i^2$ is said to follow the chi-square distribution with ν degrees of freedom and the probability that $X^2 \leq \chi^2$ is given by $P(\chi^2|\nu)$.

Cumulants

26.4.3 $\qquad \kappa_{n+1} = 2^n n!\nu \qquad (n=0, 1, \ldots)$

Series Expansions

26.4.4

$$Q(\chi^2|\nu)=2Q(\chi)+2Z(\chi)\sum_{r=1}^{\frac{\nu-1}{2}}\frac{\chi^{2r-1}}{1\cdot 3\cdot 5\ldots(2r-1)}$$

(ν odd) and $\chi=\sqrt{\chi^2}$

26.4.5

$$Q(\chi^2|\nu)=\sqrt{2\pi}Z(\chi)\left\{1+\sum_{r=1}^{\frac{\nu-2}{2}}\frac{\chi^{2r}}{2\cdot 4\ldots(2r)}\right\}$$

(ν even)

26.4.6

$$P(\chi^2|\nu)=\left(\frac{1}{2}\chi^2\right)^{\nu/2}\frac{e^{-\chi^2/2}}{\Gamma\left(\frac{\nu+2}{2}\right)}\left\{1+\sum_{r=1}^{\infty}\frac{\chi^{2r}}{(\nu+2)(\nu+4)\cdots(\nu+2r)}\right\}$$

26.4.7 $$P(\chi^2|\nu)=\frac{1}{\Gamma\left(\frac{\nu}{2}\right)}\sum_{n=0}^{\infty}\frac{(-1)^n(\chi^2/2)^{\frac{\nu}{2}+n}}{n!\left(\frac{\nu}{2}+n\right)}$$

Recurrence and Differential Relations

26.4.8 $$Q(\chi^2|\nu+2)=Q(\chi^2|\nu)+\frac{(\chi^2/2)^{\nu/2}e^{-\chi^2/2}}{\Gamma\left(\frac{\nu}{2}+1\right)}$$

26.4.9 $$\frac{\partial^m Q(\chi^2|\nu)}{\partial(\chi^2)^m}=\frac{1}{2^m}\sum_{j=0}^{m}\binom{m}{j}(-1)^{m+j}Q(\chi^2|\nu-2j)$$

Continued Fraction

26.4.10 $$^*Q(\chi^2|\nu)=\frac{(\chi^2)^{\nu/2}e^{-\chi^2/2}}{2^{\nu/2}\Gamma(\nu/2)}\left\{\frac{1}{\chi^2/2+}\,\frac{1-\nu/2}{1+}\,\frac{1}{\chi^2/2+}\,\frac{2-\nu/2}{1+}\,\frac{2}{\chi^2/2+}\cdots\right\}$$

Asymptotic Distribution for Large ν

26.4.11 $P(\chi^2|\nu)\sim P(x)$ where $x=\dfrac{\chi^2-\nu}{\sqrt{2\nu}}$

Asymptotic Expansions for Large χ^2

26.4.12

$$Q(\chi^2|\nu)\sim\frac{(\chi^2)^{\frac{\nu}{2}-1}e^{-\chi^2/2}}{2^{\nu/2}\Gamma(\nu/2)}\sum_{j=0}^{\infty}(-1)^j\frac{\Gamma\left(1-\frac{\nu}{2}+j\right)}{\Gamma\left(1-\frac{\nu}{2}\right)}\frac{2^{j+1}}{(\chi^2)^j}$$

Approximations to the Chi-Square Distribution for Large ν

26.4.13

	Approximation	*Condition*
$Q(\chi^2\vert\nu)\approx Q(x_1)$,	$x_1=\sqrt{2\chi^2}-\sqrt{2\nu-1}$	$(\nu>100)$

26.4.14

$$Q(\chi^2|\nu)\approx Q(x_2),\qquad x_2=\frac{(\chi^2/\nu)^{1/3}-\left(1-\frac{2}{9\nu}\right)}{\sqrt{2/9\nu}}\qquad(\nu>30)$$

26.4.15

$$Q(\chi^2|\nu)\approx Q(x_2+h_\nu),\qquad h_\nu=\frac{60}{\nu}h_{60}\qquad(\nu>30)$$

Values of h_{60}

x	h_{60}	x	h_{60}	x	h_{60}
−3.5	−.0118	−1.0	+.0006	+1.5	−.0005
−3.0	−.0067	−.5	.0006	2.0	+.0002
−2.5	−.0033	.0	+.0002	2.5	.0017
−2.0	−.0010	+.5	−.0003	3.0	.0043
−1.5	+.0001	1.0	−.0006	3.5	.0082

Approximations for the Inverse Function for Large ν

If $Q(\chi_p^2|\nu)=p$ and $Q(x_p)=1-P(x_p)=p$, then

	Approximation	*Condition*
26.4.16	$\chi_p^2\approx\frac{1}{2}\left\{x_p+\sqrt{2\nu-1}\right\}^2$	$(\nu>100)$
26.4.17	$\chi_p^2\approx\nu\left\{1-\frac{2}{9\nu}+x_p\sqrt{\frac{2}{9\nu}}\right\}^3$	$(\nu>30)$
26.4.18	$\chi_p^2\approx\nu\left\{1-\frac{2}{9\nu}+(x_p-h_\nu)\sqrt{\frac{2}{9\nu}}\right\}^3$	$(\nu>30)$

where h_ν is given by **26.4.15.**

Relation to Other Functions

26.4.19 Incomplete gamma function

$$\frac{\gamma(a,x)}{\Gamma(a)}=P(\chi^2|\nu),\qquad \nu=2a,\ \chi^2=2x$$

$$\frac{\Gamma(a,x)}{\Gamma(a)}=Q(\chi^2|\nu)$$

26.4.20 Pearson's incomplete gamma function

$$I(u,p)=\frac{1}{\Gamma(p+1)}\int_0^{u\sqrt{p+1}}t^pe^{-t}dt=P(\chi^2|\nu)$$

$$\nu=2(p+1),\ \chi^2=2u\sqrt{p+1}$$

26.4.21 Poisson distribution

$$Q(\chi^2|\nu)=\sum_{j=0}^{c-1}e^{-m}\frac{m^j}{j!},\qquad c=\frac{\nu}{2},\ m=\frac{\chi^2}{2},\ (\nu\text{ even})$$

$$Q(\chi^2|\nu)-Q(\chi^2|\nu-2)=e^{-m}\frac{m^{c-1}}{(c-1)!}$$

26.4.22 Pearson Type III

$$\left[\frac{ab}{e}\right]^{ab}\int_{-a}^{x}\left(1+\frac{t}{a}\right)^{ab}e^{-bt}dt=P(\chi^2|\nu)$$

$$\nu=2ab+2,\ \chi^2=2b(x+a)$$

26.4.23 Incomplete moments of Normal distribution

$$\int_0^x t^n Z(t)dt=\begin{cases}(n-1)!!\dfrac{P(\chi^2|\nu)}{2} & (n \text{ even})\\ \dfrac{(n-1)!!}{\sqrt{2\pi}}P(\chi^2|\nu) & (n \text{ odd})\end{cases}$$

$$\chi^2=x^2,\ \nu=n+1$$

26.4.24 Generalized Laguerre Polynomials

$$n!L_n^{(\alpha)}(x)=\frac{\sum_{j=0}^{n+1}(-1)^{n+j}\binom{n+1}{j}Q(\chi^2|\nu+2-2j)}{2^n[Q(\chi^2|\nu+2)-Q(\chi^2|\nu)]}$$

$$x=\chi^2/2,\ \alpha=\nu/2$$

Non-Central χ^2 Distribution Function

26.4.25

$$P(\chi'^2|\nu,\lambda)=\sum_{j=0}^{\infty}e^{-\lambda/2}\frac{(\lambda/2)^j}{j!}P(\chi'^2|\nu+2j)$$

where $\lambda\geq 0$ is termed the non-centrality parameter.

Relation of Non-Central χ^2 Distribution With $\nu=2$ to the Integral of Circular Normal Distribution ($\sigma^2=1$) Over an Offset Circle Having Radius R and Center a Distance $r=\sqrt{\lambda}$ From the Origin. (See **26.3.24–26.3.27.**)

26.4.26

$$\iint_A g(x,y,0)\,dxdy=P(\chi^2=R^2|\nu=2,\lambda)$$

$$=1-\sum_{j=0}^{\infty}\frac{e^{-\lambda/2}\lambda^j}{2^j j!}Q(R^2|2+2j)$$

Approximations to the Non-Central χ^2 Distribution

$$a=\nu+\lambda\qquad b=\frac{\lambda}{\nu+\lambda}$$

	Approximating Function	*Approximation*	
26.4.27	χ^2 distribution	$P(\chi'^2\|\nu,\lambda)\approx P\left(\frac{\chi^2}{1+b}\middle\|\nu^*\right)$,	$\nu^*=\frac{a}{1+b}$
26.4.28	Normal distribution	$P(\chi'^2\|\nu,\lambda)\approx P(x)$,	$x=\frac{(\chi'^2/a)^{1/3}-\left[1-\frac{2}{9}\left(\frac{1+b}{a}\right)\right]}{\sqrt{\frac{2}{9}\left(\frac{1+b}{a}\right)}}$
26.4.29	Normal distribution	$P(\chi'^2\|\nu,\lambda)\approx P(x)$,	$x=\left[\frac{2\chi'^2}{1+b}\right]^{\frac{1}{2}}-\left[\frac{2a}{1+b}-1\right]^{\frac{1}{2}}$

Approximations to the Inverse Function of Non-Central χ^2 Distribution

If $Q(\chi_p'^2|\nu,\lambda)=p$, $Q(\chi_p^2|\nu^*)=p$, and $Q(x_p)=p$ then

	Approximating Variable	*Approximation to the Inverse Function*
26.4.30	χ^2	$\chi_p'^2\approx(1+b)\chi_p^2$
26.4.31	Normal	$\chi_p'^2\approx\frac{1+b}{2}\left[x_p+\sqrt{\frac{2a}{1+b}-1}\right]^2$
26.4.32	Normal	$\chi_p'^2\approx a\left[x_p\sqrt{\frac{2}{9}\left(\frac{1+b}{a}\right)}+1-\frac{2}{9}\left(\frac{1+b}{a}\right)\right]^3$

Properties of Chi-Square, Non-Central Chi-Square, and Related Quantities

$$a=\nu+\lambda \qquad b=\frac{\lambda}{\nu+\lambda}$$

$$\psi(z)=\frac{d}{dz}\ln\Gamma(z), \qquad \psi^{(n)}(z)=\frac{d^n}{dz^n}\psi(z)$$

	Variable	Mean	Variance	Coefficient of skewness (γ_1)	Coefficient of excess (γ_2)
26.4.33	χ^2	ν	2ν	$\frac{2^{3/2}}{\sqrt{\nu}}$	$12\nu^{-1}$
26.4.34	$\sqrt{2\chi^2}$	$(2\nu-1)^{\frac{1}{2}}\{1+[16\nu(\nu-1)]^{-1}\}+O(\nu^{-7/2})$	$1-\frac{1}{4\nu}-\frac{1}{8\nu^2}+\frac{5}{64\nu^3}-O(\nu^{-4})$	$\frac{1}{\sqrt{2\nu}}\left[1+\frac{5}{8\nu}-\frac{1}{128\nu^2}\right]+O(\nu^{-7/2})$	$\frac{3}{2^3}\frac{1}{\nu^2}\left[1+\frac{3}{2\nu}\right]+O(\nu^{-4})$
26.4.35	$(\chi^2/\nu)^{1/3}$	$1-\frac{2}{3^2\nu}+\frac{80}{3^7\nu^3}+O(\nu^{-4})$	$\frac{2}{3^2\nu}-\frac{104}{3^7\nu^3}+O(\nu^{-4})$	$\frac{2^{7/2}}{3^3\nu^{3/2}}\left[1+\frac{8}{3^2\nu}\right]+O(\nu^{-7/2})$	$-\frac{4}{9\nu}\left[1+\frac{16}{9\nu}\right]+O(\nu^{-3})$
26.4.36	$\ln(\chi^2/\nu)$	$\psi\left(\frac{\nu}{2}\right)-\ln\left(\frac{\nu}{2}\right)=-\frac{1}{\nu}-\frac{1}{3\nu^2}+O(\nu^{-4})$	$\psi'\left(\frac{\nu}{2}\right)=\frac{2}{\nu-1}\left[1-\frac{1}{3(\nu-1)^2}\right]+O((\nu-1)^{-5})$	$\frac{\psi''\left(\frac{\nu}{2}\right)}{\psi'\left(\frac{\nu}{2}\right)^{3/2}}=-\sqrt{\frac{2}{\nu-1}}\left[1-\frac{1}{2(\nu-1)^2}\right]+O((\nu-1)^{-9/2})$	$\frac{\psi^{(3)}\left(\frac{\nu}{2}\right)}{\psi'\left(\frac{\nu}{2}\right)^2}=\frac{4}{\nu-1}\left[1+\frac{4}{3(\nu-1)^2}\right]+O((\nu-1)^{-5})$
26.4.37	χ'^2	a	$2a(1+b)$	$\left(\frac{2}{1+b}\right)^{3/2}(1+2b)a^{-\frac{1}{2}}$	$\frac{12}{a}\frac{(1+3b)}{(1+b)^2}$
26.4.38	$\sqrt{2\chi'^2}$	$[2a-(1+b)]^{\frac{1}{2}}+O(a^{-3/2})$	$(1+b)-\frac{a^{-1}}{4}[8b+(1+b)(1-7b)]+O(a^{-2})$	$\frac{a^{-\frac{1}{2}}(1-b)(1+3b)}{2^{\frac{1}{2}}(1+b)^{3/2}}+O(a^{-1})$	$\frac{3b(b+2)}{(1+b)^2}+O(a^{-2})$
26.4.39	$(\chi'^2/a)^{1/3}$	$1-\frac{2}{3^2}\frac{1+b}{a}-\frac{40}{3^4}\frac{b^2}{a^2}+O(a^{-3})$	$\frac{2}{9}a^{-1}(1+b)+\frac{16}{27}a^{-2}b^2+O(a^{-3})$	$\left(\frac{2}{1+b}\right)^{3/2}b^2a^{-\frac{1}{2}}+O(a^{-3/2})$	$-\frac{4}{3^3}\frac{(1+3b+12b^2-44b^3)}{a(1+b)^3}-O(a^{-2})$

26.5. Incomplete Beta Function

26.5.1

$$I_x(a,b)=\frac{1}{B(a,b)}\int_0^x t^{a-1}(1-t)^{b-1}dt \qquad (0\leq x\leq 1)$$

26.5.2

$$I_x(a,b)=1-I_{1-x}(b,a)$$

Relation to the Chi-Square Distribution

If X_1^2 and X_2^2 are independent random variables following chi-square distributions **26.4.1** with ν_1 and ν_2 degrees of freedom respectively, then $\frac{X_1^2}{X_1^2+X_2^2}$ is said to follow a beta distribution with ν_1 and ν_2 degrees of freedom and has the distribution function

26.5.3

$$P\left\{\frac{X_1^2}{X_1^2+X_2^2}\leq x\right\}=\frac{1}{B(a,b)}\int_0^x t^{a-1}(1-t)^{b-1}dt$$
$$=I_x(a,b) \qquad a=\frac{\nu_1}{2},\ b=\frac{\nu_2}{2}$$

Series Expansions ($0<x<1$)

26.5.4

$$I_x(a,b)=\frac{x^a(1-x)^b}{aB(a,b)}\left\{1+\sum_{n=0}^{\infty}\frac{B(a+1,n+1)}{B(a+b,n+1)}x^{n+1}\right\}$$

26.5.5

$$I_x(a,b)=\frac{x^a(1-x)^{b-1}}{aB(a,b)}\left\{1+\sum_{n=0}^{\infty}\frac{B(a+1,n+1)}{B(b-n-1,n+1)}\left(\frac{x}{1-x}\right)^{n+1}\right\}$$
$$=\frac{x^a(1-x)^{b-1}}{aB(a,b)}\left\{1+\sum_{n=0}^{s-2}\frac{B(a+1,n+1)}{B(b-n-1,n+1)}\left(\frac{x}{1-x}\right)^{n+1}\right\}+I_x(a+s,b-s)$$

26.5.6

$$1-I_x(a,b)=I_{1-x}(b,a)$$
$$=\frac{(1-x)^b}{B(a,b)}\sum_{i=0}^{a-1}(-1)^i\binom{a-1}{i}\frac{(1-x)^i}{b+i} \quad \text{(integer a)}$$

26.5.7

$$1-I_x(a,b)=I_{1-x}(b,a)$$
$$=(1-x)^{a+b-1}\sum_{i=0}^{a-1}\binom{a+b-1}{i}\left(\frac{x}{1-x}\right)^i \quad \text{(integer a)}$$

Continued Fractions

26.5.8

$$I_x(a,b)=\frac{x^a(1-x)^b}{aB(a,b)}\left\{\frac{1}{1+}\frac{d_1}{1+}\frac{d_2}{1+}\cdots\right\}$$

$$d_{2m+1}=-\frac{(a+m)(a+b+m)}{(a+2m)(a+2m+1)}x$$

$$d_{2m}=\frac{m(b-m)}{(a+2m-1)(a+2m)}x$$

Best results are obtained when $x<\frac{a-1}{a+b-2}$. Also the $4m$ and $4m+1$ convergents are less than $I_x(a,b)$ and the $4m+2$, $4m+3$ convergents are greater than $I_x(a,b)$.

26.5.9

$$I_x(a,b)=\frac{x^a(1-x)^{b-1}}{aB(a,b)}\left[\frac{e_1}{1+}\frac{e_2}{1+}\frac{e_3}{1+}\cdots\right]$$

$$x<1 \qquad e_1=1$$

$$e_{2m}=-\frac{(a+m-1)(b-m)}{(a+2m-2)(a+2m-1)}\frac{x}{1-x}$$

$$e_{2m+1}=\frac{m(a+b-1+m)}{(a+2m-1)(a+2m)}\frac{x}{1-x}$$

Recurrence Relations

26.5.10

$$I_x(a,b)=xI_x(a-1,b)+(1-x)I_x(a,b-1)$$

26.5.11

$$I_x(a,b)=\frac{1}{x}\{I_x(a+1,b)-(1-x)I_x(a+1,b-1)\}$$

26.5.12

$$\left[I_x(a,b)=\right]\frac{1}{a(1-x)+b}\{bI_x(a,b+1)+a(1-x)I_x(a+1,b-1)\}$$

26.5.13

$$I_x(a,b)=\frac{1}{a+b}\{aI_x(a+1,b)+bI_x(a,b+1)\}$$

26.5.14

$$I_x(a,a)=\frac{1}{2}I_{1-x'}\left(a,\frac{1}{2}\right), \qquad x'=4\left(x-\frac{1}{2}\right)^2\left[,\ x\leq\frac{1}{2}^*\right]$$

26.5.15

$$I_x(a,b)=\frac{\Gamma(a+b)}{\Gamma(a+1)\Gamma(b)}x^a(1-x)^{b-1}+I_x(a+1,b-1)$$

26.5.16

$$I_x(a,b)=\frac{\Gamma(a+b)}{\Gamma(a+1)\Gamma(b)}x^a(1-x)^b+I_x(a+1,b)$$

Asymptotic Expansions

26.5.17

$$1-I_x(a,b)=I_{1-x}(b,a)\sim\frac{\Gamma(b,y)}{\Gamma(b)}$$
$$-\frac{1}{24N^2}\left\{\frac{y^be^{-y}}{(b-2)!}(b+1+y)\right\}$$
$$+\frac{1}{5760N^4}\left\{\frac{y^be^{-y}}{(b-2)!}[(b-3)(b-2)(5b+7)(b+1+y)-(5b-7)(b+3+y)y^2]\right\}$$
$$y=-N\ln x,\qquad N=a+\frac{b}{2}-\frac{1}{2}$$

26.5.18

$$I_x(a,b)\sim\frac{\Gamma(a,w)}{\Gamma(a)}+\frac{e^{-w}w^a}{\Gamma(a)}\left\{\frac{(a-1-w)}{2b}+\frac{1}{(2b)^2}\left(\frac{a^3}{2}-\frac{5}{3}a^2+\frac{3}{2}a-\frac{1}{3}-w\left[\frac{3}{2}a^2-\frac{11}{6}a+\frac{1}{3}\right]+w^2\left(\frac{3}{2}a-\frac{1}{6}\right)-\frac{1}{2}w^3\right)\right\}$$
$$w=b\left(\frac{x}{1-x}\right)$$

26.5.19

$$I_x(a,b)\sim P(y)-Z(y)\left[a_1+\frac{a_2(y-a_1)}{1+a_2}+\frac{a_3(1+y^2/2)}{1+a_2}+\cdots\right]$$
$$a_1=\frac{2}{3}(b-a)[(a+b-2)(a-1)(b-1)]^{-1/2}$$
$$a_2=\frac{1}{12}\left[\frac{1}{a-1}+\frac{1}{b-1}-\frac{13}{a+b-1}\right]$$
$$a_3=-\frac{8}{15}\left[a_1\left(a_2+\frac{3}{a+b-2}\right)\right]$$
$$y^2=2\left[(a+b-1)\ln\frac{a+b-1}{a+b-2}+(a-1)\ln\frac{a-1}{(a+b-1)x}+(b-1)\ln\frac{b-1}{(a+b-1)(1-x)}\right]$$

and y is taken negative when $x<\dfrac{a-1}{a+b-2}$

Approximations

26.5.20 If $(a+b-1)(1-x)\leq.8$

$$I_x(a,b)=Q(\chi^2|\nu)+\epsilon,$$
$$|\epsilon|<5\times10^{-3}\text{ if }a+b>6$$
$$\chi^2=(a+b-1)(1-x)(3-x)-(1-x)(b-1),$$
$$\nu=2b$$

26.5.21 If $(a+b-1)(1-x)\geq.8$

$$I_x(a,b)=P(y)+\epsilon,$$
$$|\epsilon|<5\times10^{-3}\text{ if }a+b>6$$
$$y=\frac{3\left[w_1\left(1-\frac{1}{9b}\right)-w_2\left(1-\frac{1}{9a}\right)\right]}{\left[\frac{w_1^2}{b}+\frac{w_2^2}{a}\right]^{\frac{1}{2}}},$$
$$w_1=(bx)^{1/3},\quad w_2=[a(1-x)]^{1/3}$$

Approximation to the Inverse Function

26.5.22 If $I_{x_p}(a,b)=p$ and $Q(y_p)=p$ then

$$x_p\approx\frac{a}{a+be^{2w}}$$
$$w=\frac{y_p(h+\lambda)^{\frac{1}{2}}}{h}-\left(\frac{1}{2b-1}-\frac{1}{2a-1}\right)\left(\lambda+\frac{5}{6}-\frac{2}{3h}\right)$$
$$h=2\left(\frac{1}{2a-1}+\frac{1}{2b-1}\right)^{-1},\qquad\lambda=\frac{y_p^2-3}{6}$$

Relations to Other Functions and Distributions

	Function	*Relation*
26.5.23	Hypergeometric function	$\frac{1}{B(a,b)}\frac{x^a}{a}F(a,1-b;a+1;x)=I_x(a,b)$
26.5.24	Binomial distribution	$\sum_{s=a}^{n}\binom{n}{s}p^s(1-p)^{n-s}=I_p(a,n-a+1)$
26.5.25	"	$\binom{n}{a}p^a(1-p)^{n-a}=I_p(a,n-a+1)-I_p(a+1,n-a)$
26.5.26	Negative binomial distribution	$\sum_{s=a}^{n}\binom{n+s-1}{s}p^nq^s=I_q(a,n)$
26.5.27	Student's distribution	$\frac{1}{2}[1-A(t\vert\nu)]=\frac{1}{2}I_x\left(\frac{\nu}{2},\frac{1}{2}\right),\quad x=\frac{\nu}{\nu+t^2}$
26.5.28	F-(variance-ratio) distribution	$Q(F\vert\nu_1,\nu_2)=I_x\left(\frac{\nu_2}{2},\frac{\nu_1}{2}\right),\quad x=\frac{\nu_2}{\nu_2+\nu_1F}$

26.6. F-(Variance-Ratio) Distribution Function

26.6.1

$$P(F|\nu_1,\nu_2)=\frac{\nu_1^{\frac{1}{2}\nu_1}\nu_2^{\frac{1}{2}\nu_2}}{B\left(\frac{1}{2}\nu_1,\frac{1}{2}\nu_2\right)}\int_0^F t^{\frac{1}{2}(\nu_1-2)}(\nu_2+\nu_1 t)^{-\frac{1}{2}(\nu_1+\nu_2)}dt \qquad (F\geq 0)$$

26.6.2

$$Q(F|\nu_1,\nu_2)=1-P(F|\nu_1,\nu_2)=I_x\left(\frac{\nu_2}{2},\frac{\nu_1}{2}\right)$$

where

$$x=\frac{\nu_2}{\nu_2+\nu_1 F}$$

Relation to the Chi-Square Distribution

If X_1^2 and X_2^2 are independent random variables following chi-square distributions **26.4.1** with ν_1 and ν_2 degrees of freedom respectively, then the distribution of $F=\frac{X_1^2/\nu_1}{X_2^2/\nu_2}$ is said to follow the variance ratio or F-distribution with ν_1 and ν_2 degrees of freedom. The corresponding distribution function is $P(F|\nu_1,\nu_2)$.

Statistical Properties

26.6.3

mean: $$m=\frac{\nu_2}{\nu_2-2} \qquad (\nu_2>2)$$

variance: $$\sigma^2=\frac{2\nu_2^2(\nu_1+\nu_2-2)}{\nu_1(\nu_2-2)^2(\nu_2-4)} \qquad (\nu_2>4)$$

third central moment:

$$\mu_3=\left(\frac{\nu_2}{\nu_1}\right)^3\frac{8\nu_1(\nu_1+\nu_2-2)(2\nu_1+\nu_2-2)}{(\nu_2-2)^3(\nu_2-4)(\nu_2-6)} \qquad (\nu_2>6)$$

moments about the origin:

$$\mu_n'=\left(\frac{\nu_2}{\nu_1}\right)^n\frac{\Gamma\left(\frac{\nu_1+2n}{2}\right)}{\Gamma\left(\frac{\nu_1}{2}\right)}\frac{\Gamma\left(\frac{\nu_1-2n}{2}\right)}{\Gamma\left(\frac{\nu_2}{2}\right)} \qquad (\nu_2>2n)$$

characteristic function:

$$\phi(t)=E(e^{iFt})=M\left(\frac{\nu_1}{2},-\frac{\nu_2}{2},-\frac{\nu_2}{\nu_1}it\right)$$

Series Expansions

$$x=\frac{\nu_2}{\nu_2+\nu_1 F}$$

26.6.4

$$Q(F|\nu_1,\nu_2)=x^{\nu_2/2}\left[1+\frac{\nu_2}{2}(1-x)+\frac{\nu_2(\nu_2+2)}{2\cdot 4}(1-x)^2+\ldots+\frac{\nu_2(\nu_2+2)\ldots(\nu_2+\nu_1-4)}{2\cdot 4\ldots(\nu_1-2)}(1-x)^{\frac{\nu_1-2}{2}}\right] \qquad (\nu_1 \text{ even})$$

26.6.5

$$Q(F|\nu_1,\nu_2)=1-(1-x)^{\nu_1/2}\left[1+\frac{\nu_1}{2}x+\frac{\nu_1(\nu_1+2)}{2\cdot 4}x^2+\ldots+\frac{\nu_1(\nu_1+2)\ldots(\nu_2+\nu_1-4)}{2\cdot 4\ldots(\nu_2-2)}x^{\frac{\nu_2-2}{2}}\right] \qquad (\nu_2 \text{ even})$$

26.6.6

$$Q(F|\nu_1,\nu_2)=x^{\frac{\nu_1+\nu_2-2}{2}}\left[1+\frac{\nu_1+\nu_2-2}{2}\left(\frac{1-x}{x}\right)+\frac{(\nu_1+\nu_2-2)(\nu_1+\nu_2-4)}{2\cdot 4}\left(\frac{1-x}{x}\right)^2+\ldots+\frac{(\nu_1+\nu_2-2)\ldots(\nu_2+2)}{2\cdot 4\ldots(\nu_1-2)}\left(\frac{1-x}{x}\right)^{\frac{\nu_1-2}{2}}\right] \qquad (\nu_1 \text{ even})$$

26.6.7

$$Q(F|\nu_1,\nu_2)=1-(1-x)^{\frac{\nu_1+\nu_2-2}{2}}\left[1+\frac{\nu_1+\nu_2-2}{2}\left(\frac{x}{1-x}\right)+\ldots+\frac{(\nu_1+\nu_2-2)\ldots(\nu_1+2)}{2\cdot 4\ldots(\nu_2-2)}\left(\frac{x}{1-x}\right)^{\frac{\nu_2-2}{2}}\right] \qquad (\nu_2 \text{ even})$$

26.6.8

$$Q(F|\nu_1,\nu_2)=1-A(t|\nu_2)+\beta(\nu_1,\nu_2) \qquad (\nu_1,\nu_2 \text{ odd})$$

$$A(t|\nu_2)=\begin{cases}\frac{2}{\pi}\left\{\theta+\sin\theta\left[\cos\theta+\frac{2}{3}\cos^3\theta+\ldots+\frac{2\cdot 4\ldots(\nu_2-3)}{3.5\ldots(\nu_2-2)}\cos^{\nu_2-2}\theta\right]\right\} & \text{for } \nu_2>1\\ \frac{2\theta}{\pi} & \text{for } \nu_2=1\end{cases}$$

$$\beta(\nu_1,\nu_2)=\begin{cases}\frac{2}{\sqrt{\pi}}\frac{\left(\frac{\nu_2-1}{2}\right)!}{\left(\frac{\nu_2-2}{2}\right)!}\sin\theta\cos^{\nu_2}\theta\left\{1+\frac{\nu_2+1}{3}\sin^2\theta+\cdots+\frac{(\nu_2+1)(\nu_2+3)\ldots(\nu_1+\nu_2-4)}{3\cdot 5\ldots(\nu_1-2)}\sin^{\nu_1-3}\theta\right\} & \text{for } \nu_2>1\\ 0 & \text{for } \nu_1=1\end{cases}$$

where

$$\theta=\arctan\sqrt{\frac{\nu_1}{\nu_2}F}$$

Reflexive Relation

If $F_p(\nu_1,\nu_2)$ and $F_{1-p}(\nu_2,\nu_1)$ satisfy

$$Q(F_p(\nu_1,\nu_2)|\nu_1,\nu_2)=p$$

$$Q(F_{1-p}(\nu_2,\nu_1)|\nu_2,\nu_1)=1-p$$

26.6.9 then

$$F_p(\nu_1, \nu_2) = \frac{1}{F_{1-p}(\nu_2, \nu_1)}$$

Relation to Student's *t*-Distribution Function (See **26.7**)

26.6.10 $Q(F|\nu_1=1, \nu_2) = 1 - A(t|\nu_2) \qquad t = \sqrt{F}$

Limiting Forms

26.6.11

$$\lim_{\nu_2\to\infty} Q(F|\nu_1, \nu_2) = Q(\chi^2|\nu_1), \qquad \chi^2 = \nu_1 F$$

26.6.12

$$\lim_{\nu_1\to\infty} Q(F|\nu_1, \nu_2) = P(\chi^2|\nu_2), \qquad \chi^2 = \frac{\nu_2}{F}$$

Approximations

26.6.13

$$Q(F|\nu_1, \nu_2) \approx Q(x), \quad (\nu_1 \text{ and } \nu_2 \text{ large}) \qquad x = \frac{F - \frac{\nu_2}{\nu_2 - 2}}{\frac{\nu_2}{\nu_2 - 2}\sqrt{\frac{2(\nu_1+\nu_2-2)}{\nu_1(\nu_2-4)}}}$$

26.6.14

$$Q(F|\nu_1, \nu_2) \approx Q(x), \qquad x = \frac{\sqrt{(2\nu_2-1)\frac{\nu_1}{\nu_2}F} - \sqrt{2\nu_1 - 1}}{\sqrt{1+\frac{\nu_1}{\nu_2}F}}$$

26.6.15

$$Q(F|\nu_1, \nu_2) \approx Q(x), \qquad x = \frac{F^{1/3}\left(1-\frac{2}{9\nu_2}\right) - \left(1-\frac{2}{9\nu_1}\right)}{\sqrt{\frac{2}{9\nu_1} + F^{2/3}\frac{2}{9\nu_2}}}$$

Approximation to the Inverse Function

26.6.16 If $Q(F_p|\nu_1, \nu_2) = p$, then

$F_p \approx e^{2w}$ where w is given by **26.5.22**, with

$\nu_1 = 2b, \; \nu_2 = 2a$

Non-Central *F*-Distribution Function

26.6.17

$$P(F'|\nu_1, \nu_2, \lambda) = \int_0^{F'} p(t|\nu_1, \nu_2, \lambda)dt = 1 - Q(F'|\nu_1, \nu_2, \lambda)$$

where

$$p(t|\nu_1, \nu_2, \lambda) = \sum_{j=0}^{\infty} e^{-\lambda/2}\frac{(\lambda/2)^j}{j!}\frac{(\nu_1+2j)^{\frac{\nu_1+2j}{2}}\nu_2^{\nu_2/2}}{B\left(\frac{\nu_1+2j}{2}, \frac{\nu_2}{2}\right)} \times t^{\frac{\nu_1+2j-2}{2}}[\nu_2 + (\nu_1+2j)t]^{-(\nu_1+2j+\nu_2)/2}$$

and $\lambda \geq 0$ is termed the non-centrality parameter.

Relation of Non-Central *F*-Distribution Function to Other Functions

	Function	*Relation*
26.6.18	*F*-distribution	$P(F'\|\nu_1, \nu_2, \lambda) = \sum_{j=0}^{\infty} e^{-\lambda/2}\frac{(\lambda/2)^j}{j!}P(F'\|\nu_1+2j, \nu_2)$ $P(F'\|\nu_1, \nu_2, \lambda=0) = P(F'\|\nu_1, \nu_2)$
26.6.19	Non-central *t*-distribution	$P(F'\|\nu_1=1, \nu_2, \lambda) = P(t'\|\nu, \delta), \; t' = \sqrt{F'}, \; \nu = \nu_2, \; \delta = \sqrt{\lambda}$
26.6.20	Incomplete Beta function	$P(F'\|\nu_1, \nu_2) = \sum_{j=0}^{\infty} e^{-\lambda/2}\frac{(\lambda/2)^j}{j!}I_x\left(\frac{\nu_1}{2}+j, \frac{\nu_2}{2}\right),$ $x = \frac{\nu_1 F'}{\nu_1 F' + \nu_2}$
26.6.21	Confluent hypergeometric function	$P(F'\|\nu_1, \nu_2, \lambda) = \sum_{i=0}^{\frac{\nu_2}{2}-1}\frac{2e^{-\lambda/2}}{(\nu_1+\nu_2)B\left(\frac{\nu_1}{2}+i+1, \frac{\nu_2}{2}-i\right)} \times$ $x^{\frac{\nu_1}{2}+1}(1-x)^{\frac{\nu_2}{2}-i-1}M\left(\frac{\nu_1+\nu_2}{2}, \frac{\nu_1}{2}+i+1, \frac{\lambda x}{2}\right)$ $\left(\nu_2 \text{ even and } x = \frac{\nu_2}{\nu_1 F' + \nu_2}\right)$

Series Expansion

26.6.22

$$P(F'|\nu_1,\nu_2,\lambda)=e^{-\frac{\lambda}{2}(1-x)}\,x^{\frac{1}{2}(\nu_1+\nu_2-2)}\sum_{i=0}^{\frac{\nu_2}{2}-1}T_i\qquad(\nu_2\text{ even})$$

where

$$T_0=1$$

$$T_1=\frac{1}{2}(\nu_1+\nu_2-2+\lambda x)\frac{1-x}{x}$$

$$T_i=\frac{1-x}{2i}[(\nu_1+\nu_2-2i+\lambda x)T_{i-1}+\lambda(1-x)T_{i-2}]$$

$$x=\frac{\nu_2}{\nu_1F'+\nu_2}$$

Limiting Forms

26.6.23

$$\lim_{\nu_2\to\infty}P(F'|\nu_1,\nu_2,\lambda)=P(\chi'^2|\nu,\lambda),\qquad \chi'^2=\nu_1F',\ \nu=\nu_1$$

26.6.24

$$\lim_{\nu_1\to\infty}P(F'|\nu_1,\nu_2,\lambda)=Q(\chi^2|\nu),\qquad \chi^2=\frac{\nu_2(1+c^2)}{F'}$$

where $\lambda/\nu_1\to c^2$ as $\nu_1\to\infty$.

Approximations to the Non-Central *F*-Distribution

26.6.25 $P(F'|\nu_1,\nu_2,\lambda)\approx P(x_1)$, $\qquad(\nu_1$ and ν_2 large)

where

$$x_1=\frac{F'-\frac{\nu_2(\nu_1+\lambda)}{\nu_1(\nu_2-2)}}{\frac{\nu_2}{\nu_1}\left[\frac{2}{(\nu_2-2)(\nu_2-4)}\left\{\frac{(\nu_1+\lambda)^2}{\nu_2-2}+\nu_1+2\lambda\right\}\right]^{\frac{1}{2}}}$$

26.6.26

$$P(F'|\nu_1,\nu_2,\lambda)\approx P(F|\nu_1^*,\nu_2),$$

$$F=\frac{\nu_1}{\nu_1+\lambda}F',\ \nu_1^*=\frac{(\nu_1+\lambda)^2}{\nu_1+2\lambda}$$

26.6.27

$$P(F'|\nu_1,\nu_2,\lambda)\approx P(x_2),$$

$$x_2=\frac{\left[\frac{\nu_1F'}{(\nu_1+\lambda)}\right]^{1/3}\left[1-\frac{2}{9\nu_2}\right]-\left[1-\frac{2(\nu_1+2\lambda)}{9(\nu_1+\lambda)^2}\right]}{\left[\frac{2}{9}\frac{\nu_1+2\lambda}{(\nu_1+\lambda)^2}+\frac{2}{9\nu_2}\left(\frac{\nu_1}{\nu_1+\lambda}F'\right)^{2/3}\right]^{\frac{1}{2}}}$$

26.7. Student's *t*-Distribution

If X is a random variable following a normal distribution with mean zero and variance unity, and χ^2 is a random variable following an independent chi-square distribution with ν degrees of freedom, then the distribution of the ratio $\frac{X}{\sqrt{\chi^2/\nu}}$ is called Student's t-distribution with ν degrees of freedom. The probability that $\frac{X}{\sqrt{\chi^2/\nu}}$ will be less in absolute value than a fixed constant t is

26.7.1

$$A(t|\nu)=P_r\left\{\left|\frac{X}{\sqrt{\chi^2/\nu}}\right|\leq t\right\}$$

$$=\left[\sqrt{\nu}B\left(\frac{1}{2},\frac{\nu}{2}\right)\right]^{-1}\int_{-t}^{t}\left(1+\frac{x^2}{\nu}\right)^{-\frac{\nu+1}{2}}dx$$

$$=1-I_x\left(\frac{\nu}{2},\frac{1}{2}\right),\qquad(0\leq t<\infty)$$

where

$$x=\frac{\nu}{\nu+t^2}$$

Statistical Properties

26.7.2

mean: $\quad m=0$

variance: $\quad\sigma^2=\frac{\nu}{\nu-2}\qquad(\nu>2)$

skewness: $\quad\gamma_1=0$

excess: $\quad\gamma_2=\frac{6}{\nu-4}\qquad(\nu>4)$

moments:

$$\mu_{2n}=\frac{1\cdot3\ldots(2n-1)\nu^n}{(\nu-2)(\nu-4)\ldots(\nu-2n)}\qquad(\nu>2n)$$

$$\mu_{2n+1}=0$$

characteristic function:

$$\phi(t)=E\left[\exp\left(it\frac{X}{\sqrt{\chi^2/\nu}}\right)\right]=\frac{\left(\frac{|t|}{2\sqrt{\nu}}\right)^{\nu/2}}{\pi\Gamma(\nu/2)}Y_{\frac{\nu}{2}}\left(\frac{|t|}{\sqrt{\nu}}\right)$$

Series Expansions

$$\left(\theta=\arctan\frac{t}{\sqrt{\nu}}\right)$$

26.7.3

$$A(t|\nu)=\begin{cases}\frac{2}{\pi}\left\{\theta+\sin\theta\left[\cos\theta+\frac{2}{3}\cos^3\theta+\ldots+\frac{2\cdot4\ldots(\nu-3)}{1\cdot3\ldots(\nu-2)}\cos^{\nu-2}\theta\right]\right\} & (\nu>1\text{ and odd})\\ \frac{2}{\pi}\theta & (\nu=1)\end{cases}$$

26.7.4

$$A(t|\nu)=\sin\theta\left\{1+\frac{1}{2}\cos^2\theta+\frac{1\cdot3}{2\cdot4}\cos^4\theta+\ldots+\frac{1\cdot3\cdot5\ldots(\nu-3)}{2\cdot4\cdot6\ldots(\nu-2)}\cos^{\nu-2}\theta\right\}\qquad(\nu\text{ even})$$

Asymptotic Expansion for the Inverse Function

If $A(t_p|\nu)=1-2p$ and $Q(x_p)=p$, then

26.7.5

$$t_p \sim x_p+\frac{g_1(x_p)}{\nu}+\frac{g_2(x_p)}{\nu^2}+\frac{g_3(x_p)}{\nu^3}+\ldots$$

$$g_1(x)=\frac{1}{4}(x^3+x)$$

$$g_2(x)=\frac{1}{96}(5x^5+16x^3+3x)$$

$$g_3(x)=\frac{1}{384}(3x^7+19x^5+17x^3-15x)$$

$$g_4(x)=\frac{1}{92160}(79x^9+776x^7+1482x^5-1920x^3-945x)$$

Limiting Distribution

26.7.6

$$\lim_{\nu\to\infty} A(t|\nu)=\frac{1}{\sqrt{2\pi}}\int_{-t}^{t} e^{-x^2/2}dx=A(t)$$

Approximation for Large Values of t and $\nu\leq 5$

26.7.7 $$A(t|\nu)\approx 1-2\left\{\frac{a_\nu}{t^\nu}+\frac{b_\nu}{t^{\nu+1}}\right\}$$

ν	1	2	3	4	5
a_ν	.3183	.4991	1.1094	3.0941	9.948
b_ν	.0000	.0518	−.0460	−2.756	−14.05

Approximation for Large ν

26.7.8 $$A(t|\nu)\approx 2P(x)-1, \qquad x=\frac{t\left(1-\frac{1}{4\nu}\right)}{\sqrt{1+\frac{t^2}{2\nu}}}$$

Non-Central t-Distribution

26.7.9

$$P(t'|\nu,\delta)=$$

$$\frac{1}{\sqrt{\nu}B\left(\frac{1}{2},\frac{\nu}{2}\right)}\int_{-\infty}^{t'}\left(\frac{\nu}{\nu+x^2}\right)^{\frac{\nu+1}{2}} e^{-\frac{1}{2}\frac{\nu\delta^2}{\nu+x^2}} Hh_\nu\left(\frac{-\delta x}{\sqrt{\nu+x^2}}\right)dx$$

$$=1-\sum_{j=0}^{\infty} e^{-\delta^2/2}\frac{(\delta^2/2)^j}{2j!} I_x\left(\frac{\nu}{2},\frac{1}{2}+j\right), \qquad x=\frac{\nu}{\nu+t'^2}$$

where δ is termed the non-centrality parameter.

Approximation to the Non-Central t-Distribution

26.7.10

$$P(t'|\nu,\delta)\approx P(x) \qquad \text{where } x=\frac{t'\left(1-\frac{1}{4\nu}\right)-\delta}{\left(1+\frac{t'^2}{2\nu}\right)^{\frac{1}{2}}}$$

26.8. Methods of Generating Random Numbers and Their Applications [9]

Random digits are digits generated by repeated independent drawings from the population 0, 1, 2, . . ., 9 where the probability of selecting any digit is one-tenth. This is equivalent to putting 10 balls, numbered from 0 to 9, into an urn and drawing one ball at a time, replacing the ball after each drawing. The recorded set of numbers forms a collection of random digits. Any group of n successive random digits is known as a *random number*.

Several lengthy tables of random digits are available (see references). However, the use of random numbers in electronic computers has resulted in a need for random numbers to be generated in a completely deterministic way. The numbers so generated are termed pseudo-random numbers. The quality of pseudo-random numbers is determined by subjecting the numbers to several statistical tests, see [26.55], [26.56]. The purpose of these statistical tests is to detect any properties of the pseudo-random numbers which are different from the (conceptual) properties of random numbers.

[9] The authors wish to express their appreciation to Professor J. W. Tukey who made many penetrating and helpful suggestions in this section.

Experience has shown that the congruence method is the most preferable device for generating random numbers on a computer. Let the sequence of pseudo-random numbers be denoted by $\{X_n\}$, $n=0, 1, 2, \ldots$. Then the congruence method of generating pseudo-random numbers is

$$X_{n+1}=aX_n+b(\text{mod } T)$$

where b and T are relatively prime. The choice of T is determined by the capacity and base of the computer; a and b are chosen so that: (1) the resulting sequence $\{X_n\}$ possesses the desired statistical properties of random numbers, (2) the period of the sequence is as long as possible, and (3) the speed of generation is fast. A guide for choosing a and b is to make the correlation between the numbers be near zero, e.g., the correlation between X_n and X_{n+s} is

$$\rho_s=\frac{1-6\frac{b_s}{T}\left(1-\frac{b_s}{T}\right)}{a_s}+e$$

where

$$a_s=a^s \ (\text{mod } T)$$
$$b_s=(1+a+a^2+\ldots+a^{s-1})b \ (\text{mod } T)$$
$$|e|<a_s/T$$

which occur in

$$X_{n+s}=a_sX_n+b_s \pmod T$$

When a is chosen so that $a \approx T^{1/2}$, the correlation $\rho_1 \approx T^{-1/2}$.

The sequence defined by the multiplicative congruence method will have a full period of T numbers if

(i) b is relatively prime to T
(ii) $a=1 \pmod p$ if p is a prime factor of T
(iii) $a=1 \pmod 4$ if 4 is a factor of T.

Consequently if $T=2^q$, b need only be odd, and $a=1 \pmod 4$. When $T=10^q$, b need only be not divisible by 2 or 5, and $a=1 \pmod{20}$. The most convenient choices for a are of the form $a=2^s+1$ (for binary computers) and $a=10^s+1$ (for decimal computers). This results in the fastest generation of random numbers as the operations only require a shift operation plus two additions. Also any number can serve as the starting point to generate a sequence of random digits. A good summary of generating pseudo-random numbers is [26.51].

Below are listed various congruence schemes and their properties.

Congruence methods for generating random numbers

$X_{n+1}=aX_n+b \pmod T$, T and b relatively prime

	a	b	T	Period	X_0	Special cases for which random numbers have passed statistical tests for randomness[10]
26.8.1	$1+t^s$	odd	$T=t^q$	t^q	$0 \le X_0 < T$	$T=2^{35}$, X_0 unknown; $a=2^7+1$, $b=1$; $T=2^{47}$, $a=2^9+1$, $b=29741\ 09625\ 8473$, $X_0=76293\ 94531\ 25$.
26.8.2	$r2^s \pm 1$ (r odd, $s \ge 2$)	0	$T=t^q$	t^{q-s}	relatively prime to T	$T=2^{40}$, 2^{43}, $X_0=1$; $a=5^{17}(s=2)$ $T=2^{36}$, $X_0=1$; $T=2^{39}$, $X_0=1-2^{-39}$, .5478126193; $a=5^{13}(s=2)$ $T=2^{35}$, $X_0=1$; $a=5^{15}(s=2)$
26.8.3	$r2^s \pm 1$ (r odd, $s \ge 2$)	0	$T=t^q \pm 1$	(varies)	relatively prime to T	$T=2^{35}+1$, $X_0=10{,}987{,}654{,}321$; $a=23$; period $\approx 10^6$ $T=10^8+1$, $X_0=47{,}594{,}118$; $a=23$; period $\approx 5.8\times 10^6$
26.8.4	7^{4s+1}	0	$T=10^q$	$5\cdot 10^{q-3}$	relatively prime to T	$T=10^{10}$, $X_0=1$; $a=7$ $T=10^{11}$, $X_0=1$; $a=7^{13}$
26.8.5	3^{4s+1} ($s=0, 2, 3, 4$)	0	$T=10^q$	$5\cdot 10^{q-2}$	relatively prime to T	

[10] X_0 given is the starting point for random numbers when statistical tests were made.

When the numbers are generated using a congruence scheme, the least significant digits have short periods. Hence the entire word length cannot be used. If one desired random numbers with as many digits as possible, one would have to modify the congruence schemes. One way is to generate the numbers mod $T \pm 1$. This unfortunately reduces the period.

Generation of Random Deviates

Let $\{X\}$ be a generated sequence of independent random numbers having the domain $(0, T)$. Then $\{U\}=\{T^{-1}X\}$ is a sequence of random deviates (numbers) from a uniform distribution on the interval (0, 1). This is usually a necessary preliminary step in the generation of random deviates having a given cumulative distribution function $F(y)$ or probability density function $f(y)$. Below are summarized some general techniques for producing arbitrary random deviates. (In what follows $\{U\}$ will always denote a sequence of random deviates from a uniform distribution on the interval (0, 1).)

1. Inverse Method

The solutions $\{y\}$ of the equations $\{u=F(y)\}$ form a sequence of independent random deviates with cumulative distribution function $F(y)$. (If $F(y)$ has a discontinuity at $y=y_0$, then whenever u is such that $F(y_0-0)<u<F(y_0)$, select y_0 as the corresponding deviate.) Generally the inverse method is not practical unless the inverse function $y=F^{-1}(u)$ can be obtained explicitly or can be conveniently approximated.

2. Generating a Discrete Random Variable

Let Y be a discrete random variable with point probabilities $p_i=Pr\{Y=y_i\}$ for $i=1, 2, \ldots$.

The direct way to generate Y is to generate $\{U\}$ and put $Y=y_i$ if

$$p_1+p_2+ \ldots +p_{i-1}<U<p_1+p_2+ \ldots +p_i.$$

However, this method requires complicated machine programs that take too long.

An alternative way due to Marsaglia [26.53] is simple, fast, and seems to be well suited to high-speed computations. Let p_i for $i=1, 2, \ldots, n$ be expressed by k decimal digits as $p_i=.\delta_{1i}\delta_{2i} \ldots \delta_{ki}$ where the δ's are the decimal digits. (If the domain of the random variable is infinite, it is necessary to truncate the probability distribution at p_n.) Define

$$P_0=0,\ P_r=10^{-r}\sum_{i=1}^{n}\delta_{ri} \text{ for } r=1, 2, \ldots, k, \text{ and}$$

$$\Pi_s=\sum_{r=0}^{s}10^rP_r,\ s=1, 2, \ldots, k.$$

Number the computer memory locations by 0, 1, 2, . . . , Π_k-1. The memory locations are divided into k mutually exclusive sets such that the sth set consists of memory locations Π_{s-1}, $\Pi_{s-1}+1, \ldots, \Pi_s-1$. The information stored in the memory locations of the sth set consists of y_1 in δ_{s1} locations, y_2 in δ_{s2} locations, . . . , y_n in δ_{sn} locations.

Denote the decimal expansion of the uniform deviates generated by the computer by $u=\cdot d_1d_2d_3 \ldots$ and finally let $a\{m\}$ be the contents of memory location m. Then if

$$\sum_{i=0}^{s-1}P_i\leq U<\sum_{i=0}^{s}P_i$$

put

$$y=a\left\{d_1d_2 \ldots d_s+\Pi_{s-1}-10^s\sum_{i=1}^{s-1}P_i\right\}.$$

This method is perhaps the best all-around method for generating random deviates from a discrete distribution. In order to illustrate this method consider the problem of generating deviates from the binomial distribution with point probabilities

$$p_i=\binom{n}{i}p^i(1-p)^{n-i}$$

for $n=5$ and $p=.20$. The point probabilities to 4 D are

Value of Random Variable	*Point Probabilities*
0	$p_0=0.3277$
1	$p_1=\ .4096$
2	$p_2=\ .2048$
3	$p_3=\ .0512$
4	$p_4=\ .0064$
5	$p_5=\ .0003$

and thus $P_0=0$, $P_1=.9$, $P_2=.07$, $P_3=.027$, $P_4=.0030$ from which $\Pi_0=0$, $\Pi_1=9$, $\Pi_2=16$, $\Pi_3=43$, $\Pi_4=73$. The 73 memory locations are divided into 4 mutually exclusive sets such that

Set	*Memory Locations*
1	0, 1, . . . , 8
2	9, 10, . . . , 15
3	16, . . . , 42
4	43, . . . , 72

Among the nine memory locations of set 1, zero is stored $\delta_{10}=3$ times, 1 is stored $\delta_{11}=4$ times, 2 is stored $\delta_{12}=2$ times; the seven locations of set 2 store 0 $\delta_{20}=2$ times and 3 $\delta_{23}=5$ times; etc. A summary of the memory locations is set out below:

	Value of Random Variable					
	0	1	2	3	4	5
Frequency (set 1)	3	4	2	0	0	0
Frequency (set 2)	2	0	0	5	0	0
Frequency (set 3)	7	9	4	1	6	0
Frequency (set 4)	7	6	8	2	4	3

Then to generate the random variables if

$0\leq u<.9$	put	$y=a\{d_1\}$
$.9\leq u<.97$		$y=a\{d_1d_2-81\}$
$.97\leq u<.997$		$y=a\{d_1d_2d_3-954\}$
$.997\leq u<1.000$		$y=a\{d_1d_2d_3d_4-9927\}$

3. Generating a Continuous Random Variable

The method for generating deviates from a discrete distribution can be adapted to random variables having a continuous distribution. Let $F(y)$ be the cumulative distribution function and assume that the domain of the random variable is (a,b) where the interval is finite. (If the domain is infinite, it must be truncated at (say) the points a and b.) Divide the interval $(b-a)$ into n sub-intervals of length Δ ($n\Delta=b-a$) such that the boundary of the ith interval is (y_{i-1}, y_i) where $y_i=a+i\Delta$ for $i=0, 1, \ldots, n$. Now define a discrete distribution having domain

$$\left\{z_i=\frac{y_i+y_{i-1}}{2}\right\}$$

with point probabilities $p_i=F(y_i)-F(y_{i-1})$. Finally, let W be a random variable having a uniform distribution on $\left(-\frac{\Delta}{2}, \frac{\Delta}{2}\right)$. This can be done by setting $W=\Delta\left(U-\frac{1}{2}\right)$. Then random deviates from the distribution function $F(y)$, can be generated (approximately) by setting $y=z+w=z+\Delta\left(u-\frac{1}{2}\right)$. This is simply an approximate decomposition of the continuous random variable into the sum of a discrete and continuous random variable. The discrete variable can be generated quickly by the method described previously. The smaller the value of Δ the better will be the approximation. Each number can be generated by using the leading digits of U to generate the discrete random variable Z and the remaining digits forming a uniformly distributed deviate having (0,1) domain.

4. Acceptance-Rejection Methods

In what follows the random variable Y will be assumed to have finite domain (a, b). If the domain is infinite, it must be truncated for computational purposes at (say) the points a and b. Then the resulting random deviates will only have this truncated domain.

a) Let f be the maximum of $f(y)$. Then the procedure for generating random deviates is: (1) generate a pair of uniform deviates U_1, U_2; (2) compute a point $y=a+(b-a)u_2$ in (a, b); (3) if $u_1<f(y)/f$ accept y as the random deviate, otherwise reject the pair (u_1, u_2) and start again. The acceptance ratio of deviates actually produced is $[(b-a)f]^{-1}$. Hence the acceptance ratio decreases as the domain increases. One way to increase the acceptance ratio is to divide the interval (a, b) into mutually exclusive sub-intervals and then carry out the acceptance-rejection process. For this purpose let the interval (a, b) be divided into k sub-intervals such that the end points of the jth interval are (ξ_{j-1}, ξ_j) with $\xi_0=a$, $\xi_k=b$ and $\int_{\xi_{j-1}}^{\xi_j} f(y)dy=p_j$; further let the maximum of $f(y)$ in the jth interval be f_j. Then to generate random deviates from $f(y)$, generate n pairs of deviates $(u_{1s}, u_{2s}) s=1, 2, \ldots, n$. Assign $[np_j]$ such pairs to the jth interval and compute $y_j=\xi_{j-1}+(\xi_j-\xi_{j-1})u_{2s}$. If $u_{1s}<f(y_j)/f_j$ accept y_j as a deviate. The acceptance ratio of this method is

$$\sum_{j=1}^{k} p_j\,[(\xi_j-\xi_{j-1})f_j]^{-1}$$

b) Let $F(y)$ be such that $f(y)=f_1(y)f_2(y)$ where the domain of y is (a, b). Let f_1 and f_2 be the maximum of $f_1(y)$ and $f_2(y)$ respectively. Then the procedure for generating random deviates having the probability density function $f(y)$ is: (1) generate U_1, U_2, U_3; (2) define $z=a+(b-a)u_3$; (3) if both $u_1<\frac{f_1(z)}{f_1}$ and $u_2<\frac{f_2(z)}{f_2}$, take z as the random deviate; otherwise take another sample of three uniform deviates. The acceptance ratio of this method is $[(b-a)f_1f_2]^{-1}$ and can be increased by dividing (a, b) into sub-intervals as in the previous case.

c) Let the probability density function of Y be

$$f(y)=\int_\alpha^\beta g(y, t)dt, \ (\alpha\leq t\leq\beta), \ (a\leq y\leq b).$$

Let g be the maximum of $g(y, t)$. Then the procedure for generating random deviates having the probability density function $f(y)$ is: (1) generate U_1, U_2, U_3; (2) define $s=\alpha+(\beta-\alpha)u_2$; $z=a+(b-a)u_3$; (3) if $u_1<\frac{g(z, s)}{g}$, take z as the random deviate; otherwise take another sample of three. The acceptance ratio for this method is $[(b-a)g]^{-1}$ and can be increased by dividing the domain of t and y into sub-domains.

5. Composition Method

Let $g_z(y)$ be a probability density function which depends on the parameter z; further let $H(z)$ be the cumulative distribution function for z. In order to generate random deviates Y having the frequency function

$$f(y)=\int_{-\infty}^{\infty} g_z(y)dH(z)$$

one draws a deviate having the cumulative distribution function $H(z)$; then draws a second sample having the probability density function $g_z(y)$.

6. Generation of Random Deviates From Well Known Distributions

a. Normal distribution

(1) *Inverse method:* The inverse method depends on having a convenient approximation to the inverse function $x=P^{-1}(u)$ where

$$u=(2\pi)^{-1/2}\int_{-\infty}^{x} e^{-t^2/2}dt.$$

Two ways of performing this operation are to (i) use **26.2.23** with $t=\left(\ln\frac{1}{u^2}\right)^{1/2}$ or (ii) approximate $x=P^{-1}(u)$ piecewise using Chebyshev polynomials, see [26.54].

(2) *Sum of uniform deviates:* Let U_1, U_2, . . ., U_n be a sequence of n uniform deviates. Then

$$X_n=\left(\sum_{i=1}^{n} U_i-\frac{n}{2}\right)\left(\frac{n}{12}\right)^{-1/2}$$

will be distributed asymptotically as a normal random deviate. When $n=12$, the maximum errors made in the normal deviate are 9×10^{-3} for $|X|<2$, 9×10^{-1} for $2<|X|<3$. An improvement can be made by taking a polynomial function of X_n (say)

$$X_n^*=X_n \sum_{s=0}^{k} a_{2s}X_n^{2s}$$

as the normal deviate where a_{2s} are suitable coefficients. These coefficients may be calculated using (say) Chebyshev polynomials or simply by making the asymptotic random deviate agree with the correc normal deviate at certain specified points. When $n=12$, the maximum error in the normal deviate is 8×10^{-4} using the coefficients

$a_0=9.8746$ $\quad a_6=(-7)-5.102$

$a_2=(-3)3.9439$ $\quad a_8=(-7)1.141$

$a_4=(-5)7.474$

(3) *Direct method:* Generate a pair of uniform deviates (U_1, U_2). Then

$$X_1=(-2\ln U_1)^{1/2}\cos 2\pi U_2,$$

$X_2=(-2\ln U_1)^{1/2}\sin 2\pi U_2$ will be a pair of independent normal random deviates with mean zero and unit variance. This procedure can be modified by calculating $\cos 2\pi U$ and $\sin 2\pi U$ using an acceptance rejection method; e.g., (1) generate (U_1, U_2); (2) if $(2U_1-1)^2+(2U_2-1)^2\leq1$ generate a third uniform deviate U_3, otherwise reject the pair and start over; (3) calculate $y_1=(-\ln u_3)^{1/2}\dfrac{u_1^2-u_2^2}{u_1^2+u_2^2}$, $y_2=\pm2(-\ln u_3)^{1/2}\dfrac{u_1u_2}{u_1^2+u_2^2}$ ($\pm$ random). Both y_1 and y_2 are the desired random deviates.

(4) *Acceptance-rejection method:* 1) Generate a pair of uniform deviates (U_1, U_2); 2) compute $x=-\ln u_1$; 3) if $e^{-\frac{1}{2}(x-1)^2}\geq u_2$ (or equivalently $(x-1)^2\leq-2(\ln u_2)$ accept x, otherwise reject the pair and start over. The quantity will be the required normal deviate with mean zero and unit variance.

b. Bivariate normal distribution

Let $\{X_1, X_2\}$ be a pair of independent normal deviates with mean zero and unit variance. Then $\{X_1, \rho X_1+(1-\rho^2)^{1/2}X_2\}$ represent a pair of deviates from a bivariate normal distribution with zero means, unit variances, and correlation coefficient ρ.

c. Exponential distribution

(1) *Inverse method:* Since $F(x)=e^{-x/\theta}$, $X=-\theta\ln U$ will be a deviate from the exponential distribution with parameter θ.

(2) *Acceptance-rejection method:* 1) Generate a pair of independent uniform deviates (U_0, U_1); 2) if $U_1<U_0$ generate a third value U_2; 3) if $U_1+U_2<U_0$ generate a fourth value U_3, etc.; 4) continue generating uniform deviates until an n is obtained such that $U_1+U_2+\ldots+U_{n-1}<U_0<U_1+\ldots+U_n$; 5) if n is even reject the procedure and start a fresh trial with a new value of U_0, otherwise if n is odd take $X=\theta U_0$ as the desired deviate; 6) in general if t is the number of trials until an acceptable sequence is obtained $X=\theta(t+U_0)$. The random deviates produced in this way follow an exponential distribution with parameter θ. One can expect to generate approximately six uniform deviates for every exponential deviate.

(3) *Discrete Distribution Method:* Let Y and n be discrete random variables with point probabilities

$$Pr\{Y=r\}=(e-1)e^{-(r+1)} \qquad r=0, 1, 2, \ldots$$

$$Pr\{n=s\}=[s!(e-1)]^{-1} \qquad s=1, 2, 3, \ldots.$$

Then $X=Y+\min(U_1, U_2, \ldots, U_n)$ will follow an exponential distribution. The average value of n is 1.58 so that one needs, on the average, only 1.58 u's from which the minimum is selected.

26.9. Use and Extension of the Tables

Use of Probability Function Inequalities

Example 1. Let X be a random variable with finite mean and variance equal to m and σ^2, respectively. Use the inequalities for probability functions **26.1.37, 40, 41** to place lower bounds on

$$A(t)=F(t)-F(-t)=P\left\{\frac{|X-m|}{\sigma}\leq t\right\}$$

for $t=1(1)4$.

Lower bounds on $A(t)=F(t)-F(-t)$

$t=1$	2	3	4	*Remarks*
0	.7500	.8889	.9375	no knowledge of $F(t)$; **26.1.37**
.5556	.8889	.9506	.9722	$F(t)$ is unimodal and continuous; **26.1.40**
0	.8182	.9697	.9912	$F(t)$ is such that $\mu_4=3$; **26.1.41**

It is of interest to note that the standard normal distribution is unimodal, has mean zero, unit variance $\mu_4=3$, is continuous, and such that

$$A(t)=P(t)-P(-t)$$
$$=.6827,\ .9545,\ .9973,\ \text{and}\ .9999$$

for $t=1$, 2, 3 and 4 respectively.

Interpolation for $P(x)$ in Table 26.1

Example 2. Compute $P(x)$ for $x=2.576$ to fifteen decimal places using a Taylor expansion.

Writing $x=x_0+\theta$ we have

$$P(x)=P(x_0)+Z(x_0)\theta+Z^{(1)}(x_0)\frac{\theta^2}{2!}$$
$$+Z^{(2)}(x_0)\frac{\theta^3}{3!}+Z^{(3)}(x_0)\frac{\theta^4}{4!}+\ldots$$

Taking $x_0=2.58$ and $\theta=-4\times10^{-3}$ we calculate the successive terms to 16D

+.99505	99842	42230		
−	5	72204	35976	6
−		2952	57449	6
−		8	63097	8
−			1439	4
−				9
.99500	24676	84265	7	

The result correct to 17D is

$$P(2.576)=.99500\ 24676\ 84264\ 98$$

Calculation for Arbitrary Mean and Variance

Example 3. Find the value to 5D of

$$P\{X\leq .50\}=\frac{1}{2\sqrt{2\pi}}\int_{-\infty}^{.5}e^{-1/2\left(\frac{t-1}{2}\right)^2}dt$$

using **26.2.8** and **Table 26.1.**

This represents the probability of the random variable being less than or equal to .5 for a normal distribution with mean $m=1$ and variance $\sigma^2=4$. Using **26.2.8** we have

$$P\{X\leq .5\}=P\left(\frac{.5-1}{2}\right)=P(-.25)$$

Since $P(-x)=1-P(x)$, we have

$$P(-.25)=1-P(.25)=1-.59871=.40129$$

where a two-term Taylor series was used for interpolation. Note that when interpolating for $P(x)$ for a value of x midway between the tabulated values we can write $x=x_0+.01$ and a two-term Taylor series is $P(x)=P(x_0)+Z(x_0)10^{-2}$. Thus one need only multiply $Z(x_0)$ by 10^{-2} and add the result to $P(x_0)$.

Calculation of $P(x)$ for x Approximate

Example 4. Using **Table 26.1,** find $P(x)$ for $x=1.96$, when there is a possible error in x of $\pm5\times10^{-3}$.

This is an example where the argument is only known approximately. The question arises as to how many decimal places one should retain in $P(x)$. If Δx and $\Delta P(x)$ denote the error in x and the resulting error in $P(x)$, respectively, then

$$\Delta P(x)\approx Z(x)\Delta x$$

Hence $\Delta P(1.960)=3\times10^{-4}$ which indicates that $P(1.960)$ need only be calculated to 4D. Therefore $P(1.960)=.9750$.

Inverse Interpolation for $P(x)$

Example 5. Find the value of x for which $P(x)=.97500\ 00000\ 00000$ using **Table 26.1** and determining as many decimal places as is consistent with the tabulated function.

For inverse interpolation the tabulated function $P(x)$ may be regarded as having a possible error of $.5\times10^{-15}$. Hence

$$\Delta x\approx\frac{\Delta P(x)}{Z(x)}=\frac{.5\times10^{-15}}{Z(x)}$$

Let $P(x_0)$ correspond to the closest tabulated value of $P(x)$. Then a convenient formula for inverse interpolation is

$$x=x_0+t+\frac{x_0t^2}{2}+\frac{2x_0^2+1}{6}t^3$$

where

$$t=\frac{P(x)-P(x_0)}{Z(x_0)}$$

If only the first two terms (i.e., $x=x_0+t$) are used, the error in x will be bounded by $\frac{x}{8}\times10^{-4}$ and the true value will always be greater than the value thus calculated.

With respect to this example, $\Delta x\approx10^{-14}$ and thus the interpolated value of x may be in error by one unit in the fourteenth place. The closest value to $P(x)=.97500\ 00000\ 00000$ is $P(x_0)=.97500\ 21048\ 51780$ with $x_0=1.96$. Hence using the preceding inverse interpolation formulas with

$$t=-.00003\ 60167\ 31129$$

and carrying fifteen decimals we have the successive terms

$+$1.96000	00000	00000
$-$ .00003	60167	31129
$+$	12	71261
$-$		68
		0
$+$1.95996	39845	40064

Edgeworth Asymptotic Expansion

Example 6. Find the Edgeworth asymptotic expansion **26.2.49** for the c.d.f. of chi-square.

Method 1. Expansion for χ^2

Let

$$Q(\chi^2|\nu)=1-F(t)$$

where

$$t=\frac{\chi^2-\nu}{(2\nu)^{\frac{1}{2}}}$$

Since the values of γ_1 and γ_2 **26.4.33** are

$$\gamma_1=2\sqrt{2}/\nu^{\frac{1}{2}}$$

$$\gamma_2=12/\nu,$$

we obtain, by using the first two bracketed terms of **26.2.49**

$$F(t)\sim P(t)-\frac{1}{\nu^{\frac{1}{2}}}\left[\frac{\sqrt{2}}{3}Z^{(2)}(t)\right]+\frac{1}{\nu}\left[\frac{1}{2}Z^{(3)}(t)+\frac{1}{9}Z^{(5)}(t)\right]$$

The Edgeworth expansion is an asymptotic expansion in terms of derivatives of the normal distribution function. It is often possible to transform a random variable so that the distribution of the transformed random variable more closely approximates the normal distribution function than does the distribution of the original random variable. Hence for the same number of terms, greater accuracy may be achieved by using the transformed variable in the expansion. Since the distribution of $\sqrt{2\chi^2}$ is more closely approximated by a normal distribution than χ^2 itself (as judged by a comparison of the values of γ_1 and γ_2), we would expect that the Edgeworth asymptotic expansion of $\sqrt{2\chi^2}$ would be superior to that of χ^2.

Method 2. Expansion for $\sqrt{2\chi^2}$. Let

$$Q(\chi^2|\nu)=1-F(t)=1-F\left(\frac{\sqrt{2\chi^2}-(2\nu-1)^{\frac{1}{2}}}{\left(1-\frac{1}{4\nu}\right)^{\frac{1}{2}}}\right)$$

where $(2\nu-1)^{\frac{1}{2}}$ and $1-\frac{1}{4\nu}$ are the mean and variance to terms of order ν^{-2} of $\sqrt{2\chi^2}$ (see **26.4.34**). The values of γ_1 and γ_2 for $\sqrt{2\chi^2}$ are

$$\gamma_1\approx\frac{1}{\sqrt{2\nu}}\left[1+\frac{5}{8\nu}\right]\qquad\gamma_2\approx\frac{3}{4\nu^2}$$

Thus we obtain

$$F(t)\sim P(t)-\frac{1}{\nu^{\frac{1}{2}}}\left[\frac{\sqrt{2}}{12}\left(1+\frac{5}{8\nu}\right)Z^{(2)}(t)\right]+\frac{1}{\nu}\left[\frac{1}{32\nu}Z^{(3)}(t)+\frac{1}{144}\left(1+\frac{5}{8\nu}\right)^2Z^{(5)}(t)\right]$$

For numerical examples using these expansions see **Example 12.**

Calculation of $L(h, k, \rho)$

Example 7. Find $L(.5, .4, .8)$. Using **26.3.20**

$$\sqrt{h^2-2\rho hk+k^2}=\sqrt{.09}=.3$$

$$L(.5, .4, .8)=L(.5, 0, 0)+L(.4, 0, -.6)$$

Reference to **Figure 26.2** yields

$$L(.5, 0, 0)+L(.4, 0, -.6)=.16+.08=.24$$

The answer to 3D is $L(.5, .4, .8)=.250$.

Calculation of the Bivariate Normal Probability Function

Example 8. Let X and Y follow a bivariate normal distribution with parameters $m_x=3$, $m_y=2$, $\sigma_x=4$, $\sigma_y=2$, and $\rho=-.125$. Find the value of $P_r\{X\geq 2,\ Y\geq 4\}$ using **26.3.20** and **Figures 26.2, 26.3.**

Since $P_r\{X\geq h, Y\geq k\}=L\left(\frac{h-m_x}{\sigma_x}, \frac{k-m_y}{\sigma_y}, \rho\right)$ we have $P\{X\geq 2,\ Y\geq 4\}=L(-.25, 1, -.125)$. Using **26.3.20**

$$L(-.25, 1, -.125)=L(-.25, 0, .969)+L(1, 0, .125)-\frac{1}{2}$$

Figure 26.2 only gives values for $h>0$, however, using the relationship **26.3.8** with $k=0$, $L(-h, 0, \rho)$ $=\frac{1}{2}-L(h, 0, -\rho)$ and thus $L(-.25, 0, .969)$ $=\frac{1}{2}-L(.25, 0, -.969)$. Therefore $L(-.25, 1, -.125)$ $=-L(.25, 0, -.969)+L(1, 0, .125)=-.01+.09=.08$.

The answer to 3D is $L(-.25,\ 1.,\ -.125)=.080$.

Integral of a Bivariate Normal Distribution Over a Polygon

Example 9. Let the random variables X and Y have a bivariate normal distribution with parameters $m_x=5$, $\sigma_x=2$, $m_y=9$, $\sigma_y=4$, and $\rho=.5$. Find the probability that the point (X, Y) be inside the triangle whose vertices are $A=(7, 8)$, $B=(9, 13)$, and $C=(2, 9)$.

When obtaining the integral of a bivariate normal distribution over a polygon, it is first necessary to use **26.3.22** in order to transform the variates so that one deals with a circular normal distribution. The polygon in the region of the transformed variables is then divided into configurations such that the integral over any selected configuration can be easily obtained. Below are listed some of the most useful configurations.

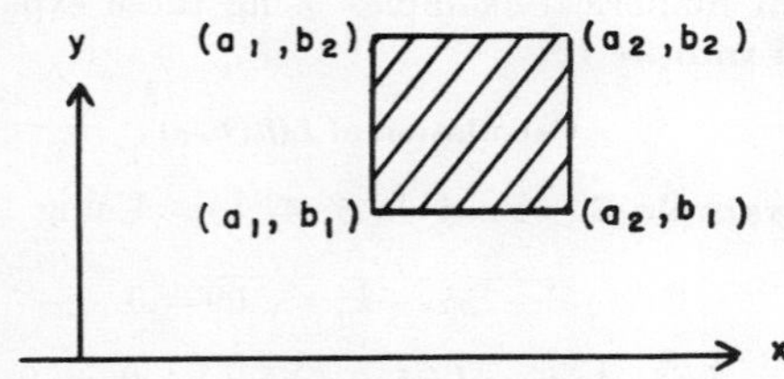

FIGURE 26.5

$$\int_{a_1}^{a_2}\int_{b_1}^{b_2} g(x, y, 0)dxdy=[P(a_2)-P(a_1)][P(b_2)-P(b_1)]$$

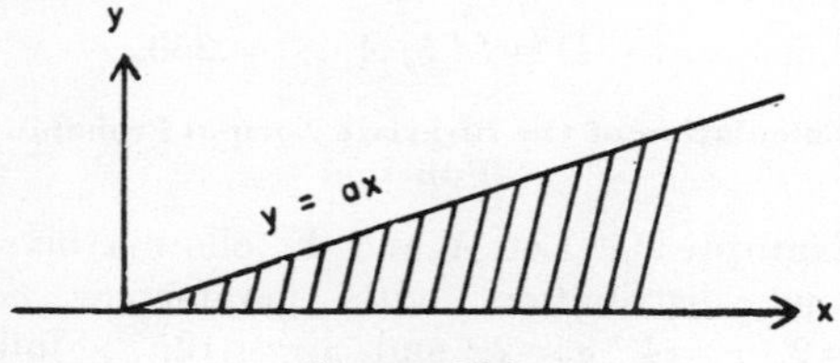

FIGURE 26.6

$$\int_0^{\infty}\int_0^{ax} g(x, y, 0)dxdy=\frac{\arctan a}{2\pi}$$

FIGURE 26.7

$$\int_0^{h}\int_0^{\frac{k}{h}x} g(x, y, 0)dxdy=V(h, k)^{11}$$

[11] See **26.3.23** for definition of $V(h, k)$.

For the following two configurations we define

$$h=\frac{|t_2s_1-t_1s_2|}{[(s_2-s_1)^2+(t_2-t_1)^2]^{\frac{1}{2}}}$$

$$k_1=\frac{|s_1(s_2-s_1)+t_1(t_2-t_1)|}{[(s_2-s_1)^2+(t_2-t_1)^2]^{\frac{1}{2}}}$$

$$k_2=\frac{|s_2(s_2-s_1)+t_2(t_2-t_1)|}{[(s_2-s_1)^2+(t_2-t_1)^2]^{\frac{1}{2}}}$$

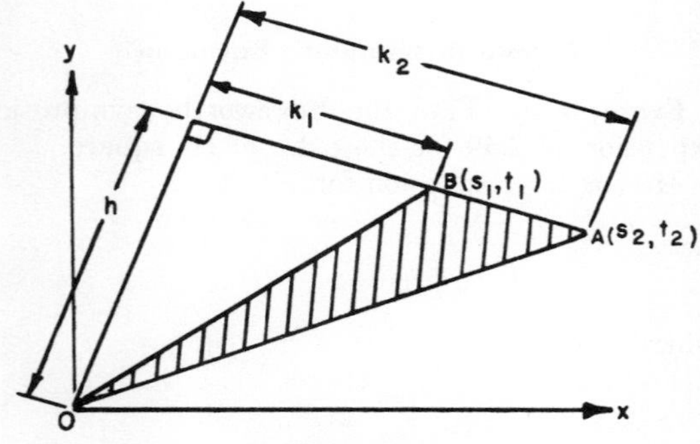

FIGURE 26.8

$$\iint_{\Delta AOB} g(x, y, 0)dxdy=V(h, k_2)-V(h, k_1)$$

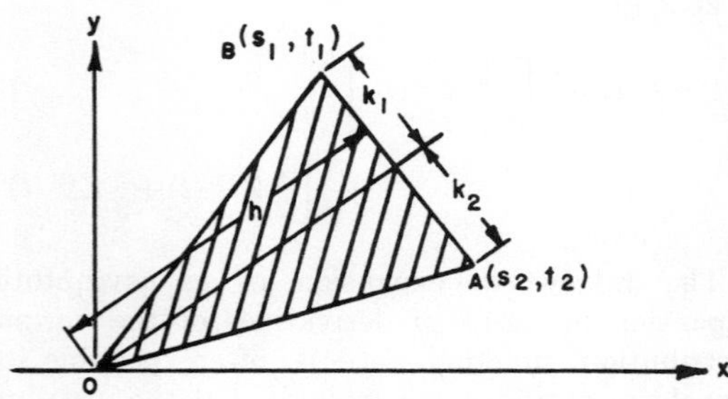

FIGURE 26.9

$$\iint_{\Delta AOB} g(x, y, 0)dxdy=V(h, k_2)+V(h, k_1)$$

Using the circularizing transformation **26.3.22** for our example results in

$$s=\frac{1}{\sqrt{3}}\left(\frac{x-5}{2}+\frac{y-9}{4}\right)$$

$$t=-\frac{1}{1}\left(\frac{x-5}{2}-\frac{y-9}{4}\right)$$

The vertices of the triangle in the (s, t) coordinates become $A=(\sqrt{3}/4, \quad -5/4)$, $B=(\sqrt{3}, \quad -1)$ and $C=\left(-\frac{\sqrt{3}}{2}, \frac{3}{2}\right)$. These points are plotted below. From the figure it is seen that the desired probability is the sum of the probabilities that the point having the transformed variables as coordinates is inside the triangles AOB, AOC, and BOC.

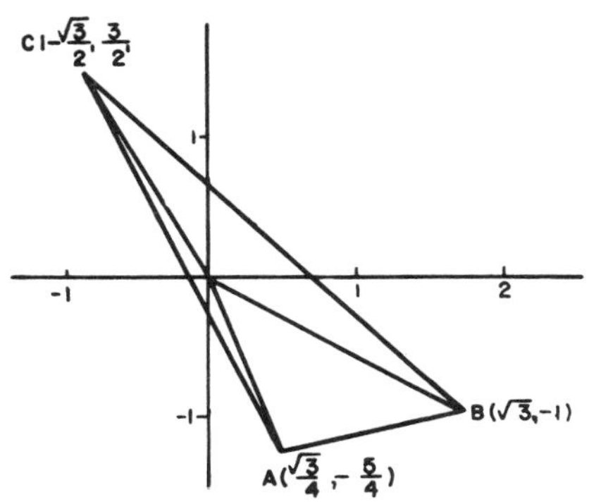

FIGURE 26.10

For these three triangles we have

	h	k_1	k_2
ΔAOB	$\frac{2}{7}\sqrt{21}$	$\sqrt{7}/14$	$\frac{4}{7}\sqrt{7}$
ΔAOC	$\frac{1}{74}\sqrt{111}$	$\frac{8}{37}\sqrt{37}$	$\frac{21}{74}\sqrt{37}$
ΔBOC	$\frac{1}{13}\sqrt{39}$	$\frac{7}{13}\sqrt{13}$	$\frac{6}{13}\sqrt{13}$

From the graph it is seen that the probability over AOB may be found in the same manner as that over **Figure 26.8**, and over AOC and BOC the probabilities may be found as that over **Figure 26.9.**

Hence

$$\iint_{\Delta} g(x, y, .5)dxdy=\iint_{\Delta ABC} g(s, t, 0)dsdt$$

$$=\iint_{\Delta AOB} g(s, t, 0)dsdt+\iint_{\Delta AOC} g(s, t, 0)dsdt$$

$$+\iint_{\Delta BOC} g(s, t, 0)dsdt$$

and consequently using **26.3.23** and **Figure 26.2**

$$\iint_{\Delta AOB} g(s, t, 0)dsdt=V\left(\frac{2}{7}\sqrt{21}, \frac{4\sqrt{7}}{7}\right)-V\left(\frac{2}{7}\sqrt{21}, \frac{\sqrt{7}}{14}\right)$$

$$=\left[\frac{1}{4}+L(1.31, 0, -.76)-L(0, 0, -.76)-\frac{1}{2}Q(1.31)\right]$$

$$-\left[\frac{1}{4}+L(1.31, 0, -.14)-L(0, 0, -.14)-\frac{1}{2}Q(1.31)\right]$$

$$=L(1.31, 0, -.76)-L(0, 0, -.76)$$

$$-L(1.31, 0, -.14)+L(0, 0, -.14)$$

$$=.00-.11-.04+.23=.08$$

$$\iint_{\Delta AOC} g(s, t, 0)dsdt=V\left(\frac{\sqrt{111}}{74}, \frac{8\sqrt{37}}{37}\right)+V\left(\frac{\sqrt{111}}{74}, \frac{21\sqrt{37}}{74}\right)$$

$$=\left[\frac{1}{4}+L(.14, 0, -.99)-L(0, 0, -.99)-\frac{1}{2}Q(.14)\right]$$

$$+\left[\frac{1}{4}+L(.14, 0, -1)-L(0, 0, -1)-\frac{1}{2}Q(.14)\right]$$

$$=.01+.02=.03$$

$$\iint_{\Delta BOC} g(s, t, 0)dsdt=V\left(\frac{\sqrt{39}}{13}, \frac{7\sqrt{13}}{13}\right)+V\left(\frac{\sqrt{39}}{13}, \frac{6\sqrt{13}}{13}\right)$$

$$=\left[\frac{1}{4}+L(.48, 0, -.97)-L(0, 0, -.97)-\frac{1}{2}Q(.48)\right]$$

$$+\left[\frac{1}{4}+L(.48, 0, -.96)-L(0, 0, -.96)-\frac{1}{2}Q(.48)\right]$$

$$=.05+.04=.09$$

Thus adding all parts, the probability that X and Y are in triangle ABC is $=.08+.03+.09=.20$. The answer to 3D is .211.

Calculation of a Circular Normal Distribution Over an Offset Circle

Example 10. Let X and Y have a circular normal distribution with $\sigma=1000$. Find the probability that the point (X, Y) falls within a circle having a radius equal to 540 whose center is displaced 1210 from the mean of the circular normal distribution.

In units of σ, the radius and displacement from the center are, respectively, $R=\frac{540}{1000}=.54$ and $r=\frac{1210}{1000}=1.21$. The problem is thus reduced to finding the probability of X and Y falling in a circle of radius $R=.54$ displaced $r=1.21$ from the center of the distribution where $\sigma=1$.

Since $R<1$, the approximation **26.3.25** is used. This results in

$$P(R^2|2, r^2)=\frac{2(.54)^2}{4+(.54)^2}\exp\frac{-2(1.21)^2}{4+(.54)^2}$$
$$=(.1359)e^{-.6823}=.06869$$

The answer to 5D is .06870.

Interpolation for $Q(\chi^2|\nu)$

Example 11. Find $Q(25.298|20)$ using the interpolation formula given with **Table 26.7.**

Taking $\chi^2=25$, $\theta=.298$ and applying the interpolation formula results in

$$Q(25.298|20)=\frac{1}{8}\{Q(25|16)\theta^2+Q(25|18)(4\theta-2\theta^2)+Q(25|20)(8-4\theta+\theta^2)\}$$
$$=\frac{1}{8}\{(.06982)(.088804)+(.12492)(1.014392)+(.20143)(6.896804)\}$$
$$=.19027$$

A less accurate interpolate may be obtained by setting θ^2 equal to zero in the above formula. This results in the value .19003. The correct value to 6D is $Q(25.298|20)=.190259$.

On the other hand if $\chi^2=25.298$ is assumed to have an error of $\pm 5\times 10^{-4}$, then how large an error arises in $Q(\chi^2|\nu)$? Denoting the error in χ^2 by $\Delta\chi^2$ and the resulting error in $Q(\chi^2|\nu)$ by $\Delta Q(\chi^2|\nu)$, we then have the approximate relationship

$$\Delta Q(\chi^2|\nu)\approx\frac{\partial Q(\chi^2|\nu)}{\partial\chi^2}\,\Delta\chi^2$$

Using **26.4.8** we can write

$$\frac{\partial Q(\chi^2|\nu)}{\partial\chi^2}=\frac{1}{2}\,[Q(\chi^2|\nu-2)-Q(\chi^2|\nu)]$$

and

$$\Delta Q(\chi^2|\nu)\approx\frac{1}{2}\,[Q(\chi^2|\nu-2)-Q(\chi^2|\nu)]\Delta\chi^2$$

For practical purposes it is sufficient to evaluate the derivative to one or two significant figures. Consequently we can write

$$\frac{\partial Q(\chi^2|\nu)}{\partial\chi^2}\approx\frac{\partial Q(\chi_0^2|\nu)}{\partial\chi^2}$$

where χ_0^2 is the closest value to χ^2 for which Q is tabulated. Hence

$$\Delta Q(\chi^2|\nu)\approx\frac{1}{2}\,[Q(\chi_0^2|\nu-2)-Q(\chi_0^2|\nu)]\Delta\chi^2$$

For this example $\Delta\chi^2=\pm 5\times 10^{-4}$ and $\chi_0^2=25$. This results in

$$\Delta Q(\chi^2|\nu)=\frac{1}{2}\,(-.076)(\pm 5)10^{-4}=\pm 2\times 10^{-5}$$

as the possible error in $Q(\chi^2|\nu)$.

Calculation of $Q(\chi^2|\nu)$ Outside the Range of Table 26.7

Example 12. Find the value of $Q(84|72)$.

Since this value is outside the range of **Table 26.7** we can approximate $Q(84|72)$ by (1) using the Edgeworth expansion for $Q(\chi^2|\nu)$ given in **Example 6,** (2) the cube root approximation **26.4.14,** (3) the improved cube root approximation **26.4.15** or (4) the square root approximation **26.4.13.** The results of using all four methods are presented below:

1. Edgeworth expansion

The successive terms of the Edgeworth expansion for the distribution of chi-square result in

$$\begin{aligned}1-Q(84|72)=&.841345\\&.000000\\&.001120\\ \hline &.842465\end{aligned}$$

Hence $Q(84|72)=.15754$.

The successive terms of the Edgeworth expansion for the distribution of $\sqrt{2\chi^2}$ result in

$$\begin{aligned}1-Q(84|72)=&.842544\\&-.000034\\&-.000138\\ \hline &.842372\end{aligned}$$

Hence $Q(84|72)=.15764$.

2. Cube root approximation 26.4.14

Using the cube root approximation we have

$$Q(84|72)=Q(x)$$

where

$$x=\frac{\left(\frac{84}{72}\right)^{1/3}\left[1-\frac{2}{9(72)}\right]}{\left[\frac{2}{9(72)}\right]^{\frac{1}{2}}}=1.0046$$

This results in $Q(84|72)=Q(1.0046)=1-P(1.0046)=.15754$.

Table 26.1 NORMAL PROBABILITY FUNCTION AND DERIVATIVE

x	$P(x)$	$Z(x)$	$Z^{(1)}(x)$
0.00	0.50000 00000 00000	0.39894 22804 01433	0.00000 00000 00000
0.02	0.50797 83137 16902	0.39886 24999 23666	-0.00797 72499 98473
0.04	0.51595 34368 52831	0.39862 32542 04605	-0.01594 49301 68184
0.06	0.52392 21826 54107	0.39822 48301 95607	-0.02389 34898 11736
0.08	0.53188 13720 13988	0.39766 77055 11609	-0.03181 34164 40929
0.10	0.53982 78372 77029	0.39695 25474 77012	-0.03969 52547 47701
0.12	0.54775 84260 20584	0.39608 02117 93656	-0.04752 96254 15239
0.14	0.55567 00048 05907	0.39505 17408 34611	-0.05530 72437 16846
0.16	0.56355 94628 91433	0.39386 83615 68541	-0.06301 89378 50967
0.18	0.57142 37159 00901	0.39253 14831 20429	-0.07065 56669 61677
0.20	0.57925 97094 39103	0.39104 26939 75456	-0.07820 85387 95091
0.22	0.58706 44226 48215	0.38940 37588 33790	-0.08566 88269 43434
0.24	0.59483 48716 97796	0.38761 66151 25014	-0.09302 79876 30003
0.26	0.60256 81132 01761	0.38568 33691 91816	-0.10027 76759 89872
0.28	0.61026 12475 55797	0.38360 62921 53479	-0.10740 97618 02974
0.30	0.61791 14221 88953	0.38138 78154 60524	-0.11441 63446 38157
0.32	0.62551 58347 23320	0.37903 05261 52702	-0.12128 97683 68865
0.34	0.63307 17360 36028	0.37653 71618 33254	-0.12802 26350 23306
0.36	0.64057 64332 17991	0.37391 06053 73128	-0.13460 78179 34326
0.38	0.64802 72924 24163	0.37115 38793 59466	-0.14103 84741 56597
0.40	0.65542 17416 10324	0.36827 01403 03323	-0.14730 80561 21329
0.42	0.66275 72731 51751	0.36526 26726 22154	-0.15341 03225 01305
0.44	0.67003 14463 39407	0.36213 48824 13092	-0.15933 93482 61761
0.46	0.67724 18897 49653	0.35889 02910 33545	-0.16508 95338 75431
0.48	0.68438 63034 83778	0.35553 25285 05997	-0.17065 56136 82879
0.50	0.69146 24612 74013	0.35206 53267 64299	-0.17603 26633 82150
0.52	0.69846 82124 53034	0.34849 25127 58974	-0.18121 61066 34667
0.54	0.70540 14837 84302	0.34481 80014 39333	-0.18620 17207 77240
0.56	0.71226 02811 50973	0.34104 57886 30353	-0.19098 56416 32997
0.58	0.71904 26911 01436	0.33717 99438 22381	-0.19556 43674 16981
0.60	0.72574 68822 49927	0.33322 46028 91800	-0.19993 47617 35080
0.62	0.73237 11065 31017	0.32918 39607 70765	-0.20409 40556 77874
0.64	0.73891 37003 07139	0.32506 22640 84082	-0.20803 98490 13813
0.66	0.74537 30853 28664	0.32086 38037 71172	-0.21177 01104 88974
0.68	0.75174 77695 46430	0.31659 29077 10893	-0.21528 31772 43407
0.70	0.75803 63477 76927	0.31225 39333 66761	-0.21857 77533 56733
0.72	0.76423 75022 20749	0.30785 12604 69853	-0.22165 29075 38294
0.74	0.77035 00028 35210	0.30338 92837 56300	-0.22450 80699 79662
0.76	0.77637 27075 62401	0.29887 24057 75953	-0.22714 30283 89724
0.78	0.78230 45624 14267	0.29430 50297 88325	-0.22955 79232 34894
0.80	0.78814 46014 16604	0.28969 15527 61483	-0.23175 32422 09186
0.82	0.79389 19464 14187	0.28503 63584 89007	-0.23372 98139 60986
0.84	0.79954 58067 39551	0.28034 38108 39621	-0.23548 88011 05281
0.86	0.80510 54787 48192	0.27561 82471 53457	-0.23703 16925 51973
0.88	0.81057 03452 23288	0.27086 39717 98338	-0.23836 02951 82537
0.90	0.81593 98746 53241	0.26608 52498 98755	-0.23947 67249 08879
0.92	0.82121 36203 85629	0.26128 63012 49553	-0.24038 33971 49589
0.94	0.82639 12196 61376	0.25647 12944 25620	-0.24108 30167 60083
0.96	0.83147 23925 33162	0.25164 43410 98117	-0.24157 85674 54192
0.98	0.83645 69406 72308	0.24680 94905 67043	-0.24187 33007 55702
1.00	0.84134 47460 68543	0.24197 07245 19143	-0.24197 07245 19143

$$Z(x)=\frac{1}{\sqrt{2\pi}}e^{-\frac{1}{2}x^2} \quad P(x)=\int_{-\infty}^{x} Z(t)dt \quad Z^{(n)}(x)=\frac{d^n}{dx^n}Z(x) \quad He_n(x)=(-1)^n Z^{(n)}(x)/Z(x)$$

Table 26.1 NORMAL PROBABILITY FUNCTION AND DERIVATIVE

x	$P(x)$	$Z(x)$	$Z^{(1)}(x)$
1.00	0.84134 47460 68543	0.24197 07245 19143	-0.24197 07245 19143
1.02	0.84613 57696 27265	0.23713 19520 19380	-0.24187 45910 59767
1.04	0.85083 00496 69019	0.23229 70047 43366	-0.24158 88849 33101
1.06	0.85542 77003 36091	0.22746 96324 57386	-0.24111 78104 04829
1.08	0.85992 89099 11231	0.22265 34987 51761	-0.24046 57786 51902
1.10	0.86433 39390 53618	0.21785 21770 32551	-0.23963 73947 35806
1.12	0.86864 31189 57270	0.21306 91467 75718	-0.23863 74443 88804
1.14	0.87285 68494 37202	0.20830 77900 47108	-0.23747 08806 53704
1.16	0.87697 55969 48657	0.20357 13882 90759	-0.23614 28104 17281
1.18	0.88099 98925 44800	0.19886 31193 87276	-0.23465 84808 76986
1.20	0.88493 03297 78292	0.19418 60549 83213	-0.23302 32659 79856
1.22	0.88876 75625 52166	0.18954 31580 91640	-0.23124 26528 71801
1.24	0.89251 23029 25413	0.18493 72809 63305	-0.22932 22283 94499
1.26	0.89616 53188 78700	0.18037 11632 27080	-0.22726 76656 66121
1.28	0.89972 74320 45558	0.17584 74302 97662	-0.22508 47107 81008
1.30	0.90319 95154 14390	0.17136 85920 47807	-0.22277 91696 62150
1.32	0.90658 24910 06528	0.16693 70417 41714	-0.22035 68950 99062
1.34	0.90987 73275 35548	0.16255 50552 25534	-0.21782 37740 02216
1.36	0.91308 50380 52915	0.15822 47903 70383	-0.21518 57149 03721
1.38	0.91620 66775 84986	0.15394 82867 62634	-0.21244 86357 32434
1.40	0.91924 33407 66229	0.14972 74656 35745	-0.20961 84518 90043
1.42	0.92219 61594 73454	0.14556 41300 37348	-0.20670 10646 53034
1.44	0.92506 63004 65673	0.14145 99652 24839	-0.20370 23499 23768
1.46	0.92785 49630 34106	0.13741 65392 82282	-0.20062 81473 52131
1.48	0.93056 33766 66669	0.13343 53039 51002	-0.19748 42498 47483
1.50	0.93319 27987 31142	0.12951 75956 65892	-0.19427 63934 98838
1.52	0.93574 45121 81064	0.12566 46367 89088	-0.19101 02479 19414
1.54	0.93821 98232 88188	0.12187 75370 32402	-0.18769 14070 29899
1.56	0.94062 00594 05207	0.11815 72950 59582	-0.18432 53802 92948
1.58	0.94294 65667 62246	0.11450 48002 59292	-0.18091 75844 09682
1.60	0.94520 07083 00442	0.11092 08346 79456	-0.17747 33354 87129
1.62	0.94738 38615 45748	0.10740 60751 13484	-0.17399 78416 83844
1.64	0.94949 74165 25897	0.10396 10953 28764	-0.17049 61963 39173
1.66	0.95154 27737 33277	0.10058 63684 27691	-0.16697 33715 89966
1.68	0.95352 13421 36280	0.09728 22693 31467	-0.16343 42124 76865
1.70	0.95543 45372 41457	0.09404 90773 76887	-0.15988 34315 40708
1.72	0.95728 37792 08671	0.09088 69790 16283	-0.15632 56039 08007
1.74	0.95907 04910 21193	0.08779 60706 10906	-0.15276 51628 62976
1.76	0.96079 60967 12518	0.08477 63613 08022	-0.14920 63959 02119
1.78	0.96246 20196 51483	0.08182 77759 92143	-0.14565 34412 66014
1.80	0.96406 96808 87074	0.07895 01583 00894	-0.14211 02849 41609
1.82	0.96562 04975 54110	0.07614 32736 96207	-0.13858 07581 27097
1.84	0.96711 58813 40836	0.07340 68125 81657	-0.13506 85351 50249
1.86	0.96855 72370 19248	0.07074 03934 56983	-0.13157 71318 29989
1.88	0.96994 59610 38800	0.06814 35661 01045	-0.12810 99042 69964
1.90	0.97128 34401 83998	0.06561 58147 74677	-0.12467 00480 71886
1.92	0.97257 10502 96163	0.06315 65614 35199	-0.12126 05979 55581
1.94	0.97381 01550 59548	0.06076 51689 54565	-0.11788 44277 71856
1.96	0.97500 21048 51780	0.05844 09443 33451	-0.11454 42508 93565
1.98	0.97614 82356 58492	0.05618 31419 03868	-0.11124 26209 69659
2.00	0.97724 98680 51821	0.05399 09665 13188	-0.10798 19330 26376

$Z(x)=\frac{1}{\sqrt{2\pi}}e^{-\frac{1}{2}x^2}$ $\quad P(x)=\int_{-\infty}^{x} Z(t)dt$ $\quad Z^{(n)}(x)=\frac{d^n}{dx^n}Z(x)$ $\quad He_n(x)=(-1)^n Z^{(n)}(x)/Z(x)$

Table 26.1 NORMAL PROBABILITY FUNCTION AND DERIVATIVE

x	$P(x)$	$Z(x)$	$Z^{(1)}(x)$
2.00	0.97724 98680 51821	0.05399 09665 13188	−0.10798 19330 26376
2.02	0.97830 83062 32353	0.05186 35766 82821	−0.10476 44248 99298
2.04	0.97932 48371 33930	0.04980 00877 35071	−0.10159 21789 79544
2.06	0.98030 07295 90623	0.04779 95748 82077	−0.09846 71242 57079
2.08	0.98123 72335 65062	0.04586 10762 71055	−0.09539 10386 43794
2.10	0.98213 55794 37184	0.04398 35959 80427	−0.09236 55515 58897
2.12	0.98299 69773 52367	0.04216 61069 61770	−0.08939 21467 58953
2.14	0.98382 26166 27834	0.04040 75539 22860	−0.08647 21653 94921
2.16	0.98461 36652 16075	0.03870 68561 47456	−0.08360 68092 78504
2.18	0.98537 12692 24011	0.03706 29102 47806	−0.08079 71443 40218
2.20	0.98609 65524 86502	0.03547 45928 46231	−0.07804 41042 61709
2.22	0.98679 06161 92744	0.03394 07631 82449	−0.07534 84942 65037
2.24	0.98745 45385 64054	0.03246 02656 43697	−0.07271 09950 41882
2.26	0.98808 93745 81453	0.03103 19322 15008	−0.07013 21668 05919
2.28	0.98869 61557 61447	0.02965 45848 47341	−0.06761 24534 51938
2.30	0.98927 58899 78324	0.02832 70377 41601	−0.06515 21868 05683
2.32	0.98982 95613 31281	0.02704 80995 46882	−0.06275 15909 48766
2.34	0.99035 81300 54642	0.02581 65754 71588	−0.06041 07866 03515
2.36	0.99086 25324 69428	0.02463 12693 06382	−0.05812 97955 63063
2.38	0.99134 36809 74484	0.02349 09853 58201	−0.05590 85451 52519
2.40	0.99180 24640 75404	0.02239 45302 94843	−0.05374 68727 07623
2.42	0.99223 97464 49447	0.02134 07148 99923	−0.05164 45300 57813
2.44	0.99265 63690 44652	0.02032 83557 38226	−0.04960 11880 01271
2.46	0.99305 31492 11376	0.01935 62767 31737	−0.04761 64407 60073
2.48	0.99343 08808 64453	0.01842 33106 46862	−0.04568 98104 04218
2.50	0.99379 03346 74224	0.01752 83004 93569	−0.04382 07512 33921
2.52	0.99413 22582 84668	0.01667 01008 37381	−0.04200 86541 10200
2.54	0.99445 73765 56918	0.01584 75790 25361	−0.04025 28507 24416
2.56	0.99476 63918 36444	0.01505 96163 27377	−0.03855 26177 98086
2.58	0.99505 99842 42230	0.01430 51089 94150	−0.03690 71812 04906
2.60	0.99533 88119 76281	0.01358 29692 33686	−0.03531 57200 07583
2.62	0.99560 35116 51879	0.01289 21261 07895	−0.03377 73704 02686
2.64	0.99585 46986 38964	0.01223 15263 51278	−0.03229 12295 67374
2.66	0.99609 29674 25147	0.01160 01351 13703	−0.03085 63594 02449
2.68	0.99631 88919 90825	0.01099 69366 29406	−0.02947 17901 66807
2.70	0.99653 30261 96960	0.01042 09348 14423	−0.02813 65239 98941
2.72	0.99673 59041 84109	0.00987 11537 94751	−0.02684 95383 21723
2.74	0.99692 80407 81350	0.00934 66383 67612	−0.02560 97891 27258
2.76	0.99710 99319 23774	0.00884 64543 98237	−0.02441 62141 39135
2.78	0.99728 20550 77299	0.00836 96891 54653	−0.02326 77358 49935
2.80	0.99744 48696 69572	0.00791 54515 82980	−0.02216 32644 32344
2.82	0.99759 88175 25811	0.00748 28725 25781	−0.02110 17005 22701
2.84	0.99774 43233 08458	0.00707 11048 86019	−0.02008 19378 76295
2.86	0.99788 17949 59596	0.00667 93237 39203	−0.01910 28658 94119
2.88	0.99801 16241 45106	0.00630 67263 96266	−0.01816 33720 21246
2.90	0.99813 41866 99616	0.00595 25324 19776	−0.01726 23440 17350
2.92	0.99824 98430 71324	0.00561 59835 95991	−0.01639 86721 00294
2.94	0.99835 89387 65843	0.00529 63438 65311	−0.01557 12509 64014
2.96	0.99846 18047 88262	0.00499 28992 13612	−0.01477 89816 72293
2.98	0.99855 87580 82660	0.00470 49575 26934	−0.01402 07734 30263
3.00	0.99865 01019 68370	0.00443 18484 11938	−0.01329 55452 35814

$Z(x)=\frac{1}{\sqrt{2\pi}}e^{-\frac{1}{2}x^2}$ $P(x)=\int_{-\infty}^{x} Z(t)dt$ $Z^{(n)}(x)=\frac{d^n}{dx^n}Z(x)$ $He_n(x)=(-1)^n Z^{(n)}(x)/Z(x)$

Table 26.1 NORMAL PROBABILITY FUNCTION AND DERIVATIVE

x	$P(x)$	$Z(x)$	$Z^{(1)}(x)$
3.00	0.99865 01020	(-3) 4.43184 8412	(-2) -1.32955 45
3.05	0.99885 57932	(-3) 3.80976 2098	(-2) -1.16197 74
3.10	0.99903 23968	(-3) 3.26681 9056	(-2) -1.01271 39
3.15	0.99918 36477	(-3) 2.79425 8415	(-3) -8.80191 40
3.20	0.99931 28621	(-3) 2.38408 8201	(-3) -7.62908 22
3.25	0.99942 29750	(-3) 2.02904 8057	(-3) -6.59440 62
3.30	0.99951 65759	(-3) 1.72256 8939	(-3) -5.68447 75
3.35	0.99959 59422	(-3) 1.45873 0805	(-3) -4.88674 82
3.40	0.99966 30707	(-3) 1.23221 9168	(-3) -4.18954 52
3.45	0.99971 97067	(-3) 1.03828 1296	(-3) -3.58207 05
3.50	0.99976 73709	(-4) 8.72682 6950	(-3) -3.05438 94
3.55	0.99980 73844	(-4) 7.31664 4628	(-3) -2.59740 88
3.60	0.99984 08914	(-4) 6.11901 9301	(-3) -2.20284 69
3.65	0.99986 88798	(-4) 5.10464 9743	(-3) -1.86319 72
3.70	0.99989 22003	(-4) 4.24780 2706	(-3) -1.57168 70
3.75	0.99991 15827	(-4) 3.52595 6824	(-3) -1.32223 38
3.80	0.99992 76520	(-4) 2.91946 9258	(-3) -1.10939 83
3.85	0.99994 09411	(-4) 2.41126 5802	(-4) -9.28337 33
3.90	0.99995 19037	(-4) 1.98655 4714	(-4) -7.74756 34
3.95	0.99996 09244	(-4) 1.63256 4088	(-4) -6.44862 81
4.00	0.99996 83288	(-4) 1.33830 2258	(-4) -5.35320 90
4.05	0.99997 43912	(-4) 1.09434 0434	(-4) -4.43207 88
4.10	0.99997 93425	(-5) 8.92616 5718	(-4) -3.65972 79
4.15	0.99998 33762	(-5) 7.26259 3030	(-4) -3.01397 61
4.20	0.99998 66543	(-5) 5.89430 6776	(-4) -2.47560 88
4.25	0.99998 93115	(-5) 4.77186 3654	(-4) -2.02804 21
4.30	0.99999 14601	(-5) 3.85351 9674	(-4) -1.65701 35
4.35	0.99999 31931	(-5) 3.10414 0706	(-4) -1.35030 12
4.40	0.99999 45875	(-5) 2.49424 7129	(-4) -1.09746 87
4.45	0.99999 57065	(-5) 1.99917 9671	(-5) -8.89634 95
4.50	0.99999 66023	(-5) 1.59837 4111	(-5) -7.19268 35
4.55	0.99999 73177	(-5) 1.27473 3238	(-5) -5.80003 62
4.60	0.99999 78875	(-5) 1.01408 5207	(-5) -4.66479 20
4.65	0.99999 83403	(-6) 8.04718 2456	(-5) -3.74193 98
4.70	0.99999 86992	(-6) 6.36982 5179	(-5) -2.99381 78
4.75	0.99999 89829	(-6) 5.02950 7289	(-5) -2.38901 60
4.80	0.99999 92067	(-6) 3.96129 9091	(-5) -1.90142 36
4.85	0.99999 93827	(-6) 3.11217 5579	(-5) -1.50940 52
4.90	0.99999 95208	(-6) 2.43896 0746	(-5) -1.19509 08
4.95	0.99999 96289	(-6) 1.90660 0903	(-6) -9.43767 45
5.00	0.99999 97133	(-6) 1.48671 9515	(-6) -7.43359 76

Table 26.7 PROBABILITY INTEGRAL OF χ^2-DISTRIBUTION, INCOMPLETE GAMMA FUNCTION CUMULATIVE SUMS OF THE POISSON DISTRIBUTION

ν	χ^2=0.001	0.002	0.003	0.004	0.005	0.006	0.007	0.008	0.009	0.010
	m=0.0005	0.0010	0.0015	0.0020	0.0025	0.0030	0.0035	0.0040	0.0045	0.0050
1	0.97477	0.96433	0.95632	0.94957	0.94363	0.93826	0.93332	0.92873	0.92442	0.92034
2	0.99950	0.99900	0.99850	0.99800	0.99750	0.99700	0.99651	0.99601	0.99551	0.99501
3	0.99999	0.99998	0.99996	0.99993	0.99991	0.99988	0.99984	0.99981	0.99977	0.99973
4							0.99999	0.99999	0.99999	0.99999

ν	χ^2=0.01	0.02	0.03	0.04	0.05	0.06	0.07	0.08	0.09	0.10
	m=0.005	0.010	0.015	0.020	0.025	0.030	0.035	0.040	0.045	0.050
1	0.92034	0.88754	0.86249	0.84148	0.82306	0.80650	0.79134	0.77730	0.76418	0.75183
2	0.99501	0.99005	0.98511	0.98020	0.97531	0.97045	0.96561	0.96079	0.95600	0.95123
3	0.99973	0.99925	0.99863	0.99790	0.99707	0.99616	0.99518	0.99412	0.99301	0.99184
4	0.99999	0.99995	0.99989	0.99980	0.99969	0.99956	0.99940	0.99922	0.99902	0.99879
5			0.99999	0.99998	0.99997	0.99995	0.99993	0.99991	0.99987	0.99984
6							0.99999	0.99999	0.99999	0.99998

ν	χ^2=0.1	0.2	0.3	0.4	0.5	0.6	0.7	0.8	0.9	1.0
	m=0.05	0.10	0.15	0.20	0.25	0.30	0.35	0.40	0.45	0.50
1	0.75183	0.65472	0.58388	0.52709	0.47950	0.43858	0.40278	0.37109	0.34278	0.31731
2	0.95123	0.90484	0.86071	0.81873	0.77880	0.74082	0.70469	0.67032	0.63763	0.60653
3	0.99184	0.97759	0.96003	0.94024	0.91889	0.89643	0.87320	0.84947	0.82543	0.80125
4	0.99879	0.99532	0.98981	0.98248	0.97350	0.96306	0.95133	0.93845	0.92456	0.90980
5	0.99984	0.99911	0.99764	0.99533	0.99212	0.98800	0.98297	0.97703	0.97022	0.96257
6	0.99998	0.99985	0.99950	0.99885	0.99784	0.99640	0.99449	0.99207	0.98912	0.98561
7		0.99997	0.99990	0.99974	0.99945	0.99899	0.99834	0.99744	0.99628	0.99483
8			0.99998	0.99994	0.99987	0.99973	0.99953	0.99922	0.99880	0.99825
9				0.99999	0.99997	0.99993	0.99987	0.99978	0.99964	0.99944
10					0.99999	0.99998	0.99997	0.99994	0.99989	0.99983
11							0.99999	0.99998	0.99997	0.99995
12									0.99999	0.99999

ν	χ^2=1.1	1.2	1.3	1.4	1.5	1.6	1.7	1.8	1.9	2.0
	m=0.55	0.60	0.65	0.70	0.75	0.80	0.85	0.90	0.95	1.00
1	0.29427	0.27332	0.25421	0.23672	0.22067	0.20590	0.19229	0.17971	0.16808	0.15730
2	0.57695	0.54881	0.52205	0.49659	0.47237	0.44933	0.42741	0.40657	0.38674	0.36788
3	0.77707	0.75300	0.72913	0.70553	0.68227	0.65939	0.63693	0.61493	0.59342	0.57241
4	0.89427	0.87810	0.86138	0.84420	0.82664	0.80879	0.79072	0.77248	0.75414	0.73576
5	0.95410	0.94488	0.93493	0.92431	0.91307	0.90125	0.88890	0.87607	0.86280	0.84915
6	0.98154	0.97689	0.97166	0.96586	0.95949	0.95258	0.94512	0.93714	0.92866	0.91970
7	0.99305	0.99093	0.98844	0.98557	0.98231	0.97864	0.97457	0.97008	0.96517	0.95984
8	0.99753	0.99664	0.99555	0.99425	0.99271	0.99092	0.98887	0.98654	0.98393	0.98101
9	0.99917	0.99882	0.99838	0.99782	0.99715	0.99633	0.99537	0.99425	0.99295	0.99147
10	0.99973	0.99961	0.99944	0.99921	0.99894	0.99859	0.99817	0.99766	0.99705	0.99634
11	0.99992	0.99987	0.99981	0.99973	0.99962	0.99948	0.99930	0.99908	0.99882	0.99850
12	0.99998	0.99996	0.99994	0.99991	0.99987	0.99982	0.99975	0.99966	0.99954	0.99941
13	0.99999	0.99999	0.99998	0.99997	0.99996	0.99994	0.99991	0.99988	0.99983	0.99977
14			0.99999	0.99999	0.99999	0.99998	0.99997	0.99996	0.99994	0.99992
15						0.99999	0.99999	0.99999	0.99998	0.99997
16									0.99999	0.99999

$$Q(\chi^2|\nu)=1-P(\chi^2|\nu)=\left[2^{\frac{\nu}{2}}\Gamma\left(\frac{\nu}{2}\right)\right]^{-1}\int_{\chi^2}^{\infty}e^{-\frac{t}{2}}t^{\frac{\nu}{2}-1}dt=\left[\Gamma\left(\frac{\nu}{2}\right)\right]^{-1}\int_{\frac{1}{2}\chi^2}^{\infty}e^{-t}t^{\frac{\nu}{2}-1}dt=\sum_{j=0}^{c-1}e^{-m}m^j/j! \quad (\nu \text{ even, } c=\tfrac{1}{2}\nu,\ m=\tfrac{1}{2}\chi^2)$$

PROBABILITY INTEGRAL OF χ^2-DISTRIBUTION, INCOMPLETE GAMMA FUNCTION Table 26.7
CUMULATIVE SUMS OF THE POISSON DISTRIBUTION

ν	$\chi^2=2.2$	2.4	2.6	2.8	3.0	3.2	3.4	3.6	3.8	4.0
	$m=1.1$	1.2	1.3	1.4	1.5	1.6	1.7	1.8	1.9	2.0
1	0.13801	0.12134	0.10686	0.09426	0.08327	0.07364	0.06520	0.05778	0.05125	0.04550
2	0.33287	0.30119	0.27253	0.24660	0.22313	0.20190	0.18268	0.16530	0.14957	0.13534
3	0.53195	0.49363	0.45749	0.42350	0.39163	0.36181	0.33397	0.30802	0.28389	0.26146
4	0.69903	0.66263	0.62682	0.59183	0.55783	0.52493	0.49325	0.46284	0.43375	0.40601
5	0.82084	0.79147	0.76137	0.73079	0.69999	0.66918	0.63857	0.60831	0.57856	0.54942
6	0.90042	0.87949	0.85711	0.83350	0.80885	0.78336	0.75722	0.73062	0.70372	0.67668
7	0.94795	0.93444	0.91938	0.90287	0.88500	0.86590	0.84570	0.82452	0.80250	0.77978
8	0.97426	0.96623	0.95691	0.94628	0.93436	0.92119	0.90681	0.89129	0.87470	0.85712
9	0.98790	0.98345	0.97807	0.97170	0.96430	0.95583	0.94631	0.93572	0.92408	0.91141
10	0.99457	0.99225	0.98934	0.98575	0.98142	0.97632	0.97039	0.96359	0.95592	0.94735
11	0.99766	0.99652	0.99503	0.99311	0.99073	0.98781	0.98431	0.98019	0.97541	0.96992
12	0.99903	0.99850	0.99777	0.99680	0.99554	0.99396	0.99200	0.98962	0.98678	0.98344
13	0.99961	0.99938	0.99903	0.99856	0.99793	0.99711	0.99606	0.99475	0.99314	0.99119
14	0.99985	0.99975	0.99960	0.99938	0.99907	0.99866	0.99813	0.99743	0.99655	0.99547
15	0.99994	0.99990	0.99984	0.99974	0.99960	0.99940	0.99913	0.99878	0.99832	0.99774
16	0.99998	0.99996	0.99994	0.99989	0.99983	0.99974	0.99961	0.99944	0.99921	0.99890
17	0.99999	0.99999	0.99998	0.99996	0.99993	0.99989	0.99983	0.99975	0.99964	0.99948
18			0.99999	0.99998	0.99997	0.99995	0.99993	0.99989	0.99984	0.99976
19				0.99999	0.99999	0.99998	0.99997	0.99995	0.99993	0.99989
20						0.99999	0.99999	0.99998	0.99997	0.99995
21								0.99999	0.99999	0.99998
22										0.99999

ν	$\chi^2=4.2$	4.4	4.6	4.8	5.0	5.2	5.4	5.6	5.8	6.0
	$m=2.1$	2.2	2.3	2.4	2.5	2.6	2.7	2.8	2.9	3.0
1	0.04042	0.03594	0.03197	0.02846	0.02535	0.02259	0.02014	0.01796	0.01603	0.01431
2	0.12246	0.11080	0.10026	0.09072	0.08209	0.07427	0.06721	0.06081	0.05502	0.04979
3	0.24066	0.22139	0.20354	0.18704	0.17180	0.15772	0.14474	0.13278	0.12176	0.11161
4	0.37962	0.35457	0.33085	0.30844	0.28730	0.26739	0.24866	0.23108	0.21459	0.19915
5	0.52099	0.49337	0.46662	0.44077	0.41588	0.39196	0.36904	0.34711	0.32617	0.30622
6	0.64963	0.62271	0.59604	0.56971	0.54381	0.51843	0.49363	0.46945	0.44596	0.42319
7	0.75647	0.73272	0.70864	0.68435	0.65996	0.63557	0.61127	0.58715	0.56329	0.53975
8	0.83864	0.81935	0.79935	0.77872	0.75758	0.73600	0.71409	0.69194	0.66962	0.64723
9	0.89776	0.88317	0.86769	0.85138	0.83431	0.81654	0.79814	0.77919	0.75976	0.73992
10	0.93787	0.92750	0.91625	0.90413	0.89118	0.87742	0.86291	0.84768	0.83178	0.81526
11	0.96370	0.95672	0.94898	0.94046	0.93117	0.92109	0.91026	0.89868	0.88637	0.87337
12	0.97955	0.97509	0.97002	0.96433	0.95798	0.95096	0.94327	0.93489	0.92583	0.91608
13	0.98887	0.98614	0.98298	0.97934	0.97519	0.97052	0.96530	0.95951	0.95313	0.94615
14	0.99414	0.99254	0.99064	0.98841	0.98581	0.98283	0.97943	0.97559	0.97128	0.96649
15	0.99701	0.99610	0.99501	0.99369	0.99213	0.99029	0.98816	0.98571	0.98291	0.97975
16	0.99851	0.99802	0.99741	0.99666	0.99575	0.99467	0.99338	0.99187	0.99012	0.98810
17	0.99928	0.99902	0.99869	0.99828	0.99777	0.99715	0.99639	0.99550	0.99443	0.99319
18	0.99966	0.99953	0.99936	0.99914	0.99886	0.99851	0.99809	0.99757	0.99694	0.99620
19	0.99985	0.99978	0.99969	0.99958	0.99943	0.99924	0.99901	0.99872	0.99836	0.99793
20	0.99993	0.99990	0.99986	0.99980	0.99972	0.99962	0.99950	0.99934	0.99914	0.99890
21	0.99997	0.99995	0.99993	0.99991	0.99987	0.99982	0.99975	0.99967	0.99956	0.99943
22	0.99999	0.99998	0.99997	0.99996	0.99994	0.99991	0.99988	0.99984	0.99978	0.99971
23	0.99999	0.99999	0.99999	0.99998	0.99997	0.99996	0.99994	0.99992	0.99989	0.99986
24			0.99999	0.99999	0.99999	0.99998	0.99997	0.99996	0.99995	0.99993
25					0.99999	0.99999	0.99999	0.99998	0.99998	0.99997
26								0.99999	0.99999	0.99998
27									0.99999	0.99999

$\phi=\frac{1}{2}\left(\chi^2-\chi_0^2\right)$ $\qquad w=\nu-\nu_0>0$

Interpolation on χ^2

$$Q(\chi^2|\nu)=Q\left(\chi_0^2\middle|\nu_0-4\right)\left[\tfrac{1}{2}\phi^2\right]+Q\left(\chi_0^2\middle|\nu_0-2\right)\left[\phi-\phi^2\right]+Q\left(\chi_0^2\middle|\nu_0\right)\left[1-\phi+\tfrac{1}{2}\phi^2\right]$$

Double Entry Interpolation

$$Q\left(\chi^2\middle|\nu\right)=Q\left(\chi_0^2\middle|\nu_0-4\right)\left[\tfrac{1}{2}\phi^2\right]+Q\left(\chi_0^2\middle|\nu_0-2\right)\left[\phi-\phi^2-w\phi\right]+Q\left(\chi_0^2\middle|\nu_0-1\right)\left[\tfrac{1}{2}w^2-\tfrac{1}{2}w+w\phi\right]$$

$$+Q\left(\chi_0^2\middle|\nu_0\right)\left[1-w^2-\phi+\tfrac{1}{2}\phi^2+w\phi\right]+Q\left(\chi_0^2\middle|\nu_0+1\right)\left[\tfrac{1}{2}w^2+\tfrac{1}{2}w-w\phi\right]$$

Table 26.7 PROBABILITY INTEGRAL OF χ^2-DISTRIBUTION, INCOMPLETE GAMMA FUNCTION CUMULATIVE SUMS OF THE POISSON DISTRIBUTION

ν	$\chi^2=6.2$	6.4	6.6	6.8	7.0	7.2	7.4	7.6	7.8	8.0
	$m=3.1$	3.2	3.3	3.4	3.5	3.6	3.7	3.8	3.9	4.0
1	0.01278	0.01141	0.01020	0.00912	0.00815	0.00729	0.00652	0.00584	0.00522	0.00468
2	0.04505	0.04076	0.03688	0.03337	0.03020	0.02732	0.02472	0.02237	0.02024	0.01832
3	0.10228	0.09369	0.08580	0.07855	0.07190	0.06579	0.06018	0.05504	0.05033	0.04601
4	0.18470	0.17120	0.15860	0.14684	0.13589	0.12569	0.11620	0.10738	0.09919	0.09158
5	0.28724	0.26922	0.25213	0.23595	0.22064	0.20619	0.19255	0.17970	0.16761	0.15624
6	0.40116	0.37990	0.35943	0.33974	0.32085	0.30275	0.28543	0.26890	0.25313	0.23810
7	0.51660	0.49390	0.47168	0.45000	0.42888	0.40836	0.38845	0.36918	0.35056	0.33259
8	0.62484	0.60252	0.58034	0.55836	0.53663	0.51522	0.49415	0.47349	0.45325	0.43347
9	0.71975	0.69931	0.67869	0.65793	0.63712	0.61631	0.59555	0.57490	0.55442	0.53415
10	0.79819	0.78061	0.76259	0.74418	0.72544	0.70644	0.68722	0.66784	0.64837	0.62884
11	0.85969	0.84539	0.83049	0.81504	0.79908	0.78266	0.76583	0.74862	0.73110	0.71330
12	0.90567	0.89459	0.88288	0.87054	0.85761	0.84412	0.83009	0.81556	0.80056	0.78513
13	0.93857	0.93038	0.92157	0.91216	0.90215	0.89155	0.88038	0.86865	0.85638	0.84360
14	0.96120	0.95538	0.94903	0.94215	0.93471	0.92673	0.91819	0.90911	0.89948	0.88933
15	0.97619	0.97222	0.96782	0.96296	0.95765	0.95186	0.94559	0.93882	0.93155	0.92378
16	0.98579	0.98317	0.98022	0.97693	0.97326	0.96921	0.96476	0.95989	0.95460	0.94887
17	0.99174	0.99007	0.98816	0.98599	0.98355	0.98081	0.97775	0.97437	0.97064	0.96655
18	0.99532	0.99429	0.99309	0.99171	0.99013	0.98833	0.98630	0.98402	0.98147	0.97864
19	0.99741	0.99679	0.99606	0.99521	0.99421	0.99307	0.99176	0.99026	0.98857	0.98667
20	0.99860	0.99824	0.99781	0.99729	0.99669	0.99598	0.99515	0.99420	0.99311	0.99187
21	0.99926	0.99905	0.99880	0.99850	0.99814	0.99771	0.99721	0.99662	0.99594	0.99514
22	0.99962	0.99950	0.99936	0.99919	0.99898	0.99873	0.99843	0.99807	0.99765	0.99716
23	0.99981	0.99974	0.99967	0.99957	0.99945	0.99931	0.99913	0.99892	0.99867	0.99837
24	0.99990	0.99987	0.99983	0.99978	0.99971	0.99963	0.99953	0.99941	0.99926	0.99908
25	0.99995	0.99994	0.99991	0.99989	0.99985	0.99981	0.99975	0.99968	0.99960	0.99949
26	0.99998	0.99997	0.99996	0.99994	0.99992	0.99990	0.99987	0.99983	0.99978	0.99973
27	0.99999	0.99999	0.99998	0.99997	0.99996	0.99995	0.99993	0.99991	0.99989	0.99985
28		0.99999	0.99999	0.99999	0.99998	0.99998	0.99997	0.99996	0.99994	0.99992
29				0.99999	0.99999	0.99999	0.99998	0.99998	0.99997	0.99996
30						0.99999	0.99999	0.99999	0.99999	0.99998

ν	$\chi^2=8.2$	8.4	8.6	8.8	9.0	9.2	9.4	9.6	9.8	10.0
	$m=4.1$	4.2	4.3	4.4	4.5	4.6	4.7	4.8	4.9	5.0
1	0.00419	0.00375	0.00336	0.00301	0.00270	0.00242	0.00217	0.00195	0.00175	0.00157
2	0.01657	0.01500	0.01357	0.01228	0.01111	0.01005	0.00910	0.00823	0.00745	0.00674
3	0.04205	0.03843	0.03511	0.03207	0.02929	0.02675	0.02442	0.02229	0.02034	0.01857
4	0.08452	0.07798	0.07191	0.06630	0.06110	0.05629	0.05184	0.04773	0.04394	0.04043
5	0.14555	0.13553	0.12612	0.11731	0.10906	0.10135	0.09413	0.08740	0.08110	0.07524
6	0.22381	0.21024	0.19736	0.18514	0.17358	0.16264	0.15230	0.14254	0.13333	0.12465
7	0.31529	0.29865	0.28266	0.26734	0.25266	0.23861	0.22520	0.21240	0.20019	0.18857
8	0.41418	0.39540	0.37715	0.35945	0.34230	0.32571	0.30968	0.29423	0.27935	0.26503
9	0.51412	0.49439	0.47499	0.45594	0.43727	0.41902	0.40120	0.38383	0.36692	0.35049
10	0.60931	0.58983	0.57044	0.55118	0.53210	0.51323	0.49461	0.47626	0.45821	0.44049
11	0.69528	0.67709	0.65876	0.64035	0.62189	0.60344	0.58502	0.56669	0.54846	0.53039
12	0.76931	0.75314	0.73666	0.71991	0.70293	0.68576	0.66844	0.65101	0.63350	0.61596
13	0.83033	0.81660	0.80244	0.78788	0.77294	0.75768	0.74211	0.72627	0.71020	0.69393
14	0.87865	0.86746	0.85579	0.84365	0.83105	0.81803	0.80461	0.79081	0.77666	0.76218
15	0.91551	0.90675	0.89749	0.88774	0.87752	0.86683	0.85569	0.84412	0.83213	0.81974
16	0.94269	0.93606	0.92897	0.92142	0.91341	0.90495	0.89603	0.88667	0.87686	0.86663
17	0.96208	0.95723	0.95198	0.94633	0.94026	0.93378	0.92687	0.91954	0.91179	0.90361
18	0.97551	0.97207	0.96830	0.96420	0.95974	0.95493	0.94974	0.94418	0.93824	0.93191
19	0.98454	0.98217	0.97955	0.97666	0.97348	0.97001	0.96623	0.96213	0.95771	0.95295
20	0.99046	0.98887	0.98709	0.98511	0.98291	0.98047	0.97779	0.97486	0.97166	0.96817
21	0.99424	0.99320	0.99203	0.99070	0.98921	0.98755	0.98570	0.98365	0.98139	0.97891
22	0.99659	0.99593	0.99518	0.99431	0.99333	0.99222	0.99098	0.98958	0.98803	0.98630
23	0.99802	0.99761	0.99714	0.99659	0.99596	0.99524	0.99442	0.99349	0.99245	0.99128
24	0.99888	0.99863	0.99833	0.99799	0.99760	0.99714	0.99661	0.99601	0.99532	0.99455
25	0.99937	0.99922	0.99905	0.99884	0.99860	0.99831	0.99798	0.99760	0.99716	0.99665
26	0.99966	0.99957	0.99947	0.99934	0.99919	0.99902	0.99882	0.99858	0.99830	0.99798
27	0.99981	0.99977	0.99971	0.99963	0.99955	0.99944	0.99932	0.99917	0.99900	0.99880
28	0.99990	0.99987	0.99984	0.99980	0.99975	0.99969	0.99962	0.99953	0.99942	0.99930
29	0.99995	0.99993	0.99991	0.99989	0.99986	0.99983	0.99979	0.99973	0.99967	0.99960
30	0.99997	0.99997	0.99996	0.99994	0.99993	0.99991	0.99988	0.99985	0.99982	0.99977

$$Q(\chi^2|\nu)=1-P(\chi^2|\nu)=\left[2^{\frac{\nu}{2}}\Gamma\left(\frac{\nu}{2}\right)\right]^{-1}\int_{\chi^2}^{\infty}e^{-\frac{t}{2}}t^{\frac{\nu}{2}-1}dt=\left[\Gamma\left(\frac{\nu}{2}\right)\right]^{-1}\int_{\frac{1}{2}\chi^2}^{\infty}e^{-t}t^{\frac{\nu}{2}-1}dt=\sum_{j=0}^{c-1}e^{-m}m^j/j!\;(\nu\text{ even},\ c=\tfrac{1}{2}\nu,\ m=\tfrac{1}{2}\chi^2)$$

27. Miscellaneous Functions

27.1. Debye Functions

Series Representations

27.1.1

$$\int_0^x \frac{t^n dt}{e^t-1} = x^n\left[\frac{1}{n} - \frac{x}{2(n+1)} + \sum_{k=1}^{\infty} \frac{B_{2k}x^{2k}}{(2k+n)(2k)!}\right] \qquad (|x|<2\pi, n\geq 1)$$

(For Bernoulli numbers B_{2k}, see chapter **23.**)

27.1.2

$$\int_x^{\infty} \frac{t^n dt}{e^t-1} = \sum_{k=1}^{\infty} e^{-kx}\left[\frac{x^n}{k} + \frac{nx^{n-1}}{k^2} + \frac{(n)(n-1)x^{n-2}}{k^3} + \ldots + \frac{n!}{k^{n+1}}\right] (x>0, n\geq 1)$$

Relation to Riemann Zeta Function (see chapter **23**)

27.1.3

$$\int_0^{\infty} \frac{t^n dt}{e^t-1} = n!\zeta(n+1).$$

[27.1] J. A. Beattie, Six-place tables of the Debye energy and specific heat functions, J. Math. Phys. **6**, 1–32 (1926).

$\frac{3}{x^3}\int_0^x \frac{y^3dy}{e^y-1}$, $\frac{12}{x^3}\left[\int_0^x \frac{y^3dy}{e^y-1} - \frac{3x}{e^x-1}\right]$, $x=0(.01)24$, 6S.

[27.2] E. Grüneisen, Die Abhängigkeit des elektrischen Widerstandes reiner Metalle von der Temperatur, Ann. Physik. (5) **16**, 530–540 (1933).

$\frac{20}{x^4}\int_0^x \frac{t^4dt}{e^t-1} - \frac{4x}{e^x-1}$, $x=0(.1)13(.2)18(1)20(2)52(4)80$, 4S.

Table 27.1 **Debye Functions**

x	$\frac{1}{x}\int_0^x \frac{t\,dt}{e^t-1}$	$\frac{2}{x^2}\int_0^x \frac{t^2dt}{e^t-1}$	$\frac{3}{x^3}\int_0^x \frac{t^3dt}{e^t-1}$	$\frac{4}{x^4}\int_0^x \frac{t^4dt}{e^t-1}$
0.0	1.000000	1.000000	1.000000	1.000000
0.1	0.975278	0.967083	0.963000	0.960555
0.2	0.951111	0.934999	0.926999	0.922221
0.3	0.927498	0.903746	0.891995	0.884994
0.4	0.904437	0.873322	0.857985	0.848871
0.5	0.881927	0.843721	0.824963	0.813846
0.6	0.859964	0.814940	0.792924	0.779911
0.7	0.838545	0.786973	0.761859	0.747057
0.8	0.817665	0.759813	0.731759	0.715275
0.9	0.797320	0.733451	0.702615	0.684551
1.0	0.777505	0.707878	0.674416	0.654874
1.1	0.758213	0.683086	0.647148	0.626228
1.2	0.739438	0.659064	0.620798	0.598598
1.3	0.721173	0.635800	0.595351	0.571967
1.4	0.703412	0.613281	0.570793	0.546317
1.6	0.669366	0.570431	0.524275	0.497882
1.8	0.637235	0.530404	0.481103	0.453131
2.0	0.606947	0.493083	0.441129	0.411893
2.2	0.578427	0.458343	0.404194	0.373984
2.4	0.551596	0.426057	0.370137	0.339218
2.6	0.526375	0.396095	0.338793	0.307405
2.8	0.502682	0.368324	0.309995	0.278355
3.0	0.480435	0.342614	0.283580	0.251879
3.2	0.459555	0.318834	0.259385	0.227792
3.4	0.439962	0.296859	0.237252	0.205915
3.6	0.421580	0.276565	0.217030	0.186075
3.8	0.404332	0.257835	0.198571	0.168107
4.0	0.388148	0.240554	0.181737	0.151855
4.2	0.372958	0.224615	0.166396	0.137169
4.4	0.358696	0.209916	0.152424	0.123913
4.6	0.345301	0.196361	0.139704	0.111957
4.8	0.332713	0.183860	0.128129	0.101180
5.0	0.320876	0.172329	0.117597	0.091471
5.5	0.294240	0.147243	0.095241	0.071228
6.0	0.271260	0.126669	0.077581	0.055677
6.5	0.251331	0.109727	0.063604	0.043730
7.0	0.233948	0.095707	0.052506	0.034541
7.5	0.218698	0.084039	0.043655	0.027453
8.0	0.205239	0.074269	0.036560	0.021968
8.5	0.193294	0.066036	0.030840	0.017702
9.0	0.182633	0.059053	0.026200	0.014368
9.5	0.173068	0.053092	0.022411	0.011747
10.0	0.164443	0.047971	0.019296	0.009674

Planck's Radiation Function

Table 27.2

$f(x)=x^{-5}(e^{1/x}-1)^{-1}$

x	$f(x)$	x	$f(x)$	x	$f(x)$	x	$f(x)$	x	$f(x)$
0. 050	0. 007	0. 10	4. 540	0. 20	21. 199	0. 40	8. 733	0. 9	0. 831
0. 055	0. 025	0. 11	6. 998	0. 22	20. 819	0. 45	6. 586	1. 0	0. 582
0. 060	0. 074	0. 12	9. 662	0. 24	19. 777	0. 50	5. 009	1. 1	0. 419
0. 065	0. 179	0. 13	12. 296	0. 26	18. 372	0. 55	3. 850	1. 2	0. 309
0. 070	0. 372	0. 14	14. 710	0. 28	16. 809	0. 60	2. 995	1. 3	0. 233
0. 075	0. 682	0. 15	16. 780	0. 30	15. 224	0. 65	2. 356	1. 4	0. 178
0. 080	1. 137	0. 16	18. 446	0. 32	13. 696	0. 70	1. 875	1. 5	0. 139
0. 085	1. 752	0. 17	19. 692	0. 34	12. 270	0. 75	1. 508	2. 0	0. 048
0. 090	2. 531	0. 18	20. 539	0. 36	10. 965	0. 80	1. 225	2. 5	0. 021
0. 095	3. 466	0. 19	21. 025	0. 38	9. 787	0. 85	1. 005	3. 0	0. 010
0. 100	4. 540	0. 20	21. 199	0. 40	8. 733	0. 90	0. 831	3. 5	0. 006

$x_{max}=.20140\ 52353 \qquad f(x_{max})=21.20143\ 58.$

[27.3] Miscellaneous Physical Tables, Planck's radiation functions and electronic functions, MT 17 (U.S. Government Printing Office, Washington, D.C., 1941).

$$R_\lambda=c_1\lambda^{-5}(e^{c_2/\lambda T}-1)^{-1},\ R_{0-\lambda}=\int_0^\lambda R_\lambda d\lambda,$$

$$N_\lambda=2\pi c\lambda^{-4}(e^{c_2/\lambda T}-1)^{-1},\ N_{0-\lambda}=\int_0^\lambda N_\lambda d\lambda$$

Table I: $\frac{R_\lambda}{R_{\lambda\,max}}, \frac{R_{0-\lambda}}{R_{0-\infty}}, \frac{N_\lambda}{N_{\lambda\,max}}, \frac{N_{0-\lambda}}{N_{0-\infty}}$ for $\lambda T=[.05(.001).1(.005).4(.01).6(.02)1(.05)2]$cm $K°$.

Table II: R_λ, $R_{0-\lambda}$, N_λ, $N_{0-\lambda}$ ($T=1000°$ K) for $\lambda=[.5(.01)1(.05)4(.1)6(.2)10(.5)20]$ microns.

Table III: N_λ for $\lambda=[.25(.05)1.6(.2)3(1)10]$ microns, $T=[1000°(500°)3500°$ K and $6000°$ K].

Einstein Functions

Table 27.3

x	$\frac{x^2e^x}{(e^x-1)^2}$	$\frac{x}{e^x-1}$	$\ln(1-e^{-x})$	$\frac{x}{e^x-1}-\ln(1-e^{-x})$
0. 00	1. 00000	1. 00000	$-\infty$	∞
0. 05	0. 99979	0. 97521	−3. 02063	3. 99584
0. 10	0. 99917	0. 95083	−2. 35217	3. 30300
0. 15	0. 99813	0. 92687	−1. 97118	2. 89806
0. 20	0. 99667	0. 90333	−1. 70777	2. 61110
0. 25	0. 99481	0. 88020	−1. 50869	2. 38888
0. 30	0. 99253	0. 85749	−1. 35023	2. 20771
0. 35	0. 98985	0. 83519	−1. 21972	2. 05491
0. 40	0. 98677	0. 81330	−1. 10963	1. 92293
0. 45	0. 98329	0. 79182	−1. 01508	1. 80690
0. 50	0. 97942	0. 77075	−0. 93275	1. 70350
0. 55	0. 97517	0. 75008	−0. 86026	1. 61035
0. 60	0. 97053	0. 72982	−0. 79587	1. 52569
0. 65	0. 96552	0. 70996	−0. 73824	1. 44820
0. 70	0. 96015	0. 69050	−0. 68634	1. 37684
0. 75	0. 95441	0. 67144	−0. 63935	1. 31079
0. 80	0. 94833	0. 65277	−0. 59662	1. 24939
0. 85	0. 94191	0. 63450	−0. 55759	1. 19209
0. 90	0. 93515	0. 61661	−0. 52184	1. 13844
0. 95	0. 92807	0. 59910	−0. 48897	1. 08809
1. 00	0. 92067	0. 58198	−0. 45868	1. 04065
1. 05	0. 91298	0. 56523	−0. 43069	0. 99592
1. 10	0. 90499	0. 54886	−0. 40477	0. 95363
1. 15	0. 89671	0. 53285	−0. 38073	0. 91358
1. 20	0. 88817	0. 51722	−0. 35838	0. 87560
1. 25	0. 87937	0. 50194	−0. 33758	0. 83952
1. 30	0. 87031	0. 48702	−0. 31818	0. 80520
1. 35	0. 86102	0. 47245	−0. 30008	0. 77253
1. 40	0. 85151	0. 45824	−0. 28315	0. 74139
1. 45	0. 84178	0. 44436	−0. 26732	0. 71168
1. 50	0. 83185	0. 43083	−0. 25248	0. 68331

Table 27.3 **Einstein Functions**

x	$\frac{x^2e^x}{(e^x-1)^2}$	$\frac{x}{e^x-1}$	$\ln(1-e^{-x})$	$\frac{x}{e^x-1}-\ln(1-e^{-x})$
1.6	0.81143	0.40475	−0.22552	0.63027
1.7	0.79035	0.37998	−0.20173	0.58171
1.8	0.76869	0.35646	−0.18068	0.53714
1.9	0.74657	0.33416	−0.16201	0.49617
2.0	0.72406	0.31304	−0.14541	0.45845
2.1	0.70127	0.29304	−0.13063	0.42367
2.2	0.67827	0.27414	−0.11744	0.39158
2.3	0.65515	0.25629	−0.10565	0.36194
2.4	0.63200	0.23945	−0.09510	0.33455
2.5	0.60889	0.22356	−0.08565	0.30921
2.6	0.58589	0.20861	−0.07718	0.28578
2.7	0.56307	0.19453	−0.06957	0.26410
2.8	0.54049	0.18129	−0.06274	0.24403
2.9	0.51820	0.16886	−0.05659	0.22545
3.0	0.49627	0.15719	−0.05107	0.20826
3.2	0.45363	0.13598	−0.04162	0.17760
3.4	0.41289	0.11739	−0.03394	0.15133
3.6	0.37429	0.10113	−0.02770	0.12883
3.8	0.33799	0.08695	−0.02262	0.10958
4.0	0.30409	0.07463	−0.01849	0.09311
4.2	0.27264	0.06394	−0.01511	0.07905
4.4	0.24363	0.05469	−0.01235	0.06705
4.6	0.21704	0.04671	−0.01010	0.05681
4.8	0.19277	0.03983	−0.00826	0.04809
5.0	0.17074	0.03392	−0.00676	0.04068
5.2	0.15083	0.02885	−0.00553	0.03438
5.4	0.13290	0.02450	−0.00453	0.02903
5.6	0.11683	0.02078	−0.00370	0.02449
5.8	0.10247	0.01761	−0.00303	0.02065
6.0	0.08968	0.01491	−0.00248	0.01739

[27.4] H. L. Johnston, L. Savedoff and J. Belzer, Contributions to the thermodynamic functions by a Planck-Einstein oscillator in one degree of freedom, NAVEXOS p. 646, Office of Naval Research, Department of the Navy, Washington, D.C. (1949). Values of $x^2e^x(e^x-1)^{-2}$, $x(e^x-1)^{-1}$, $-\ln(1-e^{-x})$ and $x(e^x-1)^{-1}-\ln(1-e^{-x})$ for $x=0(.001)3(.01)14.99$, 5D with first differences.

27.4. Sievert Integral

$$\int_0^\theta e^{-x\sec\phi}d\phi$$

Relation to the Error Function

27.4.1

$$\int_0^\theta e^{-x\sec\phi}d\phi\sim\sqrt{\frac{\pi}{2x}}\,e^{-x}\,\mathrm{erf}\left(\sqrt{\frac{x}{2}}\,\theta\right)\qquad(x\to\infty)$$

(For erf, see chapter **7.**)

Representation in Terms of Exponential Integrals

27.4.2

$$\int_0^\theta e^{-x\sec\phi}d\phi=\int_0^{\frac{\pi}{2}}e^{-x\sec\phi}d\phi-\sum_{k=0}^{\infty}\alpha_k(\cos\theta)^{2k+1}E_{2k+2}\left(\frac{x}{\cos\theta}\right)$$

$$\left(x\geq0,\,0<\theta<\frac{\pi}{2}\right)$$

$$\alpha_0=1,\,\alpha_k=\frac{1\cdot3\cdot5\ldots(2k-1)}{2\cdot4\cdot6\ldots(2k)}$$

(For $E_{2k+2}(x)$, see chapter **5.**)

Relation to the Integral of the Bessel Function $K_0(x)$

27.4.3

$$\int_0^{\frac{\pi}{2}}e^{-x\sec\phi}d\phi=\mathrm{Ki}_1(x)=\int_x^\infty K_0(t)dt\text{ where}$$

$$x^{\frac{1}{2}}e^x\mathrm{Ki}_1(x)\sim(\tfrac{1}{2}\pi)^{\frac{1}{2}}\left\{1-\frac{5}{8x}+\frac{129}{128x^2}-\frac{2655}{1024x^3}+\frac{301035}{32768x^4}-\ldots\right\}$$

(For $\mathrm{Ki}_r(x)$, see chapter **11.**)

[27.5] National Bureau of Standards, Table of the Sievert integral, Applied Math. Series— (U.S. Government Printing Office, Washington, D.C. In press).

$x=0(.01)2(.02)5(.05)10,\ \theta=0°(1°)90°$, 9D.

[27.6] R. M. Sievert, Die v-Strahlungsintensität an der Oberfläche und in der nächsten Umgebung von Radiumnadeln, Acta Radiologica **11**, 239–301 (1930).

$\int_0^\phi e^{-A\sec\phi}d\phi,\ \phi=30°(1°)90°,\ A=0(.01).5$, 3D.

Sievert Integral $\int_0^\theta e^{-x\sec\phi}\,d\phi$ **Table 27.4**

$x\backslash\theta$	10°	20°	30°	40°	50°	60°	75°	90°
0.0	0.174533	0.349066	0.523599	0.698132	0.872665	1.047198	1.308997	1.570796
0.1	0.157843	0.315187	0.471456	0.625886	0.777323	0.923778	1.123611	1.228632
0.2	0.142749	0.284598	0.424515	0.561159	0.692565	0.815477	0.968414	1.023680
0.3	0.129099	0.256978	0.382255	0.503165	0.617194	0.720366	0.837712	0.868832
0.4	0.116754	0.232040	0.344209	0.451198	0.550154	0.636769	0.727031	0.745203
0.5	0.105589	0.209522	0.309957	0.404629	0.490508	0.563236	0.632830	0.643694
0.6	0.095492	0.189191	0.279118	0.362893	0.437428	0.498504	0.552287	0.558890
0.7	0.086361	0.170833	0.251353	0.325486	0.390178	0.441478	0.483134	0.487198
0.8	0.078103	0.154256	0.226354	0.291957	0.348109	0.391204	0.423535	0.426062
0.9	0.070634	0.139289	0.203845	0.261901	0.310642	0.346851	0.371996	0.373579
1.0	0.063880	0.125775	0.183579	0.234956	0.277267	0.307694	0.327288	0.328286
1.2	0.052247	0.102553	0.148899	0.189138	0.221027	0.242523	0.254485	0.254889
1.4	0.042733	0.083620	0.120780	0.152298	0.176336	0.191533	0.198885	0.199051
1.6	0.034951	0.068183	0.097979	0.122667	0.140792	0.151541	0.156087	0.156156
1.8	0.028587	0.055597	0.079488	0.098829	0.112497	0.120105	0.122932	0.122961
2.0	0.023381	0.045335	0.064492	0.079644	0.089954	0.095342	0.097108	0.097121
2.2	0.019123	0.036967	0.052329	0.064201	0.071979	0.075797	0.076905	0.076911
2.4	0.015641	0.030145	0.042463	0.051766	0.057635	0.060342	0.061040	0.061043
2.6	0.012793	0.024582	0.034460	0.041750	0.046179	0.048100	0.048541	0.048542
2.8	0.010463	0.020045	0.027968	0.033680	0.037024	0.038387	0.038667	0.038668
3.0	0.008558	0.016347	0.022700	0.027177	0.029702	0.030670	0.030848	0.030848
3.5	0.005178	0.009817	0.013477	0.015912	0.017164	0.017576	0.017634	0.017634
4.0	0.003132	0.005896	0.008005	0.009330	0.009951	0.010128	0.010147	0.010147
4.5	0.001895	0.003542	0.004756	0.005478	0.005787	0.005862	0.005869	0.005869
5.0	0.001147	0.002127	0.002828	0.003221	0.003374	0.003407	0.003409	0.003409
5.5	0.000694	0.001278	0.001682	0.001896	0.001972	0.001986	0.001987	0.001987
6.0	0.000420	0.000768	0.001001	0.001117	0.001155	0.001162	0.001162	0.001162
6.5	0.000254	0.000461	0.000596	0.000659	0.000678	0.000681	0.000681	0.000681
7.0	0.000154	0.000277	0.000355	0.000389	0.000399	0.000400	0.000400	0.000400
7.5	0.000093	0.000167	0.000211	0.000230	0.000235	0.000235	0.000235	0.000235
8.0	0.000056	0.000100	0.000126	0.000136	0.000139	0.000139	0.000139	0.000139
8.5	0.000034	0.000060	0.000075	0.000081	0.000082	0.000082	0.000082	0.000082
9.0	0.000021	0.000036	0.000045	0.000048	0.000048	0.000048	0.000048	0.000048
9.5	0.000012	0.000022	0.000027	0.000028	0.000029	0.000029	0.000029	0.000029
10.0	0.000008	0.000013	0.000016	0.000017	0.000017	0.000017	0.000017	0.000017

27.5. $f_m(x)=\int_0^\infty t^m e^{-t^2-\frac{x}{t}}dt$ and Related Integrals

$m=0, 1, 2 \ldots$

Differential Equations

27.5.1 $$xf_m'''-(m-1)f_m''+2f_m=0$$

27.5.2 $$f_m'=-f_{m-1}\qquad (m=1, 2, \ldots)$$

Recurrence Relation

27.5.3 $$2f_m=(m-1)f_{m-2}+xf_{m-3}\qquad (m\geq 3)$$

Power Series Representations

27.5.4 $$2f_1(x)=\sum_{k=0}^{\infty}(a_k\ln x+b_k)x^k$$

$$a_k=\frac{-2a_{k-2}}{k(k-1)(k-2)}\qquad b_k=\frac{-2b_{k-2}-(3k^2-6k+2)a_k}{k(k-1)(k-2)}$$

$$a_0=a_1=0\qquad a_2=-b_0$$

$$b_0=1\qquad b_1=-\sqrt{\pi}\qquad b_2=\frac{3}{2}(1-\gamma)$$

(For γ, see chapter **6**.)

27.5.5

$$2f_1(x)=1-\sqrt{\pi}x+.6342x^2+.5908x^3-.1431x^4$$
$$-.01968x^5+.00324x^6+.000188x^7\ldots$$
$$-x^2\ln x(1-.08333x^2+.001389x^4-.0000083x^6+\ldots)$$

27.5.6

$$2f_2(x)=\frac{\sqrt{\pi}}{2}-x+\frac{\sqrt{\pi}}{2}x^2-.3225x^3-.1477x^4+.03195x^5$$
$$+.00328x^6-.000491x^7-.0000235x^8\ldots$$
$$+x^3\ln x(\tfrac{1}{3}-.01667x^2+.000198x^4-\ldots)$$

27.5.7

$$2f_3(x)=1-\frac{\sqrt{\pi}}{2}x+\frac{x^2}{2}-.2954x^3+.1014x^4+.02954x^5$$
$$-.00578x^6-.00047x^7+.000064x^8\ldots$$
$$-x^4\ln x(.0833-.00278x^2+.000025x^4-\ldots)$$

Asymptotic Representation

27.5.8

$$f_m(x)\sim\sqrt{\frac{\pi}{3}}\,3^{-\frac{m}{2}}v^{\frac{m}{2}}e^{-v}\left(a_0+\frac{a_1}{v}+\frac{a_2}{v^2}+\ldots+\frac{a_k}{v^k}+\ldots\right)\qquad(x\to\infty)$$

$$v=3\left(\frac{x}{2}\right)^{2/3}$$

$$a_0=1,\ a_1=\frac{1}{12}(3m^2+3m-1)$$

$$12(k+2)a_{k+2}=-(12k^2+36k-3m^2-3m+25)a_{k+1}$$
$$+\tfrac{1}{2}(m-2k)(2k+3-m)(2k+3+2m)a_k\qquad(k=0,1,2\ldots)$$

27.5.9 $$g_1(x)+ig_2(x)=\int_0^\infty t^3e^{-t^2+i\frac{x}{t}}dt$$

27.5.10

$$g_1(x)=\mathscr{R}f_3(ix)\qquad g_2(x)=-\mathscr{I}f_3(ix)$$

Asymptotic Representation

27.5.11

$$g_1(x)=\left(\frac{\pi}{3}\right)^{1/2}\frac{x}{2}\exp\left[-\frac{3}{2}\left(\frac{x}{2}\right)^{2/3}\right](A\sin\theta+B\cos\theta)$$

27.5.12

$$g_2(x)=-\left(\frac{\pi}{3}\right)^{1/2}\frac{x}{2}\exp\left[-\frac{3}{2}\left(\frac{x}{2}\right)^{2/3}\right](A\cos\theta-B\sin\theta)$$

$$\theta=\frac{3}{2}\sqrt{3}\left(\frac{x}{2}\right)^{2/3}$$

$$A\sim a_0-a_3\left(\frac{2}{x}\right)^2+\frac{1}{2}\left[a_1\left(\frac{2}{x}\right)^{2/3}-a_2\left(\frac{2}{x}\right)^{4/3}-a_4\left(\frac{2}{x}\right)^{8/3}+a_5\left(\frac{2}{x}\right)^{10/3}-\ldots\right]\qquad(x\to\infty)$$

$$B\sim\frac{\sqrt{3}}{2}\left[a_1\left(\frac{2}{x}\right)^{2/3}+a_2\left(\frac{2}{x}\right)^{4/3}-a_4\left(\frac{2}{x}\right)^{8/3}-a_5\left(\frac{2}{x}\right)^{10/3}+\ldots\right]\qquad(x\to\infty)$$

$$a_0=1\qquad a_1=.972222\qquad a_2=.148534$$
$$a_3=-.017879\qquad a_4=.004594\qquad a_5=-.000762$$

[27.7] M. Abramowitz, Evaluation of the integral $\int_0^\infty e^{-u^2-x/u}du$, J. Math. Phys. **32**, 188–192 (1953).

[27.8] H. Faxén, Expansion in series of the integral $\int_y^\infty \exp[-x(t\pm t^{-n})]t^{\epsilon}dt$, Ark. Mat., Astr., Fys. **15**, 13, 1–57 (1921).

[27.9] J. E. Kilpatrick and M. F. Kilpatrick, Discrete energy levels associated with the Lennard-Jones potential, J. Chem. Phys. **19**, 7, 930–933 (1951).

[27.10] U. E. Kruse and N. F. Ramsey, The integral $\int_0^\infty y^3\exp\left(-y^2+i\frac{x}{y}\right)dy$, J. Math. Phys. **30**, 40 (1951).

[27.11] O. Laporte, Absorption coefficients for thermal neutrons, Phys. Rev. **52**, 72–74 (1937).

[27.12] H. C. Torrey, Notes on intensities of radio frequency spectra, Phys. Rev. **59**, 293 (1941).

[27.13] C. T. Zahn, Absorption coefficients for thermal neutrons, Phys. Rev. **52**, 67–71 (1937). $\int_0^\infty y^ne^{-y-x/\sqrt{y}}dy$ for $n=0,\frac{1}{2},1$; $x=0(.01).1(.1)1$.

$$f_m(x)=\int_0^\infty t^m e^{-t^2-\frac{x}{t}}\,dt$$

Table 27.5

x	$f_1(x)$	$f_2(x)$	$f_3(x)$	x	$f_1(x)$	$f_2(x)$	$f_3(x)$	x	$f_1(x)$	$f_2(x)$	$f_3(x)$
0.00	0.5000	0.4431	0.5000	0.1	0.4263	0.3970	0.4580	0.6	0.2255	0.2415	0.3025
0.01	0.4914	0.4382	0.4956	0.2	0.3697	0.3573	0.4204	0.7	0.2015	0.2202	0.2793
0.02	0.4832	0.4333	0.4912	0.3	0.3238	0.3227	0.3864	0.8	0.1807	0.2011	0.2584
0.03	0.4753	0.4285	0.4869	0.4	0.2855	0.2923	0.3557	0.9	0.1626	0.1839	0.2392
0.04	0.4676	0.4238	0.4826	0.5	0.2531	0.2654	0.3278	1.0	0.1466	0.1685	0.2215
0.05	0.4602	0.4191	0.4784								

x	$\mathscr{R}f_3(ix)$	$-\mathscr{I}f_3(ix)$	x	$\mathscr{R}f_3(ix)$	$-\mathscr{I}f_3(ix)$	x	$\mathscr{R}f_3(ix)$	$-\mathscr{I}f_3(ix)$
0.0	0.50000	0.00000	4.0	−0.2626	0.0430	8.0	0.06078	−0.09808
0.2	0.49019	0.08754	4.2	−0.2552	+0.0094	8.5	0.07562	−0.07131
0.4	0.46229	0.16933	4.4	−0.2441	−0.0214	9.0	0.08221	−0.04496
0.6	0.41950	0.24139	4.6	−0.2299	−0.0490	9.5	0.08191	−0.02082
0.8	0.36543	0.30136	4.8	−0.2132	−0.0734	10.0	0.07626	−0.00010
1.0	0.30366	0.34805	5.0	−0.1945	−0.0944	10.5	0.06684	+0.01654
1.2	0.23746	0.38122	5.2	−0.1745	−0.1120	11.0	0.05507	0.02889
1.4	0.16972	0.40127	5.4	−0.1536	−0.1263	11.5	0.04224	0.03707
1.6	0.10288	0.40910	5.6	−0.1322	−0.1374	12.0	0.02937	0.04146
1.8	+0.03892	0.40592	5.8	−0.1108	−0.1455	12.5	0.01727	0.04259
2.0	−0.02062	0.39314	6.0	−0.0896	−0.1507	13.0	+0.00650	0.04109
2.2	−0.0746	0.3722	6.2	−0.0691	−0.1533	13.5	−0.00259	0.03758
2.4	−0.1221	0.3448	6.4	−0.0493	−0.1535	14.0	−0.00982	0.03268
2.6	−0.1629	0.3122	6.6	−0.0307	−0.1515	14.5	−0.01517	0.02696
2.8	−0.1966	0.2759	6.8	−0.0132	−0.1476	15.0	−0.01872	0.02089
3.0	−0.2233	0.2371	7.0	+0.00286	−0.14211	16.0	−0.02118	+0.00921
3.2	−0.2432	0.1971	7.2	0.01749	−0.13518	17.0	−0.01906	−0.00022
3.4	−0.2565	0.1569	7.4	0.03061	−0.12709	18.0	−0.01435	−0.00650
3.6	−0.2639	0.1173	7.6	0.04220	−0.11805	19.0	−0.00879	−0.00965
3.8	−0.2657	0.0792	7.8	0.05224	−0.10830	20.0	−0.00360	−0.01021

Compiled from U. E. Kruse and N. F. Ramsey, The integral $\int_0^\infty y^3 \exp\left(-y^2+i\frac{x}{y}\right)dy$, J. Math. Phys. **30**, 40 (1951) (with permission).

27.6. $f(x)=\int_0^\infty \frac{e^{-t^2}}{t+x}\,dt$

Power Series Representation

27.6.1

$$f(x)=-e^{-x^2}\ln x+e^{-x^2}\left[\sqrt{\pi}\sum_{k=0}^\infty \frac{x^{2k+1}}{k!(2k+1)}-\sum_{k=1}^\infty \frac{x^{2k}}{k!\,2k}-\frac{\gamma}{2}\right]$$

27.6.2

$$=-e^{-x^2}\ln x+\frac{1}{2}\sum_{k=0}^\infty \frac{(-1)^k\psi(k+1)x^{2k}}{k!}+\sqrt{\pi}\sum_{k=0}^\infty \frac{(-2)^k x^{2k+1}}{1\cdot 3\cdot 5\ \ldots\ (2k+1)}$$

(For γ and the digamma function $\psi(x)$, see chapter **6.**)

Relation to the Exponential Integral

27.6.3 $f(x)=-\frac{1}{2}\,e^{-x^2}\,\mathrm{Ei}\,(x^2)+\sqrt{\pi}e^{-x^2}\int_0^x e^{t^2}dt$

(For Ei (x) see chapter **5**; $e^{-x^2}\int_0^x e^{t^2}\,dt$ see chapter **7**

Asymptotic Representation

27.6.4

$$f(x)\sim\frac{\sqrt{\pi}}{2}\left[\frac{1}{x}+\frac{1}{2x^3}+\frac{1\cdot 3}{4x^5}+\frac{1\cdot 3\cdot 5}{8x^7}+\ldots\right]-\frac{1}{2}\left[\frac{1}{x^2}+\frac{1}{x^4}+\frac{2!}{x^6}+\frac{3!}{x^8}+\ldots\right]\qquad (x\to\infty)$$

[27.14] A. Erdélyi, Note on the paper "On a definite integral" by R. H. Ritchie, Math. Tables Aids Comp. **4**, 31, 179 (1950).

[27.15] E. T. Goodwin and J. Staton, Table of $\int_0^\infty \frac{e^{-u^2}}{u+x}\,du$, Quart. J. Mech. Appl. Math. **1**, 319 (1948). $x=0(.02)2(.05)3(.1)10$. Auxiliary function for $x=0(.01)1$.

[27.16] R. H. Ritchie, On a definite integral, Math. Tables Aids Comp. **4**, 30, 75 (1950).

Table 27.6 $f(x)=\int_0^\infty \frac{e^{-t^2}}{t+x}\,dt$

x	$f(x)+\ln x$	x	$f(x)+\ln x$	x	$f(x)$	x	$f(x)$	x	$f(x)$
0.00	−0.2886	0.50	0.2704	1.0	0.6051	2.0	0.3543	3.0	0.2519
0.05	−0.2081	0.55	0.3100	1.1	0.5644	2.1	0.3404	3.5	0.2203
0.10	−0.1375	0.60	0.3479	1.2	0.5291	2.2	0.3276	4.0	0.1958
0.15	−0.0735	0.65	0.3842	1.3	0.4980	2.3	0.3157	4.5	0.1762
0.20	−0.0146	0.70	0.4192	1.4	0.4705	2.4	0.3046	5.0	0.1602
0.25	+0.0402	0.75	0.4529	1.5	0.4460	2.5	0.2944	5.5	0.1468
0.30	0.0915	0.80	0.4854	1.6	0.4239	2.6	0.2848	6.0	0.1356
0.35	0.1398	0.85	0.5168	1.7	0.4040	2.7	0.2758	6.5	0.1259
0.40	0.1856	0.90	0.5472	1.8	0.3860	2.8	0.2673	7.0	0.1175
0.45	0.2290	0.95	0.5766	1.9	0.3695	2.9	0.2594	7.5	0.1102
0.50	0.2704	1.00	0.6051	2.0	0.3543	3.0	0.2519	8.0	0.1037

27.7. Dilogarithm

(Spence's Integral for $n=2$)

27.7.1 $$f(x)=-\int_1^x \frac{\ln t}{t-1}\,dt$$

Series Expansion

27.7.2 $$f(x)=\sum_{k=1}^{\infty}(-1)^k\frac{(x-1)^k}{k^2}\qquad(2\geq x\geq 0)$$

Functional Relationships

27.7.3

$$f(x)+f(1-x)=-\ln x\ln(1-x)+\frac{\pi^2}{6}\qquad(1\geq x\geq 0)$$

27.7.4

$$f(1-x)+f(1+x)=\frac{1}{2}f(1-x^2)\qquad(1\geq x>0)$$

27.7.5 $$f(x)+f\left(\frac{1}{x}\right)=-\frac{1}{2}(\ln x)^2\qquad(0\leq x\leq 1)$$

27.7.6

$$f(x+1)-f(x)=-\ln x\ln(x+1)-\frac{\pi^2}{12}-\frac{1}{2}f(x^2)$$

$$(2\geq x\geq 0)$$

Relation to Debye Functions

27.7.7 $$f(e^{-t})=-f(e^t)-\frac{t^2}{2}=\int_0^t\frac{t\,dt}{e^t-1}$$

[27.17] L. Lewin, Dilogarithms and associated functions (Macdonald, London, England, 1958).

[27.18] K. Mitchell, Tables of the function $\int_0^z \frac{-\log|1-y|}{y}\,dy$, with an account of some properties of this and related functions, Phil. Mag. **40**, 351–368 (1949). $x=-1(.01)1$; $x=0(.001).5$, 9D.

[27.19] E. O. Powell, An integral related to the radiation integrals, Phil. Mag. **7**, 34, 600–607 (1943). $\int_1^x \frac{\log y}{y-1}\,dy$, $x=0(.01)2(.02)6$, 7D.

[27.20] A. van Wijngaarden, Polylogarithms, by the Staff of the Computation Department, Report R24, Mathematisch Centrum, Amsterdam, Holland (1954). $F_n(z)=\sum_{h=1}^{\infty}h^{-n}z^h$ for $z=x=-1(.01)1$; $z=ix$, for $x=0(.01)1$; $z=e^{i\pi\alpha/2}$ for $\alpha=0(.01)2$, 10D.

Dilogarithm

Table 27.7

$$f(x)=-\int_1^x \frac{\ln t}{t-1}\,dt$$

x	$f(x)$	x	$f(x)$	x	$f(x)$	x	$f(x)$	x	$f(x)$
0. 00	1. 64493 4067	0. 10	1. 29971 4723	0. 20	1. 07479 4600	0. 30	0. 88937 7624	0. 40	0. 72758 6308
0. 01	1. 58862 5448	0. 11	1. 27452 9160	0. 21	1. 05485 9830	0. 31	0. 87229 1733	0. 41	0. 71239 5042
0. 02	1. 54579 9712	0. 12	1. 25008 7584	0. 22	1. 03527 7934	0. 32	0. 85542 7404	0. 42	0. 69736 1058
0. 03	1. 50789 9041	0. 13	1. 22632 0101	0. 23	1. 01603 0062	0. 33	0. 83877 6261	0. 43	0. 68247 9725
0. 04	1. 47312 5860	0. 14	1. 20316 7961	0. 24	0. 99709 9088	0. 34	0. 82233 0471	0. 44	0. 66774 6644
0. 05	1. 44063 3797	0. 15	1. 18058 1124	0. 25	0. 97846 9393	0. 35	0. 80608 2689	0. 45	0. 65315 7631
0. 06	1. 40992 8300	0. 16	1. 15851 6487	0. 26	0. 96012 6675	0. 36	0. 79002 6024	0. 46	0. 63870 8705
0. 07	1. 38068 5041	0. 17	1. 13693 6560	0. 27	0. 94205 7798	0. 37	0. 77415 3992	0. 47	0. 62439 6071
0. 08	1. 35267 5161	0. 18	1. 11580 8451	0. 28	0. 92425 0654	0. 38	0. 75846 0483	0. 48	0. 61021 6108
0. 09	1. 32572 8728	0. 19	1. 09510 3088	0. 29	0. 90669 4053	0. 39	0. 74293 9737	0. 49	0. 59616 5361
0. 10	1. 29971 4723	0. 20	1. 07479 4600	0. 30	0. 88937 7624	0. 40	0. 72758 6308	0. 50	0. 58224 0526

27.8. Clausen's Integral and Related Summations

27.8.1

$$f(\theta)=-\int_0^\theta \ln\left(2\sin\frac{t}{2}\right)dt=\sum_{k=1}^\infty \frac{\sin k\theta}{k^2} \qquad (0\leq\theta\leq\pi)$$

Series Representation

27.8.2

$$f(\theta)=-\theta\ln|\theta|+\theta+\sum_{k=1}^\infty \frac{(-1)^{k-1}}{(2k)!}B_{2k}\frac{\theta^{2k+1}}{2k(2k+1)} \qquad \left(0\leq\theta<\frac{\pi}{2}\right)$$

27.8.3

$$f(\pi-\theta)=\theta\ln 2-\sum_{k=1}^\infty \frac{(-1)^{k-1}}{(2k)!}B_{2k}(2^{2k}-1)\frac{\theta^{2k+1}}{2k(2k+1)} \qquad (\pi/2<\theta<\pi)$$

Functional Relationship

27.8.4 $f(\pi-\theta)=f(\theta)-\frac{1}{2}f(2\theta) \qquad \left(0\leq\theta\leq\frac{\pi}{2}\right)$

Relation to Spence's Integral

27.8.5

$$if(\theta)=g(e^{i\theta})+\frac{\theta^2}{4} \text{ where } g(x)=\int_1^x \frac{dt}{t}\ln|1+t|$$

Summable Series

27.8.6

$$\sum_{n=1}^\infty \frac{\cos n\theta}{n}=-\ln\left(2\sin\frac{\theta}{2}\right) \qquad (0<\theta<2\pi)$$

$$\sum_{n=1}^\infty \frac{\cos n\theta}{n^2}=\frac{\pi^2}{6}-\frac{\pi\theta}{2}+\frac{\theta^2}{4} \qquad (0\leq\theta\leq2\pi)$$

$$\sum_{n=1}^\infty \frac{\cos n\theta}{n^4}=\frac{\pi^4}{90}-\frac{\pi^2\theta^2}{12}+\frac{\pi\theta^3}{12}-\frac{\theta^4}{48} \qquad (0\leq\theta\leq2\pi)$$

$$\sum_{n=1}^\infty \frac{\sin n\theta}{n}=\frac{1}{2}(\pi-\theta) \qquad (0<\theta<2\pi)$$

$$\sum_{n=1}^\infty \frac{\sin n\theta}{n^3}=\frac{\pi^2\theta}{6}-\frac{\pi\theta^2}{4}+\frac{\theta^3}{12} \qquad (0\leq\theta\leq2\pi)$$

$$\sum_{n=1}^\infty \frac{\sin n\theta}{n^5}=\frac{\pi^4\theta}{90}-\frac{\pi^2\theta^3}{36}+\frac{\pi\theta^4}{48}-\frac{\theta^5}{240} \qquad (0\leq\theta\leq2\pi)$$

[27.21] A. Ashour and A. Sabri, Tabulation of the function $\psi(\theta)=\sum_{n=1}^\infty \frac{\sin n\theta}{n^2}$, Math. Tables Aids Comp. **10**, 54, 57–65 (1956).

[27.22] T. Clausen, Über die Zerlegung reeller gebrochener Funktionen, J. Reine Angew. Math. **8**, 298–300 (1832). $x=0°(1°)180°$, 16D.

[27.23] L. B. W. Jolley, Summation of series (Chapman Publishing Co., London, England, 1925).

[27.24] A. D. Wheelon, A short table of summable series, Report No. SM–14642, Douglas Aircraft Co., Inc., Santa Monica, Calif. (1953).

Table 27.8 **Clausen's Integral**

$$f(\theta)=-\int_0^\theta \ln\left(2\sin\frac{t}{2}\right)dt$$

$\theta°$	$f(\theta)+\theta\ln\theta$	$\theta°$	$f(\theta)$	$\theta°$	$f(\theta)$	$\theta°$	$f(\theta)$	$\theta°$	$f(\theta)$
0	0. 000000	15	0. 612906	30	0. 864379	60	1. 014942	90	0. 915966
1	0. 017453	16	0. 635781	32	0. 886253	62	1. 014421	95	0. 883872
2	0. 034908	17	0. 657571	34	0. 906001	64	1. 012886	100	0. 848287
3	0. 052362	18	0. 678341	36	0. 923755	66	1. 010376	105	0. 809505
4	0. 069818	19	0. 698149	38	0. 939633	68	1. 006928	110	0. 767800
5	0. 087276	20	0. 717047	40	0. 953741	70	1. 002576	115	0. 723427
6	0. 104735	21	0. 735080	42	0. 966174	72	0. 997355	120	0. 676628
7	0. 122199	22	0. 752292	44	0. 977020	74	0. 991294	125	0. 627629
8	0. 139664	23	0. 768719	46	0. 986357	76	0. 984425	130	0. 576647
9	0. 157133	24	0. 784398	48	0. 994258	78	0. 976776	135	0. 523889
10	0. 174607	25	0. 799360	50	1. 000791	80	0. 968375	140	0. 469554
11	0. 192084	26	0. 813635	52	1. 006016	82	0. 959247	145	0. 413831
12	0. 209567	27	0. 827249	54	1. 009992	84	0. 949419	150	0. 356908
13	0. 227055	28	0. 840230	56	1. 012773	86	0. 938914	160	0. 240176
14	0. 244549	29	0. 852599	58	1. 014407	88	0. 927755	170	0. 120755
15	0. 262049	30	0. 864379	60	1. 014942	90	0. 915966	180	0. 000000

27.9. Vector-Addition Coefficients

(Wigner coefficients or Clebsch-Gordan coefficients)

Definition

27.9.1

$$(j_1j_2m_1m_2|j_1j_2jm)=\delta(m,m_1+m_2)\cdot\sqrt{\frac{(j_1+j_2-j)!(j+j_1-j_2)!(j+j_2-j_1)!(2j+1)}{(j+j_1+j_2+1)!}}$$

$$\cdot\sum_k\frac{(-1)^k\sqrt{(j_1+m_1)!(j_1-m_1)!(j_2+m_2)!(j_2-m_2)!(j+m)!(j-m)!}}{k!(j_1+j_2-j-k)!(j_1-m_1-k)!(j_2+m_2-k)!(j-j_2+m_1+k)!(j-j_1-m_2+k)!}$$

$$\delta(i,k)=\begin{cases}1, & i=k\\ 0, & i\neq k\end{cases}$$

Conditions

27.9.2 $j_1, j_2, j=+n$ or $+\frac{n}{2}$ $\qquad$ (n=integer)

27.9.3 $j_1+j_2+j=n$

27.9.4 j_1+j_2-j

27.9.5 j_1-j_2+j $\Bigg\}\geq 0$

27.9.6 $-j_1+j_2+j$

27.9.7 $m_1, m_2, m=\pm n$ or $\pm\frac{n}{2}$

27.9.8 $|m_1|\leq j_1,\ |m_2|\leq j_2,\ |m|\leq j$

27.9.9 $(j_1j_2m_1m_2|j_1j_2jm)=0 \qquad m_1+m_2\neq m$

Special Values

27.9.10 $(j_10m_10|j_10jm)=\delta(j_1,j)\delta(m_1,m)$

27.9.11 $(j_1j_200|j_1j_2j0)=0 \qquad j_1+j_2+j=2n+1$

27.9.12 $(j_1j_1m_1m_1|j_1j_1jm)=0 \qquad 2j_1+j=2n+1$

Symmetry Relations

27.9.13

$$(j_1j_2m_1m_2|j_1j_2jm) = (-1)^{j_1+j_2-j}(j_1j_2-m_1-m_2|j_1j_2j-m)$$

27.9.14 $$=(j_2j_1-m_2-m_1|j_2j_1j-m)$$

27.9.15 $$=(-1)^{j_1+j_2-j}(j_2j_1m_1m_2|j_2j_1jm)$$

27.9.16

$$=\sqrt{\frac{2j+1}{2j_1+1}}(-1)^{j_2+m_2}(jj_2-mm_2|jj_2j_1-m_1)$$

27.9.17

$$=\sqrt{\frac{2j+1}{2j_1+1}}(-1)^{j_1-m_1+j-m}(jj_2m-m_2|jj_2j_1m_1)$$

27.9.18

$$=\sqrt{\frac{2j+1}{2j_1+1}}(-1)^{j-m+j_1-m_1}(j_2jm_2-m|j_2jj_1-m_1)$$

27.9.19

$$=\sqrt{\frac{2j+1}{2j_2+1}}(-1)^{j_1-m_1}(j_1jm_1-m|j_1jj_2-m_2)$$

27.9.20

$$=\sqrt{\frac{2j+1}{2j_2+1}}(-1)^{j_1-m_1}(jj_1m-m_1|jj_1j_2m_2)$$

Table 27.9.1

$(j_1\ \tfrac{1}{2}\ m_1\ m_2\,|\,j_1\ \tfrac{1}{2}\ j\ m)$

$j=$	$m_2=\tfrac{1}{2}$	$m_2=-\tfrac{1}{2}$
$j_1+\tfrac{1}{2}$	$\sqrt{\frac{j_1+m+\frac{1}{2}}{2j_1+1}}$	$\sqrt{\frac{j_1-m+\frac{1}{2}}{2j_1+1}}$
$j_1-\tfrac{1}{2}$	$-\sqrt{\frac{j_1-m+\frac{1}{2}}{2j_1+1}}$	$\sqrt{\frac{j_1+m+\frac{1}{2}}{2j_1+1}}$

Table 27.9.2

$(j_1\ 1\ m_1\ m_2\,|\,j_1\ 1\ j\ m)$

$j=$	$m_2=1$	$m_2=0$	$m_2=-1$
j_1+1	$\sqrt{\frac{(j_1+m)(j_1+m+1)}{(2j_1+1)(2j_1+2)}}$	$\sqrt{\frac{(j_1-m+1)(j_1+m+1)}{(2j_1+1)(j_1+1)}}$	$\sqrt{\frac{(j_1-m)(j_1-m+1)}{(2j_1+1)(2j_1+2)}}$
j_1	$-\sqrt{\frac{(j_1+m)(j_1-m+1)}{2j_1(j_1+1)}}$	$\frac{m}{\sqrt{j_1(j_1+1)}}$	$\sqrt{\frac{(j_1-m)(j_1+m+1)}{2j_1(j_1+1)}}$
j_1-1	$\sqrt{\frac{(j_1-m)(j_1-m+1)}{2j_1(2j_1+1)}}$	$-\sqrt{\frac{(j_1-m)(j_1+m)}{j_1(2j_1+1)}}$	$\sqrt{\frac{(j_1+m+1)(j_1+m)}{2j_1(2j_1+1)}}$

Table 27.9.3 $(j_1\ \tfrac{3}{2}\ m_1\ m_2 \mid j_1\ \tfrac{3}{2}\ j\ m)$

$j=$	$m_2=\tfrac{3}{2}$	$m_2=\tfrac{1}{2}$
$j_1+\tfrac{3}{2}$	$\sqrt{\frac{(j_1+m-\frac{1}{2})(j_1+m+\frac{1}{2})(j_1+m+\frac{3}{2})}{(2j_1+1)(2j_1+2)(2j_1+3)}}$	$\sqrt{\frac{3(j_1+m+\frac{1}{2})(j_1+m+\frac{3}{2})(j_1-m+\frac{3}{2})}{(2j_1+1)(2j_1+2)(2j_1+3)}}$
$j_1+\tfrac{1}{2}$	$-\sqrt{\frac{3(j_1+m-\frac{1}{2})(j_1+m+\frac{1}{2})(j_1-m+\frac{3}{2})}{2j_1(2j_1+1)(2j_1+3)}}$	$-(j_1-3m+\tfrac{3}{2})\sqrt{\frac{j_1+m+\frac{1}{2}}{2j_1(2j_1+1)(2j_1+3)}}$
$j_1-\tfrac{1}{2}$	$\sqrt{\frac{3(j_1+m-\frac{1}{2})(j_1-m+\frac{1}{2})(j_1-m+\frac{3}{2})}{(2j_1-1)(2j_1+1)(2j_1+2)}}$	$-(j_1+3m-\tfrac{1}{2})\sqrt{\frac{j_1-m+\frac{1}{2}}{(2j_1-1)(2j_1+1)(2j_1+2)}}$
$j_1-\tfrac{3}{2}$	$-\sqrt{\frac{(j_1-m-\frac{1}{2})(j_1-m+\frac{1}{2})(j_1-m+\frac{3}{2})}{2j_1(2j_1-1)(2j_1+1)}}$	$\sqrt{\frac{3(j_1+m-\frac{1}{2})(j_1-m-\frac{1}{2})(j_1-m+\frac{1}{2})}{2j_1(2j_1-1)(2j_1+1)}}$

$j=$	$m_2=-\tfrac{1}{2}$	$m_2=-\tfrac{3}{2}$
$j_1+\tfrac{3}{2}$	$\sqrt{\frac{3(j_1+m+\frac{3}{2})(j_1-m+\frac{1}{2})(j_1-m+\frac{3}{2})}{(2j_1+1)(2j_1+2)(2j_1+3)}}$	$\sqrt{\frac{(j_1-m-\frac{1}{2})(j_1-m+\frac{1}{2})(j_1-m+\frac{3}{2})}{(2j_1+1)(2j_1+2)(2j_1+3)}}$
$j_1+\tfrac{1}{2}$	$(j_1+3m+\tfrac{3}{2})\sqrt{\frac{j_1-m+\frac{1}{2}}{2j_1(2j_1+1)(2j_1+3)}}$	$\sqrt{\frac{3(j_1+m+\frac{3}{2})(j_1-m-\frac{1}{2})(j_1-m+\frac{1}{2})}{2j_1(2j_1+1)(2j_1+3)}}$
$j_1-\tfrac{1}{2}$	$-(j_1-3m-\tfrac{1}{2})\sqrt{\frac{j_1+m+\frac{1}{2}}{(2j_1-1)(2j_1+1)(2j_1+2)}}$	$\sqrt{\frac{3(j_1+m+\frac{1}{2})(j_1+m+\frac{3}{2})(j_1-m-\frac{1}{2})}{(2j_1-1)(2j_1+1)(2j_1+2)}}$
$j_1-\tfrac{3}{2}$	$-\sqrt{\frac{3(j_1+m-\frac{1}{2})(j_1+m+\frac{1}{2})(j_1-m-\frac{1}{2})}{2j_1(2j_1-1)(2j_1+1)}}$	$\sqrt{\frac{(j_1+m-\frac{1}{2})(j_1+m+\frac{1}{2})(j_1+m+\frac{3}{2})}{2j_1(2j_1-1)(2j_1+1)}}$

Table 27.9.4 $(j_1\ 2\ m_1\ m_2 | j_1\ 2\ j\ m)$

$j=$	$m_2=2$	$m_2=1$	$m_2=0$
j_1+2	$\sqrt{\frac{(j_1+m-1)(j_1+m)(j_1+m+1)(j_1+m+2)}{(2j_1+1)(2j_1+2)(2j_1+3)(2j_1+4)}}$	$\sqrt{\frac{(j_1-m+2)(j_1+m+2)(j_1+m+1)(j_1+m)}{(2j_1+1)(j_1+1)(2j_1+3)(j_1+2)}}$	$\sqrt{\frac{3(j_1-m+2)(j_1-m+1)(j_1+m+2)(j_1+m+1)}{(2j_1+1)(2j_1+2)(2j_1+3)(j_1+2)}}$
j_1+1	$-\sqrt{\frac{(j_1+m-1)(j_1+m)(j_1+m+1)(j_1-m+2)}{2j_1(j_1+1)(j_1+2)(2j_1+1)}}$	$-(j_1-2m+2)\sqrt{\frac{(j_1+m+1)(j_1+m)}{2j_1(2j_1+1)(j_1+1)(j_1+2)}}$	$m\sqrt{\frac{3(j_1-m+1)(j_1+m+1)}{j_1(2j_1+1)(j_1+1)(j_1+2)}}$
j_1	$\sqrt{\frac{3(j_1+m-1)(j_1+m)(j_1-m+1)(j_1-m+2)}{(2j_1-1)2j_1(j_1+1)(2j_1+3)}}$	$(1-2m)\sqrt{\frac{3(j_1-m+1)(j_1+m)}{(2j_1-1)j_1(2j_1+2)(2j_1+3)}}$	$\frac{3m^2-j_1(j_1+1)}{\sqrt{(2j_1-1)j_1(j_1+1)(2j_1+3)}}$
j_1-1	$-\sqrt{\frac{(j_1+m-1)(j_1-m)(j_1-m+1)(j_1-m+2)}{2(j_1-1)j_1(j_1+1)(2j_1+1)}}$	$(j_1+2m-1)\sqrt{\frac{(j_1-m+1)(j_1-m)}{(j_1-1)j_1(2j_1+1)(2j_1+2)}}$	$-m\sqrt{\frac{3(j_1-m)(j_1+m)}{(j_1-1)j_1(2j_1+1)(j_1+1)}}$
j_1-2	$\sqrt{\frac{(j_1-m-1)(j_1-m)(j_1-m+1)(j_1-m+2)}{(2j_1-2)(2j_1-1)2j_1(2j_1+1)}}$	$-\sqrt{\frac{(j_1-m+1)(j_1-m)(j_1-m-1)(j_1+m-1)}{(j_1-1)(2j_1-1)j_1(2j_1+1)}}$	$\sqrt{\frac{3(j_1-m)(j_1-m-1)(j_1+m)(j_1+m-1)}{(2j_1-2)(2j_1-1)j_1(2j_1+1)}}$

$j=$	$m_2=-1$	$m_2=-2$
j_1+2	$\sqrt{\frac{(j_1-m+2)(j_1-m+1)(j_1-m)(j_1+m+2)}{(2j_1+1)(j_1+1)(2j_1+3)(j_1+2)}}$	$\sqrt{\frac{(j_1-m-1)(j_1-m)(j_1-m+1)(j_1-m+2)}{(2j_1+1)(2j_1+2)(2j_1+3)(2j_1+4)}}$
j_1+1	$(j_1+2m+2)\sqrt{\frac{(j_1-m+1)(j_1-m)}{j_1(2j_1+1)(2j_1+2)(j_1+2)}}$	$\sqrt{\frac{(j_1-m-1)(j_1-m)(j_1-m+1)(j_1+m+2)}{j_1(2j_1+1)(j_1+1)(2j_1+4)}}$
j_1	$(2m+1)\sqrt{\frac{3(j_1-m)(j_1+m+1)}{(2j_1-1)j_1(2j_1+2)(2j_1+3)}}$	$\sqrt{\frac{3(j_1-m-1)(j_1-m)(j_1+m+1)(j_1+m+2)}{(2j_1-1)j_1(2j_1+2)(2j_1+3)}}$
j_1-1	$-(j_1-2m-1)\sqrt{\frac{(j_1+m+1)(j_1+m)}{(j_1-1)j_1(2j_1+1)(2j_1+2)}}$	$\sqrt{\frac{(j_1-m-1)(j_1+m)(j_1+m+1)(j_1+m+2)}{(j_1-1)j_1(2j_1+1)(2j_1+2)}}$
j_1-2	$-\sqrt{\frac{(j_1-m-1)(j_1+m+1)(j_1+m)(j_1+m-1)}{(j_1-1)(2j_1-1)j_1(2j_1+1)}}$	$\sqrt{\frac{(j_1+m-1)(j_1+m)(j_1+m+1)(j_1+m+2)}{(2j_1-2)(2j_1-1)2j_1(2j_1+1)}}$

Table 27.9.5 [By use of symmetry relations, coefficients may be put in standard form $j_1 \leq j_2 \leq j$ and $m \geq 0$]

m_2	m	j_1	j	$(j_1 j_2 m_1 m_2 \vert j_1 j_2 j m)$	
			$j_2=1/2$		
$-1/2$	0	$1/2$	1	$\sqrt{1/2}$	0.70711
$1/2$	0	$1/2$	1	$\sqrt{1/2}$	0.70711
$1/2$	1	$1/2$	1		1.00000
			$j_2=1$		
-1	0	1	1	$\sqrt{1/2}$	0.70711
0	0	1	1		0.00000
1	0	1	1	$-\sqrt{1/2}$	-0.70711
0	1	1	1	$\sqrt{1/2}$	0.70711
1	1	1	1	$-\sqrt{1/2}$	-0.70711
0	$1/2$	$1/2$	$3/2$	$\sqrt{2/3}$	0.81650
1	$1/2$	$1/2$	$3/2$	$\sqrt{1/3}$	0.57735
1	$3/2$	$1/2$	$3/2$		1.00000
-1	0	1	2	$\sqrt{1/6}$	0.40825
0	0	1	2	$\sqrt{2/3}$	0.81650
1	0	1	2	$\sqrt{1/6}$	0.40825
0	1	1	2	$\sqrt{1/2}$	0.70711
1	1	1	2	$\sqrt{1/2}$	0.70711
1	2	1	2		1.00000
			$j_2=3/2$		
$-1/2$	$1/2$	1	$3/2$	$\sqrt{8/15}$	0.73030
$1/2$	$1/2$	1	$3/2$	$-\sqrt{1/15}$	-0.25820
$3/2$	$1/2$	1	$3/2$	$-\sqrt{2/5}$	-0.63246
$1/2$	$3/2$	1	$3/2$	$\sqrt{2/5}$	0.63246
$3/2$	$3/2$	1	$3/2$	$-\sqrt{3/5}$	-0.77460
$-1/2$	0	$1/2$	2	$\sqrt{1/2}$	0.70711
$1/2$	0	$1/2$	2	$\sqrt{1/2}$	0.70711
$1/2$	1	$1/2$	2	$\frac{1}{2}\sqrt{3}$	0.86603
$3/2$	1	$1/2$	2		0.50000
$3/2$	2	$1/2$	2		1.00000
$-3/2$	0	$3/2$	2		0.50000
$-1/2$	0	$3/2$	2		0.50000
$1/2$	0	$3/2$	2		-0.50000
$3/2$	0	$3/2$	2		-0.50000
$-1/2$	1	$3/2$	2	$\sqrt{1/2}$	0.70711
$1/2$	1	$3/2$	2		0.00000
$3/2$	1	$3/2$	2	$-\sqrt{1/2}$	-0.70711
$1/2$	2	$3/2$	2	$\sqrt{1/2}$	0.70711
$3/2$	2	$3/2$	2	$-\sqrt{1/2}$	-0.70711
$-1/2$	$1/2$	1	$5/2$	$\sqrt{3/10}$	0.54772
$1/2$	$1/2$	1	$5/2$	$\sqrt{3/5}$	0.77460
$3/2$	$1/2$	1	$5/2$	$\sqrt{1/10}$	0.31623
$1/2$	$3/2$	1	$5/2$	$\sqrt{3/5}$	0.77460
$3/2$	$3/2$	1	$5/2$	$\sqrt{2/5}$	0.63246
$3/2$	$5/2$	1	$5/2$		1.00000

Subject Index

D

E

F

G

H

K

L

M

N

T

U

V

W

Z

Index of Notations

Notation — Greek Letters

Miscellaneous Notations

NOTES

NOTES